Rinden – cortical.

Nebennierenrinde – " (adrenal cortical)

# A GERMAN-ENGLISH DICTIONARY
# FOR CHEMISTS

# A GERMAN-ENGLISH DICTIONARY

# FOR

# CHEMISTS

BY

## AUSTIN M. PATTERSON, Ph.D.

*Formerly Vice-President and Professor of Chemistry, Antioch College,
and Principal Specialist in Chemical Education, U. S.
Office of Education*

*SECOND EDITION*
*Ninth Printing*

NEW YORK
JOHN WILEY & SONS, Inc.
London: CHAPMAN & HALL, Limited

The Publishers and the Author will be grateful to any of the readers of this volume who will kindly call their attention to any errors of omission or of commission that they may find therein. It is intended to make our publications standard works of study and reference, and, to that end, the greatest accuracy is sought. It rarely happens that early editions are free from errors; but it is the endeavor of the Publishers to have them removed immediately upon being discovered, and it is therefore desired that the Author may be aided in his task of revision, from time to time, by the kindly criticism of readers.

JOHN WILEY & SONS, Inc.

440 FOURTH AVENUE.

SECOND EDITION
*Ninth Printing, October, 1947*

PRINTED IN U. S. A.

# PREFACE TO THE SECOND EDITION

This new edition of the Dictionary reflects the growth of the science, the appearance of new technical books (especially German–English vocabularies), and the contributions of readers. The words of general meaning have been carefully re-examined with the aid of Morgan's German Frequency Word Book; some, which are uncommon or unlikely to be found in technical literature, have been discarded, while others have been inserted for the first time. A glossary of terms relating to atomic structure by Dr. H. V. Knorr and the author, which first appeared in *The American Physics Teacher*, has been incorporated. Many new abbreviations have also been included.

The vocabulary has grown to about 42,000 entries, not to mention the increase due to numerous additional meanings of old words. In order to save space it has been necessary to adopt the paragraph style for entries beginning with the same word element, but not in such a way as to disturb the alphabetic order. As in the first edition, words which have the same, or practically the same, spelling in both languages have been omitted unless for some special reason.

Attention is again called to the INTRODUCTION, and to the definitions of common prefixes and suffixes scattered through the Vocabulary.

New German–English vocabularies chiefly consulted: Mayer, Chemisches Fachwörterbuch; Hoyer-Kreuter-Schlomann, Technologisches Wörterbuch (6th edition); Webel, Technical and Scientific Dictionary; Hebert-Hirsch, New German–English Dictionary; Freeman, Fachwörterbuch der Metallurgie; Artschwager, Dictionary of Biological Equivalents; Partridge, Dictionary of Bacteriological Equivalents.

Among the contributors particular mention should be made of Dr. D. D. Berolzheimer, Mr. E. J. Crane and other members of the *Chemical Abstracts* staff, Dr. C. C. Davis, Dr. Francis C. Frary, and Dr. Geo. C. O. Haas. The author is also under special obligation to Prof. William T. Hall (for the second time), Dr. Paul Rothemund, and Miss Janet D. Scott, who have spent laborious hours on the proofs. The present edition owes much to the above persons and to all others who have furnished additions and corrections.

YELLOW SPRINGS, OHIO,                    AUSTIN M. PATTERSON
    November, 1934.

# PREFACE TO THE FIRST EDITION

As the title is meant to imply, this book is not solely a dictionary of chemical terms. It includes words from related fields of science and, what is perhaps a novelty in a technical dictionary, a *general* vocabulary (see the INTRODUCTION). More attention has also been paid to abbreviations, prefixes and suffixes than in the average work of its kind. For historical reasons a number of old terms are defined; where these might be confused with modern meanings they are distinguished by the label "*Old Chem.*" or in some other way. It should be remembered, too, that some terms which have been replaced in chemistry are still in use in pharmacy or industry.

If some of the chemical industries do not seem to be represented in due proportion, this must be ascribed to the fact that glossaries of them are not available and that war conditions have made it extremely difficult to secure German books. It is hoped that these departments may be added to in a later edition.

The INTRODUCTION is intended especially for students and classes in chemical German, but the sections on nomenclature should be of general interest.

The author is indebted to many friends, most of them assistant editors of "Chemical Abstracts," for information in their respective fields and for the loan of books. He is specially indebted to Prof. William T. Hall, of the Massachusetts Institute of Technology, and to Prof. C. W. Foulk, of Ohio State University, who have read the proofs and whose suggestions have been of great value.

Dictionary authorities chiefly consulted: *General:* Muret-Sanders, Encyclopädisches Wörterbuch; Flügel-Schmidt-Tanger, Wörterbuch; Duden, Orthographisches Wörterbuch. *Technical:* Eger, Technologisches Wörterbuch; Harras, ditto; Lang-Meyers, German-English Medical Dictionary; and various special vocabularies. Text-books, journals and dealers' catalogs have also been examined for words.

The publishers have offered every facility for improving the dictionary and the author invites correspondence as to errors and omissions.

AUSTIN M. PATTERSON.

XENIA, OHIO, January, 1917.

# GERMAN LETTERS

## With Their Roman Equivalents

| | | | | |
|---|---|---|---|---|
| 𝔄𝔞 | A a | | 𝔒𝔬 | O o |
| 𝔄̈𝔞̈ | Ä ä | | 𝔒̈𝔬̈ | Ö ö |
| 𝔅𝔟 | B b | | 𝔓𝔭 | P p |
| ℭ𝔠 | C c | | 𝔔𝔮 | Q q |
| 𝔇𝔡 | D d | | 𝔕𝔯 | R r |
| 𝔈𝔢 | E e | | 𝔖 𝔰 𝔰 | S s |
| 𝔉𝔣 | F f | | 𝔗𝔱 | T t |
| 𝔊𝔤 | G g | | 𝔘𝔲 | U u |
| ℌ𝔥 | H h | | 𝔘̈𝔲̈ | Ü ü |
| 𝔍𝔦 | I i | | 𝔙𝔳 | V v |
| 𝔍𝔧 | J j | | 𝔚𝔴 | W w |
| 𝔎𝔨 | K k | | 𝔛𝔵 | X x |
| 𝔏𝔩 | L l | | 𝔜𝔶 | Y y |
| 𝔐𝔪 | M m | | 𝔷𝔷 | Z z |
| 𝔑𝔫 | N n | | ß | ss |

# ABBREVIATIONS

| | | | | |
|---|---|---|---|---|
| *a.* | adjective. | | *Metal.* | Metallurgy. |
| *abbrev.* | abbreviation. | | *Micros.* | Microscopy. |
| *adv.* | adverb. | | *Min.* | Mineralogy. |
| *Agric.* | Agriculture. | | *n.* | neuter noun. |
| *Anat.* | Anatomy. | | *Obs.* | obsolete. |
| *Arith.* | Arithmetic. | | *Org.* | Organic. |
| *Astron.* | Astronomy. | | *p.a.* | participial adjective. |
| *Bact.* | Bacteriology. | | *Petrog.* | Petrography. |
| *Biol.* | Biology, Biological. | | *Pharm.* | Pharmacy. |
| *Bot.* | Botany. | | *Photog.* | Photography. |
| *Calico* | Calico Printing. | | *Physiol.* | Physiology. |
| *Ceram.* | Ceramics. | | *pl.* | plural. |
| *cf.* | compare. | | *p.p.* | past participle. |
| *Chem.* | Chemistry. | | *pr.* | present. |
| *Com.* | Commerce. | | *prep.* | preposition. |
| *conj.* | conjunction. | | *pret.* | preterit. |
| *Cryst.* | Crystallography. | | *pron.* | pronoun. |
| *Elec.* | Electricity. | | *Pyro.* | Pyrotechnics. |
| *esp.* | especially. | | *sing.* | singular. |
| *Expl.* | Explosives. | | *sp.* | species. |
| *f.* | feminine noun. | | *specif.* | specifically. |
| *fig.* | figuratively. | | *subj.* | subjunctive. |
| *gen.* | genitive. | | *Tech.* | Technical. |
| *Geol.* | Geology. | | *Teleg.* | Telegraphy. |
| *Geom.* | Geometry. | | *Thermochem.* | Thermochemistry. |
| *interj.* | interjection. | | *v.aux.* | auxiliary verb. |
| *m.* | masculine noun. | | *v.i.* | intransitive verb. |
| *Mach.* | Machinery. | | *v.r.* | reflexive verb (with sich). |
| *Math.* | Mathematics. | | *v.t.* | transitive verb. |
| *Mech.* | Mechanics. | | *Zoöl.* | Zoölogy. |
| *Med.* | Medicine. | | | |

# INTRODUCTION

To the advanced worker in chemistry a knowledge of German is almost indispensable, since a very large proportion of chemical literature is published in that language. Even if he has had a good general course in German (which is too often not the case), he must become familiar with an immense special vocabulary which no dictionary can give completely. It is hoped, therefore, that the following hints as to the use of this dictionary will be found helpful.

**General Words.** A general vocabulary which is superior to many pocket dictionaries has been included, for two reasons: first, to save the user the trouble of looking up the more common German words in a separate dictionary; and secondly, because many general words have one or more technical meanings. In a general work these meanings are often either absent or buried among other senses. In this dictionary the special chemical meaning is put first or indicated in some way, the aim being in all cases to give the user immediately the meaning he is most likely to be seeking.

**Self-evident Words.** Words which are common to English and German (even with a slight variation in spelling), and which are therefore so readily recognized that they are not likely to be looked up, are omitted from the vocabulary, unless there is a special reason for inserting them.

**Spelling.** Owing to official German spelling reforms, many variant spellings appear in the current literature. In this book both old and new forms are freely given, or what seems to be the prevailing chemical usage is followed, tho in doubtful cases the official form is preferred. Those who wish to know the correct official spellings should consult Duden's " Orthographisches Wörterbuch " (inexpensive) or some similar book. For ordinary purposes it will suffice to know the following changes, which are not all invariable, but which apply to many words:

c (hard) becomes **k,** as in Kohäsion.

c (with sound of ts) becomes **z,** as in Zylinder.

**fff** and similar triplets lose one member, as Schiffahrt for Schifffahrt.

**i** becomes **ie** in the verb ending -ieren (formerly -iren).

**ph** becomes **f,** as in Efeu (formerly Epheu).

**th** becomes **t,** as in Ton (formerly Thon).

**ti** becomes **zi** in certain cases, as in Reagenzien.

Umlauts are represented by two dots (never by e), as Ä instead of Ae. In this dictionary the only effect of an umlaut on the vocabulary order is to make the word follow a word of the same spelling without the umlaut. Thus fällen immediately follows fallen and is not placed under fae-. Similarly Äther is found under At-, not under Aet-.

In the vocabulary s is used to represent both ſ and ß, and ss for ß (and sometimes for SZ when the word is spelled in capitals; thus STRASZE would be found as Strasse).

**Noun Endings.** Since the case endings of nouns are occasionally puzzling, a résumé of the ways in which German nouns may form nominative plurals from nominative singulars may be of assistance (note especially 7):

1. No change, as Kasten from Kasten.
2. Umlaut, as Vögel from Vogel.
3. Ending -e, as Jahre from Jahr.
4. Umlaut and -e, Bäume from Baum.
5. Ending -er and umlaut if possible, Männer from Mann, Kinder from Kind.
6. Ending -n, -en, or -nen, Blumen from Blume, Doktoren from Doktor, Wirtinnen from Wirtin.
7. Plurals from Latin and Greek neuters: Studien from Studium, Materialien from Material, Dramen from Drama.

The other cases are either the same as the corresponding nominative or formed from it, as follows: genitive singular, -en, -ens, -es, -n, -ns, or -s; dative and accusative singular and dative plural, -n or -en.

**Irregular Verbs.** The preterite, past participle, and present third singular (indicative) of *simple* verbs are given in all cases where the student might miss finding the meaning. In the case of compound verbs, if the irregular parts are not given one can easily find them by going back to the simple form; thus, if *verschob* is not found, *schob* is looked for and found to be the preterite of *schieben*, whence *verschob* is the preterite of *verschieben*. Again, if *zerrissen* were not found, the form *gerissen* would be looked up, because it is the corresponding part of the simple verb; it is the past participle of *reissen*, and accordingly *zerrissen* is from *zerreissen*. Regularly formed " strong " past participles like *gebacken* are not systematically entered because they merely prefix *ge-* to the infinitive. Participles used as adjectives are " run in " after the verbs from which they are derived. For the inflection of verbs, adjectives, etc., a grammar must be consulted.

**Adverbs.** Since in German nearly any adjective may be used adverbially without change of form, the user of the dictionary is ordinarily left to form these adverbial meanings for himself.

**Prefixes and Suffixes.** Combining forms are given plentifully in the vocabulary in the hope that the reader may often be able to determine the meaning of words that are not found in the dictionary. He is earnestly urged to make use of them, especially the suffixes, which are likely to be overlooked. Some of those defined are: -ähnlich, -artig, -bar, -de, -el, -en, -er, -erlei, -ern, -fach, -falt, -faltig, -förmig, -haft, -haltig, -heit, -icht, -ieren, -ig, -in, -isch, -keit, -lich, -ling, -los, -mässig, -nis, -ös, -sam, -schaft, -ung, -ür, -wärts, -weise.

**Abbreviations.** Many abbreviations found in German chemical literature but not in English are entered in the vocabulary in their proper places, as if the letters composing them spelled a word. An abbreviation is often converted from singular to plural by doubling the final letter; as, *Lsg.*, Lösung; *Lsgg.*, Lösungen.

**Inorganic Nomenclature.** Compounds may be named in German merely by compounding the names of the elements; as, *Jodkalium* (potassium iodide), *Siliziumfluorwasserstoff* (hydrogen silicofluoride, fluosilicic acid). Words formed from the names of two elements are usually to be translated by giving the *-ide* ending to the first part (Jodkalium, potassium iod*ide*).

Compounds are also named in a manner more like the English method; as, *Strontiumchlorid* (strontium chloride), *Kaliumsulfid* (potassium sulfide). To indicate a lower compound the ending *-ür* is used where *-ous* or *sub-* would occur in English; as, *Kupferchlorür* (cuprous chloride), *Silberchlorür* (silver subchloride). In corresponding names *-id* and *-ür* are contrasted like *-ic* and *-ous* in English; thus, *Kupferchlorid*, in addition to its general sense of "copper chloride," is used particularly to designate cupric chloride. Another way of distinguishing between two compounds of the same elements is by the use of Latin combining forms; as, *Cuprochlorid*, cuprous chloride; *Cuprichlorid*, cupric chloride; or by the use of di-, tri-, etc., as in English. For the old prefixes zweifach, dreifach, etc., see the Vocabulary.

Higher and lower oxides are distinguished as *-oxyd* and *-oxydul* (*Eisenoxyd*, ferric oxide; *Eisenoxydul*, ferrous oxide) or by Latin forms (*Ferrioxyd*, ferric oxide; *Ferrooxyd*, ferrous oxide).

Names of acids in German are formed very simply by attaching the word Säure to some other word; as, *Salzsäure* (literally "salt acid"), hydrochloric acid; *Osmiumsäure*, osmic acid. These names are translated into English by attaching the ending *-ic acid* to a suitable combining form; as, *Zinnsäure* (literally "tin acid"), stannic acid, from *stannum*, Latin for tin. Hydracids are designated in German by the ending *-wasserstoffsäure;* as, *Bromwasserstoffsäure*, hydrobromic acid. The German equivalent of *-ous* in naming acids is *-ig;* as, *schweflige Säure*, or, less commonly, *Schwefligsäure*, sulfurous acid. Similarly, *unter-* corresponds to *hypo-* and *über-* to *per-* (*unterchlorige Säure*, hypochlorous acid; *Übermangansäure*, permanganic acid). Any acid name may form an adjective ending in *-sauer;* as, *salpetersaure Lösung*, nitric acid solution; *mangan-*

*saures Blei*, manganate of lead; *mangansaures Salz*, salt of manganic acid, manganate. Latin names for salts are also used; as, *Manganat*, manganate; and these occur in combination; as, *Bleimanganat*, lead manganate; *Chromisulfat*, chromic sulfate.

Words ending in *-it* in German, as, for instance, the names of a great many minerals, should as a rule be translated with the ending *-ite;* as, *Kainit*, kainite (not kainit). If it seems best to retain the original spelling of a trade name it should be placed in quotation marks to show that it has not been translated; as, *Permutit*, permutite or "permutit."

**Organic Nomenclature.** There has been much carelessness in translating German organic names, and as a result many uncouth forms are seen in English articles. The following rules represent the usage of the American Chemical Society as embodied in the "Directions to Abstractors," and this harmonizes well with the best usage in Great Britain:

(1) Translate *oxy-* by *hydroxy-* when it designates hydroxyl, as is commonly the case. When *oxy-* designates the ketonic group it is preferably translated *keto-*.

(2) Translate names of compounds the chief function of which is alcoholic (or phenolic) so that the name ends in *-ol;* as, glycerol, resorcinol, mannitol, pinacol (not pinacone).

(3) When the German ending *-ol* does not indicate hydroxyl it should be translated *-ole* (as, anisole, indole), or in the case of a few hydrocarbons *-ene* (as, *Benzol*, benzene; *Toluol*, toluene; *Styrol*, styrene).

(4) The ending *-in* should be translated *-ine* in the case of basic substances and *-in* elsewhere; as, aniline, glycine, palmitin, albumin. (But for names of alcohols see (2)).

(5) The form *amido-* should be so translated only when it is in combination with an acid group. Usually it is to be translated *amino-;* as, *Amidopropionsäure*, aminopropionic acid; *Amidophenol*, aminophenol. The same holds for imido-, anilido-, etc.

(6) In such combining forms as bromo-, cyano-, chloro-, nitro-, the connective *o* is to be used invariably (with the exception of a few well-established words such as acetamide, cyanamide); as, *Chlorbenzol*, chlorobenzene; *Chloressigsäure*, chloroacetic acid. This usage is by no means universal, but those who can not reconcile themselves to such spellings as "bromoacetic" should at least avoid the German forms bromphenol, acetphenetidine, benzhydrol, etc., and use the connecting *o* before consonants.

(7) The German ending *-an* should be translated *-ane* if it is the name of a hydrocarbon (or parent heterocyclic compound) which is *fully saturated;* otherwise, *-an*. Examples: methane, menthane, tolan, furan, pentosan.

(8) Most German simple names of organic acids are correctly translated by substituting *-ic acid* for *-säure*. Some of the exceptions are old-

established names such as Milchsäure (lactic acid) and Valeriansäure (valeric acid). Elements coming before -*säure* that are likely to be dropped in translating are: vowels (*Syringasäure*, syringic acid; *Benzoesäure*, benzoic acid), *us* (*Cheiranthussäure*, cheiranthic acid), *um* or *ium* (*Cnidiumsäure*, cnidic acid). An *o* should be *inserted* in translating German Geneva names of acids (hydrocarbon name plus -säure), as, *Pentensäure*, pentenoic acid (not pentenic acid).

When the name ends in -*insäure* the translator *may* substitute -*ic acid* for this unless another acid already bears the resulting name; thus *Akridinsäure* is often called acridic acid instead of the longer acridinic acid, but *Mekoninsäure* should be translated meconinic acid because *Mekonsäure* has preëmpted the translation meconic acid. Such exceptions are given in the dictionary as far as possible, but in doubtful cases the longer form "-inic acid" would be the safer.

Names ending in -*carbonsäure* are translated -*carboxylic acid*, not -carbonic acid.

The student should be warned against confusing chemical endings and case endings; for example, -*en* may be equivalent to the English -*ene* or only a plural sign: *Terpenen* means not terpenene but terpenes; *Ketone* means not ketone but ketones; *Terpene*, not terpene but terpenes.

**How to Handle Difficulties.** If the word sought is not in the vocabulary, or if its meaning is not clear, the experienced dictionary user still has many resources. He is often able to "puzzle out" an obscure word, and the student should practise the art, using the context to guide him. A few possibilities are suggested:

1. The word may be a variant spelling. See *Spelling*, above, and look up other possible forms.

2. It may be an inflected form of a word given in the dictionary. See *Noun Endings* and *Irregular Verbs*, above. A thoro knowledge of German grammar is of course the best assistance here.

3. The word may be a verb with a separated prefix, such as *ab*, *an*, or *zu*. Look for this in the part of the sentence that follows, and hunt the meaning under the compound verb, or, if necessary, deduce what meaning you can from the meanings of the prefix and the simple verb. For example, in the sentence *es fängt an zu sieden*, the meaning of *fängt an* is found under *anfangen*. Such compound verbs are very numerous, and if not found in the vocabulary their meanings can often be guessed, for the prefixes are in reality merely adverbs attached to the verb.

4. The word may be formed from some word which is in the vocabulary by the addition of one or more prefixes or suffixes (see the paragraph on

these, above). A number of these combining forms are common in chemical writings, as *ent-*, *-frei*, *-los*, *-widrig*, and their meanings should be familiar. So also verbal nouns are freely formed from verbs by capitalizing the infinitive or by substituting *-ung* for *-en*, as Schmelzen or Schmelzung from schmelzen, and these cannot all be given.

5. The word may be a *compound* of two or more words. The capacity of German to form such compounds is much greater than that of English, and while a large number are found in this dictionary they are only a small part of those in the literature. Many words drop or add letters in combining. The general meaning of many such combining forms is given in the vocabulary. Occasionally the beginner may make a wrong division of a compound word, and he should bear this in mind; for instance, Gastrolle is from Gast and Rolle, not from Gas and Trolle. See also the rule for dropping one member of a triplet letter (under *Spelling*, above). In deciphering the meaning of compound words the student who is able will frequently find it helpful to think of the Latin or Greek equivalents; thus, Überführung means trans-ference; Königswasser means aqua regia; Lichtmesser, photo-meter.

Persistent practice is the great essential to acquiring a foreign language vocabulary and sensing its word order and idioms. At the outset the chemical student will find it very helpful to read in German elementary chemical text-books with the subject matter of which he is familiar. This will serve the double purpose of review and German practice. Further hints on learning to read technical literature in a foreign language will be found in Crane and Patterson's "Guide to the Literature of Chemistry" (pp. 231–3, John Wiley & Sons, New York, 1927).

The following books on chemical German are available: DeVries, "German for Chemists" (Chem. Pub. Co.); Greenfield, "Introduction to Chemical German" (Heath & Co.); King and Fromherz, "German-English Chemical Terminology" (Murby & Co., London); Phillips, "Chemical German" (Chem. Pub. Co.).

# GERMAN-ENGLISH DICTIONARY FOR CHEMISTS

## A

**a.,** *abbrev.* (aus) of; (an, am) on; (asymmetrisch) asymmetric(al); ana-.

**A,** *abbrev.* (Arbeit) work; (Atomgewicht) atomic weight.

**A.,** *abbrev.* Alkohol; Annalen der Chemie; ampere(s).

**Ä.,** *abbrev.* (Äther) ether.

**Aal,** *m.* eel.

**a.a.O.,** *abbrev.* (an anderen Orten) elsewhere; (an angeführten, or angegebenen, Orte) in the place cited.

**Aar,** *m.* eagle.

**Aas,** *n.* fleshings, scrapings (from hides); carrion, carcass; groats.

**aasen,** *v.t.* flesh (hides).

**Aas-schmiere,** *f.* (*Leather*) flesh-side dubbing. **-seite,** *f.* (*Leather*) flesh side.

**ab,** *adv.* off, away, down.—*prep.* from, since.— **— und zu,** to and fro; off and on.

**Abakafaser,** *f.* abacá (Manila hemp) fiber.

**abändern,** *v.t.* modify, change, alter, vary, amend.

**Abänderung,** *f.* modification; alteration; variation; amendment; variant.

**abarbeiten,** *v.t.* work off; rough-work; tire out.

**Abart,** *f.* variety, modification.

**abarten,** *v.i.* vary; deviate; degenerate.

**abätmen, abatmen,** *v.t.* glow (a cupel); cupel; anneal.

**abätzen,** *v.t.* corrode, corrode off, eat away. —**abätzend,** *p.a.* corrosive, corroding.

**Abb.,** *abbrev.* (Abbildung) cut, illustration.

**Abbau,** *m.* decomposition, disintegration, analysis (as opposed to synthesis), degradation; demolishing; (*Mining*) working; (*Physiol.*) catabolism.

**abbauen,** *v.t.* decompose, disintegrate, analyze, degrade, etc. (see Abbau).

**Abbaustufe,** *f.* step or stage in decomposition or degradation.

**abbeissen,** *v.t.* bite off; nip off.

**Abbeizdruck,** *m.* (*Calico*) discharge printing.

**abbeizen,** *v.t.* remove with corrosives; scour; (*Metal.*) dip, pickle; (*Calico*) discharge; (*Leather*) dress.—**abbeizend,** *p.a.* corrosive.

**Abbeizmittel,** *n.* corrosive.

**Abbeizung,** *f.* scouring, etc. (see abbeizen).

**abbersten,** *v.i.* burst off, crack off, fly off.

**abberufen,** *v.t.* call away, recall.

**abbestellen,** *v.t.* revoke, countermand.

**abbiegen, abbeugen,** *v.t.* bend off, bend aside, deflect; snap off; (*Grammar*) inflect.

**Abbild,** *n.* copy, image, likeness.

**abbilden,** *v.t.* portray, copy, model; describe, represent.

**Abbildung,** *f.* illustration, cut; representation, portrait, copy.

**Abbildungsvermögen,** *n.* resolving power (of a microscope).

**abbimsen,** *v.t.* rub with pumice; (*Leather*) friz, fluff, buff.

**abbinden,** *v.t.* unbind, untie, loosen; tie off; remove (by chemical combination); castrate; frame.—*v.i.* (of cement, etc.) set.

**Abbindezeit,** *f.* setting time (of cement, etc.)

**Abbitte,** *f.* apology; deprecation.

**abbitten,** *v.t.* apologize for; beg.—**abbittend,** *p.a.* deprecatory.

**abblasen,** *v.t.* blow away, blow off, blow; distill off.—*v.i.* (of gases) expand.

**abblassen,** *v.i.* fade, lose color, grow pale.

**abblättern,** *v.r.& i.* scale off, exfoliate; desquamate; shed the leaves.—*v.t.* strip of leaves.

**Abblätterung.** *f.* exfoliation; stripping of leaves.

**Abblätterungsmittel,** *n.* exfoliative.

**abbläuen,** *v.t.* blue (fabrics).—*v.i.* lose blue color.

**abbleichen,** *v.t.* bleach, bleach out.—*v.i.* fade; finish bleaching; pale.

**abblenden,** *v.t.* screen off.

**abblicken,** *v.i.* (*Metal.*) grow dull after the flash or "blick."

**abblitzen,** *v.i.* miss fire, cease lightening.

**abblühen,** *v.i.* cease blooming; fade, wither.

**abböschen,** *v.t.* slope, slant.

**Abbrand,** *m.* burnt or roasted ore; waste (in forging, etc.); loss by burning, consumption; calcination.

**abbrauchen,** *v.t.* use up, wear out.

**abbrauen,** *v.t.* brew (thoroly).—*v.i.* finish brewing.

**abbraunen,** *v.i.* lose brown color.

**abbräunen,** *v.t.* brown, dye brown (thoroly).—*v.i.* lose brown color.

**abbrausen,** *v.t.* rinse off.—*v.i.* cease effervescing; cease roaring; go off with a roar.

**abbrechen,** *v.t.* break off, break up, interrupt, discontinue, remove; deduct.—*v.i.* break off, leave off.

**abbreiten,** *v.t.* stretch out, flatten.

**abbremsen,** *v.t.* check, retard.

**abbrennbar,** *a.* combustible, deflagrable.

**Abbrennbarkeit,** *f.* combustibility, deflagrability.

**abbrennen,** *v.i.* burn off, away, or down; deflagrate; miss fire.—*v.t.* burn off, away or down; deflagrate; calcine; fire off; temper; distill off; dip, pickle; cauterize; sear, singe; (*Ceram.*) finish firing.

**Abbrenner,** *m.* deflagrator.

**Abbrenn-glocke,** *f.* deflagrating jar. **-löffel,** *m.* deflagrating spoon.

**Abbrennung,** *f.* burning off, etc. (see abbrennen).

**abbringen,** *v.t.* bring off, get off, turn off; dissuade; lead astray.

**abbröckeln,** *v.i.* scale off, chip off; crumble away.—*v.t.* break off in bits.

**Abbruch,** *m.* breaking off or down; fragment; damage; breach; demolition.

**abbrüchig,** *a.* crumbly, friable, brittle; detrimental.

**abbrühen,** *v.t.* scald, seethe, parboil.

**Abbrühkessel,** *m.* scalding kettle.

**abbuffen,** *v.t.* buff.

**abbürsten,** *v.t.* brush off, brush.

**Abdachung,** *f.* slope, declivity; unroofing.

**Abdampf,** *m.* exhaust steam.

**Abdampf-,** evaporating; exhaust-steam. **-apparat,** *m.* evaporating apparatus.

**abdampfen,** *v.t. & i.* evaporate; volatilize (solids); boil down.

**Abdampfen,** *n.* evaporation.

**abdämpfen,** *v.t.* evaporate; volatilize; steam; scald; stew; quench (charcoal); damp.

**Abdampf-gefäss,** *n.* evaporating vessel. **-kapelle,** *f.* evaporating capsule. **-kasserole,** *f.* evaporating pan. **-kessel,** *m.* evaporating kettle or pan. **-kolben,** *m.* evaporating flask. **-leitung,** *f.* exhaust-steam line. **-maschine,** *f.* evaporator; (*Ceram.*) slip kiln. **-ofen,** *m.* (*Ceram.*) slip kiln. **-pfanne,** *f.* evaporating pan. **-rückstand,** *m.* residue on evaporation. **-schale,** *f.* evaporating dish or basin. **-temperatur,** *f.* temperature of evaporation. **-trichter,** *m.* evaporating funnel.

**Abdampfung,** *f.* evaporation; volatilization.

**Abdampfungs-gefäss,** *n.* evaporating vessel. **-kessel,** *m.* evaporating kettle or pan. **-pfanne,** *f.* evaporating pan. **-rückstand,** *m.* residue on evaporation.

**Abdampfvorrichtung,** *f.* evaporating apparatus, evaporator.

**abdanken,** *v.t.* dismiss, retire.—*v.i.* resign, retire.

**abdarren,** *v.t.* dry, kiln-dry, desiccate, cure (by drying); (*Metal.*) liquate.

**Abdarrtemperatur,** *f.* (*Brewing*) finishing temperature.

**abdecken,** *v.t.* uncover, unroof; skin, flay; cover.

**Abdeckplatte,** *f.* cover plate.

**Abdeckung,** *f.* uncovering; flaying; covering.

**Abdeckvorrichtung,** *f.* covering device.

**abdekantieren,** *v.t.* decant.

**abdestillieren,** *v.t.* distill off, distill.

**abdichten,** *v.t.* make tight, calk, lute, seal, pack.

**Abdichtung,** *f.* making tight, calking, luting, sealing, packing.

**abdicken,** *v.t.* boil down, evaporate down, thicken (by boiling), inspissate.

**Abdickung,** *f.* boiling down, etc. (see abdicken).

**abdörren,** *v.t.* dry up, dry thoroly, parch, roast.

**Abdörrofen,** *m.* refining furnace.

**Abdraht,** *m.* turnings.

**abdrehen,** *v.t.* turn off (gas, etc.); turn (on a lathe); twist off; unscrew.

**Abdreh-maschine,** *f.* lathe; (*Ceram.*) finishing machine. **-späne,** *m.pl.* turnings. **-spindel,** *f.* (*Ceram.*) finishing machine.

**abdringen,** *v.t.* extort (from).

**abdrosseln,** *v.t.* throttle, choke, shut off.

**Abdruck,** *m.* copy, impression, print; cast; printing, copying; counterpart.

**abdrucken,** *v.t.* print; stamp; copy (by pressure).

**abdrücken,** *v.t.* press off; force out; fire (a gun).

**Abdruckmasse,** *f.* molding material.

**abduften,** *v.i.* lose aroma or smell.

**abdunkeln,** *v.t.* darken, sadden (colors).—*v.i.* grow darker.

**abdunsten,** *v.i.* evaporate.

**Abdunsten,** *n.* evaporation.

**abdünsten,** *v.t.* evaporate; graduate (brine).

**Abdunstung, Abdünstung,** *f.* evaporation.

**Abdünstungshaus,** *n.* (*Salt*) graduation house.

**abecelich,** *a.* alphabetic.

**abeichen,** *v.t.* gage, adjust (measures).

**Abelmoschkorn, Abelmoschuskorn,** *n.* abelmosk seed.

**Abel-prüfer,** *m.* Abel tester. **-test,** *m.* Abel test.

**Abend,** *m.* evening, night. **-brot, -essen,** *n.* supper. **-land,** *n.* western country, West, Occident.

**abendländisch,** *a.* western, occidental.

**Abendmahl,** *n.* evening meal, supper.

**abends,** *adv.* in the evening.

**abendwärts,** *adv.* westward.

Abenteuer, *n.* adventure.

aber, *conj.* but, however.

Aberglaube, *m.* superstition.

aberkennen, *v.t.* dispossess.—*v.i.* pass sentence.

abermalig, *a.* repeated, further, new.

abermals, *adv.* again.

aberwitzig, *a.* crazy, foolish.

Abessinien, *n.* Abyssinia.

abfachen, *v.t.* classify; partition.

abfahrbar, *a.* removable.

abfahren, *v.i.* depart, leave.—*v.t.* carry off, cart off; take off, remove.

Abfahrt, *f.* departure; emigration.

Abfall, *m.* falling off; decrease, deterioration, decline, loss; slope, declivity; desertion; contrast; (also *pl.* Abfälle) waste, refuse, by-product, chips, parings, cuttings, scrap, tailings, garbage, etc.

Abfall-. waste, refuse; descending. -brennstoff, *m.* refuse fuel. -eimer, *m.* waste bucket, waste pail. -eisen, *n.* scrap iron.

abfallen, *v.i.* fall off; descend; diminish, decrease; decay; be lost or wasted; lose flesh; slope; deviate; desert; be rebuffed; contrast badly.—abfallend, *p.a.* falling off; deciduous; sloping.

Abfallerzeugnis, *n.* waste product.

Abfälleverwertung, *f.* utilization of waste.

Abfall-fett, *n.* waste fat or grease. -gut, *n.* waste material (to be treated for recovery).

abfällig, *a.* falling off, sloping, etc. (see abfallen); adverse.

Abfall-kohle, *f.* waste coal or charcoal. -lauge, *f.* spent lye. -marke, *f.* (*Dyeing*) off shade. -öl, *n.* waste oil. -produkt, *n.* by-product. -salz, *n.* waste salt. -säure, *f.* waste acid, spent acid. -stoff, *m.* waste material, specif. sewage. -topf, *m.* waste jar. -vernichtung, *f.* destruction of waste. -ware, *f.* rejected ware, culls. -wasser, *n.* waste water, sewage.

abfangen, *v.t.* catch, capture, intercept; tap (molten metal).

Abfangverfahren, *n.* interception process.

abfärben, *v.t.* dye (thoroly).—*v.i.* lose color, crock; (*Min.*) give a colored streak; (*Paper*) rub off.

abfärbig, *a.* liable to crock or rub off.

abfasern, *v.i. & r.* lose fibers, fuzz; unravel.

abfassen, *v.t.* write, word, compose, draw up; catch, seize; bend (iron).

Abfasser, *m.* writer.

abfedern, *v.t.* provide with springs.

Abfegemittel, *n.* detergent.

abfegen, *v.t.* sweep away; clean.—abfegend, *p.a.* detergent.

abfeilen, *v.t.* file off.

Abfeilicht, *n.* filings.

abfertigen, *v.t.* send off, despatch.

Abfett, *m.* fat taken off, skimmings.

abfetten, *v.t.* take fat or grease from.

abfeuern, *v.t.* fire off.

abfiedeln, *v.t.* (*Metal.*) skim off.

abfiltrieren, abfiltern, *v.t.* filter off.

Abfiltrierung, *f.* filtering off, filtration.

abfinden, *v.t.* pay off, satisfy.

Abfindung, *f.* indemnification, satisfaction.

abflachen, *v.t.* make flat, level; bevel.—abgeflacht, *p.a.* flat, shallow.

Abflachung, *f.* beveling, bevel; (of a curve) rounding off.

abflammen, *v.t.* singe, gas; grease, tallow (hides).

abflauen, *v.t.* wash, scour (ore), buddle.

abfleckecht, *a.* fast to rubbing, not spotting.

abflecken, *v.i.* stain, make stains.

abfleischen, *v.t.* flesh (hides).

abfliessen, *v.i.* flow away, off or down, discharge, drain.

Abfluss, *m.* flowing off, efflux, discharge; outlet; drain pipe; effluent; waste water. -geschwindigkeit, *f.* velocity of discharge. -hahn, *m.* discharge cock. -kühler, *m.* a condenser which leads the condensate away, efflux condenser (contrasted with Rückflusskühler). -leitung, *f.* outlet pipe, drain pipe. -menge, *f.* amount of discharge. -rinne, *f.* outlet trough, discharge gutter. -rohr, -röhrchen, *n.* discharge tube, outlet tube, waste pipe, escape pipe. -wasser, *n.* waste water.

abformen, *v.t.* form, shape, mold; copy, imitate.

abfressen, *v.t.* eat away or up; corrode (off); remove by caustics; consume.

Abfrischen, *n.* (*Brewing*) changing of steep water.

Abfuhr, *f.* removal; transport, carriage. -dünger, *m.* night soil.

abführen, *v.t.* lead off, draw off, carry away, remove; send (goods); draw (wire); exhaust (steam); (*Med.*) evacuate, purge —abführend, *p.a.* (*Med.*) purgative, laxative, aperient, efferent, excretory.—abführendes Brausepulver, Seidlitz powder.

Abführ-gang, *m.* (*Physiol.*) efferent duct. -mittel, *n.* purgative, aperient. -pille, *f.* cathartic pill, purgative pill. -salz, *n.* aperient salt.

Abführung, *f.* leading off, etc. (see abführen); outlet; discharge.

Abführungsrohr, *n.* discharge tube or pipe.

Abfüll-apparat, *m.* emptying apparatus, etc. (see abfüllen); (*Brewing*) racker. -bütte, *f.* (*Brewing*) racking square.

abfüllen, *v.t.* empty, draw off (wine, etc).

drain off; rack, decant; take off, skim off (scum or dross).

**Abfüll-flasche,** f. bottle or jar into which something is emptied or drawn off. **-pipette,** f. delivery pipette. **-schlauch,** m. (*Brewing*) racking hose. **-vorrichtung,** f. emptying contrivance or apparatus.

**Abfurchung,** f. division, segmentation.

**abfüttern, abfuttern,** v.t. case, line; feed.

**Abgabe,** f. delivery; giving off, emission, evolution, escape (of gases, etc.); tax, duty; (*Com.*) draft; royalty.

**Abgang,** m. waste; loss; decrease, decline; going off, leaving; escape (of gases, etc.); miscarriage; sale, market.

**abgängig,** a. waste; wanting; salable; decrepit.

**Abgangsrohr,** n. waste pipe.

**abgären,** v.i. ferment; cease fermenting.

**Abgas,** n. waste gas; flue gas; exhaust gas.

**abgäschen,** v.i. cease foaming or fermenting.

**abgautschen,** v.t. (*Paper*) couch.

**abgeben,** v.t. give up or off, part with; deliver; yield; serve as, act as.—v.r. occupy oneself.

**abgebrochen,** p.p. of abbrechen.

**abgebunden,** p.p. of abbinden.

**abgedroschen,** p.a. trite, hackneyed.

**abgeflacht,** p.a. see abflachen.

**abgegriffen,** p.a. worn, worn-out.

**abgehen,** v.i. pass off, come off, go away, pass away.

**abgehoben,** p.p. of abheben.

**abgelegen,** p.a. remote, retired.

**Abgeltung,** f. remuneration, compensation.

**abgemessen,** p.a. see abmessen.

**abgeneigt,** p.a. disinclined.

**Abgeordnete,** m. deputy, delegate.

**abgeplattet,** p.a. see abplatten.

**abgerben,** v.t. tan (thoroly).

**abgerundet,** p.a. see abrunden.

**Abgesandte,** m. envoy, delegate.

**Abgeschäumtes,** n. skimmings.

**abgeschieden,** p.a. see abscheiden.

**abgeschliffen,** p.p. of abschleifen.

**abgeschmackt,** p.a. tasteless, insipid; absurd.

**abgeschmolzen,** p.p. of abschmelzen.

**abgeschwefelt,** p.a. desulfurized, etc. (see abschwefeln).

**abgesehen,** p.a. see absehen.

**abgespannt,** p.a. see abspannen.

**abgestanden,** p.a. see abstehen.

**abgestrichen,** p.p. of abstreichen.

**abgestumpft,** p.a. see abstumpfen.

**abgetan,** p.p. of abtun.

**abgetrieben,** p.p. of abtreiben.

**abgewinnen,** v.t. win, win away.

**abgewogen,** p.p. of abwägen.

**abgewöhnen,** v.t. wean, break of a habit.

**abgezogen,** p.p. of abziehen.

**abgiessen,** v.t. pour off, decant; (*Founding*) cast.

**Abglanz,** m. reflection.

**abglätten,** v.t. polish, polish off.

**abgleichen,** v.t. make equal, equalize; level; smooth; justify (coins); balance (accounts).

**abgleiten,** v.i. glide off, slide off, glance.

**abglühen,** v.t. heat thoroly, make red-hot, anneal; mull (wine).—v.r. cease glowing, cool gradually.

**abgreifen,** v.t. read off; wear out.

**abgrenzbar,** a. definable, limitable.

**abgrenzen,** v.t. mark off; bound; define.

**Abgrenzung,** f. demarcation, boundary.

**Abgrund,** m. abyss, precipice.

**Abguss,** m. pouring off, decanting; casting, cast.

**abh.,** *abbrev.* (abhängig) dependent.

**Abh.,** *abbrev.* (Abhandlung) treatise, paper.

**abhaaren,** v.t. remove hair from, depilate, unhair.

**abhalten,** v.t. keep off or back, detain, deter, hinder; endure; hold (a meeting).

**Abhaltung,** f. hindrance, impediment; holding, celebration.

**abhandeln,** v.t. treat (of), discuss, examine into; buy; bargain for.

**abhanden,** adv. missing, lost.

**Abhandlung,** f. treatise, paper, dissertation, discourse; transaction.

**Abhang,** m. slope, declivity.

**abhangen,** v.i. depend; slope; hang down.

**abhängen,** v.t. take off or down, disconnect.

**abhängig,** a. dependent; sloping.

**Abhängigkeit,** f. dependence; slope.

**abhären,** v.t. = abhaaren.

**abhärten,** v.t. harden; temper (iron or steel); (*Med.*) strengthen.

**abharzen,** v.t. take resin from.

**abhäuten,** v.t. skin; peel; abrade; (*Founding*) free of scum.

**abheben,** v.t. lift off, take off; skim off.

**abhebern,** v.t. siphon off.

**abhelfen,** v.t. help, remedy, correct.

**abhellen,** v.t. clarify, clear; fine (wine).—v.r. become clear.

**abhetzen,** v.t. overwork, harass.

**Abhilfe,** f. remedy, redress.

**Abhitze,** f. waste heat.

**abhobeln,** v.t. plane off, plane, smooth.

**abhold,** a. unfavorable, averse.

**abholen,** v.t. fetch off, call for.

**abhören,** v.t. hear; examine; audit.

**Abhub,** m. matter lifted off: scum, waste, dross, etc.

**Abiesöl,** n. fir oil, abies oil.

**Abietinsäure,** f. abietic acid.

**Abirrung,** f. deviation, aberration.

**Abk.,** *abbrev.* (Abkürzung) abbreviation.

**abkalken,** *v.t.* unlime.

**abkälten,** *v.t.* cool, cool down.

**abkanten,** *v.t.* bevel; trim; fold.

**abkarten,** *v.t.* prearrange, plot.

**abkehren,** *v.t.* turn away or aside, avert; divert; sweep, brush (off).

**abkeltern,** *v.t.* press (wine).

**abklappen,** *v.t.* swing aside or out; move the flaps of; open.

**abklären,** *v.t.* clarify, clear, defecate, fine; (according to method) filter, decant, elutriate, etc.; decolor (sugar); brighten (a color); strip off, boil off (a dye).—*v.r.* clear, clear up.

**Abklär-flasche,** *f.* decanting bottle (or flask). **-gefäss,** *n.* decanting vessel. **-topf,** *m.* decanting jar.

**Abklärung,** *f.* clarification, etc. (see abklären).

**Abklärungs-flasche,** *f.* = Abklärflasche. **-gefäss,** *n.* decanting vessel. **-methode,** *f.* method of clarification. **-mittel,** *n.* clarifying agent.

**abklingen,** *v.i.* die away, die out; lose radioactivity.

**abklopfen,** *v.t.* beat; beat off, knock off; scale off; (*Med.*) auscultate.

**abklören,** *v.t.* boil out (for redyeing).

**abknallen,** *v.i.* go off, explode.—*v.t.* fire off.

**abkneifen,** *v.t.* pinch off, nip off.

**abknicken,** *v.t.* bend (sharply); crack or snap off.

**abknistern,** *v.i.* decrepitate.

**Abknisterung,** *f.* decrepitation.

**abkochecht,** *a.* fast to boiling.

**abkochen,** *v.t.* boil, decoct; boil off; reboil.

**Abkochmittel,** *n.* decoction medium.

**Abkochung,** *f.* decoction; boiling.

**abkommen,** *v i.* get off; be spared; grow out of use.

**Abkommen,** *n.* agreement; disuse.

**Abkömmling,** *m.* derivative; descendant.

**abkratzen,** *v.t.* scrape off, scrape.

**abkrücken,** *v.t.* rake off.

**Abkühlapparat,** *m.* cooler, refrigerator.

**abkühlen,** *v.t. & i.* cool, cool down, chill, refrigerate; anneal.

**Abkühl-fass,** *n.* cooler, cooling vat; (*Glass*) annealing oven. **-gefäss,** *n.* cooling vessel. **-mittel,** *n.* cooling agent, refrigerant.

**Abkühlung,** *f.* cooling, refrigeration; annealing.

**Abkühlungs-fläche,** *f.* cooling surface. **-kurve,** *f.* cooling curve. **-mittel,** *n.* refrigerant. **-oberfläche,** *f.* cooling surface. **-zeit,** *f.* time of cooling.

**Abkühlverlust,** *m.* loss from cooling.

**Abkunft,** *f.* origin, descent; breed, stock.

**abkürzen,** *v.t.* shorten, abbreviate; truncate.

**Abkürzung,** *f.* abbreviation.

**abladen,** *v.t.* unload, discharge.

**ablagern,** *v.t. & i.* deposit; store; age, mellow, mature, season.—*v.r.* deposit, settle, subside.

**Ablagerung,** *f.* deposit; deposition; storage.

**Ablagerungsmenge,** *f.* amount of deposit.

**Ablass,** *m.* draining, discharge; cessation; discount; drain, outlet.

**ablassen,** *v.t.* let off, draw off, discharge, decant, drain; anneal (steel); deduct.— *v.i.* leave off, cease; (of colors) fade or come off.

**Ablass-hahn,** *m.* delivery cock, discharge cock, drain cock. **-rohr,** *n.,* **-röhre,** *f.* outlet tube or pipe. **-ventil,** *n.* outlet valve, drain valve.

**Ablauf,** *m.* running off, discharge, outlet, drain; sink; effluent; filtrate; slope; expiration (of time); result, event.

**ablaufen,** *v.i.* run off or down, drain; expire.

**Ablauf-flüssigkeit,** *f.* discharge liquid, drainage liquid. **-hahn,** *m.* = Ablasshahn. **-öl,** *n.* expressed oil; run oil. **-rohr,** *n.,* **-röhre,** *f.* outlet tube, waste pipe. **-trichter,** *m.* draining funnel, condensing funnel (inverted funnel with tubulated rim for carrying off condensed vapors).

**Ablauge,** *f.* spent lye, spent liquor, waste liquor; washing out.

**ablaugen,** *v.t.* lixiviate; wash out lye from; steep in lye.

**abläutern,** *v.t.* clarify, purify, refine, fine; strain; draw off; wash (ore).

**Abläuterung,** *f.* clarification, etc. (see abläutern).

**Abläuterungsvorrichtung,** *f.* clarifying apparatus.

**Ableben,** *n.* death.

**ablegen,** *v.t.* lay aside or off: unwind, unroll.

**Ableger,** *m.* (of plants) layer, slip, scion.

**ablehnen,** *v.t.* decline, challenge, reject, refuse; turn aside.

**ableitbar,** *a.* derivable, etc. (see ableiten).

**ableiten,** *v.t.* derive; turn aside, lead off, carry off.—*v.r.* be derived (from).

**Ableiterohr,** *n.* delivery tube or pipe.

**Ableitung,** *f.* derivation; derivative; deduction; carrying off; drainage; channel; turning aside.

**Ableitungs-mittel,** *n.* revulsive; derivative. **-rohr,** *n.,* **-röhre,** *f.* delivery tube, delivery pipe; drain conduit.

**ablenken,** *v.t.* turn off, deflect; diffract; distract.—*i.* turn aside, deviate.

**Ablenkung,** *f.* deflection; diffraction; diversion; deviation.

**Ablenkungskraft,** *f.* deflecting force.

**Ablese-.** reading. **-fehler,** *m.* error in reading **-lupe,** *f.* reading lens.

**ablesen,** *v.t.* read off; pluck off, pick, gather.

**Ablesevorrichtung,** *f.* reading device.

**Ablesung,** *f.* reading (off), observation; gathering, harvest, crop.

**Ablesungsfehler,** *m.* error in reading.

**ablichten,** *v.t.* (*Dyeing*) reduce, shade, strip.

**abliefern,** *v.t.* deliver.

**Ablieferung,** *f.* delivery.

**ablohnen,** *v.t.* pay off.

**ablöschbar,** *a.* slakable (lime); temperable.

**ablöschen,** *v.t.* quench; slake (lime); temper (iron or steel); smother, extinguish (fire).

**Ablöschflüssigkeit,** *f.* quenching or tempering liquid.

**ablösen,** *v.t.* loosen; detach; split off; dissolve; relieve.—*v.r.* come loose, come off. —**ablösend,** *p.a.* (*Med.*) resolvent.

**Ablösung,** *f.* loosening, etc. (see ablösen).

**Ablösungs-fläche,** *f.* cleavage surface; (*Geol.*) jointing plane, joint. **-richtung,** *f.* (*Cryst.*) cleavage plane.

**ablöten,** *v.t.* unsolder.

**Abluft,** *f.* outgoing air.

**ablüften,** *v.t.* expose to the air, air.

**Abluftrohr,** *n.* air outlet tube (or pipe).

**ablutieren,** *v. t.* unlute.

**abmachen,** *v.t.* loosen, detach; settle, arrange.

**Abmachung,** *f.* taking off; arrangement, settlement, agreement; stipulation.

**abmagern,** *v. i.* lose flesh.

**abmahnen,** *v.t.* dissuade, warn.

**abmaischen,** *v.t. & i.* finish mashing.

**Abmaischtemperatur,** *f.* final temperature (of mashing).

**abmatten,** *v.t.* fatigue, exhaust; deaden (gold).

**abmessbar,** *a.* measurable, mensurable.

**abmessen,** *v.t.* measure off.—**abgemessen,** *p.a.* measured, precise.

**Abmessung,** *f.* measurement; adjustment; dimension.

**abmindern,** *v.t.* lessen, diminish.

**abnagen,** *v.t.* gnaw (off); erode.

**Abnahme,** *f.* decrease, decline, diminution; taking off or away; sale.

**abnarben,** *v.t.* buff; scrape.

**abnehmbar,** *a.* removable, detachable.

**abnehmen,** *v.t.* take off, take away, remove; infer.—*v.i.* decrease, decline, diminish, wane.

**Abnehmer,** *m.* buyer, purchaser; customer.

**Abneigung,** *f.* deviation, slope; disinclination.

**abnorm,** *a.* abnormal, anomalous, irregular.

**Abnormität,** *f.* abnormality, anomaly, irregularity.

**abnutschen,** *v.t.* =absaugen.

**abnutzen, abnützen,** *v.t.* use up, wear out.

**Abnutzung, Abnützung,** *f.* wear, wasting, abrasion, attrition.

**Aböl,** *n.* waste oil.

**abölen,** *v.t.* oil off; remove oil from; oil thoroly.

**Abonnement,** *n.* subscription.

**Abonnent,** *m.* subscriber.

**abonnieren,** *v.i.* subscribe.

**aboxydieren,** *v.t.* oxidize off, remove by oxidation.

**abpälen,** *v.t.* unhair, depilate.

**abpassen,** *v.t.* measure, fit, adjust.

**abplatten,** *v.t.* flatten.—**abgeplattet,** *p.a.* flattened, oblate.

**abprallen,** *v.i.* rebound, be reflected.

**Abprallung,** *f.* rebound, resiliency, reverberation; (*Optics*) reflection.

**abpressen,** *v.t.* press or squeeze off; separate by pressing; express.

**Abprodukt,** *n.* waste product, by-product.

**abpumpen,** *v.t.* pump off; drain by pumping.

**Abputz,** *m.* plaster, plastering.

**abputzen,** *v.t.* plaster; clean off, trim, dress; cut off.

**abquetschen,** *v.t.* squeeze off, squeeze out.

**abquicken,** *v.t.* purify; refine with mercury; separate (gold or silver) from amalgam.

**abrahmen,** *v.t.* take the cream from, skim.

**Abrahmer,** *m.* skimmer.

**abraten,** *v.t.* dissuade, warn.

**abrauchen,** *v.t. & i.* evaporate (with fuming).

**abräuchern,** *v.t.* fumigate thoroly.

**Abrauch-raum,** *m.* evaporating space or chamber. **-schale,** *f.* evaporating dish or vessel.

**Abraum,** *m.* rubbish, trash, rubble.

**abräumen,** *v.t.* take away, clear away; clear (of something); empty.

**Abräumen,** *n.* (*Brewing*) clearing the kiln.

**Abraum-salze,** *n. pl.* abraum salts (saline deposits overlying the rock salt at Stassfurt and elsewhere). **-stoff,** *m.* waste.

**abrechnen,** *v.t.* deduct; reckon off.—*v.i.* settle.

**Abrechnung,** *f.* deduction, discount; settlement; calculation; account.

**Abrede,** *f.* agreement; denial.

**abreiben,** *v.t.* rub off, scrape, scour, rub smooth, abrade; grind (colors).

**Abreibung,** *f.* rubbing off or down; abrasion; attrition.

**abreisen,** *v.i.* depart.

**abreissen,** *v.t.* tear off, pull off, remove; pull down; draw.—*v.i.* break.

**abresten,** *v.t.* (*Brewing*) decant.

**Abrichtelauge,** *f.* (*Soap*) weak caustic liquor.

**abrichten,** *v.t.* fit, adjust, true; train.

**Abrieb,** *m.* rubbings, grindings, dust.

**Abriss,** *m.* outline, sketch, design.

**abrollen,** *v.t.* roll off, unroll, unfold, uncoil.

**abröschen,** *v.t.* air (paper).

**abrosten,** *v.i.* rust off or away, corrode.

**abrösten,** *v.t.* roast thoroly.

**Abrostung,** *f.* rusting, corrosion.

**Abröstung,** *f.* thoro roasting.

**abröten,** *v.t.* dye red, color red.—*v.i.* lose red color.

**abrunden,** *v.t.* round off, round, finish off.— **abgerundet,** *p.a.* rounded off; (of glass edges) fire-polished; round (numbers).

**abrussecht,** *a.* fast to rubbing, not crocking.

**abrussen,** *v.i.* (of colored goods) rub off, crock.

**abrüsten,** *v.i.* disarm.

**absacken,** *v.t.* sack; unload.—*v.i.* sink down; shrink.

**absagen,** *v.t.* countermand, renounce.

**absalzen,** *v.t.* salt (thoroly).

**absättigen,** *v.t.* saturate, neutralize.

**Absättigung,** *f.* saturation, neutralization.

**Absatz,** *m.* deposit, sediment; pause; paragraph; sale; heel (of a shoe). **-gefäss,** *n.* sedimentation vessel, settling tank.

**absätzig,** *a.* interrupted; (of wool) inferior, faulty.

**absatzweise,** *adv.* interruptedly, intermittently, fractionally.

**absäuern,** *v.t.* acidify, sour.

**Absaug(e)-flasche,** *f.* suction flask, filtering flask. **-haube,** *f.* suction hood. **-kolben,** *m.* suction flask, filter flask. **-leitung,** *f.* suction piping, suction line.

**absaugen,** *v.t.* suck off; filter with suction; draw off by suction, exhaust, aspirate; (*Dyeing*) hydro-extract.

**Absaugentfeuchter,** *m.* vacuum desiccator.

**Absaug(e)öffnung,** *f.* suction outlet.

**Absauger,** *m.* (*Paper*) suction box; (*Dyeing*) hydro-extractor.

**Absaug(e)trockenofen,** *m.* vacuum drying oven.

**Absaugflasche,** etc. see Absaug(e)flasche, etc.

**Absaugung,** *f.* sucking off, suction, etc. (see absaugen).

**Absaugungsanlage,** *f.* suction installation.

**abschaben,** *v.t.* scrape off; clean; scrape, abrade.

**Abschabsel,** *n.* scrapings, shavings.

**abschaffen,** *v.t.* do away with, abolish.

**abschälen,** *v.t.* shell, peel, pare, bark, decorticate.—*v.r.* peel off, scale off, come off.

**abschalten,** *v.t.* disconnect.

**Abschälung,** *f.* shelling, etc. (see abschälen).

**abschattieren,** *v.t. & i.* shade off.

**abschätzen,** *v.t.* estimate, value, appraise.

**Abschaum,** *m.* scum, skimmings, dross.

**abschäumen,** *v.t.* skim off, skim.

**Abschäumer,** *m.* skimming apparatus; skimmer.

**Abschaum-löffel,** *m.* skimmer, skimming ladle. **-sieb,** *n.* skimming sieve.

**Abschäumung,** *f.* skimming off, skimming.

**abscheidbar,** *a.* separable.

**Abscheide-gefäss,** *n.* separating vessel. **-kammer,** *f.* separating chamber; condensation chamber.

**abscheiden,** *v.t.* separate; part, disengage, eliminate; refine (metals); secrete.—*v.r.* separate, be precipitated, be deposited; be separated.—*v.i.* depart.—**abgeschieden,** *p.a.* departed, deceased.

**Abscheider,** *m.* separator; refiner.

**Abscheidung,** *f.* separation; elimination; deposit; secretion; departure.

**Abscheidungs-mittel,** *n.* means of separation; precipitant. **-produkt,** *n.* secretion. **-verfahren,** *n.* separation process. **-vorrichtung,** *f.* separator.

**abscheren,** *v.t.* shear off, cut off.

**Abscheu,** *m.* horror; loathing.

**abscheuern,** *v.t.* scour (off), rub off; cleanse.

**Abscheuerung,** *f.* scouring; attrition.

**abscheulich,** *a* horrible, detestable.

**abschichten,** *v.t.* separate into layers.

**Abschied,** *m.* parting, departure; dismissal, discharge; farewell.

**abschiefern,** *v.i.* flake or scale off; exfoliate.

**abschiessen,** *v.t.* shoot off.—*v.i.* shoot off or down; (of colors) fade, lose color.

**abschirmen,** *v.t.* screen off.

**Abschirmungszahl,** *f.* screening number, screening constant.

**abschlacken,** *v.t.* remove slag from.

**Abschlag,** *m.* fragments, chips, etc.; rebound; outlet; deduction, reduction; instalment.

**abschlagen,** *v.t.* beat or knock off or back; take to pieces; refuse; turn off; drain; (*Founding*) stop (molten metal); (*Pharm.*) sieve.—*v.i.* abate; fall (in price).

**abschlämmen, abschlammen,** *v.t.* wash, elutriate; decant.

**Abschlämmung,** *f.* washing; decantation.

**abschleifen,** *v.t.* grind off, grind, rub off; polish; sharpen.

**Abschleifung,** *f.* grinding off, attrition; polishing; sharpening.

**abschleimen,** *v.t.* rid of slime, slime, clarify (sugar).

**abschlemmen,** *v.t.* wash, elutriate; decant.

**abschleppen,** *v.t.* draw off, carry away.

**Abschleudermaschine,** *f.* centrifugal, centrifuge; hydro-extractor.

**abschleudern,** *v.t.* centrifuge; hydro-extract (yarn, etc.); separate in a centrifugal; fling off.

**abschlichten,** *v.t.* smooth, plane.

**abschliessen,** *v.t.* occlude; close, shut off; seclude; separate; conclude.—**abschliessend,** *p.a.* conclusive, final, positive.

**Abschliessung,** *f.* occlusion, etc. (see abschliessen).

**Abschluss,** *m.* = Abschliessung; closing device, shut-off. **-hahn,** *m.* stopcock. **-schie'>er,** *m.* slide valve. **-vorrichtung,** *f.* closing device.

**abschmeckend,** *a.* of unpleasant flavor; insipid.

**Abschmelzdraht,** *m.* fuse wire, fusible wire.

**abschmelzen,** *v.t.* melt off, melt, fuse, separate by melting; seal off, seal.

**Abschmelz-konstante,** *f.* fusion coefficient. **-sicherung,** *f.* (*Elec.*) safety fuse.

**Abschmelzung,** *f.* melting off, etc. (see abschmelzen); (*Metal.*) liquation.

**abschmieren,** *v.t.* grease (thoroly).

**abschmirgeln,** *v.t.* polish with emery.

**abschmutzen,** *v.i.* rub off, soil.

**Abschn.,** *abbrev.* (Abschnitt) section.

**Abschneideapparat,** *m.* (*Mach.*) cutter.

**abschneiden,** *v.t.* cut off, cut away, cut; (*Math.*) truncate.—*v.i.* be cut off, end.

**Abschnitt,** *m.* cutting, chip; segment; portion, section, division; period (of time).

**Abschnitzel,** *n.* shred, chip, paring.

**abschnüren,** *v.t.* untie; mark off, lay off.

**abschöpfen,** *v.t.* skim off, skim; ladle out.

**abschrägen,** *v.t.* slope, slant, bevel, taper.

**Abschrägung,** *f.* sloping, slope, bevel, taper.

**abschrauben,** *v.t.* screw off, unscrew.

**abschrecken,** *v.t.* chill, cool; quench (metals, etc.); render (water) lukewarm; deter, frighten off.

**Abschreckung,** *f.* chilling, etc. (see abschrecken).

**abschreiben,** *v.t.* write off, copy; revoke.

**abschreiten,** *v.t.* step off; pace off.

**Abschrift,** *f.* copy; duplicate.

**abschuppen,** *v.i.* scale off, flake off.

**abschüssig,** *a.* steep.

**abschütten,** *v.t.* pour off, run off.

**abschwächen,** *v.t. & r.* weaken; diminish, decrease, reduce; soften; mellow (leather); (*Photog.*) clear.

**Abschwächer,** *m.* (*Photog.*) clearing agent.

**Abschwächung,** *f.* weakening, etc. (see abschwächen).

**abschwärzen,** *v.t.* blacken.—*v.i.* lose black color, come off black.

**abschweelen,** *v.t.* = abschwelen.

**abschwefeln,** *v.t.* free of sulfur, desulfurize; coke (coal); less commonly, impregnate with sulfur.

**Abschwefelung,** *f.* desulfurization.

**Abschweifung,** *f.* deviation; digression.

**abschwelen, abschweelen,** *v.t.* calcine, roast.

**abschwemmen,** *v.t.* wash, rinse; wash away.

**abschwenken,** *v.t.* wash off, rinse; wash away.

**abschwingen,** *v.t.* centrifuge, hydro-extract; fan, winnow.

**abschwirren,** *v.t.* whiz, centrifuge.

**abschwitzen,** *v.t.* depilate (leather).

**Abscisse,** *f.* abscissa.

**absehbar,** *a.* perceivable, observable.—**in absehbarer Zeit,** within any predeterminable time.

**absehen,** *v.t.* see, perceive; aim at.—*v.i.* (with von) disregard, let alone.—**abgesehen,** *p.a.* (with von) not mentioning, apart from.

**Abseide,** *f.* floss silk.

**abseifen,** *v.t.* clean with soap; wash out the soap from.

**abseigern,** *v.t.* separate by fusion; (*Metal.*) liquate.

**Abseihbier,** *n.* drawings; residue beer in chip cask.

**Abseihebeutel,** *m.* filtering bag.

**abseihen,** *v.t.* filter, filter off, strain, decant, percolate.

**Abseihung,** *f.* filtration, etc. (see abseihen).

**abseits,** *adv.* aside, apart.

**absenden,** *v.t.* send off or away; forward.

**absengen,** *v.t.* singe off, singe, flame.

**absenken,** *v.t.* lower.

**Absenkung,** *f.* lowering.

**absetzen,** *v.t.* deposit; put down or off; interrupt; put in type; depose.—*v.r.* settle, subside, deposit.

**Absetzung,** *f.* deposition, etc. (see absetzen); sedimentation; sediment.

**Absetzzisterne,** *f.* settling cistern.

**Absicht,** *f.* intention, purpose, view.

**absichtlich,** *a.* intentional.

**absieben,** *v.t.* sieve, screen.

**absieden,** *v.t.* decoct, extract by boiling, boil.

**absinken,** *v.i.* sink away, sink down.

**Absinth,** *m.* wormwood; absinth.

**absinthan, absinthartig,** *a.* absinthine.

**absiphonieren,** *v.t.* siphon off.

**Absitzbütte,** *f.* (*Brewing*) settling tub.

**absitzen,** *v.i.* deposit, settle; dismount.

**absol.,** *abbrev.* (absolut) absolute.

**absolut,** *a.* absolute; (of oils) essential.

**Absoluttrockengewicht,** *n.* absolute dry weight (all moisture having been expelled).

**absondern,** *v.t.* separate, detach, isolate; insulate; abstract; extract, segregate; (*Physiol.*) secrete, excrete.—**absondernd,** *p.a.* (*Physiol.*) secretory, secreting, excreting.

**Absonderung,** *f.* separation, etc. (see absondern); (*Geol.*) jointing.

**Absonderungs-flüssigkeit,** *f.* secretory fluid, secretion. **-stoff,** *m.* secreted material. **-vorgang,** *m.* process of secretion.

**Absorbens,** *n.* absorbent.

**Absorbentia,** *n.pl.* absorbents.

**absorbierbar,** *a.* absorbable.

**Absorbierbarkeit,** *f.* absorbability.

**absorbieren,** *v.t.* absorb.—**absorbierend,** *p.a.*

absorbent, absorptive.—**absorbierendes Mittel**, absorbent, absorptive.

**Absorbierung**, *f.* absorbing, absorption.

**absorptiometrisch**, *a.* absorptiometric.

**Absorptions-anlage**, *f.* absorption equipment or plant. **-apparat**, *m.* absorption apparatus.

**absorptionsfähig**, *a.* absorptive, absorbent.

**Absorptions-fähigkeit**, *f.* capability of absorbing, absorptive power. **-farbe**, *f.* absorption color. **-flasche**, *f.* absorption bottle, absorption flask. **-flüssigkeit**, *f.* absorption liquid. **-gefäss**, *n.* absorption vessel. **-gesetz**, *n.* law of absorption. **-kraft**, *f.* absorptive power. **-mittel**, *n.* absorbent. **-rohr**, *n.*, **-röhre**, *f.* absorption tube. **-schlange**, *f.* absorption coil. **-streifen**, *m.* absorption band. **-turm**, *m.* absorption tower. **-verbindung**, *f.* absorption compound. **-verfahren**, *n.* absorption process. **-vermögen**, *n.* absorptive power, absorption capacity. **-wärme**, *f.* heat of absorption.

**abspalten**, *v.t.& i.* split off, cleave off, separate.

**Abspaltung**, *f.* splitting off, cleavage, separation.

**abspannen**, *v.t.* relieve from tension, release (a spring, etc.); relax; (allow to) expand; cut off (steam).—**abgespannt**, *p.a.* released, etc.; unstrung, unnerved.

**Abspannung**, *f.* release (from tension); relaxation; expansion; lassitude.

**abspateln**, *v.t.* scrape off (with a spatula).

**absperren**, *v.t.* shut off, cut off, confine, stop, block.

**Absperr-flüssigkeit**, *f.* confining liquid, sealing liquid. **-glied**, *n.* shut-off. **-hahn**, *m.* stopcock. **-ventil**, *n.* cut-off valve, stop valve, check valve.

**abspielen**, *v.t.* play.—*v.r.* take place.

**abspitzen**, *v.t.* sharpen to a point, point.

**absplittern**, *v.t., i.& r.* splinter off.

**absprechen**, *v.t.* deny; discuss; arrange.—*v.i.* pass judgment.—**absprechend**, *p.a.* peremptory, positive.

**absprengen**, *v.t.* break, spring or burst off; drive off; blast.

**Absprenger**, *m.* (for glass tubes) cutter.

**abspringen**, *v.i.* leap or fly off; burst off, crack off; rebound; (of wood) warp, start; (of iron) be red-short.—**abspringend**, *p.a.* in contrast; desultory.

**abspritzen**, *v.t.* wash off or down (with a jet); spray.

**absprudeln**, *v.i.* bubble away.

**Absprung**, *m.* leaping off or rebounding; contrast; fragment; (*Physics*) reflection.

**abspülen**, *v.t.* wash off, wash, cleanse, rinse; wash away.

**Abspülung**, *f.* washing off, etc. (see abspülen).

**abstammen**, *v.i.* descend, come; be derived.

**Abstammung**, *f.* origin, descent, derivation.

**Abstand**, *m.* distance, interval, difference; desisting, renouncement.—**Abstand nehmen**, desist (from).

**abständig**, *a.* deteriorated; flat, stale.

**abstatten**, *v.t.* render, give.

**abstäubecht**, *a.* not crocking.

**abstäuben, abstauben**, *v.t.* dust off, dust.—*v.i.* (of colors) crock.

**abstechen**, *v.t.* tap, draw, run off; drain; etch (a picture); cut off; cut up.

**Abstecher**, *m.* (*Metal.*) tapper; excursion.

**abstecken**, *v.t.* mark out.

**abstehen**, *v.i.* grow stale, decay, decompose; stand off; desist.—**abgestanden**, *p.a.* stale, flat, dead; decayed.

**absteigen**, *v.i.* descend.

**Abstellbrett**, *n.* storage board or shelf.

**abstellen**, *v.t.* turn off, shut off, stop; put off, put away; annul.

**Abstell-hahn**, *m.* stopcock. **-vorrichtung**, *f.* cut-off device.

**absterben**, *v.i.* die, fade, wither, decay; (of lime) air-slack; (*Sugar*) change from transparent to opaque crystalline mass.

**abstergieren**, *v.t.* cleanse.

**Abstich**, *m.* tapping, drawing; running; tapped metal; contrast. **-loch**, *n.*, **-öffnung**, *f.* tap hole.

**abstimmen**, *v.i.* disagree; vote.—*v.t.* tune.

**abstoppen**, *v.t.* stop off, stop up, stop.

**abstöpseln**, *v.t.* unstop, uncork.

**abstossen**, *v.t.* repel; push off, rub off, scrape off.—**abstossend**, *p.a.* repelling, repulsive.

**Abstossung**, *f.* repulsion; pushing off.

**Abstrahl**, *m.* reflected ray.

**abstrahlen**, *v.t.* reflect.—*v.i.* be reflected.

**Abstrahlung**, *f.* reflection.

**Abstrebekraft**, *f.* centrifugal force.

**abstreichen**, *v.t.* wipe or scrape off; skim; strike out; deduct.

**Abstreicher**, *m.* scraper.

**Abstreich-löffel**, *m.* skimming ladle, skimmer. **-messer**, *n.* (*Calico*) doctor (literally, scraping-off knife).

**abstreifen**, *v.t.* strip off, skin.

**abstreiten**, *v.t.* dispute, contest.

**Abstrich**, *m.* skim, scum, dross, specif. a scum of arsenates, etc., on molten lead; deduction. **-blei**, *n.* lead skim (see Abstrich).

**abströmen**, *v.i.* flow away, flow off.

**abstufen**, *v.t.* gradate; graduate.—*v.r.* grade, grade off.

**Abstufung**, *f.* gradation; graduation.

**abstumpfen**, *v.t.* neutralize, saturate (acids); truncate; blunt, dull, deaden.—**abgestumpft**, *p.a.* neutralized, etc.; blunt, dull.

**Abstumpfung**, *f.* neutralization, etc. (see abstumpfen).

**Abstumpfungsfläche,** f. (*Cryst.*) truncating face.

**abstürzen,** v.t. throw down, dump; remove the lid from.—v.i. fall down; fall off.

**absuchen,** v.t. search, examine; pick off, clear off.

**Absud,** m. decoction, extract; (*Dyeing*) specif., iron or chrome mordant.

**Absüssbottich,** m. edulcorating vat.

**absüssen,** v.t. sweeten, purify by washing, edulcorate; wash out, wash (a precipitate).

**Absüss-kessel,** m. edulcorating vessel. -spindel, f. (*Sugar*) sweet-water spindle (or hydrometer).

**Absüssung,** f. sweetening, etc. (see absüssen).

**Absüsswasser,** n. (*Sugar*) sweet water.

**Absynt,** m. = Absinth.

**Abszisse,** f. abscissa.

**Abt,** m. abbot.

**abtasten,** v.t. feel out.

**abtauen,** v.t. thaw off, thaw, melt.

**abteilen,** v.t. separate, divide, divide off; graduate; classify.

**Abteilung,** f. division; graduation; part, section, class, lot.

**abthun,** v.t. = abtun.

**abtönen,** v.t. tone down, shade off.

**abtöten,** v.t. destroy, kill.

**abtragen,** v.t. carry off, clear off; wear out.

**abtränken,** v.t. (*Leather*) fill up with tan liquor.

**Abtreibe-herd,** m. refining hearth. -mittel, n. expulsive agent; abortifacient.

**abtreiben,** v.t. drive off, expel; separate (by distillation); refine (by cupellation), cupel; (*Med.*) abort.—**abtreibend,** p.a. (*Med.*) abortefacient.

**Abtreibeofen,** m. cupel furnace.

**Abtreibgas,** n. expelled gas.

**Abtreibung,** f. driving off, etc. (see abtreiben).

**abtrennbar,** a. separable.

**abtrennen,** v.t. separate; dissociate; dissever; detach; disconnect.

**abtreten,** v.t. tread, tread down, tread off; transfer, convey; yield, cede.—v.i. retire, yield; alight.

**Abtretung,** f. treading, etc. (see abtreten); transfer, cession; retirement.

**abtriefen,** v.i. trickle down, drip.

**abtrocknen,** v.t. dry off, dry; wipe dry.

**Abtropfbrett,** n. draining board or shelf.

**abtröpfeln,** v.i. drop, drip, trickle.

**abtropfen,** v.i. drop (off), drip, drain, dry.

**Abtropfer,** m. drainer, drip board, etc.

**Abtropf-gefäss,** n. drainer. -gestell, n. draining stand, dropping horse. -pfanne, f. drain pan, drainer; (in tin plating) list pot.

-platte, f. draining plate. -schale, f. draining dish or basin, drainer (with perforated bottom).

**abtun,** v.t. put or take off; settle.

**abwägen,** v.t. weigh off, weigh, weigh out; level; ponder.

**abwällen,** v.t. boil gently, simmer.

**Abwandlung,** f. modification.

**Abwärme,** f. waste heat, lost heat.

**abwärmen,** v.t. heat, warm.

**Abwärmeverlust,** m. waste-heat loss.

**abwarten,** v.t. wait for, wait on.

**abwärts,** adv. downward, down; off, away.

**Abwärtstransformator,** m. (*Elec.*) step-down transformer.

**abwaschen,** v.t. wash, wash off, wash out, rinse, cleanse.

**Abwaschung,** f. washing, etc. (see abwaschen); lotion.

**Abwasser,** n. waste water, waste liquor; specif., sewage. -leitung, f. drain.

**abwässern,** v.t. wash; free from water, drain, dry.

**Abwasser-reinigung,** f. waste-water purification. -rohr, n. waste pipe, drain pipe.

**abwechseln,** v.t. & i. alternate, vary.—**abwechselnd,** p.a. alternating, alternate, intermittent; variable.

**Abwechselung,** f. change, variation, alternation.

**Abweg,** m. by-way; wrong way.

**Abwehr,** f. warding off, defense.

**abwehren,** v.t. ward off, prevent.

**Abwehr-ferment,** n. protective ferment (or enzyme), defensive ferment (or enzyme). -mittel, n. prophylactic.

**abweichen,** v.t. & i. soak, soak off, soften (by steeping), macerate.

**abweichen,** v.i. deviate, diverge, depart, vary. —**abweichend,** p.a. deviating, divergent, irregular.

**Abweichung,** f. deviation; variation; declination (of the needle); (*Opt.*) aberration; anomaly.

**abweisen,** v.t. send away; refuse.

**abweissen,** v.t. whiten.—v.i. lose whiteness.

**abwelken,** v.t. wilt, wither, dry; (*Leather*) sammy.

**abwenden,** v.t. turn off, avert.

**abwerfen,** v.t. throw off or out; run off (slag); give off; discharge; reject; (*Com.*) yield.

**Abwerf-ofen,** m. refining furnace. -pfanne, f. refining pan; (*Tinning*) list pot.

**abwesend,** a. absent.

**Abwesenheit,** f. absence.

**abwickeln,** v.t. wind off, unwind; wind up; (*Math.*) rectify.

**abwiegen,** v.t. = abwägen.

**abwischen,** v.t. wipe off, wipe.

**Abwurf,** *m.* throwing off; something thrown off, offal; coarse plaster, roughcast.

**abzahlen,** *v.t.* pay, pay off.

**abzählen,** *v.t.* count, count off.

**abzapfen,** *v.t.* draw off, tap.

**abzehren,** *v.i.,* *r.& t.* waste (away); corrode.

**Abzehrung,** *f.* wasting (away); corrosion.

**Abzeichen,** *n.* mark, sign, label; (*pl.*) insignia.

**Abzieh-bild,** *n.* transfer picture or design, decalcomania. **-blase,** *f.* retort, alembic.

**abziehen,** *v.t.* draw off, take away, remove; rack, decant (liquids); bottle; distill, rectify; tap; skim; skin; subtract; abstract; transfer (designs); degum (silk); (*Dyeing*) strip, boil off (color); (*Leather*) strip, clear.—*v.i.* depart, leave, (of gases) escape.—**abgezogene Wasser,** distilled liquor(s).

**Abzieh-halle,** *f.* (*Brewing*) racking room. **-kolben,** *m.* retort, alembic. **-mittel,** *n.* (*Dyeing*) stripping agent.

**Abzug,** *m.* hood, fume cupboard; scum, dross, specif. a scum on molten lead, sharp slag; outlet, drainage, drain; vent; drawing off; deduction; proof sheet.

**Abzugs-blei,** *n.* lead obtained from dross. **-dampf,** *m.* drawn-off vapor; specif., exhaust steam. **-gas,** *n.* chimney gas, flue gas. **-kanal,** *m.* sewer, drain; discharge duct. **-kupfer,** *n.* copper obtained from dross (cf. Abzug). **-raum,** *m.* hood. **-rohr,** *n.,* **-röhre,** *f.* waste pipe, drain tube, drain pipe, outlet tube or pipe. **-schacht,** *m.* hood flue. **-schrank,** *m.* hood, fume cupboard. **-vorrichtung,** *f.* constant-level apparatus (for water baths). **-werke,** *n.pl.* (*Metal.*) scum, dross.

**abzweigen,** *v.t.* trim off, detach.—*v.r.* branch off.

**Abzweigleitung,** *f.* branch line.

**Abzweigung,** *f.* branching, branch.

**Ac-.** for words beginning Ac- see also Ak- and Az-.

**Acajou,** *m.* acajou (see Akajou).

**Ac Blei.** actinium lead.

**Acceleren,** *pl.* accelerators.

**accessorisch,** *a.* accessory.

**Accise,** *f.* excise.

**Accracopalinsäure,** *f.* accracopalinic acid.

**Accracopalsäure,** *f.* accracopalic acid.

**Aceanthrenchinon,** *n.* aceanthrenequinone.

**Acenaphten,** *n.* acenaphthene. **-chinon,** *n.* acenaphthenequinone.

**Acenaphtylen,** *n.* acenaphthylene.

**Acet-.** acet-; aceto-, acetic. **-anhydrid,** *n.* acetic anhydride.

**Acetat-lösung,** *f.* acetate solution. **-seide,** *f.* acetate silk.

**Acetessig-äther,** **-ester,** *m.* acetoacetic ester. **-säure,** *f.* acetoacetic acid.

**Acetindruck,** *m.* acetin printing.

**Acetolyse,** *f.* acetolysis.

**acetometrisch,** *a.* acetometric.

**Aceton-lösung,** *f.* acetone solution. **-öl,** *n.* acetone oil. **-säure,** *f.* acetonic (α-hydroxyisobutyric) acid.

**Acetopersäure, Acetpersäure,** *f.* peracetic acid.

**Acetsäure,** *f.* acetic acid.

**Acetylen-anstalt,** *f.* acetylene plant. **-bindung,** *f.* acetylene linkage, triple bond. **-brenner,** *m.* acetylene burner. **-erzeuger,** *m.* acetylene generator. **-kohlenwasserstoff,** *m.* acetylene hydrocarbon. **-kupfer,** *n.* copper acetylide. **-reihe,** *f.* acetylene series. **-russ,** *m.* acetylene black. **-schweissung,** *f.* acetylene welding.

**Acetylessigsäure,** *f.* acetoacetic acid.

**acetylierbar,** *a.* capable of being acetylated.

**acetylieren,** *v.t.* acetylate.

**Acetylierkolben,** *m.* acetylating flask.

**Acetylierung,** *f.* acetylation.

**Acetylierungs-kolben,** *m.* acetylation flask. **-mittel,** *n.* acetylating agent.

**Acetyl-säure,** *f.* acetic acid. **-schwefelsäure,** *f.* acetylsulfuric acid. **-senföl,** *n.* acetyl mustard oil. **-zahl,** *f.* acetyl number.

**Achat,** *m.* agate.

**achat-artig,** *a.* agate-like, agatine. **-haltig,** *a.* containing agate, agatiferous.

**Achat-mörser,** *m.* agate mortar. **-porzellan,** *n.* agate ware. **-schale,** *f.* agate dish. **-schneide,** *f.* agate knife edge.

**Achillenöl,** *n.* achillea oil.

**achromatisch,** *a.* achromatic.

**Achse,** *f.* axis; axle, shaft.

**Achsel,** *f.* shoulder; (*Physiol.*) axilla.

**Achsel-.** shoulder, axillary.

**Achsen-.** axis, axial, axle. **-drehung,** *f.* rotation. **-kreuz,** *n.* system of coördinates. **-öl,** *n.* axle oil.

**achsensymmetrisch,** *a.* axially symmetrical.

**Achsen-verhältnis,** *n.* axial ratio. **-winkel,** *m.* axial angle.

**achsig, achsial,** *a.* axial.

**Achslager,** *n.* axle bearing.

**acht,** *a.* eight.

**Acht,** *f.* attention, care.—**ausser — lassen,** disregard, neglect.

**achtbar,** *a.* respectable, honorable.

**achtbasisch,** *a.* octabasic.

**achte,** *a.* eighth.

**Achteck,** *n.* octagon.

**achteckig,** *a.* octagonal, eight-angled.

**Achtel,** *n.* eighth.

**Achtel-.** (in old names) octo-, octa-; as, **Achtelkohleneisen,** octoferric carbide, and **Achtelschwefeleisen,** octoferric sulfide.

**achten,** *v.t.* regard, respect, esteem.—*v.i.* pay attention, see (to).

**ächten,** *v.t.* outlaw.

**Achter,** *m.* figure-of-eight, figure 8. **-schale,** *f.* shell of eight electrons, octet shell.

**Achtflach,** *n.* octahedron.

**achtflächig,** *a.* octahedral.

**Achtflächner,** *m.* octahedron.

**acht-gliedrig,** *a.* eight-membered. **-kantig,** *a.* octagonal.

**Achtring,** *m.* eight-membered ring.

**achtsam,** *a.* careful, heedful.

**achtseitig,** *a.* eight-sided.

**Achtung,** *f.* attention, notice; esteem, respect.

**achtungsvoll,** *adv.* respectfully.

**achtwertig,** *a.* octavalent.

**Achtwertigkeit,** *f.* octavalence.

**achtzehn,** *a.* eighteen.

**Achtzehnerperiode,** *f.,* period of eighteen.

**achtzig,** *a.* eighty.

**ächzen,** *v.i.* groan.

**acidifizieren,** *v.t.* acidify.

**Acidifizierung,** *f.* acidification.

**Acidimetrie,** *f.* acidimetry.

**acidimetrisch,** *a.* acidimetric(al).

**Acidität,** *f.* acidity.

**acidylieren,** *v.t.* acylate.

**Acker,** *m.* field, land; acre. **-bau,** *m.* agriculture, farming. **-bauchemie,** *f.* agricultural chemistry. **-bauwissenschaft,** *f.* science of agriculture. **-boden,** *m.* arable soil, surface soil. **-bohne,** *f.* field bean, broad bean (*Vicia faba*). **-doppen,** *f.pl.* valonia.

**Ackerei,** *f.* tillage.

**Acker-erde,** *f.* (arable) soil. **-günsel,** *m.* ground pine (*Ayuga chamaepitys*). **-kamille,** *f.* wild camomile (*Matricaria*). **-mennig,** *m.* agrimony. **-minze,** *f.* corn mint (*Mentha arvensis*).

**ackern,** *v.t.* till, cultivate.

**Aconit-.** see Akonit-.

**acyclisch, acyklisch,** *a.* acyclic.

**acylieren,** *v.t.* acylate.

**a.d.,** *abbrev.* (an der, an dem, etc.) at the, on, on the, to the.

**ad,** *prep.* (Latin) to, up to.

**adäquat.** *a.* adequate.

**Addend,** *n.* something to be added, addendum.

**addieren,** *v.t.* add. — **addierend,** *p.a.* additive.—*adv.* additively.

**additionell,** *a.* additional, addition.

**additionsfähig,** *a.* capable of addition.

**Additions-fähigkeit,** *f.* additive power. **-reaktion,** *f.* addition reaction, additive reaction. **-verbindung,** *f.* addition compound.

**Additivität,** *f.* additivity.

**Additivitätsbeziehung,** *f.* additivity relation.

**Address-.** see Adress-.

**Adel,** *m.* nobility.

**adelig,** *a.* noble.

**adeln,** *v.t.* ennoble; dignify.

**Ader,** *f.* vein (in various senses). **-haut,** *f.* choroid. **-häutchen,** *n.* chorion.

**aderig, äderig,** *a.* veiny, veined, streaked venous, vascular.

**Aderlass,** *m.* venesection.

**adern, ädern,** *v.t.* vein; grain, marble.

**Aderwasser,** *n.* serum.

**adhärieren,** *v.i.* adhere.

**Adhäsion,** *f.* adhesion.

**Adhäsions-kraft,** *f.* adhesive power; force of adhesion. **-vermögen,** *n.* adhesive power.

**adhäsiv,** *a.* adhesive.

**Adiabate,** *f.* adiabatic curve.

**adiabatisch,** *a.* adiabatic.

**Adiowanöl,** *n.* ajowan oil.

**adipid,** *a.* fat, fatty.

**adipidieren,** *v.t.* grease.

**Adipinsäure,** *f.* adipic acid.

**Adipocire,** *n.* adipocere.

**adipös,** *a.* adipose.

**Adipoweinsäure,** *f.* adipotartaric acid.

**adjustieren,** *v.t.* adjust, regulate.

**Adler,** *m.* eagle. **-stein,** *m.* eaglestone, aetites. **-vitriol,** *m.* Salzburg vitriol (mixed cupric and ferrous sulfate).

**adlig,** *a.* noble.

**adoucieren,** *v.t.* sweeten; wash, edulcorate; temper, anneal; decarbonize (iron).

**Adoucier-gefäss,** *n.* annealing pot; edulcorating vessel. **-ofen,** *m.* tempering furnace, annealing furnace. ¶

**Adr.,** *abbrev.* (Adresse) address.

**Adressant,** *m.* writer; sender.

**Adressat,** *m.* person addressed; consignee.

**Adressbuch,** *n.* directory.

**Adresse,** *f.* address, direction.

**adressieren,** *v.t.* address; forward.

**adrig,** *a.* =aderig.

**Adsorbat, Adsorbend, Adsorbendum,** *n.* adsorbed substance, adsorbate.

**Adsorbens,** *m.* (*pl.* Adsorbentien) adsorbing substance, adsorbent.

**adsorbierbar,** *a.* adsorbable.

**Adsorbierbarkeit,** *f.* adsorbability.

**adsorbieren,** *v.t.* adsorb.

**Adsorptions-haut,** *f.,* **-häutchen,** *n.* adsorbed film, adsorption film. **-hülle,** *f.* adsorption shell or sheath. **-verbindung,** *f.* adsorption compound. **-wärme,** *f.* heat of adsorption.

**adstringierend,** *a.* astringent.—**adstringierendes Mittel,** astringent.

**Adular,** *m.* adularia.

**Advokat,** *m.* lawyer.

**Ae.,** *abbrev.* (Äther) ether.

**Å.E.,** *abbrev.* (Ångströmeinheit) Ångström unit.

Ae-. for words beginning Ae- see also Ä-.

aerobisch, aerobiontisch, *a.* aërobic.

Aerogengas, *n.* aerogene gas.

aerostatisch, *a.* aërostatic.

Aetz-. see Ätz-.

Affe, *m.* ape, monkey.

äffen, *v.t.* ape, mock.

Affenbrotbaum, *m.* baobab tree.

Affiche, *f.* poster, bill.

Affinade, *f.* washed raw sugar.

Affination, *f.* refining (esp. of gold by treating with sulfuric acid and of sugar by washing from mother liquor).

affinieren, *v.t.* refine.

Affinierung, *f.* refining.

Affinität, *f.* affinity.

Affinitäts-einheit, *f.* unit of affinity. -lehre, *f.* doctrine of affinity. -rest, *m.* affinity residue, residual affinity. -richtung, *f.* direction of affinity.

Affinivalenz, *f.* atomicity, valence.

After-. pseudo-, false, secondary, neo-, after-, back-, hind-; anal, rectal. -kohle, *f.* slack coal, slack. -kristall, *m.* pseudomorph. -moos, *n.* alga, algae. -schörl, *m.* axinite. -silber, *n.* silver containing dross.

A.G., A.-G., *abbrev.* (Atomgewicht) atomic weight; (Aktiengesellschaft) joint-stock company.

Agaricinsäure, *f.* agaric acid, agaricic acid.

Agens, *n.* agent.

Agentur, *f.* agency.

Agenzien, *m.pl.* agents.

Agfa, *abbrev.* Aktien-Gesellschaft für Anilinfarbenfabrikation.

agglutinieren, *v.t.& i.* agglutinate.

Aggregat, *n.* aggregate; outfit. -zustand, *m.* state of aggregation.

aggressiv, *a.* aggressive, offensive.

Agio, *n.* premium, agio.

Agitakel, *n.* stirrer.

Agrikultur, *f.* agriculture. -chemie, *f.* agricultural chemistry.

Agtstein, *m.* amber.

Ägypten, *n.* Egypt.

Ägypterblau, *n.* Egyptian blue.

ägyptisch, *a.* Egyptian.

Ahlbeere, *f.* black currant.

Ahle, *f.* awl, punch; black cherry.

Ahn, *m.* grandfather; ancestor.

Ahne, *f.* awn, chaff; grandmother.

ähneln, *v.i.& r.* resemble.

ahnen, *v.t.* anticipate; surmise.

ähnlich, *a.* similar; analogous, resembling, like. -ähnlich. similar to, resembling, -like, -oid.

Ähnlichkeit, *f.* similarity, resemblance, likeness.

Ahnung, *f.* presentiment, anticipation.

Ahorn, *m.* maple. -melasse, *f.* maple sirup.

-saft, *m.* maple sap. -säure, *f.* aceric acid. -zucker, *m.* maple sugar.

Ähre, *f.* ear, spike.

Ährenfrüchte, *f.pl.* grains, cereals.

Aichamt, aichen, *v.t.*, etc., see Eichamt, eichen, etc.

Ajowanöl, Ajoranöl, *n.* ajowan oil.

ajustieren, *v.t.* adjust.

Ajustiertisch, *m.* adjusting table.

Akajou, *m.* acajou (either cashew or mahogany tree). -harz, *n.* acajou resin.

Akaridentod, *m.* acaricide.

Akaroidharz, *n.* acaroid resin.

Akaschu, *m.* =Akajou.

Akazie, *f.* acacia.

Akazien-gummi, *n.* acacia gum, gum arabic. -öl, *n.* acacia oil.

Akazin, *n.* gum arabic.

Akeeöl, *n.* akee oil.

akkommodieren, *v.t.* accommodate.

Akkordarbeit, *f.* piece work, job work.

Akkumulator, *m.* accumulator, storage battery. -säure, *f.* battery acid, electrolyte. -zelle, *f.* storage-battery cell.

akkumulieren, *v.t.* accumulate.

Akonitinsäure, aconitic acid.

Akonit-knollen, *f.pl.* aconite root, aconite. -säure, *f.* aconitic acid.

Akridin-gelb, *n.* acridine yellow. -säure, *f.* acridic acid, acridinic acid.

Akrylsäure, *f.* acrylic acid.

Akt, *m.* act, action, deed.

Akte, *f.* act, deed, document, file, record.

Aktenpapier, *n.* deed paper, record paper.

Akt.-Ges., *abbrev.* of Aktiengesellschaft.

Aktie, *f.* share.

Aktiengesellschaft, *f.* joint-stock company.

aktinisch, *a.* actinic.

Aktinismus, *m.* actinism.

Aktinochemie, *f.* actinochemistry.

aktinometrisch, *a.* actinometric.

Aktionär, *m.* shareholder, stockholder.

aktiv, *a.* active.

Aktiva, Aktiven, *n.pl.* assets.

aktivieren, *v.t.* activate.

Aktivierung, *f.* activation.

Aktivierungszahl, *f.* activation number.

Aktivität, *f.* activity.

aktuell, *a.* actual; present; important.

Akustik, *f.* acoustics.

akustisch, *a.* acoustic.

Akzeptor, *m.* acceptor.

akzessorisch, *a.* accessory.

Akzidenzdruck, *m.* display printing.

Akzise, *f.* excise.

Alabastergips, *m.* plaster of Paris (best grade).

Alakreatin, *n.* alacreatine.

Alakreatinin, *n.* alacreatinine.

Alant, m. elecampane. -beere, f. black currant. -kampher, m. helenin. -öl, n. elecampane oil. -wurzel, f. (Pharm.) inula, elecampane.
alarmieren, v.t. alarm.
Alaun, m. alum.— — von Rocca, roche alum, Roman alum.
alaunartig, a. alumish, aluminous.
Alaun-bad, n. alum bath. -beize, f. (Dyeing) aluminous mordant; alum bath; (Leather) aluming, also alum steep. -brühe, f. (Leather) alum steep.
alaunen, v.t. alum.
Alaunerde, f. alumina.
alaunerdehaltig, a. aluminiferous.
Alaun-erdesulfat, n. sulfate of alumina (aluminum sulfate). -erz, n. alunite. -fass, n. (Leather) alum vat. -fels, m. alunite. -festigkeit, f. (Paper) alum resistance.
alaun-förmig, a. aluminiform. -gar, a. dressed with alum, alumed, tawed.
Alaun-gerber, m. tawer. -gerberei, f. tawing; tawery. -gips, m. artificial marble (made with alum and gypsum).
alaunhaltig, a. containing alum, aluminous, aluminiferous.
Alaunhütte, f. alum works.
alaunieren, v.t. alum.
alaunig, a. aluminous.
Alaun-kies, m. aluminous pyrites. -kuchen, m. alum cake. -lauge, f. alum liquor. -leder, n. alum leather. -lösung, f. alum solution. -mehl, -pulver, n. powdered alum, precipitated alum.
alaunsauer, a. aluminate of.—alaunsaures Salz, aluminate.
Alaun-schiefer, m., -schiefererz, n. alum slate, alum shale. -seife, f. aluminous soap. -sieden, n. alum boiling, alum making. -sieder, m. alum boiler. -siederei, f. alum works. -stein, -spat, m. alum stone, alunite.
alaunt, p.a. alumed.
Alaunung, f. aluming.
Alaun-wasser, n. alum water. -wurzel, f. alumroot.
albuminartig, a. albuminoid.
Albumingehalt, m. albumin content.
albuminisieren, v.t. albuminize.
Albuminisierung, f. albuminization.
Albumin-kupfer, n. copper albuminate. -stoff, m. albuminous substance, protein.
Alchimie, Alchemie, f. alchemy.
alchimistisch, a. alchemistic(al).
Aldehydgrün, n. aldehyde green.
aldehydhaltig, a. containing aldehyde.
Aldehydharz, n. aldehyde resin.
aldehydisch, a. aldehydic.

Aldehydsäure, f. aldehyde acid, aldehydic acid.
Alembrothsalz, n. alembroth, salt of alembroth ($2NH_4Cl \cdot HgCl_2 \cdot H_2O$).
alepisch, a. Aleppo.—alepischer Gallapfel, Aleppo gall.
Alfa, f. esparto (Stipa tenacissima).
Algarot(t)pulver, n. powder of Algaroth, algarot, algaroth (SbOCl).
Alge, f. alga, seaweed.
algebraisch, a. algebraic.
Algerien, n. Algeria.
Algol-blau, n. algol blue. -farbe, f., -farbstoff, m. algol dye. -rot, n. algol red.
alicyclisch, a. alicyclic.
aliphatisch, a. aliphatic.
Alit, n., Alith, m. (Cement) alite.
alitieren, v.t. (Steel) alite (coat with alumina).
Alizarin-blau, n. alizarin blue. -chinon, n. alizarinquinone. -färberei, f. alizarin dyeing. -gelb, n. alizarin yellow. -rot, n. alizarin red. -schwarz, n. alizarin black.
alizyklisch, a. alicyclic.
Alk., abbrev. (Alkohol) alcohol.
alkal., abbrev. (alkalisch) alkaline.
Alkaleszenz, f. alkalescence.
alkali-arm, a. poor in alkali. -artig, a. alkaloidal, alkaloid. -beständig, a. resistant to alkalies. -bildend, a. alkaligenous.
Alkali-blau, n. alkali blue. -chlorid, n. alkali chloride.
alkaliecht, a. fast to alkali.
Alkalien, n.pl. alkalies.
alkali-enthaltend, a. =alkalihaltig. -fest, a. alkali-proof.
Alkali-gehalt, m. alkali content. -gelb, n. alkali yellow. -halogenid, n. alkali halide.
alkalihaltig, a. containing alkali.
Alkali-hydrat, n. alkali hydrate (hydroxide). -lauge, f. alkali liquor, lye.
alkalilöslich, a. soluble in alkali, alkalisoluble.
Alkali-lösung, f. solution of alkali, alkaline liquor. -menge, f. amount of alkali. -messer, m. alkalimeter. -messung, f. alkalimetry. -metrie, f. alkalimetry.
alkalimetrisch, a. alkalimetric.
alkalinisch, a. alkaline.—alkalinische Erde, alkaline earth.
Alkalinität, f. alkalinity.
Alkali-rückstand, m. alkali residue. -salz, n. alkali (metal) salt.
Alkalisator, m. alkalizer.
alkalisch, a. alkaline.—alkalische Erde, alkaline earth.—alkalische Erdmetalle, alkaline-earth metals.—alkalische Luft, alkaline air (Priestley's name for ammonia).—alkalisch machen, render alkaline, alkalize.—alkalisch reagierend, giving an alkaline reaction.

alkalisierbar, *a.* alkalizable.

alkalisieren, *v.t.* render alkaline, alkalize.

Alkalisierung, *f.* alkalization.

Alkalität, *f.* alkalinity.

Alkali-zelle, *f.* (*Elec.*) alkaline cell. -zellstoff, *m.* alkali cellulose.

Alkalizität, *f.* alkalinity.

alkaloidartig, *a.* alkaloid-like, alkaloidal.

alkaloidisch, *a.* alkaloidal.

Alkaloid-lösung, *f.* alkaloidal solution. -vergiftung, *f.* alkaloid poisoning.

Alkamin, *n.* alcamine.

Alkannarot, *n.* alkanna red, anchusin.

Alkogel, *n.* alcogel.

alkoh., *abbrev.* (alkoholisch) alcoholic.

alkoholartig, *a.* alcohol-like, alcoholic.

Alkohol-artigkeit, *f.* alcoholicity. -auszug, *m.* alcoholic extract. -dampf, *m.* alcohol vapor.

alkohol-enthaltend, *a.* containing alcohol, alcoholic. -fest, *a.* alcohol-proof. -frei, *a.* alcohol-free, non-alcoholic.

Alkohol-gärung, *f.* alcoholic fermentation. -gehalt, *m.* alcohol content.

alkoholhaltig, *a.* containing alcohol, alcoholic.

alkoholisch, *a.* alcoholic.—alkoholische Getränke, alcoholic beverages.

alkoholschwässerig, *a.* aqueous-alcoholic.

alkoholisierbar, *a.* alcoholizable.

alkoholisieren, *v.t.* alcoholize.

Alkoholisierung, *f.* alcoholization.

alkohollöslich, *a.* soluble in alcohol.

Alkoholmesser, *m.* alcoholometer.

alkoholometrisch, *a.* alcoholometric.

Alkoholpräparat, *n.* alcoholic preparation.

alkoholreich, *a.* containing much alcohol.

Alkohol-säure, *f.* alcohol acid. -tafel, *f.* alcohol table.

alkoholunlöslich, *a.* insoluble in alcohol.

Alkoholvergiftung, *f.* alcoholic poisoning.

Alkoholyse, *f.* alcoholysis.

Alkoholzusatz, *m.* addition of alcohol.

Alkosol, *n.* alcosol.

Alkoven, *m.* alcove, recess.

alkoxyalkylieren, *v.t.*, convert into an alkoxy compound by alkylation.

Alkylhaloid, *n.* alkyl halide.

alkylieren, *v.t.* introduce alkyl into, alkylate.

Alkylierung, *f.* alkylation.

Alkylierungsmittel, *n.* alkylating agent.

Alkylrest, *n.* alkyl residue, alkyl group.

all, *a.* all, whole, every.—vor allem, above all.

allantoisch, *a.* allantoic.

Allantosäure, Allantoissäure, *f.* allantoic acid (allantoin).

allda, *adv.* there.

alledem, all that.—bei alledem, for all that, after all

Allee, *f.* avenue, alley.

allein, *a.* alone, single.—*adv.* only, merely.—*conj.* but, still.

Alleinhandel, *m.* monopoly.

alleinig, *a.* sole, unique.

alleinstehend, *p.a.* isolated, insulated; unmarried.

allelotrop, *a.* allelotropic.

allenfalls, *adv.* perhaps; at best.

allenthalben, *adv.* everywhere.

aller-best, *a.* best (of all), very best. -dings, *adv.* to be sure, it is true, of course. -feinst, *a.* finest (of all), very fine. -grösst, *a.* greatest (of all), very greatest. -hand, *a.* of all kinds, all sorts of.

Allerheiligenholz, *n.* logwood.

aller-jüngst, *a.* very recent. -lei, *a.* all kinds of.

Allerleigewürz, *n.* allspice.

aller-letzt, *a.* very last, ultimate; very recent. -neuest, *a.* very newest or latest. -wärts, *adv.* everywhere. -wesentlichst, *a.* most essential. -wichtigst, *a.* most important.

alles, *n.* all, everything.—vor allem, before all, above all, in the first place.

allfällig, *a.* eventual.—*adv.* eventually.

allg., *abbrev.* (allgemein) general; generally.

allgemach, *adv.* gradually, by degrees.

allgemein, *a.* general; common; (*Med.*) constitutional; epidemic.—*adv.* generally, commonly. -giltig, -gültig, *a.* of general validity.

alljährlich, *a.* yearly, annual.

allmählich, *a.* gradual.—*adv.* gradually, by degrees.

Alloisomerie, *f.* alloisomerism.

allomerisch, *a.* allomeric.

Allomerismus, *m.* allomerism.

allomorph, *a.* allomorphic.

Allomorphismus, *m.* allomorphism.

Allonge, *f.* adapter; fly leaf.

Alloschleimsäure, *f.* allomucic acid.

allotrop, *a.* allotropic.

Allotropie, *f.* allotropy, allotropism.

allotropisch, *a.* allotropic.

Allotropismus, *m.* allotropism.

Alloxur-basen, *f.pl.* alloxuric bases (purine bases). -körper, *m.pl.* alloxuric substances (purine substances).

Allozimtsäure, *f.* allocinnamic acid.

allseitig, *a.* on all sides; universal; versatile.

alltäglich, *a.* daily; commonplace; (*Med.*) quotidian.

Allyl-jodid, *n.* allyl iodide. -rhodanid, *n.* allyl thiocyanate. -senföl, *n.* allyl mustard oil. -verbindung, *f.* allyl compound.

allzu, *adv.* too much, altogether too.

Almeroder Tiegel. Hessian crucible.

Aloe, *f.* aloes.

**aloehaltig**, *a.* aloetic.
**Aloe-hanf**, *m.* aloe hemp (agave). **-holz**, *n.* agalloch. **-mittel**, *n.* (*Med.*) aloetic. **-saft**, *m.* aloe juice, aloes.
**Aloetinsäure, Aloesäure**, *f.* aloetic acid.
**aloetisch**, *a.* aloetic.
**Alpha-milchsäure**, *f.* ($\alpha$-)lactic acid. **-strahlen**, *m.pl.* alpha rays.
**Alpranken**. bittersweet (*Solanum dulcamara*).
**Alquifoux**, *n.* alquifou, potter's lead.
**Alraun**, *m.*, **Alraune, Alrune**, *f.* mandrake.
**Alraunwurzel**, *f.* (*Pharm.*) mandragora.
**als**, *conj.* as, like; than, except; when; as if.
**alsbald**, *adv.* at once.
**alsdann**, *adv.* then.
**also**, *adv. & conj.* accordingly, therefore, so, thus, then, i.e.
**alt**, *a.* old, aged, ancient. **-backen**, *p.a.* stale. **-bekannt**, *p.a.* long-known, well known.
**Alteisen**, *n.* old iron, scrap iron.
**Alter**, *n.* age, old age.
**Alterantia**, *n.pl.* alteratives.
**altern**, *v.i.* age, grow old; decline.—*v.t.* age.
**alternieren**, *v.i.* alternate.—**alternierend**, *p.a.* alternating, alternate.
**Alters-**. old-age, senile, age, of age.
**Altertum**, *n.* antiquity.
**Altertumskunde**, *f.* archeology.
**Alterung**, *f.* aging.
**Alterungshärtung**, *f.* age-hardening.
**Alt-gesell**, *m.* foreman. **-gold**, *n.* old gold. **-gummi**, *n.* old rubber, used rubber.
**Althee**, *f.* marsh mallow (*Althaea officinalis*); (*Pharm.*) althaea. **-wurzel**, *f.* (*Pharm.*) althaea.
**altklug**, *a.* precocious.
**Alt-malz**, *n.* stored malt. **-messing**, *n.* old brass. **-metall**, *n.* old metal, scrap metal. **-papier**, *n.* old paper, used paper. **-schaden-wasser**, *n.* (*Pharm.*) yellow mercurial lotion. **-stoff**, *m.* old material, waste.
**Aluchiharz**, *n.* acouchi resin, aluchi resin.
**Aludelofen**, *m.* aludel furnace.
**Aluminium**, *n.* aluminum, aluminium. **-blech**, *n.* sheet aluminum. **-bor**, *n.* aluminum boride. **-draht**, *m.* aluminum wire. **-feil-späne**, *m.pl.* aluminum filings. **-fluorwas-serstoffsäure**, *f.* fluoaluminic acid. **-guss**, *m.* aluminum casting.
**aluminiumhaltig**, *a.* containing aluminum.
**Aluminium-hydrat**, *n.* aluminum hydroxide. **-kaliumsulfat**, *n.* aluminum potassium sulfate. **-legierung**, *f.* aluminum alloy. **-messing**, *n.* aluminum brass. **-oxydhydrat**, *n.* aluminum hydroxide. **-pulver**, *n.* aluminum powder. **-rhodanid**, *n.* aluminum thiocyanate. **-rohr**, *n.*, **-röhre**, *f.* aluminum pipe or tube. **-salz**, *n.* aluminum salt. **-stange**, *f.* aluminum rod or bar.

**aluminothermisch**, *a.* aluminothermic.
**Aluminoxyd**, *n.* aluminum oxide.
**am**, *abbrev.* an dem.
**amalgamierbar**, *a.* amalgamable.
**amalgamieren**, *v.t.* amalgamate.
**Amalgamierung**, *f.* amalgamation.
**Amarant**, *m.* amaranth. **-holz**, *n.* purpleheart, purplewood.
**Amause**, *f.* enamel.
**Amazonenstein**, *m.* Amazon stone, amazo-nite.
**Amber**, *m.* amber; (grauer) ambergris.
**amberartig**, *a.* amberlike, amber.
**Amber-fett, -harz**, *n.* ambrain. **-kraut**, *n.* cat thyme (*Teucrium marum*). **-öl**, *n.* oil of amber, amber oil. **-stoff**, *m.* ambrain.
**Amboss**, *m.* anvil; (*Anat.*) incus.
**Ambra**, *m.,f.& n.* amber.—**gelber —**, yellow or ordinary amber.—**grauer —**, ambergris. **—flüssiger —**, liquidambar. **-baum**, *m.* amber tree. **-fett**, *n.* ambrain. **-holz**, *n.* yellow sandalwood. **-öl**, *n.* oil of amber.
**ambulant**, *a.* moving about, traveling, ambulant.
**Ameise**, *f.* ant.
**Ameisen-**. formic. **-aldehyd**, *n.* formalde-hyde. **-äther**, *m.* formic ether (ethyl for-mate). **-geist**, *m.* (*Pharm.*) spirit of ants (a mixture of formic acid, alcohol and water). **-naphta**, *n.* = Ameisenäther. **-per-säure**, *f.* performic acid.
**ameisensauer**, *a.* of or combined with formic acid, formate of.—**ameisensaures Salz**, formate.
**Ameisensäure**, *f.* formic acid. **-nitril**, *n.* formonitrile (HCN). **-sulfonsäure**, *f.* sulfo-formic acid.
**Ameisenspiritus**, *m.* = Ameisengeist.
**Amerikaner**, *m.* American.
**amerikanisch**, *a.* American.
**Ametall**, *n.* nonmetal.
**Amethystfarbe**, *f.* amethyst color.
**Amiant**, *m.* amianthus (silky asbestos).
**amiantartig**, *a.* amianthine.
**Amidgruppe**, *f.* amido (or amino) group, amidogen.
**amidieren**, *v.t.* amidate, convert into an amide.
**Amidierung**, *f.* amidation.
**Amido-**. amino-, amido- (should be trans-lated amido- only when the compound is of amide nature, otherwise amino-). **-benzol**, *n.* aminobenzene. **-essigsäure**, *f.* amino-acetic acid. **-kohlensäure**, *f.* amidocarbonic acid (carbamic acid). **-säure**, *f.* amino acid. **-schwefelsäure**, *f.* amidosulfuric acid (sul-famic acid, $NH_2SO_3H$). **-sulfosäure**, *f.* amidosulfuric (sulfamic) acid; aminosul-fonic acid.

Amidsäure, *f.* amide acid, amic acid.

-amidsäure, *f.* -amic acid.

aminartig, *a.* amine-like.

aminieren, *v.t.* aminate, convert into an amine.

Aminosäure, *f.* amino acid. -rest, *m.* amino acid residue.

Amino-verbindung, *f.* amino compound. -zucker, *m.* amino sugar.

Aminsäure, *f.* amino acid; amic acid.

-aminsäure, *f.* -amic acid.

Ammiak, *n.* ammine.

Ammon, *m.* ammonia.—oxalsauer —, oxalate of ammonia, ammonium oxalate.

Ammon-. ammonium; ammonia. -alaun, *m.* ammonia alum, ammonium alum. -chlorid, *n.* ammonium chloride. -eisenalaun, *m.* ammonium iron alum. -formiat, *n.* ammonium formate.

Ammoniak, *n.* ammonia (in old names of salts equivalent to ammonium, as salzsaures —, ammonium chloride); ammoniac. -alaun, *m.* ammonia alum.

ammoniakalisch, *a.* ammoniacal.

ammoniakarm, *a.* poor in ammonia.

Ammoniakbestimmung, *f.* determination of ammonia.

ammoniakbindend, *a.* combining with ammonia.

Ammoniak-dampf, *m.* ammonia vapor. -entwicklung, *f.* evolution of ammonia. -flasche, *f.* ammonia bottle, flask or cylinder. -flüssigkeit, *f.* ammonia water, aqueous ammonia; (*Tech.*) ammoniacal liquor. -gas, *n.* ammonia gas. -gummi, *m.* gum ammoniac, ammoniac.

ammoniakhaltig, *a.* containing ammonia, ammoniacal.

Ammoniak-harz, *n.* = Ammoniakgummi. -kupferchlorür, *n.* ammoniacal cuprous chloride. -leitung, *f.* conduction of ammonia; ammonia piping or line. -lösung, *f.* ammonia solution. -messer, *m.* ammonia meter. -pflanze, *f.* ammoniac plant. -pflaster, *n.* ammoniac plaster. -prüfer, *m.* ammonia tester.

ammoniakreich, *a.* rich in ammonia.

Ammoniak-rest, *m.* ammonia residue (amidogen, $NH_2$). -rohr, *n.* ammonia tube or pipe. -salpeter, *m.* ammonia saltpeter (ammonium nitrate). -salz, *n.* ammonium salt. -seife, *f.* ammonia soap. -stickstoff, *m.* ammonia nitrogen. -verbindung, *f.* ammonia compound; ammonium compound. -verfahren, *n.* ammonia process. -wasser, *n.* ammonia water; (*Tech.*) ammoniacal liquor. -weinstein, *m.* ammonium potassium tartrate. -zusatz, *m.* addition of ammonia.

Ammonium bromatum. (*Pharm.*) ammonium bromide.

Ammonium chloratum. (*Pharm.*) ammonium chloride.

Ammonium jodatum. (*Pharm.*) ammonium iodide.

Ammonium-jodid, *n.* ammonium iodide. -platinchlorid, *n.* ammonium platinichloride (chloroplatinate). -rest, *m.* ammonium radical. -rhodanid, *n.* ammonium thiocyanate. -salz, *n.* ammonium salt. -seife, *f.* ammonia soap. -sulfhydrat, *n.* ammonium hydrosulfide. -sulfocyanid, *n.* ammonium thiocyanate. -verbindung, *f.* ammonium compound. -zinnchlorid, *n.* ammonium chlorostannate, pink salt.

Ammon-jodid, *n.* ammonium iodide. -karbonat, *n.* carbonate of ammonia. -karbonit, *n.* ammoncarbonite (trade name of an explosive). -nitrat, *n.* ammonium nitrate. -persulfat, *n.* ammonium persulfate. -platinchlorid, *n.* ammonium platinichloride (chloroplatinate). -pulver, *n.* an explosive made by evaporating ammonium nitrate solution with powdered charcoal. -rest, *m.* ammonium radical ($NH_4$). -rhodanid, *n.* ammonium thiocyanate. -salpeter, *m.* ammonium nitrate. -salpetersprengstoff, *m.* ammonium nitrate explosive. -salz, *n.* ammonium salt. -seife, *f.* ammonia soap. -sulfat, *n.* ammonium sulfate. -sulfatsalpeter, *m.* a mixture or compound of ammonium sulfate and nitrate. -sulfit, *n.* ammonium sulfite. -verbindung, *f.* ammonium compound. -zinnchlorid, *n.* ammonium chlorostannate, pink salt.

Amnios-flüssigkeit, *f.* amniotic fluid. -säure, *f.* amniotic acid (allantoin). -wasser, *n.* amniotic fluid.

amorph, amorphisch, *a.* amorphous.

am.P., *abbrev.* (amerikanisches Patent) American patent.

Ampel, *f.* = Ampulla.

Amperestunde, *f.* (*Elec.*) ampere-hour.

Ampfer, *m.* sorrel, dock (*Rumex*).

amphichroitisch, *a.* amphichroic.

amphoter, *a.* amphoteric.

Ampulle, Ampulla, *f.* ampulla; (*Pharm.*) ampoule.

Ampullenfabrikation, *f.* manufacture of ampoules.

ampullenförmig, *a.* ampulliform.

Amt, *n.* office, post, employment, business; board, court, council.

amtlich, *a.* official.

Amtmann, *m.* magistrate.

Amts-bericht, *m.* official report. -blatt, *n.* official gazette.

Amyläther, *m.* amyl ether.

**Amylobrennerei,** *f.* distilling with the amylo process.

**amyloklastisch,** *a.* amyloclastic.

**Amylolyse,** *f.* amylolysis.

**Amyloverfahren,** *n.* (*Alcohol*) amylo process (of saccharification).

**Amyl-oxydhydrat,** *n.* amyl alcohol. **-verbindung,** *f.* amyl compound.

**an,** *prep.* at, by, along, against, to; in, on; near to, about; in respect to, by way of.— *adv.* on, onward, along, up.—**an sich,** in itself, in themselves, *per se,* intrinsically.

**an-.** (with verbs) at, toward, on, commence to, continue to.

**-an.** (*Org. Chem.*), in the names of *saturated* hydrocarbons and heterocyclic parent compounds, -ane; in other cases, -an; as, Meth*an,* methane; Menth*an,* menthane; Pyr*an,* pyran; Ureth*an,* urethan.

**An.,** *abbrev.* (Anmerkung) note, remark.

**anaerob,** *a.* anaerobic.

**analog,** *a.* analogous.

**Analogon,** *n.* analog.

**Analysator,** *m.* analyzer.

**Analyse,** *f.* analysis.

**Analysen-.** analytical. **-befund,** *m.* analytical finding or result. **-bericht,** *m.* report of analyses, analytical report. **-fehler,** *m.* analytical error.

**analysenfertig,** *a.* ready for analysis.

**Analysen-formel,** *f.* analysis formula, empirical formula. **-gewicht,** *n.* analytical weight. **-material,** *n.* analytical material. **-methode,** *f.* analytical method.

**analysenrein,** *a.* analytically pure, for analyses.

**Analysen-trichter,** *m.* analytical funnel. **-wage,** *f.* analytical balance.

**analysierbar,** *a.* analyzable.

**analysieren,** *v.t.* analyze.

**Analytiker,** *m.* analyst.

**analytisch,** *a.* analytical, analytic.

**Anämie,** *f.* anemia.

**Ananas,** *f.* pineapple. **-äther,** *m.,* **-essenz,** *f.* pineapple essence (ethyl butyrate).

**anaphylaktisch,** *a.* anaphylactic.

**Anaphylaxe, Anaphylaxie,** *f.* anaphylaxis.

**anarbeiten,** *v.t.* join, attach.

**anästhetisch,** *a.* anesthetic.—**anästhetisches Mittel,** anesthetic.

**Anatas,** *m.* anatase.

**anatomisch,** *a.* anatomical.

**anätzen,** *v.t.* cauterize; begin to etch, begin to corrode; etch on.

**Anätzung,** *f.* cauterization.

**anbacken,** *v.t.& i.* bake on, burn on; bake slightly; stick on.

**anbahnen,** *v.t.* pave the way for.

**Anbau,** *m.* cultivation, culture; addition, wing; colony.

**anbauen,** *v.t.* grow, cultivate; build on, add.

**anbei,** *adv.* herewith.

**anbeizen,** *v.t.* mordant.

**anbelangen,** *v.t.* relate to; concern.

**anberaumen,** *v.t.* appoint.

**anbeten,** *v.t.* adore.

**Anbetracht,** *m.* consideration.

**anbetreffen,** *v.t.* concern.

**anbieten,** *v.t.* offer, hold out, tender.

**anbinden,** *v.t.* tie, bind.

**anblaken,** *v.t.* blacken, smoke.

**anblasen,** *v.t.* blow in (a blast furnace); seal on (with the blast).

**anbläuen,** *v.t.* blue, tinge with blue.

**Anblick,** *m.* sight, aspect, view.

**anblicken,** *v.t.* look at.

**anbluten,** *v.i.* (of colors) bleed, run.

**anbohren,** *v.t.* bore, tap; perforate.

**anbräunen,** *v.t.* brown.

**anbrennen,** *v.t.* set fire to, light; scorch; calcine.—*v.i.* catch fire, begin to burn; calcine.

**anbringen,** *v.t.* place; mount, install; dispose of, sell; lodge (a complaint).—**angebracht,** *p.a.* fitting, suitable, applicable.

**Anbruch,** *m.* decay; fracture; first ore; opening (of a mine); daybreak.

**anbrüchig,** *a.* decaying, putrescent, spoiled, rotten, moldy.

**Anbrüchigkeit,** *f.* putrescence, putridity, rottenness, moldiness.

**anbrühen,** *v.t.* scald, infuse, steep (in hot water).

**Anchovisöl,** *n.* anchovy oil.

**Anchusasäure,** *f.* anchusic acid (anchusin).

**Andacht,** *f.* devotion; devotions.

**andampfen,** *v.t.& i.* deposit by evaporation.

**Andaöl,** *n.* anda oil.

**andauern,** *v.i.* last, continue, persist.—**andauernd,** *p.a.* lasting, continual, steady.

**Andenken,** *m.* remembrance, memory.

**ander,** *a.* other, another, else.

**änderbar,** *a.* alterable, changeable.

**Anderbarkeit,** *f.* alterability, changeability.

**ändern,** *v.t.* alter, change.

**andernfalls,** *adv.* else, otherwise.

**anders,** *adv.* otherwise, differently.—**wenn —,** if instead, provided.

**anderseits,** *adv.* on the other hand, on the other side.

**anderswertig,** *a.* of another valence.

**anderthalb,** *a.* sesqui-; one and a half. **-basisch,** *a.* sesquibasic. **-fach,** *a.* one and a half times; sesqui-. **-faches Chlorid,** sesquichloride. **-faches Oxyd,** sesquioxide. **-fachkohlensauer, -kohlensauer,** *a.* sesquicarbonate of.

**Änderung,** *f.* change, alteration, variation.

**anderwärts,** *adv.* elsewhere.

**anderweitig,** *a. & adv.* in another place or way, otherwise, further.

**andeuten,** *v.t.* indicate, signify; intimate, hint.

**Andeutung,** *f.* indication, etc. (see andeuten).

**Andorn,** *m.,* **-kraut,** *n.* horehound.

**andorren,** *v.i.* dry on, adhere by drying.

**Andrang,** *m.* rush, crowd, congestion; urgency.

**andrehen,** *v.t.* twist on, screw on, turn on.

**andringen,** *v.i.* press, rush.—*v.t.* press, push.

**andrücken,** *v.t.* press on, press close.

**andunkeln,** *v.i.* darken.

**andunsten, andünsten,** *v.i.* be deposited by evaporation.

**aneignen,** *v.t.* assimilate; appropriate, acquire.

**aneinander,** *adv.* together. **-fügen,** *v.t.* join.

**anekeln,** *v.t.* disgust.

**Anelland,** *n.* a ring joined to another by "ortho fusion," anellated ring (see anellieren).

**anellieren,** *v.t.* (*Org. Chem.*) join by "ortho fusion" (as the two rings in naphthalene), anellate.

**Anellierung,** *f.* anellation (see anellieren).

**Anemoninsäure,** *f.* anemoninic acid.

**Anemon-kampher,** *m.* anemonin. **-säure,** *f.* anemonic acid.

**anerbieten,** *v.t.* offer, proffer, tender.

**anerk.,** *abbrev.* (anerkannt) recognized.

**anerkannt,** *p.p.* of anerkennen.

**anerkennbar,** *a.* recognizable.

**anerkennen,** *v.t.* recognize; acknowledge; admit; appreciate.

**Anerkennung,** *f.* recognizing, recognition, etc. (see anerkennen).

**Aneth,** *n.* dill.

**Anethol,** *n.* anethole.

**anfächeln,** *v.t.* fan.

**anfachen,** *v.t.* fan, blow; kindle.

**Anfachung,** *f.* fanning, kindling.

**anfahren,** *v.t.* carry near, bring up; start (machinery); attack, snub.—*v.i.* approach, arrive.

**Anfall,** *m.* amount formed or collected; attack; fit; stay, prop.

**anfallen,** *v.i.* fall on, fall; accumulate, accrue, result; (of dyes) go on.—**anfallend,** *p.a.* resulting; aggressive.

**anfällig,** *a.* susceptible.

**Anfälligkeit,** *f.* susceptibility.

**Anfang,** *m.* beginning; origin.

**anfangen,** *v.t. & i.* begin, commence.

**Anfänger,** *m.* beginner.

**anfänglich,** *a.* original, initial, incipient.— *adv.* at first, originally.

**anfangs,** *adv.* at first, originally.

**Anfangs-.** initial, beginning, first, primary; original. **-bahn,** *f.* initial orbit or path. **-buchstabe,** *m.* initial, capital (letter).

**-druck,** *m.* initial pressure. **-ergebnis,** *n.* initial product or yield. **-erzeugnis,** *f.* initial product, first product. **-glied,** *n.* initial member, first member (of a series). **-lösung,** *f.* initial or original solution. **-niveau,** *n.* initial level. **-phase,** *f.* initial phase. **-produkt,** *m.* initial product, first product. **-punkt,** *m.* initial point; zero. **-temperatur,** *f.* initial temperature. **-wert,** *m.* initial value. **-zustand,** *m.* initial state or condition.

**anfärben,** *v.t.* color, dye, paint, tint, tinge; start dyeing.

**anfassen,** *v.t.* seize, handle; undertake.—*v.r.* feel.

**anfaulen,** *v.i.* begin to rot.—**anfaulend,** *p.a.* putrescent.—**angefault,** *p.a.* rotten, decayed.

**anfechten,** *v.t.* combat, attack; trouble, concern.

**anfertigen,** *v.t.* make ready, make, manufacture.

**Anfertigung,** *f.* making, manufacture; composition.

**anfetten,** *v.t.* grease; lubricate, oil.

**anfeuchten,** *v.t.* moisten, damp, wet.

**Anfeuchter,** *m.* moistener; (*Brewing*) sparger.

**Anfeuchtung,** *f.* moistening, damping, wetting.

**anfeuern,** *v.t.* light, fire; prime; inflame, excite.

**Anfeuerung,** *f.* priming.

**anfirnissen,** *v.t.* varnish (over).

**anflehen,** *v.t.* implore, supplicate.

**anfliegen,** *v.i.* effloresce; grow spontaneously; (of dyes) rush on; fly on, fly; occur.—**angeflogen,** *p.a.* incrusted.

**Anflug,** *m.* incrustation, coating; efflorescence; tinge, tint, slight admixture; smattering; flying (against), flight; onset; young wood; copse.

**Anfluss,** *m.* alluvium; onflow, afflux.

**anfordern,** *v.t.* demand, require.

**Anforderung,** *f.* demand, requirement, claim.

**Anfr.,** *abbrev.* (Anfrage) inquiry.

**Anfrage,** *f.* inquiry; demand.

**anfragen,** *v.i.* inquire.

**anfressen,** *v.t.* corrode; erode; eat at; attack.

**Anfressung,** *f.* corrosion, etc. (see anfressen).

**anfrieren,** *v.i.* freeze on.

**anfrischen,** *v.t.* freshen, refresh, revive; reduce or refine (metals); varnish (paintings).

**Anfrisch-herd,** **-ofen,** *m.* refining furnace.

**Anfrischung,** *f.* freshening, etc. (see anfrischen).

**anfügen,** *v.t.* join, attach, affix, annex.

**anfühlen,** *v.t.* feel, touch, handle.

**Anfühlen,** *n.* feel, touch.

**anführen,** *v.t.* lead; adduce; quote; mention; impose on.

**Anführungszeichen,** *n.pl.* quotation marks.

anfüllen, v.t. fill, fill up; prime; charge.

Ang., abbrev. (Angebot) offer.

Angabe, f. statement; specification, estimate; report; information; indication (of an instrument); instruction; plan.—Angaben, pl. data.

angängig, angänglich, a. feasible, admissible.

angeätzt, p.p. of anätzen.

Angeb., abbrev. (Angebot) offer.

angeben, v.t. state, declare, tell; specify; accuse; indicate; devise.

angeblich, a. stated; alleged; pretended; nominal.

angeboren, p.a. inborn, innate, congenital.

Angebot, n. offer, bid, quotation.

angebracht, p.a. see anbringen.

angebrannt, p.p. of anbrennen.

angefeuchtet, p.p. of anfeuchten.

angeflogen, p.a. see anfliegen.

angefressen, p.p. of anfressen.

angeglüht, p.p. of anglühen; red-hot.

angegriffen, p.p. of angreifen.

Angehäufe, n. conglomerate; heap, aggregate.

angehen, v.i. begin (to grow, burn, decay, etc.); go on, (of dyes) be absorbed; be feasible; be passable.—v.t. approach; concern.

angehören, v.i. belong (to); pertain (to); be related (to).

angehörig, a. belonging, related.

Angehörige, pl. relatives, relations; adherents; inhabitants.

Angel, f. hinge; hook; pivot; axis.

angelaufen, p.p. of anlaufen; coated, tarnished.

angelegen, p.a. see anliegen.

Angelegenheit, f. concern; affair.

angelegentlich, a. earnest, urgent.

Angelikasäure, Angelicasäure, f. angelic acid.

angem., abbrev. (angemeldet) (of a patent) applied for.

angemessen, p.a. suitable, adequate.

angenähert, p.a. see annähern.

angenehm, a. pleasant, agreeable.

angenommen, p.a. see annehmen.

angepasst, p.a. see anpassen.

angereichert, p.p. of anreichern.

angesäuert, p.p. of ansäuern.

angeschmolzen, p.p. of anschmelzen.

angeschwemmt, p.a. alluvial.

angesehen, p.a. see ansehen.

angesessen, p.a. resident; settled.

Angesicht, n. face, countenance; look.

angesichts, adv. in face of, in view of.

angestammt, a. hereditary; inborn.

Angestellte, m. employee; appointee; official.

angew., abbrev. (angewandt) applied; employed.

angewandt, p.a. see anwenden.

angewöhnen, v.t. accustom.

angezeigt, p.a. see anzeigen.

angezogen, p.a. see anziehen.

angiessen, v.t. pour on; water; (Founding) cast on; (Ceramics) color by a coat of clay.

angliedern, v.t. join on, link on.

Angliederung, f. union; affiliation.

anglühen, v.t. heat to glowing, glow; mull (wine).—v.r. begin to glow.

angreifbar, a. capable of being attacked or affected.

Angreifbarkeit, f. attackability.

angreifen, v.t. attack, act on, affect; corrode (metals); lay hold of; fatigue; undertake.

angrenzen, v.t. border on, adjoin.—angrenzend, p.a. adjacent, adjoining.

Angriff, m. attack; handling; undertaking.— in — nehmen, take in hand, take up.

Angst, f. anxiety, fright, agony.

ängstigen, v.t. alarm, frighten, worry.

ängstlich, a. anxious; scrupulous; alarming.

Anguss, m. pouring on, etc. (see angiessen); (Founding) feedhead; (Ceram.) engobe. -farbe, f. colored coating clay.

anhaften, v.i. adhere, be attached (to).—anhaftend, p.a. adhering; adhesive; inherent.

Anhalt, m. support; hold; stop, pause.

anhalten, v.t. stop, stay, halt.—v.i. stop; hold on, persist; solicit.—anhaltend, p.a. continuous, persistent, lasting; astringent.

Anhaltpunkt, Anhaltspunkt, m. stopping point, station; criterion; essential point; (Mech.) fulcrum.

Anhaltungsmittel, n. astringent.

Anhang, m. addition, appendix, appendage, supplement; attachment; followers; (Anat.) appendix.

anhangen, v.i. adhere, hang on.—anhangend, anhängend, p.a. adhering, adhesive.

anhängen, v.t. attach, affix, append, add; (Mach.) throw in, connect.

Anhänger, m. follower, adherent; appendage; tag; trailer.

anhängig, a. adhering; appended, annexed; pending.

anhänglich, a. attached; faithful.

Anhängsel, n. appendage; amulet.

Anhangskraft, f. adhesive force, adhesion.

Anhauch, m. tinge; breathing on.

anhauchen, v.t. breathe upon; tinge.

anhäufen, v.t. aggregate; accumulate.—v.r. accumulate.

Anhäufung, f. aggregation; accumulation; agglomeration.

anheben, v.t., i.& r. begin.—v.t. lift, raise.

anheften, v.t. fasten to, attach.

anheimfallen, v.i. (with dative) fall into, undergo, suffer; fall (to), devolve (on).

anheimstellen, v.t. commit, submit.

anheischig, *a*, bound, pledged.

anheizen, *v.t.* heat (a little), begin to heat.

anher, *adv.* hither.—bis —, hitherto.

Anhöhe, *f.* elevation, hill; rising ground.

anhören, *v.t.* listen to, hear.—*v.r.* sound.

Anhydrämie, *f.* anhydremia.

anhydrisch, *a.* anhydrous.

anhydrisieren, *v.t.* render anhydrous, dehydrate.—*v.r.* become anhydrous.

Anhydrisierungsmittel, *n.* dehydrating agent.

Anhydrosäure, *f.* anhydro acid (an acid, such as pyrosulfuric, which is formed from a polybasic acid by elimination of water).

Anhydroxyd, *n.* anhydrous oxide, anhydride.

Anilido-. anilino-, anilido- (cf. Amido-).

Anilin-blau, *n.* aniline blue. -braun, *n.* aniline brown. -dampf, *m.* aniline vapor. -fabrik, *f.* aniline works. -farbe, *f.* aniline color. -farbstoff, *m.* aniline dye. -gelb, *n.* aniline yellow. -grün, *n.* aniline green. -öl, *n.* aniline oil. -rot, *n.* aniline red. -salz, *n.* aniline salt. -schwarz, *n.* aniline black. -tinte, *f.* aniline ink. -vergiftung, *f.* aniline poisoning.

Anilismus, *m.* anilinism, anilism.

animalisch, *a.* animal.

animalisieren, *v.t.* animalize.

Anime-gummi, -harz, *n.* animé, gum animé.

Anis, *m.* anise; aniseed. -branntwein, *m.* anisette. -geist, *m.* (*Pharm.*) spirit of anise; anisette. -kampher, *m.* anise camphor, anethole. -likör, *m.* anisette.

Anisol, *n.* anisole.

Anisöl, *n.* aniseed oil, anise oil.

anisometrisch, *a.* anisometric.

anisotrop, anisotropisch, *a.* anisotropic.

Anis-same, -samen, *m.* aniseed, (*Pharm.*) anise. -säure, *f.* anisic acid. -wasser, *n.* anisette.

ankalken, *v.t.* limewash, whitewash.

Ankauf, *m.* buying, purchasing, purchase. -preis, *m.* purchase price, cost.

Anker, *m.* anchor; (*Elec.*) armature. -strom. *m.* (*Elec.*) armature current. -wicklung, *f.* armature winding.

ankitten, *v.t.* fasten with cement, cement.

anklagen, *v.t.* accuse, charge.

Anklang, *m.* concord, accord; approval; sympathy.

ankleben, *v.t.* stick on, glue on, paste on, agglutinate, attach.—*v.i.* stick, adhere.—anklebend, *p.a.* adhesive, agglutinative.

ankleiden, *v.t.& r.* dress.

anklingen, *v.i.* grow stronger, increase.

anknüpfen, *v.t.* fasten (by tying), join, connect; enter upon, engage in.—*v.i.* start (at or from), refer (to).

Anknüpfungspunkt, *m.* point of contact.

ankochen, *v.t.* bring to the boil, begin to boil.

ankohlen, *v.t.* char partially.

Ankohlung, *f.* partial charring.

ankommen, *v.i.* arrive; approach; succeed; be important; depend; (*Brewing*) start fermenting.

Ankömmling, *m.* newcomer, novice; new product, novelty.

ankreiden, *v.t.* chalk; chalk up.

ankündigen, ankünden, *v.t.* announce, publish.

Ankündigung, *f.* announcement, notice; prospectus.

Ankunft, *f.* arrival.

ankuppeln, *v.t.* couple (on), attach.

Anl., *abbrev.* Anlage.

Anlage, *f.* laying on, etc. (see anlegen); establishment, plant; installation, equipment; construction; design; outline; arrangement; investment; tax; attached paper; tendency; talent.

anlagern, *v.t.* add (on), take up; accumulate.

Anlagerung, *f.* addition, etc. (see anlagern).

Anlagerungs-erzeugnis, *n.* addition product. -verbindung, *f.* addition compound.

anlangen, *v.i.* arrive.—*v.t.* concern.—anlangend, *prep.* concerning, as for.

Anlass, *m.* occasion, motive; occurrence; letting in; starting.

anlassen, *v.t.* temper, anneal (glass or metals); let in, turn on, start (going).—*v.r.* appear, look.

Anlasser, *m.* starting device, starter.

Anlass-farbe, *f.* (*Steel*) temper color. -härte, *f.* tempering hardness.

anlässlich, *adv.* occasionally; apropos (of).

Anlass-ofen, *m.* tempering furnace, annealing oven. -wirkung, *f.* tempering effect, annealing effect.

Anlauf, *m.* tarnish; tarnishing; swelling; slope; starting (of machinery); (*Mach.*) catch, tappet, shoulder, etc.; onset, run, attack; concourse, crowd.

anlaufen, *v.i.* become coated (with oxide, moisture, mold, etc.), tarnish, become dull or dim; (of dyed goods) recolor; swell, intumesce; increase; (*Mach.*) start; amount; run; crowd.

Anlauf-farbe, *f.* (*Metal.*) tempering color. -temperatur, *f.* tempering temperature. -zeit, *f.* filling time (of a pipeline); (*Mach.*) starting period.

anlegen, *v.t.* lay or put on, apply, fix; invest; found; lay out; plan.—*v.r.* deposit, settle.

Anlehen, *m.* loan.

anlehnen, *v.t.& r.* lean (against or on), rest, be supported (by); (of a door) nearly close.

Anlehnung, *f.* leaning; dependence; support.

Anleihe, *f.* loan.

anleimen, *v.t.* glue on, glue.

anleiten, v.t. lead, guide, conduct; instruct.

Anleitung, f. leading, conducting; instruction; (of books) introduction, guide, key.

anliegen, v.i. be adjacent, lie near; join; fit; concern; entreat.—angelegen, p.a. interesting; important.

Anliegen, n. proximity; request.

anlöten, v.t. solder, solder on; cause to adhere.

Anlötung, f. soldering, etc. (see anlöten).

Anm., abbrev. (Anmerkung) note, remark.

anmachen, v.t. slack (lime or gypsum); mix, temper, dilute, wet, treat, prepare, flavor, adulterate; fasten on, attach; light (a fire).

Anmachwasser, n. mixing water; water of plasticity.

anmassen, v.t. assume; usurp.

anmelden, v.t. announce, advertise, declare; apply for (a patent); register, enter.

Anmeldung, f. announcement, etc. (see anmelden).

anmengen, v.t. mix, blend, temper, dilute.

Anmerkung, f. note, remark, comment.

anmischen, v.t. mix.

Anmut, f. grace, charm.

anmuten, v.t. expect, ask; please.

Ann., abbrev. Annalen der Chemie.

annähern, v.t.& r. approach, approximate, bring or draw near.—annähernd, p.a. approximate; approaching.—angenähert, p.a. approximate.

Annäherung, f. approximation, approach.

Annäherungsgrad, m. degree of approximation.

Annahme, f. assumption, hypothesis; acceptance.

Annalin, n. annaline (a prepared calcium sulfate).

annässen, v.t. moisten a little, damp.

annehmbar, a. acceptable.

annehmen, v.t. assume, suppose; take, accept; adopt; take, take up (colors).—angenommen, p.a. assuming; false, fictitious.

Annehmung, f. assumption, etc. (see annehmen).

annektieren, v.t. annex.

annetzen, v.t. moisten, damp.

annieten, v.t. rivet, rivet on.

Annonce, f. advertisement.

annoncieren, v.t. advertise, announce.

Anoden-dichte, f. anode density, anodic density. -schlamm, m. anode slime, anode mud. -spannung, f. anode potential.

anodisch, a. anodic.

anölen, v.t. oil, coat with oil.

anomal, anomalisch, a. anomalous.

anordnen, v.t. arrange, regulate, order.

Anordnung, f. arrangement, disposition, regulation.

anorg., abbrev. (anorganisch) inorganic.

Anorganiker, m. inorganic chemist.

anorganisch, a. inorganic.

anormal, a. abnormal.

anoxydieren, v.t. oxidize.

anpassen, v.t. adapt, adjust, fit, suit.— anpassend, p.a. suitable, fit.—angepasst, p.a. adapted, adjusted, suited, appropriate.

Anpassung, f. adaptation, adjustment.

Anpassungsfähigkeit. f. adaptability.

Anprall, m. impact; contusion.

anprallen, v.i. strike, impinge (forcibly).

anpreisen, v.t. commend, recommend.

anpudern, v.t. powder.

anputzen, v.t. dress up, adorn, decorate.

anquicken, v.t. amalgamate.

Anquick-fass, n. amalgamating tub. -silber, n. silver amalgam.

Anquickung, f. amalgamation.

Anrat, m. advice, counsel.

anrauchen, v.t. smoke.

anräuchern, v.t. fumigate; perfume.

Anräucherung, f. fumigation; perfuming.

anrechnen, v.t. charge; ascribe; count.

Anrecht, n. claim, title, right.

Anrede, f. address.

anreden, v.t. address, speak to.

anregbar, a. capable of being excited.

anregen, v.t. excite; stimulate; incite; activate; set going; interest; suggest, mention.— anregend, p.a. exciting; stimulating, stimulant; interesting.

Anregung, f. stimulation; stimulus, impulse; suggestion.

Anregungs-grenze, f. excitation limit. -potential, n., -spannung, f. excitation potential. -stärke, f. strength of excitation. -wahrscheinlichkeit, f. probability of excitation.

anreiben, v.t. rub, rub on; grind (colors).

anreichern, v.t. enrich, strengthen, concentrate.

Anreicherung, f. enrichment, concentration.

Anreichlech, m. enriched matte.

anreihen, v.t. arrange in a series; attach to a series, add.

anreizen, v.t. stimulate; instigate.

anrichten, v.t. prepare, dress; perform, produce; serve; mix (colors).

Anrichter, m. assayer; (ore) dresser.

Anriss, m. initial tear or break; surface crack.

anrosten, v.t. begin to rust; become fixed by rust.

Anrostung, f. rusting (on); corrosion.

anrufen, v.t. call; call up; call upon.

anrühren, v.t. touch, handle; stir; mix; temper; touch on, refer to.

anrussen, v.t. smoke, soot.

ans, abbrev. an das.

ansagen, v.t. announce, state.

ansalzen, *v.t.* salt lightly.

ansammeln, *v.t.* collect, gather, accumulate, amass; (*Physics*) focus.

Ansammlung, *f.* collection, etc. (see ansammeln); aggregation, heap, mass; throng.

Ansatz, *m.* deposit, sediment; attachment, added piece, lug, shoulder, etc.; appendage; insertion; preparing, mixture; ingredients; rate; item; onset; tendency; (*Dyeing*) standard; extension, annex; starting material, start (as yeast). **-bad,** *n.* (*Dyeing*) first bath, initial bath. **-punkt,** *m.* point of attachment or insertion. **-rohr,** *n.* attached tube (or pipe), insert tube, connecting tube; nozzle. **-stück,** *n.* attached piece or part, attachment.

ansäuern, *v.t.* acidify, acidulate; sour; (*Baking*) add yeast to.

Ansäuerung, *f.* acidification; souring.

Ansaugehub, *m.* suction stroke.

ansaugen, *v.t.& i.* suck, suck in, suck up.

Ansaug-heber, *m.* siphon. **-rohr,** *n.* suction tube, suction pipe.

Ansaugung, *f.* suction.

**-ansäure. -anoic** acid (Geneva system); **-anic** acid.

anschaffen, *v.t.* provide, supply; purchase.

anschauen, *v.t.* look at, view, consider.

anschaulich, *a.* clear, plain.

Anschauung, *f.* mode of viewing, view, idea; observation; perception; intuition.

Anschauungsweise, *f.* point of view, standpoint.

Anschein, *m.* appearance; likelihood.

anscheinen, *v.i.* appear.—*v.t.* shine on.—anscheinend, *p.a.* apparent.

anschichten, *v.t.* pile in layers, stratify.

anschicken, *v.r.* prepare.

Anschieber, *m.* lengthening piece; (*Brewing*) workman; (*Baking*) kissing crust.

Anschiessen, *v.i.* shoot into crystals, crystallize; shoot; rush; be adjacent.

Anschiessgefäss, *n.* crystallizing vessel, crystallizer.

anschimmeln, *v.i.* begin to mold.

Anschlag, *m.* stroke, impact; posting up, placard; estimate; plan, attempt; projection, stop.

anschlagen, *v.t.* strike at; fasten, affix; aim; estimate.

anschlägig, *a.* ingenious.

Anschlagwert, *m.* estimated value.

anschlämmen, *v.t.* suspend; elutriate, wash; deposit (mud, etc.); make into a paste; smear with mud or slime.

anschleifen, *v.t.* grind, polish.

anschliessen, *v.t.* fasten (on), attach, annex, connect; join; fit.—*v.r.* join; concur (in), agree (with).

Anschluss, *m.* joining; junction, connection; enclosure, something annexed.

anschmauchen, *v.t.* smoke, soot.

anschmelzen, *v.t.* melt or fuse on (to), join by fusion; solder.—*v.i.* begin to melt; adhere by fusion.

Anschmelzherd, *m.* melting furnace, smelting furnace.

anschmiegen, *v.t.* cause to cling (to), press (to).—*v.r.* cling (to).

anschmieren, *v.t.* smear; adulterate; cheat.

anschmutzen, *v.t.* soil.

anschrauben, *v.t.* screw on.

anschreiben, *v.t.* write down, note down.

Anschrift, *f.* address.

anschüren, *v.t.* stir up, stir, keep going (fire).

Anschuss, *m.* crystallization; crop (of crystals); shooting; rush. **-gefäss,** *n.* crystallizing vessel, crystallizer.

anschütten, *v.t.* pour on, discharge on; fill up.

anschwängern, *v.t.* saturate, impregnate.

Anschwänzapparat, *m.* sprinkler, sparger.

anschwänzen, *v.t.* sprinkle, sparge.

anschwärzen, *v.t.* blacken; slander.

anschwefeln, *v.t.* treat or fumigate with sulfur.

anschweissen, *v.t.* weld on, weld together.

anschwellen, *v.i.* swell, swell out; increase.

anschwöden, *v.t.* paint (the flesh side of hides) with lime.

ansehen, *v.t.* look at, see, regard; esteem.—angesehen, *p.a.* important, prominent.

Ansehen, *n.* appearance; standing, reputation.

ansehnlich, *a.* considerable, important.

ansetzen, *v.r.* crystallize; effloresce; be deposited.—*v.t.* set on, apply, attach; prepare, mix; charge (a furnace); form, produce; establish.—*v.i.* make a start, try.

Ansetzung, *f.* crystallization, etc. (see ansetzen).

Ansicht, *f.* view; inspection; opinion.

ansichtig, *a.* cognizant.

ansieden, *v.t.* boil, boil on; scorify; blanch; mordant (by boiling).—Ansieden und Abdunkeln, stuffing and saddening.

Ansiede-probe, *f.* scorification assay. **-scherbe,** *f.* **-scherben,** *m.* scorifier.

Ansiedung, *f.* boiling, etc. (see ansieden).

ansinnen, *v.t.* expect, require; attribute.

ansintern, *v.i.* sinter; form sinter.

anspannen, *v.t.* strain, stretch, bend; hitch.

anspielen, *v.i.* hint, allude; begin to play.

anspitzen, *v.t.* point, sharpen.

Anspr., *abbrev.* (Anspruch) claim, demand.

ansprechen, *v.t.* address; claim; ask; please; (with für) declare to be, pronounce, consider to be.—*v.i.* emit a sound, sound; respond (to).

**ansprengen,** *v.t.* blow up, blast; sprinkle; urge on.

**Anspruch,** *m.* claim; demand.—in — nehmen, engage, engross, tax; use.

**anspruchslos,** *a.* unassuming, unpretending.

**anstählen,** *v.t.* steel.

**Anstalt,** *f.* institution, establishment, plant, station; preparation, arrangement.

**Anstand,** *m.* delay; hesitation; behavior, propriety.

**anständig,** *a.* suitable, fit, proper; decent.

**anstandslos,** *a.* unhesitating.

**anstatt,** *prep.* instead of.

**anstäuben,** *v.t.* dust, powder.

**anstechen,** *v.t.* pierce, tap, open.

**anstecken,** *v.t.* stick on, fasten; infect; light (a fire).—**ansteckend,** *p.a.* infectious; contagious.

**Ansteckung,** *f.* infection; contagion.

**Ansteckungsstoff,** *m.* infectious matter.

**anstehen,** *v.i.* be near or next; be becoming; be pleasing; be deferred; hesitate; (of rocks) crop out.

**ansteigen,** *v.i.* rise, ascend.

**Anstellbottich,** *m.* (*Brewing*) starting tub.

**anstellen,** *v.t.* institute, make; install, set going, start; prepare; pitch (wort); appoint, employ; plan.—*v.r.* behave; pretend.

**Ansteller,** *m.* employer.

**Anstellhefe,** *f.* (*Brewing*) pitching yeast.

**anstellig,** *a.* skilful, handy.

**Anstelltemperatur,** *f.* (*Brewing*) pitching temperature.

**Anstellung,** *f.* instituting, etc. (see anstellen); situation, employment.

**Anstieg,** *m.* rise, ascent.

**anstiften,** *v.t.* contrive, cause.

**anstocken,** *v.i.* become moldy.

**Anstoss,** *m.* collision; impulse, impetus; offense; butt joint.

**anstossen,** *v.t.* crush, prepare by crushing; strike against, impinge upon; offend.—*v.i.* strike, impinge; be adjacent; stumble; stammer; offend.—**anstossend,** *p.a.* adjacent, contiguous.

**Anstrebekraft,** *f.* centripetal force.

**anstreben,** *v.i.* strive toward; oppose.—*v.t.* strive for.

**Anstreiche,** *f.* paint, color.

**anstreichen,** *v.t.* paint, coat, color, varnish; mark; underscore.

**anstrengen,** *v.t.* stretch, strain, exert.

**Anstrich,** *m.* paint, painting, coat; varnish; dye; tint, color; appearance. **-farbe,** *f.* painting color.

**ansuchen,** *v.t.* apply, request.

**Ansud,** *m.* boiling, etc. (see ansieden).

**ansüssen,** *v.t.* edulcorate; sweeten slightly.

**antaphrodisisch,** *a.* auaphrodisiac.

**anteeren,** *v.t.* tar.

**anteigen,** *v.t.* stir into a paste, make a paste of.

**Anteil, Antheil,** *m.* constituent; portion, share; interest, sympathy.

**antemetisch,** *a.* antiemetic.

**Anthocyan,** *n.* anthocyanin, anthocyan.

**Anthrac-.** see also Anthraz-.

**Anthracen-blau,** *n.* anthracene blue. **-farbstoff,** *m.* anthracene dye. **-öl,** *n.* anthracene oil.

**Anthrachinolin,** *n.* anthraquinoline.

**Anthrachinon,** *n.* anthraquinone. **-azin,** *n.* anthraquinonazine.

**Anthradichinon,** *n.* anthradiquinone.

**Anthrahydrochinon,** *n.* anthrahydroquinone.

**Anthrazen,** *n.* anthracene. **-farbstoff,** *m.*, **-farbe,** *f.* dye. **-öl,** *n.* anthracene oil.

**Anthrazit,** *n.* anthracite.

**anthrazitartig,** *a.* anthracitic.

**Anthrazitkohle,** *f.* anthracite coal, anthracite.

**Anthrazyl,** *n.* anthracyl.

**Anthroesäure,** *f.* anthroic acid.

**Antianaphylaxie,** *f.* antianaphylaxis.

**Antichlor,** *n.* antichlor, antichlorine.

**Antifäulnis,** *f.* antifouling.

**antik,** *a.* antique; old.

**Antikatalysator,** *m.* anticatalyst.

**antikatalytisch,** *a.* anticatalytic.

**Antiklopf-eigenschaft,** *f.* antiknock property. **-mittel,** *n.* antiknock agent.

**Antikörper,** *m.* antisubstance, antibody (cf. Körper).

**Antimon,** *n.* antimony. **-arsen,** *n.* (*Min.*) allemontite.

**antimonartig,** *a.* like antimony; antimonial.

**Antimon-blei,** *n.* (*Metal.*) lead containing antimony, antimonial lead. **-bleiblende,** *f.* boulangerite. **-blende,** *f.* kermesite. **-blüte,** *f.* antimony bloom, valentinite. **-butter,** *f.* butter of antimony ($SbCl_3$). **-chlorid,** *n.* antimony chloride, specif. antimony pentachloride. **-chlorür,** *n.* antimony trichloride. **-erz,** *n.* antimony ore. **-fahlerz,** *n.* tetrahedrite. **-gehalt,** *m.* antimony content. **-gelb,** *n.* antimony yellow. **-glanz,** *m.* antimony glance, antimonite. **-goldschwefel,** *m.* golden antimony sulfide ($Sb_2S_5$). **-halogen,** *n.* antimony halide.

**antimonhaltig,** *a.* containing antimony; antimonial.

**antimonig, antimonicht,** *a.* antimonious.—**antimonige Säure,** antimonious acid.

**antimonigsauer,** *a.* of or combined with antimonious acid, antimonite of.

**Antimonigsäureanhydrid,** *n.* antimony trioxide.

**antimonisch,** *a.* antimonial, antimonic.

**Antimonium,** *n.* antimony.

**Antimon-kermes,** *m.& n.* kermes mineral. **-kupferglanz,** *m.* antimonial copper glance (bournonite or chalcostibite). **-legierung,** *f.* antimony alloy. **-nickel,** *n.* (*Min.*) breithauptite. **-nickelglanz,** *m.* ullmannite. **-ocker,** *m.* antimony ocher (usually cervantite). **-oxychlorür,** *n.* antimony oxychloride (SbOCl). **-oxyd,** *n.* antimony oxide, specif. antimony trioxide. **-safran,** *m.* antimonial saffron, crocus of antimony. **-salz,** *n.* antimony salt, specif. a double compound of antimony trifluoride and ammonium sulfate.

**antimonsauer,** *a.* of or combined with antimonic acid, antimonate of.

**Antimon-säure,** *f.* antimonic acid. **-silber,** *n.* antimonial silver, dyscrasite. **-silberblende,** *f.* pyrargyrite. **-silberglanz,** *m.* stephanite. **-spiegel,** *m.* antimony mirror. **-sulfid,** *n.* antimony sulfide, specif. antimony pentasulfide. **-sulfür,** *n.* antimony trisulfide. **-verbindung,** *f.* antimony compound. **-wasserstoff,** *m.* antimony hydride, stibine. **-zinnober,** *m.* kermes mineral.

**antiphlogistisch,** *a.* antiphlogistic.

**antipodisch,** *a.* antipodal, opposite.

**antipyretisch,** *a.* antipyretic.

**Antiquariat,** *n.* second-hand bookstore.

**antiquarisch,** *a.* (of books) second-hand.

**Antisepticum, Antiseptikum,** *n.* antiseptic.

**antiseptisch,** *a.* antiseptic.

**antiskorbutisch,** *a.* antiscorbutic.

**Antiweinsäure,** *f.* antitartaric acid.

**Antlitz,** *n.* countenance, face.

**Antoniusfeuer,** *n.* St. Anthony's fire (erysipelas).

**Antonskraut,** *n.* willow herb (*Chamaenerion angustifolium*).

**Antrag,** *m.* proposal, proposition.

**antragen,** *v.t.* lay on, apply; propose, offer.

**anträufeln,** *v.i.* drip (on).

**antreffen,** *v.t.* hit upon, meet with; find.

**antreiben,** *v.t.* drive on, drive against, drive in; hoop (casks); start (a fire); incite, urge on.

**antreten,** *v.t.* enter on, set out on; approach; accost; tread down.

**Antrieb,** *m.* impulse, impulsion; (*Mach.*) drive; motive.

**Antritt,** *m.* beginning, entrance, first step.

**Antrittsvorlesung,** *f.* inaugural lecture.

**antrocknen,** *v.i.* dry on; begin to dry.

**antun,** *v.t.* put on; do to; do violence to.

**Antwort,** *f.* answer, reply.

**antworten,** *v.t.& i.* answer, reply.

**anvertrauen,** *v.t.* trust, confide.

**anverwandt,** *p.a.* related.

**anvisieren,** *v.t.* sight at, sight.

**Anw.,** *abbrev.* (Anwendung) employment, use.

**Anwachs,** *m.* increase, swelling.

**anwachsen,** *v.i.* grow, increase; adhere; grow on, grow together; grow up; take root.

**Anwalt,** *m.* attorney; deputy.

**Anwandlung,** *f.* fit, attack.

**anwärmen,** *v.t.* warm, heat (moderately); dry (by heating).—*v.i.* warm, begin to heat.

**Anwartschaft,** *f.* expectancy.

**anwässern,** *v.t.* moisten slightly.

**anweichen,** *v.t.* soften; soak slightly.

**anweisen,** *v.t.* point out, show; assign; direct; instruct.

**anweissen,** *v.t.* whitewash, whiten.

**Anweisung,** *f.* direction, instruction; money order, check, draft; assignment.

**anwendbar,** *a.* usable, applicable, adaptable, practicable, available.

**Anwendbarkeit,** *f.* applicability, practicability, availability.

**anwenden,** *v.t.* apply, employ, use.—**angewandt,** *p.a.* applied, practical; employed.

**Anwendung,** *f.* application, employment, use.

**Anwendungsweise,** *f.* mode of application.

**anwerfen,** *v.t.* throw, throw on; roughcast; (*Mach.*) start.

**anwesend,** *a.* present.

**Anwesenheit,** *f.* presence.

**anwidern,** *v.t.* disgust, offend.

**Anwuchs,** *m.* growth, increase.

**Anwurf,** *m.* roughcast; priming; deposit; first draft.

**Anz.,** *abbrev.* (Anzahl) number.

**Anzahl,** *f.* number.

**anzahlen,** *v.t.* pay on account.

**anzapfen,** *v.t.* tap.

**Anzeichen,** *n.* sign, indication, symptom, omen.

**Anzeige,** *f.* information; indication; (of an instrument) reading; notice, report, circular, advertisement, dispatch; sign, mark.

**anzeigen,** *v.t.* inform, announce, advertise; indicate; show.—**angezeigt,** *p.a.* advisable, proper, fit.

**Anzeigengebühren,** *f.pl.* advertising rates.

**Anzeiger,** *m.* indicator; (*Math.*) exponent; informer, advertiser.

**Anzeigevorrichtung,** *f.* indicating device.

**anzementieren,** *v.t.* cement on.

**anzetteln,** *v.t.* plot; (*Weaving*) warp.

**anziehen,** *v.t.* draw, pull, attract; absorb; tighten; stretch; raise, grow; put on (clothes); quote.—*v.i.* take effect, hold well; set, harden; attract moisture; approach; advance.—**anziehend,** *p.a.* attractive; astringent.—**angezogen,** *p.a.* (of malt) slack.

**Anziehung,** *f.* attraction, etc. (see anziehen); adhesion; (*Physiol.*) adduction.

**Anziehungskraft,** *f.* attractive power, attraction; adhesive power.

**anzinnen,** *v.t.* coat with tin, tin.

**Anzucht,** *f.* raising, cultivation, culture.

**anzuckern,** *v.t.* sprinkle with sugar.

**Anzug,** *m.* clothes, clothing; approach; entrance.

**anzünden,** *v.t.* ignite, kindle, light.

**Anzünder,** *m.* igniter, lighter.

**Anzündung,** *f.* ignition, lighting.

**Aorte,** *f.* aorta.

**Aorten-.** aortic.

**Aouaraöl,** *n.* African palm oil.

**A.P.,** *abbrev.* (amerikanisches Patent) American patent.

**Apfel,** *m.* apple.

**Apfeläther, Äpfeläther,** *m.* malic ether (ethyl malate); essence of apple (genuine or artificial).

**Apfelbranntwein,** *m.* apple brandy, apple jack.

**Äpfeleisenextrakt,** *n.* (*Pharm.*) ferrated extract of apples.

**Apfel-most,** *m.* cider. **-mus,** *m.* apple sauce.

**Apfelöl, Äpfelöl,** *n.* apple oil.

**Apfelsalbe,** *f.* pomatum.

**apfelsauer, äpfelsauer,** *a.* of or combined with malic acid, malate of.

**Apfelsäure, Äpfelsäure,** *f.* malic acid.

**Apfelsine,** *f.* (sweet) orange.

**Apfelsinen-saft,** *m.* orange juice. **-schalenöl,** *n.* orange-peel oil, essence of orange.

**Apfelwein, Äpfelwein,** *m.* cider.

**Aphel,** *n.* aphelion. **-abstand,** *m.* aphelion distance.

**aphlogistisch,** *a.* aphlogistic.

**aphoristisch,** *a.* aphoristic(al).

**Apiol,** *n.* apiole.

**aplanatisch,** *a.* aplanatic.

**Apocampher,** *m.* apocamphor. **-säure,** *f.* apocamphoric acid.

**Apochinen,** *n.* apoquinene.

**Apochinin,** *n.* apoquinine.

**apochromatisch,** *a.* apochromatic.

**Apogluzinsäure,** *f.* apoglucic acid.

**Apohydrochinin,** *n.* apohydroquinine.

**Apokaffein,** *n.* apocaffeine.

**Apokamphersäure,** *f.* apocamphoric acid.

**Apokodein,** *n.* apocodeine.

**aposteriorisch,** *a.* *a posteriori*.

**Apotheke,** *f.* drugstore, chemist's shop, apothecary's shop.

**Apotheker,** *m.* pharmacist, druggist, (in England) pharmaceutical chemist, apothecary. **-buch,** *n.* dispensatory; pharmacopeia. **-farbe,** *f.* drug color, pharmacist's color. **-gewicht,** *n.* apothecary's weight. **-kunst,** *f.* apothecary's art, pharmacy. **-ordnung,** *f.* dispensatory. **-verein,** *m.* pharmaceutical society, organization of druggists. **-wa(a)ge,** *f.* druggist's scales, apothecary's scales. **-waren,** *f.pl.* drugs. **-warenhändler,** *m.* druggist. **-wesen,** *n.* pharmaceutical matters. **-wissenschaft,** *f.* pharmacology.

**App.,** *abbrev.* Apparat.

**Apparat,** *m.* apparatus.

**Apparate-bau,** *m.* construction of apparatus. **-brett,** *n.* apparatus board; instrument board.

**Apparatenkunde,** *f.* knowledge relating to apparatus.

**Apparatetisch,** *m.* apparatus table; working table.

**apparativ,** *a.* pertaining to apparatus.

**Apparatur,** *f.* apparatus (collectively), equipment.

**appellieren,** *v.i.* appeal.

**appetitlich,** *a.* appetizing, delicious.

**applizieren,** *v.t.* apply.

**Applizierung,** *f.* application.

**Appret,** *n.* (*Textiles*) dressing, finishing.

**appretieren,** *v.t.* dress, finish (cloth).

**Appretur,** *f.* finishing, dressing; finish, dressing, size.

**appreturecht,** *a.* unaffected by finishing.

**Appretur-masse,** *f.* dressing, sizing, size. **-mittel,** *n.* finishing agent, dressing material, dressing. **-verfahren,** *n.* finishing process.

**approbieren,** *v.t.* approve.

**Aprikose,** *f.* apricot.

**Aprikosenkernöl,** *n.* apricot kernel oil.

**apyrisch,** *a.* apyrous, incombustible.

**Äquator,** *m.* equator.

**Aquavit,** *m.* aqua vitae, whisky; *pl.* spirits.

**äqui-.** equi-.

**äquimolekular,** *a.* equimolecular.

**Äquipartition,** *f.* equipartition.

**äquipotential, -tiell,** *a.* equipotential.

**äquivalent,** *a.* equivalent.

**Äquivalent,** *n.* equivalent. **-gewicht,** *n.* equivalent weight, combining weight.

**Äquivalenz,** *f.* equivalence.

**Aquoverbindung,** *f.* aquo compound.

**Araber,** *m.* Arab, Arabian.

**Arabien,** *n.* Arabia.

**Arabin-gummi,** *n.* gum arabic. **-säure,** *f.* arabic acid, arabin.

**arabisch,** *a.* Arabic, Arabian.—**arabischer Balsam,** balsam of Mecca, balm of Gilead. —**arabisches Gummi,** gum arabic.

**Arachinsäure,** *f.* arachic (or arachidic) acid.

**Arachisöl,** *n.* arachis oil, peanut oil.

**Aräometer,** *n.*, **Aräomesser,** *m.* hydrometer, areometer.

**Aräometrie,** *f.* hydrometry, areometry.

**aräometrisch,** *a.* hydrometric, areometric.

**Arbeit,** *f.* work, labor; working; fermentation;

task, job; workmanship; piece of work, (scientific) investigation.

arbeiten, v.i. work; ferment; (of wood) warp. —v.i. work, perform, make.—arbeitend, p.a. working, active.

Arbeiter, m. worker, laborer, workman.

Arbeit-geber, m. employer. -nehmer, m. workman, employee.

Arbeits-. working, work, of work or labor, operating.

arbeitsam, a. industrious; laborious.

Arbeits-änderung, f. change in work. -äquivalent, n. mechanical equivalent. -aufwand, m. expenditure of work. -druck, m. working pressure. -einheit, f. unit of work. -einstellung, f. strike.

arbeitsfähig, a. capable of work; able-bodied.

Arbeits-fähigkeit, f. capacity for performing work. -fläche, f. bearing surface; working surface. -gang, m. working state, operation; course of manufacture. -hub, m. working stroke. -kammer, f. laboratory; work room. -kraft, f. working power, working faculty. -kräfte, f.pl. labor. -leistung, f. performance of work; efficiency; output. -lohn, m. wages, pay.

arbeitslos, a.& adv. without work, unemployed.

Arbeits-methode, f. method of work (or working). -ordnung, f. working regulation.

arbeitsparend, a. labor-saving.

Arbeits-raum, m. laboratory; work room. -tisch, m. work table; laboratory table. -vermögen, n. (Physics) energy. -verrichtung, f. performance of work. -weise, f. method of working, procedure; workmanship.

Arbeitswert, m. value in work. — der Wärme, mechanical equivalent of heat.

Arbeitszimmer, n. work room; laboratory; workshop; office; study.

Arbitrium, n. arbitrament.

Archiv, n. record office; pl. records, archives (often used in names of periodicals).

Areal, n. area.

Arecanuss, Arekanuss, f. areca nut.

arg, a. bad; strong, severe, enormous.

Arg, n. harm, mischief.

Argentinien, m. Argentina.

ärgerlich, a. angry; vexatious.

arglos, a. harmless; unsuspecting.

Argwohn, n. suspicion.

arithmetisch, a. arithmetical.

arktisch, a. arctic.

arm, a. poor; low, weak; (of gas, etc.) lean.

Arm, m. arm (in various senses); branch; cross bar (of a balance).

-arm. poor (in), low (in).

Armatur, f. fitting, mounting; armature.

Arm-binde, m. sling. -blei, n. refined lead (from which the silver has been removed).

Armee, f. army.

Ärmel, m. sleeve.

armenisch, a. Armenian.

ärmer, a. poorer.

armieren, v.t. arm, equip; reinforce (concrete).

ärmlich, a. poor.

armselig, a. poor, wretched, paltry.

Armut, f. poverty.

Arnika-blüten, f.pl. arnica flowers, (Pharm.) arnica. -wurzel, f. arnica rhizome, arnica root.

Arom, n. aroma.

Aromaten, pl. aromatic substances.

aromatisch, a. aromatic.—aromatisches Mittel, (Pharm.) aromatic.

aromatisieren, v.t. aromatize, scent, perfume.

Aromatisierung, f. aromatization.

Aron, m. arum.

Aronsstärke, f. arum starch.

Arrak, m. arrack.

arretieren, v.t. arrest.

Arretierung, f. arrest; stop, detent.

arrodieren, v.t. erode.

Arrowmehl, n. arrowroot flour, (Pharm.) arrowroot, maranta.

Arsen, n. arsenic. -antimon, n. antimony arsenide. -bestimmung, f. arsenic determination. -blende, f. arsenic blend (gelbe, orpiment; rote, realgar). -blüte, f. arsenic bloom, arsenolite (As₂O₃). -chlorid, n. (any) arsenic chloride. -dampf, m. arsenic vapor, arsenical vapor. -eisen, n. iron arsenide. -eisensinter, m. pitticite. -erz, n. arsenic ore. -fahlerz, n. tennantite. -fleck, m. arsenic spot or stain.

arsen-frei, a. free from arsenic, arsenic-free. -führend, a. arseniferous.

Arsen-gehalt, m. arsenic content. -glas, n. =Arsenikglas. -halogen, n. arsenic halide.

arsenhaltig, a. arsenical, containing arsenic.

arsenig, a. arsenious.—arsenige Säure, arsenious acid.

arsenigsauer, a. of or combined with arsenious acid, arsenite of.

Arsenigsäure, f. arsenious acid. -salz, n. arsenite.

Arsenik, m. arsenic.—gelber —, orpiment.— roter —, realgar.—weisser —, white arsenic, arsenic trioxide.

Arsenikfahlerz, n. tennantite.

Arsenikalien, f.pl. arsenicals, arsenical compounds or preparations.

arsenikalisch, a. arsenical.

Arsenikalkies, m. leucopyrite.

Arsenik-antimon, n. antimony arsenite. -blei, n. lead arsenide. -bleispat, m.

mimetite. **-blumen,** *f.pl.,* **-blüte,** *f.* = Arsenblüte. **-eisen,** *n.* = Arseneisen. **-erz,** *n.* arsenic ore. **-fahlerz,** *n.* tennantite. **-gegengift,** *n.* arsenic antidote. **-glas,** *n.* arsenic glass, vitreous arsenic trioxide; **(gelbes)** orpiment; **(rotes)** realgar.

**arsenikhaltig,** *a.* = arsenhaltig.

**Arsenik-hütte,** *f.* arsenic works. **-jodür,** *n.* = Arsenjodür. **-kies,** *m.* arsenical pyrites (either arsenopyrite or löllingite). **-kobalt,** *m.* cobalt arsenide. **-kupfer,** *n.* copper arsenide. **-metall,** *n.* = Arsenmetall. **-nickel,** *n.* nickel arsenide. **-öl (ätzendes),** caustic oil of arsenic (AsCl₃). **-präparat,** *n.* = Arsenpräparat. **-probe,** *f.* arsenic test. **-rubin,** *m.* realgar. **-salz,** *n.* salt of arsenic, arsenate or arsenite.

**arseniksauer,** *a.* = arsensauer.

**Arseniksäure,** *f.* arsenic acid.—**unvollkommene —,** *f.* arsenious acid.

**Arsenik-schwarz,** *n.* arsenic black. **-silber,** *n.* arsenical silver. **-silberblende,** *f.* (*Min.*) proustite. **-sinter,** *m.* scorodite. **-spiegel,** *m.* arsenic mirror. **-spiessglanz,** *m.* allemontite. **-verbindung,** *f.* arsenic compound. **-vitriol,** *m.* arsenic sulfate.

**Arsen-jodid,** *n.* arsenic iodide, specif. arsenic triiodide. **-jodür,** *n.* = arsenic diiodide (AsI₂). **-kies,** *m.* = Arsenikkies. **-kobalt,** *m.* cobalt arsenide. **-kupfer,** *n.* copper arsenide. **-legierung,** *f.* arsenic alloy. **-lösung,** *f.* arsenic solution. **-metall,** *n.* metallic arsenide; metallic arsenic. **-nickel,** *m.* nickel arsenide; (*Min.*) niccolite. **-nickelglanz,** *m.* gersdorffite. **-nickelkies,** *m.* niccolite.

**Arsenobenzol,** *n.* arsenobenzene.

**Arsen-oxyd,** *n.* arsenic oxide, specif. arsenic trioxide. **-präparat,** *n.* arsenical preparation, arsenical. **-rohr,** *n.,* **-röhre,** *f.* arsenic tube. **-rotgültigerz,** *n.* proustite. **-rubin,** *m.* realgar. **-salz,** *n.* arsenic salt.

**arsensauer,** *a.* of or combined with arsenic acid, arsenate of.

**Arsen-säure,** *f.* arsenic acid. **-silber,** *n.* silver arsenide. **-silberblende,** *f.* proustite. **-spiegel,** *m.* arsenic mirror. **-sulfid,** *n.* arsenic sulfide, esp. the pentasulfide. **-sulfür,** *n.* arsenic trisulfide. **-verbindung,** *f.* arsenic compound. **-vergiftung,** *f.* arsenic poisoning. **-wasserstoff,** *m.* arsenic hydride, arseniuretted hydrogen (specif. arsine, AsH₃). **-zink,** *n.* zinc arsenide.

**Arsinigsäure,** *f.* arsinous acid, arsinic acid (better translated arsinic acid when referring to compounds of the formula RR'AsO.OH).

**Arsinsäure,** *f.* arsonic acid, arsinic acid (better translated arsonic acid when refer-

ring to compounds of the formula RAsO(OH)₂).

**Art,** *f.* kind, sort, species, variety; nature; manner, way; race, breed; *pl.* manners; (*Biol.*) species. (Used as a suffix to give a generic meaning; as, *Pecharten,* pitches, *i.e.,* kinds of pitch).

**arten,** *v.i.* be of a (certain) kind, be like; thrive.—*v.t.* form, modify.—**geartet,** disposed, -natured.

**arteriell,** *a.* arterial.

**Arterien-.** arterial.

**artesisch,** *a.* artesian.

**artificiell,** *a.* artificial.

**artig,** *a.* good, polite, agreeable.

**-artig.** A suffix attached to nouns and adjectives to form adjectives, and signifying " of the kind or nature of," " resembling," " like; " as, *schwefelartig,* like sulfur, sulfurous.

**Artikel,** *m.* article; goods, material; entry, item; (*Calico*) style.

**Artischocke,** *f.* artichoke.

**arylieren,** *v.t.* arylate.

**Arznei, Arzenei,** *f.* medicine; *pl.* drugs.

**Arznei-.** medicinal, medical, medicated. **-bereiter,** *m.* pharmacist. **-bereitung,** *f.* preparing of medicines, pharmacy. **-buch,** *n.* pharmacopeia; dispensatory. **-essig,** *m.* medicated vinegar. **-fläschchen,** *n.* small medicine bottle. **-flasche,** *f.* medicine bottle. **-form,** *f.* medicinal form. **-formel,** *f.* medical formula. **-gabe,** *f.* dose (of medicine). **-gemisch,** *n.* medicinal mixture. **-geruch,** *m.* medicinal smell. **-geschmack,** *m.* medicinal taste. **-gewicht,** *n.* officinal weight. **-handel,** *m.* drug trade. **-händler,** *m.* druggist. **-körper,** *m.* medicinal substance.

**arzneikräftig,** *a.* medicinal, curative, therapeutic.

**Arznei-kraut,** *n.* medicinal plant, medicinal herb. **-kugel,** *f.* (*Pharm.*) bolus. **-lehre,** *f.* pharmacology.

**arzneilich,** *a.* medicinal, medical, pharmaceutical.

**Arznei-mass,** *n.* officinal measure. **-mischung,** *f.* medicinal mixture.

**Arzneimittel,** *n.* medicine, remedy. **-kunde,** *f.* pharmacology. **-lehre,** *f.* pharmacology. **-träger,** *m.* (*Pharm.*) menstruum; excipient.

**Arznei-pflanze,** *f.* medicinal plant. **-seife,** *f.* medicinal soap. **-sirup,** *m.* medicated sirup. **-stoff,** *m.* medicinal substance, pharmaceutical. **-verordnung,** **-verschreibung,** *f.* (medical) prescription. **-ware,** *f.* drug. **-warenkunde,** *f.* pharmacology. **-wesen,** *n.* pharmaceutical affairs. **-wissenschaft,** *f.* pharmacology; medical science.

Arzt, *m.* physician, doctor.

Ärzte-schaft, *f.* medical profession, medicine. -verein, *m.* medical society.

ärztlich, *a.* medical.

A.S., *abbrev.* (Ampère-Stunde) ampere-hour.

Asant, Asand, *m.*—stinkender —, asafetida.— wohlriechender —, gum benzoin.

Asantöl, *n.* asafetida oil.

Asarumkampher, *m.* asarum camphor, asaron.

Asbest, *m.* asbestos.

asbestartig, *a.* asbestoid, asbestiform, amianthine.

Asbest-drahtnetz, *n.* asbestos wire gauze. -faser, *f.* asbestos fiber. -gewebe, *n.* asbestos cloth. -handschuh, *m.* asbestos glove. -papier, *n.* asbestos paper. -pappe, *f.* asbestos board. -platte, *f.* asbestos plate or board. -schale, *f.* asbestos dish. -schicht, *f.* asbestos layer or bed. -schiefer, *m.* asbestos slate. -schirm, *m.* asbestos screen. -schnur, *f.* asbestos twine or cord. -wolle, *f.* asbestos wool.

Asch-blau, *n.* zaffer. -blei, *n.* native bismuth.

Asche, *f.* ash, ashes.

aschefrei, *a.* free from ash, ash-free.

Äschel, Aschel, *m.* (*Metal.*) sullage.

aschen, *v.t.* ash.

Aschen-bad, *n.* ash bath. -bestandteil, *m.* ash constituent. -bestimmung, *f.* ash determination. -dünger, *m.* cinereal manure, cinereal. -ermittelung, *f.* determination of ash. -fall, *f.* ash pit, ash pan.

aschen-fleckig, *a.* (*Metal.*) specked with sullage. -frei, *a.* ash-free.

Aschen-gehalt, *m.* ash content. -lauge, *f.* lye from ashes. -ofen, *m.* calcining oven. -salz, *n.* potash. -trecker, -zieher, *m.* tourmaline (old name).

Äscher, *m.* (*Leather*) tanner's pit, lime pit; (*Soap*) ash cistern (also, ashes); (*Masonry*) slaked lime; (*Ceram.*) tin ashes. -brühe, -flüssigkeit, *f.* (*Leather*) lime liquor.

aschereich, *a.* rich in ash, high in ash.

Äscher-fass, *n.* (*Leather*) liming tub. -kalk, *m.* (*Leather*) lime.

äschern, *v.t.* ash; (*Leather*) lime.

Äscherofen, *m.* (*Ceram.*) frit kiln.

Äscherung, *f.* ashing; (*Leather*) liming.

aschfarben, *a.* ash-colored, ashy.

äschig, äschicht, *a.* ashy.

Aschraum, *m.* ash box, ash pit.

Äsculetin, *n.* esculetin, aesculetin.

Äsculin, *n.* esculin, aesculin.

aseptisch, *a.* aseptic.

asiatisch, *a.* Asiatic.

Äskuletin, *n.* esculetin, aesculetin.

Äskulin, *n.* esculin, aesculin.

Asparaginsäure, *f.* aspartic acid.

Aspe, *f.* aspen (tree).

Asphalt-beton, *m.* asphalt(ic) concrete. -firnis, *m.* asphalt varnish.

asphaltfrei, *a.* asphalt-free.

Asphaltgestein, *n.* native asphalt.

asphalthaltig, *a.* containing asphalt, asphaltic, bituminiferous.

asphaltieren, *v.t.* asphalt.

asphaltisch, *a.* asphaltic.

Asphalt-kitt, *m.* asphalt cement, asphalt mastic. -lack, *m.* asphalt varnish. -mastix, *m.* = Asphaltkitt. -pappe, *f.* asphalt board. -pech, *n.* bituminous pitch. -pflaster, *n.* asphalt pavement.

asphaltreich, *a.* rich in asphalt.

Asphalt-stein, *m.* native asphalt. -verfahren, *n.* asphalt process, bitumen process.

aspirieren, *v.i.* aspire.—*v.t.* aspirate.

ass, *pret.* of essen.

Assanierung, *f.* sanitation.

Assekuranz, *f.* insurance.

assekurieren, *v.t.* insure.

assimilatorisch, *a.* assimilatory, assimilative.

assimilierbar, *a.* assimilable.

Assimilierbarkeit, *f.* assimilability.

assimilieren, *v.t.* assimilate.

Assistent, *m.* assistant.

Association, *f.* association; (*Org. Chem.*) coupling.

associieren, *v.t.* associate.

assortieren, *v.t.* assort, sort.

assouplieren, *v.t.* render pliable, supple.

assoziieren, *v.t.* associate.

Ast, *m.* branch, bough; leg (of a tube); knot (in wood).

Astronom, *m.* astronomer.

astronomisch, *a.* astronomical.

astrophysikalisch, *a.* astrophysical.

asymmetrisch, *a.* asymmetric, asymmetrical.

asymptotisch, *a.* asymptotic.

asynchron, *a.* asynchronous.

At., *abbrev.* (Atom) atom; (Atmosphäre) atmosphere.

-at. (in names of salts, etc.) -ate.

Atem, *m.* breath, breathing, respiration; spirit.

Atem-. of breathing, respiratory.

atembar, *a.* respirable.

Atem-einsatz, *m.* drum (of a German mask). -gerät, *n.* = Atmungsgerät.

äterisch, *a.* ethereal.

At.-Gew., *abbrev.* (Atomgewicht) atomic weight.

äth., *abbrev.* (ätherisch) ethereal.

Äthal, *n.* ethal (cetyl alcohol).

Äthan, *n.* ethane; *pl.* paraffins, hydrocarbons of the ethane series. -al, *n.* ethanal (acetaldehyde). -oyl, *n.* ethanoyl (acetyl). -säure, *f.* ethanoic acid (acetic acid).

Äthebenin, *n.* ethebenine.

**Äthebenol,** *n.* ethebenol.

**Äthen,** *n.* ethene (ethylene). **-yl,** *n.* ethenyl.

**Äther,** *m.* ether (in older names frequently equivalent to *ester*).

**ätherähnlich,** *a.* etherlike, ethereal.

**Ätherart,** *f.* kind of ether; *pl.* ethers.

**ätherartig,** *a.* ethereal.

**Äther-auszug,** *m.* ethereal extract, ether extract. **-bildung,** *f.* ether formation, etherification. **-dampf,** *m.* ether vapor.

**ätherifizieren,** *v.t.* etherify.

**Ätherifizierung,** *f.* etherification.

**Ätherin,** *n.* etherin.

**ätherisch,** *a.* ethereal; essential, volatile (oils). **-riechend,** *a.* of ethereal odor.

**ätherisierbar,** *a.* etherizable.

**ätherisieren,** *v.t.* etherize.

**atherman,** *a.* athermanous.

**äthern,** *v.t.* etherize.

**Äther-prober,** *m.* ether tester. **-säure,** *f.* ether acid (compound which is both an ether and an acid); lampic acid (*Obs.*). **-schicht,** *f.* ether layer. **-schwefelsäure,** *f.* alkylsulfuric acid, specif. ethylsulfuric acid. **-schwingung,** *f.* vibration of the ether, ethereal vibration. **-verlust,** *m.* loss or waste of ether. **-weingeist,** *m.* (*Pharm.*) spirit of ether (solution of ether in alcohol)

**Äthiden,** *n.* ethidene, ethylidene.

**Äthin,** *n.* ethyne, ethine (acetylene).

**Äthionsäure,** *f.* ethionic acid.

**athmen,** *v.* = atmen.

**Äthoxalyl,** *n.* ethoxalyl.

**Äthoxy-.** ethoxy-.

**Äthoxyl,** *n.* ethoxyl.

**Äthyl,** *n.* ethyl. **-al,** *n.* ethylal.

**äthylalkoholisch,** *a.* ethyl-alcoholic.

**Äthyl-at,** *n.* ethylate. **-äther,** *m.* ethyl ether. **-blau,** *n.* ethyl blue.

**Äthylen,** *n.* ethylene. **-bindung,** *f.* ethylene linkage, double bond. **-jodid,** *n.* ethylene iodide. **-oxyd,** *n.* ethylene oxide. **-reihe,** *f.* ethylene series.

**Äthyl-grün,** *n.* ethyl green. **-gruppe,** *f.* ethyl group. **-gummi,** *n.* ethyl rubber.

**Äthyliden,** *n.* ethylidene. **-milchsäure,** *f.* ethylidene lactic acid.

**Äthyl-jodid,** *n.* ethyl iodide, iodoethane. **-rot,** *n.* ethyl red. **-schwefelsäure,** *f.* ethylsulfuric acid. **-senföl,** *n.* ethyl mustard oil ($C_2H_5NCS$). **-verbindung,** *f.* ethyl compound. **-wasserstoff,** *m.* ethyl hydride (ethane). **-zinnsäure,** *f.* ethylstannic acid.

**Ätio-.** etio-, aetio-.

**Ätiologie,** *f.* etiology, aetiology.

**Atlas,** *m.* satin; atlas.

**atlasartig,** *a.* satiny, satined.

**Atlas-erz,** *n.,* **-kies,** *m.* fibrous malachite. **-gips,** *m.* fibrous gypsum.

**atlasglänzend,** *a.* of satiny luster, satiny.

**Atlas-holz,** *n.* satinwood. **-papier,** *n.* glazed paper. **-spat, -stein,** *m.* satin spar (fibrous calcium carbonate).

**Atm.,** *abbrev.* (Atmosphäre) atmosphere(s).

**atmen,** *v.i.* breathe, respire.—*v.t.* breathe.

**Atmolyse,** *f.* atmolysis.

**Atmosphäre,** *f.* atmosphere.

**Atmosphärendruck,** *m.* atmospheric pressure.

**atmosphärisch,** *a.* atmospheric.

**Atmosphärilien,** *pl.* substances in the atmosphere.

**Atmung,** *f.* breathing, respiration.

**Atmungs-.** of breathing, respiratory. **-gerät,** *n.* breathing apparatus, respirator. **-gift,** *n.* respiratory poison. **-grösse,** *f.* respiration quotient. **-nahrungsmittel,** *n.* respiratory food.

**atomar,** *a.* atomic.

**atomartig,** *a.* atomic; atom-like.

**Atom-begriff,** *m.* conception of the atom. **-bewegung,** *f.* atomic motion. **-bindungsvermögen,** *n.,* **atombindende Kraft,** atomic combining power, valence. **-gewicht,** *n.* atomic weight. **-gewichtstabelle, -gewichtstafel,** *f.* table of atomic weights. **-gramm,** *n.* gram atom. **-gruppe,** *f.* group of atoms, atomic group. **-gruppierung,** *f.* atomic grouping.

**atomhaltig,** *a.* atomic.

**Atom-hülle,** *f.* atomic shell. **-hypothese,** *f.* atomic hypothesis.

**Atomigkeit,** *f.* atomicity.

**atomisch,** *a.* atomic.

**Atomismus,** *m.* atomism.

**Atomistik,** *f.* atomistics.

**atomistisch,** *a.* atomistic, atomic.

**Atomizität,** *f.* atomicity.

**Atom-kern,** *m.* atomic nucleus. **-lage,** *f.* atomic layer; atomic position. **-lehre,** *f.* doctrine of atoms, atomic theory. **-mechanik,** *f.* mechanics of the atom. **-modell,** *n.* atomic model. **-nummer,** *f.* atomic number. **-refraktion,** *f.* atomic refraction. **-rest,** *m.* atomic residue (= Atomrumpf). **-ring,** *m.* ring of atoms. **-rumpf,** *m.* core of the atom, atomic core (the atom minus the outer electrons).

**atomtheoretisch,** *a.* of or according to the atomic theory.

**Atom-theorie,** *f.* atomic theory. **-verband,** *m.,* **-verbindung,** *f.* union of atoms, atomic union. **-verkettung,** *f.* linking of atoms, atomic linkage. **-verschiebung,** *f.* atomic displacement. **-volum, -volumen,** *n.* atomic volume. **-wärme,** *f.* atomic heat. **-wertigkeit,** *f.* atomic valence. **-zahl,** *f.* atomic number; number of atoms. -zeichen, *n.* atomic symbol.

Atramentstein, *m.* inkstone, native copperas.

Atranorinsäure, *f.* atranorinic acid.

Atranorsäure, *f.* atranoric acid.

Atrolaktinsäure, *f.* atrolactic acid.

Atropasäure, *f.* atropic acid.

attenuieren, *v.t.* attenuate.

Attest, *n.* certificate.

Attich, *m.* dwarf elder, danewort.

Atü., *abbrev.* (Atmosphärenüberdruck) atmospheres excess pressure.

Ätz-. caustic, corrosive; (*Calico*) discharging, discharge. -alkali, *n.* caustic alkali. -alkalilösung, *f.* caustic alkaline solution.

ätzalkalisch, *a.* caustic alkaline.

Ätz-ammoniak, *n.* caustic ammonia (ammonium hydroxide), ammonia water. -artikel, *m.* (*Calico*) discharge style.

ätzbar, *a.* corrodible; (*Calico*) dischargeable.

Ätz-barkeit, *f.* corrodibility. -baryt, *m.* caustic baryta (barium hydroxide). -beizdruck, *n.* discharge printing. -beize, *f.* chemical discharge, discharge mordant. -druck, *n.* discharge printing.

Ätze, *f.* corrosion; etching; cauterization; etching liquid, esp. aqua fortis; (*Calico*) discharge.

ätzen, *v.t.* corrode; etch, bite; cauterize; (*Calico*) discharge.—ätzend, *p.a.* caustic, corrosive.—ätzend machen, render caustic, causticize.—ätzender Kalk = Ätzkalk.

Ätz-farbe, *f.* etching ink; (*Calico*) discharge paste. -figur, *f.* etching figure, etched figure. -gift, *n.* caustic poison. -grund, *m.* etching ground.

Ätzkali, *n.* caustic potash. -lauge, *f.* caustic potash lye, caustic potash solution. -lösung, *f.* caustic potash solution. -stück, *n.* piece of caustic potash.

Ätzkalk, *m.* caustic lime (gebrännter, quicklime; gelöschter, slaked lime). -lösung, *f.* lime water.

Ätz-kraft, *f.* causticity; corrosiveness. -lack, *m.* discharge lake. -lauge, *f.* caustic lye, caustic liquor. -mittel, *n.* corrosive, caustic; (*Calico*) chemical discharge.

Ätznatron, *n.* caustic soda. -lauge, *f.* caustic soda lye, caustic soda solution. -lösung, *f.* caustic soda solution. -stück, *n.* piece of caustic soda.

Ätzpapp, *m.* (*Calico*) resist.

ätzpolieren, *v.t.* polish with acid or other etching agent, etch-polish.

Ätz-probe, *f.* etching test or sample. -pulver, *n.* caustic powder; etching powder. -schliff, *m.* ground section for etching (as of metals). -silber, *n.* lunar caustic (silver nitrate). -stein, *m.* lapis causticus, (fused) caustic

potash; lunar caustic (silver nitrate). -stoff, *m.* caustic, corrosive. -strontian, *m.* caustic strontia (strontium oxide or hydroxide). -sublimat, *n.* corrosive sublimate (mercuric chloride). -tinte, *f.* etching ink.

Ätzung, *f.* corrosion; etching; cauterization.

Ätz-verfahren, *n.* caustic process, corrosive process, etching process. -wasser, *n.* caustic water; etching liquid, specif. aqua fortis; mordant. -weiss, *n.* (*Calico*) white discharge. -wirkung, *f.* corrosive action; (*Calico*) action of the discharge.

a.u.a., *abbrev.* (auch unter andern) also among others.

auch, *adv.& conj.* also, too; indeed, even.— — nicht, neither, not . . . either.

Aue, *f.* islet; meadow.

Auer-brenner, *m.* Welsbach burner. -licht, *n.* Welsbach light. -metall, *n.* Welsbach metal (pyrophoric cerium alloy).

auf, *prep.* on, upon, in, at; about; into, to.— *adv.& prefix.* up, upward, open.— — dass, in order that.— — einmal, at once.— — und ab, up and down; to and fro.

aufarbeiten, *v.t.* work up; finish (a task).

aufatmen, *v.i.* breathe hard, breathe again.

aufätzen, *v.t.* corrode or etch upon, etch; (*Med.*) open with caustic.

Aufbau, *m.* building up, synthesis; building, erection; (super) structure; display.

aufbauen, *v.t.* build up, synthesize; erect. —aufbauend, *p.a.* synthetic.

aufbäumen, *v.i.* show (metallic) luster.— *v.t.* beam, wind up.

Aufbauprinzip, *n.* construction principle (governing the structure of atoms).

aufbeizen, *v.t.* = aufätzen.

aufbereiten, *v.t.* prepare; dress (ores).

Aufbereitung, *f.* preparation; dressing (of ores).

Aufbereitungsverlust, *m.* loss from preparation or (of ores) dressing.

aufbersten, *v.i.* burst, crack.

aufbessern, *v.t.* improve, ameliorate.

aufbewahren, *v.t.* keep, store, preserve.

Aufbewahrung, *f.* keeping, storage, preservation.

Aufbewahrungsdauer, *f.* length of storage.

aufbiegen, *v.t.* bend up, turn up; open, unfold.

aufbieten, *v.t.* call out, summon; exert; abuse.

aufbinden, *v.t.* tie up, fasten; untie, loosen.

aufblähen, *v.t., i.& r.* swell, swell up, bulge out, expand.

aufblasen, *v.t.* blow up, inflate.

aufblättern, *v.i.* (*Min. & Med.*) exfoliate.

Aufblick, *m.* (*Assaying*) fulguration, blick; look upward.

**aufblicken,** *v.i.* (*Assaying*) brighten, give the " blick "; look up.

**aufblitzen,** *v.i.* flash, flash up.

**aufblühen,** *v.i.* blossom, unfold; form a flower-like mass (before the blowpipe); develop.

**aufbohren,** *v.t.* bore open, bore.

**aufbrauchen,** *v.t.* use up, consume.

**aufbrausen,** *v.i.* effervesce; ferment; roar; fly into a passion:—**aufbrausend,** *p.a.* effervescent; fermenting.

**aufbrechen,** *v.t.* break up, break open.— *v.i.* open, break, burst.

**aufbrennen,** *v.t.* burn up, consume; refine (metals); brand; burn on; treat by burning, specif. sulfur (wine).

**aufbringen,** *v.t.* bring (up), lift (up); put (up), set (up); raise; anger, provoke.

**aufbrodeln,** *v.i.* bubble up, boil up.

**aufbrühen,** *v.t.* boil up, boil.

**aufdampfen,** *v.i.* evaporate; smoke.

**aufdarren,** *v.t.* dry, desiccate.

**aufdecken,** *v.t.* uncover, disclose.

**aufdocken,** *v.t.* wind up, roll up; bundle, shock.

**aufdörren,** *v.t.* dry, desiccate.

**aufdrängen,** *v.r.* obtrude oneself.

**aufdrehen,** *v.t.* screw open, untwist; turn on (as gas); turn up; (*Ceram.*) throw.

**aufdringen,** *v.t.* press upon, obtrude upon.

**Aufdringlichkeit,** *f.* obtrusiveness, importunity.

**Aufdruck,** *m.* printing; print.

**aufdrücken,** *v.t.* impress, imprint, stamp.

**aufduften,** *v.i.* give off an odor or fragrance.

**aufdunsten,** *v.i.* evaporate.

**aufdünsten,** *v.t.* evaporate.

**aufeinander,** *adv.* one upon (or after) another.

**Aufeinanderfolge,** *f.* succession, series.

**aufeinanderfolgend,** *p.a.* consecutive, successive.

**Aufelektron,** *n.* outer electron, valence electron.

**Aufenthalt,** *m.* stay, stop; abode, residence.

**auferlegen,** *v.t.* impose (on or upon); punish.

**auffahren,** *v.i.* rise up, drive up, fly up, start up.

**auffallen,** *v.i.* fall (on); strike; astonish.— **auffallend,** *p.a.* incident; striking, remarkable.

**auffällig,** *a.* = auffallend.

**auffalten,** *v.t.* unfold, open; fold up, fold.

**Auffangbehälter,** *m.* collecting vessel, receiver.

**Auffange-.** collecting. **-gefäss,** *n.* collecting vessel, receiver. **-glas,** *n.* (*Optics*) object glass.

**auffangen,** *v.t.* collect; intercept; catch.

**Auffänger,** *m.* collector; collecting vessel, receiver.

**Auffang-rohr,** *n.,* **-röhre,** *f.* collecting tube, pipe or cylinder. **-schale,** *f.* collecting dish or basin; drip pan.

**auffärben,** *v.t.* dye anew, redye.

**Auffärber,** *m.* job dyer.

**auffasern,** *v.t.* separate into fibers, unravel.

**auffassen,** *v.t.* conceive, perceive, comprehend; interpret; catch up.

**Auffassung,** *f.* conception; perception; comprehension.

**auffeuchten,** *v.t.* moisten, wet.

**auffinden,** *v.t.* detect, discover, find, find out.

**aufflackern,** *v.i.* flare up; deflagrate.

**aufflammen,** *v.i.* flame up, blaze, deflagrate.

**auffliegen,** *v.i.* blow up, explode; fly up, rise.

**auffliessen,** *v.i.* flow on, run on.

**Aufforderung,** *f.* request; appeal; demand.

**auffressen,** *v.t.* corrode; eat up.

**auffrischen,** *v.t.* freshen (up), revive, restore, renew; regenerate; (*Brewing*) change (steep water), refresh (yeast).

**Auffrischung,** *f.* freshening, etc. (see auffrischen).

**aufführen,** *v.t.* erect, raise; perform; charge (in an account), enter, note; register; adduce, bring in (as evidence).

**auffüllen,** *v.t.* fill up, make up, fill.

**Auffüllung,** *f.* filling up, filling.

**Aufgabe,** *f.* task, problem; function; giving up; delivery; order; lesson; theme.

**Aufgabe-.** charging, feeding; issuing, sending.

**Aufgabensammlung,** *f.* collection of problems.

**Aufgabevorrichtung,** *f.* charging device, feeder.

**Aufgang,** *m.* rising, going up, ascent; disappearance.

**aufgären,** *v.i.* ferment, effervesce.

**aufgeben,** *v.t.* give up, give, deliver; charge, feed (a furnace or the like); propose.

**aufgebläht,** *p.p.* of aufblähen.

**Aufgebot,** *n.* summons; levy; bans.

**aufgebracht,** *p.p.* of aufbringen.

**aufgedunsen,** *p.a.* swollen.

**aufgehen,** *v.i.* go up, rise, swell; ferment; appear; open, come open; unfold; be spent or consumed; evaporate; be merged; (of dyes) go on, be absorbed; (of plants) come up, shoot; (*Arith.*) leave no remainder.

**Aufgeld,** *n.* premium; extra charge.

**aufgelegt,** *p.a.* see auflegen.

**aufgeschliffen,** *p.p.* of aufschleifen.

**aufgeschlossen,** *p.p.* of aufschliessen.

**aufgeschmolzen,** *p.p.* of aufschmelzen.

**aufgesogen,** *p.p.* of aufsaugen.

**aufgeweckt,** *p.a.* lively, clever.

**aufgichten,** *v.t.* (*Metal.*).

**aufgiessen,** *v.t.* infuse; pour on, pour upon.

**aufgischen,** *v.i.* foam up, boil up; ferment.

**Aufguss,** *m.* infusion. **-apparat,** *m.* sparger. **-gefäss,** *n.* infusion vessel, digester. **-tier-**

chen, *n.pl.* Infusoria. **-verfahren,** *n.* infusion process or method; mashing process.

**aufhacken,** *v.t.* cut up, stir up.

**aufhalten,** *v.t.* hold up, support; stop, detain, obstruct.—*v.r.* stop, stay; find fault.

**aufhängen,** *v.t.* hang up, hang, suspend.

**Aufhänger,** *m.* hanger; rack.

**Aufhängung,** *f.* hanging (up), suspension.

**aufhäufen,** *v.t.* heap up, pile up, store up.

**aufheben,** *v.t.* lift up, raise; pick up; lay up, preserve; break up, abolish; annul, destroy, neutralize; seize; (of colors) compensate, be complementary to; reduce (a fraction) to lowest terms.

**Aufhebung,** *f.* lifting up, etc. (see aufheben).

**aufheitern,** *v.t.& r.* clear up, brighten up.

**aufhellen,** *v.t.& r.* clear up, clarify, brighten, make lighter (in color).

**Aufhellungsmittel,** *n.* clearing agent.

**aufholen,** *v.t.* draw up, haul up, raise.

**aufhören,** *v.i.* stop, cease, discontinue, end; desist.

**aufkippen,** *v.t.* tilt up, tip up.

**aufkitten,** *v.t.* cement on.

**aufklappbar,** *a.* capable of opening, hinged.

**aufklappen,** *v.t.* open (something leaved, as a book).

**aufklären,** *v.t.* clear up; explain; enlighten.—*v.r.* clear up, clear.

**Aufklärung,** *f.* clearing up, elucidation; information; explanation; enlightenment.

**aufkleben,** *v.t.* paste on; paste up.

**aufkochen,** *v.t.& i.* boil up, boil; boil again.

**Aufkochgefäss,** *n.* boiler; reboiler.

**aufkommen,** *v.i.* advance; come into use; come up, get up.

**aufkratzen,** *v.t.* scratch up, scratch; rake, stir (a fire); dress, nap (fabrics); card (wool).

**aufkräusen,** *v.i.* (*Brewing*) form a head, esp. curly head.

**aufkühlen,** *v.t.* (*Brewing*) aerate.

**aufkündigen,** *v.t.* give notice or warning of; recall.

**aufkupfern,** *v.t.* coat with copper, copper.

**Aufl.,** *abbrev.* (Auflage) edition.

**aufladen,** *v.t.* load; (*Elec.*) charge.

**Auflage,** *f.* edition, impression (of a book); duty, tax; (*Mech.*) rest, support; overlayer, superimposed layer. **-fläche,** *f.* bearing surface.

**Auflager,** *n.* support, bearing.

**auflagern,** *v.t.* store up, store; superpose.—*v.i.* form a layer, aggregate.

**Auflauf,** *m.* swelling; puff; mob, crowd.

**auflaufen,** *v.i.* run up, come up, rise, swell.—*v.t.* feed, supply (to a furnace, etc.); beam, wind up.

**aufleben,** *v.i.* revive.

**auflegen,** *v.t.* lay on or up; apply; impose; print, publish.—**aufgelegt,** *p.a.* disposed, inclined.

**auflehnen,** *v.r.* lean (upon); rebel (against).

**auflesen,** *v.t.* pick up, gather.

**aufleuchten,** *v.i.* light up, shine.

**aufliegen,** *v.i.* lie (on), rest (on); weigh (on); be incumbent (on).

**auflockern,** *v.t.* loosen up, loosen; relax.

**Auflockerung,** *f.* loosening; relaxation.

**auflösbar,** *a.* soluble; resolvable.

**Auflösbarkeit,** *f.* solubility; resolvability.

**auflösen,** *v.t.* dissolve; loosen, untie, undo; resolve, decompose, dissipate; solve.— *v.r.* dissolve; deliquesce.—**auflösend,** *p.a.* solvent, dissolvent.

**Auflöser,** *m.* dissolver, etc. (see auflösen); (*Paper*, etc.) mixer.

**auflöslich,** *a.* soluble.

**Auflöslichblau,** *n.* soluble blue.

**Auflöslichkeit,** *f.* solubility.

**Auflösung,** *f.* solution; dissolving; unloosening, undoing; resolution, decomposition, dissolution, analysis (as opposed to synthesis); (of malt) mellowness, friability.

**auflösungsfähig,** *a.* capable of solution, soluble.

**Auflösungs-gefäss,** *n.* dissolving vessel, dissolver. **-geschwindigkeit,** *f.* velocity of solution, resolution, etc. **-grenze,** *f.* (*Micros.*) limit of resolution. **-kraft,** *f.* dissolving power; resolving power. **-mittel,** *n.* solvent. **-pfanne,** *f.* (*Sugar*) blow-up pan, clarifier. **-vermögen,** *n.* solvent power; (of a microscope) resolving power. **-wärme,** *f.* heat of solution.

**auflöten,** *v.t.* solder on; unsolder.

**aufmachen,** *v.t.* open, undo; put up; make up. —*v.r.* prepare; get up, rise.

**Aufmaischen,** *n.* second mashing.

**aufmerksam,** *a.* attentive, observing.— machen, call (one's) attention (to).

**Aufmerksamkeit,** *f.* attention, attentiveness.

**aufmischen,** *v.t.* mix up.

**Aufnahme,** *f.* taking up; absorbing, absorption; dissolving; admission; reception; fashion; survey, sketch; taking of (photographs); (photographic) picture, photograph.

**aufnahmefähig,** *a.* absorbable; absorptive.

**Aufnahme-fähigkeit,** *f.* absorbability, absorptivity. **-kolben,** *m.* absorption flask. **-vermögen,** *n.* absorptive power.

**aufnehmen,** *v.t.* take up; absorb; dissolve; admit, receive; draw, survey; take (a photograph); borrow.—**aufnehmend,** *p.a.* absorbing, absorptive.

**Aufnehmer,** *m.* receiver; absorber; etc. (see aufnehmen).

**aufnötigen,** *v.t.* force upon.

**aufpassen,** *v.t.* fit on.—*v.i.* be watching.

**aufperlen,** *v.i.* bubble up, bubble.

**aufplatzen,** *v.i.* burst, blow up, explode.

**aufprägen,** *v.t.* imprint, impress on, stamp on.

**Aufprall,** *m.* bound, rebound; impact; shock.

**aufputzen,** *v.t.* trim up, clean up, decorate.

**aufquellen,** *v.i.* swell, swell up; well up.—*v.t.* cause to swell, swell.

**Aufquellung,** *f.* swelling, etc. (see aufquellen).

**aufraffen,** *v.t.* rake up, collect.

**aufräumen,** *v.t.* clear up, clear away, clear, open.—**aufgeräumt,** *p.a.* in good spirits.

**aufrechnen,** *v.t.* count up, count.

**aufrecht,** *a. & adv.* upright, erect.

**Aufrechthaltung,** *f.* maintenance.

**aufregen,** *v.t.* excite, stimulate, irritate; agitate, rouse, alarm.—**aufregend,** *p.a.* irritant, stimulant; alarming.

**Aufregungsmittel,** *n.* irritant; stimulant.

**aufreissen,** *v.t.* tear up, tear open; crack, split; design, plot.—*v.i.* crack, split.

**aufrichten,** *v.t.* set up, raise, erect; comfort.

**aufrichtig,** *a.* sincere, genuine.

**Aufriss,** *m.* elevation; sketch, design.

**aufrollen,** *v.t.* roll up; unroll.

**aufrücken,** *v.t. & i.* move up, advance.

**Aufruf,** *m.* call, summons.

**aufrühren,** *v.t.* stir, stir up.

**Aufrührer,** *m.* stirrer; agitator, rebel.

**aufrunden,** *v.t.* (*Math.*) round off.

**aufrütteln,** *v.t.* shake up, shake.

**aufsagen,** *v.t.* recite; revoke; give warning.

**aufsammeln,** *v.t.* collect; gather.

**Aufsatz,** *m.* something set on; attachment; head, headpiece; neck; top; dome; set (of china); essay, treatise, article, paper; (*Dyeing*) topping; (*Calico*) cover print. **-farbe,** *f.* (*Dyeing*) topping color. **-teil,** *m.* supplement (to a periodical).

**aufsäuern,** *v.t.* acidify (again).

**aufsaugbar,** *a.* absorbable.

**Aufsaugbarkeit,** *f.* absorbability.

**Aufsaugeflüssigkeit,** *f.* absorbing liquid, absorption liquid.

**aufsaugen,** *v.t.* suck up, absorb; aspirate.—**aufsaugend,** *p.a.* absorbent, absorptive.—**aufsaugendes Mittel,** absorbent.

**Aufsauger,** *m.* absorber.

**Aufsaugung,** *f.* absorption; suction.

**Aufsaugungs-fähigkeit,** *f.* absorptive ability or capacity. **-verfahren,** *n.* absorption process or method. **-wärme,** *f.* heat of absorption.

**aufschäumen,** *v.i.* foam up, froth.

**aufschichten,** *v.t.* pile, arrange in layers, stratify.

**Aufschichtung,** *f.* stratification.

**aufschieben,** *v.t.* put off, postpone; push open; push on.

**Aufschlag,** *m.* impact; percussion; increase (in price or tax); cuff, facing; warp; bound (of a ball); (*Med.*) application.

**Aufschlagebuch,** *n.* reference book.

**aufschlagen,** *v.t.* strike up or open; open, unfold; unbung (casks); handle (hides); set up, erect; raise; apply (as a poultice).—*v.r.* spring up; strike; rise (in price).

**Aufschlagzünder,** *m.* percussion fuse.

**aufschlämmen,** *v.t.* suspend, make into a paste, reduce to slime.

**Aufschlämmung,** *f.* suspension; reduction to paste or slime; slime; paste.

**aufschleifen,** *v.t.* grind on; engrave on.

**aufschlemmen,** *v.* = aufschlämmen.

**Aufschliessarbeit,** *f.* work, task or operation of decomposition.

**aufschliessbar,** *a.* capable of being decomposed.

**aufschliessen,** *v.t.* decompose, open up, convert into non-refractory form (as silicates by fusion with alkali carbonates); hydrolyze (as starch); break up, disintegrate; unlock, open; disclose, explain.

**Aufschliessmischung,** *f.* decomposition mixture.

**Aufschliessung,** *f.* decomposition, etc. (see aufschliessen).

**Aufschluss,** *m.* decomposition, etc. (see aufschliessen); information, explanation. **-grad,** *m.* degree of decomposition. **-mittel,** *n.* decomposing agent. **-verfahren,** *n.* decomposition process, disintegration process.

**aufschmelzen,** *v.t.* melt on; fuse on; melt down; melt away; melt open or apart.

**aufschneiden,** *v.t.* cut open, dissect.—*v.i.* brag.

**Aufschnitt,** *m.* cutting open; cut, incision; sliced meat.

**aufschraubbar,** *a.* capable of being unscrewed; capable of being screwed on or up.

**aufschrauben,** *v.t.* unscrew; screw on, screw up; turn up (as gas).

**aufschrecken,** *v.t.* startle.

**aufschreiben,** *v.t.* write down, record.

**Aufschrift,** *f.* label, inscription; address.

**Aufschub,** *m.* putting off, delay.

**aufschütteln,** *v.t.* shake up, shake.

**aufschütten,** *v.t.* put on; lay up, store up.

**Aufschüttung,** *f.* putting on; charging; stoking; storing; dike, bank.

**aufschwefeln,** *v.t.* treat with sulfur, sulfur.

**aufschweissen,** *v.t.* weld on or together.

**aufschwellen,** *v.i.* swell up, tumefy.

**aufschwemmen,** *v.t.* deposit (silt, etc.); float or wash upon; swell up, bloat; soak.

**Aufschwemmung,** *f.* depositing; deposit; suspension; swelling, bloating; soaking.

**Aufschwung,** *m.* rising, rise; advance; growth.

**Aufsehen,** *n.* looking up; sensation.

**Aufseher,** *m.* overseer, inspector, superintendent, foreman.

**aufsetzbar,** *a.* capable of being put on (set up, or drawn up), attachable.

**aufsetzen,** *v.t.* set up, put up, erect; put on; draw up (writings); (*Dyeing*) top; (*Calico*) cover-print.—*v.i.* sit up; mount.

**Aufsicht,** *f.* inspection; superintendence, supervision, control; (of drawings) plan.

**aufsieden,** *v.t.* boil; boil again; boil out; blanch (silver).—*v.i.* boil up.

**Aufsieden,** *n.* boiling up, ebullition.

**aufspalten,** *v.t.* split (up), cleave; slit, slot.—*v.i.* split, burst.

**Aufspaltung,** *f.* splitting up, cleavage (of compounds).

**aufspannen,** *v.t.* stretch, spread; unfold, spread out.

**aufspeichern,** *v.t.* lay up, store, accumulate.

**Aufspeicherung,** *f.* storage, accumulation.

**aufsperren,** *v.t.* open wide.

**aufsprengen,** *v.t.* blow up, blast; force open.

**aufspringen,** *v.i.* crack, split; spring up.

**aufspritzen,** *v.t. & i.* squirt up; spray on.

**aufsprudeln,** *v.i.* boil up, bubble up, effervesce.

**aufspunden, aufspünden,** *v.t.* unbung.

**Aufst.,** *abbrev.* Aufstellung.

**aufstapeln,** *v.t.* pile, stack, store, store up.

**aufstechen,** *v.t.* pick or pierce open; lance; stir up.

**aufstehen,** *v.i.* stand up, rise; stand open.

**aufsteigen,** *v.i.* rise, ascend; swell; boil; spit.

**aufstellen,** *v.t.* set up, put up; erect; advance, adduce; draw up; formulate (an equation).

**Aufstellung,** *f.* erection; arrangement; formulation; statement.

**aufstöbern,** *v.t.* ferret out, discover.

**aufstossen,** *v.i.* ferment anew; become acid (wine); chance (upon).—*v.t.* push up, push open.

**aufstreichen,** *v.t.* spread on, brush on; stain (paper).

**aufstreuen,** *v.t.* sprinkle, strew.

**Aufstrich,** *m.* spreading or brushing on, coat, stain; up stroke; auction.

**aufstützen,** *v.t.* prop, prop up, support.

**aufsuchen,** *v.t.* seek out, search for.

**aufsummen, -summieren,** *v.t. & r.* sum up.

**auftauchen,** *v.i.* emerge, spring up.

**auftauen,** *v.i.* thaw, melt.

**Auftaupunkt,** *m.* thawing point.

**aufteilen,** *v.t.* distribute, allot.

**Auftrag,** *m.* putting on, coating, coat (of color); order; commission, charge.

**auftragen,** *v.t.* lay on, apply; charge (a furnace); draw, plot, protract; order; serve up.

**aufträufeln, auftraufen,** *v.t.* drop on, pour on drop by drop.—*v.i.* drop, fall in drops.

**Auftreff-.** impact, collision.

**auftreffen,** *v.i.* strike (against).

**auftreiben,** *v.t.* sublime; blow, blow up (glass); distend, inflate; drive up; beat out; procure.

**auftrennen,** *v.t.* sever, rip up, rip open.

**auftreten,** *v.i.* enter, appear, occur, come forth; step; proceed.

**Auftreten,** *n.* appearance; occurrence; behavior.

**Auftrieb,** *m.* buoyancy; lift; plankton.

**Auftritt,** *m.* entrance, appearance; step; scene.

**auftrocknen,** *v.t.* dry up, dry.—*v.i.* dry up, dry on.

**auftun,** *v.t.* open, disclose.—*v.r.* become visible.

**auftürmen,** *v.t.* heap up, pile up.—*v.r.* tower.

**aufvulkanisieren,** *v.t.* vulcanize (on).

**aufwallen,** *v.i.* bubble up, bubble, boil up, boil.

**Aufwallung,** *f.* bubbling, ebullition, effervescence.

**Aufwand,** *m.* expenditure; expense; display.

**aufwärmen,** *v.t.* warm up, warm (again).

**aufwarten,** *v.t.* wait on, pay respects to.

**aufwärts,** *adv.* upward.

**Aufwärtstransformator,** *m.* (*Elec.*) step-up transformer.

**aufwaschen,** *v.t.* wash, cleanse, scour.

**aufweichen,** *v.t.* moisten, wet, soak; soften; temper (colors).—*v.i.* soak; soften.—**aufweichend,** *p.a.* emollient.

**aufweisen,** *v.t.* show, exhibit, display.

**aufweiten,** *v.t.* widen, stretch, expand.

**aufwenden,** *v.t.* employ, devote, spend.

**Aufwendung,** *f.* employment; expenditure, outlay.

**aufwerfen,** *v.t.* throw up; throw open; dig; propose, put.

**aufwickeln,** *v.t.* wind up, wrap up; unwind, unwrap.

**aufwiegen,** *v.t.* counterbalance, compensate.

**aufzählen,** *v.t.* count up, count; pay down.

**aufzehren,** *v.t.* absorb; eat up, consume.

**Aufzehrung,** *f.* absorption; consumption.

**aufzeichnen,** *v.t.* record; draw, trace; note.

**Aufzeichnung,** *f.* record; design; note; item.

**aufziehen,** *v.t.* draw up, raise up; wind up; open; loosen; raise, cultivate; rouse, agitate (yeast); educate; mount.—*v.i.* appear; (of dyes) go on, be absorbed.

**Aufziehkrücke,** *f.* (*Brewing*) rouser.

**aufzischen,** *v.i.* rush up with hissing, fizz.

**Aufzug,** *m.* elevator, crane, hoist; pump; drawing up; parade; act (of a play).

**Augapfel,** *m.* eyeball, apple of the eye.

**Auge,** *n.* eye; bubble (in liquids, bread, etc.); luster (on fabrics); (*Bot.*) bud, eye.—**ins-fassen,** have in view; gaze at.

**Augen-.** eye, visual, ocular, optic. **-achat,** *m.* (*Min.*) cat's-eye. **-blick,** *m.* moment, instant.

**augenblicklich,** *a.* instantaneous; immediate; momentary, temporary; present.—*adv.* for the moment; at present; instantly.

**Augenblicks-.** instantaneous.

**Augenbraue,** *f.* eyebrow.

**augenfällig,** *a.* conspicuous, evident.

**Augen-fehler,** *m.* visual error. **-feld,** *n.* field of vision. **-flüssigkeit,** *f.* (glasartige) vitreous humor; (wasserartige) aqueous humor. **-höhle,** *f.* eye socket, orbit.

**Augenhöhlen-.** orbital.

**Augen-kammerwasser,** *n.* aqueous humor. **-licht,** *n.* eyesight. **-lid,** *n.* eyelid. **-linse,** *f.* crystalline lens; eye lens, eyepiece. **-marmor,** *m.* eye-spotted marble. **-merk,** *n.* object in view, aim. **-nichts,** *n.* nihil album (zinc oxide). **-pinsel,** *m.* eye brush (a small, soft camel's hair brush). **-punkt,** *m.* point of sight, visual point. **-ring,** *m.* iris. **-schein,** *m.* appearance; inspection.

**augenscheinlich,** *a.* apparent, evident.

**Augen-schützer,** *m.* protecting spectacles, goggles. **-schwarz,** *n.* retinal pigment. **-stein,** *m.* white vitriol, zinc sulfate; a variety of chalcedony; lacrimal calculus. **-stern,** *m.* pupil (of the eye). **-täuschung,** *f.* optical ilusilon. **-trost,** *m.* eyebright (*Euphrasia officinalis*). **-wimper,** *f.* eyelash. **-wurzel, -wurz,** *f.* dandelion; wood anemone; mountain parsley.

**augitartig, augithaltig, augitisch,** *a.* augitic.

**Auri-.** auric, auri-. **-chlorid,** *n.* auric chloride. **-chlorwasserstoffsäure,** *f.* chloroauric acid. **-cyanid,** *n.* auric cyanide; auricyanide. **-cyanwasserstoffsäure,** *f.* cyanoauric acid. **-hydroxyd,** *n.* auric hydroxide. **-oxyd,** *n.* auric oxide. **-pigment,** *n.* orpiment. **-rhodanwasserstoffsäure,** *f.* aurithiocyanic acid. **-sulfid,** *n.* auric sulfide. **-verbindung,** *f.* auric compound.

**Auro-.** aurous, auro-. **-chlorid,** *n.* aurous chloride. **-chlorwasserstoffsäure,** *f.* chloroaurous acid, HAuCl$_2$. **-cyanid,** *n.* aurous cyanide; aurocyanide. **-cyanwasserstoffsäure,** *f.* aurocyanic acid. **-kaliumcyanid,** *n.* potassium aurocyanide. **-oxyd,** *n.* aurous oxide. **-rhodanwasserstoffsäure,** *f.* aurothiocyanic acid. **-verbindung,** *f.* aurous compound.

**aus,** *prep.* out of, from, away from.—*adv.& prefix.* out, forth; over, done; in front.

**ausarbeiten,** *v.t.* work out, prepare, finish off, finish, perfect, elaborate.

**ausarten,** *v.i.* degenerate; develop (adversely).

**ausäthern,** *v.t.* extract with ether.

**ausatmen,** *v.t.* breathe out, exhale.

**Ausatmungsluft,** *f.* exhaled air.

**ausätzen,** *v.t.* cauterize; destroy by caustics; discharge (colors).

**Ausbau,** *m.* completion; development; extension.

**ausbauchen,** *v.t.* swell, hollow out; emboss.— *v.i.* bulge, swell.

**Ausbauchung,** *f.* bulging, swelling; enlargement, bulb.

**ausbauen,** *v.t.* complete; improve; exhaust.

**ausbedingen,** *v.t.* stipulate, reserve.

**ausbeizen,** *v.t.* remove with corrosive.

**ausbessern,** *v.t.* mend, repair; correct.

**ausbeulen,** *v.t.* swell out, round out.

**Ausbeute,** *f.* yield; crop; output; gain, profit.

**ausbeuten,** *v.t.* make the best of, turn to account; exploit; (*Agric.*) cultivate; (*Mining*) work, win.

**ausbiegen,** *v.t.& i.* turn out, bend out.

**ausbilden,** *v.t.& i.* form; develop, improve, perfect; educate.

**Ausbildung,** *f.* formation, etc. (see ausbilden).

**ausbitten,** *v.t.* request, insist upon, invite.

**Ausblase-dampf,** *m.* exhaust steam. **-hahn,** *m.* blow-off cock; drain cock.

**ausblasen,** *v.t.* blow out; blow off, stop (a blast furnace); exhaust (steam).—**ausgeblasen,** *p.a.* blown out, etc.; exhaust (steam).

**ausbleiben,** *v.i.* be absent; be missing, be omitted, fail to appear or occur.

**Ausbleiben,** *n.* absence, nonappearance, nonoccurrence, nonarrival.

**ausbleichen,** *v.t.* bleach out.—*v.i.* fade.

**Ausbleichung,** *f.* fading; bleaching out, bleaching.

**Ausbleichverfahren,** *n.* bleaching-out process.

**ausbleien,** *v.t.* line with lead.

**Ausblick,** *m.* outlook, prospect.

**ausblühen,** *v.i.* effloresce; cease blooming.

**Ausblühung,** *f.* efflorescence.

**ausbohren,** *v.t.* bore out, drill.

**ausbraten,** *v.t.* roast out; heat.

**ausbrechen,** *v.t.* break out, take out; clear (a furnace); work (a lode); cut off, prune; vomit.—*v.i.* break out, break off; occur.

**ausbreiten,** *v.t.& r.* spread out, spread, extend; diffuse; floor (grain, etc.).

**Ausbreitung,** *f.* spreading out, etc. (see ausbreiten); propagation (of wave motion).

**ausbrennen,** *v.t.* burn out; burn (thoroly); anneal (metals); frit (glass); (*Med.*) cauterize.—*v.i.* burn out.

**ausbringen,** *v.t.* yield, produce; bring out, take away.

**Ausbruch,** *m.* wine of the first press; outburst, outbreak, explosion, eruption; excavation.

**ausbrühen,** *v.t.* scald, parboil.

**ausbrüten,** *v.t.* incubate.

**ausbuchten,** *v.t.*, *i.& r.* bend out, bow out.

**ausdampfen,** *v.i.* evaporate; cease steaming.

**ausdämpfen,** *v.t.* steam, clean with steam; evaporate; smoke out.

**Ausdampfung,** *f.* evaporation.

**Ausdauer,** *f.* endurance, continuance, perseverance.

**ausdecken,** *v.t.* cleanse, wash.

**ausdehnbar,** *a.* expansible; extensible, ductile.

**Ausdehnbarkeit,** *f.* expansibility; extensibility.

**ausdehnen,** *v.t.*, *r.& i.* expand; stretch, extend, distend, dilate; spread (gold).—**ausgedehnt,** *p.a.* expanded, etc.; extensive.

**ausdehnsam,** *a.* = ausdehnbar.

**Ausdehnsamkeit,** *f.* = Ausdehnbarkeit.

**Ausdehnung,** *f.* expansion; spread, extent; extension, dilatation, distention; (*Math.*) dimension.

**Ausdehnungs-koeffizient,** *m.* expansion coefficient. **-vermögen,** *n.* expansibility; extensibility; dilatability. **-zahl,** *f.* expansion coefficient.

**ausdenken,** *v.t.* think out, devise, conceive.

**ausdeuten,** *v.t.* interpret.

**ausdörren,** *v.t.* dry up, desiccate; season (timber).

**ausdrehen,** *v.t.* turn out; strip (a screw).

**Ausdruck,** *m.* expression.

**ausdrucken,** *v.t.* finish printing; print in full; use up in printing.

**ausdrücken,** *v.t.* express; press out, squeeze out.

**ausdrücklich,** *a.* express, explicit; intentional.

**ausdruckslos,** *a.* expressionless.

**ausdünnen,** *v.t.* thin out, thin.

**Ausdunst,** *m.* evaporation, exhalation.

**ausdünstbar, ausdunstbar,** *a.* evaporable.

**Ausdünstbarkeit,** *f.* evaporability.

**ausdünsten, ausdunsten,** *v.i.* evaporate; transpire; perspire.—*v.t.* exhale.

**Ausdünstung, Ausdunstung,** *f.* evaporation; exhalation; transpiration; perspiration; emanation, vapor.

**Ausdünstungs-apparat,** *m.* evaporating apparatus. **-messer,** *m.* atmometer.

**auseinander,** *adv.* apart, asunder, separately. **-fahren,** *v.i.* diverge, go apart; break up. **-falten,** *v.t.* unfold, open out. **-gehen,** *v.i.* fall apart, break up; separate. **-nehmen,** *v.t.* take apart, disconnect. **-reissen,** *v.t.* tear apart, disrupt. **-setzen,** *v.t.* explain, set forth; put or set apart.

**auserkoren,** *p.a.* chosen, selected.

**auserlesen,** *p.a.* select; exquisite.

**ausersehen,** *v.t.* mark out, choose.

**ausfahren,** *v.i.* drive out; go out; break out.—*v.t.* export.

**Ausfall,** *m.* precipitation, precipitate; falling out or off; deficiency, deficit; result; sortie, attack.

**ausfällbar,** *a.* precipitable.

**ausfallen,** *v.i.* precipitate, deposit; fall or come out; result; be omitted.

**ausfällen,** *v.t.* precipitate.

**Ausfällung,** *f.* precipitation.

**Ausfallwinkel,** *m.* angle of reflection.

**ausfärben,** *v.t.* finish dyeing, dye (completely); extract the color from, exhaust.

**Ausfärbvorrichtung,** *f.* color extractor.

**ausfaulen,** *v.i.* rot out; (of sewage) digest.

**ausfertigen,** *v.t.* make out, draw up, make ready, dispatch.

**ausfetten,** *v.t.* deprive of fat or grease, scour (wool).

**ausfeuern,** *v.t.* burn out (casks); warm (a room).

**ausfindig machen.** find out.

**ausfleischen,** *v.t.* flesh (hides).

**ausfliessen,** *v.i.* flow or issue out; discharge; emanate.

**ausflocken,** *v.i.* separate in flakes or flocks.

**Ausflockung,** *f.* separation in flocks.

**Ausflucht,** *f.* evasion; subterfuge.

**Ausflug,** *m.* flight; excursion.

**Ausfluss,** *m.* outflow, efflux; effluent; discharge; emanation; secretion; outlet, mouth; result. **-geschwindigkeit,** *f.* velocity of outflow; efflux velocity, rate of discharge. **-hahn,** *m.* outflow cock, discharge cock. **-loch,** *n.* outlet. **-rohr,** *n.*, **-röhre,** *f.* outflow tube or pipe, discharge pipe. **-zeit,** *f.* time of outflow or discharge.

**ausfolgen,** *v.t.* deliver up.

**ausformen,** *v.t.* shape out, perfect; form; develop, improve.

**ausforschen,** *v.t.* search out, investigate.

**ausfragen,** *v.t.* question, examine.

**ausfräsen,** *v.t.* countersink; (*Mach.*) shape.

**ausfressen,** *v.t.* corrode (out), eat out.

**ausfrieren,** *v.t.* freeze out; concentrate by freezing; freeze thoroly.—*v.i.* freeze up; deteriorate thru freezing; cease freezing.

**Ausfuhr,** *f.* export(ation); elimination.

**ausführbar,** *a.* practicable, feasible; exportable.

**Ausfuhrbewilligung,** *f.* export license.

**ausführen,** *v.t.* carry out, execute; amplify, explain; clean, purge; export; lead out; erect; (*Metal.*) assay.

**ausführlich,** *a.* full, complete, detailed.— *adv.* in full, *in extenso,* amply.

**Ausführung,** *f.* carrying out, etc. (see ausführen); excretion; model, pattern, specimen; detailed statement; construction, make, style.

**Ausführungsmittel,** *n.* purgative.

**ausfüllen,** *v.t.* fill, fill up, fill out; empty.

**Ausfüllmasse, Ausfüllungsmasse,** *f.* filling (for teeth).

**Ausfüllstoff,** *m.* filling or packing material.

**ausfuttern,** *v.t.* line.

**ausfüttern,** *v.t.* line; coat; feed, fatten.

**Ausfütterung,** *f.* lining.

**Ausgabe,** *f.* expense, expenditure; edition; issue; distribution.

**ausgähren,** *v.i.* = ausgären.

**Ausgang,** *m.* starting out, going out, departure; outlet, egress; ending, end; outcome, result; exportation.

**Ausgangs-.** starting, initial; outlet; export. **-erzeugnis,** *n.* starting product, initial product. **-gleichung,** *f.* initial equation, starting equation. **-lösung,** *f.* initial solution, original solution, parent solution. **-material,** *n.* initial material, starting material, raw material. **-niveau,** *n.* initial level. **-produkt,** *n.* starting product, initial product; raw product. **-punkt,** *m.* starting point. **-röhre,** *f.* outlet pipe, waste pipe, eduction pipe. **-stellung,** *f.* initial position. **-stoff,** *m.* initial substance or material, starting material, parent material, primary material.

**ausgären,** *v.i.* ferment sufficiently; cease fermenting; rise (from fermentation).—*v.t.* throw off (by fermentation); weld (steel).

**ausgeben,** *v.t.* yield, produce; give out; spend; edit; publish; issue.—*v.i.* (of slaking lime) swell.

**ausgeblasen,** *p.a.* see ausblasen.

**ausgehen,** *v.i.* go out; proceed, emanate; come off or out, fade; fail; stop; (*Baking*) ferment; (*Mining*) crop out.—**ausgehend,** *p.a.* outgoing; export.

**ausgekocht,** *p.a.* see auskochen.

**ausgelassen,** *p.a.* see auslassen.

**ausgemacht,** *p.a.* see ausmachen.

**ausgenommen,** *prep.* except.

**ausgeprägt,** *p.a.* marked, decided.

**ausgerben,** *v.t.* tan fully; weld (steel).

**ausgeschieden,** *p.p.* of ausscheiden.

**ausgeschlossen,** *p.a.* see ausschliessen.

**ausgeschmolzen,** *p.p.* of ausschmelzen.

**ausgesprochen,** *p.a.* see aussprechen.

**Ausgestaltung,** *f.* working out, development; conformation; equipment.

**ausgesucht,** *p.a.* see aussuchen.

**ausgewachsen,** *p.a.* see auswachsen.

**ausgewogen,** *p.a.* of auswägen.

**ausgezeichnet,** *p.a.* see auszeichnen.

**ausgezogen,** *p.p.* of ausziehen.

**ausgiebig,** *a.* productive, fertile, abundant.

**Ausgiebigkeit,** *f.* productiveness, fertility, abundance; (of a dye) yield, strength.

**ausgiessen,** *v.t.* pour out, run out; fill up by pouring; put out (fire).

**Ausgiessung,** *f.* effusion; pouring out, etc. (see ausgiessen).

**ausgischen,** *v.i.* cease frothing.

**Ausgleich,** *m.* = Ausgleichung.

**ausgleichen,** *v.t.* equalize, adjust; compensate; balance; level; settle.—**ausgleichende Farbe,** compensation or complementary color.

**Ausgleichung,** *f.* equalization, etc. (see ausgleichen); equilibrium.

**ausgleiten,** *v.i.* slip; glide out.

**ausglühen,** *v.t.* glow (thoroly), ignite; anneal; calcine; roast.—*v.i.* cease glowing; burn out.

**Ausglühtopf,** *m.* (*Glass*) annealing pot.

**Ausglühung,** *f.* glowing, etc. (see ausglühen).

**ausgraben,** *v.t.* dig out, dig, excavate, exhume; engrave.

**Ausguss,** *m.* lip; spout; outlet, drain, sink; pouring out, delivery; casting; effusion. **-leitung,** *f.* outlet piping, discharge piping. **-masse,** *f.* casting composition, filling compound. **-mörser,** *m.* lipped mortar. **-pfanne,** *f.* mold (for ingots). **-röhre,** *f.* drain tube or pipe, waste pipe. **-ventil,** *n.* discharge valve. **-wasser,** *n.* waste water.

**aushalten,** *v.t.* endure, stand; (*Mining*) pick out, sort.—*v.i.* hold out, last.

**aushändigen,** *v.t.* hand over.

**Aushang,** *m.* placard, poster.

**Aushängeschild,** *n.* sign-board, sign.

**ausharren,** *v.i.* persist; persevere.—**ausharrend,** *p.a.* persistent.

**ausharten,** *v.t.* harden; (*Metal.*) temper.

**ausharzen,** *v.i.* exude resinous matter; (*Leather*) spew.

**aushauchen,** *v.t.& i.* breathe out, exhale.

**Aushauchung,** *f.* exhalation.

**ausheben,** *v.t.* draw out, lift out, select; levy; dislocate.

**aushebern,** *v.t.* siphon out.

**aushecken,** *v.t.* hatch.

**aushelfen,** *v.i. with dative.* help out, assist.

**Aushilfsmittel,** *n.* expedient, makeshift.

**aushilfsweise,** *adv.* temporarily, as an expedient, in an emergency.

**aushöhlen,** *v.t.* hollow out, excavate.

**aushülsen,** *v.t.* husk, shell, peel.

**auskalten,** *v.t.& i.* cool (thoroly), chill.

**auskehlen,** *v.t.* channel, groove, flute.

**auskeimen,** *v.i.* germinate; cease germinating.

**auskitten,** *v.t.* fill with cement, cement.

**auskleiden,** *v.t.* line (as an oven); disguise.

**Auskleidung,** *f.* lining; disguise.

**ausklingen,** *v.i.* die away.

**auskochen,** *v.t.* boil out, boil, decoct; extract by boiling; clean by boiling, scour, buck.—**ausgekocht,** *p.a.* extracted, etc.; spent (hops).—**auskochender Sprengschuss,** blown-out shot.

**Auskocher,** m. boiler; bucking keir.

**Auskochung,** f. boiling out, etc. (see auskochen).

**Auskohlbad,** n. carbonizing bath.

**auskohlen,** v.t. carbonize (as wool).

**Auskohlung,** f. carbonization.

**Auskohlungsverfahren,** n. carbonizing process.

**auskommen,** v.i. come out, get out; manage, get on.

**auskörnen,** v.t. free from grains; thresh (grain); gin (cotton).

**auskratzen,** v.t. scratch out, scrape out, rake out.

**auskristallisieren,** v.t.& i. crystallize out, crystallize.

**Auskristallisierung,** f. crystallization.

**auskrücken,** v.t. rake out.

**auskrystallisieren.** =auskristallisieren.

**auskühlen,** v.i. cool thoroly.

**Auskunft,** f. information; report; resource.

**Auskunfts-buch,** n. information book. **-mittel,** n. expedient, resort.

**auskuppeln,** v.t. disconnect, disengage.

**ausl.,** abbrev. (ausländisch) foreign.

**ausladen,** v.t. unload, discharge.

**Auslage,** f. outlay, expense; display; show window.

**Ausland,** n. foreign country.—im —, ins —, nach dem —, abroad.

**Ausländer,** m. foreigner, alien.

**ausländisch,** a. foreign, alien; exotic.

**Auslass,** m. outlet, vent; exhaust.

**auslassen,** v.t. let out, emit, discharge; exhaust (steam); melt, render; leave out.—v.r. express oneself.—**ausgelassen,** p.a. let out, etc.; extravagant, wanton.

**Auslass-röhre,** f. outlet tube or pipe, discharge pipe. **-ventil,** n. escape valve, delivery valve.

**Auslauf,** m. outlet, mouth; running out; outflow, discharge; leaking; outrun, outspread.

**auslaufen,** v.i. run out; leak out, leak; blot; (of colors) run, bleed; project; stop running; set out.

**Ausläufer,** m. runner; offshoot, branch; (Spect.) attendant line, satellite.

**Auslauf-flasche,** f. overflow flask. **-probe,** f. (Metal., etc.) pouring test. **-rohr,** n., **-röhre,** f. outlet tube (or pipe), discharge tube (or pipe). **-spitze,** f. discharge tip (as of a buret). **-zeit,** f. time of outflow.

**Auslauge-.** lixiviating, leaching, extraction. **-behälter,** m. lixiviating tank. **-hülse,** f. extraction thimble. **-kasten,** m. lixiviating vat, leaching vat.

**auslaugen,** v.t. leach out, leach, lixiviate, extract; wash out, wash; steep or wash in lye, buck.

**Auslauger,** m. leacher. extracter.

**Auslaugetrichter,** m. extraction funnel.

**Auslaugung,** f. leaching out, etc. (see auslaugen).

**ausleeren,** v.t. empty out, empty, evacuate, drain; purge.

**Ausleerungsmittel,** n. (Med.) evacuant, esp. a purgative.

**auslegen,** v.t. lay out; exhibit; inlay, veneer; interpret; explain.

**Auslese,** f. selection; choice wine.

**auslesen,** v.t. pick out, select, sort; read thru.

**ausleuchten,** v.t. extinguish.—v.i.& r. cease giving light.

**Auslieferung,** f. delivery, giving up.

**auslöffeln,** v.t. spoon out, ladle out.

**auslösbar,** a. capable of being dissolved out, etc. (see auslösen).

**auslöschen,** v.t. extinguish; blot out.

**Auslöschung,** f. extinction, extinguishment.

**auslösen,** v.t. dissolve out; release; liberate; loosen; relieve; uncouple, disengage.

**Auslösung,** f. dissolving out, etc. (see auslösen); release (of a balance).

**auslüften,** v.t. ventilate, air.

**ausmachen,** v.t. take out, put out; shell; gut; end, settle; find out; matter, amount to; constitute.—**ausmachend,** p.a. constituent, essential.—**ausgemacht,** p.a. certain; thoro.

**ausmalen,** v.t. paint, color; describe.

**Ausmass,** m. delivery; overall dimension.

**ausmergeln,** v.t. exhaust.

**ausmessen,** v.t. measure out, gage.

**ausmitteln,** v.t. ascertain.

**ausmultiplizieren,** v.t. multiply out.

**Ausmündung,** f. orifice, outlet, mouth.

**Ausnahme,** f. exception.

**ausnahmelos, ausnahmslos,** a. without exception.

**ausnahmsweise,** adv. exceptionally.

**ausnehmen,** v.t. take out, draw; except, exclude; choose.—v.r. look, appear.—**ausnehmend,** p.a. exceptional, uncommon, exceeding.—adv. exceedingly.

**ausnutzbar,** a. exhaustible; utilizable.

**ausnutzen,** v.t. use up, exhaust, work out; utilize, make the most of, turn to profit.

**Ausnutzung,** f. using up, etc. (see ausnutzen); efficiency.

**Ausnutzungskoeffizient,** m. utilization coefficient.

**ausölen,** v.t. oil.

**auspichen,** v.t. pitch.

**auspinseln,** v.t. paint or apply with a brush.

**auspressen,** v.t. press out, press, express; squeeze; force (out).

**ausproben, ausprobieren,** v.t. try, try out, test (thoroly).

**Auspuff,** m. (Mach.) exhaust, escape. **-dampf,** m. exhaust steam; exhaust vapor. **-gas,** n.

exhaust gas, burnt gas. **-hub,** *m.* exhaust stroke. **-ventil,** *n.* exhaust valve.

**auspumpen,** *v.t.* pump out, exhaust.

**ausputzen,** *v.t.* clean out, clean, polish; dress out.

**ausquetschen,** *v.t.* squeeze out, crush out, wring out.

**ausradieren,** *v.t.* erase.

**ausräuchern,** *v.t.* fumigate; smoke, smoke out.

**Ausräucherung,** *f.* fumigation; smoking.

**ausräumen,** *v.t.* clear out, clean out, remove.

**ausrechnen,** *v.t.* calculate, compute.

**Ausrede,** *f.* evasion, excuse; utterance.

**ausreden,** *v.t.* utter; dissuade.—*v.i.* finish speaking.—*v.r.* excuse oneself.

**ausreiben,** *v.t.* rub out, scrape, scour, cleanse.

**ausreichen,** *v.i.* suffice.—*v.t.* seize.—**ausreichend,** *p.a.* sufficient.

**ausreichern,** *v.t.* enrich, strengthen.

**ausreinigen,** *v.t.* clean out, clean thoroly, purge.

**ausreissen,** *v.t.* pull out, tear out.—*v.i.* run away.

**ausrenken,** *v.t.* sprain; dislocate.

**ausrichten,** *v.t.* straighten; align; orient; adjust; give; perform, do; (*Mining*) discover, explore.

**Ausrichtung,** *f.* straightening, etc. (see ausrichten).

**ausringen,** *v.t.* wring out, squeeze out.

**ausrotten,** *v.t.* root up, exterminate.

**ausrücken,** *v.t.* disengage, ungear.—*v.i.* march out.

**Ausrücker,** *m.* disengaging gear.

**ausrufen,** *v.t.& i.* cry out, call out.

**Ausrufung,** *f.* crying out, exclamation; proclamation.

**ausrüsten,** *v.t.* fit out, equip, supply; finish (cloth).

**Ausrüstung,** *f.* equipment, outfit.

**Aussaat,** *f.* sowing; inoculation; seed.

**aussäen,** *v.t.* seed, inoculate (with crystals).

**Aussage,** *f.* statement, assertion, declaration.

**aussagen,** *v.t.* express, assert, affirm, state; testify, depose.

**aussaigern,** *v.t.* =ausseigern.

**aussalzbar,** *a.* capable of being salted out.

**aussalzen,** *v.t.* salt out, separate by addition of salt; (*Soap*) grain.

**Aussalzung,** *f.* salting out; (*Soap*) graining.

**Aussatz,** *m.* display (of wares); leprosy; scurf.

**aussäuern,** *v.t.* deprive of acid, deacidify.

**aussaugen,** *v.t.* suck out, suck dry, drain, exhaust.

**ausschaltbar,** *a.* capable of being cut out or switched off.

**ausschalten,** *v.t.* cut out, switch out, take out, remove, eliminate, exclude.

**Ausschalter,** *m.* (*Elec.*) cut-out, circuit breaker.

**Ausschank,** *m.* retailing (of liquor); public house.

**ausschärfen,** *v.t.* neutralize, deaden, dull (colors); bevel.

**ausscheiden,** *v.t.* separate; set free, liberate, eliminate, precipitate, extract; secrete, excrete; sort.

**Ausscheidung,** *f.* separation, etc. (see ausscheiden).

**Ausscheidungsmittel,** *n.* separating agent; precipitant.

**ausschenken,** *v.t.* pour out; sell (liquors) by retail.

**ausschiessen,** *v.t.* cast out, reject; discharge; shoot out.—*v.i.* shoot up.

**ausschirren,** *v.t.* ungear; unharness.

**ausschl.,** *abbrev.* (ausschliesslich) exclusive.

**ausschlacken,** *v.t.* clear of dross.

**Ausschlag,** *m.* throwing out, removal; throw, deflection (as of a galvanometer); exudation, scum, efflorescence; sprout, shoot; breaking out, eruption; lining, trimming; turning of the scale, result; (*Brewing*) run of wort from the kettle. **-bütte,** *f.* (*Brewing*) underback. **-eisen,** *n.* punch; piercer; tool for pounding ore.

**ausschlagen,** *v.t.* knock, throw, or punch out, remove; express (oils, etc.); turn out (wort) from the kettle; flatten, planish; line, cover; stretch; refuse.—*v.i.* break out; effloresce; (of a balance beam) turn; bud; strike out; turn out, prove; (*Leather*) spew.

**ausschlaggebend,** *a.* decisive.

**Ausschlag-winkel,** *m.* angle of deflection. **-würze,** *f.* finished wort.

**ausschlämmen,** *v.t.* wash out, cleanse (from slime).

**ausschleifen,** *v.t.* grind, whet; (*Soap*) grain.

**Ausschleudermaschine,** *f.* centrifuge.

**ausschleudern,** *v.t.* expel by centrifugal force, centrifuge, spin out; hydro-extract (yarns, etc.).

**ausschliessen,** *v.t.* shut out, exclude; except.
—**ausgeschlossen,** *p.a.* out of the question.

**ausschliesslich,** *a.* exclusive; exceptional.

**Ausschluss,** *m.* exclusion; exception.

**ausschmelzen,** *v.t.* melt out, render; (of metals) liquate; melt, fuse; purify by melting.—*v.i.* melt out; cease melting.

**Ausschmelzung,** *f.* melting out, etc. (see ausschmelzen).

**ausschmieren,** *v.t.* smear; copy; cheat.

**ausschneiden,** *v.t.* cut out, excise; prune; retail.

**Ausschnitt,** *m.* cutting out, cut; notch; hole (cut out), opening; sector; retail.

**ausschöpfen,** *v.t.* scoop out, ladle out; drain.

**Ausschöpfkelle,** *f.* ladle; scoop.

**ausschreiben,** *v.t.* write out, write in full; copy; summon; appoint, impose.

**Ausschreitung,** *f.* excess.

**Ausschuss,** *m.* refuse, scrap, waste; culls; committee; shooting out, emission.

**ausschütteln,** *v.t.* shake out, shake, agitate.

**ausschwefeln,** *v.t.* fumigate with sulfur.

**ausschweifend,** *p.a.* excessive; dissolute.

**ausschweissen,** *v.t.* weld out, cleanse (iron) by welding; bleed.

**ausschwemmen,** *v.t.* wash out, flush; rinse.

**ausschwenken,** *v.t.* whirl, centrifuge, hydro-extract.

**Ausschwenkmaschine,** *f.* centrifugal, hydro-extractor.

**Ausschwingmaschine,** *f.* centrifuge.

**ausschwirren,** *v.t.* whiz, hydro-extract.

**ausschwitzen,** *v.t.& i.* exude; sweat.

**aussehen,** *v.i.* look, appear; look out.

**Aussehen,** *n.* appearance.

**ausseigern,** *v.t.* liquate, separate by liquation.

**Ausseigerung,** *f.* liquation, eliquation.

**aussen,** *adv.* out, outside, outward; abroad.

**Aussen-.** outside, external, outer.

**aussenden,** *v.t.* emit, send out.

**Aussen-elektron,** *n.* outer electron. **-fläche,** *f.* outer surface. **-haut,** *f.* outer skin or membrane. **-korrosion,** *f.* external corrosion. **-leitung,** *f.* (*Brewing & Elec.*) outer circuit. **-luft,** *f.* external air, atmosphere. **-schicht,** *f.* outer layer. **-seite,** *f.* outer side, outside. **-taster,** *m.* outside calipers. **-welt,** *f.* external world.

**ausser,** *prep.* out of; except; beside, in addition to.—*conj.* except, unless.

**äusser,** *a.* outer, outward, exterior, external.

**Ausserbetriebsetzung,** *f.* shutting down, putting out of operation.

**ausserdem,** *adv.* besides, moreover.

**Äussere,** *n.* exterior, outside; external appearance.

**aussergewöhnlich,** *a.* extraordinary, unusual.

**ausserhalb,** *adv.& prep.* outside, beyond.

**äusserlich,** *a.* outer, outward, external; apparent; superficial; extrinsic.—*adv.* outwardly, apparently.

**äussern,** *v.t.* utter, express, manifest.

**ausserordentlich,** *a.* extraordinary, unusual.—*adv.* exceedingly, unusually.

**äusserst,** *a.* utmost, extreme; outmost.—*adv.* extremely, utterly.

**Äusserung,** *f.* manifestation, expression, utterance.

**ausserwesentlich,** *a.* nonessential.

**aussetzen,** *v.t.* set out, put out, expose; suspend, put off, postpone; line, face; censure.

—*v.i.* crop out; stop, pause.—**aussetzend,** *p.a.* intermittent, discontinuous.

**Aussetzung,** *f.* setting out, etc. (see aussetzen).

**Aussicht,** *f.* outlook, view, prospect, chance.—**in — nehmen,** contemplate.

**aussichts-los,** *a.* hopeless. **-reich,** *a.* promising.

**aussickern,** *v.i.* trickle (or ooze) out, percolate; cease trickling.

**aussieden,** *v.t.* boil out, boil; blanch (silver).

**aussinnen,** *v.t.* contrive, invent.

**aussintern,** *v.i.* trickle out, ooze out.

**aussoggen,** *v.t.& i.* =soggen.

**aussöhnen,** *v.t.* reconcile; expiate.

**aussondern,** *v.t.* separate; secrete, excrete; sort; reject.

**ausspannen,** *v.t.* stretch, spread, extend; tenter; slacken; unharness; carry off.

**Aussparung,** *f.* opening; saving (up).

**Aussprache,** *f.* pronunciation.

**aussprechen,** *v.t.* pronounce; express, declare; speak out.—**ausgesprochen,** *p.a.* pronounced, decided.

**aussprengen,** *v.t.* blast; sprinkle (water); noise abroad.

**ausspringen,** *v.i.* spring out, spring off, fly off, crack; project.—**ausspringend,** *p.a.* salient.

**ausspritzen,** *v.t.* spurt out, squirt out; wash by squirting; inject.

**Ausspruch,** *m.* utterance, saying; decision.

**aussprühen,** *v.t.* throw out, eject, emit.—*v.i.* be thrown out, dart out, fly out.

**Aussprungswinkel,** *m.* angle of reflection.

**ausspülen,** *v.t.* wash out, wash, rinse out, rinse; flush.

**Ausstand,** *m.* strike; (*pl.*) arrears.

**ausständig,** *a.* outstanding; wanting.

**ausstatten,** *v.t.* furnish, supply; get up, fit out; endow.

**Ausstattung,** *f.* fitting, equipment, outfit; get-up; dowry.

**ausstäuben,** *v.t.* dust, winnow.

**ausstechen,** *v.t.* dig out, cut out, pierce; engrave.

**ausstehen,** *v.t.* stand, endure.—*v.i.* stand out; be owing; strike.

**aussteifen,** *v.t.* stiffen, stay, reinforce.

**ausstellen,** *v.t.* put out; lay out, exhibit; draw up; censure.

**Aussteller,** *m.* exhibitor; drawer, giver (of a bill, etc.), undersigner.

**Ausstellung,** *f.* putting out; exhibition, show; display; censure.

**Ausstellungsglas,** *n.* display glass, specimen jar (or tube).

**Ausstich,** *m.* choicest wine.

**ausstopfen,** *v.t.* stuff.

**Ausstoss,** *m.* expulsion, etc. (see ausstossen); retailing (of liquors); (*Brewing*) output.

**ausstossen,** *v.t.* throw out, thrust out; expel, eject, extrude, eliminate, discharge, emit; flesh (hides); utter.—*v.i.* burst forth; froth out; (of liquids) work out.

**Ausstoss-ladung,** *f.* bursting charge. **-system,** *n.* (*Brewing*) cleansing system.

**Ausstossung,** *f.* expulsion, etc. (see ausstossen).

**ausstrahlen,** *v.t. & i.* radiate, emit or be emitted.

**Ausstrahlung,** *f.* radiation.

**Ausstrahlungs-fläche,** *f.* radiating surface. **-vermögen,** *n.* radiating power, emissivity.

**ausstrecken,** *v.t.* stretch, spread.

**ausstreichen,** *v.t.* strike out, erase; smooth out, level; spread out, smear.

**Ausstrich,** *m.* striking out, etc. (see ausstreichen); smear; streak; (*Mining*) stream tin.

**ausströmen,** *v.i.* emanate, escape, stream out, flow out.

**Ausströmung,** *f.* emanation, effusion, escape, efflux, effluence, flow.

**Ausströmungsrohr,** *n.* delivery pipe or tube.

**aussuchen,** *v.t.* search out, select, choose, sort. —**ausgesucht,** *p.a.* picked, exquisite.

**Aussucher,** *m.* sorter.

**aussüssen,** *v.t.* wash (a precipitate), edulcorate; sweeten; (*Brewing*) sparge.

**Aussüss-glas,** *n.* wash bottle (for washing precipitates). **-pumpe,** *f.* leaching pump. **-rohr,** *n.,* **-röhre,** *f.* washing tube. **-vorrichtung,** *f.* wash bottle (for precipitates); sparger.

**austarieren,** *v. t.* tare.

**Austausch,** *m.* exchange, interchange; barter. **-azidität,** *f.* exchange acidity.

**austauschbar,** *a.* exchangeable, interchangeable.

**austauschen,** *v.t.* exchange, interchange; barter.

**austauschsauer,** *a.* (rendered) acid by exchange of ions.

**austeeren,** *v.t.* tar.

**austeilen,** *v.t.* distribute.

**Auster,** *f.* oyster.

**austilgen,** *v.t.* destroy, efface, obliterate.

**Austonen,** *n.* change in (color) tone.

**Austrag,** *m.* decision, issue.

**austragen,** *v.t.* deliver; distribute; carry out; decide; report.—*v.i.* amount; cease bearing.

**Australien,** *n.* Australia.

**austreibbar,** *a.* capable of being driven out or expelled.

**austreiben,** *v.t.* expel, drive out, drive off; separate, set free; eject.

**Austreibung,** *f.* expulsion, etc. (see austreiben).

**austreten,** *v.i.* step out, go out; issue; leave, retire; (*Optics*) emerge; (*Physiol.*) extravasate.

**Austritt,** *m.* stepping out, etc. (see austreten); escape; effusion (of blood); emergence (of rays); landing, balcony, antechamber.

**austrocknen,** *v.t. & i.* dry up, dry, desiccate; drain; season (wood).—**austrocknendes Mittel,** drying agent.

**Austrockner,** *m.* desiccator.

**Austrocknung,** *f.* drying up, etc. (see austrocknen).

**auströpfeln, austropfen,** *v.i.* drop out, drip out; cease dropping or dripping.

**ausüben,** *v.t.* exert; practise, carry on; execute.

**auswachsen,** *v.i.* grow out; germinate, sprout; grow up; grow together.—**ausgewachsen,** *p.a.* grown out, etc.; full-grown.

**auswägbar,** *a.* capable of being weighed out, weighable.

**auswägen,** *v.t.* weigh out; calibrate by weighing.

**Auswahl,** *f.* choice, selection.

**auswählen,** *v.t.* choose, select.—**auswählend,** *p.a.* selective.

**Auswahl-prinzip,** *n.* selection principle. **-regel,** *f.* selection rule.

**auswalzen,** *v.t.* roll out.

**auswandern,** *v.i.* emigrate.

**auswärmen,** *v.t.* anneal; roast.

**Auswärm(e)ofen,** *m.* annealing furnace.

**auswärtig,** *a.* outward; foreign.

**auswärts,** *adv.* outward, without, abroad.

**auswaschbar,** *a.* capable of being washed out.

**auswaschen,** *v.t.* wash out, wash, rinse; edulcorate; scour (fabrics).

**Auswaschflasche,** *f.* wash bottle.

**Auswaschung,** *f.* washing out, etc. (see auswaschen).

**auswässern,** *v.t.* soak; water.—*v.i.* be soaked.

**auswechselbar,** *a.* exchangeable; interchangeable.

**auswechseln,** *v.t.* exchange; interchange.

**Ausweg,** *m.* way out, outlet, vent; expedient, shift.

**ausweichen,** *v.i.* turn out or aside; escape.— *v.t.* soften out, detach by soaking; soak; evade.—**ausweichend,** *p.a.* evasive, elusive.

**Ausweichung,** *f.* deviation; deflection; evasion; escape; soaking.

**ausweiden,** *v.t.* eviscerate, draw.

**Ausweis,** *m.* proof; evidence; report.

**ausweisen,** *v.t.* prove; turn out, expel; banish.

**auswendig,** *a.* outer, exterior.—*adv.* by heart.

**auswerfen,** *v.t.* throw out, eject, discharge; reject.

**Auswertung,** *f.* valuation, value.

**auswettern,** *v.t.* weather.

**auswinden,** *v.t.* wring out, wrench out; unscrew.

**auswintern,** *v.t.* weather; winter-season.

**auswirken,** *v.t.* work out; take out (salt from the pans); knead (dough); procure.

**auswittern,** *v.i.* effloresce; weather; (of timber) season.—*v.t.* weather, season; get scent of.

**Auswitterung,** *f.* efflorescence; weathering; seasoning (of timber).

**Auswuchs,** *m.* outgrowth, excrescence; germination.

**auswuchten,** *v.t.* counterbalance, balance.

**Auswurf,** *m.* throwing out, discharge; expectoration; excretion; refuse, trash. **-leitung,** *f.* discharge piping. **-rohr,** *n.,* **-röhre,** *f.* discharge pipe or tube. **-stoffe,** *m.pl.* excretions, excrement.

**auszacken,** *v.t.* indent, notch, jag.

**Auszehrung,** *f.* consumption.

**auszeichnen,** *v.t.* mark out, distinguish.— **ausgezeichnet,** *p.a.* excellent, distinguished.

**Auszeichnung,** *f.* distinction; label, mark.

**ausziehbar,** *a.* capable of being extracted, etc. (see ausziehen).

**ausziehen,** *v.t.* extract; exhaust (drugs, etc.); draw out, draw, pull out; fade (colors); abstract; pull off, undress; stretch, extend. —*v.r.* stretch, extend.—*v.i.* move.—**ausgezogen,** *p.a.* extracted, etc.; (of a line) solid (not broken or dotted), continuous.

**Ausziehtisch,** *m.* extension table.

**Ausziehung,** *f.* extraction; undressing.

**Auszug,** *m.* extract; essence, tincture, infusion, decoction (according to circumstances); removal, exodus; drawer; abstract; bill, note; (*Milling*) superfine flour. **-mehl,** *n.* superfine flour.

**autogen,** *a.* autogenic, autogenous.

**Autokatalysator,** *m.* autocatalyst.

**Autokatalyse,** *f.* autocatalysis.

**autokatalytisch,** *a.* autocatalytic.

**Autoklav,** *m.* autoclave.

**Autolyse,** *f.* autolysis.

**automatisch,** *a.* automatic.

**Autor,** *m.* author.

**Autoracemisierung,** *f.* autoracemization.

**Autorenregister,** *n.* author index.

**autorisieren,** *v.t.* authorize.

**Autorität,** *f.* authority.

**autoxydabel,** *a.* autoxidizable.

**Avidität,** *f.* avidity.

**avisieren,** *v.t.* inform, notify.

**Avivage,** *f.* reviving, etc. (see avivieren).

**avivierecht,** *a.* unaffected by brightening.

**avivieren,** *v.t.* revive, restore; (*Dyeing*) brighten, clear (also tone, top); scroop (silk).

**ä.W.,** *abbrev.* (äussere Weite) outside diameter.

**Axe,** *f.* axis.

**axialsymmetrisch,** *a.* axisymmetric(al).

**Axt,** *f.* ax; hatchet.

**AZ.,** *abbrev.* (Acetylzahl) acetyl number.

**Aze-.** see also Ace-.

**Azelainsäure,** *f.* azelaic acid.

**Azetal,** *n.* acetal.

**Azetat,** *n.* acetate.

**Azeto-.** aceto-.

**Azetolyse,** *f.* acetolysis.

**Azeton,** *n.* acetone.

**Azetyl,** *n.* acetyl.

**Azetylen,** *n.* acetylene.

**Azi-, azi-.** see also Aci-, aci-.

**Aziäthan,** *n.* aziethane.

**Azid,** *n.* azide; (sometimes, in combination) acid. **-cellulose,** *f.* acid cellulose.

**Azidimetrie,** *f.* acidimetry.

**Azidität,** *f.* acidity.

**Aziditätsgrad,** *m.* degree of acidity.

**Azido-.** azido-; (sometimes) acido-. **-essigsäure,** *f.* azidoacetic acid (diazoacetic acid).

**Azo-benzol,** *n.* azobenzene. **-blau,** *n.* azo blue.

**azocyclisch,** *a.* azocyclic.

**Azo-farbe,** *f.* azo dye, azo color. **-farbstoff,** *m.* azo dye. **-gelb,** *n.* azo yellow. **-gruppe,** *f.* azo group. **-körper,** *m.* azo compound. **-rot,** *n.* azo red. **-säureblau,** *n.* azo acid blue.

**Azot,** *n.* nitrogen.

**Azo-toluol,** *m.* azotoluene. **-verbindung,** *f.* azo compound.

**Azoxy-benzol,** *n.* azoxybenzene. **-verbindung,** *f.* azoxy compound.

**azurblau, azurn,** *a.* azure.

**Azurstein,** *m.* lapis lazuli.

**azyklisch,** *a.* acyclic.

**Azyl,** *n.* acyl.

**azylieren,** *v.t.* acylate.

# B

**B.,** *abbrev.* Berichte der Deutschen Chemischen Gesellschaft; (Bildung) formation.

**Bach,** *m.* brook, stream.

**bacillär,** *a.* bacillary.

**Bacille,** *f.* bacillus.

**Bacillen-.** of or pertaining to bacilli.

**bacillenvernichtend,** *a.* bacillicide.

**Back-.** baking; coking; dried. **-apfel,** *m.* dried apple.

**Backe,** *f.,* **Backen,** *m.* cheek; (of a clamp) jaw.

**Backen-.** cheek, buccal.

**backen,** *v.t.* bake; (in a pan) fry; dry (fruits); roast (ores); burn (tile, etc.); cement (steel).—*v.i.* bake; cake, coke (of coal); stick (of pottery in the kiln).

**Backenzahn,** *m.* molar tooth.

**Bäcker,** *m.* baker.

**Backerei,** *f.* baking.

**Bäckerei,** *f.* bakery; baker's trade.

**backfähig,** *a.* capable of baking; capable of caking.

**Back-fähigkeit,** *f.* capacity for baking (or for caking). **-kohle,** *f.* caking coal, coking coal. **-masse,** *f.* baking dough; a kind of confection (as of nuts and sugar). **-obst,** *n.* dried fruit. **-ofen,** *m.* baking oven, oven. **-pfanne,** *f.* baking pan, frying pan. **-pulver,** *n.* baking powder. **-stein,** *m.* (burnt) brick. **-steinofen,** *m.* brick kiln.

**bäckt,** *pr. 3 sing.* of backen.

**Back-werk,** *n.* pastry. **-wert,** *m.* baking value. **-zahn,** *m.* molar tooth.

**Bad,** *n.* bath; (*Tech.*) dip, steep; watering place.

**Bade-.** bath, bathing.

**baden,** *v.t.* bathe.

**Bade-salz,** *n.* bath salt. **-seife,** *f.* bath soap.

**Badflüssigkeit,** *f.* bath liquid, bath solution.

**Badianöl,** *n.* star anise oil.

**badisch,** *a.* of Baden.

**Badspannung,** *f.* bath tension, cell voltage.

**Bael,** *f.* (*Bot.*) bel (*Aegle marmelos*).

**Bagassefeuerung,** *f.* bagasse furnace.

**Bagger,** *m.* dredger, excavator.

**baggern,** *v.t.* dredge.

**Baggertorf,** *m.* dredged peat.

**bähen,** *v.t.* foment; toast (bread); warm, heat.

**Bahn,** *f.* way, road, track; path; orbit; trajectory; railway; breadth (of cloth).

**bahnbrechend,** *p.a.* pioneer, epoch-making.

**Bahnebene,** *f.* orbital plane.

**bahnen,** *v.t.* beat, smooth, clear (a way).

**Bahn-hof,** *m.* station. **-schleife, -schlinge,** *f.,* orbital loop. **-übergang,** *m.* orbital transition. **-zug,** *m.* railway train.

**Bahre,** *f.* barrow, stretcher; bier.

**Bähungsmittel,** *n.* (*Med.*) fomentation agent.

**Bai,** *f.* bay. **-salz,** *n.* bay salt, sea salt.

**Bajonett,** *n.* bayonet. **-rohr,** *n.,* **-röhre,** *f.* bayonet tube (a combustion tube with bayonet-like end).

**Bakterie,** *f.* bacterium.

**bakteriell,** *a.* bacterial.

**Bakterien,** *f.pl.* bacteria.

**bakterienartig,** *a.* bacteroid, bacterial.

**Bakterienfarbe,** *f.* bacterial stain.

**bakterienförmig,** *a.* bacteriform.

**Bakterien-gehalt,** *m.* bacterial content. **-gift,** *n.* bacterial toxin; bactericide.

**bakterienhaltig,** *a.* containing bacteria.

**Bakterien-kunde,** **-lehre,** *f.* bacteriology. **-stamm,** *m.* bacterial strain.

**bakterientötend,** *p.a.* bactericidal.

**Bakteriolog, -loge,** *m.* bacteriologist.

**Bakteriologie,** *f.* bacteriology.

**bakteriologisch,** *a.* bacteriological.

**Bakteriolyse,** *f.* bacteriolysis.

**bakteriolytisch,** *a.* bacteriolytic.

**bakterizid,** *a.* bactericidal.

**Bakterizidie,** *f.* bactericidal action.

**Balancier,** *m.* beam.

**balancieren,** *v.t. & i.* balance.

**Balatagummi,** *m.* balata gum.

**bald,** *adv.* soon, presently; almost.—*conj.* — ... —, now ... then; **so — als,** as soon as.

**baldig,** *a.* quick, early.

**Baldrian,** *m.* valerian. **-äther,** *m.* valeric ester, specif. ethyl valerate. **-öl,** *n.* valerian oil. **-salz,** *n.* valerate. **-säure,** *f.* valeric acid. **-wurzel,** *f.* valerian root, valerian.

**Balg,** *m.* skin; bellows; husk, pod, shell; (*Med.*) cyst; follicle; urchin.

**Balken,** *m.* beam; girder; (*Anat.*) corpus callosum. **-wage,** *f.* beam balance.

**Ball,** *m.* ball; globe; (*Soda*) ball soda, black ash.

**Ballaststoff,** *m.* ballast material (as a substance that does not take part in a reaction).

**ballen,** *v.t. & i.* ball (together), form into balls, conglomerate.

**Ballen,** *m.* bale; pack, bundle; ball.

**ballig,** *a.* convex, bulged.

**ballistisch,** *a.* ballistic.

**Ballofen,** *m.* balling furnace.

44

**Ballon,** *m.* carboy; balloon flask (spherical flask with short neck); balloon. **-entleerer,** *m.* carboy emptier. **-filter,** *n.* filtering flask (of porous porcelain). **-gas,** *n.* balloon gas. **-gestell,** *n.* carboy holder. **-kipper,** *m.* carboy tilter or inclinator.

**ballotieren,** *v.i.* ballot.

**Balsam,** *m.* balsam, balm. **-apfel,** *m.* balsam apple, balm apple (*Momordica*). **-baum,** *m.* balsam tree (any of various balsameaceous trees).

**balsamerzeugend,** *a.* balsamiferous.

**Balsam-flasche,** *f.* balsam bottle. **-harz,** *n.* balsamic resin. **-holz,** *n.* xylobalsamum, balm-of-Gilead wood.

**balsamieren,** *v.t.* embalm; perfume.

**balsamisch,** *a.* balsamic, balmy.—**balsamisches Mittel,** balsamic.

**Balsam-kraut,** *n.* costmary; moschatel. **-pappel,** *f.* balsam poplar, tacamahac. **-tanne,** *f.* balsam fir (*Abies balsamea*); spruce (esp. Norway spruce, *Picea abies*).

**Bambus,** *m.* bamboo. **-rohr,** *n.* bamboo. **-zucker,** *m.* bamboo sugar, tabasheer.

**Banane,** *f.* banana.

**Bananenwachs,** *n.* pisang wax.

**Bancazinn,** *n.* Banca tin.

**band,** *pret.* of binden.

**Band,** *n.* volume; binding; band; ribbon, tape, strap, belt, hoop; hinge; bond, tie, ligament. **-achat,** *m.* banded agate, ribbon agate.

**bandähnlich,** *a.* ribbonlike, striped, streaked; ligamentous.

**Bande,** *f.* edge, border; band; gang.

**Bandeisen,** *n.* hoop iron, band iron.

**Bandenlinie,** *f.* band line.

**Band-förderer,** *m.* belt conveyor. **-kante,** *f.* edge of a band, band head. **-mass,** *n.* tape measure. **-stahl,** *m.* band steel, hoop steel. **-trockner,** *m.* belt drier. **-wurm,** *m.* tapeworm.

**Baniane,** *m.* banyan, banyan tree.

**Bank,** *f.* bench; bank; bed, layer, stratum.—**Banken,** *f.pl.* bank.

**Bank-anweisung,** *f.* check, bank note. **-bruch,** *m.* bankruptcy.

**bankerott,** *a.* bankrupt.

**Bankett,** *n.* banquet.

**Bankier,** *m.* banker.

**bankrott,** *a.* bankrupt.

**Bankulnuss,** *f.* candlenut. **-öl,** *n.* candlenut oil.

**Bankwesen,** *n.* banking.

**Bann,** *m.* ban; jurisdiction; spell.

**bannen,** *v.t.* banish; confine; enchant.

**bar,** *a.* bare; pure, sheer; cash; destitute (of). **—für —, gegen —,** for cash.

**-bar.** An adjective suffix usually attached to verb roots and equivalent to -able, -ible;

as, *haltbar,* stable (keepable), durable, tenable.

**Bär,** *m.* bear; debt; (*Mech.*) ram, monkey.

**Barbar,** *m.* barbarian.

**Barbier,** *m.* barber.

**barbieren,** *v.t.* shave; cheat.

**Barchent,** *m.* fustian.

**Bären-klau,** *f.* bear's-breech (*Acanthus mollis* or, incorrectly, the cow parsnip, *Heracleum sphondylium*). **-traube,** *f.* bearberry (*Arctostaphylos uva-ursi*). **-wurzel,** *f.* saxifrage.

**Bärfett,** *n.* bear fat.

**barg,** *pret.* of bergen.

**Barium-.** see Baryum-.

**Barke,** *f.* shallow vat, back, beck; bark, barge.

**Bärlapp,** *m.,* **-kraut,** *n.* lycopodium, club moss. **-mehl,** *n.,* **-samen,** *m.* lycopodium (powder).

**Bärlauch,** *m.* ramson (*Allium ursinum*).

**Bärme,** *f.* yeast, barm.

**barmherzig,** *a.* merciful.

**Barnstein,** *m.* brick.

**Barockperlen,** *f.pl.* baroque pearls.

**Barometer-säule,** *f.* barometric column. **-stand,** *m.* height of the barometer, barometric height.

**Barpreis,** *m.* cash price.

**Barre,** *f.,* **Barren,** *m.* bar; ingot.

**Barren-einguss,** *m.,* **-form,** *f.* ingot mold.

**Barsch,** *m.* perch (fish).

**Barschaft,** *f.* cash; property.

**barst,** *pret.* of bersten.

**Bart,** *m.* beard; bur, seam; ward (of a key).

**bärtig,** *a.* bearded.

**bartlos,** *a.* beardless.

**Bartseife,** *f.* shaving soap.

**Bärwurzel,** *f.* saxifrage; spicknel.

**Baryt,** *m.* baryta (BaO or Ba(OH)$_2$); (*Min.*) barite (BaSO$_4$).

**barytartig,** *a.* barytic.

**Baryt-erde,** *f.* barium oxide, baryta. **-filter,** *m.& n.* barium sulfate filter. **-flusspat,** *m.* fluorite containing barium.

**barytführend,** *a.* barytic.

**Barytgelb,** *n.* barium yellow (BaCrO$_4$).

**barythaltig,** *a.* containing barium.

**Baryt-hydrat,** *n.* barium hydroxide. **-lauge,** *f.* barium hydroxide solution. **-lösung,** *f.* baryta (Ba(OH)$_2$) solution. **-salpeter,** *m.* barium nitrate, (*Min.*) nitrobarite. **-spat,** *m.,* **-stein,** *m.* (*Min.*) barite. **-wasser,** *n.* baryta water. **-weiss,** *n.* permanent white, blanc fixe (BaSO$_4$).

**Baryum,** *n.* barium. **-hydrat,** *n.* barium hydroxide. **-hyperoxyd,** *n.* barium peroxide, barium dioxide. **-platincyanür,** *n.* barium platinocyanide. **-salz,** *n.* barium salt.

**Barzahlung,** *f.* cash payment.

**bas.,** *abbrev.* (basisch) basic.

**basaltähnlich,** *a.* basaltoid, basaltic.

Basaltfelsen, m. basaltic rock.

basaltförmig, a. basaltiform.

Basaltgestein, n. basaltic rock.

basalthaltig, a. containing basalt.

basaltieren, v.t. convert (slag) into a material resembling basalt.

basaltisch, a. basaltic.

Basaltsteingut, n. (Ceram.) basalt (ware).

Base, f. base; basis; aunt; cousin.

Baseler Grün. Basle green, Paris green.

Basenaustausch, m. base exchange.

basenbildend, a. base-forming, basifying.

Basen-bildner, m. base former, basifier. -wert, m. base value.

Basicität, f. basicity.

Basidie, f., Basidium, n. basidium.

Basidienpilze, m.pl. Basidiomycetes.

basieren, v.t. base.—v.i. be based.

Basilicum, Basilicumkraut, Basilien, Basilienkraut, Basilikum, n. (sweet) basil.

Basilicumsalbe, f. (Med.) basilicon.

Basis, f. base; basis.

basisch, a. basic. -essigsauer, a. basic acetate of, subacetate of. -salpetersauer, a. basic nitrate of, subnitrate of.

Basis-ecke, f. -eck, n. base angle. -fläche, f. basal surface. -ion, n. basic ion.

Basizität, Basität, f. basicity.

Basler Blau, Baslerblau, n. Basel blue.

Bassin, n. tank, cistern, reservoir; basin; bowl.

Bastand, abbrev. (Barometerstand) height of barometer.

Bastard, m. hybrid.

Bastern, m. raw sugar.

Basterzucker, m. bastard sugar, raw sugar.

Bast-faser, f. bast fiber. -körper, m. (Bot.) bast tissue, phloëm. -papier, n. manila paper. -seide, f. raw silk.

bat, pret. of bitten.

batavisch, a. Batavian.

Batist, m. cambric; batiste.

batschen, v.t. ret (flax, etc.).

Batterie-glas, n. (glass) battery jar. -zündung, f. battery ignition.

Batzen, m. large soft lump; large amount.

Bau, m. structure; constitution; construction; building; make; cultivation. -art, f. construction, design, style. -breite, f. over-all breadth.

Bauch, m. belly, abdomen; stomach; swelling, bulge; bulb (of a retort).

Bauch-. abdominal, ventral.

Bauchdecken-. epigastric, abdominal.

Bäuche, bäuchen, etc. = Beuche, beuchen, etc.

Bauch-fell, n. peritoneum. -füssler, m. gastropod. -höhle, f. abdominal cavity.

bauchig, a. bellied, convex.

Bauchspeichel, m. pancreatic juice. -drüse, f. pancreas.

Bauchweh, n. colic, abdominal pain.

bauen, v.t. build, construct; work, cultivate.

Bauer, m. builder; farmer, peasant; jack; cage.

Bauerde, f. soil.

Bauer-gut, n. farm. -hof, m. farm; country house.

Bauernsand, m. molding sand.

Bauerstand, m. peasantry.

bau-fähig, a. (of land) arable; (of mines) workable. -fällig, a. out of repair; decaying.

Bau-holz, n. timber. -ingenieur, m. structural engineer. -kunst, f. architecture, (art of) building or construction. -länge, f. over-all length.

baulich, a. structural, constructional.

Baulichkeit, f. structure, building, edifice.

Baum, m. tree; (Mech.) beam, bar, arbor. -achat, m. dendritic agate, moss agate.

baum-ähnlich, -artig, a. arborescent, treelike.

Baumaterial, n. building material.

Baumégrad, m. degree Baumé.

Baumeister, m. architect, builder.

baumeln, v.i. dangle.

baumförmig, a. dendritic, arborescent.

Baum-garten, m. orchard; nursery. -öl, n. olive oil, sweet oil. -ölseife, f. olive oil soap, Venetian soap.

Baumörtel, m. building mortar, common mortar.

Baum-rinde, f. bark, rind. -schlag, m. foliage. -schule, f. nursery. -schwamm, m. agaric. -senf, m. candytuft. -stamm, m. tree trunk.

baumstark, a. robust.

Baum-stein, m. (Min.) dendrite. -wachs, n. grafting wax. -wollabfall, m. cotton waste. -wolle, f. cotton.

baumwollen, a. cotton.

Baumwollen-abfall, m. cotton waste. -blau, n. cotton blue. -samen, m. cottonseed.

Baumwoll-faden, m. cotton fiber; cotton thread; cotton twine. -farbstoff, m. cotton dye. -garn, n. cotton yarn. -gelb, n. cotton yellow. -gewebe, n. cotton fabric, cotton goods. -kernöl, n. cottonseed oil. -pfropfen, m. cotton plug, cotton stopper. -rot, n. cotton red. -samen, m., -saat, f. cottonseed. -samenöl, n. cottonseed oil. -scharlach, n. cotton scarlet. -wachs, n. cotton wax. -waren, f.pl. cotton goods. -watte, f. cotton wadding; cotton padding or pad. -wurzelrinde, f. cotton root bark. -zwirn, m. cotton thread.

Bau-riss, m. building plan. -sand, m. building sand, mortar sand.

Bausch, m. pad, compress; bundle; lump; plug, wad.

Bäuschchen, n. little pad, plug.

bauschen, *v.i.* swell out, bag, bulge.—*v.t.* puff up; refine (tin).

Bauschung, *f.* swelling, etc. (see bauschen); crease (in fabrics).

Bau-stahl, *m.* structural steel. -stein, *m.* building stone, brick. -stoff, *m.* building material, structural material; (*Physiol.*) nutrient. -stoffwechsel, *m.* constructive metabolism, anabolism.

Baute, *f.* structure, building.

Bau-werk, *n.* building, structure, edifice. -zwecke, *m.pl.* building purposes.

Baybeerenbaum, *m.* bebeeru, greenheart tree.

bayerisch, *a.* Bavarian.

Bayern, *n.* Bavaria.

Bayöl, *n.* oil of bay.

bayrisch, *a.* Bavarian.

Bayrischblau, *n.* Bavarian blue.

bazillär, *a.* bacillary.

Bazille, *f.*, Bazillus, *m.*, bacillus.

Bd., *abbrev.* (Band) volume.

Bde., *abbrev.* (Bände) volumes.

Bdellion, Bdellium, *n.* bdellium.

be-. A verbal prefix which, when prefixed to verbs, usually denotes completeness or thoroness; as, *bedenken*, consider. With nouns it signifies "to provide with," as *bekalken*, to lime; with adjectives, "to make . . . ," as *bereichern*, enrich.

beabsichtigen, *v.t.* intend, have in view.

beachten, *v.t.* consider; notice, observe.

beachtenswert, *a.* worth attention; noteworthy, remarkable.

Beamte, Beamter, *m.* official; officer.

beanspruchen, *v.t.* require; claim.

Beanspruchung, *f.* requirement; claim; stress; strain.

beanstanden, *v.t.* object to, complain of.

beantragen, *v.t.* propose.

beantworten, *v.t.* answer, reply to.

Beantwortung, *f.* answer, reply.

bearbeiten, *v.t.* work; manipulate; make, dress, machine, till, etc.; treat; edit.

beaufsichtigen, *v.t.* superintend, inspect.

beauftragen, *v.t.* charge; authorize.

beben, *v.i.* quake, tremble; (*Physics*) vibrate.

beblättert, *a.* having leaves, leafly.

bebrüten, *v.t.* incubate.

Becher, *m.* beaker; cup; goblet, bowl; (*Bot.*) calyx. -bürste, *f.* beaker brush. -chen, *n.* little cup. -glas, *n.* beaker. -glaskolben, -kolben, *m.* Erlenmeyer flask. -mensur, *f.* measuring cup. -werk, *n.* bucket conveyor.

Becken, *n.* basin; vessel; (*Anat.*) pelvis; cymbal.

Becken-. (*Anat.*) pelvic.

Beckmann'sche Umlagerung. Beckmann rearrangement.

Becquerelstrahlen, *m.pl.* Becquerel rays.

Bed., *abbrev.* Bedeutung.

Bedacht, *m.* consideration; care.

Bedachung, *f.* roofing.

bedanken, *v.r.* thank; decline.

Bedarf, *m.* need, demand, requirement.

Bedarfsgegenstand, *m.* requirement, requisite, necessary article.

bedauerlich, *a.* regrettable.

bedauern, *v.t.* regret; pity.

bedecken, *v.t.* cover; (*Sugar*) bottom, clay.

bedenken, *v.t.* consider, heed, care for.—*v.r.* bethink oneself; hesitate.

Bedenken, *n.* consideration; hesitation; scruple.

bedenklich, *a.* doubtful; questionable; serious.

bedeuten, *v.t.* mean, signify; point out, state. —bedeutend, *p.a.* considerable, important.

bedeutsam, *a.* significant; imposing.

Bedeutung, *f.* meaning, signification; importance.

bedeutungslos, *a.* insignificant; meaningless.

bedienen, *v.t.* serve, attend; operate.—*v.r.* help oneself, make use.

Bedienung, *f.* service, attendance; operation; attention; servants.

bedingen, *v.t.* stipulate; contract for; limit, restrict.—bedingt, *p.a.* conditioned, limited, conditional; hypothetical.

Bedingung, *f.* condition, stipulation, term; limitation, restriction.

bedrucken, *v.t.* print, print upon.

Bedruckung, *f.* printing, impression.

Bedrückung, *f.* oppression.

bedürfen, *v.i.* be in need; (*with gen.*) need, require, want.

Bedürfnis, *n.* want, requirement, necessity.

beehren, *v.t.* honor, favor.—*v.r.* have the honor.

beeifern, *v.r.* strive, endeavor.

beeilen, *v.r.* hasten, hurry.

beeinflussen, *v.t.* influence.

Beeinflussung, *f.* influence.

beeinträchtigen, *v.t.* injure, encroach upon.— beeinträchtigend, *p.a.* injurious, detrimental.

beeisen, *v.t.* cover with ice; cover with iron; alum (silk).

beenden, beendigen, *v.t.* finish, end.

beengen, *v.t.* narrow, cramp.

beerben, *v.t.* be heir to.

beerdigen, *v.t.* bury.

Beere, *f.* berry.

Beerengrün, *n.* sap green.

Beer-esche, *f.* service tree (*Sorbus domestica*). -gelb, *n.* buckthorn yellow. -schwamm, *m.* frambesia, yaws.

Beet, *n.* (garden) bed.

befähigen, *v.t.* enable, qualify.

befahl, *pret.* of befehlen.

**befangen**, *p.a.* embarrassed; prejudiced.

**befassen**, *v.t.* handle; deal with.—*v.r.* engage, be engaged, meddle (in or with).

**Befehl**, *m.* command, order, precept.

**befehlen**, *v.t.* command, order; commend, entrust.—**befehlend**, *p.a.* imperative.

**befestigen**, *v.t.* fasten, fix, attach; establish; fortify.

**Befestigungsmittel**, *n.* fixing agent.

**befeuchten**, *v.t.* moisten, dampen; wet, water.

**Befeuchtung**, *f.* moistening, dampening.

**Befeuchtungskammer**, *f.* moistening chamber.

**befiehlt**, *pr. 3 sing.* of befehlen.

**befinden**, *v.t.* find, think.—*v.r.* be, feel.

**Befinden**, *n.* condition, state; opinion.

**befindlich**, *a.* existing, present, situated.

**beflecken**, *v.t.* spot, stain, soil, blot, blur.

**befleissen, befleissigen**, *v.r.* apply oneself (to).—**beflissen**, *p.a.* studious, intent.

**befliss**, *pret.* of befleissen.

**beflissen**, *p.a.* see befleissen.

**beföhle**, *pret. subj.* of befehlen.

**befohlen**, *p.p.* of befehlen.

**befolgen**, *v.t.* follow (advice); obey (a command).

**befördern**, *v.t.* forward; further, promote, aid.

**Beförderung**, *f.* forwarding; conveyance, shipment; promotion, advancement; encouragement, stimulation.

**Beförderungsmittel**, *n.* aid, promoter, means of forwarding; (*Med.*) adjuvant.

**befrachten**, *v.t.* load.

**befreien**, *v.t.* set free, liberate, free; rescue, relieve, clear.

**befremden**, *v.t.* surprise.

**befremdlich**, *a.* strange, surprising.

**befriedigen**, *v.t.* satisfy, please.—**befriedigend**, *p.a.* satisfactory.

**befruchten**, *v.t.* fertilize, fecundate.

**Befugnis**, *f.* right, authority, warrant.

**Befund**, *m.* state, condition, circumstances; finding, award.

**befürchten**, *v.t.* fear, apprehend; suspect.

**befürworten**, *v.t.* recommend, support.

**begaben**, *v.t.* endow.

**begann**, *pret.* of beginnen.

**begasen**, *v.t.* gas; fumigate.

**begeben**, *v.r.* go; happen; give up.

**Begebenheit**, *f.* occurrence, event; adventure.

**begegnen**, *v.i.* meet; happen; behave.

**begehen**, *v.t.* celebrate; commit; walk through.

**Begeher**, *n.* desire, demand.

**begehren**, *v.t.* desire, crave, want, demand.

**begeistern**, *v.t.* inspire, animate.—*v.r.* enthuse.

**begichten**, *v.t.* charge (a furnace).

**Begier, Begierde**, *f.* desire; avidity, affinity.

**begierig**, *a.* desirous, eager.

**begiessen**, *v.t.* wet, moisten; water, irrigate.

**Beginn**, *m.* beginning.

**beginnen**, *v.t.& i.* begin.

**begipsen**, *v.t.* plaster.

**beglaubigen**, *v.t.* certify, attest, confirm.

**begleiten**, *v.t.* accompany, attend.

**Begleiter**, *m.* attendant, companion; guide.

**Begleit-erscheinung**, *f.* attendant phenomenon. **-farbe**, *f.* (*Calico*) fitting color. **-körper, -stoff**, *m.* accompanying substance (or body), impurity.

**beglücken**, *v.t.* bless, favor.

**begnadigen**, *v.t.* pardon, favor.

**begnügen**, *v.r.* be content.

**begönne**, *pret. subj.* of beginnen.

**begonnen**, *p.p.* of beginnen.

**begraben**, *v.t.* bury; conceal.

**Begräbnis**, *n.* burial; tomb.

**begreifen**, *v.t.* conceive, understand; include, comprise; imply.

**begreiflich**, *a.* conceivable, intelligible.

**begrenzen**, *v.t.* bound, limit, terminate; define.

**Begrenzung**, *f.* limit, boundary.

**Begriff**, *m.* conception, idea, notion.

**begrifflich**, *a.* conceptual, abstract.

**Begriffsbestimmung**, *f.* definition.

**begründen**, *v.t.* establish; base; prove; confirm.

**Begründung**, *f.* establishment; foundation.

**begrüssen**, *v.t.* salute, greet.

**begünstigen**, *v.t.* favor; promote.

**Beguss**, *m.*, **-masse**, *f.* (*Ceram.*) slip, engobe.

**begutachten**, *v.t.* pass judgment on.

**Begutachtung**, *f.* opinion, judgment, appraisal, award.

**begütert**, *a.* wealthy.

**begütigen**, *v.t.* appease.

**behaart**, *a.* hairy.

**behaftet**, *a.* affected, afflicted.

**behagen**, *v.t.* please.

**Behagen**, *n.* pleasure, comfort.

**behaglich**, *a.* agreeable, comfortable.

**behalten**, *v.t.* keep, retain; (*Math.*) carry.

**Behälter**, *m.* container, receiver, receptacle, tank, reservoir, vessel, etc.; conservatory.

**Behältnis**, *n.* container, case, box, bin, etc.

**behandelbar**, *a.* susceptible of treatment, workable.

**behandeln**, *v.t.* treat; handle, manipulate, work.

**Behandlung**, *f.* treatment, etc. (see behandeln).

**Behandlungs-mittel**, *m.* agent, reagent. **-weise**, *f.* method of treatment.

**beharren**, *v.i.* continue, persist, persevere.

**beharrlich**, *a.* persistent, constant; persevering; stubborn.

**Beharrung**, *f.* continuance, permanence, persistence, perseverance; obstinacy.

**Beharrungs-vermögen**, *n.* (*Physics*) inertia.

-zustand, *m.* permanence; persistence; resistance (of a machine).

behaupten, *v.t.* maintain, assert.

Behauptung, *f.* assertion, proposition; maintaining.

Behausung, *f.* lodging, abode.

beheben, *v.t.* remove, eliminate.

beheizen, *v.t.* heat.

Beheizung, *f.* heating.

Behelf, *m.* shift, device.

Behen-nuss, *f.* ben nut. -öl, *n.* oil of ben. -säure, *f.* behenic acid.

beherbergen, *v.t.* harbor, shelter.

beherrschen, *v.t.* rule, control, command.

beherzigen, *v.t.* take to heart, consider.

beherzigenswert, *a.* worthy of consideration.

beherzt, *p.a.* courageous.

behilflich, *a.* helpful.

behindern, *v.t.* hinder.

Behinderung, *f.* hindrance, hindering.

Behörde, *f.* authority, magistrate.

behördlich, *a.* official.

Behuf, *m.* purpose, object; behalf.

behufs, *prep.* in behalf of, in order to.

behüten, *v.t.* guard.

behutsam, *a.* cautious, careful.

bei, *prep.* at, near, by; on, in, about; with.

beibehalten, *v.t.* retain, keep, continue.

Beiblatt, *n.* supplement, supplementary sheet.

beibringen, *v.t.* administer; produce; impart; teach.

Beibringungsmittel, *n.* vehicle (as for drugs).

beidäugig, *a.* binocular.

beide, *a.* both; either. -mal, *adv.* both times.

beiderseits, *adv.* on both sides, mutually.

beidlebig, *a.* amphibious.

Beifall, *m.* approval, applause.

beifällig, *a.* approving, favorable.

beifolgend, *p.a.* inclosed, annexed.

beifügen, *v.t.* add, annex, attach, subjoin.

Beifuss, *m.* artemisia.

Beigabe, *f.* addition, supplement.

beigeben, *v.t.* add.

beigemischt, *p.a.* admixed.

Beigeschmack, *m.* aftertaste, tang, flavor.

Beiheft, *n.* supplemental part or number, supplement. (The word is sometimes used in titles of periodicals; as, Kolloidchemische *Beihefte*.)

Beihilfe, *f.* help, assistance.

Beil, *n.* hatchet; (grosses) ax.

Beilage, *f.* addition, supplement, appendix; enclosure.

beiläufig, *a.* incidental.

beilegen, *v.t.* add, enclose; settle; attribute.

Beilstein, *m.* axstone, nephrite.

Beiluft, *f.* admixed air.

beim. =bei dem.

beimengen, *v.t.* admix, add.

Beimengung, *f.* admixture; impurity.

beimessen, *v.t.* attribute.—*v.r.* assume.

beimischen, *v.t.* admix, mix with.

•Beimischung, *f.* admixture, mixture; infusion.

beimpfen, *v.t.* inoculate.

Bein, *n.* bone; leg.

beinah, beinahe, *adv.* almost, nearly.

Beiname, *m.* surname; nickname.

Bein-asche, *f.* bone ash. -brech, *m.& n.* (*Bot.*) bog asphodel; (*Min.*) osteocolla. -kleider, *pl.* trousers, breeches. -mehl, *n.* bone meal. -schwarz, bone black. -türkis, *m.* bone turquoise, odontolite. -wurz, *f.* comfrey (*Symphytum officinale*).

beiordnen, *v.t.* adjoin, coordinate.

beipflichten, *v.i.* assent, agree.

beisammen, *adv.* together.

Beisatz, *m.* addition, admixture; alloy.

Beischmack, *m.* =Beigeschmack.

Beisein, *n.* presence.

beiseite, *adv.* aside, apart.

beisetzen, *v.t.* bury, inter.

Beispiel, *n.* example.

beispiellos, *a.* unexampled, unparalleled.

beispielsweise, *adv.* for example.

beispringen, *v.i.* assist.

Beissbeere, *f.* cayenne pepper.

beissen, *v.t.* bite.—*v.i.* bite, smart, burn.— beissend, *p.a.* biting, sharp, pungent, acrid.

Beiss-probe, *f.* (*Brewing*) biting test. -zange, *f.* nippers, pincers.

Beistand, *m.* assistance; supporter.

beistehen, *v.t.* stand by, assist.

beisteuern, *v.t.* contribute.

beistimmen, *v.i.* agree, concur.

Beitel, *m.* chisel.

Beitrag, *m.* contribution; share, quota; dues.

beitragen, *v.t.& i.* contribute.

beitreiben, *v.t.* collect; drive in.

beitreten, *v.t.* accede, join.

beiwohnen, *v.i.* be present; cohabit.

Beiwort, *n.* adjective; epithet.

Beiz-artikel, *m.* (*Calico*) mordant style. -bad, *n.* mordant bath, pickling bath, etc. (see Beize). -brühe, *f.* (*Leather*) bate, drench. -bütte, *f.* (*Leather*) drench pit. -charakter, *m.* (*Dyeing*) mordant character.

Beize, *f.* corrosive; corrosion; (*Dyeing*) mordant; disinfectant; disinfection; (*Med.*) caustic, cauterization; (*Leather*) bate, drench; (*Metal.*) pickle; etching; staining; stain.

beizen, *v.t.* corrode; mordant; cauterize; steep; bate, drench (hides); etch; pickle; blanch (metals); disinfect; stain; sauce (tobacco).—beizend, *p.a.* corroding, etc.; corrosive, caustic; disinfectant.

Beizendruck, *m.* mordant printing.

**beizenfärben,** v.t. dye on a mordant.

**Beizen-farbstoff,** m. mordant dye. **-gelb,** n. mordant yellow.

**Beizer,** m. pickler, etcher, etc. (see beizen).

**Beiz-farbe,** f. mordant color. **-farbstoff,** m. mordant dye. **-flüssigkeit,** f. corrosive liquid, caustic liquor; mordant liquor; steeping liquor; (*Leather*) bate, drench; disinfecting liquid. **-gelb,** n. mordant yellow. **-gerät,** n. apparatus for mordanting, steeping, etc. (see beizen). **-kraft,** f. corrosive or caustic power; causticity; mordant strength; disinfecting power. **-mittel,** n. corrosive; caustic; mordant; disinfectant. **-ofen,** m. (*Tin Plate*) scaling furnace. **-stoff,** m. (*Dyeing*) mordant.

**Beizung,** f. corroding, etc. (see beizen).

**Beizwasser,** n. = Beizflüssigkeit.

**bejahen,** v.t. affirm.

**bejahrt,** a. aged.

**bekalken,** v.t. lime.

**bekämpfen,** v.t. combat, oppose.

**bekannt,** p.a. see bekennen.

**bekanntlich, bekanntermassen,** adv. as is known; notoriously.

**Bekannt-machung,** f. publication, announcement, notice, bulletin. **-schaft,** f. acquaintance; knowledge.

**bekennen,** v.t. confess, acknowledge.—**bekannt,** p.a. known; noted, famous; acquainted (with).

**Bekenntnis,** n. confession; acknowledgment.

**beklagen,** v.t. deplore; pity.—v.r. complain.

**bekleben,** v.t. paste; placard; label; cover.

**beklecken, bekleckern, beklecksen,** v.t. blur, blotch, blot, daub.

**bekleiden,** v.t. cover, coat, line, face, box; clothe; invest; occupy.

**Bekleidung,** f. casing, lining, jacket, coating, clothing, etc. (see bekleiden).

**bekommen,** v.t. get, receive.—v.i. agree (with).

**bekräftigen,** v.t. confirm, assert.

**bekränzen,** v.t. wreathe, festoon.

**bekritteln,** v.t. censure.

**bekrusten,** v.t. incrust, crust.

**Bekrustung,** f. incrustation.

**bekümmern,** v.t. afflict, trouble.

**bekupfern,** v.t. copper.

**-bel. -ble.**

**Bela,** f. (*Bot.*) bel (*Aegle marmelos*).

**beladen,** v.t. load, charge, burden.

**Beladen,** n., **Beladung,** f. loading, charging; load, cargo, freight.

**Belag,** m. = Beleg.

**belagern,** v.t. besiege.

**Belang,** m. importance; amount.

**belangen,** v.t. concern; bring action against.

**belanglos,** a. unimportant.

**belassen,** v.t. leave.

**belasten,** v.t. load, weight, burden; charge.

**belästigen,** v.t. trouble, bother.

**Belästigung,** f. annoyance, trouble.

**Belastung,** f. load, burden; charge; burdening; debit; (*Med.*) taint.

**Belastungsfähigkeit,** f. carrying capacity.

**belaufen,** v.r. amount.

**beleben,** v.t. vivify, quicken, enliven; revive, resuscitate; brighten, freshen (colors).— **belebt,** p.a. alive; lively.

**belecken,** v.t. lick; play upon.

**beledern,** v.t. cover with leather, leather.

**Beleg,** m. covering, coating, lining; floor; proof; document. **-analyse,** f. analysis giving experimental proof; check analysis.

**belegen,** v.t. cover, line, face, overlay, coat; prove, check; illustrate.

**Belegung,** f. covering, coating.

**belehren,** v.t. instruct, advise.

**Belehrung,** f. instruction, advice.

**beleibt,** a. stout.

**beleidigen,** v.t. offend, wrong, insult.

**beleimen,** v.t. glue, cover with glue.

**beleuchten,** v.t. light, illuminate; examine.

**Beleuchtung,** f. lighting, illumination; elucidation; examination.

**Beleuchtungsmittel,** n. illuminant.

**Belgien,** n. Belgium.

**belichten,** v.t. expose (to light); irradiate.

**Belichtung,** f. exposure (to light); irradiation.

**Belichtungskarte,** f. (*Dyeing*) exposure card.

**belieben,** v.t. like, choose.—v.i. be pleasing.— **beliebt,** p.a. popular, favorite.

**Belieben,** n. inclination, pleasure.

**beliebig,** a. optional, any, whatever.—adv. optionally, at pleasure.

**beliebt,** p.a. see belieben.

**Belit,** n., **Belith,** m. (*Cement*) belite.

**bellen,** v.i. bark; clamor.

**belohnen,** v.t. reward.

**belustigen,** v.t. amuse, divert.

**Bem.,** abbrev. of Bemerkung.

**bemächtigen,** v.r. take possession.

**bemalen,** v.t. paint, color, stain.

**bemänteln,** v.t. cover; color, varnish; palliate.

**bemerkbar,** a. perceptible; noticeable; remarkable.

**bemerken,** v.t. note, remark, notice.

**bemerkenswert,** a. worthy of note, remarkable.

**bemerklich,** a. = bemerkbar.

**Bemerkung,** f. observation, remark, note.

**bemessen,** v.t. proportion, measure.—p.a. measured, exact; symmetrical.

**bemittelt,** a. well-to-do.

**bemodert,** p.a. moldy.

**bemoost,** p.a. mossy.

**bemühen,** v.t. trouble.—v.r. trouble; endeavor, strive.

**bemustern**, *v.t.* sample; match, (*Dyeing*) dye to pattern, imitate; ornament, figure.

**benachbart**, *p.a.* neighboring, adjacent, vicinal.

**benachrichtigen**, *v.t.* inform, notify.

**benachteiligen**, *v.t.* prejudice, hurt.

**Benediktinerlikör**, *m.* benedictine.

**benehmen**, *v.t.* take away, remove; affect, make dizzy.—*v.r.* behave.

**Benehmen**, *n.* behavior, conduct.

**benennen**, *v.t.* name, call.

**Benennung**, *f.* nomenclature; name, naming, title, denomination, term.

**Beneöl**, *n.* oil of ben.

**benetzen**, *v.t.* wet; moisten; sprinkle.

**Benetzungswärme**, *f.* heat of wetting.

**Bengel**, *m.* club; clapper; boor, chap.

**Benincopal-insäure**, *f.* benincopalinic acid. **-säure**, *f.* benincopalic acid.

**Benit, Benitzucker**, *m.* barley sugar.

**Ben-öl**, *n.* oil of ben. **-säure**, *f.* benic acid (behenic acid).

**benutzen**, *v.t.* use, employ.

**Benutzer**, *m.* user.

**Benz-.** benz-, benzo- (preferably the latter before consonants; as, *Benztriazin*, benzotriazine). **-arsinigsäure**, *f.* benzarsinous acid. **-arsinsäure**, *f.* benzarsinic (benzarsonic) acid.

**Benzin**, *n.* benzine; gasoline, petrol. **-dampf**, *m.* benzine (or gasoline) vapor. **-ersatzstoff**, *m.* benzine (or gasoline) substitute. **-seife**, *f.* benzine soap. **-wagen**, *m.* gasoline automobile, petrol car.

**Benzochin-.** benzoquin-. **-hydron**, *n.* benzoquinhydrone.

**Benzochinon**, *n.* benzoquinone.

**Benzoe**, *n.&f.* benzoin (gum). **-äther**, *m.* benzoic ether (ethyl benzoate). **-baum**, *m.* benzoin tree (*Styrax benzoin*). **-blumen**, *f.pl.* flowers of benzoin.

**Benzoechtblau**, *n.* benzo fast blue.

**Benzoe-gummi**, *n.* gum benzoin, benzoin. **-harz**, *n.* benzoin (the resin). **-lorbeer**, *m.* spicebush (*Benzoin benzoin*). **-salz**, *n.* benzoate.

**benzoesauer**, *a.* of benzoic acid, benzoate of.

**Benzoesäure**, *f.* benzoic acid. **-äther**, *m.* benzoic ester, specif. ethyl benzoate.

**benzoesäurehaltig**, *a.* containing benzoic acid.

**Benzoeschmalz**, *n.* benzoinated lard, benzoated lard.

**benzoiniert**, *p.a.* benzoinated, benzoated.

**Benzol**, *n.* benzene ($C_6H_6$); benzol (commercial mixture).—**90er —,** 90 per cent benzol. **-bindung**, *f.* benzene linkage. **-derivat**, *n.* benzene derivative.

**Benzoleinsäure**, *f.* benzoleic acid.

**Benzolichtrot**, *n.* benzo light red.

**benzolisch**, *a.* benzene.

**Benzol-kern**, *m.* benzene nucleus. **-kohlenwasserstoffe**, *m.pl.* benzene hydrocarbons. **-lack**, *m.* benzol varnish. **-sulfosäure**, **-sulfonsäure**, *f.* benzenesulfonic acid, phenylsulfonic acid.

**Benzo-persäure**, *f.* perbenzoic acid. **-schwarzblau**, *n.* benzo black-blue.

**benzoylieren**, *v.t.* benzoylate, introduce benzoyl into.

**Benzoylwasserstoff**, *m.* benzoyl hydride (benzaldehyde).

**beobachten**, *v.t.* observe.

**Beobachter**, *m.* observer.

**Beobachtung**, *f.* observation; observance.

**Beobachtungs-gabe**, *f.* faculty for observation. **-fehler**, *m.* error of observation. **-rohr**, *n.*, **-röhre**, *f.* observation tube (as for a polariscope or spectroscope).

**beölen**, *v.t.* oil.

**bepacken**, *v.t.* load.

**bepichen**, *v.t.* pitch.

**bequem**, *a.* convenient; easy; comfortable.

**bequemen**, *v.r.* conform, comply.

**Bequemlichkeit**, *f.* convenience, comfort; indolence.

**ber.**, *abbrev.* (berechnet) calculated.

**Ber.**, *abbrev.* (Bericht, Berichte) report(s); specif. Berichte der Deutschen Chemischen Gesellschaft.

**Berapp**, *m.* rough plaster, brown coat.

**beraten**, *v.t.* advise; consult.

**Berat. Ing.**, *abbrev.* (Beratender Ingenieur) consulting engineer.

**beratschlagen**, *v.r.* consult, deliberate.

**Beratung**, *f.* consultation, deliberation; conference, council.

**berauben**, *v.t.* rob, deprive.

**beräuchern**, *v.t.* fumigate.

**berauschen**, *v.t.* intoxicate.—**berauschende Getränke**, intoxicating liquors.

**Berauschungsmittel**, *n.* intoxicant.

**Berberin**, *n.* berberine; barberry. **-saft**, *m.* barberry juice.

**Berberisrinde**, *f.* barberry bark.

**Berberitze**, *f.* barberry, berberis.

**berechenbar**, *a.* calculable; appreciable.

**berechnen**, *v.t.* calculate, compute; charge.

**Berechnung**, *f.* calculation; account.

**Berechnungsweise**, *f.* mode or method of calculation.

**berechtigen**, *v.t.* entitle, authorize, qualify.

**Berechtigung**, *f.* authorization, right.

**bereden**, *v.t.* persuade; talk over; defame.

**Beredsamkeit**, *f.* eloquence.

**Bereich**, *m.* reach, range; domain, district.

**bereichern**, *v.t.* enrich.

**bereifen**, *v.t.* cover with frost, frost; hoop.

**Bereifung**, *f.* tire equipment, tires; hoar frost.

**bereit**, *a.* ready, prepared.

**bereiten**, *v.t.* prepare, make ready, make.

**bereits**, *adv.* already.

**Bereitung**, *f.* preparation; manufacture.

**bereitwillig**, *a.* ready, willing, eager, prompt.

**bereuen**, *v.t.* repent, regret.

**Berg**, *m.* mountain; (*Mining*) gang, waste; (*Paper*) breasting (of a rag engine).

**Berg-**. mountain; rock; mineral; native. (See the following entries.)

**bergab**, *adv.* down hill.

**Berg-ader**, *f.* lode, vein. **-alaun**, *m.* rock alum, roche alum (Roman alum); alum stone, alunite.

**bergan**, *adv.* up hill.

**Berg-arbeit**, *f.* mining. **-art**, *f.* gang, matrix, vein stuff. **-asche**, *f.* an inferior kind of mineral blue. **-balsam**, *m.* petroleum. **-bau**, *m.* mining. **-baukunde**, *f.* science of mining. **-blau**, *n.* mineral blue (blue basic carbonate of copper). **-braun**, *n.* umber. **-butter**, *f.* (*Min.*) impure iron alum, iron sulfate or zinc sulfate.

**bergen**, *v.t.* save, shelter, conceal.—**geborgen**, *p.a.* safe; well off.

**Berg-erz**, *n.* raw ore. **-farbe**, *f.* ocher.

**bergfein**, *a.* (*Min.*) native.

**Berg-fett**, *n.* mountain tallow, ozocerite. **-flachs**, *m.* mountain flax, amianthus. **-fleisch**, *n.* mountain flesh (a variety of asbestos). **-fluss**, *m.* colored quartz; fluorite. **-gang**, *m.* vein, lode. **-gelb**, *n.* mountain yellow, yellow ocher. **-glas**, *n.* rock crystal (transparent quartz). **-glimmer**, *m.* margarite. **-gold**, *n.* gold found in primitive rocks. **-grün**, *n.* mineral green, green verditer (green basic copper carbonate). **-guhr**, *m.* mountain milk, agaric mineral (earthy calcium carbonate). **-gut**, *n.* minerals. **-haar**, *n.* amianthus. **-harz**, *n.* mineral pitch, asphalt.

**bergharzig**, *a.* asphaltic, bituminous.

**Bergholz**, *m.* rock wood (ligniform asbestos).

**bergig**, *a.* mountainous; hilly.

**Berg-kalk**, *m.* (*Geol.*) mountain limestone. **-kiesel**, *m.* rock flint, chert; felsite. **-kohle**, *f.* (mineral) coal. **-kork**, *m.* mountain cork (a light form of asbestos). **-kristall**, **-krystall**, *m.* rock crystal (transparent quartz). **-kupfer**, *n.* native copper. **-lasur**, *f.* azurite. **-leder**, *n.* mountain leather (a form of asbestos). **-mann**, *m.* miner.

**bergmännisch**, *a.* mining, pertaining to miners.

**Berg-mehl**, *n.* mountain flour (or meal), kieselguhr. **-melisse**, *f.* calamint. **-milch**, *m.* mountain milk, agaric mineral (earthy calcium carbonate). **-minze**, **-münze**, *f.* lit., mountain mint (applied to several men-

thaceous plants, as catnip or catmint, calamint, field basil, etc.). **-naphta**, *f.* mineral naphtha, petroleum. **-öl**, *n.* petroleum. **-papier**, *n.* mountain paper (a form of asbestos). **-pech**, *n.* mineral pitch, asphalt. **-petersilie**, *f.* mountain parsley. **-rot**, *n.* realgar; Indian red; cinnabar. **-salz**, *n.* rock salt. **-schule**, *f.* school of mines. **-schwaden**, *m.* fire damp; choke damp. **-schwefel**, *m.* native sulfur. **-seife**, *f.* mountain soap (kind of clay); rock butter (impure iron or zinc sulfate). **-talg**, *m.* mountain tallow, ozocerite; rock butter (impure iron or zinc sulfate). **-tee**, *m.* mountain tea, wintergreen. **-teegeist**, *m.* spirit of wintergreen, spirit of gaultheria. **-teeöl**, *n.* oil of wintergreen. **-teer**, *m.* mineral tar, maltha. **-torf**, *m.* mountain peat.

**Bergung**, *f.* saving, sheltering; salvage.

**Berg-unschlitt**, *m.* = Bergbutter. **-wachs**, *n.* mineral wax, ozocerite. **-werk**, *n.* mine. **-wesen**, *n.* mining. **-wetter**, *n.* (*Mining*) damp. **-wolle**, *f.* mineral wool (asbestos). **-zinn**, *n.* native tin. **-zinnerz**, *n.* mine tin (cassiterite). **-zinnober**, *m.* native cinnabar. **-zunder**, *m.* mountain tinder (asbestos).

**Bericht**, *m.* report; notice, information.

**berichten**, *v.t.* inform, advise, notify.—*v.i.* report (on).

**Berichterstatter**, *m.* reporter, correspondent.

**berichtigen**, *v.t.* adjust, correct; settle (an account).

**berieseln**, *v.t.* cause to flow or trickle over; spray; water, irrigate.

**Berieselungs-kühler**, *m.* trickle cooler, spray cooler. **-verflüssiger**, *m.* spray condenser.

**Berl. Ber.**, *abbrev.* (Berliner Berichte) Berichte der deutschen chemischen Gesellschaft.

**Berliner-blau**, *n.* Berlin blue, Prussian blue. **-blausäure**, *f.* hydrocyanic acid. **-grün**, *n.* Prussian green. **-rot**, *n.* Berlin red (a red lake color). **-säure**, *f.* prussic acid. **-weiss**, *n.* a kind of white lead.

**Bernstein**, *m.* amber.—**schwarzer —**, jet.

**Bernstein-**. amber; succinic, succinyl, succino-. **-alaun**, *m.* aluminous amber. **-aldehyd**, *n.* succinaldehyde.

**bernsteinartig**, *a.* amber-like.

**Bernstein-erde**, *f.* mineral amber. **-fett**, *n.* ambrain. **-firnis**, *m.* amber varnish. **-geist**, *m.* spirit of amber. **-lack**, *m.* amber varnish. **-öl**, *n.* oil of amber, oleum succini. **-salz**, *n.* succinate.

**bernsteinsauer**, *a.* of succinic acid, succinate of.

**Bernsteinsäure**, *f.* succinic acid.

**berosten**, *v.i.* rust, become rusty.

**bersten**, *v.t.* burst, explode, rupture. crack.

**Bertram,** m. pellitory (*Anacyclus pyrethrum* and similar plants). **-(s)wurzel, -wurz,** f. pellitory, pyrethrum (root of *Anacyclus pyrethrum*).

**berüchtigt,** p.a. notorious.

**berücksichtigen,** v.t. bear in mind, regard, consider.

**Berücksichtigung,** f. regard, consideration.

**Beruf,** m. calling, occupation, profession.

**berufen,** v.t. call, appoint.—v.r. appeal.

**Berufkraut,** n. any of various plants, specif. (*Pharm.*) fleabane (*Erigeron*).

**Berufs-.** professional, occupational, vocational. **-genossenschaft,** f. professional association; coöperative association.

**berufsmässig,** a. professional.

**Berufung,** f. convening, convocation; nomination, appointment; (*Law*) appeal.

**beruhen,** v.i. rest, depend.

**beruhigen,** v.t. quiet; reassure.—v.r. become quiet, moderate, abate.—**beruhigend,** p.a. quieting, sedative.

**Beruhigungsmittel,** n. sedative; anodyne.

**berühmt,** p.a. famous, celebrated.

**berühren,** v.t. touch; touch on.—**berührend,** p.a. touching, tangent.

**Berührende,** f. tangent.

**Berührung,** f. contact; touching.

**Berührungs-ebene,** f. tangential plane. **-elektrizität,** f. contact electricity. **-fläche,** f. surface of contact. **-linie,** f. tangent. **-stelle,** f. place of contact; mark (made by touching something).

**berussen,** v.t. soot, smoke, smut.

**Beryll,** m. beryl.

**beryllartig,** a. like beryl, berylline.

**Beryllerde,** f. beryllia (BeO).

**Beryllium-gehalt,** m. beryllium content. **-salz,** n. beryllium salt.

**bes.,** *abbrev.* (besonders) especially.

**besagen,** v.t. mean, signify.

**besänftigen,** v.t. appease, soothe.

**Besatz,** m. border, edging, trimming; (*Metal.*) fettling; charge (of a crucible).

**Besatzung,** f. garrison, crew.

**beschädigen,** v.t. damage.

**beschaffen,** v.t. procure; supply; make, execute.—p.a. constituted, conditioned.

**Beschaffenheit,** f. nature; state, condition; quality; disposition.

**beschäftigen,** v.t. occupy, busy, employ.

**Beschäftigung,** f. occupation, business.

**Beschau,** f. examination, inspection.

**beschauen,** v.t. examine, inspect; behold.

**beschaulich,** a. contemplative.

**beschäumt,** p.a. covered with foam, foamy.

**Bescheid,** m. decision, answer; information.

**bescheiden,** v.t. assign; inform; order; summon.—v.r. be content.

**bescheiden,** a. modest, unassuming.

**bescheinigen,** v.t. certify.

**beschenken,** v.t. present.

**bescheren,** v.t. give, bestow.

**beschicken,** v.t. load, charge, feed; prepare; mix; manage, attend to; exhibit.

**Beschickung,** f. loading, charging; load, charge; management; (*Minting*) alloy.

**Beschiessung,** f. bombardment.

**beschirmen,** v.t. shelter, cover; protect.

**Beschlag,** m. coating of some kind, as efflorescence, moisture on glass, tarnish on metals, clay to protect from heat, etc.; fitting, mounting, hooping, etc.; shoeing, shoe (of a horse); seizure.

**beschlagen,** v.i. become coated, as with moisture, oxide, or mold; effloresce; tarnish; give an incrustation (before the blowpipe).—v.t. cover, mount or fit (with iron, metal, leather, etc.); lute; shoe (a horse).—p.a. versed, skilled.

**beschlagnehmen,** v.t. seize, attach; arrest.

**beschleunigen,** v.t. accelerate; hasten.

**Beschleuniger,** m. accelerator.

**Beschleunigung,** f. acceleration; despatch.

**Beschleunigungsmittel,** n. accelerator.

**beschliessen,** v.t. finish, close; determine, resolve, decide.

**Beschluss,** m. conclusion; determination, decision; locking up, bond.—**einen — fassen,** pass a resolution, resolve, vote, decide. **-fassung,** f. conclusion, decision.

**beschmieren,** v.t. smear.

**beschmutzen,** v.t. soil, stain.

**beschneiden,** v.t. cut, trim, pare, dress; cut off, curtail.

**beschneit,** p.a. snow-covered.

**Beschönigung,** f. gloss, varnish; palliation.

**beschränken,** v.t. limit, confine.—**beschränkt,** p.a. limited, narrow.

**Beschränktheit,** f. limitedness.

**beschreiben,** v.t. describe; write on.

**Beschreibung,** f. description.

**beschuldigen,** v.t. accuse.

**Beschussprobe,** f. shooting test.

**beschützen,** v.t. protect.

**beschwefeln,** v.t. sulfur.

**Beschwerde,** f. trouble, annoyance; complaint; malady.

**beschweren,** v.t. load; weight; charge; burden, annoy.—v.r. complain.

**beschwerlich,** a. burdensome, troublesome.

**Beschwerung,** f. loading, etc. (see beschweren).

**Beschwerungsmittel,** n. loading material, weighting agent.

**beschwichtigen,** v.t. allay, appease, soothe.

**beseelen,** v.t. animate, inspirit.

**besehen,** v.t. look at; inspect, examine.

**beseitigen,** v.t. remove, do away with.

Beseitigung, *f.* removal.

Besen, *m.* broom. -ginster, *m.*, -kraut, *n.* broom (*Cytisus scoparius*); (*Pharm.*) scoparius. -stiel, *m.* broomstick.

besessen, *p.p.* of besitzen.

besetzen, *v.t.* set, trim, border, stock, fit; charge (a furnace or the like); occupy; fill (a position); engage.

Besetzungszahl, *f.* number of electrons in a completed shell.

besichtigen, *v.t.* inspect, view; survey.

besiegen, *v.t.* defeat, conquer.

besinnen, *v.r.* consider; recollect.—besonnen, *p.a.* considerate; discreet.

Besinnung, *f.* consideration; recollection; consciousness.

besinnungslos, *a.* unconscious.

Besitz, *m.* possession; property.

besitzen, *v.t.* possess, occupy, hold.

Besitzer, *m.* possessor, owner; occupant.

Besitztum, *n.* possession, property.

Besitzung, *f.* = Besitz.

besonder, *a.* particular, special, specific; separate; singular, odd.

Besonderheit, *f.* peculiarity, individuality; particular.

besonders, *adv.* especially; separately; singularly.

besonnen, *p.a.* see besinnen.

besorgen, *v.t.* care for, attend to; do, effect; fear.—besorgt, *p.a.* anxious; careful.

Besorgnis, *f.* apprehension, fear; concern.

Bespannung, *f.* covering (as of cloth).

bespinnen, *v.t.* cover.—besponnen, *p.a.* covered.

besprechen, *v.t.* discuss; arrange; conjure.

Besprechung, *f.* discussion; conference.

besprengen, *v.t.* sprinkle.

bespritzen, *v.t.* sprinkle, spray, spatter.

bespülen, *v.t.* wash, bathe.

Bessemer-birne, *f.* Bessemer converter. -ei, *f.* Bessemer (steel) plant; Bessemerizing. -eisen, *n.* Bessemer iron.

bessemern, *v.t.* bessemerize.

Bessemer-schlacke, *f.* Bessemer slag. -stahl, *m.* Bessemer steel. -verfahren, *n.* Bessemer process.

besser, *a.& adv.* better.

bessern, *v.t.* better; correct.—*v.r.* grow better.

Best., *abbrev.* (Bestimmung) determination; (Bestellung) order; (Bestand) amount.

Bestand, *m.* duration, stability; existence; amount, stock.

beständig, *a.* stable; constant, durable, permanent; proof; fast (colors); steady, steadfast.—— machen, render stable, etc.; stabilize.

Beständigkeit, *f.* stability, etc. (see beständig).

Bestandteil, *m.* constituent; ingredient.

bestärken, *v.t.* confirm; strengthen.

bestätigen, *v.t.* confirm, ratify.—*v.r.* hold true.

Bestätigung, *f.* confirmation, verification; sanction; legalization.

bestatten, *v.t.* bury, inter.

bestäuben, *v.t.* dust, powder, cover with dust; pollinate.—bestäubt, *p.a.* dusty; pulverulent.

beste, *a.* best.—am besten, best.

bestechen, *v.t.* stitch; bribe; charm.

Besteck, *n.* case, set (of instruments); cover (at table).

bestehen, *v.i.* consist; exist; persist, insist.— *v.r.* resist; encounter; pass.—— aus, consist of.

Bestehen, *n.* composition; existence; persistence.

bestellen, *v.t.* order, appoint, engage; deliver; arrange; till, plant.

Besteller, *m.* (*Com.*) orderer.

Bestellschein, *m.* order blank, requisition blank.

Bestellung, *f.* ordering, etc. (see bestellen); (*Com.*) order, commission.

bestenfalls, *adv.* at best.

besteuern, *v.t.* tax, assess.

Bestie, *f.* beast, brute.

bestimmbar, *a.* determinable.

bestimmen, *v.t.* determine; fix, design, allot, define.—bestimmt, *p.a.* determined, definite, fixed, appointed, certain.

Bestimmtheit, *f.* definiteness; determination; certainty.

Bestimmung, *f.* determination; appointment; definition; provision; destiny.

Bestimmungsmethode, *f.* method of determination.

bestossen, *v.t.* trim, plane, shape; hit.

bestrafen, *v.t.* punish.

bestrahlen, *v.t.* irradiate, expose (to rays); illuminate.

Bestrahlung, *f.* irradiation, exposure (to rays).

bestreben, *v.r.* strive, endeavor.

Bestrebung, *f.* striving, effort, endeavor; tendency.

bestreichen, *v.t.* coat, smear, spread; brush, stroke; sweep (over).

bestreiten, *v.t.* dispute; defray.

bestreuen, *v.t.* strew, sprinkle, powder.

bestürzen, *v.t.* charge, feed; cover; perplex, dismay, amaze.

Besuch, *m.* visit; company.

besuchen, *v.t.* visit, resort to, attend.

besudeln, *v.t.* soil, contaminate.

betagt, *p.a.* aged; due.

betalgen, *v.t.* tallow.

Betastrahlen, *m.pl.* beta rays.

**betätigen,** *v.t.* operate; put into operation, start; prove, manifest.

**Betätigung,** *f.* operation; starting; activity; proving.

**betäuben,** *v.t.* deafen, stun, stupefy.

**Betäubung,** *f.* stunning, stupefying; stupor; narcosis.

**Betäubungsmittel,** *n.* narcotic.

**betauen,** *v.t.* cover with dew, bedew.

**Bete,** *f.* beet, beetroot.

**beteeren,** *v.t.* tar.

**beteiligen,** *v.t.* give a share to, concern.—*v.r.* participate.—**beteiligt,** *p.a.* concerned, interested.

**Betel-nuss,** *f.* betel nut. **-pfeffer,** *m.* betel pepper, betel.

**beteuern,** *v.t.* protest, swear to.

**betiteln,** *v.t.* entitle, name.

**Beton,** *m.* concrete (made with cement), béton. **-bruch,** *m.* broken concrete; concrete fracture. **-eisen,** *n.* reinforcing iron.

**betonen,** *v.t.* accent, emphasize.

**Betonie,** *f.*, **Betonienkraut,** *n.* betony; water betony, water figwort.

**betonieren,** *v.t.* concrete, cover or lay with, or form of, concrete.—**betoniert,** *p.a.* concrete.

**Betonschicht,** *f.* layer of concrete.

**betr.,** *abbrev.* (betreffend) concerning, concerned.

**Betracht,** *m.* consideration, regard, account.

**betrachten,** *v.t.* consider; regard; view, examine.

**beträchtlich,** *a.* considerable, important.

**Betrachtung,** *f.* consideration, reflection; inspection.

**Betrag,** *m.* amount, sum.

**betragen,** *v.t.* amount to.—*v.r.* behave.

**Betragen,** *n.* behavior, conduct.

**Betreff,** *m.* reference, regard (to).—**in dessen,** as regards that.

**betreffen,** *v.t.* concern; befall; catch.—**betreffend,** *p.a.* concerning, concerned.—**betroffen,** *p.a.* disconcerted, dazed.

**betreffs,** *adv. with gen.* as regards.

**betreiben,** *v.t.* carry on, conduct, pursue.

**betreten,** *v.t.* tread upon, enter upon.—*p.a.* beaten; confused.

**Betrieb,** *m.* work, working, operation, management; trade; works, factory; impulse, impulsion.—**im —,** in operation; in practice.—**in — setzen,** set in operation, set going.

**Betriebs-.** working, operating; industrial.

**betriebsam,** *a.* active, industrious.

**Betriebs-anlage,** *f.* plant, works. **-chemiker,** *m.* industrial chemist, works chemist. **-druck,** *m.* working pressure.

**betriebsfähig,** *a.* in working order.

**Betriebs-kontrolle,** *f.* control of (technical) operations. **-kosten,** *f.pl.* operating expenses. **-kraft,** *f.* motive power. **-laboratorium,** *n.* works laboratory, industrial laboratory. **-leiter,** *m.* manager. **-spannung,** *f.* (*Elec.*) operating voltage. **-stoff,** *m.* fuel; working material. **-stoffwechsel,** *m.* functional metabolism, basal metabolism. **-substanz,** *f.* working substance. **-technik,** *f.* operating technique, operating practice. **-wasser,** *n.* water for industrial use. **-zeit,** *f.* working hours; shift; working season, campaign; operating time (required for any process).

**betroffen,** *p.a.* see betreffen.

**Betrug,** *m.* fraud, deception.

**betrügen,** *v.t.* cheat, defraud, dupe.

**Bett,** *n.* bed.

**betteln,** *v.i.* beg.

**betten,** *v.t.* imbed, embed, bed; put to bed.

**Bett-stelle,** *f.* bedstead. **-tuch,** *n.* sheet.

**Bettung,** *f.* bedding, bed.

**Bettwanze,** *f.* bedbug.

**betupfen, betüpfen,** *v.t.* dab, dip, tip; spot.

**Beuche,** *f.* bucking, bowking; bucking lye.

**beuchen,** *v.t.* buck (steep or boil in lye or suds).

**Beuch-fass,** *n.* bucking tub. **-kessel,** *m.* bucking kier. **-lauge,** *f.* bucking lye. **-wasser,** *n.* buck.

**Beuge,** *f.* bend, bow.

**beugen,** *v.t.* bend; deflect; diffract (light); inflect (words); bow, humble.

**beugsam,** *a.* =biegsam.

**Beugung,** *f.* bending, etc. (see beugen); flexure, flexion.

**Beugungsgitter,** *n.* diffraction grating.

**Beule,** *f.* bump, swelling; boil; blister.

**beunruhigen,** *v.t.* disquiet, trouble.

**beurkunden,** *v.t.* authenticate, verify.

**beurteilen,** *v.t.* judge, estimate, criticize.

**Beurteilung,** *f.* judging, judgment; valuation, estimation; estimate; criticism.

**Beute,** *f.* booty, spoil, prize; trough.

**Beutel,** *m.* bag; pouch; purse; (*Med.*) sac, cyst. **-filter,** *n.* bag filter.

**beuteln,** *v.t.* bolt, sift.—*v.r.* bag.

**Beutel-sieb,** *n.* bolting sieve, bolter. **-tuch,** *n.* bolting cloth. **-zeug,** *n.* bolting apparatus; bolting cloth.

**Bevölkerung,** *f.* population.

**bevollmächtigen,** *v.t.* empower, authorize.

**bevor,** *conj.* before.

**bevorstehen,** *v.i.* approach, impend.

**bevorzugen,** *v.t.* prefer, favor.

**bewaffnen,** *v.t.* arm; equip; aid.

**Bewaffnung,** *f.* armament; equipment; armature (of a magnet).

**bewahren,** *v.t.* keep, preserve, protect.

**bewähren,** *v.t.* verify, approve, confirm.—*v.r.* prove true, prove good.

Bewahrungsmittel, *n.* preservative; prophylactic.

bewältigen, *v.t.* overcome, master.

bewandert, *a.* versed, skilled.

Bewandtnis, *f.* case, state.

bewässern, *v.t.* water, moisten, sprinkle, irrigate.

Bewässerung, *f.* watering, etc. (see bewässern).

bewegbar, *a.* movable, mobile.

bewegen, *v.t.& i.* move; induce.—bewegende Kraft, motive power.

Beweger, *m.* motor; mover; agitator.

Bewegkraft, *f.* motive power.

beweglich, *a.* movable, moving; versatile.

Beweglichkeit, *f.* mobility.

Beweglichkeitsart, *f.* kind of mobility, degree of freedom.

Bewegung, *f.* motion; movement, moving; stir, commotion.

Bewegungs-. motive, motor, motion. -kraft, *f.* motive force, motive power. -lehre, *f.* mechanics; kinematics; kinetics. -maschine, *f.* motor. -zustand, *m.* state of motion.

Beweis, *m.* proof, evidence; argument. -analyse, *f.* documentary analysis.

beweisen, *v.t.* prove, demonstrate; show.—*v.r.* prove.

Beweis-führung, *f.* demonstration; reasoning. -kraft, *f.* conclusiveness, demonstrative power.

bewenden, *v.i.* rest, drop.

Bewerber, *m.* candidate, applicant, aspirant.

bewerfen, *v.t.* plaster; pelt.

bewerkstelligen, *v.t.* accomplish, perform, effect.

bewerten, *v.t.* estimate, value, rate.

Bewertung, *f.* estimation, valuation, rating.

bewickeln, *v.t.* wrap round, envelop.

bewilligen, *v.t.* grant, permit.

Bewilligung, *f.* permission, consent; license.

bewirken, *v.t.* effect, cause, exert.

bewirten, *v.t.* entertain, treat.

bewirtschaften, *v.t.* manage, run; work.

Bewitterung, *f.* weathering.

bewog, *pret.* of bewegen.

bewogen, *p.p.* of bewegen.

bewohnen, *v.t.* inhabit, occupy.

Bewohner, *m.* inhabitant, occupant, tenant.

bewundern, *v.t.* admire.

Bewurf, *m.* plastering, plaster, roughcast.

bewusst, *a.* conscious, aware; known.

bewusstlos, *a.* unconscious; senseless.

Bewusstsein, *n.* consciousness; knowledge.

bez., *abbrev.* (beziehungsweise) respectively, or; (bezogen) related; (bezahlt) paid.

bezahlen, *v.t.* pay.

Bezahlung, *f.* payment, settlement.

bezähmen, *v.t.* tame, restrain.

bez. auf, *abbrev.* (bezogen auf) referred to, relative to.

bezeichnen, *v.t.* mark, label; indicate; signify, denote.—bezeichnend, *p.a.* characteristic.

Bezeichnung, *f.* marking, notation; mark, sign, symbol; designation; note.

Bezeichnungsweise, *f.* manner (or method) of notation.

bezetteln, *v.t.* label.

bezeugen, *v.t.* testify, certify.

beziehen, *v.t.* draw (money); order, buy (goods); enter; relate, refer; cover.—*v.r.* relate, refer; be overcast.

Beziehung, *f.* relation; reference, respect.

beziehungsweise, *adv.* respectively, or, and/or.

beziffern, *v.t.* mark with figures or ciphers, number.—*v.r.* amount.

Bezirk, *m.* circuit, district.

Bezirks-. district. -verein, *m.* district union.

Bezoar-säure, *f.* bezoardic acid (ellagic acid). -stein, *m.* bezoar stone, bezoar. -wurzel, *f.* (*Pharm.*) contrayerva.

bezogen, *p.p.* of beziehen.

Bezug, *m.* relation, reference; drawing.

bezüglich, *a.& prep.* relative, with reference (to), respecting, regarding.

Bezugnahme, *f.* reference.

Bezugs-bedingungen, *n.pl.* (*Com.*) terms. -linie, *f.* reference line. -quelle, *f.* source of supply. -wert, *m.* reference value; relative value.

bezw., *abbrev.* beziehungsweise.

bezwecken, *v.t.* aim at, intend; peg.

bezweifeln, *v.t.* doubt, (call in) question.

bezwingen, *v.t.* subdue; restrain.

Bibel, *f.* Bible.

Biber, *m.* beaver. -geil, *n.* castor, castoreum. -geilkampher, *m.* castorin. -nell, -nelle, *f.* burnet saxifrage (*Pimpinella saxifraga*). -schwanz, *m.* flat roofing tile.

Bibirin, *n.* bebeerine. -säure, *f.* bebeeric acid.

Bibliothek, *f.* library.

Bibliothekar, *m.* librarian.

Bichromatlösung, *f.* dichromate solution.

bichromsauer, *a.* of or combined with bichromic (dichromic) acid, bichromate of.

bicyclish, *a.* bicyclic.

biegbar, *a.* capable of being bent, flexible.

Biege, *f.* bend, bow. -festigkeit, *f.* bending strength, transverse strength.

biegen, *v.t.* bend; curve; diffract, refract (light); inflect (words).—*v.r.* bend, (of wood) warp.—*v.i.* bend.

Biege-rohr, *n.*, -röhre, *f.* (glass) tube for bending. -spannung, *f.* bending stress. -zahl, *f.* bending number, bend-test number.

biegsam, *a.* flexible, pliable, pliant; ductile.

**Biegsamkeit,** *f.* flexibility; pliability; ductility.

**Biegung,** *f.* bending, etc. (see biegen); bend; flexure.

**Biegungsfestigkeit,** *f.* =Biegefestigkeit.

**Biene,** *f.* bee.

**Bienen-harz,** *n.,* **-kitt,** *m.* bee glue, propolis. **-wachs,** *n.* beeswax.

**Bier,** *n.* beer; **(englisches)** ale. **-blume,** *f.* head (froth) of beer. **-brauen,** *n.* beer brewing. **-essig,** *m.* malt vinegar, beer vinegar. **-grand,** *m.* (*Brewing*) underback. **-hefe,** *f.* beer yeast, brewer's yeast. **-kessel,** *m.* (*Brewing*) boiling copper, boiler. **-pech,** *n.* brewer's pitch. **-prober,** *m.* beer tester, specif. beer hydrometer. **-schöne,** *f.* fining for beer. **-sieder,** *m.* (*Brewing*) kettleman. **-stein,** *m.* hard deposit from wort, beer scale. **-untersuchung,** *f.* examination of beer, beer analysis. **-wa(a)ge,** *f.* beer gage, beer hydrometer. **-würze,** *f.* beer wort, wort. **-zeug,** *n.& m.* beer yeast.

**Biestmilch,** *f.* colostrum.

**bieten,** *v.t.* offer; bid; show.

**Bijouterie,** *f.,* **-waren,** *f.pl.* jewelry.

**Bilanz,** *f.* balance; balance sheet.

**Bild,** *n.* image; figure; form; picture; diagram; idea, description.

**Bild.,** *abbrev.* (Bildung) formation.

**bilden,** *v.t.* form; shape, fashion; educate, cultivate, civilize.—*v.r.* form.—**bildend,** *p.a.* forming, etc.; component, constituent; formative; plastic (art).

**Bilderachat,** *m.* figured agate.

**Bildhauer,** *m.* sculptor. **-gips,** *m.* sculptor's plaster. **-kitt, -leim,** *m.* badigeon. **-marmor,** *m.* statuary marble.

**bildlich,** *a.* figurative; typical.

**bildlos,** *a.* amorphous.

**Bildmarmor,** *m.* figured marble.

**Bildner,** *m.* component, constituent; former.

**Bildnis,** *n.* image, portrait, picture, likeness.

**bildsam,** *a.* plastic; flexible, ductile.

**Bildsamkeit,** *f.* plasticity; flexibility.

**bildschön,** *a.* most beautiful.

**Bild-stecher,** *m.* engraver. **-stein,** *m.* figure stone, agalmatolite.

**Bildung,** *f.* formation; shape; structure; organization; education, culture.

**Bildungs-.** formation; formative; educational. **-energie,** *f.* energy of formation. **-gleichung,** *f.* equation of formation; structural equation. **-wärme,** *f.* heat of formation. **-weise,** *f.* mode of formation.

**Bild-werk,** *n.* sculpture, carving. **-zeichen,** *n.* symbol.

**Billard,** *n.* billiards; billiard-table.

**Billet,** *n.* ticket; note.

**billig,** *a.* fair, just, reasonable; cheap.

**billigen,** *v.t.* approve of.

**Billigkeit,** *f.* equity, reasonableness; cheapness.

**Bilse,** *f.,* **Bilsenkraut,** *n.* henbane, hyoscyamus.

**Bimetall-.** bimetallic.

**Bims,** *m.* pumice, pumice stone. **-beton,** *m.* pumice (stone) concrete.

**bimsen,** *v.t.* rub with pumice stone, pumice.

**Bimsstein, Bimstein,** *m.* pumice stone, pumice.

**bimsstein-ähnlich, -artig,** *a.* pumiceous.

**Bimssteinseife,** *f.* pumice soap.

**bin,** *pr.* 1 *sing.* of sein; am.

**binär,** *a.* binary.

**Binarkies,** *m.* marcasite.

**Binde,** *f.* band; bandage; ligature; necktie. **-elektron,** *n.* binding electron, valence electron. **-gewebe,** *f.* connective tissue. **-glied,** *n.* connecting member or link. **-haut,** *f.* conjunctiva. **-kraft,** *f.* combining power; binding power (of cements). **-material,** *n.* binding material. **-mittel,** *n.* binding agent or material; cement, adhesive, agglutinant, medium.

**binden,** *v.t.* bind; fix, combine, unite; tie, tie up; constrain.—*v.i.* bind; combine; set (of cement, etc.); harden.—**gebunden,** *p.a.* bound, combined, etc.—**gebundene Wärme,** latent heat.

**Binde-strich,** *m.* hyphen. **-substanz,** *f.* cement; (*Physiol.*) connective substance. **-ton,** *m.* ball clay. **-vermögen,** *n.* binding power; combining power; (of clays) plasticity. **-zeit,** *f.* (*Cement*) setting time.

**Bindfaden,** *m.* string, packthread.

**bindig,** *a.* binding, cohesive.

**Bindung,** *f.* binding, etc. (see binden, *v.t.& v.i.*); combination, union; linkage; bond.

**bindungsfähig,** *a.* capable of binding, of combining, etc. (see binden).

**Bindungsfähigkeit,** *f.* =Bindevermögen.

**bindungsisomer,** *a.* showing isomerism due to different modes of union of the atoms (sometimes merely to different positions of a double bond).

**Bindungs-mittel,** *n.* =Bindemittel. **-vermögen,** *n.* =Bindevermögen. **-wärme,** *f.* heat of combination. **-weise,** *f.* mode of union.

**Bingel,** *f.,* **-kraut,** *n.* *Bot.* mercury (*Mercurialis*).

**binnen,** *prep.* within.

**Binnen-.** internal, inner, inside, inland. **-druck,** *m.* internal pressure. **-handel,** *m.* domestic trade. **-raum,** *m.* inner or interior space. **-steuer,** *f.* internal revenue.

**Binse,** *f.* rush; rattan.

**Biochemie,** *f.* biochemistry.

**biochemisch,** *a.* biochemical.

**biogen,** *a.* related to the life process, biogenic.

**Biolog, Biologe,** *m.* biologist.

**biologisch,** *a.* biological.

**Biophysik,** *f.* biophysics.

**Bioxyd,** *n.* bioxide, dioxide.

**Biquadrat,** *n.* (*Math.*) fourth power.

**birgt,** *pr. 3 sing.* of bergen.

**Birke,** *f.* birch.

**birken,** *a.* birch, birchen.

**Birken-kampher,** *m.* birch camphor, betulin. **-kohle,** *f.* birch charcoal. **-rindenöl, -öl,** *n.* oil of betula, oil of sweet birch. **-teer,** *m.* birch tar.

**Birnäther,** *m.* =Birnenäther.

**Birne,** *f.* pear; pear-shaped object, as a bulb or ampoule; (*Metal.*) converter; (*Elec.*) bulb.

**Birnen-äther,** *m.,* **-essenz,** *f.* pear ether, pear essence. **-öl,** *n.* pear oil (amyl acetate). **-wein,** *m.* perry.

**birnenförmig,** *a.* =birnförmig.

**Birnessig,** *m.* pear vinegar.

**birnförmig,** *a.* pear-shaped, pyriform.

**Birn-most,** *m.* pear juice, (new) perry. **-öl,** *n.* pear oil. **-wein,** *m.* perry.

**birst,** *pr. 2 & 3 sing.* of bersten.

**bis,** *prep.* till, until, up to.—*conj.* till, until. — **— auf,** until; even to; except.

**Bisam,** *m.* musk.

**bisamartig,** *a.* musky.

**Bisamkorn,** *n.* musk seed, abelmosk seed.

**bisher,** *adv.* hitherto, as yet.

**bisherig,** *a.* hitherto till now.

**bislang,** *adv.* as yet, thus far.

**biss,** *pret.* of beissen.

**Biss,** *m.* bite; sting.

**Bisschen,** *n.* bit, little bit.

**Bissen,** *m.* morsel, bit; (*Med.*) bolus.

**bisubstituiert,** *a.* disubstituted.

**bisweilen,** *adv.* sometimes, occasionally.

**Bitte,** *f.* request, prayer.

**bitten,** *v.t.* ask, beg, invite.

**Bitter-erde,** *f.* magnesia. **-harz,** *n.* bitter resin. **-holz,** *n.* bitterwood; quassia. **-kalk, -kalkspat,** *m.* dolomite. **-klee,** *m.* buck bean (*Menyanthes*). **-kleesalz,** *n.* oxalic acid. **-kochsalz,** *n.* magnesium chloride.

**bitterlich,** *a.* bitterish.—*adv.* bitterly.

**Bitterling,** *m.* bitter mineral water.

**bitterlos,** *a.* free from bitterness.

**Bittermandel,** *f.* bitter almond. **-geist,** *m.* spirit (or essence) of bitter almond. **-öl,** *n.* oil of bitter almond, benzaldehyde; (künstliches) nitrobenzene.

**Bittermittel,** *n.* bitter, bitters.

**bittern,** *v.t.* make bitter.—*v.i.* be bitter.

**Bitter-rinde,** *f.* bitter bark, specif. amargoso. **-salz,** *n.* Epsom salt (magnesium sulfate). **-salzerde,** *f.* magnesia. **-säure,** *f.* picric acid. **-spat,** *m.* magnesite; (sometimes) dolomite, bitter spar. **-stein,** *m.* nephrite;

saussurite; picrolite. **-stoff,** *m.* bitter principle.

**bittersüss,** *a.* bittersweet.

**Bitter-süss,** *n.* bittersweet. **-süssigkeit,** *f.* bittersweetness. **-wasser,** *n.* bitter water (**◦**ontaining Epsom salt); (*Pharm.*) bitter-almond water. **-wurzel,** *f.* gentian root.

**bituminisieren,** *v.t.* bituminize.

**Bituminisierung,** *f.* bituminization.

**bituminös,** *a.* bituminous.

**bizyklisch,** *a.* bicyclic.

**Blachmal,** *n.* dross (on melted silver); niello.

**blähen,** *v.t.* inflate, swell; cause flatulence.

**Blähsucht,** *f.* flatulence.

**Blähungsmittel,** *n.* carminative.

**blähungstreibend,** *p.a.* carminative.

**blaken,** *v.i.* smoke.

**blamieren,** *v.t.* expose to ridicule.

**Blanc fixe.** blanc fixe, permanent white.

**blanchieren,** *v.t.* blanch, whiten.

**Blanchissure,** *f.* light spot (due to imperfect dyeing).

**blank,** *a.* bright, clear, clean, polished; smooth; uncovered, bare; white, blank. **-beizen,** *v.t.* pickle, dip (metals).

**Blank-draht,** *m.* bright wire; galvanized wire. **-holz,** *n.* logwood.

**blankkochen,** *v.t.* (*Sugar*) boil down without graining.

**blanko,** *a.* blank.

**blankputzen,** *v.t.* polish, scour.

**Blank-reiben,** *n.* polishing. **-tran,** *m.* clear, light-yellow cod oil.

**Blas-.** blast. **-apparat,** *m.* blast apparatus. **-balg,** *m.* bellows.

**Bläschen,** *n.* small bubble, bleb; vesicle.

**Bläschen-.** vesicular.

**Blase,** *f.* bubble, bleb; blister, vesicle; cavity; bladder; bladder-shaped vessel, as the body of a retort or still; still.

**Blase-.** blowing, blast. **-balg,** *m.* bellows. **-lampe,** *f.* blast lamp.

**blasen,** *v.t.* blow; (*Metal.*) smelt in a blast furnace; inject (steam).

**Blasen-.** bubble; bladder, vesical, vesico-; vesicular; blister. **-bildung,** *f.* bubble formation; blister formation. **-galle,** *f.* bile from the gall bladder. **-gärung,** *f.* bubbling (or bubble) fermentation. **-grün,** *n.* sap green. **-käfer,** *m.* Spanish fly, cantharis. **-kirsche,** *f.* bladder cherry, alkekengi. **-kupfer,** *n.* blister copper. **-pflaster,** *n.* (*Pharm.*) blister plaster, specif. cantharides cerate. **-säure,** *f.* uric acid. **-stahl,** *m.* blister steel. **-stein,** *m.* urinary calculus. **-tang,** *m.* bladder wrack (*Fucus vesiculosus*).

**blasen-weise,** *adv.* in bubbles, bubble by bubble. **-ziehend,** *p.a.* blistering, vesicatory.

**Blase-ofen,** *m.* blowing furnace; blast furnace. **-probe,** *f.* bubble test.

**Bläserei,** *f.* (glass) blowing, glassblowing shop.

**Blase-rohr,** *n.* blowpipe, blast pipe; nozzle (of bellows). **-tisch,** *m.* blast-lamp table; blowpipe table.

**blasig,** *a.* blistery, blistered, vesicular.— **blasiger Kupferstein,** pimple metal.

**Blasig-keit,** *f.* blistered state. **-werden,** *n.* blistering.

**Blas-lampe,** *f.* blast lamp. **-rohr,** *n.*, **-röhre,** *f.* blast pipe, blast tube.

**blass,** *a.* pale. **-gelb,** *a.* pale yellow. **-rot,** *a.* pale red, pink. **-rötlich,** *a.* pale reddish, pinkish.

**bläst,** *pr. 3 sing.* of blasen.

**Blastisch,** *m.* =Blasetisch.

**Blatt,** *n.* leaf; lamina, lamella, plate, flake; sheet (of paper); blade; journal, newspaper. **-blau,** *n.* phyllocyanin. **-blei,** *n.* sheet lead.

**Blättchen,** *n.* lamina, lamella; small leaf, leaflet; flake; foil; slip (of paper).

**blättchenartig,** *a.* lamelliform, laminiform.

**Blättchenpulver,** *n.* leaf powder; flake powder.

**Blatteisen,** *n.* sheet iron.

**Blatter,** *f.* blister, pimple; *pl.* smallpox.

**Blätter,** *pl.* of Blatt.

**Blätter-.** foliated, lamellar, laminated. **-aldehyd,** *n.* aldehyde of leaves (2-hexenal). **-blende,** *f.* foliated zinc blend. **-bruch,** *m.* lamellar cleavage. **-erde,** *f.* potassium acetate. *Obs.* **-erz,** *n.* foliated tellurium (nagyagite).

**blätterförmig,** *a.* in the form of leaflets or flakes; laminated; leaf-shaped.

**Blätter-gelb,** *n.* xanthophyll. **-gips,** *m.* selenite.

**blätterig,** *a.* leafy, foliated, laminated.

**Blätter-kies,** *m.* lamellar pyrites. **-kohle,** *f.* foliated coal, slate coal.

**blättern,** *v.r.* flake, exfoliate.

**Blätter-spat,** *m.* foliaceous spar. **-stein,** *m.* variolite. **-tellur,** *n.* foliated tellurium (nagyagite). **-ton,** *m.* foliated clay. **-zeolith,** *m.* foliated zeolite (heulandite).

**Blatt-feder,** *f.* leaf spring. **-federchen,** *n.* = Blattkeim. **-gelb,** *n.* xanthophyll. **-gewebe,** *n.* leaf tissue, mesophyll. **-gold,** *n.* leaf gold, gold leaf, gold foil. **-grün,** *n.* leaf green, chlorophyll. **-keim,** *m.* plumule, (of malt, etc.) acrospire. **-kupfer,** *n.* sheet copper. **-lack,** *m.* shellac. **-mark,** *n.* (*Bot.*) mesophyll. **-metall,** *n.* sheet metal; leaf metal, foil.

**blättrig,** *a.* =blätterig.

**Blatt-silber,** *n.* silver leaf. **-stahl,** *m.* sheet steel. **-zinn,** *n.* tin foil.

**blau,** *a.* blue.—**blaue Erde,** blue earth, specif. earthy vivianite.— **— schillern,** give a blue iridescence.

**Blau,** *n.* blue. **-asche,** *f.* saunders blue. **-beere,** *f.* bilberry, whortleberry.

**blaubrüchig,** *a.* brittle at blue heat.

**Blau-brüchigkeit,** *f.* (*Iron*) blue-shortness. **-carmin,** *n.* indigo carmine. **-dämpfen,** *n.* (*Ceram.*) blue-smoking.

**Bläue,** *f.* blue; blueness.

**Blaueisen-erde,** *f.* earthy vivianite. **-erz,** *n.* vivianite. **-spat,** *n.*, **-stein,** *m.* vivianite. **(faseriger)** crocidolite.

**bläueln,** *v.t.* blue; beetle.

**blauen, bläuen,** *v.t.* blue; dye blue.—*v.i.* turn blue.

**Blau-erei,** *f.* indigo dyehouse. **-erz,** *n.* vivianite. **-farbe,** *f.* blue color; smalt. **-farbenglas,** *n.* smalt. **-färber,** *m.* dyer in blue. **-färbung,** *f.* blue coloration, blue color. **-fäule,** *f.* sap rot, sap stain (of wood). **-gas,** *n.* Blau gas (named from its inventor).

**blau-gesäuert,** *a.* (*Old Chem.*) of or combined with hydrocyanic acid, cyanide of. **-glühend,** *a.* blue-hot. **-grau,** *a.* blue-gray. **-grün,** *a.* blue-green.

**Blauholz,** *n.* logwood. **-schwarz,** *n.* logwood black. **-späne,** *m.pl.* logwood chips.

**Blau-kohl,** *m.* red cabbage. **-kreuzgeschoss,** *n.* " blue cross " projectile or shell. **-kreuzkampfstoff,** *m.* (*Mil.*) " blue cross " shell filling (diphenylchloroarsine or some other sternutative). **-küpe,** *f.* blue vat, specif. indigo vat.

**bläulich,** *a.* bluish. **-grau,** *a.* bluish-gray.

**Blau-mühle,** *f.* smalt mill. **-ofen,** *m.* flowing furnace. **-öl,** *n.* (*Org. Chem.*) cerulignol. **-papier,** *n.* blue-print paper. **-pause,** *f.* blue-print tracing, blue print. **-probe,** *f.* blue test.

**blaurot,** *a.* blue-red, violet.

**Blau-salz,** *n.* potassium ferrocyanide. **-sand,** *m.* coarsest smalt.

**blausauer,** *a.* of or combined with hydrocyanic acid, cyanide of.—**gelbes blausaures Kali,** potassium ferrocyanide.—**rotes blausaures Kali,** potassium ferricyanide.

**Blausäure,** *f.* hydrocyanic acid.

**blausäurehaltig,** *a.* containing hydrocyanic acid.

**Blau-säurevergiftung,** *f.* hydrocyanic-acid poisoning. **-schörl,** *m.* cyanite.

**blauschwarz,** *a.* blue-black.

**Blau-spat,** *m.* lazulite. **-stein,** *m.* bluestone, blue vitriol; lazulite; (*Metal.*) blue metal, blue matte. **-stich,** *m.* bluish tinge or tint. **-stift,** *m.* blue pencil. **-stoff,** *m.* cyanogen. **-sucht,** *f.* cyanosis.

**Bläuung**, *f.* bluing.

**blau-verschoben**, *p.a.* displaced toward the blue. **-violett**, *a.* blue-violet.

**Blauvitriol**, *n.* blue vitriol.

**blauwarm**, *a.* blue-hot.

**Blauwasser**, *n.* eau céleste (cupric ammonium sulfate solution).

**Blech**, *n.* plate, sheet, sheet metal, specif. sheet iron; foil; **(weisses)** tin plate; **(schwarzes)** black iron plate. **-büchse**, *f.* tin can. **-dose**, *f.* tin box; tin can, tin. **-eisen**, *n.* sheet iron.

**blechen, blechern**, *a.* tin (plate).

**Blech-flasche**, *f.* narrow-necked tin vessel. **-gefäss**, *n.* tin (plate) vessel. **-glühofen**, *m.* plate-heating furnace. **-hafen**, *m.*, **-kanne**, *f.*, tin can. **-kasten**, *m.* tin box; sheet-iron box. **-lack**, *m.* tinplate varnish; sheet-metal varnish. **-rohr**, *n.* sheet-iron tube; tin tube. **-schmied**, *m.* tinner. **-tafel**, *f.* sheet iron, iron plate. **-trichter**, *m.* tin funnel. **-trommel**, *f.* tin (plate) drum. **-ware**, *f.* tinware.

**Blei**, *n.* lead. **-abgang**, *m.* lead dross, lead scoria. **-ader**, *f.* lead vein. **-antimonerz**, *n.*, **-antimonglanz**, *m.* zinkenite. **-arbeit**, *f.* lead smelting; plumbing. **-arsenglanz**, *m.* sartorite. **-arsenik**, *m.* lead arsenate; lead arsenide. **-art**, *f.* kind or variety of lead.

**bleiartig**, *a.* leadlike, leady, plumbeous.

**Blei-asche**, *f.* lead dross; lead ash; the gray film of oxide on lead exposed to air. **-azetat**, *n.* lead acetate. **-bad**, *n.* lead bath. **-baum**, *m.* lead tree, arbor saturni.

**bleiben**, *v.i.* remain, stay, last.—**bleibend**, *p.a.* permanent, lasting, durable, stable, (of colors) fast; persistent.—**bleibende Härte**, permanent hardness.— **— stehen**, remain standing; stop.

**Blei-blech**, *n.* sheet lead. **-blüte**, *f.* mimetite. **-buchse, -büchse**, *f.* lead box, case or can.

**bleich**, *a.* pale, white.

**Bleich-anlage**, *f.* bleaching establishment, bleaching plant, bleachery. **-anstalt**, *f.* bleachery. **-bad**, *n.* bleaching liquor.

**bleichbar**, *a.* capable of being bleached.

**Bleichchlor**, *n.* chlorine for bleaching; active chlorine.

**Bleiche**, *f.* bleaching; bleachery; paleness, whiteness.

**bleichen**, *v.t.* bleach; whiten; blanch.—*v.i.* lose color, fade; turn white or pale.

**Bleicher**, *m.* bleacher.

**Bleich-erde**, *f.* bleaching earth, fuller's earth. **-erei**, *f.* bleaching; bleachery. **-fähigkeit**, *f.* capability of being bleached, bleachability. **-fass**, *n.* bleaching vat. **-fleck**, *m.* bleaching stain. **-flotte**, *f.* bleaching liquor. **-flüssigkeit**, *f.* bleaching liquor. **-gefäss**, *n.*

bleaching vessel. **-grad**, *m.* degree of bleaching; degree of bleachability. **-gut**, *n.* batch of cloth for bleaching. **-holländer**, *m.* (*Paper*) poaching engine, poacher. **-hülfsmittel**, *n.* something used to assist bleaching, bleaching assistant. **-kalk**, *m.* chloride of lime (bleaching powder). **-kasten**, *m.* bleaching vat. **-kessel**, *m.* bleaching boiler or kier. **-lauge**, *f.* bleaching lye (or liquor). **-mittel**, *n.* bleaching agent, decolorant. **-prozess**, *m.* bleaching process. **-pulver**, *n.* bleaching powder.

**Bleichromat**, *n.* lead chromate.

**Bleich-salz**, *n.* bleaching salt (chloride of lime, sodium hypochlorite, etc.). **-sand**, *m.* bleached sand. **-säure**, *f.* chloric acid. **-seife**, *f.* bleaching soap. **-soda**, *n.* bleaching soda. **-vermögen**, *n.* bleaching power. **-vorbereitungsmittel**, *n.* preliminary bleaching assistant. **-wasser**, *n.* bleaching liquor; chlorine water. **-wirkung**, *f.* bleaching action or effect. **-zweck**, *m.* bleaching purpose(s).

**Blei-dampf**, *m.* lead vapor, lead fume. **-draht**, *m.* lead wire. **-erde**, *f.* earthy cerussite.

**bleiern**, *a.* lead, leaden; dull, heavy.

**Blei-erz**, *n.* lead ore. **-essig**, *m.* vinegar of lead (aqueous solution of basic lead acetate). **-extrakt**, *m.* = Bleiessig. **-fahlerz**, *n.* bournonite. **-farbe**, *f.* lead color.

**blei-farben, -farbig**, *a.* lead-colored.

**Blei-feder**, *f.* lead pencil. **-flasche**, *f.* lead bottle. **-folie**, *f.* lead foil.

**blei-frei**, *a.* free from lead. **-führend**, *a.* lead-bearing, plumbiferous.

**Blei-gang**, *m.* (*Mining*) lead vein. **-gehalt**, *m.* lead content. **-gelb**, *n.* massicot; lead chromate. **-giesser**, *m.* plumber; lead founder. **-glanz**, *m.* lead glance, galena. **-glas**, *n.* lead glass; (*Min.*) anglesite. **-glasur**, *f.* lead glaze. **-glätte**, *f.* litharge. **-glimmer**, *m.* cerussite in micaceous form.

**bleigrau**, *a.* lead-gray.

**Blei-grube**, *f.* lead mine. **-gummi**, *m.* lead-pencil eraser; (*Min.*) plumboresinite.

**bleihaltig**, *a.* containing lead, plumbiferous.

**Blei-hornerz**, *n.* **-hornspat**, *m.* phosgenite. **-hütte**, *f.* lead works. **-ion**, *n.* lead ion. **-jodid**, *n.* lead iodide. **-kalk**, *m.* lead calx, lead oxide. **-kammer**, *f.* lead chamber. **-könig**, *m.* lead regulus. **-krankheit**, *f.* lead poisoning, plumbism. **-kugel**, *f.* lead ball; lead bullet. **-lasur**, *f.* linarite. **-leder**, *n.* (*Metal.*) silver containing much lead. **-legierung**, *f.* lead alloy. **-lot**, *n.* lead solder; plummet; plumb line. **-löter**, *m.* lead burner. **-lötung**, *f.* lead soldering. **-mangan**, *n.* lead-manganese. **-mennige**, *f.* minium, red lead. **-mine**, *f.* lead mine; lead (for pencils). -niere, *f.* (*Min.*) bindheimite. -ocker, *m.* lead ocher. -ofen, *m.* lead furnace. -öl, *n.* (*Pharm.*) lead acetate in oil of turpentine. -oxyd, *n.* lead oxide, specif. PbO; (rotes) minium. -oxydsalz, *n.* lead salt, specif. a salt of bivalent lead. -oxydul, *n.* lead suboxide, $Pb_2O$; (sometimes) lead monoxide, PbO. -oxyduloxyd, *n.* minium, $Pb_3O_4$. -papier, *n.* lead paper (for hydrogen sulfide tests); lead foil. -peroxyd, *n.* lead dioxide, $PbO_2$. -pflaster, *n.* lead plaster. -pflastersalbe, *f.* (*Pharm.*) diachylon ointment. -raffination, *f.* lead refining. -rauch, *m.* lead fume, lead smoke. -rohr, *n.*, -röhre, *f.* lead tube or pipe. -röstprozess, *m.* lead roasting. -rot, *n.* red lead, minium. -safran, *m.* orange lead. -salbe, *f.* (*Pharm.*) cerate of lead subacetate. -salpeter, *m.* lead nitrate. -salz, *n.* lead salt. -sammler, *m.* lead accumulator; lead storage battery.

bleisauer, *a.* of or combined with plumbic acid, plumbate of.

Blei-säure, *f.* plumbic acid. -schale, *f.* lead dish, lead basin. -schlacke, *f.* lead slag. -schlich, *m.* (*Mining*) lead slime. -schrot, *n.* lead shot. -schwamm, *m.* lead sponge, spongy lead. -sicherung, *f.* lead fuse. -spat, *n.* cerussite; (gelber) wulfenite; (roter) crocoisite. -speise, *f.* lead speiss. -spiegel, *m.* specular galena. -staub, *m.* lead dust. -stein, *m.* lead matte. -stift, *m.* lead pencil, pencil. -sulfat, *n.* lead sulfate. -verbindung, *f.* lead compound. -vergiftung, *f.* lead poisoning. -verhüttung, *f.* lead smelting. -vitriol, *m.* lead vitriol, lead sulfate, (*Min.*) anglesite. -vitriolspat, *m.* anglesite. -wasser, *n.* lead water, Goulard water. -weiss, *n.* white lead. -weisssalbe, *f.* lead carbonate ointment. -wismut, *n.* lead-bismuth. -zinnober, *m.* red lead, minium. -zucker, *m.* sugar of lead, lead acetate. -zuckersalbe, *f.* lead acetate ointment.

Blendart, *f.* hybrid.

Blende, *f.* blend, glance (specif. zinc blend, ZnS); blind, screen, diaphragm, stop; border.

blenden, *v.t.* blind, dazzle.

bleuueln, *v.t.* beat, beetle; blue.

blf., *abbrev.* (blätterförmig) in leaflets or flakes.

Blick, *m.* look, view, glance; flash; (*Metal.*) flashing (as of molten silver), fulguration, "blick."

blicken, *v.i.* glance, look; shine; (*Metal.*) flash, lighten, give the "blick."

Blick-feld, *n.* field of vision. -gold, *n.* refined gold still containing silver. -silber, *n.*

(*Metal.*) silver containing 5–10 per cent impurities.

blieb, *pret.* of bleiben.

blies, *pret.* of blasen.

blind, *a.* blind; dull, tarnished; false; (of tests) blank.

Blind-darm, *m.* caecum. -heit, *f.* blindness. -kohle, *f.* underburned charcoal. -leitwert, *m.* (*Elec.*) susceptance. -schlauch, flexible tube closed at one end. -widerstand, *m.* (*Elec.*) reactance.

blinken, blinkern, *v.i.* gleam, sparkle.

Blitz, *m.* lightning; flash. -licht, *n.* flashlight. -photographie, *f.* flashlight photography. -pulver, *n.* lycopodium. -röhre, *f.* fulgurite.

Block, *m.* block; pig; ingot; (tree) trunk; log. -blei, *n.* pig lead. -färbung, *f.* (*Micros.*) staining *in toto.* -hahn, *m.* stopcock. -mühle, *f.* block mill. -schnitt, *m.* die, matrix. -seigerung, *f.* (*Metal.*) segregation (in an ingot). -zinn, *n.* block tin.

Blödsinn, *m.* imbecility, insanity; nonsense.

bloss, *a.* bare, naked, nude; mere, sole.—*adv.* merely, only; barely; nakedly.

Blösse, *f.* bareness; unhaired hide, pelt.

blosslegen, *v.t.* lay bare, strip.

Blt., *abbrev.* (Blättchen) leaflets, lamellas.

blühen, *v.i.* bloom, blossom; flourish.

Blume, *f.* flower; bloom; aroma, bouquet.

blümen, *v.t.* flower, figure.

Blumen-blatt, *n.* petal. -gelb, *n.* any yellow flower pigment. -kohl, *m.* cauliflower. -seite, *f.* (*Leather*) hair side. -staub, *m.* pollen. -tee, *m.* imperial tea. -topf, *m.* flower pot.

blumig, *a.* bloomy, flowery.

Blunze, Blunzen, *f.* a kind of German sausage or its casing.

Blut, *n.* blood. -achat, *m.* blood agate. -ader, *f.* vein.

blutarm, *a.* bloodless, anemic; very poor.

Blutbahn, *f.* blood vessel.

blutbildend, *a.* blood-forming.

Blut-blume, *f.* arnica; bloodflower (*Haemanthus*). -druck, *m.* blood pressure.

Blüte, *f.* blossom, flower, bloom.

Blut-egel, *m.* leech. -eiweiss, *n.* blood albumin, serum albumin.

bluten, *v.i.* bleed; suffer; (of colors) bleed, run.

Blüten-blatt, *n.* petal. -hüllenblatt, *n.* sepal. -öl, *n.* flower oil, attar. -staub, *m.* pollen.

Blutentziehungsmittel, *n.* hemagogue.

Blütenweiss, *n.* a form of calcium sulfate used in loading paper.

Blut-farbe, *f.* blood color; blood pigment. -farbstoff, *m.* coloring matter of the blood, blood pigment. -faserstoff, *m.* fibrin. -fleck, -flecken, *m.* blood stain. -fluss, *m.* hemorrhage.

**blutflüssig,** *a.* hemorrhagic.

**Blut-flüssigkeit,** *f.* blood plasma. **-gefäss,** *n.* blood vessel.

**blutgierig,** *a.* bloodthirsty.

**Blut-gift,** *n.* blood toxin. **-holz,** *n.* logwood.

**blutig,** *a.* bloody.

**Blut-kohle,** *f.* blood charcoal. **-körperchen,** *n.* blood corpuscle. **-kraut,** *n.* any of various blood-red or blood-stanching plants. **-kuchen,** *m.* blood clot; placenta. **-lauf,** *m.* circulation of the blood.

**Blutlaugensalz,** *n.* potassium ferrocyanide (often with *adj.* gelbes).—**rotes —,** potassium ferricyanide.

**blut-leer,** *a.* anemic, bloodless. **-los,** *a.* bloodless.

**Blut-mehl,** *n.* blood meal. **-mittel,** *n.* (*Med.*) blood tonic. **-plättchen,** *n.* blood plate, blood platelet.

**blutrot,** *a.* blood-red.

**Blut-rot,** *n.* hemoglobin. **-ruhr,** *f.* dysentery. **-säure,** *f.* thiocyanic acid. *Obs.* **-scheibe,** *f.* blood corpuscle. **-schlag,** *m.* apoplexy. **-seuche,** *f.* anthrax. **-stein,** *m.* bloodstone, hematite.

**blutstillend,** *p.a.* blood-stanching, hemostatic, styptic.

**Blut-strom,** *m.* blood stream. **-sucht,** *f.* hemophilia. **-untersuchung,** *f.* examination of blood. **-vergiftung,** *f.* blood poisoning. **-wasser,** *n.* blood serum. **-wolle,** *f.* blood wool, plucked wool. **-wurz, -wurzel,** *f.* any of various plants of red sap or supposed blood-stanching properties, specif. bloodroot (either *Sanguinaria canadensis* or *Potentilla tormentilla*).

**Bock,** *m.* he-goat, buck; (*Brewing*) bock beer; (*Tech.*) trestle, jack, horse; blunder. **-asche,** *f.* coal ashes. **-holz,** *n.* guaiacum wood, lignum-vitae.

**bockig, böckig,** *a.* resistant, refractory.

**Bock-leder,** *n.* goat leather, kid. **-nuss,** *f.* souari nut (fruit of *Caryocar*). **-säure,** *f.* hircic acid (a mixture). **-seife,** *f.* mountain soap (kind of clay).

**Bocks-horn,** *n.* fenugreek. **-hörnlein,** *n.* carob bean.

**Boden,** *m.* soil; earth, ground, land; bottom; base; floor; loft, garret. **-analyse,** *f.* soil analysis. **-art,** *f.* (kind or variety of) soil. **-blatt,** *n.* flat bottom. **-hals,** *m.* neck or tubulation at the bottom. **-hefe,** *f.* grounds, dregs, lees (of yeast). **-kolloid,** *n.* soil colloid. **-körper,** *m.* a substance at the bottom of a liquid, a solid phase; soil substance. **-kupfer,** *n.* (*Copper*) bottoms. **-mehl,** *n.* fecula, starch. **-nährstoff,** *m.* soil nutrient. **-probe,** *f.* soil test; soil sample. **-satz,** *m.* deposit, sediment, dregs, bottoms, foot;

(*Salt*) bitterings. **-säure,** *f.* soil acid. **-stein,** *m.* bottom stone, sole (of a furnace); (*Salt*) bittern; bed stone (of a mill). **-teig,** *m.* underdough. **-untersuchung,** *f.* soil investigation, examination of soil. **-ventil,** *n.* bottom valve. **-wasser,** *n.* ground water. **-ziegel,** *m.* paving tile.

**bog,** *pret.* of biegen.

**Bogen,** *m.* bow, arc, bend, curve, curvature, arch; (*Elec.*) arc; sheet (of paper). **-flamme,** *f.* arc flame.

**bogenförmig,** *a.* bowed, curved, arched.

**Bogen-lampe,** *f.* arc lamp. **-licht,** *n.* arc light. **-linie,** *f.* curved line. **-stück,** *n.* curved piece; (*Brewing*) return bend.

**Bohle,** *f.* plank.

**Böhmen,** *n.* Bohemia.

**böhmisch,** *a.* Bohemian.

**Bohne,** *f.* bean.

**bohnen,** *v.t.* wax.

**Bohnen-erz,** *n.* =Bohnerz. **-kraut,** *n.* summer savory (*Satureia hortensis*). **-kuchen,** *m.* bean cake. **-mehl,** *m.* bean meal.

**Bohnerwachs,** *n.* polishing wax.

**Bohn-erz,** *n.* pea ore (oölitic limonite). **-wachs,** *n.* polishing wax.

**bohren,** *v.t.* bore, drill.

**Bohrer,** *m.* borer, perforator, gimlet, auger, drill, bit.

**Bohr-gut,** *n.* material obtained by boring. **-loch,** *n.* borehole, drill hole. **-mehl,** *n.* borings, bore dust. **-probe,** *f.* core sample; boring test. **-span,** *m.* boring. **-stock,** *m.* boring stock, borer.

**Bohrung,** *f.* boring, bore, bore hole.

**Boje,** *f.* buoy.

**Bol,** *m.* =Bolus.

**Bolivien,** *n.* Bolivia.

**Bolle,** *f.* bulb.

**Bollwerk,** *n.* bulwark.

**Bologneser,** *m.* Bolognese, Bologna.— — **Flasche,** Bologna flask.— — **Spat,** Bologna stone.

**Bolus,** *m.,* **-erde,** *f.* bole.—**roter Bolus,** reddle.—**weisser Bolus,** kaolin.

**Bolzen,** *m.* bolt; peg, pin; prop. **-mutter,** *f.* nut (to a bolt). **-scheibe,** *f.* washer (for a bolt).

**Bombage,** *f.* (*Canning*) swell.

**Bombe,** *f.* bomb, shell.

**Bomben-ofen,** *m.* bomb furnace. **-rohr,** *n.* bomb tube.

**Bomse,** *f.* (*Ceram.*) support.

**Bonitierung,** *f.* valuation, appraisement.

**Boot,** *n.* boat.

**Bor,** *n.* boron.

**Bor-.** boric, boron, boro-, etc. **-ameisensäure,** *f.* boroformic acid.

**Borat,** *n.* borate.

**Bor-äthan,** *n.* borethane, boroethane. **-äthyl,** *n.* borethyl (triethylborine).

**Borax-honig,** *m.* borax honey. **-kalk,** *m.* calcium borate. **-perle,** *f.* borax bead.

**boraxsauer,** *a.* =borsauer.

**Borax-säure,** *f.* boric acid. **-see,** *m.* borax lake. **-spat,** *m.* boracite. **-weinstein,** *m.* boryl potassium tartrate, (*Pharm.*) tartarus boratus.

**Borazit,** *n.* boracite.

**Bor-butan,** *n.* borobutane. **-chlorid,** *n.* boron chloride.

**Bord,** *m.* border, edge, rim; (ship) board.

**bordeauxrot,** *a.* Bordeaux red, claret.

**Bordelaiser Brühe.** Bordeaux mixture.

**bördeln,** *v.t.* border, edge, flange.

**Boretsch,** *m.* borage.

**Bor-fluorid,** *n.* boron fluoride; borofluoride. **-fluorwasserstoffsäure,** *f.*, **-fluorwasserstoff,** *m.* fluoboric acid, hydrofluoboric acid, $HBF_4$. **-flusssäure,** *f.* fluoboric acid.

**Borg,** *m.* borrowing, credit.

**Borgehalt,** *m.* boron content.

**borgen,** *v.t.* borrow; (less often) lend.

**Borium,** *n.* boron.

**Borjodid,** *n.* boron iodide.

**Borke,** *f.* bark; rind; crust, scab.

**Bormethyl,** *n.* trimethylborine, boron methyl, $B(CH_3)_3$.

**Born,** *m.* spring, well; (*Salt*) salt pit; brine.

**Borokalzit,** *n.* borocalcite.

**Borsalbe,** *f.* (*Pharm.*) boric acid ointment.

**borsauer,** *a.* of or combined with boric acid, borate of.

**Borsäure,** *f.* boric acid. **-weinstein,** *m.* = Boraxweinstein.

**Börse,** *f.* purse; Exchange.

**Borst,** *m.* burst, crack, fissure.

**Borstahl,** *m.* boron steel.

**Borste,** *f.* bristle; fissure, crack.

**börste,** *pret. subj.* of bersten.

**Borstickstoff,** *m.* boron nitride.

**borstig,** *a.* cracked; bristly; surly.

**Borte,** *f.* border, edging; lace.

**Bor-verbindung,** *f.* boron compound. **-wasser,** *n.* boric-acid solution. **-wasserstoff,** *m.* boron hydride. **-wolframsäure,** *f.* borotungstic acid. **Böschung,** *f.* slope, sloping.

**Böschungswinkel,** *m.* angle of slope.

**böse,** *a.* bad, evil; harmful, noxious; sore, aching.—**böses Wesen,** epilepsy.—**böses Wetter,** choke damp.

**bossieren,** *v.t.* emboss; chase; dress.

**Bossierwachs,** *n.* molding wax.

**bot,** *pret.* of bieten.

**Botanik,** *f.* botany.

**Botaniker,** *m.* botanist.

**botanisch,** *a.* botanical.

**Bote,** *m.* messenger.

**Botschaft,** *f.* message; embassy; *pl.* tidings.

**Böttcher,** *m.* cooper.

**Bottich,** *m.* vat, tub, tun, tank, back, vessel. **-kühler,** *m.* (*Brewing*) attemperator.

**Bouteille,** *f.* bottle.

**Bouteillenglas,** *n.* bottle glass.

**brach,** *pret.* of brechen.

**brach,** *a.* fallow.

**brachte,** *pret.* of bringen.

**Brack,** *m.* refuse.

**brackig,** *a.* brackish.

**Brambeere,** *f.* blackberry.

**Bramme,** *f.* slab (of iron), bloom.

**Brand,** *m.* burning; fire; charge (of a kiln or oven); blight, smut; gangrene, slough; brand.

**Brand-.** burn(ing), fire, incendiary. **-balsam,** *m.* ointment for burns. **-bombe,** *f.* incendiary bomb. **-erz,** *n.* inflammable ore (as bituminous shale, or as idrialite).

**brandfest,** *a.* fireproof.

**Brand-fleck,** **-flecken,** *m.* burn. **-gelb,** *n.* reddish yellow. **-geschoss,** *n.* incendiary shell. **-gold,** *n.* refined gold. **-granate,** *f.* incendiary shell. **-harz,** *n.* empyreumatic resin.

**brandig,** *a.* burnt; blasted; gangrenous.

**Brand-kitt,** *m.* fireproof cement or lute. **-lunte,** *f.* slow match.

**brandmarken,** *v.t.* brand.

**Brand-messer,** *m.* pyrometer. **-mittel,** *n.* escharotic; remedy for burns; remedy for gangrene. **-öl,** *n.* empyreumatic oil (obtained by destructive distillation). **-probe,** *f.* fire test, fire assay. **-riss,** *m.* fire crack. **-salbe,** *f.* salve for burns. **-satz,** *m.,* **-zeug,** *n.* (*Mil.*) an incendiary composition. **-schaden,** *m.* damage from fire. **-schiefer,** *m.* bituminous shale. **-silber,** *n.* refined silver. **-stein,** *m.* brick.

**brandstiftend,** *a.* incendiary.

**Brandstiftung,** *f.* incendiarism, arson.

**Brandung,** *f.* surf, breaker.

**Brand-versicherung,** *f.* fire insurance. **-wunde,** *f.* burn. **-ziegel,** *m.* firebrick.

**Bränke,** *f.* =Brenke.

**brannte,** *pret.* of brennen.

**Brannt-hefe,** *f.* spent yeast. **-kalk,** *m.* caustic lime, quicklime.

**Branntwein,** *m.* spirits (brandy, whisky, etc.). **-blase,** *f.* still (for spirits). **-brenner,** *m.* distiller. **-brennerei,** *f.* distillation (of spirits); distillery. **-essig,** *m.* brandy vinegar. **-geist,** *m.* rectified spirit, alcohol. **-hefe,** *f.* alcohol ferment (*Saccharomyces cerevisii*). **-mixture,** *f.* (*Pharm.*) mixture of brandy, brandy mixture. **-prober,** *m.* alcoholometer. **-vergiftung,** *f.* alcoholic poisoning. **-wa(a)ge,** *f.* alcoholometer.

**branstig,** *a.* of a burnt smell or taste.

Brasil, Brasilien, n. Brazil. -holz, n. Brazil wood.

brasilianisch, a. Brazilian, Brazil.

Brasil-insäure, f. brazilinic acid. -kopalinsäure, f. brazilcopalinic acid. -kopalsäure, f. brazilcopalic acid. -säure, f. brazilic acid.

Brassidinsäure, f. brassidic acid.

Brassinsäure, f. brassic acid (brassidic acid).

brät, pr.3 sing. of braten.

braten, v.t. roast; calcine; grill, broil, fry; burn, scorch.

Braten, m. roast (meat). -fett, n. drippings.

Bratfrischarbeit, f. roasting and refining.

Brau, Bräu, m. brew, quantity brewed at one time; malt liquor.

Braubottich, m. brewing vat or tun.

Brauch, m. custom, usage.

brauchbar, a. useful, serviceable.

brauchen, v.t. use; want, need.

Braue, f. (eye)brow.

brauen, v.t. & i. brew.

Brauer, m. brewer.

Brauerei, f. brewing; brewery.

Brauerlack, m. brewer's varnish.

Brau-gerste, f. brewing barley. -haus, Bräuhaus, n., Brauhof, m. brewery. -industrie, f. brewing industry, brewing. -kessel, m. (Brewing) kettle, copper. -malz, n. brewing malt. -meister, m. master brewer.

braun, a. brown; bay (horse); dark (person). —brauner Glaskopf, limonite.

Braun, n. brown. -bleierz, n. pyromorphite.

Bräune, f. quinsy; angina; brownness; (Min.) =Braunerz.

Brauneisen-erz, n. =Brauneisenstein. -ocker, m. brown iron ocher. -stein, m. brown iron ore, limonite.

Braunelle, f. =Brunelle.

bräunen, v.t. brown; dye brown; bronze.

Braun-erz, n. limonite; vivianite; sphalerite. -färbung, f. brown color(ation).

braun-gefärbt, a. brown-colored. -gelb, a. brownish-yellow, yellowish-brown.

Braunglühhitze, f. dark red heat.

braungrün, a. brown-green.

Braun-heil, n. =Brunelle. -holz, n. logwood. -kalk, m. dolomite. -kohle, f. brown coal, lignite.

braunkohlenhaltig, a. lignitiferous, lignitic.

Braunkohlen-koks, m. lignite coke. -schiefer, m. lignite shale. -schwelerei, f. lignite coking; lignite-coking plant. -schwelgas, n. gas from lignite distillation. -teer, m. lignite tar. -teeröl, n. lignite tar oil. -teerpech, n. lignite pitch.

Braun-kräusen, f.pl. (Brewing) fuzzy heads. -lauge, f. brown liquor.

bräunlich, a. brownish. -gelb, a. brownish-yellow.

Braunmanganerz, n. (Min.) manganite.

braunrot, a. brown-red.

Braunrot, n. brown red; colcothar; Indian red.

braunrötlich, a. reddish-brown.

Braunschliff, m. (Paper) steamed mechanical wood pulp.

braunschwarz, a. brown-black, very dark brown.

Braunschweig, n. Brunswick.

Braunschweiger, a. Brunswick. -grün, n. Brunswick green.

Braun-späne, m.pl. logwood shavings. -spat, m. dolomite.

Braunstein, m. pyrolusite ($MnO_2$); (roter) rhodochrosite; (schwarzer) hausmannite. -blende, f. alabandite. -kies, m. alabandite. -kiesel, m. rhodonite. -rahm, -schaum, m. bog manganese, wad.

Brauntran, m. (Leather) blubber, thick cod oil.

Bräunung, f. browning; brown coloring; dyeing brown; bronzing.

Braupfanne, f. =Braukessel.

Brause, f. effervescence; sprinkler, rose, sprinkling can.

Brause-. effervescing, effervescent. -bad, n. shower bath. -lithiumcitrat, n. (Pharm.) effervescent lithium citrate. -magnesia, f. (Pharm.) (effervescing) solution of magnesium citrate. -mischung, f. effervescing mixture.

brausen, v.i. effervesce, froth; roar; buzz.—brausend, p.a. effervescent.

Brause-pulver, n. effervescing powder; (englisches) Seidlitz powder. -salz, n. effervescent salt. -ton, m. bituminous clay. -wasser, n. soda water. -wein, m. sparkling wine.

Braut, f. bride, betrothed.

Brau-wasser, n. water for brewing; mash liquor, liquor. -wesen, n. brewing business.

brav, a. brave, gallant, good.

Brech-. breaking; broken; emetic. -arznei, f. emetic. -backen, f.pl. crusher jaws.

brechbar, a. refrangible; breakable, brittle.

Brech-barkeit, f. refrangibility, etc. (see brechbar). -bohne, f. kidney bean (Phaseolus vulgaris). -eisen, n. crowbar.

brechen, v.t. break; refract; mine, quarry; crush, pulverize; vomit; pluck; fold; blend (colors); boil off (silk); sprout.—v.i. break; crease, crinkle; (of dye baths) change, decompose. —gebrochen, p.a. broken, etc.; fractional; crooked, bent; worn out; ruined.

brechenerregend, a. emetic.

Brecher, m. breaker, crusher, etc. (see brechen).

Brech-haufen, m. (Brewing) broken piece. -körner, n.pl. castor beans. -kraft, f. (Opt.) refractive power. -mittel, n. emetic.

-neigung, f. (Med.) nausea. -nuss, f. nux vomica. -stange, f. crowbar, pinch bar. -stoff, m. emetic, specif. emetine.

Brechung, f. breaking, etc. (see brechen); (Physics) refraction.

Brechungs-ebene, f. (Optics) plane of refraction. -exponent, m. refractive index. -verhältnis, n. refractive index. -vermögen, n. refractive power. -winkel, m. angle of refraction.

Brech-walzwerk, n. crushing rolls (or rollers). -wein, m. (Pharm.) wine of antimony, antimonial wine. -weinstein, m. tartar emetic. -werk, n. crusher. -wurzel, -wurz, f. ipecacuanha, ipecac.

Brei, m. (something of porridgelike consistency) pulp, mash, paste, slurry; magma; porridge, pap; (Ceram.) slip.

breiartig, breiig, breiicht, a. pulpy, pappy, pasty, semifluid, semiliquid.

breit, a. broad, wide; flat.

Breite, f. breadth, width; latitude.

breiten, v.t. spread, extend, flatten.

Breitleder, n. sole leather.

Breiumschlag, m. poultice, cataplasm.

breiweich, a. pulpy, pappy.

Brekzie, f. breccia.

Bremer, a. Bremen. -blau, n. Bremen blue. -grün, n. Bremen green.

Bremse, f. brake; gadfly.

bremsen, v.t. brake, check, retard.

Brems-strahlen, f.pl. rays due to retarding of particles. -strahlung, f. radiation due to retarding of particles (usually continuous radiation).

Bremsung, f. checking, retarding.

Brenkas, n. fine East-Indian tin.

Brenke, f. (Brewing) yeast tub.

Brenn-. burning, of combustion, calorific; distilling; (Optics, etc.) focal. -apparat, m. distilling apparatus, still; branding machine. -arbeit, f. fire assaying. -ätzverfahren, n. pyrography.

brennbar, a. combustible, burnable.—brennbare Luft, inflammable air (hydrogen).

Brenn-barkeit, f. combustibility. -blase, f. alembic, still. -cylinder, m. (Pharm.) moxa. -ebene, f. focal plane.

brennen, v.t. burn; calcine, roast; distill; fire, bake; anneal; refine; char; scald; singe; cauterize; brand; curl (hair).—v.i. burn; smart.—brennend, p.a. burning; caustic; pungent; ardent.—gebrannt, p.a. burnt, calcined, etc.—gebrannte Erde, terra cotta. — gebrannte Magnesia, magnesia usta (MgO).—gebrannte Wasser, distilled liquors.

Brenner, m. burner; distiller; brickmaker; lime burner.

Brennerei, f. distillery; distillation; plant (for burning lime, etc.); kiln; burning (of lime, brick, etc.). -betrieb, m. distillery management or operation. -hefe, f. distillery yeast.

Brennermündung, f. orifice of a burner.

Brenn-gas, n. combustible gas, fuel gas. -gerste, f. distilling barley. -geschwindigkeit, f. velocity of combustion, of burning or of distillation. -glas, n. burning glass. -gut, n. material to be burned or distilled. -helm, m. still head. -herd, m. hearth; refining furnace. -holz, n. firewood. -kapsel, f. sagger. -kegel, m. (Ceram.) pyrometric cone. -kolben, m. distilling flask, alembic. -linie, f. focal line. -linse, f. burning glass, convex lens. -luft, f. inflammable air (hydrogen). -material, n. combustible material, fuel. -materialverbrauch, m. fuel consumption. -mittel, n. caustic, corrosive. -nessel, f. (stinging) nettle (Urtica). -ofen, m. burning oven, baking oven, kiln, furnace, roasting furnace, calcining furnace, etc. -öl, n. burning oil; fuel oil. -punkt, m. focal point, focus. -schwindung, f. (Ceram.) shrinkage in firing. -silber, n. amalgam for silvering. -spiegel, m. concave mirror. -spiritus, m. alcohol for burning. -stahl, m. blister steel.

Brennstoff, m. fuel, combustible; (Old Chem.) phlogiston. -aufwand, m. fuel consumption. -ausnutzung, f. utilization of fuel. -verbrauch, m. fuel consumption. -wert, m. fuel value. -ziegel, m. fuel briquet.

Brenn-stunde, f. burning hour, lamp hour. -wärme, f. heat of combustion; calcining heat, etc. (see brennen). -weite, f. focal distance, focal length. -wert, m. fuel value, calorific value. -zeit, f. time of burning, etc. (see brennen). -ziegel, m. firebrick; fuel briquet. -zone, f. zone of combustion. -zylinder, m. = Brenncylinder.

Brenz, n. empyreuma, combustible.

Brenz-. pyro-. -apfelsäure, f. maleic acid. -cain, n. (Pharm.) pyrocain. -catechin, n. pyrocatechol, pyrocatechin. -essigäther, -essiggeist, m. acetone. -gallussäure, f. pyrogallic acid. -harz, n. = Brandharz.

brenzholzsauer, a. of or combined with pyroligneous acid.

Brenz-holzsäure, f. pyroligneous acid. -katechin, n. pyrocatechol, pyrocatechin.

brenzlich, brenzlig, a. empyreumatic, tarry; burnt.—brenzlige Säuren, pyro acids.

Brenz-öl, n. empyreumatic oil. -säure, f. pyro acid. -schleimsäure, f. pyromucic acid. -terebinsäure, f. pyroterebic acid. -traubenalkohol, m. pyroracemic alcohol. -traubensäure, f. pyroracemic acid. -weinsäure, f. pyrotartaric acid.

**Brett,** *n.* board, plank; shelf; office.
**brettern,** *a.* of boards, boarded.
**Brett-mühle,** *f.* sawmill. **-stückchen,** *n.* piece of board.
**Brezel,** *f.* pretzel.
**Brezzie,** *f.* breccia.
**bricht,** *pr. 3 sing.* of brechen.
**Brief,** *m.* letter; paper, packet. **-chen,** *n.* note. **-geld,** *n.* postage.
**brieflich,** *a.* written.—*adv.* by letter, in writing.
**Brief-marke,** *f.* postage stamp. **-papier,** *n.* writing paper. **-schaften,** *f. pl.* writings, papers. **-stempel,** *m.* postmark. **-tisch,** *m.* desk. **-umschlag,** *m.* envelope, wrapper. **-wechsel,** *m.* correspondence.
**Bries,** *n.* thymus. **-eldrüse,** *f.* thymus gland.
**briet,** *pret.* of braten.
**Brikett,** *n.* briquet, briquette. **-bindemittel,** *n.* binder for briquets, briquet cement.
**brikettieren,** *v.t.* briquet.
**brillant,** *a.* brilliant.
**Brillant-gelb,** *n.* brilliant yellow. **-grün,** *n.* brilliant green. **-weiss,** *n.* brilliant white.
**Brille,** *f.* spectacles, eyeglasses.
**Brillenofen,** *m.* spectacle furnace.
**bringen,** *v.t.* bring; carry, take, put.
**brisant,** *a.* shattering, disruptive, brisant. —**brisanter Sprengstoff,** high explosive, disruptive.
**Brisanz,** *f.* shattering power. **-sprengstoff,** *m.* high explosive, disruptive.
**Brise,** *f.* breeze.
**Bröckchen,** *n.* small bit, small piece, crumb.
**bröckelig,** *a.* brittle, friable, fragile.
**Bröckeligkeit,** *f.* brittleness, friability.
**bröckeln,** *v.t.* crumble.
**Bröckelstärke,** *f.* lump starch.
**brocken,** *v.t.* crumble, break up.
**Brocken,** *m.* lump, fragment; crumb. **-gestein,** *n.* (*Petrog.*) breccia. **-glas,** *n.* broken glass, cullet. **-stärke,** *f.* lump starch. **-stein,** *m.* (*Petrog.*) breccia.
**bröcklig,** *a.* =bröckelig.
**Bröckligkeit,** *f.* brittleness, friability.
**Brod,** *n.* =Brot.
**brodeln,** *v.i.* bubble; effervesce; boil.
**Brodem, Broden,** *m.* vapor, steam, exhalation; (*Mining*) foul air, damp.
**Brokat,** *m.* brocade.
**Brom,** *n.* bromine.
**Brom-,** of or combined with bromine; bromo- (as *Brombenzoesäure,* bromobenzoic acid); bromide of (as *Brombaryum,* barium bromide). **-ammonium,** *n.* ammonium bromide. **-antimon,** *n.* antimony bromide. **-arsen,** *n.,* **-arsenik,** *m.* arsenic bromide. **-äther,** *m.* ethyl bromide. **-äthyl,** *n.* ethyl bromide. **-äthylen,** *n.* ethylene bromide. **-äthylformin,** *n.* (*Pharm.*) bro-

malin. **-atom,** *n.* bromine atom. **-baryum,** *n.* barium bromide. **-beere,** *f.* blackberry. **-benzol,** *n.* bromobenzene. **-calcium,** *n.* calcium bromide. **-cyan,** *n.* cyanogen bromide, bromocyanogen. **-dampf,** *m.* bromine vapor. **-eisen,** *n.* iron bromide. **-flasche,** *f.* bromine bottle. **-fluor,** *n.* bromine fluoride. **-gehalt,** *m.* bromine content. **-gold,** *n.* gold bromide. **-goldkalium,** *n.* potassium auribromide, potassium bromoaurate.
**bromhaltig,** *a.* containing bromine.
**Brom-hydrat,** *n.* hydrobromide; bromine hydrate. **-hydrin,** *n.* bromohydrin.
**Bromid,** *n.* bromide (especially an -ic bromide, as contrasted with Bromür).
**bromierbar,** *a.* capable of being brominated.
**bromieren,** *v.t.* brominate.
**Bromierung,** *f.* bromination.
**bromig,** *a.* bromous.
**Brom-jod,** *n.* iodine bromide. **-kalium,** *n.* potassium bromide. **-kalzium,** *n.,* **-kalk,** *m.* calcium bromide. **-kampher,** *m.* bromocamphor, (*Pharm.*) monobromated camphor. **-kohlenstoff,** *m.* carbon (tetra)-bromide. **-kupfer,** *n.* copper bromide. **-lauge,** *f.* bromine lye (solution of sodium hypobromite and bromide made by passing bromine into sodium hydroxide solution). **-lithium,** *n.* lithium bromide. **-lösung,** *f.* bromine solution. **-magnesium,** *n.* magnesium bromide. **-metall,** *n.* metallic bromide. **-methylat,** *n.* methobromide. **-natrium,** *n.* sodium bromide. **-natron,** *n.* sodium hypobromite. **-olyse,** *f.* bromolysis. **-phosphor,** *m.* phosphorus bromide. **-radium,** *n.* radium bromide. **-salz,** *n.* bromide; bromate.
**bromsauer,** *a.* of or combined with bromic acid, bromate of.
**Brom-säure,** *f.* bromic acid. **-schwefel,** *m.* sulfur bromide. **-silber,** *n.* silver bromide. **-silizium,** *n.* silicon bromide. **-spat,** *n.* bromyrite (AgBr). **-stickstoff,** *m.* nitrogen bromide. **-toluol,** *n.* bromotoluene. **-überträger,** *m.* bromine carrier.
**Bromür,** *n.* (-ous) bromide. (Used for a metal in its lower valence, as *Eisenbromür,* ferrous bromide.)
**Brom-verbindung,** *f.* bromine compound. **-vergiftung,** *f.* bromine (or bromide) poisoning. **-wasser,** *n.* bromine water. **-wasserstoff,** *m.* hydrogen bromide; hydrobromic acid.
**bromwasserstoffsauer,** *a.* of or combined with hydrobromic acid, (usually) hydrobromide of.
**Brom-wasserstoffsäure,** *f.* hydrobromic acid. **-wismut,** *m. & n.* bismuth bromide. **-zahl,** *f.* bromine number. **-zink,** *n.* zinc bromide. **-zinn,** *n.* tin bromide.

Bronce, *f.* bronze.

bronzeartig, *a.* bronzelike, bronzy.

Bronze-draht, *m.* bronze wire. -farbe, *f.* bronze color. -färben, *n.* bronzing.

bronzefarbig, *a.* bronze-colored.

Bronze-glanz, *m.* bronze luster. -guss, *m.* bronze casting. -lack, *m.* bronze varnish. -pulver, *n.* bronze powder. -tinktur, *f.* bronzing liquid.

bronzieren, *v.t.* bronze.

Bronzier-pulver, *n.* bronzing powder. -salz, *n.* bronzing salt, specif. antimony trichloride.

Bronzierung, *f.* bronzing.

bronzig, *a.* bronzy.

Brosam, Brosame, *f.* crumb, scrap.

Bröschen, *n.* sweetbread.

broschieren, *v.t.* stitch, sew, work; bind in paper cover.

Broschüre, *f.* stitched (but unbound) book; pamphlet.

Brot, *n.* bread; loaf. -backen, *n.* bread baking. -brei, *m.* bread paste.

Brötchen, *n.* roll.

Brot-gärung, *f.* panary fermentation, leavening of bread. -geschmack, *n.* (*Brewing*) steam taste. -herr, *m.* employer. -korn, *n.* breadstuff.

brotlos, *a.* unemployed, unprofitable.

Brot-masse, *f.* breadstuff. -raffinade, *f.* loaf sugar. -teig, *m.* bread dough. -zucker, *m.* loaf sugar.

Brown'sche Bewegung. Brownian movement.

Bruch, *m.* fracture; fraction; break, breaking, breach, crack, cleft; fold, crease, wrinkle, crimp; quarry; fragments, scrap; rupture, (*Med.*) hernia. -beanspruchung, *f.* breaking stress. -belastung, *f.* breaking load. -blei, *n.* scrap lead. -dehnung, *f.* breaking elongation; stretch (of paper). -eisen, *n.* scrap iron.

bruchfest, *a.* resisting breakage, tenacious.

Bruch-festigkeit, *f.* resistance to fracture, tenacity. -fläche, *f.* surface of fracture. -gewicht, *n.* fractional weight. -glas, *n.* broken glass, cullet. -gramm, *n.* fraction of a gram. -grammgewicht, *n.* fractional gram weight.

brüchig, *a.* brittle, short; friable; fragile; full of cracks; (*Geol.*) clastic, fragmental.— werden, (of fabrics) tender.

Brüchigkeit, *f.* brittleness, friability.

Bruch-kupfer, *n.* scrap copper. -last, *f.* breaking load. -metall, *n.* broken metal, scrap metal. -modul, *m.* modulus of rupture. -silber, *n.* broken silver, scrap silver. -spannung, *f.* breaking stress; tensile strength. -stein, *m.* quarry stone. -stück, *n.* fragment, shred. -teil, *m.* fraction.

Brücke, *f.* bridge; platform.

Brücken-atom, *n.* bridge atom, bridging atom. -bindung, *f.* bridge bond, bridging bond. -sauerstoff, *m.* bridging oxygen, connecting oxygen. -wa(a)ge, *f.* platform balance. -widerstand, *m.* (*Elec.*) bridge resistance.

Bruder, *m.* brother; friar.

Brühe, *f.* soupy liquid, liquor; broth, soup; gravy, sauce; (*Dyeing*) liquor, bath; (*Leather*) juice, liquor, drench, ooze; (*Tobacco*) sauce.

brühen, *v.t.* scald, treat with hot water; scour.

brühheiss, *a.* scalding hot.

Brüh-messer, *m.* (*Leather*) barkometer. -wasser, *n.* water for scalding.

brüllen, *v.i.* roar, bellow, howl.

brummen, *v.i.* hum, buzz, low, growl, grumble.

Brunelle, *f.* self-heal (*Prunella vulgaris*).

Brunierbeize, *f.* (*Metal.*) bronzing pickle.

brunieren, brünieren, *v.t.* burnish, polish; brown; bronze.—*v.i.* turn brown.

Brünierstein, *m.* burnishing stone; bloodstone.

Brunnen, *m.* well, spring; fountain; (mineral) waters. -flasche, *f.* mineral-water bottle; siphon bottle. -kresse, *f.* watercress. -salz, *n.* well salt, brine salt. -wasser, *n.* well water, spring water.

brünstig, *a.* ardent; fervent; in heat.

Brust, *f.* breast, chest; brisket.

Brust-. of the chest; thoracic; pectoral. -angst, *f.* angina pectoris. -beere, *f.* jujube, zizyphus. -drüse, *f.* mammary gland. -fell, *n.* pleura. -fellentzündung, *f.* pleurisy. -fieber, *n.* bronchitis. -gang, *m.* thoracic duct. -kasten, *m.* thorax. -korb, *m.* thorax. -krampf, *m.* asthma. -pulver, *n.* pectoral powder, specif. compound licorice powder.

brustreinigend, *p.a.* expectorant.

Brüstung, *f.* parapet, breast wall.

Brut, *f.* brood, hatch; brooding, hatching.

brüten, *v.i.* brood, hatch, incubate.

Brut-kasten, -ofen, -schrank, *m.* incubator.

Brüt-ofen, -schrank, *m.* incubator.

brutto, *a.& adv.* gross.

Brutto-formel, *f.* a formula indicating merely the number of atoms of each kind, and not their mode of union, an empirical molecular formula (e.g., $C_3H_8$). -gewicht, *n.* gross weight.

Brutwärme, *f.* blood heat.

Bruzin, *n.* brucine.

Bube, *m.* boy; knave.

Bubonenpest, *f.* bubonic plague.

Bucco-. buchu. -blätter, *n.pl.* (*Pharm.*) buchu.

Buch, *n.* book; quire. -binderkleister, *m.* bookbinder's paste.

Buchdrucker, *m.* printer. -ei, *f.* printing establishment, press; printing. -farbe, f. printing ink. -schwärze, f. printer's ink.

Buchdruck-farbe, f. printing ink. -firnis, m. printer's varnish.

Buche, f. beech.

Buch-ecker, f. beechnut. -eckernöl, -ekernöl, n. beechnut oil.

Buchel, f. beechnut.

buchen, büchen, a. beechen, of beech.

buchen, v.t. enter, book, register.

Buchen-asche, f. beech ashes. -holz, n. beechwood. -holzteer, n. beech tar. -rinde, f. beech bark. -späne, m.pl. beech shavings (or chips).

Bücher-ei, f. library; books. -verzeichnis, n. book list, book catalog.

Buch-führen, n. bookkeeping. -gold, n. leaf gold. -halter, m. bookkeeper, accountant. -handel, m. book trade, bookselling. -händler, m. bookseller; publisher.

Büchnertrichter, m. Büchner funnel.

Buch-nuss, f. beechnut. -nussöl, n. beechnut oil. -öl, n. beech(nut) oil.

Buchsbaum, m. box tree. -holz, n. boxwood.

Büchse, Buchse, f. box, chest, case, can, pot; rifle; (Mach.) bush, box, socket.

Büchsenfleisch, n. canned meat, tinned meat.

büchsenförmig, a. box-shaped.

Buchsenfrucht, f. canned fruit, tinned fruit.

Büchsen-gemüse, n. canned vegetables. -macher, n. gunsmith.

Buchsenmetal, Büchsenmetall, n. bush metal, bearing metal.

Büchsen-milch, f. condensed (or evaporated) milk. -mühle, f. barrel mill. -pulver, n. rifle powder. -schuss, m. gunshot. -stein, m. iron pyrites.

Buchstabe, m. letter; character; type.

Buchstabenrechnung, f. algebra.

buchstabieren, v.t. spell.

buchstäblich, a. literal.

Bucht, f. bay, inlet; sinus.

Buchung, f. entry.

Buchweizen, m. buckwheat.

Buckel, m. hump; knob; knot.

bücken, v.r. stoop.

Bückling, m. red herring, bloater.

Bucko-, Bucku-. buchu.

Bude, f. booth, stall, shop; hut; shed.

Büffel, m. buffalo; buff (leather). -leim, m. leather glue.

Bug, m. bend, bow; bow (of a boat).

Bügel, m. bow (any curved piece of metal, wood, or the like); hoop; guard, frame; loop; handle (of a pail, etc.); stirrup.

bügelecht, a. fast to ironing.

Bügeleisen, n. flatiron.

bügeln, v.t. iron.

Bügelschälchen, n. little dish or cup (of bent metal).

Bühne, f. platform, scaffold; stage, theater.

buk, pret. of backen.

büken, v.t. =beuchen.

Bukett, n. bouquet.

Bukko-, Bukku-. buchu.

Bulbe, f. bulb.

Bulgarien, n. Bulgaria.

Bund, m. band, tie; hoop, collar; alliance.—n. bundle, bunch.

Bündel, n. bundle, bunch; parcel, packet.

Bundes-rat, m. federal council. -tag, m. federal diet.

bündig, a. flush; valid; concise; conclusive.

Bündnis, n. alliance.

Bundstahl, m. fagot steel.

Bunsen-brenner, m. Bunsen burner. -flamme, f. Bunsen (burner) flame. -kohle, f. carbon for the Bunsen cell.

bunt, a. variegated, many-colored, motley; mottled, speckled; colored; gay, fancy, gaudy.

Bunt-bleiche, f. (Calico) branning. -druck, m. color printing; color print. -farbe, f. variegated color; (any) iron oxide pigment.

buntfärben, v.t. stain.

Buntfärberei, f. dyeing in different colors.

buntfarbig, a. variegated.

Bunt-gewebe, n. colored fabric. -kupfererz, n., -kupferkies, m. bornite. -papier, n. colored paper; fancy paper.

buntschillernd, a. iridescent, chatoyant.

Bürde, f. burden, load, charge.

Bureau, n. office; bureau.

Büretten-bürste, f. burette brush. -deckel, m. burette cap. -flasche, f. volumetric flask. -gestell, n. burette stand. -halter, m. burette holder. -klemme, f. burette clamp. -schwimmer, m. burette float. -spitze, f. burette tip. -stativ, n. burette stand, burette support. -trichter, m. funnel for filling burettes.

Burg, f. castle, stronghold.

bürge, pret. subj. of bergen.

bürgen, v.i. give bail; vouch (for).

Bürger, m. citizen; townsman; civilian. -krieg, m. civil war.

bürgerlich, a. civil; common; civilian.

Bürger-meister, m. mayor, burgomaster. -schaft, f. community; the citizens. -stand, m. citizenry; middle class. -steig, m. sidewalk.

Bürgschaft, f. security, bail.

Burgunder, m. Burgundy (wine). -harz, -pech, n. Burgundy pitch.

Büro, n. office. -zeit, f. office hours.

Bursche, m. fellow; lad; servant; student.

Bürste, f. brush.

bürsten, *v.t.* brush.

Bürsten-entladung, *f.* (*Elec.*) brush discharge. -feuer, *n.* (*Elec.*) brush sparking.

Busch, *m.* bush; copse; tuft.

Büschel, *m.* tuft, bunch, cluster; (*Elec.*) brush; bundle, pencil, beam (of rays). -entladung, *f.* (*Elec.*) brush discharge.

büschelförmig, *a.* tuft-like, clustered.

Busen, *m.* bosom, breast; bay.

Busse, *f.* penance, fine, penalty.

büssen, *v.t.* atone for, make good.

Butan, *n.* butane.

Bütte, Butte, *f.* tub, vat, back, tank, chest.

butteln, *v.i.* bubble.

büttengefärbt, *p.a.* unbleached (paper).

Büttenpapier, *n.* vat paper, handmade paper.

Butter-. butter; butyric, butyryl, butyro-.

butter-ähnlich, -artig, *a.* buttery, butyraceous.

Butter-amylester, *m.* amyl butyrate. -äther, *m.* butyric ether (ethyl butyrate). -baum, *m.* shea tree. -blume, *f.* buttercup. -farbe, *f.* butter color. -fass, *n.* churn. -fett, *n.* butter fat; butyrin. -gärung, *f.* butyric fermentation. -gelb, *n.* butter yellow.

butterhaltig, *a.* containing butter, butyraceous.

butterig, *a.* buttery.

Butter-messer, *m.* butyrometer. -milch, *f.* buttermilk.

buttern, *v.t.* churn; butter.—*v.i.* yield butter.

Butter-nuss, *f.* butternut. -persäure, *f.* perbutyric acid. -prüfer, *m.* butter tester.

buttersauer, *a.* of or combined with butyric acid, butyrate of.

Buttersäure, *f.* butyric acid. -äther, *m.* ethyl butyrate; *pl.* butyric esters. -gärung, *f.* butyric fermentation.

Butterstoff, *m.* butyrin. *Obs.*

Butyljodid, *n.* butyl iodide.

Butyropersäure, *f.* perbutyric acid.

b.w., *abbrev.* (bitte wenden) please turn over, p.t.o.

Bz., *abbrev.* (Benzol) benzene; (*Com.*) benzol.

bzgl., *abbrev.* (bezüglich) respecting.

Bzl., *abbrev.* (Benzol) benzene; (*Com.*) benzol.

Bzn., *abbrev.* (Benzin) benzine.

bzw., *abbrev.* (beziehungsweise) respectively, or.

# C

C., *abbrev.* Chemisches Zentralblatt.

ca., *abbrev.* (circa, zirka) about.

Cabesaseide, *f.* cabeça, cabesse (silk).

Cachou, *n.* catechu.

cachoutieren, *v.t.* dye with catechu or cutch.

Cadeöl, *n.* oil of cade.

Cadinöl, Cadiöl, *n.* oil of cade.

Cadmium-. see Kadmium-.

Caffee, *m.* coffee (for compounds see Kaffee-).

Cainca-säure, *f.* cahincic acid. -wurzel, *f.* cahinca (root).

Caincin, *n.* cahincin.

Cajeput-geist, *m.* spirit of cajuput. -öl, *n.* cajuput oil.

calcifizieren, *v.t.* calcify.

calcinierbar, *a.* calcinable.

calcinieren, *v.t.* calcine.

Calcinier-herd, *m.* calcining hearth. -ofen, *m.* calcining furnace or oven.

Calcinierung, *f.* calcination.

Calcium-gehalt, *m.* calcium content. -hydrür, *n.* calcium hydride (CaH₂). -jodid, *n.* calcium iodide. -salz, *n.* calcium salt. -spiegel, *m.* (*Biol.*) calcium level. -verbindung, *f.* calcium compound.

Caledonischbraun, *n.* Caledonian brown.

calibrieren, *v.t.* calibrate.

Calisayarinde, *f.* calisaya bark.

Calorienwert, *m.* caloric value.

calorimetrieren, *v.t.* measure with the calorimeter.

Calorimetrierung, *f.* calorimetric measurement.

calorimetrisch, *a.* calorimetric.

calorisch, *a.* caloric, thermal.

Cambogiasäure, *f.* gambogic acid.

cämentieren, =cementieren.

camouflieren, *v.t.* camouflage.

Campagne, *f.* campaign, (working) season.

Campane, *f.* bell jar.

Campecheholz, *n.* logwood.

Camphansäure, *f.* camphanic acid.

Campher, *m.* camphor (for compounds see Kampher-).

camphotetisch, *a.* (*Org. Chem.*) camphothetic (isocampholytic).

canadisch, *a.* Canadian.

Canarienfarbe, *f.* canary color; canarin.

canneliert, *a.* channeled.

Cannelkohle, *f.* cannel coal.

Cantharinsäure, *f.* cantharidic acid.

Cantharsäure, *f.* cantharic acid.

Caoutschuk, *m.* caoutchouc.

Capelle, etc. =Kapelle, etc.

capillar, etc. =kapillar, etc.

Capriblau, *n.* Capri blue. |

Caprinsäure, *f.* capric acid.

Capron-fett, *n.* caproin. -säure, *f.* caproic acid.

Caprylsäure, *f,* caprylic acid.

Capsel, etc. =Kapsel, etc.

Caramelgeruch, *m.* caramel odor.

Caranna-gummi, -harz, *n.* caranna (resin).

Carapa-öl, -fett, *n.* carap(a) oil.

Carbamidsäure, *f.* carbamic acid.

carbaminsauer, *a.* of or combined with carbamic acid, carbamate of.

Carbaminsäure, *f.* carbamic acid.

Carbanilsäure, *f.* carbanilic acid.

Carbäthoxy-. carbethoxy-.

Carbäthoxyl, *n.* carbethoxyl.

Carbazotsilicium, *n.* silicon carbonitride.

Carbid-kohle, *f.* carbide carbon. -ofen, *m.* carbide furnace. -verfahren, *n.* carbide process.

Carbochindolin, *n.* carboquindoline.

carbocyclisch, *a.* carbocyclic.

Carbol-. carbolic, carbolized, carbolated. -kalk, *n.* carbolated lime. -öl, *n.* carbolated oil. -salbe, *f.* (*Pharm.*) ointment of phenol.

Carbolsäure, *f.* carbolic acid. -lösung, *f.* carbolic acid solution. -seife, *f.* carbolic acid soap.

carbolschwefelsauer, *a.* (*Pharm.*) of or combined with sulfocarbolic acid, sulfocarbolate of.

Carbol-schwefelsäure, *f.* (*Pharm.*) sulfocarbolic acid, sulfophenic acid (p-phenolsulfonic acid.). -seife, *f.* carbolic soap. -sulfosäure, *f.*=Carbolschwefelsäure. -wasser, *n.* aqueous solution of phenol.

Carbon, *m.* carbon; (*Geol.*) Carboniferous.

Carbonat, *n.* carbonate. -härte, *f.* hardness due to carbonates. -ion, *n.* carbonate ion.

carbonieren, *v.t.* carbonate.

Carbonisation, *f.* carbonization; carbonation.

carbonisch, *a.* (*Geol.*) Carboniferous.

Carbonisier-anlage, -anstalt, *f.* carbonizing plant. -bad, *n.* carbonizing bath.

carbonisieren, *v.t.* carbonize; carburize; carbonate.

Carbonisierflüssigkeit, *f.* carbonizing liquor.

Carbonisierung, *f.* carbonization; carbonation.

Carbonsäure, *f.* carboxylic acid (a general term).

-carbonsäure, *f.* -carboxylic acid.

Carbonyl-gruppe, *f.* carbonyl group. -sauerstoff, *m.* carbonyl oxygen. -verbindung, *f.* carbonyl compound.

carbozyklisch, *a.* carbocyclic.

Carbür, *n.* (ous) carbide (cf. Chlorür).

Carburateur, *m.* carburetor.

carburieren, *v.t.* carburet, carburize.

Carenz, *f.* omission.

Carmin, etc. = Karmin, etc.

Carnauba-säure, *f.* carnaubic acid. -wachs, *n* carnauba wax.

Carneol, *m.* carnelian.

Caro'sche Säure. Caro's acid.

Carotin, *n.* carotene, carotin.

Carotte, *f.* carrot.

Carraghenmoos, *n.* carrageen moss, Irish moss.

Carreau, *n.* check, square.

Carub, *m.*, Carube, *f.* carob.

Cärul-, cärul-, cerul-.

caseinartig, *a.* like casein, caseous.

Casein-kitt, *m.* casein cement. -leim, *m.* casein glue. -lösung, *f.* casein solution. -natrium, *n.* sodium caseinate.

Cäsium, *n.* cesium. -alaun, *m.* cesium alum. -verbindung, *f.* cesium compound.

Cassawastärke, *f.* tapioca.

Cassia-öl, *n.* cassia oil. -rinde, *f.* cassia bark.

Cassie, *f.* cassia.

Cassien-. cassia (see Kassien-).

Cassiuspurpur, *m.* purple of Cassius.

Castillianer Seife. castile soap.

Castor-nuss, *f.* castor bean. -öl, *n.* castor oil.

Catech-. see Katech-.

Cathartinsäure, *f.* cathartic acid.

Cautel, *f.* precaution.

Cautschuk, *m.* = Kautschuk.

cbcm., *abbrev.* cubic centimeter, cc.

cbm., *abbrev.* cubic meter, cu. m.

cca., *abbrev.* (circa) about.

Ceder, *f.* cedar.

Cedern-harz, *n.* cedar resin. -öl, *n.* cedar oil.

Cedratöl, *n.* citron oil.

Cedroöl, *n.* citron oil.

Celasteröl, *n.* celastrus oil, staff-tree oil.

Celit, *n.*, Celith, *m.* (*Cement*) celite.

Cellulose-lösung, *f.* cellulose solution. -schleim, *m.* cellulose slime, pulp slime. -schwefelsäure, *f.* cellulosesulfuric acid. -zahl, *f.* cellulose number.

Celsiusgrad, *m.* Celsius (centigrade) degree.

Cement, cementieren, etc. = Zement, zementieren, etc.

censieren, *v.t.* criticize.

Censur, *f.* censorship; report.

Cent-. see Zent-.

Cer, *m.* cerium.

Cerat, *n.* cerate.

Cerealien, *pl.* cereals.

Cer-erde, *f.* cerium earth (class name). -erz, *n.* cerium ore, esp. cerite. -feuerzeug, *n.& m.* cerium lighter.

Ceri-. ceric. -chlorid, *n.* ceric chloride.

Cerinstein, *m.* (*Min.*) cerite.

Ceri-oxyd, *n.* ceric oxide. -salz, *n.* ceric salt. -sulfat, *n.* ceric sulfate.

Ceriterde, *f.* cerite earth.

Ceriverbindung, *f.* ceric compound.

Cermischmetall, *n.* misch metal (a mixture of rare-earth metals).

Cero-. cerous. -ion, *n.* cerous ion. -salz, *n.* cerous salt. -sulfat, *n.* cerous sulfate.

Cerotinsäure, *f.* cerotic acid.

Ceroverbindung, *f.* cerous compound.

Ceroxyd, *n.* cerium oxide.

Ceylonzimt, *m.* Ceylon cinnamon.

Chagrin, *m.* shagreen.

Chamäleon, *n.* chameleon; chameleon mineral (potassium manganate). -lösung, *f.* potassium permanganate solution.

Chamotte, etc. = Schamotte, etc.

Champagner, *m.* champagne. -weisse, *f.* a strongly foaming pale beer.

changierend, *a.* changeable, shot (fabrics).

Chappeseide, *f.* spun silk.

charakterisieren, *v.t.* characterize.

charakteristisch, *a.* characteristic.

chargieren, *v.t.* charge.

Charpie, *f.* lint.

Chaulmoogra-öl, Chaulmugra-öl, *n.* chaulmoogra oil. -säure, *f.* chaulmoogric acid.

Chaussee, *f.* highway.

Chef, *m.* chief, head, principal.

Cheiranthussäure, *f.* cheiranthic acid.

chem., *abbrev.* (chemisch) chemical.

Chemiatrie, *f.* chemiatry, iatrochemistry.

Chemie, *f.* chemistry.

Chemikalien, *n.pl.* chemicals. -handel, *m.* trade in chemicals.

Chemiker, *m.* chemist. -stelle, *f.* position of chemist.

chemisch, *a.* chemical.—*adv.* chemically.

Chemisch-blau, *n.* chemic blue (indigo extract). -gelb, *n.* patent yellow, Cassel yellow (lead oxychloride). -grün, *n.* sap green. -rot, *n.* Venetian red.

chemisch-rein, *a.* chemically pure. -technologisch, *a.* pertaining to chemical technology, chemico-technological.

Chemismus, *m.* chemism.

chemotaktisch, *a.* chemotactic.

-chen. little, small, -kin, -let.

Chesterkäse, *m.* Cheshire cheese.

Chibouharz, *n.* cachibou.

**Chiffer, Chiffre,** *f.* cipher.

**chilenisch,** *a.* Chilean.

**Chin-.** quin- (as in Chinin, Chinidin, etc.).

**China,** *f.* cinchona, Peruvian bark. **-alkaloid,** *n.* cinchona alkaloid. **-basen,** *f.pl.* cinchona bases, quinine bases. **-baum,** *m.* cinchona tree.

**chinabaumartig,** *a.* cinchonaceous.

**Chin-acetophenon,** *n.* quinacetophenone. **-acridin,** *n.* quinacridine. **-acridon,** *n.* quinacridone.

**China-eisenwein,** *m.* (*Pharm.*) bitter wine of iron. **-gerbsäure,** *f.* quinotannic acid.

**Chinaldin,** *n.* quinaldine. **-säure,** *f.* quinaldic acid.

**Chin-alizarin,** *n.* quinalizarin. **-amin,** *n.* quinamine.

**China-rinde,** *f.* cinchona bark, Peruvian bark. **-rindensäure,** *f.* quinic acid. **-rot,** *n.* cinchona red.

**chinasauer,** *a.* of or combined with quinic acid, quinate of.

**China-säure,** *f.* quinic acid. **-silber,** *n.* China silver (a plated alloy).

**Chinäthylin,** *n.* quinethyline.

**China-tinktur,** *f.* tincture of cinchona. **-toxin,** *n.* cinchona toxin. **-wein,** *m.* quinine wine. **-wurzel,** *f.* chinaroot.

**Chin-azolin,** *n.* quinazoline. **-azolon,** *n.* quinazolone. **-dolin,** *n.* quindoline.

**Chinen,** *n.* quinene.

**chinesisch,** *a.* Chinese.

**Chinesisch-grün,** *n.* Chinese green, lokao. **-rot,** *n.* Chinese red (basic lead chromate).

**Chinetum,** *n.* quinetum.

**Chin-hydrin,** *n.* quinhydrine. **-hydron,** *n.* quinhydrone. **-icin,** *n.* quinicine.

**Chinid,** *n.* quinide.

**Chinidin,** *n.* quinidine.

**chinieren,** *v.t.* weave or print chiné, cloud.

**Chinin,** *n.* quinine.

**Chinindolin,** *n.* quinindoline.

**Chinin-eisen, -eisencitrat,** *n.* citrate of iron and quinine. **-säure,** *f.* quininic acid. **-wein,** *m.* quinine wine.

**Chinisatin,** *n.* quinisatin.

**Chinit,** *n.* quinitol, quinite.

**Chinizarin,** *n.* quinizarin.

**Chino-.** quino-.

**chinoid,** *a.* quinoid, quinoidal.

**Chinoidin,** *n.* quinoidine.

**Chinol,** *n.* quinol.

**Chinolin,** *n.* quinoline. **-blau,** *n.* quinoline blue. **-gelb,** *n.* quinoline yellow. **-ium,** *n.* quinolinium. **-rot,** *n.* quinoline red. **-säure,** *f.* quinolinic acid.

**Chin-olizin,** *n.* quinolizine. **-olon,** *n.* quinolone. **-omethan,** *n.* quinomethan, quinomethane.

**Chinon,** *n.* quinone.

**Chino-pyran,** *n.* quinopyran. **-pyridin,** *n.* quinopyridine. **-sol,** *n.* (*Pharm.*) quinosol, chinosol. **-tin,** *n.* quinotine. **-toxin,** *n.* quinotoxin. **-tropin,** *n.* quinotropin.

**Chinova-bitter,** *n.* quinova bitter (quinovin). **-säure,** *f.* quinovic acid.

**Chin-ovin,** *n.* quinovin. **-ovose,** *f.* quinovose. **-oxalin,** *n.* quinoxaline.

**Chinoyl,** *n.* quinoyl.

**Chinuclidin,** *n.* quinuclidine.

**Chiretta,** *f.* chirata.

**Chirurg,** *m.* surgeon.

**Chirurgie,** *f.* surgery.

**chirurgisch,** *a.* surgical.

**Chlf.,** *abbrev.* chloroform.

**Chlor,** *n.* chlorine.

**Chlor-.** of or combined with chlorine, chloro- (as *Chlorbenzoesäure*, chlorobenzoic acid), chloride of (as *Chlorzink*, zinc chloride).

**chlorähnlich,** *a.* like chlorine, chlorinous.

**Chlor-alaun,** *m.* chloralum. **-alkalien,** *n.pl.* alkali-metal chlorides. **-aluminium,** *n.* aluminum chloride. **-ammon,** *m.* ammonium chloride. **-ammonium,** *n.* ammonium chloride. **-amyl,** *n.* amyl chloride. **-antimon,** *n.* antimony chloride. **-arsenik,** *n.* chloride of arsenic. **-arseniklösung,** *f.* (*Pharm.*) solution of arsenious acid, hydrochloric solution of arsenic.

**chlorartig,** *a.* like chlorine, chlorinous.

**Chlorat,** *n.* chlorate. **-chlor,** *n.* chlorine in the form of chlorate.

**Chlor-äther,** *m.* chloric ether (old name for ethylene chloride). **-äthyl,** *n.* ethyl chloride, chloroethane. **-äthylen,** *n.* ethylene chloride. **-äthyliden,** *n.* ethylidene chloride.

**Chloration,** *f.* chlorination.—*n.* chlorate ion.

**Chloratsprengstoff,** *m.* chlorate explosive.

**Chlor-azetyl,** *n.* acetyl chloride. **-barium, -baryum,** *n.* barium chloride. **-baryum-lösung,** *f.* barium chloride solution. **-benzol,** *n.* chlorobenzene. **-benzyl,** *n.* benzyl chloride. **-bestimmung,** *f.* chlorine determination. **-blei,** *n.* lead chloride. **-bleiche,** *f.* chlorine bleaching. **-bleispat,** *m.* phosgenite. **-bor,** *n.* boron chloride. **-brom,** *n.* bromine chloride. **-bromsilber,** *n.* silver chlorobromide, (*Min.*) embolite. **-calcium,** *n.* calcium chloride. **-calciumrohr,** *n.*, **-calciumröhre,** *f.* calcium chloride tube. **-chrom,** *n.* chromium chloride, specif. chromic chloride. **-chromsäure,** *f.* chlorochromic acid. **-cyan,** *n.* cyanogen chloride.

**chlorecht,** *a.* fast to chlorine.

**Chloreisen,** *n.* iron chloride, specif. ferric chloride.

**chloren,** *v.t.* chlore, chlorinate; (*Bleaching*) gas.

**Chlor-entwickler,** *m.* chlorine generator. **-entwicklung,** *f.* evolution or generation of chlorine. **-entwicklungsapparat,** *m.* chlorine generator. **-essigsäure,** *f.* chloroacetic acid.

**chlorfrei,** *a.* free from chlorine, chlorine-free.

**Chlor-gas,** *n.* chlorine gas. **-gehalt,** *m.* chlorine content. **-geruch,** *m.* chlorine odor. **-gold,** *n.* gold chloride, specif. auric chloride. **-goldnatrium,** *n.* sodium chloroaurate.

**chlorhaltig,** *a.* containing chlorine.

**Chlor-hydrat,** *n.* hydrochloride; chlorine hydrate. **-hydrin,** *n.* chlorohydrin.

**Chlorid,** *n.* chloride (esp. an -ic chloride, as contrasted with Chlorür). **-chlor,** *n.* chlorine in the form of chloride.

**chloridhaltig,** *a.* containing chloride(s).

**chlorierbar,** *a.* capable of chlorination.

**chlorieren,** *v.t.* chlorinate; (*Bleaching*) chemick.

**Chlorierer,** *m.* chlorinator.

**Chlorierung,** *f.* chlorination.

**chlorig,** *a.* chlorous.—**chlorige Säure,** chlorous acid.

**chlorigsauer,** *a.* of or combined with chlorous acid, chlorite of.

**Chlorigsäure,** *f.* chlorous acid.

**Chlorion,** *n.* chlorine ion.

**Chlorit,** *n.* chlorite. **-spat,** *m.* spathic chlorite, foliated chlorite.

**Chlor-jod,** *n.* iodine chloride, specif. iodine monochloride. **-kali,** *n.* chloride of potash (potassium hypochlorite); potassium chloride. **-kalilösung,** *f.* (*Pharm.*) solution of chlorinated potassa, Javelle water. **-kalium,** *n.* potassium chloride.

**Chlorkalk,** *m.* chloride of lime, bleaching powder. **-bad,** *n.* (*Bleaching*) chemic vat. **-flüssigkeit, -lösung,** *f.* (*Pharm.*) solution of chlorinated lime. (bleaching powder solution). **-kufe,** *f.* chemic vat. **-lauge,** *f.* bleaching-powder liquor.

**Chlorkalzium,** *n.* calcium chloride. **-rohr,** *n.*, **-röhre,** *f.* calcium chloride tube. **-röhrchen,** *n.* (small) calcium chloride tube.

**Chlorknallgas,** *n.* chlorine detonating gas (an explosive mixture of chlorine and hydrogen).

**Chlorkohlen-oxyd,** *n.* carbonyl chloride. **-oxydäther,** *m.* ethyl chlorocarbonate. **-säure,** *f.* chlorocarbonic acid. **-stoff,** *m.* carbon chloride, carbon tetrachloride (sometimes with the adj. vierfach).

**Chlor-kupfer,** *n.* copper chloride. **-lauge,** *f.* = Chlornatron. **-magnesium,** *n.* magnesium chloride. **-mangan,** *n.* manganese chloride. **-messer,** *m.* chlorometer. **-messung,** *f.* chlorometry. **-metall,** *n.* metallic chloride. **-metalloid,** *n.* chloride of a metalloid. **-methyl,** *n.* methyl chloride. **-methylat,** *m.*

methochloride. **-methylen,** *n.* methylene chloride. **-natrium,** *n.* sodium chloride. **-natron,** *n.* chloride of soda (sodium hypochlorite). **-natronlösung,** *f.* (*Pharm.*) solution of chlorinated soda, Labarraque's solution.

**Chloro-benzil,** *n.* dichlorobenzil, $C_6H_5COCCl_2$-$C_6H_5$. **-benzol,** *n.* benzal chloride.

**chloroformieren,** *v.t.* chloroform.

**Chlorojodid,** *n.* chloro-iodide, iodochloride.

**chlorometrisch,** *a.* chlorometric.

**Chlor-oxyd,** *n.* chlorine oxide. **-phosphor,** *m.* phosphorus chloride. **-pikrin,** *n.* chloropicrin. **-platin,** *n.* platinic chloride. **-quecksilber,** *n.* mercury chloride (either one). **-räucherung,** *f.* chlorine fumigation.

**chlorsauer,** *a.* of or combined with chloric acid, chlorate of.

**Chlor-säure,** *f.* chloric acid. **-säureanhydrid,** *n.* chloric anhydride. **-schwefel,** *n.* sulfur chloride. **-silber,** *n.* silver chloride. **-silicium,** *n.* silicon tetrachloride. **-soda,** *f.* = Chlornatron. **-stickstoff,** *m.* nitrogen chloride. **-strom,** *m.* stream of chlorine. **-strontium,** *n.* strontium chloride. **-sulfonsäure,** *f.* chlorosulfonic acid. **-toluol,** *n.* chlorotoluene. **-übertrager,** *m.* chlorine carrier.

**Chlorür,** *n.* (-ous) chloride, (formerly) protochloride. (Used of a metal in its lower valence, as *Eisenchlorür,* ferrous chloride.)

**Chlor-verbindung,** *f.* chlorine compound. **-wasser,** *n.* chlorine water.

**Chlorwasserstoff,** *m.* hydrogen chloride; hydrochloric acid. **-äther,** *m.* ethyl chloride.

**chlorwasserstoffsauer,** *a.* of or combined with hydrochloric acid, chloride (or hydrochloride) of.

**Chlor-wasserstoffsäure,** *f.* hydrochloric acid. **-wismut,** *n.* bismuth (tri)chloride. **-zink,** *n.* zinc chloride. **-zinn,** *n.* tin chloride. **-zinnbad,** *n.* tin-chloride bath. **-zyan,** *n.* cyanogen chloride.

**Chm.,** *abbrev.* (Chemie) chemistry.

**Chokolade,** *f.* chocolate.

**Cholalsäure,** *f.* cholalic acid (cholic acid).

**Cholämie,** *f.* (*Med.*) cholemia.

**Cholecamphersäure,** *f.* cholecamphoric acid (choloidanic acid).

**Choleinsäure,** *f.* choleic acid, choleinic acid.

**Cholesterin,** *n.* cholesterol, cholesterin. **-säure,** *f.* cholesteric acid (cholesterol).

**Cholin,** *n.* choline.

**Cholsäure,** *f.* cholic acid.

**Chondron-insäure,** *f.* chondroninic acid. **-säure,** *f.* chondronic acid.

**Chor,** *m.* chorus; choir.

**Chorde,** *f.* chord.

**Christdorn,** *m.* holly.

**Christophs-kraut,** *n.,* **-wurz,** *f.* baneberry (*Actaea*).

**Christ-palmöl,** *n.* castor oil. **-wurz,** *f.* black hellebore; spring pheasant's-eye (*Adonis vernalis*).

**Chrom,** *n.* chromium; chrome. **-alaun,** *m.* chrome alum.

**Chromat,** *n.* chromate.—**saures —,** dichromate.

**chromatisch,** *a.* chromatic.

**Chrom-bad,** *n.* chrome bath. **-beize,** *f.* chrome mordant.

**chrombeizen,** *v.t.* chrome-mordant.

**Chrom-blei,** *n.* lead chromate. **-bleispat,** *m.* (*Min.*) crocoite. **-chlorid,** *n.* chromic chloride. **-chlorür,** *n.* chromous chloride.

**chromecht,** *a.* (*Dyeing*) fast to chrome (potassium or sodium dichromate).

**Chrom-echtschwarz,** *n.* fast chrome black. **-eisen, -eisenerz,** *n.,* **-eisenstein,** *m.* chrome iron ore, chromite.

**chromenthaltend,** *a.* = chromhaltig.

**Chrom-erz,** *n.* chromium ore. **-farbe,** *f.* chrome color. **-fluorid,** *n.* chromic fluoride.

**chromgar,** *a.* chrome-tanned.

**Chrom-gehalt,** *m.* chromium content. **-gelatine,** *f.* chromatized gelatin, bichromated gelatin. **-gelb,** *n.* chrome yellow (lead chromate); Cologne yellow (lead chromate and sulfate). **-gerberei, -gerbung,** *f.* chrome tanning. **-glimmer,** *m.* chrome mica. **-grün,** *n.* chrome green.

**chromhaltig,** *a.* containing chromium, chromiferous.

**Chrom-hydroxyd,** *n.* chromic hydroxide. **-hydroxydul,** *n.* chromous hydroxide.

**Chromi-.** chromic. **-chlorid,** *n.* chromic chloride. **-cyanwasserstoffsäure,** *f.* chromicyanic acid.

**Chromierartikel,** *m.* (*Calico*) chrome style.

**chromieren,** *v.t.* chrome.

**Chromierfarbstoff,** *m.* chrome dye.

**Chromi-hydroxyd,** *n.* chromic hydroxide. **-oxyd,** *n.* chromic oxide. **-rhodanwasserstoffsäure,** *f.* chromithiocyanic acid. **-salz,** *n.* chromic salt. **-sulfat,** *n.* chromic sulfate. **-sulfocyansäure,** *f.* chromithiocyanic acid. **-verbindung,** *f.* chromic compound.

**Chrom-kali,** *n.* potassium dichromate. **-karbid,** *n.* chromium carbide. **-leder,** *n.* chrome leather. **-natron,** *n.* sodium chromate. **-nickelstahl,** *m.* chrome-nickel steel.

**Chromo-.** chromous. **-chlorid,** *n.* chromous chloride. **-hydroxyd,** *n.* chromous hydroxide. **-ion,** *n.* chromous ion.

**Chromolyse,** *f.* (*Biol.*) chromatolysis, chromolysis.

**Chromooxyd,** *n.* chromous oxide.

**chromophor,** *a.* chromophoric, chromophore, chromophorous.

**Chromoverbindung,** *f.* chromous compound.

**Chromoxychlorid,** *n.* chromium oxychloride (chromyl chloride).

**Chromoxyd,** *n.* chromium oxide, specif. chromic oxide. **-hydrat,** *n.* chromium hydroxide, specif. chromous hydroxide. **-natron,** *n.* sodium chromite. **-salz,** *n.* chromic salt.

**Chromoxydul,** *n.* chromous oxide.

**Chromoxydul-.** chromous. **-verbindung,** *f.* chromous compound.

**Chrom-rindleder,** *n.* chromed neat's leather. **-rot,** *n.* chrome red. **-salpetersäure,** *f.* chromonitric acid. **-salz,** *n.* chromium salt; chromate.

**chromsauer,** *a.* of or combined with chromic acid, chromate of.—**chromsaures Kali,** potassium chromate.—**doppelt (rotes, saures) chromsaures Kali,** potassium dichromate.

**Chromsäure,** *f.* chromic acid. **-anhydrid,** *n.* chromic anhydride. **-gemisch,** *n.* chromic acid mixture. **-lösung,** *f.* chromic acid solution. **-salz,** *n.* salt of chromic acid, chromate.

**Chrom-schwefelsäure,** *f.* chromosulfuric acid. **-silber,** *n.* silver chromate. **-stahl,** *m.* chrome steel, chromium steel. **-sulfür,** *n.* chromous sulfide. **-verbindung,** *f.* chromium compound.

**chronisch,** *a.* chronic.

**Chrysatropasäure,** *f.* chrysatropic acid.

**Chrysenchinon, Chrysochinon,** *n.* chrysenequinone, chrysoquinone.

**Chrysokoll,** *n.* chrysocolla.

**Chrysolith,** *m.* (*Min.*) chrysolite.

**Chylus,** *m.* chyle.

**Ciba-blau,** *n.* ciba blue. **-rot,** *n.* ciba red.

**Cibebe,** *f.* = Zibebe.

**Cichorie,** *f.* chicory.

**Cider-branntwein,** *m.* cider brandy, apple brandy. **-essig,** *m.* cider vinegar. **-trester,** *m.pl.* cider marc. **-wein,** *m.* (fermented) cider.

**Cie.,** *abbrev.* (Compagnie, Gesellschaft) Company, Co.

**cimolisch,** *a.* Cimolian.—**cimolische Erde,** Cimolian earth, cimolite.

**Cinchoninsäure,** *f.* cinchoninic acid.

**Cinchonsäure,** *f.* cinchonic acid.

**circa, cirka,** *adv.* about.

**cirkulieren,** *v.i.* circulate.

**Cis-körper,** *m.* cis substance. **-stellung,** *f.* cis position.

**Citat,** *n.* citation, quotation.

**citieren,** *v.t.* quote, cite; summon.

**Citrat, Citrone,** etc. = Zitrat, Zitrone, etc.

**civil,** *a.* civil; moderate.

**claircieren,** v.t. (Sugar), clear, purge.

**Cnidiumsäure,** f. cnidic acid.

**coag-.** see koag-.

**Coaks,** m. & m.pl. coke.

**Coca-blätter,** n.pl. coca leaves. **-säure,** f. cocaic acid. **-wein,** m. (Pharm.) wine of coca.

**Coccinsäure,** f. coccinic acid.

**Cochenille,** f. cochineal.

**Cochenillen-farbstoff,** m. cochineal dye. **-rot,** n. cochineal red. **-scharlach,** m. cochineal scarlet. **-schildlaus,** f. cochineal insect.

**Cochenillesäure,** f. cochenillic acid.

**Cocos,** etc. see Kokos, etc.

**Codöl,** n. cod-liver oil.

**Coff-.** caff-.

**Coffearin,** n. caffearine.

**Coffein,** n. caffeine.

**cohobieren,** v.t. cohobate.

**Colanuss,** f. cola nut.

**Colatur,** f. filtrate.

**Cölestin,** m. celestite, celestine.

**colieren,** etc. =kolieren, etc.

**Collodium,** etc. see Kollodium, etc.

**Colombin,** n. columbin.

**Colombowürzel,** f. calumba root, calumba.

**Colonne,** f. column.

**colorimetrisch,** a. colorimetric.

**Columbasäure,** f. columbic acid (from calumba).

**Columbeisen,** n. (Min.) columbite.

**Columbiakopalinsäure,** f. columbiacopalinic acid.

**Columbiakopalsäure,** f. columbiacopalic acid.

**Columbien,** n. Colombia.

**Columbowurzel,** f. calumba root, calumba.

**Colzaöl,** n. colza oil.

**com-.** see also kom-.

**combinieren,** v.t. combine.

**Commis,** m. clerk.

**comprimieren,** v.t. compress.

**Comptoir,** n. office, counting house.

**conc-.** see konz-.

**Condens-.** see Kondens-.

**conditionieren,** v.t. condition.

**conglobieren,** v.t. heap up.

**Congo-farbe,** f. Congo color, Congo dye. **-farbstoff,** m. Congo dye. **-gelb,** n. Congo yellow. **-gummi,** n. Congo rubber. **-papier,** n. Congo paper. **-rot,** n. Congo red.

**Coniin,** n. conine, coniine.

**Conimaharz,** n. conima resin, conima.

**Conserv-.** see Konserv-.

**Conspersasäure,** f. conspersic acid.

**constatieren,** v.t. ascertain, verify.

**Conto,** n. account.

**Conus,** m. cone.

**Copaiva-balsam,** m. copaiba (balsam). **-öl,** n. oil of copaiba. **-säure,** f. copaivic acid.

**Cör-.** =cer-.

**Corozonuss,** f. ivory nut.

**corr.,** abbrev. (corrigiert) corrected.

**corrigieren,** v.t. correct.

**corrodieren,** v.t. & i. corrode.

**Cörulein,** n. cerulein.

**Cöruleum,** n. ceruleum.

**Cörulignol,** n. cerulignol.

**Cörulignon,** n. cerulignone.

**Cosinus,** m. (Math.) cosine.

**Costussäure,** f. costic acid, costusic acid.

**Cotorinde,** f. coto bark.

**Cotta,** f. = Deul.

**Cottonöl,** n. cottonseed oil.

**Couleur,** f. color; caramel, burnt sugar; dark, coarse smalt; (pl.) fancy goods, colored goods.

**coupieren,** v.t. cut, cut short.

**Courant,** n. currency; price list.

**Couvert,** n. envelope; cover.

**Crackbenzin,** n. benzine or gasoline produced by " cracking."

**cracken,** v.t. crack (as petroleum).

**Cracken,** n. crackene; cracking (of oils). **-chinon,** n. crackenequinone.

**Crack-kessel,** m. cracking retort. **-prozess,** m. cracking process.

**Crackung,** f. cracking (of oils).

**Crackverfahren,** n. cracking process.

**Creme,** f. cream.

**creme, cremefarben,** a. cream-colored.

**Cremor tartari.** cream of tartar.

**Cristall,** etc. = Kristall, etc.

**Croceïnscharlach,** m. crocein scarlet.

**Croton-harz,** n. croton resin. **-öl,** n. croton oil. **-säure,** f. crotonic acid.

**Crystall-.** = Kristall-.

**Cubeben,** n. cubebene.—f.pl. cubebs. **-öl,** n. cubeb oil. **-pfeffer,** m. cubebs. **-säure,** f. cubebic acid.

**Cuiteseide,** f. boiled-off silk.

**Cultur, Cultur-.** see Kultur, Kultur-.

**Cumalin,** n. coumalin (1.2-pyrone). **-säure,** f. coumalic (or cumalic) acid.

**Cumar-.** coumar- (or cumar-).

**Cumarinsäure,** f. coumarinic (or cumarinic) acid.

**Cumaronharz,** n. coumarone resin.

**Cumarsäure,** f. coumaric (or cumaric) acid.

**Cumin-öl,** n. cumin oil. **-samen,** m. cumin seed. **-säure,** f. cumic acid, cuminic acid.

**Cumo-chinol,** n. cumoquinol. **-chinon,** n. cumoquinone.

**Cumol,** n. cumene.

**Cupri-.** cupric. **-carbonat,** n. cupric carbonate. **-chlorid,** n. cupric chloride. **-oxalat,** n.

cupric oxalate. -oxyd, n. cupric oxide. -salz, n. cupric salt. -sulfat, n. cupric sulfate. -sulfid, n. cupric sulfide. -verbindung, f. cupric compound. -weinsäure, f. cupritartaric acid.

Cupro-. cuprous; cupro-. -chlorid, n. cuprous chloride. -mangan, n. cupromanganese. -oxyd, n. cuprous oxide. -verbindung, f. cuprous compound.

Curcuma, etc. see Kurkuma, etc.

curs-. see kurs-.

Cuskhygrin, n. cuscohygrine.

Cuskorinde, f. cusco bark.

Cutin-insäure, f. cutinic acid. -säure, f. cutic acid.

Cuvette, f. bulb; cell.

Cyan, n. cyanogen.

Cyan-. of or combined with cyanogen, cyano- (as Cyanpropionsäure, cyanopropionic acid), cyanide of (as Cyanammonium, ammonium cyanide). -alkali, n. alkali cyanide. -alkyl, n. alkyl cyanide.

Cyanamid-calcium, n. calcium cyanamide. -natrium, n. sodium cyanamide.

Cyanamido-dikohlensäure, f. cyanamidodicarboxylic acid. -kohlensäure, f. cyanamidocarboxylic acid (cyanocarbamic acid).

Cyanammonium, n. ammonium cyanide.

Cyanat, n. cyanate.

Cyan-äthyl, n. ethyl cyanide. -bad, n. cyanide bath. -baryum, n. barium cyanide. -benzol, n. cyanobenzene. -bromid, n. cyanogen bromide. -calcium, n. calcium cyanide. -chlorid, n. cyanogen chloride. -doppelsalz, n. double cyanide.

Cyaneisen, n. iron cyanide. -kalium, n. potassium ferrocyanide. -verbindung, f. iron cyanogen compound, specif. a ferrocyanide.

Cyanessigsäure, f. cyanoacetic acid. -gas, n. cyanogen gas. -gold, n. gold cyanide. -goldkalium, n. potassium auri- or aurocyanide.

cyanhaltig, a. containing cyanogen.

Cyanhydrin, n. cyanohydrin.

Cyanid, n. cyanide (esp. an -ic cyanide as contrasted with Cyanür).

cyanidfrei, a. cyanide-free.

Cyan-jodid, n. cyanogen iodide. -kali, n. potassium cyanide.

cyankalisch, a. potassium-cyanide.

Cyan-kalium, -kali, n. potassium cyanide. -kaliumlösung, f. potassium cyanide solution. -kobalt, m. cobalt cyanide. -kohlensäure, f. cyanocarbonic acid. -kupfer, n. copper cyanide. -laugerei, -laugung, f. cyaniding, cyanidation. -lösung, f. cyanide solution. -metall, n. metallic cyanide. -methyl, n. methyl cyanide. -natrium, n. sodium cyanide. -platin, n. platinum cyanide.

Cyanquecksilber, n. mercury cyanide. -kalium, n. mercury potassium cyanide. -oxyd, n. mercuric cyanide.

Cyansalz, n. cyanogen salt, cyanide.

cyansauer, a. of or combined with cyanic acid, cyanate of.

Cyan-säure, f. cyanic acid; cyano acid. -schlamm, m. cyanide sludge. -senföl, n. cyanomustard oil. -silber, n. silver cyanide. -stickstoff, m. cyanonitride. -toluol, n. cyanotoluene.

Cyanür, n. (-ous) cyanide. Cf. Cyanid.

Cyanur-. cyanuric; cyanuryl. -säure, f. cyanuric acid.

Cyan-verbindung, f. cyanogen compound. -vergiftung, f. cyanogen poisoning. -wasserstoff, m. hydrogen cyanide; hydrocyanic acid.

cyanwasserstoffsauer, a. of or combined with hydrocyanic acid, cyanide of.

Cyan-wasserstoffsäure, f. hydrocyanic acid. -zink, n. zinc cyanide.

cyclisch, a. cyclic.

Cyclisieren, n. cyclization.

Cyclogeraniumsäure, f. cyclogeranic acid.

cylindern, etc. see zylindern, etc.

Cymol, n. cymene.

Cyper-. cypress; Cyprus, Cyprian; copper.

Cypern, n. Cyprus.

Cypervitriol, m. (Old Chem.) blue vitriol.

Cypressen-nuss, f. cypress cone. -öl, n. cypress oil.

cyprisch, a. Cyprian.—cyprischer Vitriol, copper sulfate.

cystenartig, a. cyst-like.

Cystenflüssigkeit, f. cystic fluid.

cystenförmig, a. = cystiform.

Cystinuriker, m. one who has cystinuria.

C.Z., abbrev. (Cellulosezahl) cellulose number; Chemisches Zentralblatt.

# D

**d.,** *abbrev.* (der, die, das) the, of the, etc.; (dieser, dieses, etc.) this, of this, etc.

**D.,** *abbrev.* (Dichte) density, specific gravity; (Deutsch) German.

**da,** *adv.* there; present; then.—*conj.* when, as, while, since.

**D.A.,** *abbrev.* (Deutsches Arzneibuch) German Pharmacopeia.

**D.A.-B.,** *abbrev.* (Deutsches Apothekerbuch) German Dispensatory.

**dabei,** *adv.* thereby, there, near, besides; therein.

**Dach,** *n.* roof; dome (of a boiler); house. **-bau, -belag,** *m.* roofing. **-blech,** *n.* sheet metal for roofing. **-boden,** *m.* loft. **-deckerei, -deckung,** *f.* roofing.

**Dachel, Dächel,** *m.* (*Metal.*) lump, bloom.

**Dach-filz,** *m.* roofing felt. **-kammer,** *f.* attic, garret. **-kohle,** *f.* upper coal. **-pappe,** *f.* composition roofing, roofing paper. **-pfanne,** *f.* pantile.

**Dachs,** *m.* badger; dachshund.

**Dachschiefer,** *m.* roofing slate.

**Dächsel,** *m.* adze.

**Dachsfett,** *n.* badger fat.

**Dachstein,** *m.* tile, slate; bituminous shale; (*Mining*) roof rock.

**dachte,** *pret.* of denken.

**Dachung,** *f.* roofing.

**Dach-wurz,** *f.* common houseleek. **-ziegel,** *m.* (roofing) tile. **-ziegelei,** *f.* tilery, tile kiln.

**dad. gek.,** *abbrev.* (dadurch gekennzeichnet) thereby characterized.

**dadurch,** *adv.* thereby, thus; thru this, by this, by that, in this way.

**dafür,** *adv.* therefor, for it; instead of it.

**dagegen,** *adv.* against it; in comparison; in return.—*conj.* on the other hand; whereas.

**daheim,** *adv.* at home.

**daher,** *adv.* hence, thence, therefore.

**dahin,** *adv.* thither, there, thereto; away, over, gone; along.

**dahingestellt,** *a.* undecided, uncertain.

**dahinstehen,** *v.i.* remain uncertain.

**dahinter,** *adv.* behind it; after that.

**damalig,** *a.* at or of that time, then being.

**damals,** *adv.* at that time, then.

**damasc-.** see damasz-.

**Damast,** *m.* damask. **-stahl,** *m.* damask steel, Damascus steel. **-stoff,** *m.* damask (the fabric).

**damaszener,** *a.* Damascene, Damascus, damask.

**damaszieren,** *v.t.* damascene, damask.

**Damaszierung,** *f.* damascening.

**Dame,** *f.* lady; queen (at cards); king (checkers).

**Damen-brett,** *n.* checkerboard. **-spiel,** *n.* checkers, draughts.

**Damhirschfell,** *n.* buckskin.

**damit,** *adv.* therewith, with, by it.—*conj.* in order that.

**Damm,** *m.* dam, dike, bank; (*Med.*) perineum.

**Dammar-firnis,** *m.* dammar varnish. **-harz,** *n.* dammar resin, dammar.

**dämmen,** *v.t.* dam, dam up, stop up; curb.

**Dammerde,** *f.* mold, humus; (*Founding*) pit sand.

**Dämmerung,** *f.* twilight, dusk; dawn.

**Dammgrube,** *f.* foundry pit.

**Dampf,** *m.* vapor; steam; fume, smoke.— **direkter —,** live steam.—**indirekter —,** exhaust steam.—**stickender —,** choke damp.

**dampfartig,** *a.* vaporous, vapory.

**Dampf-artikel,** *m.* (*Calico*) steam style. **-auflösung,** *f.* volatilization. **-bad,** *n.* steam bath; vapor bath. **-betrieb,** *m.* steam working, steam drive. **-bildung,** *f.* formation of vapor; formation of steam. **-blase,** *f.* bubble of vapor or steam; still heated by steam. **-blasen,** *n.* injecting of steam, distilling with steam. **-bleicherei,** *f.* steam bleaching; steam bleachery. **-chlor,** *n.* steam chemicking. **-darre,** *f.* steam kiln.

**dampfdicht,** *a.* steam-tight, vapor-tight.

**Dampf-dichte, -dichtigkeit,** *f.* vapor density; density of steam. **-dichtung,** *f.* steam packing. **-druck,** *m.* vapor pressure; steam pressure; steam printing. **-druckerei,** *f.* steam printing. **-druckerniedrigung,** *f.* vapor pressure lowering. **-druckmesser,** *m.* manometer; steam gage.

**dampfecht,** *a.* fast to steaming.

**dampfen,** *v.i.* give off vapor or steam, steam; evaporate; fume, smoke.

**dämpfen,** *v.t.* damp, smother; put out (fire); subdue (color or sound); treat with steam, steam, stew; evaporate (fruit).

**Dampf-entwässerer,** *m.* steam desiccator, steam drier. **-entwickelung,** *f.* evolution of vapor; steam generation. **-entwickler,** *m.* steam generator.

77

**Dampfer,** *m.* steamer, steamboat.

**Dämpfer,** *m.* damper; steamer, steam cooker.

**Dampf-erzeuger,** *m.* steam generator, boiler. **-farbe,** *f.* (*Dyeing*) steam color. **-färberei,** *f.* steam printing. **-fass,** *n.* steam drum.

**dampfförmig,** *a.* in the form of vapor or steam, vaporous.

**Dampf-gas,** *n.* dry steam, superheated steam. **-gebläse,** *n.* steam blast; steam blower. **-gummi,** *n.* dextrin. **-heizrohr,** *n.* steam (heating) pipe. **-heizung,** *f.* steam heating. **-holzschliff,** *m.* steamed mechanical wood pulp. **-hülle,** *f.* steam jacket; vaporous envelope.

**dampfig,** *a.* vapory, steamy.

**Dampfkanal,** *m.* steam pipe; steam port.

**Dampfkessel,** *m.* steam boiler. **-anlage,** *f.* steam boiler plant, steam plant. **-bekleidung,** *f.* boiler covering or casing. **-blech,** *n.* boiler plate. **-speisung,** *f.* steam boiler feed.

**Dampfkoch-.** steam boiling. **-apparat, -kessel, -topf,** *m.* steam cooker.

**Dampf-kochung,** *f.* steam cooking. **-kolben,** *m.* steam piston. **-kraft,** *f.* steam power. **-leitung,** *f.* steam piping; conduction of vapor or steam. **-leitungsrohr,** *n.* steam pipe. **-mantel,** *m.* steam jacket. **-maschine,** *f.* steam engine. **-messer,** *m.* manometer; steam gage.

**Dämpfmittel,** *n.* neutralizer (for acids).

**Dampf-mühle,** *f.* steam mill. **-ofen,** *m.* steam oven; steam furnace. **-phase,** *f.* vapor phase. **-probe,** *f.* steam test. **-rohr,** *n.*, **-röhre,** *f.* steam pipe. **-rohrleitung,** *f.* steam piping. **-schale,** *f.* evaporating dish or basin. **-schiff,** *n.* steamboat. **-schlange,** *f.* steam coil. **-schmierung,** *f.* steam lubrication. **-schwarz,** *n.* (*Dyeing*) steam black. **-schwelung,** *f.* destructive distillation with steam. **-spannung,** *f.* vapor tension; steam tension. **-strahl,** *m.* steam jet; steam blast. **-topf,** *m.* (steam) digester, autoclave; steam sterilizer. **-trichter,** *m.* steam funnel. **-trockenapparat, -trockner,** *m.* steam drier. **-trockenschrank,** *m.* steam drying oven. **-turbine,** *f.* steam turbine. **-überdruck,** *m.* excess vapor pressure; excess steam pressure. **-überhitzer,** *m.* steam superheater.

**Dämpfung,** *f.* damping, etc. (see dämpfen).

**Dämpfungsvorrichtung,** *f.* damping device, damper.

**Dampf-ventil,** *n.* steam valve. **-verbrauch,** *m.* steam consumption. **-wagen,** *m.* steam car; locomotive. **-wärme,** *f.* heat of vaporization; vaporizing temperature. **-wäscherei,** *f.* steam laundry. **-wassertopf,** *m.* steam trap. **-weg,** *m.* =Dampfkanal. **-zucker,** *m.* sugar refined with steam. **-zuführung,**

**-zuleitung,** *f.* steam supply. **-zylinderöl,** *n.* steam cylinder oil.

**danach,** *adv.* after that, thereupon, for it, accordingly.

**daneben,** *adv.* near it, beside it, besides.

**Dänemark,** *n.* Denmark.

**Dank,** *m.* thanks; reward.

**dankbar,** *a.* thankful; acceptable.

**danken,** *v.t.* thank.

**dann,** *adv.* then.

**D'Anversblau,** *n.* Antwerp blue.

**D.Ap.** *abbrev.* (Deutsches Apothekerbuch) German Dispensatory.

**daran,** *adv.* thereon, thereat, about it, of it, in it.

**darangeben,** *v.t.* give up.

**darauf,** *adv.* thereupon, thereon, afterward.

**darauffolgend,** *a.* following, subsequent.

**Darauflassen,** *n.* (*Brewing*) doubling.

**daraus,** *adv.* therefrom, thence, out of that, of it.

**darben,** *v.i.* starve.

**darbieten,** *v.t.* present, offer.

**darein,** *adv.* therein, thereinto, in there.

**darf,** *pr. 1 & 3 sing.* of dürfen.

**darin,** *adv.* therein, in it.

**darlegen,** *v.t.* exhibit, show, display; explain; lay down.

**Darlehen,** *n.* (*Com.*) loan.

**Darm,** *m.* gut, intestine.—**blinder —,** caecum. —**dicker —,** colon.—**dünner —,** small intestine.—**gerader —,** rectum.—**langer —,** ileum.—**leerer —,** jejunum.

**Darm-bein,** *n.* ilium. **-fäule,** *f.* dysentery. **-gas,** *n.* intestinal gas. **-gicht,** *f.* ileus. **-gift,** *n.* enterotoxin. **-haut,** *f.* intestinal coat. **-inhalt,** *m.* intestinal contents. **-kanal,** *n.* intestinal canal. **-kot,** *m.* feces. **-netz,** *n.* omentum. **-ruhr,** *f.* dysentery. **-saft,** *m.* intestinal juice. **-saite,** *f.* catgut. **-schlauch,** *m.* gut. **-stein,** *m.* enterolith. **-stiel,** *m.* vitelline duct. **-tiere,** *n.pl.* metazoa. **-verdauung,** *f.* intestinal digestion. **-wand,** *f.* intestinal wall.

**darnach,** *adv.* =danach.

**Darr-arbeit,** *f.* (*Metal.*) liquation. **-boden,** *m.* drying floor, kiln floor. **-brett,** *n.* drying board.

**Darre,** *f.* drying, kiln-drying; drying room or kiln; (*Brewing*) malt kiln; (*Metal.*) liquation hearth.

**darreichen,** *v.t.* offer; administer (drugs).

**darren,** *v.t.* dry, kiln-dry; kiln; (*Metal.*) liquate; (*Metal.*) torrefy.

**Darr-fax,** *m.* (*Brewing*) kilnman. **-fläche,** *f.* drying surface, kiln surface. **-holz,** *n.* kiln-dried wood. **-kammer,** *f.* drying room. **-kupfer,** *n.* liquated copper. **-malz,** *n.* kiln-dried malt, cured malt. **-ofen,** *m.* drying

kiln, drying oven; (*Metal.*) liquation hearth.
-**raum**, *m.* kiln chamber. -**reife,** *f.* (*Brewing*)
kiln fitness. -**schrank**, *m.* drying cabinet,
drying oven. -**staub**, *m.* malt dust.

**Darrung,** *f.* drying, etc. (see darren).

**Darst.,** *abbrev.* (Darstellung) preparation.

**darstellbar**, *a.* capable of being prepared, etc.
(see darstellen).

**darstellen,** *v.t.* prepare; produce, make, manufacture; exhibit, display; present; represent;
describe.

**Darstellung,** *f.* preparation; production, manufacture; exhibition, display; description;
representation; (*Math.*) construction.

**Darstellungs-verfahren,** *n.* process of preparation or production. -**weise,** *f.* method of
preparation; manner of representation,
style.

**dartun,** *v.t.* prove; verify.

**darüber,** *adv.* over it, over there, about it,
more, meantime.

**darum,** *adv.* around it, about it, therefore.

**darunter,** *adv.* thereunder, under it, among
them, by it.

**das.** see der.

**Dasein,** *n.* presence; being, existence.

**daselbst,** *adv.* there, in that place, *ibidem.*

**dasjenige,** *pron.* see derjenige.

**dass,** *conj.* that.

**dastehen,** *v.i.* stand there; stand out.

**Daten,** *n.pl.* data; dates.

**datieren,** *v.t.* date.

**Dattel,** *f.* date. -**baum,** *m.* date tree, date
palm. -**pflaume,** *f.* persimmon, date plum.
-**wein,** *m.* date wine. -**zucker,** *m.* date sugar.

**Datum,** *n.* date; datum.

**Daube,** *f.* stave.

**Dauer,** *f.* duration; durability, permanence.

**Dauer-.** permanent, continuous, lasting, perennial. -**ausscheider,** *m.* (*Biol.*) chronic
carrier. -**beobachtung,** *f.* continuous observation. -**betrieb,** *m.* continuous operation. -**bier,** *n.* lager beer. -**bleiche,** *f.* continuous bleaching. -**bruch,** *m.* (*Mech.*)
fatigue fracture. -**entladung,** *f.* continuous
discharge. -**festigkeit,** *f.* durability; (*Mech.*)
endurance. -**gewächs,** *n.* perennial plant,
perennial.

**dauerhaft,** *a.* durable, lasting, permanent;
fast (colors); tough (leather).

**Dauer-haftigkeit,** *f.* durability, permanence.
-**hefe,** *f.* permanent yeast, zymin. -**magnet,**
*m.* permanent magnet. -**milch,** *f.* sterilized
milk; condensed milk.

**dauern,** *v.i.* last, continue, endure, keep.—
**dauernd,** *p.a.* lasting, permanent; perennial.

**Dauer-präparat,** *n.* permanent preparation.
-**prüfmaschine,** *f.* endurance testing ma-

chine. -**schlagfestigkeit,** *f.* (*Mech.*) resistance to repeated impact. -**spore,** *f.* resting
spore. -**standfestigkeit,** *f.* (*Mech.*) resistance to creep stress. -**strom,** *m.* continuous
current. -**träger,** *m.* (*Biol.*) chronic carrier.
-**versuch,** *m.* endurance test.

**Daum, Daumen,** *m.* thumb; inch; (*Mech.*)
part resembling a thumb, as a cam.

**Daumenrad,** *n.* cam wheel.

**Däumling,** *m.* little thumb; (*Mech.*) cam,
knob, or the like.

**Daune,** *f.* down.

**davon,** *adv.* thereof, therefrom, thereby, away.

**davontragen,** *v.t.* carry away, obtain.

**davor,** *adv.* before it, for it, from it.

**dazu,** *adv.* thereto, therefor, besides.—**noch
dazu,** moreover.

**dazumal,** *adv.* then.

**dazwischen,** *adv.* between, between them,
inter-. -**liegend,** *a.* lying between, intermediate. -**schalten, -schieben, -stellen,** *v.t.*
put between, interpose, interpolate.

**d. Bl.,** *abbrev.* (dieses Blattes) of this journal.

**dch.,** *abbrev.* (durch) thru, by.

**DD.,** *abbrev.* (Dampfdichte) vapor density.

**D.D.,** *abbrev.* (Dichten) densities.

**DE.,** *abbrev.* (Dielektrizitätskonstante) dielectric constant.

-**de.** A suffix attached to verbal roots to form
nouns which denote the result of the action
or the thing done; as, *Zierde,* ornament,
from *zieren,* adorn.

**Debet,** *n.* debit.

**decarbonisieren,** *v.t.* decarbonize, decarburize.

**dechiffrieren,** *v.t.* decipher.

**Dechsel,** *f.* adze.

**Deck-.** covering, cover, protecting. -**anstrich,**
*m.* (*Painting*) finishing coat.

**deckbar,** *a.* coverable; superposable.

**Deckblatt,** *n.* wrapper (of a cigar); (*Bot.*)
bract.

**Decke,** *f.* cover, covering (of various kinds);
integument, coat; roof; ceiling; blanket;
(*Sugar*) cleansing, purging (also, fine
liquor); (*Brewing*) head.

**Deckel,** *m.* cover, lid. -**abfall,** *m.* carding
waste.

**deckeln,** *v.t.* provide with a cover or lid.—
**gedeckelt,** *p.a.* with cover(s), covered.

**decken,** *v.t.* cover; top (paper); cleanse, wash,
purge; clay (sugar); superpose.—*v.i.* (of
colors) cover.

**Decken,** *n.* covering; cleansing, washing;
(*Paints*) covering power, opacity; (*Sugar*)
claying; superposition. -**lampe,** *f.* ceiling
lamp, dome lamp. -**licht,** *n.* skylight.
-**strich,** *m.* (*Leather*) daub.

**Decker,** *m.* coverer; (*Tobacco*) wrapper.

**deckfähig,** *a.* of good covering power, opaque.

**Deck-fähigkeit,** *f.* covering power, opacity. **-farbe,** *f.* body color, opaque color.

**deckfarbig,** *a.* of good body, opaque.

**Deck-firnis,** *m.* covering varnish, protecting varnish. **-glas,** *n.* cover glass, glass cover. **-gläschen,** *n.* (*Micros.*) cover glass. **-kläre,** *f.*, **-klärsel,** *n.* (*Sugar*) fine liquor (claircé) for cleansing the crystals. **-kraft,** *f.* covering power, body (of pigments and dyes). **-mittel,** *n.* covering material. **-papp,** *m.*, **-pappe,** *f.* resist, resist paste. **-schicht,** *f.* covering layer, protective layer.

**Decksel,** *n.* = Deckkläre.

**Deck-sirup,** *m.* (*Sugar*) liquored sirup (obtained by cleansing the crystals with fine liquor). **-stopfen,** *n.* stopper with projecting rim.

**Deckung,** *f.* covering, cover; remittance; security; (*Geom.*) congruence.

**Deck-weiss,** *n.* zinc white. **-ziegel,** *m.* cover tile; coping brick.

**decolorieren,** *v.t.* decolorize.

**decrepitieren,** *v.i.* decrepitate.

**Decreusage,** *f.* (*Silk*) determination of gum.

**Decylsäure,** *f.* decylic acid (decoic acid).

**defekt,** *a.* defective.

**defibriniert,** *a.* defibrinated.

**definieren,** *v.t.* define.—**definiert,** *p.a.* definite.

**deflagrieren,** *v.t.* deflagrate.

**deformieren,** *v.t.* deform.

**degallieren,** *v.t.* degall.

**Degen,** *m.* sword.

**deglutieren,** *v.t.* swallow.

**degommieren,** *v.t.* degum.

**degorgieren,** *v.t.* = ausschlämmen.

**degradieren,** *v.t.* degrade.

**degraissieren, degrassieren,** *v.t.* = entfetten.

**degummieren,** *v.t.* degum, ungum, strip (silk).

**dehnbar,** *a.* capable of being stretched, extensible, (of metals) malleable, ductile; expansible, (of gases) elastic; dilatable.

**Dehnbarkeit,** *f.* extensibility, etc. (see dehnbar.)

**Dehnbarkeitsmesser,** *m.* ductilimeter.

**dehnen,** *v.t.& r.* extend, stretch; expand, dilate, distend.

**Dehnkraft,** *f.* force or power of extension or expansion.

**Dehnung,** *f.* extension; tension; expansion; dilation.

**Dehnungs-kraft,** *f.* = Dehnkraft. **-messer,** *m.* extensometer. **-wärme,** *f.* heat of extension. **-zahl,** *f.* coefficient of extension or expansion.

**Dehydratation,** *f.* dehydration.

**Dehydratisierung,** *f.* dehydration.

**dehydrieren,** *v.t.* dehydrogenize, dehydrogenate; dehydrate.

**Dehydrierung,** *f.* dehydrogenation; dehydration.

**Dehydro-camphersäure,** *f.* dehydrocamphoric acid. **-chinacridon,** *n.* dehydroquinacridone. **-chinin,** *n.* dehydroquinine. **-schleimsäure,** *f.* dehydromucic acid.

**Deich,** *m.* dike.

**Deil,** *m.* = Duel.

**dein,** *pron.* thy, thine, your, yours.

**deinige,** *pron.* thine, yours.

**dekadisch,** *a.* decadic.—**dekadische Logarithmen,** common logarithms.

**Dekaeder,** *m.* decahedron.

**dekantieren,** *v.t.* decant.

**Dekantier-gefäss,** *n.* decanting vessel. **-glas,** *n.* decanting glass, glass decanting jar. **-topf,** *m.* (earthenware) decanting jar.

**Dekantierung,** *f.* decanting, decantation.

**Dekantierzylinder,** *m.* decanting cylinder.

**dekapieren,** *v.t.* scour, pickle (metals).

**dekarbonisieren,** *v.t.* decarbonize, decarburize.

**dekatieren,** *v.t.* hot-press, steam (cloth).

**dekausticieren,** *v.t.* decausticize.

**deklinieren,** *v.t.* decline, deviate.

**Dekokt,** *n.* decoction.

**dekorieren,** *v.t.* decorate.

**dekrepitieren,** *v.i.* decrepitate.

**Dekyl,** *n.* decyl.

**deliquescieren,** *v.i.* deliquesce.

**Delle,** *f.* dent.

**Delphin,** *m.* dolphin. **-öl,** *n.* dolphin oil. **-tran,** *m.* dolphin oil.

**dem,** *article.* to the, the.—*pron.* (to) this, (to) that, (to) him, (to) it, (to) whom, (to) which.

**Demant,** *m.* diamond; adamant. **-blende,** *f.* eulytite. **-spat,** *m.* adamantine spar (corundum).

**dementsprechend,** *adv.* correspondingly, accordingly.

**demethylieren,** *v.t.* demethylate.

**demgemäss, demnach,** *adv.* accordingly.

**demnächst,** *adv.* soon after, shortly.

**demontierbar,** *a.* dismountable.

**demontieren,** *v.t.* dismount, take apart or down.

**demulzieren,** *v.i.* soften, become demulcent.

**demungeachtet,** *adv.* notwithstanding, nevertheless.

**Demut,** *f.* humility.

**den,** *article.* the; (with *pl.*) to the.—*pron.* this, that, him, it, whom, which, to these, to those.

**denaturieren,** *v.t.* denature, denaturize.

**Denaturiermittel,** *n.* denaturant.

**Denaturierung,** *f.* = denaturing.

**Denaturierungsmittel,** *n.* denaturant.

**denaturisieren,** *v. t.* = denaturieren.

**Dendrachat, Dendritenachat,** *m.* dendritic agate.

dendrisch, dendritisch, *a.* dendritic.

denen, *pron.pl.* (to) these, (to) those, (to) them.

Denitrierbad, *n.* denitrating bath.

denitrieren, *v.t.* denitrate.

Denitriermittel, *n.* denitrating agent.

Denitrierung, *f.* denitration.

denitrifizieren, *v.t.* denitrify.

Denkart, *f.* way of thinking, disposition.

denkbar, *a.* thinkable, conceivable.

denken, *v.t.& i.* think; imagine.

Denk-mal, *n.* monument; memorial. -münze, *f.* commemorative medal. -schrift, *f.* memoir; memorial.

denkwürdig, *a.* memorable, notable.

denn, *conj.* for, because, then.

dennoch, *conj.* yet, however.

Depesche, *f.* dispatch.

dephlegmieren, *v.t.* dephlegmate.

Depolarisator, *m.* depolarizer.

depolarisieren, *v.t.* depolarize.

depolymerisieren, *v.t.* depolymerize.

deprimieren, *v.t.* depress.

depur., *abbrev.* (depuratus, -a, -um) purified.

der (die, das), *article.* the; to the; (with *pl.*) of the.—*pron.* this, that, he (she, it), who which, to whom, to which.

Der., *abbrev.* (Derivat) derivative.

derart, *adv.* in such a way, so much.

derartig, *a.* such, of that kind.

derb, *a.* solid, compact, dense, firm, strong; hardy, stout; rough, rude; (*Min.*) massive.

Derb-erz, *n.* massive ore. -gehalt, *m.* solid contents, cubical contents.

Derbheit, *f.* solidity, etc. (see derb).

dereinst, *adv.* some day; once, one day.

deren, *pron.* of this, of that, of her, of it, her, its, of whom, of which, whose, of these, of those, of them, their.

derer, *pron.pl.* of these, of those, of them, their.

dergestalt, *adv.* such, so.

dergl., *abbrev.* (dergleichen) the like.

dergleichen, *a.* such, the like.

Derivat, *n.* derivative.

derjenige (diejenige, dasjenige), *pron.* that one, the one, he (she, it).

dermassen, *adv.* so much, so.

dermatisch, *a.* cutaneous.

derselbe, *a.* the same.

derzeit, *adv.* at this time; at that time.

derzeitig, *a.* of the time being; present.

des, *article.* of the.—*pron.* of this, of that, of him, of it, his, its.

des-. dis-, de-; as, *D*estillat, distillate, *des*-oxydieren, deoxidize.

des., *abbrev.* (desmotrop) desmotropic.

Desagregation, *f.* disaggregation, disintegration.

desamidieren, *v.t.* deaminate; deamidate.

Desamidierung, *f.* deamination; deamidation.

desensibilieren, *v.t.* desensitize.

desfalls, *adv.* in that case.

desgl., *abbrev.* desgleichen.

desgleichen, *adv.* likewise; ditto.

deshalb, *adv.* therefore.

Desinfektion, *f.* disinfection.

Desinfektions-mittel, *n.* disinfectant. -wasser, *n.* disinfecting liquid.

Desinfektor, *m.* disinfector; disinfectant.

desinfektorisch, *a.* disinfectant.

desinfizieren, *v.t.* disinfect.—desinfizierend, *p.a.* disinfectant.

Desinfizierung, *f.* disinfection.

Desintegrator, *m.* disintegrator.

desintegrieren, *v.t.* disintegrate.

desmotrop, *a.* desmotropic.

Desmotropie, *f.* desmotropism, desmotropy.

Desodorationsmittel, *n.* deodorizer.

desodorisieren, desodorieren, *v.t.* deodorize.

Desodorisierung, *f.* deodorization.

Desodorisierungsmittel, *n.* deodorant.

Desoxy-. deoxy-, desoxy-.

Desoxydation, *f.* deoxidation.

Desoxydationsmittel, *n.* deoxidizing agent.

desoxydieren, *v.t.* deoxidize.

Desoxydierung, *f.* deoxidation.

dessen, *pron.* of this, of that, of him, of it, his, its, of whom, of which, whose.

dessenungeachtet, *adv.* nevertheless.

Dessin, *m.& n.* design, pattern.

dest., *abbrev.* (destilliert) distilled.

Dest., *abbrev.* (Destillation) distillation.

Destillat, *n.* distillate.

Destillation, *f.* distillation.

Destillations-apparat, *m.* distilling apparatus. -aufsatz, *m.* fractionating column. -gefäss, *n.* distilling vessel. -gerät, *n.* distilling apparatus. -hut, *m.* receiver. -kolben, *m.* distilling flask. -rohr, *n.*, -röhre, *f.* distillation tube, distilling tube. -rückstand, *m.* residue from distillation. -tiegel, *m.* distilling crucible. -verfahren, *n.* distillation process. -vorlage, *f.* distillation receiver.

Destillier-apparat, *m.* distilling apparatus, still. -aufsatz, *m.* fractionating column.

destillierbar, *a.* distillable.

Destillierbarkeit, *f.* distillability.

Destillier-blase, *f.* distilling vessel, retort, body of a still. -brücke, *f.* distillation bridge.

destillieren, *v.t.* distill.

Destillier-gefäss, *n.* distilling vessel. -glas, *n.* distilling vessel (of glass). -haus, *n.* still-house. -helm, *n.* still head. -kolben, *m.* distilling flask; retort. -ofen, *m.* distilling furnace. **-rohr,** *n.* distilling tube. **-topf,** *m.* distilling pot.

**Destillierung,** *f.* distillation.

**desto,** *adv.,* **desto-.** so much, so much the. **— je . . . —. . .,** the . . . the . . .

**destomehr,** *a.& adv.* so much the more, the more.

**Destrictasäure,** *f.* destrictic acid.

**Destrictinsäure,** *f.* destrictinic acid.

**deswegen,** *adv.* for that reason, therefore.

**Detacheur,** *m.* (*Dyeing*) spot cleaner.

**Detachiermittel,** *n.,* detergent, cleaner.

**detonieren,** *v.i.* detonate.—**detonierender Sprengstoff,** (*Expl.*) detonator.

**Detoniersprengstoff,** *m.* (*Expl.*) detonator.

**deuchte,** *pret.* of dünken.

**Deul,** *m.* bloom, lump, cake (of metal).

**deutbar,** *a.* explainable, explicable.

**deuten,** *v.i.* point.—*v.t.* indicate; explain.

**deutlich,** *a.* clear, distinct, plain, evident.

**Deuto-chlorür,** *n.* deutochloride. *Obs.* **-jodür,** *n.* deutoiodide, deutiodide. *Obs.*

**deutsch,** *a.* German.—**deutsche Folie,** German foil (made from an alloy of tin).— **deutsches Geschirr,** (*Paper*) stampers.— **Deutsches Reich,** (the) German State, German Government (formerly also, German Empire).

**Deutschland,** *n.* Germany.

**Deutung,** *f.* interpretation, explanation.

**Devise,** *f.* motto, device; (*Com.*) bill.

**devonisch,** *a.* Devonian.

**Dewargefäss,** *n.,* **Dewarsches Gefäss.** Dewar vessel.

**Dextronsäure,** *f.* dextronic (*d*-gluconic) acid.

**Dezi-.** deci-. **-gramm,** *n.* decigram.

**dezimal,** *a.* decimal.

**Dezimal,** *n.,* **Dezimale,** *f.,* decimal.

**Dezimalwa(a)ge,** *f.* decimal balance.

**dgl.,** *abbrev.* (dergleichen) the like; (desgleichen) likewise, ditto.

**d.h.,** *abbrev.* (das heisst) that is, i.e.

**d.i.,** *abbrev.* (das ist) that is, i.e.

**Diachylonsalbe,** *f.* diachylon ointment.

**Dialysator,** *m.* dialyzer.

**Dialyse,** *f.* dialysis.

**dialysierbar,** *a.* dialyzable.

**dialysieren,** *v.t.* dialyze.

**Dialysierpapier,** *n.* dialyzing paper.

**dialytisch, dialysisch,** *a.* dialytic.

**diamagnetisch,** *a.* diamagnetic.

**Diamant,** *m.* diamond.

**diamantartig,** *a.* diamondlike, adamantine.

**diamanten,** *a.* adamantine; diamond.

**diamantförmig,** *a.* diamond-shaped; diamondlike.

**Diamant-glanz,** *m.* adamantine luster. **-kitt,** *m.* diamond cement. **-mörser,** *m.* diamond mortar (small steel mortar). **-pulver,** *n.*

diamond dust. **-schwarz,** *n.* diamond black. **-spat,** *m.* adamantine spar (corundum). **-stahl,** *m.* very hard steel, tool steel.

**Diamido-.** diamino-, diamido- (see Amido-). **-benzol,** *n.* diaminobenzene. **-toluol,** *n.* diaminotoluene.

**Diamin-blau,** *n.* diamine blue. **-farbstoff,** *m.* diamine dye.

**Diaminosäure,** *f.* diamino acid.

**Diaminschwarz,** *n.* diamine black.

**Dianenbaum,** *m.* arbor Dianae (silver tree).

**Dianilgelb,** *n.* dianil yellow.

**diaphan,** *a.* diaphanous.

**Diaphoresie,** *f.* diaphoresis.

**diaphoretisch,** *a.* diaphoretic.

**Diaphragma,** *n.* diaphragm.

**Diastasewirkung,** *f.* diastatic action.

**diastatisch,** *a.* diastatic.

**Diät,** *f.* diet.

**Diätetik,** *f.* dietetics.

**diätetisch,** *a.* dietetic.

**Diäth-.** dieth-.

**diatherm, diatherman,** *a.* diathermic, diathermanous.

**Diazetyl-.** diacetyl-.

**Diazo-benzol,** *n.* diazobenzene. **-essigsäure,** *f.* diazoacetic acid. **-körper,** *m.* diazo compound. **-schwarz,** *n.* diazo black.

**diazotierbar,** *a.* diazotizable.

**diazotieren,** *v.t.* diazotize.

**Diazotierung,** *f.* diazotizing, diazotization.

**Diazoverbindung,** *f.* diazo compound.

**dibenzoyliert,** *p.a.* having two benzoyl groups added, dibenzoyl-.

**Dibrombenzol,** *n.* dibromobenzene.

**Dicarbonsäure,** *f.* dicarboxylic acid.

**Dichinol,** *n.* diquinol.

**Dichinolin,** *n.* diquinoline.

**Dichinoyl,** *n.* diquinoyl.

**Dichlormethan,** *n.* dichloromethane.

**Dichroismus,** *m.* dichroism.

**dichroitisch,** *a.* dichroic.

**dichromsauer,** *a.* of or combined with dichromic acid, dichromate of.

**Dichromsäure,** *f.* dichromic acid.

**Dichrosalz,** *n.* dichroic salt.

**dicht,** *a.* tight; dense; close; firm, compact, thick, impervious; (*Min.*) massive.—*adv.* close, near, near by; tightly, densely, etc. **-brennen,** *v.t.* (*Ceram.*) vitrify.

**Dichte,** *f.* density; tightness, thickness, firmness; (of paper) bulking quality; (of paint, etc.) body. **-flasche,** *f.* specific gravity bottle. **-messer,** *m.* instrument for measuring density, densimeter; specif., hydrometer.

**dichten,** *v.t.* make tight, lute, pack, alk; condense, compact; compose (poetry).

**Dichter,** *m.* poet.

**Dichtheit,** *f.* tightness, imperviousness; density, firmness.

**Dichtigkeit,** *f.* = Dichte.

**Dichtigkeits-grad,** *m.* degree of denseness, tightness, etc.; consistency. **-messer,** *m.* = Dichtemesser.

**dichtschliessend,** *p.a.* closing tightly, tight.

**Dichtschweissung,** *f.* close weld(ing).

**Dichtung,** *f.* making tight; luting; packing, stuffing; joint; poetry.

**Dichtungs-material,** *n.,* **-stoff,** *m.* luting, calking or packing material.

**dick,** *a.* thick; dense; big, bulky, fat, swollen.

**Dick-auszug,** *m.* inspissated extract. **-darm,** *m.* large intestine, colon.

**Dicke,** *f.* thickness, etc. (see dick); consistency (of a liquid); mother, dregs.

**Dickenmesser,** *m.* thickness gage, caliper.

**Dickfarbe,** *f.* thick color, body color.

**dick-flüssig,** *a.* thickly liquid, viscous, viscid. **-grell,** *a.* (of pig iron) dead-white.

**dicklich,** *a.* thickish, somewhat thick.

**Dick-maische,** *f.* (*Brewing*) thick mash, decoction. **-milch,** *f.* curdled milk, curds. **-mittel,** *n.* thickening agent, thickener. **-öl,** *n.* thick oil, heavy oil; specif., a viscous product formed by the exposure of oil of turpentine to the air, stand oil.

**dickölig,** *a.* of the nature of a thick oil.

**Dick-pfanne,** *f.* concentration pan. **-saft,** *m.* inspissated ⸤ juice; (*Sugar*) thick juice, sirup.

**dick-schalig,** *a.* thick-shelled; (of grain) husky. **-sirupartig,** *a.* of the nature of a thick sirup. **-tafelig,** *a.* in thick plates. **-wandig,** *a.* thick-walled.

**Dicyan,** *n.* dicyanogen, cyanogen gas.

**Didym,** *n.* didymium.

**die,** *article.* the.—*pron.* this, that, these, those, she, who, which.

**Dieb,** *m.* thief. **-stahl,** *m.* theft, larceny.

**diejenige,** *pron.* see derjenige.

**Diele,** *f.* board, plank, deal.

**Dielektrikum,** *n.* dielectric.

**dielektrisch,** *a.* dielectric.

**Dielektrizitätskonstante,** *f.* dielectric constant.

**dienen,** *v.i.* serve.

**Diener,** *m.* servant.

**dienlich,** *a.* serviceable, expedient, fit.

**Dienst,** *m.* service; duty, employment.

**Dienstag,** *m.* Tuesday.

**dienstbereit,** *a.* ready for service.

**Dienst-herr,** *m.* employer, master. **-leistung,** *f.* service, functioning. **-lohn,** *m.* wages.

**dienstlos,** *a.* out of employment.

**diesbezüglich,** *a.* concerning this.

**Dieselöl,** *n.* Diesel oil.

**dieser, diese, dieses, dies,** *pron.* this, this one, the latter.—**diese,** *pl.* these.

**diesmal,** *adv.* this time, now.

**Dietrich,** *m.* skeleton key, picklock.

**differentiieren,** *v.t.* differentiate.

**Differenzial-gleichung,** *f.* differential equation. **-rechnung,** *f.* differential calculus. **-strom,** *m.* differential current.

**differenzieren,** *v.t.* differentiate.

**Differenzierung,** *f.* differentiation.

**Differenzstrom,** *m.* differential current.

**differieren,** *v.i.* differ.

**diffundieren,** *v.t.* diffuse.

**Diffuseur,** *m.* diffuser.

**diffusionsfähig,** *a.* diffusible.

**Diffusions-geschwindigkeit,** *f.* velocity of diffusion. **-hülse,** *f.* diffusion shell. **-produkt,** *n.* diffusate. **-verfahren,** *n.* diffusion process. **-vermögen,** *n.* diffusibility.

**Digallussäure,** *f.* digallic acid.

**digerieren,** *v.t.* digest.

**Digerier-flasche,** *f.* digestion bottle. **-ofen,** *m.* digestion oven, digester.

**Digerierung,** *f.* digestion.

**Digestionsalz, Digestivsalz,** *n.* digestive salt (potassium chloride).

**Digestivmittel,** *n.* digestive.

**Digestor,** *m.* digester.

**Digestorium,** *n.* hood, fume cupboard.

**Diharnstoff,** *m.* diurea(urazine).

**diheteroatomig,** *a.* diheteratomic.

**dihexaedrisch,** *a.* (*Cryst.*) dihexahedral.

**dihydratisch,** *a.* dihydric.

**Dijod-.** diiodo-.

**Dika-brot,** *n.* dika bread. **-fett,** *n.* dika fat, dika oil.

**Dikarb-.** see Dicarb-.

**Dilemöl,** *n.* dilem oil, Java oil (a kind of patchouli oil).

**Dilettant,** *m.* amateur.

**Dille,** *f.* socket, nozzle.

**Dill-kraut,** *n.* dill. **-öl,** *n.* oil of dill, dill oil. **-samen,** *m.* dill seed.

**dimensionieren,** *v.t.* dimension.

**dimer,** *a.* dimeric.

**Dimethyläther,** *m.* dimethyl ether.

**dimethyliert,** *p.a.* dimethylated, dimethyl-.

**dimetrisch,** *a.* (*Cryst.*) dimetric (tetragonal).

**Dimilchsäure,** *f.* dilactic acid (dilactylic acid).

**dimorph, dimorphisch,** *a.* dimorphous.

**Dimorphie,** *f.* **Dimorphismus,** *m.* dimorphism.

**DIN,** *abbrev.* (Deutsche Industrienormen) German industrial standards.

**Dina-.** Dinas.

**Dinapht-, Dinaphto-.** dinaphtho-.

**Dinaphtyl,** *n.* dinaphthyl.

**Dinaphtylen-.** dinaphthylene-.

**Dinaphtylin,** *n.* dinaphthyline.

**Dinas-stein,** *m.* Dinas brick, silica brick. **-ton,** *m.* Dinas clay. **-ziegel,** *m.* = Dinaziegel.

**Dinaton,** *m.* Dinas clay.

Dinatrium-. disodium.

Dinaziegel, m. Dinas brick, silica brick.

Ding, n. thing; being.

dingen, v.t. hire.—v.i. bargain.

Dinicotinsäure, f. dinicotinic acid.

dinitriert, p.a. having two nitro groups introduced, dinitro-.

Dinkel, m. spelt, German wheat.

Dinte, f. (more commonly, Tinte) ink.

diorithaltig, a. containing diorite, dioritic.

Diorsellinsäure, f. diorsellinic acid.

Dioxy-. dioxy-; dihydroxy-. (See note under Oxy-.) -benzol, n. dihydroxybenzene. -chinolin, n. dihydroxyquinoline. -chinon, n. dihydroxyquinone.

Dioxyd, n. dioxide.

Dioxy-naphtalin, n. dihydroxynaphthalene. -toluol, n. dihydroxytoluene.

diphasisch, a. diphase, diphasic.

Diphensäure, f. diphenic acid.

Diphenyl-arsenchlorür, n. diphenylarsenious chloride. -borchlorid, n. diphenylboron chloride.

Diphosphorsäure, f. diphosphoric (pyrophosphoric) acid.

Diphtal-. diphthal-.

Dipl.-Ing., abbrev. (Diplom-Ingenieur) graduate in engineering from a school of university rank.

Diploeder, n. (Cryst.) diplohedron, diploid.

dipol, a. dipolar.

Dippelsöl, n. Dippel's oil.

Diptam, m. (Bot.) dittany.

direktfärbend, a. direct-coloring, direct.

Direktive, f. instructions.

direktziehend, a. (Dyeing) direct.

Dirhodan-. dithiocyano-.

Dirigent, m. director, manager, head.

dirigieren, v.t. direct, manage, rule.

Disäure, f. diacid (often, pyro acid).

Disazo-farbstoff, m. disazo dye. -verbindung, f. disazo compound.

Dischwefelsäure, f. disulfuric acid, pyrosulfuric acid.

dischweflig, a. disulfurous, pyrosulfurous.

diskontieren, v.t. discount.

diskontinuierlich, a. discontinuous.

Diskontinuität, f. discontinuity.

diskutieren, v.t. discuss.

dispensieren, v.t. dispense; exempt, excuse.

Dispergens, m. dispersion agent.

dispergieren, v.t. disperse.—dispergierend, p.a. dispersing, dispersive.

dispers, a. dispersed, disperse.

Dispersions-grad, m. degree of dispersion. -mittel, n. dispersion agent. -vermögen, n. dispersive power.

Dispersitätsgrad, m. degree of dispersion.

Disponent, m. manager, agent, accountant.

disponibel, a. disposable, available.

disponieren, v.t. dispose.

Diss., abbrev. dissertation; dissociation.

Dissertation, f. dissertation, thesis.

dissezieren, v.t. dissect.

dissimilieren, v.t. decompose.

dissociierbar, a. dissociable.

dissociieren, v.t.& i. dissociate.

Dissoz., abbrev. (Dissoziation) dissociation.

Dissoziations-grad, m. degree of dissociation. -spannung, f. dissociation tension. -vermögen, n. dissociating power. -wärme, f. heat of dissociation. -zustand, m. dissociated condition.

dissoziierbar, a. dissociable.

dissoziieren, v.t.& i. dissociate.

Distel, f. thistle.

distillieren, v.t. distill. See Destill-.

Disulfaminsäure, f. disulfamic acid.

Disulfosäure, f. disulfonic acid.

Ditarinde, f. dita bark.

Dithiokohlensäure, f. (either) dithiocarbonic acid; specif., dithiolcarbonic acid (HSCOSH).

dithionig, a. hyposulfurous.

dithionigsauer, a. =unterschwefligsauer.

Dithionsäure, f. dithionic acid.

Dithiophosphorsäure, f. dithiophosphoric acid.

Diüberjodsäure, f. diperiodic acid.

diuretisch, a. diuretic.

Divaricatinsäure, f. divaricatinic acid.

Divaricatsäure, f. divaricatic acid.

divergierend, p.a. diverging, divergent.

dividieren, v.t. divide.

Diweinsäure, f. ditartaric acid.

Diwolframsäure, f. ditungstic acid.

Dizimmtsäure, f. dicinnamic acid.

Dizyan, n. =Dicyan.

d.J., abbrev. (dieses Jahres) of this year.

d. M., abbrev. (dieses Monats) of this month, inst.

Döbel, Dobel, m. pin, peg, dowel.

Docent, m. teacher, lecturer.

doch, conj. yet, however, surely, indeed.

Docht, m. wick. -kohle, f. (Elec.) cored carbon.

Docke, f. bundle, skein; plug; baluster; mandrel; doll; dock.

docken, v.t. wind (yarn, etc.).

Dodekaeder, n. dodecahedron.

dodekaedrisch, a. dodecahedral.

Döglingstran, m. doegling oil.

Dohle, f. jackdaw; sewer.

Dokimasie, f. docimasy.

Dokosan, n. docosane.

Dolde, f. umbel, (of hops) cone, strobile.

dolden-blumig, -blütig, a. umbelliferous.

dolieren, v.t. (Leather) pare, shave.

Dolmetsch, m. interpreter.

dolomithaltig, a. dolomitic.

**dolomitisieren,** *v.t.* (*Min.*) dolomitize.
**Dom,** *m.* dome, cupola, cover; cathedral.
**Doma,** *n.* (*Cryst.*) dome.
**Donner,** *m.* thunder. **-keil,** *m.* thunderbolt; belemnite.
**donnern,** *v.i.* thunder; strike, peal.
**Donner-stein,** *m.* thunderstone, belemnite. **-strahl,** *m.* lightning flash.
**Doppel-,** double; doubly; bi-, di-.
**doppelatomig,** *a.* diatomic.
**Doppel-bier,** *n.* double beer. **-bild,** *n.* double image. **-bindung,** *f.* double bond, double union. **-boden,** *m.* double bottom, false bottom; jacket.
**doppelbrechend,** *a.* doubly refracting.
**Doppel-brechung,** *f.* double refraction. **-brillanrscharlach,** *m.* double brilliant scarlet. **-centner,** *m.* = Doppelzentner. **-chlorid,** *n.* bichloride, dichloride.
**doppel-chromsauer,** *a.* bichromate (dichromate) of. **-farbig,** *a.* dichroic, dichromatic.
**Doppel-farbigkeit,** *f.* dichroism. **-färbung,** *f.* (*Micros.*) double staining, also counterstaining. **-gänger,** *m.* double. **-gestaltung,** *f.* dimorphism. **-gitter,** *n.* (*Elec.*) double grid. **-glocke,** *f.* double bell jar. **-jodquecksilber,** *n.* biniodide of mercury (mercuric iodide).
**doppel-kohlensauer,** *a.* bicarbonate of. **-lebig,** *a.* amphibious.
**Doppel-linie,** *f.* double line, doublet. **-mantelgefäss,** *n.* double-walled vessel. **-muffelofen,** *m.* double muffle furnace. **-ofen,** *m.* double furnace or oven.
**doppeloxalsauer,** *a.* binoxalate of.
**Doppel-oxyd,** *n.* binoxide (dioxide); double oxide. **-punkt,** *m.* (*Printing*) colon.
**doppelpolig,** *a.* bipolar.
**Doppel-salz,** *n.* double salt. **-schale,** *f.* double dish, dish with cover (as a Petri dish).
**doppel-schichtig,** *a.* two-layered. **-schlicht,** *a.* dead smooth, (of files) superfine.
**Doppelschwefeleisen,** *n.* iron disulfide.
**doppelschwefelsauer,** *a.* bisulfate of.
**Doppelschwefelsäure,** *f.* disulfuric acid.
**doppel-schwefligsauer,** *a.* bisulfite of. **-seitig,** *a.* bilateral; double-faced.
**Doppelsilikat,** *n.* double silicate; bisilicate.
**doppelsinnig,** *a.* ambiguous.
**Doppelspat,** *m.* Iceland spar.
**doppelstark,** *a.* double-strength.
**Doppel-stück,** *n.* duplicate. **-sulfat,** *n.* double sulfate; bisulfate. **-sulfit,** *n.* double sulfite; bisulfite.
**doppelt,** *a.* double, duplex, twofold; (in old names of compounds) bi-, bin-.—*adv.* doubly, twice. **-basisch,** *a.* bibasic (dibasic). **-borsauer,** *a.* biborate of.

**Doppeltchlorzinn,** *n.* stannic chloride.
**doppelt-chromsauer,** *a.* bichromate (dichromate) of. **-hochrund,** *a.* convexo-concave. **-hohl,** *a.* concavo-concave. **-kieselsauer,** *a.* bisilicate of. **-kleesauer,** *a.* binoxalate of. **-kohlensauer,** *a.* bicarbonate of. **-kohlensaures Salz,** bicarbonate. **-normal,** *a.* double normal, twice normal.
**Doppeltschwefeleisen,** *n.* iron disulfide.
**doppelt-schwefelsauer,** *a.* bisulfate (acid sulfate) of. **-schwefligsauer,** *a.* bisulfite (acid sulfite) of. **-selenigsauer,** *a.* biselenite of. **-selensauer,** *a.* biselenate of. **-titansauer,** *a.* bititanate of. **-ungesättigt,** *a.* doubly unsaturated. **-vanadinsauer,** *a.* bivanadate of. **-weinsauer,** *a.* bitartrate (acid tartrate) of. **-wolframsauer,** *a.* bitungstate of.
**Doppelumsetzung,** *f.* double decomposition.
**Doppelung,** *f.* doubling.
**Doppel-verbindung,** *f.* double compound. **-wägung,** *f.* double weighing.
**doppelwandig,** *a.* double-walled.
**Doppelweghahn,** *m.* two-way cock.
**doppelwirkend,** *p.a.* double-acting; amphichroic, amphoteric.
**Doppel-wurzel,** *f.* (*Math.*) double root. **-zentner,** *m.* double centner, 100 kilograms. **-zersetzung,** *f.* double decomposition.
**doppelzüngig,** *a.* double-dealing.
**Döpper,** *m.* (*Mach.*) riveting die.
**Dorf,** *n.* village.
**Dorn,** *m.* thorn; spine; (*Mach.*) pin, spike, tongue, bolt, mandrel, etc.; (*Metal.*) slag (of copper).
**Dornenstein,** *m.* Dornstein.
**Dörnerschlacke,** *f.* (*Metal.*) bulldog.
**dornig,** *a.* thorny, spiny.
**Dornstein,** *m.* (*Salt Manuf.*) thornstone (scale of calcium carbonate and sulfate on thorn walls).
**dorren,** *v.i.* dry; wither.
**dörren,** *v.t.* dry, desiccate; cure (by drying); scorch.
**Dörr-gemüse,** *n.* dried vegetables. **-obst,** *n.* dried fruit.
**Dorschleber-tran,** *m.* **-öl,** *n.* cod-liver oil.
**dort,** *adv.* there; yonder.
**dorthin,** *adv.* thither, there, that way.
**dortig,** *a.* of that place, in that place.
**Dose,** *f.* box; can, tin.
**Dosen-barometer,** *n.* aneroid barometer. **-konserven,** *f.pl.* canned goods, tinned goods. **-milch,** *f.* condensed (or evaporated) milk.
**dosieren,** *v.t.* determine; (*Pharm.*) dose; measure out.
**Dosierung,** *f.* determination; dosing, dosage; dose.
**Dosis,** *f.* dose.

**Dossierung,** *f.* slope.

**Dost, Dosten,** *m.* origanum, origan.

**Dostenöl,** *n.* origanum oil.

**Dostkraut,** *n.* origanum, origan.

**Dotter,** *m.* egg yolk, vitellus.—*f.* any of several plants, as wild flax.

**Dotter-.** yolk, vitelline.

**doublieren,** *v.t.* double, concentrate.

**Dozent,** *m.* teacher, lecturer.

**D. P.,** *abbrev.* (deutsches Patent) German patent.

**D.P.a.,** *abbrev.* (deutsche Patentanmeldung) application for a German patent.

**Drache, Drachen,** *m.* dragon; kite.

**Drachenblut, -gummi,** *n.* dragon's blood.

**dragieren,** *v.t.* coat (pills or the like).

**Dragun,** *m.,* **-trat, -wermutkraut,** *n.* tarragon.

**Draht,** *m.* wire; (*Spinning*) twist, thread; grain (of wood). **-bund,** *m.* coil of wire. **-bürste,** *f.* wire brush. **-dreieck,** *n.* wire triangle.

**drahten, drähtern,** *a.* of wire; wiry.—**drahten,** *v.t.* wire.

**Draht-faser,** *f.* (*Paper*) wire mold. **-gaze,** *f.* wire gauze. **-geflecht,** *n.* wire netting. **-gewebe,** *n.* wire cloth, wire gauze. **-gewicht,** *n.* wire weight, (often) rider. **-glas,** *n.* armored glass, wire glass. **-korb,** *m.* wire basket. **-lehre,** *f.* wire gage.

**drahtlos,** *a.* wireless.

**Draht-maske,** *f.* wire mask. **-netz,** *n.* wire gauze, wire net. **-prüfung,** *f.* wire testing. **-rolle,** *f.* coil of wire. **-seil,** *n.* wire cable, wire rope, wire cord. **-sieb,** *n.* wire sieve, wire screen, wire cloth. **-stift,** *m.* wire nail, wire tack, wire pin. **-zange,** *f.* pliers, nippers. **-ziehen,** *n.* wire drawing. **-zug,** *m.* wire drawing; wire mill.

**drainieren,** *v.t.* drain.

**drall,** *a.* tight; buxom.

**Drall,** *m.* twist, rifling.

**drang,** *pret.* of dringen.

**Drang,** *m.* throng, pressure, impulse, craving.

**drängen,** *v.t.& i.* press, crowd, urge; drive (gases).—**gedrängt,** *p.a.* crowded; compact; succinct.

**drasch,** *pret.* of dreschen.

**Drass,** *m.* dregs (of oil).

**drauf,** *adv.* thereupon, thereon, afterward.

**Draufsicht,** *f.* top view.

**draussen,** *adv.* without, out, abroad.

**drechseln,** *v.t.* turn (on a lathe); elaborate.

**Dreck,** *m.* dirt, dung, filth.

**Dreh-.** rotatory, rotary, rotating, rotational, revolving, turning, torsional. **-achse,** *f.* axis of rotation (or of revolution); knife edge (of a balance); pin. **-bank,** *f.* lathe.

**drehbar,** *a.* capable of being turned or twisted,

turning, rotary, rotatory, revolving.— **eingesetzt,** pivoted.

**Dreh-bewegung,** *f.* rotatory motion. **-ebene,** *f.* plane of rotation or revolution.

**drehen,** *v.t.* turn, rotate; twist; roll; spin; wind.—*v.r.* turn, rotate, revolve.—**drehend,** *p.a.* turning, etc.; rotatory.

**Dreher,** *m.* turner; rotator; (*Mech.*) crank, handle (for turning), etc.

**Dreh-feld,** *n.* (*Elec.*) rotating field. **-geschwindigkeit,** *f.* speed (or velocity) of rotation or of revolution. **-impuls,** *m.* angular momentum, moment of momentum. **-kalzinierofen,** *m.* revolving roaster. **-kraft,** *f.* torsional force. **-krankheit,** *f.* staggers. **-kreuz,** *n.* turnstile; (*Brewing*) sparger; rotating shutter. **-moment,** *n.* moment of rotation; twisting or torsional moment. **-ofen,** *n.* revolving furnace. **-punkt,** *m.* center of motion, turning point, pivot. **-richtung,** *f.* direction of rotation. **-scheibe,** *f.* potter's wheel; lapidary's wheel; turntable. **-sinn,** *m.* direction of rotation or revolution. **-späne,** *m.pl.* turnings. **-spannung,** *f.* torsional strain. **-spiegelung,** *f.* (*Cryst.*) combined rotation and reflection. **-spindel,** *f.* revolving spindle, live spindle. **-spulgalvanometer,** *n.* moving-coil galvanometer. **-stahl,** *m.* turning tool, lathe tool. **-strom,** *m.* (*Elec.*) rotary current, multiphase current.

**Drehung,** *f.* rotation, turn, turning, torsion, revolution, twisting.

**Drehungs-achse,** *f.* axis of rotation (or of revolution), turning axis. **-festigkeit,** *f.* resistance to torsion. **-grad,** *m.* degree of rotation. **-kraft,** *f.* rotatory power. **-streuung,** *f.* rotatory dispersion. **-vermögen,** *n.* rotatory power. **-winkel,** *m.* angle of rotation.

**Dreh-vektor,** *m.* rotation vector. **-vermögen,** *n.* rotatory power. **-wage,** *f.* torsion balance. **-zahl,** *f.* number of revolutions. **-zahlmesser,** *m.* revolution counter. **-zylinder,** *m.* revolving cylinder.

**drei,** *a.* three.

**drei-, Drei-.** three-, tri-, triple.

**drei-achsig,** *a.* triaxial. **-atomig,** *a.* triatomic. **-basisch,** *a.* tribasic.

**Drei-bein,** *n.* tripod. **-blatt,** *n.* trefoil.

**dreiblätterig,** *a.* three-leaved.

**Drei-brenner,** *m.* triple burner. **-bund,** *m.* triple alliance.

**dreidimensional,** *a.* tridimensional.

**Dreieck,** *n.* triangle.

**dreieckig,** *a.* triangular, three-cornered.

**Dreieckslehre,** *f.* trigonometry.

**Dreiergruppe,** *f.* group of three, 3-group.

**dreierlei,** *a.* of three kinds, of three sorts.

**Dreierstoss**, *m.* three-body collision.
**dreifach**, *a.* triple, threefold, treble, tri.—
— **Chlorantimon**, antimony trichloride.
— **Chlorjod**, iodine trichloride. — **Schwefelarsen**, arsenic trisulfide.
**Drei-farben-**. three-color, trichrome. **-farbigkeit**, *f.* trichroism.
**drei-flächig**, *a.* three-faced, trihedral. **-flammig**, *a.* three-flame, triple (burner).
**Dreifuss**, *m.* tripod.
**drei-füssig**, *a.* three-footed, tripedal. **-gliedrig**, *a.* three-membered; (*Math.*) trinomial. **-gruppig**, *a.* of three groups, three-group. **-halsig**, *a.* three-necked.
**Drei-halskolben**, *m.* three-necked flask.
**Dreiheit**, *f.* triad.
**drei-kantig**, *a.* three-cornered, triangular. **-kernig**, *a.* trinuclear.
**Dreikörper**, **-apparat**, *m.* triple-effect apparatus.
**Dreileiter-**. (*Elec.*) three-wire.
**dreimalig**, *a.* done three times, triple.
**Dreiphasenstrom**, *m.* (*Elec.*) triphase current.
**dreiphasig**, *a.* three-phase, triphase.
**Dreipunkt-**. three-point.
**dreiquantig**, *a.* of three quanta, three-quantum.
**Drei-ring**, *m.* three-membered ring. **-salz**, *n.* trisalt (neutral salt of a triacid); triple salt.
**drei-säurig**, *a.* triacid. **-schenkelig**, *a.* three-legged.
**Dreischenkelrohr**, *n.* three-way tube, T-tube.
**drei-schichtig**, *a.* three-layered. **-seitig**, *a.* three-sided, trilateral, triangular.
**dreissig**, *a.* thirty.
**dreissigste**, *a.* thirtieth.
**dreist**, *a.* bold, confident.
**Dreisteinwurzel**, *f.* feverroot (*Triosteum*).
**dreistellig**, *a.* three-place.
**Dreistoff-**. three-component, ternary. **-legierung**, *f.* three-component alloy, ternary alloy.
**drei-teilig**, *a.* three-part, tripartite. **-undeinachsig**, *a.* (*Cryst.*) monotrimetric (hexagonal). **-wandig**, *a.* three-walled, triple-walled.
**Dreiweg-**, **Dreiwege-**. three-way. **-hahn**, *m.* three-way cock. **-schalter**, *m.* three-way switch. **-stück**, *n.* three-way piece, three-way tube. **-verbindung**, *f.* three-way connection.
**dreiwertig**, *a.* trivalent.
**Dreiwertigkeit**, *f.* trivalence.
**dreiwinkelig**, *a.* triangular.
**Dreizack**, *m.* trident.
**dreizählig**, *a.* threefold, triple, ternary.
**dreizehn**, *a.* thirteen.
**Drell**, *m.* ticking.

**Dresbacherblau**, *n.* Dresbach blue (Prussian blue).
**dreschen**, *v.t.* thrash, thresh.
**drgl.**, *abbrev.* (dergleichen) the like.
**D.R.G.M.**, *abbrev.* (Deutsches Reichs-Gebrauchsmuster) German registered design. Cf. Gebrauchsmuster.
**Drillbohrer**, *m.* drill.
**drillen**, *v.t.* drill; turn.
**Drillich**, *m.* ticking, tick, drill.
**Drilling**, *m.* triplet; (*Mach.*) lantern. **-salz**, *n.* triple salt.
**drin**, *adv.* therein.
**Dr.-Ing.**, *abbrev.* (Doktor-Ingenieur) doctor-engineer (doctor of technical science and graduate in engineering).
**dringen**, *v.i.* press, rush, penetrate.—**dringend**, *p.a.* pressing, urgent.—**gedrungen**, *p.a.* compact; compelled; thickset.
**dringlich**, *a.* pressing, urgent.
**drinnen**, *adv.* within, in, indoors.
**drischt**, *pr. 3 sing.* of dreschen.
**dritt**, *a.* third.
**Drittel**, *n.* third. **-alkohol**, *m.* (*Bact.*) a mixture of alcohol with double the amount of water, Ranvier's alcohol.
**drittelsauer**, *a.* tribasic.
**Drittelsilber**, *n.* tiers-argent (silver 1, aluminum or German silver 2).
**dritthalb**, *a.* two and a half.
**droben**, *adv.* up there, above.
**Droge**, *f.* drug.
**Drogen-händler**, *m.* druggist. **-handlung**, *f.* drug business; drugstore. **-kunde**, *f.* pharmacology. **-waren**, *f.pl.* drugs.
**Drogerie**, *f* = Drogenhandlung. **-geschäft**, *n.* drug business, drug trade.
**Drogett**, **Droget**, *m.* drugget.
**Drogist**, *m.* druggist.
**Drogue**, **Droguett**, etc. see Droge, Drogett, etc.
**drohen**, *v.i.* threaten, menace.
**dröhnen**, *v.i.* rumble, boom.
**drollig**, *a.* droll, comical.
**drosch**, *pret.* of dreschen.
**Drossel**, *f.* thrush (bird); throttle; (*Elec.*) choking coil. **-ader**, *f.* jugular vein. **-bein**, *n.* collar bone.
**drosseln**, *v.t.* throttle; choke; baffle.
**Drosselventil**, *n.* throttle valve.
**D.R.P.**, *abbrev.* (Deutsches Reichs-Patent) German patent.
**D.R.P. angem.**, *abbrev.* (Deutsches Reichs-Patent angemeldet) German patent applied for.
**Dr. phil.**, *abbrev.* doctor of philosophy, Ph.D.
**drüben**, *adv.* over there, yonder.
**drüber**, *adv.* = darüber.
**Druck**, *m.* pressure; compression; oppression; impression, print, printing. **-abfall**, *m.*,

-abnahme, *f.* fall in pressure. -anstieg, *m.* rise in pressure. -apparat, *m.* pressure apparatus. -behälter, *m.* pressure reservoir. -blau, *n.* (*Dyes*) printing blue. -buchstabe, *m.* type. -destillation, *f.* pressure distillation.

druckdicht, *a.* tight.

Druck-einheit, *f.* unit of pressure. -elektrizität, *f.* piezoelectricity.

drucken, *v.t.* print; stamp.

drücken, *v.t.* press; squeeze; push; oppress.

Druckentwickelung, *f.* development of pressure.

Drucker, *m.* printer.

Drücker, *m.* trigger; handle.

Druckerei, *f.* printing; printing establishment; (*Calico*) print works.

Druckerfarbe, *f.* printer's ink.

Druck-erhitzung, *f.* heating under pressure. -erhöhung, *f.* increase of pressure. -erniedrigung, *f.* lowering of pressure.

Druckerschwärze, *f.* printer's ink.

Druck-farbe, *f.* printing color, printing ink. -fehler, *m.* misprint, typographical error.

druckfest, *a.* resistant to pressure.

Druck-festigkeit, *f.* resistance to pressure or compression, elasticity of compression. -filter, *n.* pressure filter. -firnis, *m.* printer's varnish. -flasche, *f.* pressure bottle. -gärung, *f.* pressure fermentation. -gefäss, *n.* pressure vessel. -höhe, *f.* (*Mech.*) head. -kattun, *m.* printed calico. -kessel, *m.* (*Mach.*) pressure chamber. -knopf, *m.* push button. -kolben, *m.* pressure flask; (*Mach.*) piston. -kraft, *f.* compressive force. -lack, *m.* printers' lake. -legung, *f.* publishing; impression. -leitung, *f.* high-pressure piping. -luft, *f.* compressed air. -luftpumpe, *f.* pump for compressing air. -maschine, *f.* printing machine. -messer, *m.* pressure gage, manometer. -messung, *f.* pressure measurement. -papier, *n.* printing paper. -platte, *f.* printing plate, engraving. -probe, *f.* compression test; pressure test; (of barley) squeezing test; (printer's) proof. -regler, *m.* pressure regulator. -rohr, *n.*, -röhre, *f.* pressure tube; force pipe. -sache, *f.* printed matter. -schlauch, *m.* pressure tubing. -schrift, *f.* publication; print; type. -schwarz, *n.* (*Dyes*) printing black. -seite, *f.* page. -spannung, *f.* compressive stress. -steigerung, *f.* rise of pressure. -stempel, *m.* piston; pressure stamp. -stock, *m.* (*Printing*) cut, electro. -ventil, *n.* pressure valve, discharge valve. -verfahren, *n.* printing process. -verminderung, *f.* diminution or decrease of pressure. -walze, *f.* pressing (or pressure) roller (or roll, cylinder); printing roller. -wasser, *n.* pressure water, water under pressure.

Druckwasser-. hydraulic.

Druck-welle, *f.* pressure wave. -zeug, *n.* printing cloth. -zunahme, *f.* increase of pressure.

Drudenfuss, *m.* lycopodium, club moss.

drum, drunter. =darum, darunter.

Drüschen, *n.* small gland, glandule.

Druse, *f.* druse.—*pl.* Drusen, dregs, lees; husks; glanders.

Drüse, *f.* gland.

drusen, *v.i.* become dreggy.

Drüsen-. glandular.

drüsenartig, *a.* glandular.

Drusen-asche, *f.* calcined (wine) lees. -branntwein, *m.* spirits distilled from fermented lees.

drusenförmig, *a.* drusy, drused.

Drüsen-krankheit, *f.* gland disease; scrofula. -kropf, *m.* goiter.

Drusenöl, *n.* oil from dregs of wine, grapeseed oil.

Drüsensaft, *m.* glandular secretion.

Drusenschwarz, *n.* Frankfort black (from wine lees).

drusig, drusicht, *a.* drusy, drused.

drüsig, drüsicht, *a.* glandlike; glandular.

d.s., *abbrev.* (dass sind) that is, i.e.

Dschunke, *f.* junk.

dsgl., *abbrev.* (desgleichen) likewise, ditto.

ds.J., *abbrev.* (dieses Jahres) of this year.

Dtz., Dtzd., *abbrev.* (Dutzend) dozen.

du, *pron.* thou, you.

dualistisch, *a.* dualistic.

Dübel, *m.* pin, peg, plug, dowel, key.

Dublett, *n.* doublet.

dublieren, *v.t.* double; (*Metal.*) concentrate.

Dublierstein, *m.* concentrated metal, regulus.

ducken, *v.t.* humble.—*v.r.* duck; give in.—*v.i.* submit.

Ducker, *m.* siphon; one that ducks.

Duckstein, *m.* calcareous tufa.

duff, *a.* dull.

Duft, *m.* odor; fragrance, perfume, aroma; vapor, exhalation.

düfteln, *v.i.* have a slight odor or fragrance.

duften, *v.i.* be fragrant; smell; sweat.—*v.t.* perfume.

Duftessig, *m.* aromatic vinegar.

duftig, *a.* fragrant, odorous; vaporous, misty.

Duftigkeit, *f.* =Duft.

duftlos, *a.* odorless, inodorous.

Duft-losigkeit, *f.* lack of odor. -öl, *n.* fragrant oil, perfume oil.

duftreich, *a.* fragrant; odorous.

Duftstoff, *m.*, odorous substance, aromatic principle, perfume.

Dugongöl, *n.* dugong oil.

**Duktilität,** *f.* ductility.

**Dulcit,** *n.* dulcitol, dulcite.

**dulden,** *v.t.* bear, endure, suffer.

**Dulzin,** *n.* dulcin.

**Dulzit,** *n.* dulcitol, dulcite.

**dumm,** *a.* stupid, dull, silly.

**dumpf,** *a.* damp, musty; hollow; dull; close.

**Dung,** *m.* manure, fertilizer; dung.

**dungartig,** *a.* dunglike, stercoraceous.

**Dünge-gips,** *m.* gypsum for manuring. **-jauche,** *f.* dung water, liquid manure. **-kalk,** *m.* manuring lime. **-mittel,** *n.* manure, fertilizer.

**düngen,** *v.t.* manure, fertilize.

**Düngepulver,** *n.* powdered manure.

**Dünger,** *m.* manure, fertilizer; dung. **-bedarf,** *m.* fertilizer requirement.

**Dungerde,** *f.* mold, humus, compost.

**Dünger-fabrik,** *f.* fertilizer factory. **-salz,** *n.* = Düngesalz. **-versuch,** *m.* fertilizer experiment. **-wert,** *m.* manurial value.

**Düngesalz,** *n.* saline manure, fertilizer salt.

**Dung-fabrik,** *f.* fertilizer factory. **-jauche,** *f.* dung water, liquid manure. **-mittel,** *n.* manure, fertilizer. **-pulver,** *n.* powdered manure, poudrette. **-salz,** *n.* saline manure, fertilizer salt.

**Düngung,** *f.* manuring, fertilizing.

**dunkel,** *a.* dark; dim, obscure.

**Dunkel,** *n.* dark, darkness, obscurity.

**dunkelblau,** *a.* dark blue.

**Dunkelbraun,** *n.* dark brown.

**dunkelfarbig,** *a.* dark-colored.

**Dunkel-färbung,** *f.* darkening. **-feld,** *n.* dark field, dark ground. **-feldbeleuchtung,** *f.* dark-field illumination.

**dunkelgelb,** *a.* dark yellow.

**Dunkel-glühhitze,** *f.* = Dunkelrotglut. **-grau,** *n.* dark gray.

**dunkelgrün,** *a.* dark green.

**Dunkel-heit,** *f.* darkness; obscurity. **-kammer,** *f.* dark room; camera obscura.

**dunkeln,** *v.t. & i.* darken; deepen, sadden (colors).

**dunkelrot,** *a.* dark red.

**Dunkelrot-glut,** *f.* dull red heat (about 700°). **-gültigerz, -giltigerz,** *n.* dark red silver ore (pyrargyrite).

**dünken,** *v.i.* seem, appear.

**dünn,** *a.* thin; dilute, rare, slender.

**Dünn-bier,** *n.* small beer. **-darm,** *m.* small intestine.

**Dünne,** *f.* thinness.

**dünnflüssig,** *a.* thinly liquid; watery.

**Dünn-flüssigkeit,** *f.* thinly liquid state. **-heit,** *f.* thinness, diluteness, rarity, slenderness. **-saft,** *m.* (*Sugar*) thin juice.

**dünn-schalig,** *a.* thin-skinned; thin-shelled.

**-schlagen,** *v.t.* beat out, beat thin. **-schuppig,** *a.* in thin scales.

**Dünnstein,** *m.* (*Metal.*) thin matte; (*Jewelry*) table stone.

**dünn-tafelig,** *a.* in thin plates. **-walzen,** *v.t.* roll out, roll thin. **-wandig,** *a.* thin-walled.

**Dunst,** *m.* vapor; steam, fume, damp; smoke; fine shot; flue dust. **-abzug,** *m.* hood (for fumes). **-abzugsrohr,** *n.* vent pipe.

**dunstartig,** *a.* vaporous.

**Dunstbad,** *n.* vapor bath.

**dunsten,** *v.i.* evaporate, vaporize; smoke, fume, steam.

**dünsten,** *v.i.* steam, vapor, smoke.—*v.t.* stew.

**Dunst-essig,** *m.* aromatic vinegar. **-fang,** *m.* hood.

**dunstförmig,** *a.* vaporous.

**Dunsthülle,** *f.* vaporous envelope, atmosphere.

**dunstig, dünstig,** *a.* vaporous, vapory; steamy; foggy; damp, moist.

**Dunstigkeit,** *f.* vaporousness; fogginess; dampness.

**Dunst-kreis,** *m.* atmosphere. **-loch,** *n.* vent; air hole.

**dunstlos,** *a.* vaporless, fumeless.

**Dunst-messer,** *m.* atmometer. **-rohr,** *n.* ventilating pipe.

**dupliziert,** *a.* duplicate, double.

**durch,** *prep.* thru; by, owing to.—*adv.* thru.

**durch-.** thru, thru and thru, thoroly.

**durcharbeiten,** *v.t.* work thru, work; knead (dough); elaborate; (*Dyeing*) pole.

**durchätzen,** *v.t.* eat thru, corrode.

**durchaus,** *adv.* thruout, completely, absolutely, by all means.

**durchbacken,** *v.t.* bake thoroly.

**durchbeissen,** *v.t.* bite thru, eat thru.

**durchbeizen,** *v.t.* corrode (thoroly or thru); steep thoroly.

**durchbeuteln,** *v.t.* bolt (flour).

**durchbiegen,** *v.r.* sag, bend.—*v.t.* break by bending.

**Durchbiegung,** *f.* sagging; deflection.

**Durchbiegungsmesser,** *m.* deflectometer.

**durchbittern,** *v.t.* make thoroly bitter.

**durchblasen,** *v.t.* blow thru; bubble.

**durchblättern,** *v.t.* turn the pages of, glance thru; split into lamellae.

**durchbläuen,** *v.t.* blue thoroly.

**durchbohren,** *v.t.* perforate; bore thru, punch; pierce; penetrate.

**Durchbohrung,** *f.* perforation; boring thru.

**durchbrechen,** *v.t.* break, break thru, cut, pierce, punch, perforate.—*v.i.* break thru, break out; appear; break.—**durchbrochen,** *p.a.* pierced, perforated, open-work.

**durchbrennen,** *v.t.* burn thru; burn thoroly; melt thru.—*v.i.* burn thru, burn out.

**Durchbruch,** *m.* breaking out or thru; escape

(of gas); irruption, eruption; opening, aperture, breach, crevasse; (*Brewing*) collapse (of the head).

**durchdampfen,** *v.t.* fill with vapor or fumes.

**durchdämpfen,** *v.t.* steam.

**durchdringbar,** *a.* permeable, penetrable.

**Durchdringbarkeit,** *f.* permeability, penetrability.

**durchdringen,** *v.t.& i.* penetrate; permeate, pervade.—**durchdringend,** *p.a.* penetrating, penetrative.

**durchdringlich,** *a.* permeable, pervious.

**Durchdringlichkeit,** *f.* penetrability, permeability.

**Durchdringung,** *f.* penetration; permeation.

**Durchdringungsvermögen,** *n.* penetrating power.

**durchdrücken,** *v.t.* = durchpressen.

**Durchdrungenheit,** *f.* (state of) permeation.

**durch-duften, -düften,** *v.t.* scent, perfume.

**durch-dunsten, -dünsten,** *v.t.* permeate with vapor.—*v.i.* pass thru as vapor.

**durcheinander,** *adv.* confusedly. **-schütteln,** *v.t.* shake (thoroly).

**Durchfahrt,** *f.* thorofare, passage, gateway.

**Durchfall,** *m.* diarrhea; failure.

**durchfallen,** *v.i.* fall thru; (of light) be transmitted; (of beer) clear; (of beer head) fall back; fail.

**durchfärbbar,** *a.* penetrable with color.

**durchfärben,** *v.t.* dye thoroly; color thruout.

**durchfaulen,** *v.i.* rot thru, rot completely.

**durchfeuchten,** *v.t.* soak; saturate with moisture.

**durchfeuern,** *v.t.* fire or heat thoroly.

**durchfiltrieren, -filtern,** *v.t.* filter thru, filter.

**durchfliessen,** *v.i.* flow thru.

**Durchfluss,** *m.* flowing thru, flow. **-zeit,** *f.* time of flow (thru).

**durchforschen,** *v.t.* investigate thoroly.

**Durchforschung,** *f.* examination, investigation.

**durchfressen,** *v.t.* eat thru, corrode.

**durchfrieren,** *v.t.* freeze thru, chill.

**Durchfuhr,** *f.* transport, conveyance.

**durchführbar,** *a.* practicable, feasible.

**Durchführbarkeit,** *f.* practicability, feasibility.

**durchführen,** *v.t.* lead thru, convey thru; carry thru, execute, accomplish, conduct; (*Tinplate*) dip, wash.

**Durchführung,** *f.* leading thru, etc. (see durchführen).

**Durchgang,** *m.* passage; transit.

**durchgängig,** *a.* penetrable, permeable; thoro; general, usual.

**Durchgangshahn,** *m.* straightway cock.

**durchgären,** *v.t.* ferment thoroly.

**durchgeben,** *v.t.* filter, strain.

**durchgehen,** *v.i.* go thru; run away; (of light)

be transmitted.—*v.t.* go thru, examine.——**lassen,** let thru, pass thru.—**durchgehend,** *p.a.* piercing, pervading; passing thru; transmitted (light).

**durchgehends,** *adv.* thruout; generally.

**durchgerben,** *v.t.* tan thoroly.

**Durchgerbungszahl,** *f.* degree of tanning, tanning number.

**Durchgeseihtes,** *n.* filtrate.

**durchgiessen,** *v.t.* pour thru, filter, strain.

**durchglühen,** *v.t.* heat redhot.

**Durchguss,** *m.* filter, strainer; pouring thru, filtration; gutter; sink.

**Durchhang,** *m.* sag, dip.

**durchheizen, durchhitzen,** *v.t.* heat thoroly.

**durchkälten,** *v.t.* chill thoroly.

**durchklären,** *v.t.* clear or clarify thoroly.

**durchkneten,** *v.t.* knead thoroly.

**durchkochen,** *v.t.* boil thoroly.

**durchkommen,** *v.i.* come thru, get along, recover.

**durchkreuzen,** *v.t.* cross, traverse, intersect.

**durchkühlen,** *v.t.* cool or chill thoroly.

**Durchlass,** *m.* filter, sieve; passage, opening; outlet.

**durchlassen,** *v.t.* filter, strain; transmit (light, etc.); let thru; let pass.

**durchlässig,** *a.* permeable, pervious, penetrable.

**Durchlässigkeit,** *f.* permeability, perviousness.

**Durchlassung,** *f.* filtering, etc. (see lassen); (of light, etc.) transmission.

**Durchlauf,** *m.* sieve, colander; running thru; passage; (*Med.*) diarrhea.

**durchlaufen,** *v.i.* filter; run thru.—*v.t.* run thru, pass thru, traverse.

**durchlaugen,** *v.t.* lye or lixiviate thoroly.

**durchläutern,** *v.t.* purify or refine thoroly.

**durchleiten,** *v.t.* pass thru, conduct.

**durchleuchten,** *v.t.* illuminate; irradiate.

**Durchleuchtung,** *f.* illumination.

**durchlochen,** *v.t.* perforate, punch; core (fruit).

**durchlöchern,** *v.t.* perforate; pierce, punch.

**durchlüften,** *v.t.* ventilate, air.

**durchlüftungsfähig,** *a.* capable of ventilation or aëration.

**durchmachen,** *v.t.* go thru; experience.

**durchmessen,** *v.t.* pass thru, traverse, measure.

**Durchmesser,** *m.* diameter.

**durchmischen,** *v.t.* mix thoroly; intermix.

**durchmustern,** *v.t.* examine closely, scrutinize, inspect, review, scan, explore.

**durchnässen,** *v.t.* wet thoroly, soak, steep.

**durchnehmen,** *v.t.* go over, criticize.

**durchnetzen,** *v.t.* = durchnässen.

**durchölen,** *v.t.* oil (thoroly).

**durchpressen,** *v.t. & i.* press thru, force thru, squeeze thru; strain, filter.

**Durchprüfung,** *f.* thoro testing or examining.

**durchqueren,** *v.t.* traverse, cross.

**durchräuchern,** *v.t.* fumigate; smoke thoroly.

**durchrechnen,** *v.t.* calculate; recalculate, check.

**durchreiben,** *v.t.* rub thru, strain; chafe, gall.

**durchreissen,** *v.t. & i.* tear asunder, break.

**durchrosten,** *v.i.* rust thru, rust completely.

**durchrösten,** *v.t.* roast thoroly.

**durchrühren,** *v.t.* stir thoroly.

**durchsättigen,** *v.t.* saturate.

**durchsäuern,** *v.t.* acidify; make sour; leaven thoroly.

**durchsaugen,** *v.t.* suck thru, force thru by suction.

**durchscheinen,** *v.i.* shine thru.—**durchscheinend,** *p.a.* translucent; transparent.

**durchschiessen,** *v.t.* shoot thru; insert; interleave; interline.—*v.i.* shoot (thru).

**Durchschlag,** *m.* filter, strainer; screen, sieve; punch, piercer; opening; carbon copy. **-boden,** *m.* perforated bottom.

**durchschlagen,** *v.t.* filter, strain; sieve; punch, puncture, perforate; beat thru; traverse. —*v.i.* get thru, penetrate; (of paper) blot; (*Elec.*) spark; act.

**Durchschlag-festigkeit,** *f.* (*Elec.*) dielectric strength, disruptive strength. **-papier,** *n.* copying paper, carbon paper. **-spannung,** *f.* breakdown voltage, disruptive voltage.

**durchschmelzen,** *v.t. & i.* melt thru; melt or fuse thoroly.

**durchschmieren,** *v.t.* grease or lubricate thoroly.

**durchschmolzen,** *p.p.* of durchschmelzen.

**durchschneiden,** *v.t.* intersect, cross; cut thru; pierce; cut across; traverse, cross.

**Durchschnitt,** *m.* cut, section; intersection; average, mean.

**durchschnittlich,** *a.* average.—*adv.* on an average.

**Durchschnitts-bestimmung,** *f.* average determination. **-ertrag,** *m.* average yield; average profit. **-muster,** *n.* average sample. **-probe,** *f.* average sample. **-punkt,** *m.* point of intersection. **-temperatur,** *f.* mean temperature. **-wert,** *m.* average value. **-zahl,** *f.* mean.

**Durchschuss,** *m.* woof, weft; interleaf; (*Printing*) white space, blank.

**durchschütteln,** *v.t.* shake thoroly, agitate.

**durchschwängern,** *v.t.* impregnate thoroly.

**durchschwefeln,** *v.t.* sulfur(ize) thoroly.

**durchschwelen,** *v.i.* smolder.—*v.t.* cause to smolder.

**durchschwitzen,** *v.i.* sweat, ooze thru.

**durch-seigen, -seigern, -seihen,** *v.t.* strain, filter, percolate.

**Durchseiher,** *m.* strainer, filter, percolator.

**Durchseihung,** *f.* straining, filtration, percolation.

**durchsetzen,** *v.t.* permeate, infiltrate; (*Min.*) intermingle; (*Mining*) sieve, sift; intersect; carry thru.

**Durchsicht,** *f.* view, inspection, revision.

**durchsichtig,** *a.* transparent; clear.

**Durchsichtigkeit,** *f.* transparency; clearness.

**durchsickern,** *v.i. & r.* trickle thru, filter thru, percolate.—*v.t.* strain, filter.

**durchsieben,** *v.t.* sift, sieve, screen, bolt.

**durchsieden,** *v.t.* boil thoroly.

**durchsintern,** *v.i.* trickle thru, percolate.

**durchspülen,** *v.t.* rinse well, wash well.

**durchstechen,** *v.t.* pierce, stab, cut; (*Metal.*) smelt.

**Durchstich,** *m.* piercing, cutting, cut; excavation.

**durchstossen,** *v.t.* push thru, punch.

**durchstrahlen,** *v.i.* radiate thru, shine thru. —*v.t.* penetrate with rays, irradiate.

**durchstreichen,** *v.t.* run thru, go thru; sift, screen; cross out.—**durchstreichende Linie,** trajectory.

**durchströmen,** *v.t.* stream thru, flow thru.

**Durchströmung,** *f.* streaming thru; perfusion.

**durchsüssen,** *v.t.* sweeten thoroly; edulcorate.

**durchtränken,** *v.t.* saturate, impregnate, infiltrate.

**Durchtränkung,** *f.* saturation, impregnation.

**durchtreiben,** *v.t.* drive or force thru; specif. distil.—**durchtrieben,** *p.a.* cunning, sly.

**durchtrocknen,** *v.t. & i.* dry thoroly.

**durchwachsen,** *v.t. & i.* grow thru.—*v.r.* interpenetrate, intermingle.

**Durchwanderung,** *f.* passing thru; diffusion.

**durchwärmen,** *v.t.* warm thoroly.

**durchwärmig,** *a.* diathermic.

**Durchwärmigkeit,** *f.* diathermancy.

**durchwaschen,** *v.t.* wash thru; wash thoroly.

**durchwässern,** *v.t.* soak, drench.

**durchweg,** *adv.* thruout.

**durchweichen,** *v.t. & i.* soften; soak, steep.

**durchwerfen,** *v.t.* sift, screen, bolt; traject.

**Durchwurf,** *m.* sieve, screen, riddle.

**durchzeichnen,** *v.t.* trace.

**durchziehen,** *v.t.* draw thru; intermix; traverse; penetrate.—*v.r.* pass thru.

**Durchziehglas,** *n.* (*Micros.*) slide.

**Durchzug,** *m.* passage; circulation; girder.

**dürfen,** *v.i.* be permitted; need; dare; be likely; may.

**durfte,** *pret.* of dürfen.

**dürftig,** *a.* scanty, poor; needy.

**Duro-chinon,** *n.* duroquinone. **-hydrochinon,** *n.* durohydroquinone.

**Durol**, *n.* durene.

**dürr**, *a.* dry, arid; dried, withered, dead; barren, sterile; lean; plain.

**Dürre**, *f.* dryness, etc. (see dürr); drought.

**Durst**, *m.* thirst.

**dursten, dürsten**, *v.i.* be thirsty.

**durstig**, *a.* thirsty; eager.

**Düse**, *f.* nozzle, twyer (or tuyère), blast-pipe; jet; head (of a burner).

**Düsenrohr**, *n.* blast pipe.

**düster**, *a.* dark, dusky; gloomy, sad.

**Düte, Dute**, *f.* = Tüte.

**Dutzend**, *n.* dozen.

**Dynamik**, *f.* dynamics.

**dynamisch**, *a.* dynamic.

**dystektisch**, *a.* dystectic.

**Dz., dz.,** *abbrev.* (Doppelzentner) double centner, 100 kilograms.

# E

E., *abbrev.* (Erstarrungspunkt) freezing point.

Ebbe, *f.* ebb, ebb tide.

ebd., *abbrev.* (ebenda) at that same place.

eben, *a.* even; plane; level; flat, smooth.— *adv.* evenly; exactly; even, just.

Eben, *n.* ebony. -baum, *m.* ebony tree.

Ebenbild, *n.* image, likeness.

ebenda, *adv.* at that same place.

Ebene, *f.* plane; plain.

ebenen, *v.t.* level, flatten, smooth.

ebenfalls, *adv.* likewise, also, equally.

ebenflächig, *a.* flat-surfaced, plane.

Ebenholz, *n.* ebony.

ebenieren, *v.t.* ebonize.

Ebenmass, *n.* symmetry; harmony.

ebenmässig, *a.* symmetrical, proportionate.

ebenso, *adv.* just so, just as, likewise.

ebensogut, *adv.* just as well.

ebensolch, *a.* similar, like, of the same kind.

ebensoviel, *a.* just as much, as much, as many.

Eber, *m.* boar. -esche, *f.* mountain ash, service tree. -raute, *f.* southernwood, abrotanum (*Artemisia abrotanum*). -wurz, -wurzel, *f.* carline thistle (*Carlina*); carline root.

Ebne, *n.* plane; plain.

ebnen, *v.t.* = ebenen.

ebullieren, *v.i.* boil up; break out.

ebullioskopisch, *a.* ebullioscopic.

Echappé-Öl, *n.* recovered oil.

echt, *a.* genuine, true, real; pure, unadulterated; (of colors) fast; ingrain.

Echt-baumwollblau, *n.* fast cotton blue. -blau, *n.* fast blue. -braun, *n.* fast brown. -färben, *n.* fast dyeing. -gelb, *n.* fast yellow. -grün, *n.* fast green.

Echtheit, *f.* genuineness, etc. (see echt).

Echtheitsgrad, *m.* (*Dyeing*) degree of fastness.

Echt-rot, *n.* fast red. -säurefuchsin, *n.* fast acid fuchsine. -schwarz, *n.* fast black.

Eck, *n.* angle; summit (of a crystal).

Ecke, *f.* corner, angle; edge (plane angle); summit (of a crystal); quoin.

Eckeisen, *n.* angle iron; (*Metal.*) angular iron.

Ecker, *f.* acorn; beechnut. -doppe, *f.* acorn cup.

Eckholz, *n.* squared timber.

eckig, *a.* angular, cornered, angled; awkward.

edel, *a.* noble (as applied to metals, resisting oxidation, as gold and the platinum metals and, to a lesser extent, silver and some others; as applied to gases, inert, as

argon); rare (as earths); precious (stones, etc.); (*Mining*) rich; vital (organs, parts).

Edel-erde, *f.* rare earth. -erz, *n.* rich ore, ore containing precious metals. -galmei, *m.* smithsonite. -gamander, *m.* wall germander (*Teucrium chamaedrys*). -gas, *n.* noble gas, inert gas, rare gas (any gas of the argon group). -glanz, *m.* a special lustrous finish on metal, paper or the like. -leute, *pl.* nobility, gentry. -metall, *n.* noble or precious metal (see edel).

edelmütig, *a.* noble, generous.

Edel-porzellan, *n.* hard porcelain. -rost, *m.* patina, aerugo nobilis. -salze, *n.pl.* = Abraumsalze. -spat, *m.* adularia. -stahl, *m.* refined steel; specif. any of certain superior alloy steels. -stein, *m.* precious stone, gem, jewel. -tanne, *f.* silver fir (esp. *Abies picea*).

edieren, *v.t.* edit; publish.

edulkorieren, *v.t.* edulcorate, wash.

Efeu, *m.* ivy.

Effekt, *m.* effect; power; security (stock, bond, etc.).

efferveszieren, *v.i.* effervesce.

effloreszieren, *v.i.* effloresce.

Effluvien, *n.pl.* effluvia.

Eg., *abbrev.* (Eisessig) glacial acetic acid.

egal, *a.* equal; even (colors).

egalisieren, *v.t.* equalize; level, flatten.—*v.i.* (*Dyeing*) dye evenly.

Egalisierer, *m.* equalizer; (*Dyeing*) leveling agent.

Egalität, *f.* equality, evenness.

Egel, *m.* leech.

Egge, *f.* harrow; selvage.

eggen, *v.t.* harrow.

Egoutteur, *m.* (*Paper*) dandy roll.

Egreniermaschine, *f.* (cotton) gin.

ehe, *conj.* before, ere.

Ehe, *f.* matrimony, marriage.

ehedem, *adv.* formerly.

ehemalig, *a.* former, past, late.

ehemals, *adv.* formerly.

eher, *adv.* sooner, rather.

ehern, *a.* brazen, of brass, of bronze.

eheste, *a.* soonest, next.—am ehesten, most nearly; soonest, first.

ehmalig, etc. see ehemalig, etc.

ehrbar, *a.* honorable; reputable; modest.

Ehrbegierde, *f.* ambition.

Ehre, *f.* honor; character; reputation.

**ehren,** *v.t.* honor; esteem.

**ehrenhaft,** *a.* honorable.

**Ehren-mitglied,** *n.* honorary member. **-preis,** *m.* speedwell, veronica; prize. **-rettung,** *f.* vindication; apology. **-stelle,** *f.* honor, preferment.

**ehren-voll,** *a.* honorable, creditable. **-wert,** *a.* honorable, respectable.

**Ehrgeiz,** *m.* ambition.

**ehrlich,** *a.* honest, fair, honorable, decent.

**Ei,** *n.* egg; ovum.

**Eibe,** *f.* yew.

**Eibisch,** *m.* marsh mallow (the plant). **-wurzel,** *f.* marsh mallow root. **-zucker,** *m.* marshmallow (the confection).

**Eich-amt,** *n.* gaging office. **-apfel,** *m.* oak gall, gall nut. **-baum,** *m.* oak tree.

**Eiche,** *f.* oak; gage, standard.

**Eichel,** *f.* acorn; glans penis. **-doppe,** *f.* acorn cup.

**eichelförmig,** *a.* acorn-shaped, glandiform.

**Eichel-kernöl,** *n.* acorn oil. **-zucker,** *m.* acorn sugar, quercitol.

**eichen,** *a.* oak, oaken.

**eichen,** *v.t.* gage, measure, standardize, calibrate; test or adjust (weights or measures).

**Eichen,** *n.* little egg; ovule.

**Eichen-gerbsäure,** *f.,* **-gerbstoff,** *m.* quercitannic acid, oak tannin. **-holz,** *n.* oak wood, oak. **-kern,** *m.* acorn. **-lohe,** *f.* tanbark (from oak). **-mehl,** *n.* powdered oak bark. **-rinde,** *f.* oak bark. **-rindengerbsäure,** *f.* quercitannic acid. **-rot,** *n.* oak red. **-samen,** *m.* acorn.

**Eicher,** *m.* gager.

**eichfähig,** *a.* capable of adjustment.

**Eich-gas,** *n.* standard gas. **-holz,** *n.* oak wood, oak. **-kurve,** *f.* calibration curve. **-mass,** *n.* gage, standard (measure). **-meister,** *m.* gager, adjuster. **-nagel,** *m.* gage mark. **-punkt,** *m.* reference point. **-schein,** *m.* certificate (that an instrument has been standardized).

**Eichung,** *f.* gaging, etc. (see eichen, *v.t.*).

**Eichwert,** *m.* reference value, standard value.

**Eid,** *m.* oath.

**Eidechse,** *f.* lizard.

**Eidgenoss,** *m.* confederate, ally.

**Eidotter,** *m.* egg yolk. **-fett,** *n.* lecithin.

**Eier,** *n.pl.* eggs. **-albumin,** *n.* egg albumin, ovalbumin. **-dotter,** *m.* yolk of eggs. **-drüse,** *f.* corpus luteum. **-öl,** *n.* egg-yolk oil. **-pulver,** *n.* egg powder, custard powder. **-schale,** *f.* egg shell. **-stein,** *m.* oölite, egg stone.

**eiersteinartig,** *a.* oölitic.

**Eier-stock,** *m.* ovary. **-weiss,** *n.* white of eggs.

**Eifer,** *m.* zeal, eagerness, passion. **-sucht,** *f.* jealousy; rivalry; envy.

**eiförmig,** *a.* egg-shaped, oval, ovoid.

**eifrig,** *a.* zealous, earnest, ardent, eager.

**eig.,** *abbrev.* (eigentlich) proper; properly; (eigen, eigene, etc.) see eigen.

**Eig.,** *abbrev.* (Eigenschaft) property.

**Eigelb,** *n.* egg yolk.

**eigen,** *a.* own, individual, proper, characteristic, intrinsic, specific, special, self-, idio-, auto-; odd; exact.

**Eigenart,** *f.* peculiarity, individuality.

**eigenartig,** *a.* peculiar, singular; original.

**Eigen-artigkeit,** *f.* peculiarity. **-bewegung,** *f.* proper motion, individual motion. **-drehimpuls,** *m.* proper (or characteristic) angular momentum. **-drehung,** *f.* proper rotation. **-farbe,** *f.* proper color, intrinsic color.

**eigenfarbig,** *a.* self-colored, colored.

**Eigen-frequenz,** *f.* proper or characteristic frequency. **-funktion,** *f.* proper function, characteristic function, "eigenfunktion." **-gewicht,** *n.* specific gravity; its own weight; dead weight; proper weight.

**eigen-händig,** *a.* with one's own hand. **-mächtig,** *a.* arbitrary; despotic.

**Eigen-mittel,** *n.* (*Med.*) specific remedy. **-name,** *m.* proper name.

**eigennützig,** *a.* selfish.

**eigens,** *adv.* expressly.

**Eigenschaft,** *f.* property; quality.

**Eigenschaftswort,** *n.* adjective; epithet.

**Eigen-schwingung,** *f.* proper or characteristic vibration. **-sinn,** *m.* wilfulness, stubbornness. **-strahlung,** *f.* proper or characteristic radiation.

**eigentlich,** *a.* proper, true, real, intrinsic.— *adv.* properly, really.

**Eigentum,** *n.* property.

**eigentümlich,** *a.* characteristic; peculiar; specific.

**Eigentümlichkeit,** *f.* characteristic; peculiarity.

**Eigenvergiftung,** *f.* autointoxication.

**Eigen-wärme,** *f.* specific heat; body heat. **-wert,** *m.* proper value, characteristic value, "eigenwert." **-zustand,** *m.* proper or characteristic state.

**eignen,** *v.t.* suit, qualify; appropriate.—*v.r.* be qualified, be suited, be adapted.—**geeignet,** *p.a.* suited, adapted, suitable, fit, proper.

**Eikosan,** *n.* eicosane, icosane, eikosane.

**Eil-.** quick, fast, express.

**Eiland,** *n.* island.

**Eile,** *f.* haste; speed.

**eilen,** *v.i.* hasten, hurry.

**eilfertig,** *a.* hasty.

**Eilgut,** *n.* goods shipped on post trains.

**eilig,** *a.* hasty, speedy.

**Eilzug,** *m.* express train, fast train.

**Eimer,** *m.* bucket, pail.

**ein,** *a. a,* an; one.

**ein,** *adv.* in, within, into; (of an electric switch) on.

**ein-, Ein-.** one-, single, mono-, uni-.

**einachsig,** *a.* uniaxial.

**einander,** *adv.* one another, each other.

**einarmig,** *a.* one-armed.

**einäschern,** *v.t.* incinerate, calcine; burn to ashes.

**Einäscherung,** *f.* incineration, calcination.

**einatembar,** *a.* respirable.

**einatmen,** *v.t.* inhale.

**Einatmung,** *f.* inhalation.

**einatomig,** *a.* monatomic.

**Einatomigkeit,** *f.* monatomicity.

**einätzen,** *v.t.* etch.

**Einätzung,** *f.* etching.

**einäugig,** *a.* monocular; one-eyed.

**einbadig,** *a.* single-bath.

**Einbad-schwarz,** *n.* (*Dyeing*) one-dip black. **-verfahren,** *n.* single-bath process.

**einbalsamieren,** *v.t.* embalm.

**Einbalsamierung,** *f.* embalmment.

**Einband,** *m.* binding; cover.

**einbasisch, einbasig,** *a.* monobasic.

**Einbau,** *m.* building in; installation.

**einbauen,** *v.t.* build in; fit in; install.

**einbegreifen,** *v.t.* include; imply.

**einbehalten,** *v.t.* keep back, retain.

**einbeizen,** *v.t.* etch in.

**einbetten,** *v.t.* imbed; insert.

**einbeziehen,** *v.t.* =hineinziehen.

**einbiegen,** *v.t.* bend in, turn down, deflect. —*v.r.* sag.

**Einbiegung,** *f.* curvature, inflection.

**einbilden,** *v.r.* imagine, think; pride oneself. —**eingebildet,** *p.a.* imaginary; conceited.

**Einbildung,** *f.* imagination, fancy.

**einbinden,** *v.t.* bind, bind in, fasten.

**einblasen,** *v.t.* blow in, blow into, insufflate, bubble thru, inject (gas).

**einblauen, einbläuen,** *v.t.* blue.

**Einblick,** *m.* insight.

**einbrechen,** *v.i.* break (into); break (in); begin.—*v.t.* break in.

**einbrennen,** *v.t.* burn in; anneal (colors); cauterize; brand; sulfur, match (casks).

**einbringen,** *v.t.* bring in, get in, yield; insert, introduce.

**Einbruch,** *m.* breaking in; breaking down; burglary.

**einbrühen,** *v.t.* steep in boiling water, scald.

**einbürgern,** *v.t.* adopt; naturalize.—*v.r.* gain vogue, come into use; become naturalized.

**Einbusse,** *f.* loss, damage.

**einbüssen,** *v.t.* lose.

**Eindampfapparat,** *m.* evaporating apparatus.

**eindampfen,** *v.i.* become thickened by evaporation, boil down.

**eindampfen, eindämpfen,** *v.t.* evaporate, concentrate by evaporation, boil down, inspissate; steam; smoke.

**Eindampfen,** *n.,* **Eindampfung, Eindämpfung,** *f.* evaporation, etc. (see eindampfen).

**Eindampfer,** *m.* evaporator, concentrator.

**Eindampfgerät,** *n.* evaporator.

**eindecken,** *v.t.* cover.

**Eindeckung,** *f.* covering; roofing.

**eindellen,** *v.t.* dent.

**eindeutig,** *a.* plain, clear, unequivocal.

**eindichten,** *v.t.* condense.

**Eindickanlage,** *f.* concentrating plant.

**eindickbar,** *a.* capable of being thickened or concentrated.

**Eindicke,** *f.* thickening, concentration, inspissation.

**eindicken,** *v.t.* thicken, concentrate, inspissate.

**Eindickung,** *f.* thickening, concentration, inspissation.

**Eindickungsmittel,** *n.* thickening agent.

**eindimensional,** *a.* unidimensional.

**eindorren,** *v.i.* shrink in drying; dry up.

**eindrängen,** *v.t.* force in, intrude.

**eindringen,** *v.t.* press in, penetrate, infiltrate.

**eindringlich,** *a.* impressive; forcible.

**Eindringungsfähigkeit,** *f.* penetrativity.

**Eindruck,** *m.* impression.

**eindrucken,** *v.t.* (*Calico*) block in, ground in.

**eindrücken,** *v.t.* imprint, impress, stamp; crush in; flatten; press, compress.

**Eindruckfarbe,** *f.* (*Calico*) grounding in.

**eindunsten, eindünsten,** *v.t.* evaporate down, concentrate by evaporation; impregnate with vapor.—*v.i.* evaporate down.

**Eindunstung,** *f.* evaporation; impregnation with vapor.

**einen,** *v.t.& r.* unite.

**einengen,** *v.t.* concentrate; compress, confine, narrow, contract.

**einer,** *pron.* one.

**Einer,** *m.* unit, digit.

**einerlei,** *a.* of one kind, all the same.— **— ob,** regardless of whether.

**einerseits,** *adv.* on the one hand.

**einfach,** *a.* simple; single; elementary; primary (colors); plain.—**einfacher Körper,** simple or elementary substance, element.

**einfach-.** (in old names of compounds) proto- (mono-; -ous).— **—-Bromjod,** iodine monobromide.— **—-Chlorjod,** iodine monochloride.— **—-Chlorschwefel,** protochloride of sulfur (sulfur monochloride).— **—-Chlorzinn,** protochloride of tin (stannous chloride).— **—-Schwefeleisen,** protosulfide of iron (ferrous sulfide).— **—-Schwefelmetall,**

protosulfide (monosulfide; -ous sulfide).— —-Schwefelzinn, protosulfide of tin (stannous sulfide).

einfach-brechend, a. singly refracting. -frei, a. having one degree of freedom, univariant.

Einfachheit, f. simplicity; singleness.

einfach-kohlensauer, a. neutral carbonate of. -weinsauer, a. neutral tartrate of. -wirkend, p.a. single-acting.

einfädeln, v.t. thread; contrive.

einfahren, v.t. carry in, get in, break in, break.

Einfahrt, f. entrance.

Einfall, m. falling in, fall, decay, inroad, idea; (Physics) incidence.

einfallen, v.i. fall upon, fall in, interrupt, occur; (Mining) dip; (Optics) be incident. —einfallend, p.a. (Optics) incident.

Einfalls-lot, n. perpendicular, ordinate. -strahl, m. incident ray. -winkel, m. angle of incidence.

Einfalt, f. simplicity, simpleness.

einfangen, v.t. capture, catch, seize.

Einfangung, f. capture (as of an electron).

einfärben, v.t. color or dye well; dye in the grain; ink.

einfarbig, a. of one color, monochromatic.

einfassen, v.t. enclose, fill, case, barrel; bind, trim, set; border; surround.

einfetten, v.t. grease, oil; lubricate.

Einfettung, f. greasing, oiling; lubrication.

einfeuchten, v.t. moisten, dampen, wet.

einfinden, v.r. appear.

einflammig, a. single-flame.

einflechten, v.t. weave in, interweave.

einfliessen, v.i. flow in; come in.

einflössen, v.t. instill, infuse.

Einfluss, m. influence; influx.

einflussreich, a. influential.

Einfluss-rohr, n., -röhre, f. inlet pipe, influx pipe (or tube).

einformen, v.t. (Ceram.) mold on a jigger.

einförmig, a. uniform; monotonous.

einfressen, v.t. corrode; devour.

einfrieren, v.i. freeze, congeal, freeze up.

einfügen, v.t. insert; fit in; rabbet.

Einfuhr, f. importation, import; bringing in; supply.

einführen, v.t. introduce; import; inaugurate.

Einführung, f. introduction; importation; installation.

Einfuhrwaren, f.pl. imports.

einfüllen, v.t. fill, fill in, fill up, pour in.

Einfüll-stoff, m. filling, packing. -trichter, m. funnel tube; charging hopper.

Eingabe, f. presentation; petition.

Eingang, m. entrance; importation; introduction; mouth; receipt.

eingängig, a. (Mach.) single-thread.

eingangs, adv. at the outset.

eingeben, v.t. give, administer.

eingebildet, p.a. see einbilden.

eingeboren, p.a. inborn, innate; native.

eingebrannt, p.p. of einbrennen.

eingedenk, a. mindful.

eingehen, v.i. go in, come in, enter, arrive; cease; agree; (of fabrics) shrink.—eingehend, p.a. going in, etc.; thoro, exhaustive; (Geom.) reëntrant.—adv. thoroly, exhaustively.

eingemacht, p.p. of einmachen.

Eingemachtes, n. preserves, conserves.

eingenommen, p.a. see einnehmen.

eingesalzen, p.a. see einsalzen.

eingeschichtet, p.p. of einschichten.

eingeschliffen, p.p. of einschleifen.

eingeschmolzen, p.p. of einschmelzen.

eingesprengt, p.p. of einsprengen.

eingestehen, v.i. confess; admit, grant.

Eingeweide, n. entrails, viscera.

Eingeweide-. visceral.

eingiessen, v.t. pour in; infuse.

Eingiessung, f. pouring in; infusion; transfusion.

eingipsen, v.t. set in plaster of Paris.

eingraben, v.t. engrave; dig in.

eingreifen, v.i. catch, lock, interlock; act (chemically); infringe.—eingreifend, p.a. radical.

Eingreifen, n., Eingriff, m. intervention, interference; (chemical) action; (Mach.) gearing, gear.

eingrenzen, v.t. inclose; limit; localize.

Eingriff, m. (Mach.) connection, engagement; interference. —im —, in gear.

Einguss, m. pouring in; infusion; mold; ingot; (Founding) gate, runner, sprue.

Einhalt, m. check, restraint, interruption.

einhalten, v.t. keep in, take in, stop, keep. —v.i. cease.

einhändigen, v.t. hand over, deliver.

einhauen, v.t. cut in, cut open, break in.

einheimisch, a. domestic; native; indigenous; home-made; endemic.

Einheit, f. unit; unity.

einheitlich, a. unitary; uniform, homogeneous; centralized.

Einheitlichkeit, f. uniformity, homogeneity.

Einheits-. unit; standard, normal, uniform. -masse, f. unit mass.

einhellig, a. unanimous, united.

einher, adv. along.

einholen, v.t. overtake; obtain; haul in.

einhüllen, v.t. imbed; enwrap, envelop, cover.

einig, a. united, in accord; one, one only.

einigen, v.t. unite.

einiger, pron. some; several.

einigermassen, adv. in some degree.

**Einigkeit,** *f.* unity, union, harmony.
**Einigungskitt,** *m.* cement; putty.
**einimpfen,** *v.t.* inoculate.
**einjährig,** *a.* of one year, annual.
**einkalken, einkälken,** *v.t.* treat in lime, soak in lime water.
**Einkauf,** *m.* buying, purchase.
**einkellern,** *v.t.* store (in a cellar), cellar, lay in.
**einkerben,** *v.t.* notch, indent.
**Einkerbung,** *f.* notching, notch, indentation.
**einkernig,** *a.* uninucleate, mononuclear.
**einklammern,** *v.t.* enclose in brackets or parentheses; cramp.
**Einklang,** *m.* harmony, unison.
**einkleiden,** *v.t.* clothe, dress; coat.
**einkochen,** *v.t.* boil down, evaporate.—*v.i.* thicken by boiling.
**Einkochung,** *f.* boiling down, evaporation.
**Einkommen,** *n.* income; revenue; profit.
**Einkristall,** *m.* single crystal.
**Einkünfte,** *f.pl.* income, revenue.
**einladen,** *v.t.* load in; invite.
**Einlage,** *f.* something laid or put in; inclosure; charge; filler; deposit; investment.
**einlagern,** *v.t.* intercalate; infiltrate; embed, imbed; store.
**Einlagerung,** *f.* intercalation, etc. (see einlagern).
**Einlagerungsverbindung,** *f.* intercalation compound.
**Einlass,** *m.* inlet; letting in, admission.
**einlassen,** *v.t.* let in, admit; insert, introduce.
**Einlass-rohr,** *n* , **-röhre,** *f.* inlet tube or pipe. **-ventil,** *n.* inlet valve.
**einlaufecht,** *a.* unshrinkable.
**einlaufen,** *v.i.* enter; arrive; shrink, contract.
**einlaugen,** *v.t.* soak in lye, buck.
**einlegen,** *v.t.* put, place, lay (in); soak, steep; pickle; preserve, put up (fruits, etc).; imbed; insert; inlay.
**einleiten,** *v.t.* introduce; (of gases) conduct, pass or convey in, inject; preface; initiate, start.
**Einleitung,** *f.* introduction, etc. (see einleiten); preface; preparation.
**Einleitungsrohr,** *n.* inlet tube, tube by which gases are introduced.
**einleuchten,** *v.i.* be clear.
**Einlinienspektrum,** *n.* spectrum of single lines.
**einlöten,** *v.t.* solder in.
**einmachen,** *v t* preserve, conserve, pickle; temper (lime); knead (dough); wrap up.
**Einmachesalz,** *n.* preserving salt.
**Einmachessig,** *m.* pickling vinegar.
**einmaischen,** *v.t.* (*Brewing*) dough in.
**Einmaischtemperatur,** *f.* (*Brewing*) doughing-in temperature, initial temperature (of the mash).

**einmal,** *adv.* once; ever.—**auf —,** all at once suddenly.—**nicht —,** not even.
**einmalig,** *a.* single; solitary.
**Einmalschmelzerei,** *f.* (*Iron*) single refining.
**einmarinieren,** *v.t.* pickle.
**einmauern,** *v.t.* wall in, build in, embed.
**einmischen,** *v.t.* mix in, intermix, blend.—*v.r.* interfere.
**einmünden,** *v.i.* empty, discharge; inosculate; enter, fit (in).
**einmütig,** *a.* of one mind, united.
**Einnahme,** *f.* taking in, receipt, receipts, income.
**einnehmen,** *v.t.* take in, take, receive; occupy; captivate; overcome.—**eingenommen,** *p.a.* prejudiced; infatuated; dizzy.
**Einöde,** *f.* desert, wild.
**einölen,** *v.t.* oil; lubricate.
**einordnen,** *v.t.* arrange; classify.
**Einordnung,** *f.* arrangement; classification.
**einpacken,** *v.t.* pack, pack up; imbed.
**einpassen,** *v.t.* fit in; adjust.
**Einphasen-.** (*Elec.*) single-phase.
**einphasig,** *a.* one-phase, single-phase, monophase, uniphase.
**einpökeln,** *v.t.* pickle, corn.
**einpolig,** *a.* unipolar.
**einprägen,** *v.t.* impress, imprint.
**einpressen,** *v.t.* press, compress; force in.
**einprozentig,** *a.* one-per-cent.
**einpudern,** *v.t.* powder.
**einpumpen,** *v.t.* pump in.
**einquantig,** *a.* of one quantum, one-quantum.
**Einquell-bottich,** *m.,* **-kufe,** *f.,* soaking tub, steeping vessel.
**einquellen,** *v.t.* steep, soak.
**Einquellwasser,** *n.* steeping water.
**einrahmen,** *v.t.* frame.
**Einrahmung,** *f.* framing, frame.
**einräuchern,** *v.t.* fumigate; smoke.
**Einräucherung,** *f.* fumigation.
**einräumen,** *v.t.* stow away; furnish; yield, concede.
**Einrede,** *f.* objection, protest.
**einreden,** *v.t.* talk into.—*v.i.* interrupt; object.
**einregulieren,** *v.t.* regulate.
**einreiben,** *v.t.* rub in, smear.
**Einreibesalbe,** *f.* rubbing ointment.
**Einreibung,** *f.* rubbing in, smearing; liniment, embrocation.
**Einreibungsmittel,** *n.* rubbing agent, specif. liniment.
**einreichen,** *v.t.* hand in, present.
**einreihen,** *v.t.* arrange, range, set in order; insert; enroll.
**einreihig,** *a.* single-series.
**einreissen,** *v.t.* rend; demolish.—*v.i.* tear; spread.
**einrennen,** *v.t.* melt down; run down.

**Einrennen,** *n.* melting down, first smelting.

**einrichten,** *v.t.* arrange, set right, adjust, organize, establish.

**Einrichtung,** *f.* arrangement; contrivance; establishment; installation; equipment; furniture; setting (of bones).

**Einriss,** *m.* rent, fissure, crack.

**einrosten,** *v.i.* rust in, be covered with rust.

**einrücken,** *v.t.* (*Mach.*) engage, cause to engage, throw in.

**einrühren,** *v.t.* mix by stirring, stir up; dilute; stir in; temper (mortar); beat (eggs).

**einrussen,** *v.t.* cover with soot.

**eins,** *a.* one.

**einsäen,** *v.t.* sow in (as crystals into a solution).

**einsalben,** *v.t.* grease, anoint; embalm.

**einsalzen,** *v.t.* salt, salt down, corn, brine.— **eingesalzen,** *p.a.* salted, corned, salt.

**Einsalzung,** *f.* salting, etc. (see einsalzen).

**einsam,** *a.* alone, solitary, retired.

**Einsatz,** *m.* putting in, insertion; something put in, as a tray, a nest (of boxes or the like), or a charge (in a furnace), or a liner (in a centrifugal drum). **-gewichte,** *n.pl.* weights in nests, nest of weights. **-härtung,** *f.* case-hardening. **-kessel,** *m.pl.* set of kettles. **-korb,** *m.* test-tube basket or cage. **-pulver,** *n.* cementing powder. **-stahl,** *m.* casehardened steel. **-tür,** *f.* charging door.

**einsäuern,** *v.t.* acidify, sour; vinegar, pickle; leaven.

**Einsäuerung,** *f.* acidification, souring; pickling; leavening.

**Einsäuerungsbad,** *n.* acid bath.

**Einsauge-.** absorbent; lymphatic. **-mittel,** *n.* absorbent.

**einsaugen,** *v.t.* absorb; suck up, suck in.—*v.r.* be absorbed, soak in.—**einsaugend,** *p.a.* absorbent, absorptive.

**Einsaugung,** *f.* absorption; suction.

**einsäurig,** *a.* monoacid, monacid.

**einschalten,** *v.t.* put in, insert, introduce; interpolate; switch in, switch on.

**Einschalter,** *m.* (*Elec.*) circuit closer, switch.

**einschärfen,** *v.t.* enjoin, impress.

**Einschätzung,** *f.* assessment.

**einschenken,** *v.t.* pour in, pour out (into something).

**einschichten,** *v.t.* imbed; stratify, arrange in layers; interstratify; pack.

**einschichtig,** *a.* of one layer, single.

**einschieben,** *v.t.* shove in, put in, insert.

**einschl.,** *abbrev.* (einschliesslich) inclusive(ly).

**einschläfern,** *v.t.* make drowsy, narcotize; lull. —**einschläfernd,** *p.a.* soporific, narcotic.

**Einschläferungsmittel,** *n.* soporific, narcotic.

**einschlaffen,** *v.i.* fall asleep.

**Einschlag,** *m.* wrapper, envelope; plait, fold; woof; sulfur match (for casks); striking in; handshake.

**einschlagen,** *v.t.* strike in, drive in; break; punch; wrap up, cover; follow, adopt; dip (sheet metal); sulfur (wine).—*v.i.* sink in; strike; succeed; shake hands.

**einschlägig,** *a.* belonging, pertinent, appropriate.

**Einschlagpapier,** *n.* wrapping paper.

**einschleifen,** *v.t.* grind in; engrave.

**einschliessen,** *v.t.* include, inclose, surround, seal in, lock in; occlude; embed.

**einschliesslich,** *adv.* inclusive, inclusively.

**Einschliessung,** *f.* inclusion, etc. (see einschliessen).

**einschlucken,** *v.t.* absorb; gulp down.

**einschlüpfen,** *v.i.* soak in; slip in.

**Einschluss,** *m.* inclusion, etc. (see einschliessen). **-lack,** *m.* (*Micros.*) varnish for cell making, ringing varnish. **-mittel,** *n.* (*Micros.*) embedding medium, mounting medium. **-rohr,** *n.* sealed tube. **-thermometer,** *n.& m.* thermometer with enclosed scale.

**einschmalzen,** *v.t.* grease, oil.

**einschmauchen,** *v.t.* smoke; fumigate.

**einschmelzen,** *v.t.& i.* melt down; melt in, fuse in; remelt.

**Einschmelz-flasche,** *f.* bottle closed by fusion. **-glas,** *n.* fusible glass (for sealing in platinum points, etc.). **-rohr,** *n.* **-röhre,** *f.* sealing tube (in which substances are inclosed by sealing).

**einschmieren,** *v.t.* smear, grease, lubricate.

**Einschmierung,** *f.* greasing, lubrication.

**einschneiden,** *v.t.* cut in, cut, cut up, cut out; indent.—**einschneidend,** *p.a.* incisive.

**Einschnitt,** *m.* incision, cut, notch, excavation.

**einschnüren,** *v.t.* constrict; bind up, lace up.

**Einschnürung,** *f.* constriction; (*Metal.*) necking; binding up.

**einschränken,** *v.t.* confine, limit, restrain.

**einschreiben,** *v.t.* inscribe, note, register.

**einschrumpfen,** *v.i.* shrink, shrivel.

**einschütten,** *v.t.* pour in, put in.

**einschwärzen,** *v.t.* blacken; ink.

**einschwefeln,** *v.t.* sulfur, sulfurize.

**einschwöden,** *v.t.* lime (hides).

**einsehen,** *v.t.* look into, understand, perceive.

**Einsehen,** *n.* insight, judgment.

**einseifen,** *v.t.* soap.

**ein-seigen, -seihen,** *v.t.& i.* infiltrate.

**einseitig,** *a.* one-sided, unilateral; partial.

**einsenken,** *v.t.* sink, plunge, dip; plant.

**einsetzen,** *v.t.* set in, put in, insert; plant; preserve (fruits); establish; install.

**Einsetzen,** *n.* setting in, etc. (see einsetzen); (*Metal.*) casehardening; (*Ceram.*, etc.) charging.

**Einsetzer,** *m.* combustion boat.

**Einsetz-gewichte,** *n.pl.* nest of weights. **-tür,** *f.* charging door.

**Einsicht,** *f.* examination; insight, intelligence.

**einsichtig,** *a.* intelligent, judicious.

**einsickern,** *v.i.* trickle in, soak in, infiltrate.

**einsieden,** *v.t.& i.* boil down.

**einspannen,** *v.t.* fasten in, insert, clamp, fix, attach, frame.

**einspeicheln,** *v.t.* salivate.—*v.i.* be salivated.

**einspielen,** *v.i.* balance.

**Einsprache,** *f.* objection, exception.

**einsprengen,** *v.t.* sprinkle; intersperse, disseminate; interstratify; burst open.

**einspringen,** *v.i.* spring in; (of fabrics) shrink; (of an angle) reënter.

**einspritzen,** *v.t.* squirt in, inject, syringe.

**Einspritzer,** *m.* injector; syringe.

**Einspritzhahn,** *m.* injection cock.

**Einspritzung,** *f.* injection.

**Einspruch,** *m.* objection, exception.

**einst,** *adv.* once; some time.

**einstampfen,** *v.t.* ram down, compress; stamp, reduce, pulverize.

**Einstandspreis,** *m.* cost price.

**einstäuben,** *v.t.* dust, powder.

**einstechen,** *v.t.* stick in, pierce.

**einstehen,** *v.i.* answer, guarantee.

**Einstell-.** adjusting; focusing.

**einstellbar,** *a.* adjustable.

**einstellen,** *v.t.* put in, set in; standardize (a solution); stop, suspend; adjust, regulate; put up, lay up; engage (help); (Optics) focus.—*v.r.* appear; (of a magnet) set.— **— auf,** standardize against; make up to (a standard volume).

**Einsteller,** *m.* regulator, thermostat. (See also einstellen.)

**Einstellmarke,** *f.* reference mark.

**Einstellung,** *f.* putting in, standardization, etc. (see einstellen); standard (of a solution).

**Einstich,** *m.* puncture.

**einstimmen,** *v.i.* chime in, agree, accord.

**einstimmig,** *adv.* unanimously.

**einstossen,** *v.t.* thrust in, ram in; break in.

**einstrahlen,** *v.t.* radiate upon, irradiate.

**Einstrahlung,** *f.* radiation taken in, (loosely) absorption; irradiation.

**einstreichen,** *v.t.* nick, slit (e.g. with a file); rub; take in.

**einstreuen,** *v.t.* strew, sprinkle; intersperse.

**einströmen,** *v.i.* stream in, flow in.

**Einströmungs-rohr,** *n.* **-röhre,** *f.* inlet tube or pipe, admission tube or pipe.

**Einströmventil,** *n.* inlet valve.

**einstündig,** *a.* of an hour's duration, one hour's.

**einstürzen,** *v.i.* fall in, collapse.—*v.t.* demolish.

**einstweilen,** *adv.* meanwhile, for a time.

**einsumpfen,** *v.t.* wet, soak.

**einsüssen,** *v.t.* sweeten, edulcorate.

**eintägig,** *a.* of a day's duration, one day's.

**eintauchen,** *v.t.* dip, plunge, immerse; steep. —*v.i.* dip in, sink in.

**Eintauch-refraktometer,** *n.* immersion refractometer. **-tiefe,** *f.* depth of immersion.

**Eintausch,** *m.* exchange, bartering.

**einteigen,** *v.t.* impaste, make into paste or dough; (Brewing) dough in.

**einteilen,** *v.t.* divide; distribute; separate.—**in Grade,** graduate.

**einteilig,** *a.* one-part, single.

**Einteilung,** *f.* division; graduation; separation; classification; distribution.

**eintönig,** *a.* monotonous.

**Eintracht,** *f.* harmony; unity.

**Eintrag,** *m.* entry; woof; damage, prejudice.

**eintragen,** *v.t.* carry in; introduce; add; enter, record; register; yield.

**einträglich,** *a.* profitable.

**Eintragung,** *f.* carrying in, etc. (see eintragen).

**eintränken,** *v.t.* soak, steep, impregnate; dip.

**einträufeln,** *v.t.* drop in, instill.

**eintreffen,** *v.i.* arrive; happen.

**eintreiben,** *v.t.* drive in; rub in; collect.

**eintreten,** *v.i.* enter; set in, commence; occur.

**einrichtern,** *v.t.* pour in with a funnel.

**Eintritt,** *m.* entrance, entry; admission; appearance; commencement; (Optics) incidence.

**Eintrittstemperatur,** *f.* temperature of admission.

**eintrocknen,** *v.i.* dry, dry up; shrink in drying.

**eintropfen, eintröpfeln,** *v.t.* drop in; instill.

**ein-und-einachsig,** *a.* (Cryst.) orthorhombic.

**einverleiben,** *v.t.* incorporate, embody.

**einverleihen,** *v.t.* introduce.

**Einvernehmung,** *f.* understanding.

**einverstanden,** *p.a.* agreed.

**Einverständnis,** *n.* agreement, understanding; concord, accord.

**Einw.,** *abbrev.* (Einwirkung) action, influence.

**Einwa(a)ge,** *f.* weighed portion.

**Einwägelöffel,** *m.* weighing-in spoon.

**einwägen,** *v.t.* weigh in, weigh and put in.

**einwalken,** *v.t.* full closely; force (oil, etc.) by fulling.—*v.i.& r.* shrink by fulling.

**Einwand,** *m.* objection, exception.

**einwandern,** *v.i.* immigrate.

**einwandfrei,** *a.* unobjectionable, unexceptionable.

**einwärts,** *adv.* inward.

**einwaschen,** *v.t.* wash.

**einwässerig,** *a.* (Dyeing) one-bath.

**einwässern,** *v.t.* lay in water, steep, soak.

**Einwässerung,** *f.* steeping, soaking.

**einweben,** *v.t.* inweave.—*v.r.* shrink.

**einweibig,** *a.* monogynous.

**einweichbar**, *a.* capable of being steeped, etc. (see einweichen).

**einweichen**, *v.t.* steep, soak, macerate, digest, infuse; ret (flax).

**Einweichung**, *f.* steeping, etc. (see einweichen).

**einwenden**, *v.t.* object, oppose.

**einwerfen**, *v.t.* throw in.

**einwertig**, *a.* univalent, monovalent.

**Einwertigkeit**, *f.* univalence, monovalence.

**einwickeln**, *v.t.* wrap up, wrap in, inclose.

**Einwieg-.** see Einwäg-.

**einwilligen**, *v.i.* consent, approve.

**einwirken**, *v.i.* act; exert influence.—*v.t.* work in, weave in.

**Einwirkung**, *f.* action; influence, effect.

**Einwirkungs-dauer**, *f.* duration of action. **-produkt**, *n.* resultant product.

**Einwohner**, *m.* inhabitant.

**Einwurf**, *m.* objection; reply; insertion; slot; hopper.

**Einzahlung**, *f.* payment, installment; share.

**einzehren**, *v.i.& r.* suffer loss by evaporation.

**Einzehrung**, *f.* loss by evaporation.

**Einzel-.** single, individual, particular, separate. **-beobachtung**, *f.* single observation. **-bestimmung**, *f.* single determination. **-blech**, *n.* single tinplate. **-darstellung**, *f.* single presentation, separate treatment or treatise, (sometimes) monograph. **-fall**, *m.* particular case, individual case. **-heit**, *f.* detail, particular; singleness.

**einzellig**, *a.* single-celled, unicellular.

**einzeln**, *a.* single, separate, individual.

**Einzel-potential**, single potential. **-schrift**, *f.* monograph. **-teil**, *m.* single part; detail. **-verkauf**, *m.* retail, retailing. **-vorgang**, *m.* single or separate process or reaction.

**einziehen**, *v.t.* draw in, pull in; absorb; reduce, lessen; collect; confiscate.—*v.i.* soak in, infiltrate; enter.—*v.r.* shrink, contract; retire.

**Einziehungsmittel**, *n.* absorbent.

**einzig**, *a.* only, single, unique.

**einzuckern**, *v.t.* sugar; preserve (with sugar).

**Einzug**, *m.* entry, entrance.

**eirund**, *a.* oval.

**Eis**, *n.* ice.

**Eis-.** ice, glacial, freezing. **-abkühlung**, *f.* cooling or refrigeration with ice.

**eisähnlich**, *a.* icelike, resembling ice, glacial.

**Eis-alaun**, *m.* rock alum. **-ansatz**, *m.* deposit or layer of ice.

**eisartig**, *a.* icelike, icy, glacial.

**Eis-belag, -beleg**, *m.* coating of ice. **-bereitung**, *f.* ice making. **-bildung**, *f.* formation of ice.

**Eischale**, *f.* eggshell.

**Eisen**, *n.* iron; iron instrument or utensil; horseshoe.

**Eisen-.** iron, ferro-, ferruginous. **-abbrand**, *m.* iron waste. **-abfälle**, *m.pl.* scrap iron. **-abscheidung**, *f.* separation of iron.

**eisenähnlich**, *a.* = eisenartig.

**Eisen-alaun**, *m.* iron alum (ferric potassium sulfate). **-amiant**, *m.* (*Iron*) fibrous silica. **-ammonalaun**, *m.* ammonium ferric alum. **-ammonalaunlösung**, *f.* solution of ammonium iron salt, esp. ammonium ferric alum. **-antimonerz**, *n.*, **-antimonglanz**, *m.* berthierite.

**eisenarm**, *a.* poor in iron.

**Eisenarsenik**, *n.* iron arsenide, specif. (*Min.*) löllingite or leuocopyrite.

**eisenartig**, *a.* ironlike, ferruginous, chalybeate.

**Eisen-arznei**, *f.* ferruginous remedy. **-asbest**, *m.* fibrous silica formed in iron manufacture. **-aufnahme**, *f.* absorption of iron. **-bad**, *m.* iron bath. **-bahn**, *f.* railroad, railway. **-bedarf**, *m.* iron requirement. **-beize**, *f.* iron mordant, iron liquor. **-beschwerung**, *f.* weighting with iron. **-bestimmung**, *f.* iron determination. **-beton**, *m.* ferro-concrete, reinforced concrete, armored concrete. **-betonbau**, *m.* ferro-concrete construction. **-bitterkalk**, *m.* ferruginous dolomite, ferromagnesian limestone. **-blau**, *n.*, **-blauspat**, *m.* = Blaueisenspat. **-blauerde**, *f.* earthy vivianite.

**eisenblausauer**, *a.* of or combined with ferrocyanic acid, ferrocyanide of.

**Eisen-blausäure**, *f.* ferrocyanic acid. **-blech**, *n.* sheet iron, iron plate. **-blende**, *f.* pitchblende. **-block**, *f.* ingot, bloom or block of iron. **-blumen**, *f.pl.* iron flowers (ferric chloride). **-blüte**, *f.* flos ferri (coralloid form of aragonite). **-bor**, *n.* iron boride. **-bromid**, *n.* iron bromide, specif. ferric bromide. **-bromür**, *n.* ferrous bromide. **-bromürbromid**, *n.* ferrosoferric bromide. **-bronze**, *f.* iron bronze, ferrobronze. **-brühe**, *f.* iron mordant, iron liquor. **-cement**, *m.& n.* ferro-concrete. **-chinawein**, *m.* iron and quinine wine. **-chlorid**, *n.* iron chloride, specif. ferric chloride. **-chlorür**, *n.* ferrous chloride. **-chlorürchlorid**, *n.* ferrosoferric chloride. **-chlorwasserstoff**, *m.* ferrichloric acid. **-chrom**, *n.* ferrochrome, ferrochromium; (*Min.*) chromic iron, chromite. **-chrysolith**, *m.* hyalosiderite; fayalite. **-cyanfarbe**, *f.* iron-cyanogen pigment. **-cyanid**, *n.* iron cyanide, specif. ferric cyanide; ferrocyanide. **-cyankalium**, *n.* potassium ferrocyanide. **-cyanür**, *n.* ferrous cyanide. **-cyanürzinkoxyd**, *n.* zinc ferrocyanide. **-cyanverbindung**, *f.* iron-cyanogen compound, ferro- or ferricyanogen compound. **-draht**, *m.* iron wire. **-drahtnetz**, *n.* iron gauze.

**Eisenerde,** f. terruginous earth, iron earth; (*Ceram.*) kind of hard stoneware.—**blaue —,** earthy vivianite.

**Eisen-erz,** n. iron ore. **-fällung,** f. iron precipitation. **-farbe,** f. iron color.

**eisenfarbig,** a. iron-colored.

**Eisen-feilicht,** n., **-feile,** f. **-feilspäne,** m.pl. iron filings. **-feilstaub,** m. fine iron filings. **-feinschlacke,** f. iron refinery slag. **-flasche,** f. iron cylinder (for gases). **-fleck,** m. iron spot, iron stain.

**eisenfleckig,** a. iron-stained.

**Eisenflüssigkeit,** f. iron liquid or liquor.

**eisenfrei,** a. free from iron.

**Eisen-frischerie,** f. iron refinery; iron refining, puddling. **-frischflammofen,** m. puddling furnace. **-frischschlacke,** f. finery cinders.

**eisenführend,** a. iron-bearing, ferriferous.

**Eisen-gallustinte,** f. iron-gallate ink. **-gang,** m. iron lode, iron-ore vein. **-gans,** f. iron pig. **-gaze,** f. iron gauze. **-gehalt,** m. iron content. **-gelb,** n. iron yellow. **-gestell,** n. iron stand, iron frame. **-gewinnung,** f. iron production. **-giesserei,** f. iron foundry; iron founding. **-gilbe,** f. yellow ocher. **-glanz,** m. iron glance, specular iron (form of hematite). **-glas,** n. (*Min.*) fayalite. **-glimmer,** m. micaceous iron ore (form of hematite). **-glimmerschiefer,** m. itabirite. **-granat,** m. iron garnet (almandite).

**eisengrau,** a. iron-gray.

**Eisen-graupen,** f.pl. granular bog iron ore. **-grund,** m. iron liquor. **-guss,** m. iron casting; cast iron.

**eisenhaltig,** a. containing iron, ferriferous, ferruginous, chalybeate.

**Eisenhammerschlag,** m. iron (hammer) scale.

**eisenhart,** a. as hard as iron.

**Eisen-hart, -hardt,** m. ferriferous gold sand; vervain. **-hochofen,** m. iron blast furnace. **-holz,** n. ironwood. **-hut,** m. aconite, monkshood; (*Mining*) gossan. **-hütchen, -hutkraut,** n. aconite, monkshood. **-hütte,** f. ironworks, iron mill; forge.

**Eisenhütten-kunde,** f. metallurgy of iron. **-leute,** pl. iron metallurgists. **-mann,** m. iron metallurgist. **-wesen,** n. metallurgy of iron.

**Eisen-hydroxyd,** n. ferric hydroxide. **-hydroxydul,** n. ferrous hydroxide. **-jodid,** n. iron iodide, specif. ferric iodide. **-jodür,** n. ferrous iodide. **-jodürjodid,** n. ferrosoferric iodide. **-kalium,** n. potassium ferrate. **-kaliumalaun,** m. iron potassium alum, ferric potassium sulfate. **-karbid, -karburet,** n. iron carbide.

**Eisenkies,** m. iron pyrites, pyrite.—**hexagonaler —,** pyrrhotite.—**rhombischer —,** marcasite.

**Eisen-kiesel,** m. ferruginous flint. **-kitt,** m. iron-rust cement. **-kobalterz,** n., **-kobaltkies,** m., cobaltite or smaltite rich in iron. **-kohlenoxyd,** n. iron carboxide. **-kohlenstoff,** m. iron carbide. **-kraut,** n. vervain, verbena. **-lack,** m. iron varnish. **-lebererz,** n. hepatic iron ore. **-legierung,** f. iron alloy. **-löffel,** m. iron spoon. **-lösung,** f. iron solution.

**eisenmagnetisch,** a. ferromagnetic.

**Eisen-mangan,** n. ferromanganese. **-manganerz,** n. manganiferous iron ore, ferriferous manganese ore. **-mangel,** m. lack of iron. **-mann,** m. (*Mining*) a scaly form of hematite. **-menge,** f. amount of iron. **-mennige,** f. red ocher. **-mittel,** n. (*Med.*) ferruginous remedy. **-mohr,** m. aethiops martialis ($Fe_3O_4$ as a black powder); earthy magnetite. **-molybdän,** n. ferromolybdenum. **-mulm,** m. earthy iron ore. **-nickel,** n. ferronickel. **-nickelkies,** m. pentlandite. **-niederschlag,** m. precipitate of iron. **-niere,** f. eaglestone. **-ocker, -ocher,** m. iron ocher, ocher.

**Eisenoxyd,** n. iron oxide, specif. ferric oxide. **—salpetersaures —,** ferric nitrate (and so for other salts).

**Eisenoxyd-hydrat,** n. ferric hydroxide. **-oxydul,** n. ferrosoferric oxide.

**eisenoxydreich,** a. rich in iron oxide.

**Eisenoxyd-salz,** n. ferric salt. **-sulfat,** n. ferric sulfate.

**Eisenoxydul,** n. ferrous oxide.—**salpetersaures —,** ferrous nitrate (and so for other salts).

**Eisenoxydul-hydrat,** n. ferrous hydroxide. **-oxyd,** n. ferrosoferric oxide, magnetic iron oxide ($Fe_3O_4$). **-salz,** n. ferrous salt. **-sulfat,** n. ferrous sulfate. **-verbindung,** f. ferrous compound.

**Eisen-oxydverbindung,** f. ferric compound. **-pastille,** f. (*Pharm.*) reduced iron lozenge. **-pecherz,** n. limonite; pitticite; triplite. **-phosphor,** n. iron phosphide. **-probe,** f. iron test; iron sample. **-pulver,** n. iron powder. **-quarz,** m. ferriferous quartz. **-rahm,** m. a porous form of hematite.

**eisenreich,** a. rich in iron.

**Eisen-reihe,** f. iron series. **-resin, -resinit,** m. (*Min.*) humboldtine. **-rhodanid,** n. ferric thiocyanate (or sulfocyanate). **-rhodanür,** n. ferrous thiocyanate (or sulfocyanate). **-rogenstein,** m. oölitic iron ore. **-rohr,** n. **-röhre,** f. iron pipe or tube. **-rost,** m. iron rust. **-rostwasser,** n. iron liquor, iron mordant. **-rot,** n. colcothar. **-safran,** m. saffron (or crocus) of Mars. **-salmiak,** m. (*Pharm.*) ammoniated iron, iron and ammonium chloride. **-salz,** n. iron salt. **-sand,** m. ferruginous sand. **-sau,** f. iron sow.

**eisensauer**, *a.* of or combined with ferric acid, ferrate of.

**Eisen-säuerling**, *m.* chalybeate water (mineral water containing iron salts). **-säure,** *f.* ferric acid. **-schaum,** *m.* (*Metal.*) kish; (*Min.*) = Eisenrahm. **-schlacke,** *f.* iron slag; finery cinders. **-schmelze,** *f.* iron smelting; iron smeltery; iron founding. **-schmelzhütte,** *f.* iron foundry. **-schörl,** *m.* bog iron ore.

**eisenschüssig**, *a.* ferriferous, ferruginous.

**Eisen-schutzfarbe,** *f.* protective paint for iron. **-schutzmittel,** *n.* antirusting composition, rust-proofing agent. **-schwamm,** *m.* iron sponge, spongy iron. **-schwarz,** *n.* iron black (precipitated antimony); graphite; lampblack; (*Dyeing*) copperas black. **-schwärze,** *f.* graphite; earthy magnetite; (*Dyeing*) iron liquor; (*Leather*) currier's ink. **-selenür,** *n.* ferrous selenide. **-silberglanz,** *m.* sternbergite. **-silicium,** *n.* iron silicide. **-sinter,** *m.* dross of iron, iron scale; pitticite. **-späne,** *m.pl.* iron turnings or borings. **-spat,** *m.* siderite. **-spiegel,** *m.* specular iron (hematite). **-staub,** *m.* iron dust.

**Eisenstein,** *m.* ironstone, iron ore.—**spatiger —,** spathic iron ore, siderite.

**Eisen-steinmark,** *n.* lithomarge containing iron. **-sublimat,** *n.* iron sublimate (ferric chloride). **-sulfat,** *n.* iron sulfate, specif. ferrous sulfate. **-sulfid,** *n.* iron sulfide, specif. ferric sulfide. **-sulfür,** *n.* ferrous sulfide. **-sumpferz,** *n.* bog iron ore. **-teil,** *m.* iron part. **-tiegel,** *m.* iron crucible. **-tinte,** *f.* iron ink. **-titan,** *n.* ferrotitanium; (*Min.*) ilmenite. **-ton,** *m.* clay ironstone; iron clay. **-tongranat,** *m.* almandite. **-untersuchung,** *f.* examination of iron, iron analysis. **-vanadin,** *n.* ferrovanadium. **-verbindung,** *f.* iron compound. **-verlust,** *m.* loss of iron. **-violettholz,** *n.* granadilla wood, red ebony.

**Eisenvitriol,** *m.* iron vitriol (hydrous ferrous sulfate).—**roter —,** red vitriol, botryogen.

**Eisen-wasser,** *n.* chalybeate water. **-wein,** *m.* (*Pharm.*) iron wine. **-weinstein,** *m.* (*Pharm.*) iron and potassium tartrate, tartrated iron. **-wolfram,** *n.* ferrotungsten. **-zeit,** *f.* iron age. **-zement,** *m.& n.* ferroconcrete. **-zinkblende,** *f.* marmatite. **-zinkspat,** *m.* ferruginous calamine. **-zinnerz,** *n.* ferriferous cassiterite. **-zucker,** *m.* (*Pharm.*) saccharated ferric oxide. **-zuckersirup,** *m.* (*Pharm.*) sirup of ferric oxide.

**Eisenzyan-** = Eisencyan-.

**eisern**, *a.* of iron, iron.

**Eis-erzeugung,** *f.* ice production. **-essig,** *m.* glacial acetic acid. **-farbe,** *f.* (*Dyeing*) ice color.

**eisgekühlt**, *a.* cooled with ice, ice-cooled.

**Eisglas**, *n.* frosted glass.

**eisig**, *a.* icy, icelike.

**Eisigkeit,** *f.* iciness.

**eiskalt**, *a.* ice-cold.

**Eis-kasten,** *m.* ice chest. **-kraut,** *n.* ice plant (*Mesembryanthemum crystallinum*).

**eiskühlen**, *v.t.* cool with ice.

**Eis-phosphorsäure,** *f.* glacial phosphoric acid. **-punkt,** *m.* freezing point. **-schrank,** *m.* ice box or chest, refrigerator. **-spat,** *m.* glassy feldspar, sanidine (or rhyacolite). **-stein,** *m.* cryolite. **-trichter,** *m.* ice funnel. **-wasser,** *n.* ice water. **-zacken, -zapfen,** *m.* icicle. **-zeit,** *f.* glacial period.

**eitel**, *a.* pure; idle; vain.

**Eiter,** *m.* pus.

**eiter-ähnlich, -artig,** *a.* purulent.

**Eiterbakterien,** *n.pl.* pyogenic bacteria.

**eiter-befördernd,** *a.* suppurative. **-bildend,** *a.* pyogenic.

**Eiterbildung,** *f.* suppuration, pyogenesis.

**eitererzeugend,** *p.a.* suppurative, pyogenic.

**Eitergang,** *m.* fistula.

**eiterig, eiterlich,** *a.* purulent.

**eitern**, *v.i.* suppurate.

**Eiter-pilz,** *m.* pyogenic organism. **-stoff,** *m.* purulent matter.

**Eiterung,** *f.* suppuration.

**Eiterungserreger,** *m.* suppurative agent.

**Eitervergiftung,** *f.* pyemia.

**eiterziehend,** *p.a.* suppurative, pyogenic.

**Eiweiss,** *n.* albumin; albumen, white of egg; protein.

**Eiweiss-.** albuminous, albuminoid; protein. **-abbau,** *m.* proteolysis.

**eiweiss-ähnlich,** *a.* albuminoid. **-arm,** *a.* poor in albumin or in protein.

**Eiweissart,** *f.* variety of albumin; variety of protein.

**eiweissartig,** *a.* albuminous; albuminoid; glairy.

**Eiweiss-bedarf,** *m.* albumin requirement. **-drüse,** *f.* salivary gland.

**eiweiss-förmig,** *a.* albuminous. **-haltig,** *a.* containing albumin (or albumen), albuminous; containing protein.

**Eiweiss-harnen,** *n.* albuminuria. **-körper,** *m.* albuminous substance, protein. **-leim,** *m.* albumin glue; gluten protein. **-lösung,** *f.* albumin solution. **-nahrung,** *f.* albuminous food. **-papier,** *n.* albuminized paper.

**eiweiss-reich,** *a.* rich in albumin (or in protein). **-spaltend,** *p.a.* proteolytic.

**Eiweiss-spaltung,** *f.* cleavage of albumin; protein cleavage, proteolysis. **-sparmittel,** *n.* albumin sparer; protein sparer. **-stoff,** *m.* albuminous substance, protein; albumen; albumin. **-verbindung,** *f.* albuminous compound, protein; albuminate.

Eizelle, *f.* ovum.

Eka-bor, *n.* ekaboron. -silizium, *n.* ekasilicon.

Ekel, *m.* nausea; disgust.

ekel-erregend, *a.* nauseating, disgusting. -haft, *a.* disgusting, offensive.

eklatant, *a.* brilliant, bright.

Ekrüseide, *f.* écru silk.

Ekzem, *n.* eczema.

-el. A suffix attached to verb roots to denote the instrument of an action, -er; as, *Hebel*, lever, from *heben*, lift.

Elaidinsäure, *f.* elaidic acid.

Elainsäure, *f.* oleic acid.

Elaio-, Eläo-, eleo-, elaeo-, elaio-.

Elasticität, *f.* elasticity.

elastisch, *a.* elastic.

Elastizität, *f.* elasticity.

Elastizitäts-grenze, *f.* elastic limit. -zahl, *f.* modulus of elasticity.

Elatinsäure, *f.* elatinic acid.

Elatsäure, *f.* elatic acid.

Elefanten-laus, *f.* cashew nut. -nuss, *f.* ivory nut.

elekt., *abbrev.* (elektrisch) electric.

Elekt., *abbrev.* (Elektrizität) electricity.

Elektawolle, *f.* first-class wool.

Elektivnährboden, *m.* (*Bact.*) selective medium.

Elektric-. see Elektriz-.

Elektrik, *f.* (science of) electricity.

Elektriker, *m.* electrician.

elektrisch, *a.* electric.

elektrisierbar, *a.* electrifiable.

elektrisieren, *v.t.* electrify.

Elektrisierung, *f.* electrification.

Elektrizität, *f.* electricity.

Elektrizitäts-entladung, *f.* electric discharge. -ladung, *f.* electric charge. -leiter, *m.* electric conductor. -messer, *m.* electrometer. -messung, *f.* electrometry. -wage, *f.* electrometer. -zeiger, *m.* electroscope.

Elektro-analyse, *f.* electroanalysis. -chemie, *f.* electrochemistry.

elektrochemisch, *a.* electrochemical.

Elektroden-abstand, *m.* distance between electrodes. -kohle, *f.* electrode carbon. -spannung, *f.* electrode potential.

elektro-dynamisch, *a.* electrodynamic. -galvanisch, *a.* electrogalvanic.

Elektrolyse, *f.* electrolysis.

elektrolysieren, *v.t.* electrolyze.

Elektrolyt, *m.* electrolyte. -eisen, *n.* electrolytic iron.

elektrolytisch, *a.* electrolytic.

Elektrolyt-kupfer, *n.* electrolytic copper. -nickel, *n.* electrolytic nickel. -silber, *n.* electrolytic silver.

elektromagnetisch, *a.* electromagnetic.

Elektromagnetismus, *m.* electromagnetism.

elektro-mechanisch, *a.* electromechanical. -metrisch, *a.* electrometric. -motorisch, *a.* electromotive.

Elektron, *n.* electron; electrum; amber.

Elektronen-bahn, *f.* electronic path or orbit. -drall, *m.* electron spin. -hülle, *f.* electronic shell. -röhre, *f.* electron tube. -stoss, *m.* electronic collision or impact. -theorie, *f.* theory of electrons. -zahl, *f.* number of electrons.

Elektronik, *f.* electronics.

elektronisch, *a.* electronic.

Elektro-ofen, *m.* electric furnace. -phor, *m.* electrophorus. -porzellan, *n.* electrical porcelain. -roheisen, *n.* (*Iron*) electric pig.

elektroskopisch, *a.* electroscopic.

Elektro-stahl, *m.* electric steel. -statik, *f.* electrostatics.

elektrostatisch, *a.* electrostatic.

Elektro-synthese, *f.* electrosynthesis. -techniker, *m.* electrotechnician, electrical engineer, electrician.

elektrothermisch, *a.* electrothermal.

Element, *n.* element; (*Elec.*) cell.

elementar, *a.* elementary.

Elementar-analyse, *f.* elementary analysis. -bestandteil, *m.* elementary constituent. -stoff, *m.* elementary substance, element.

Elementırt, *f.* (*Elec.*) kind of element, type of cell.

Elementen-glas, *n.* (glass) battery jar. -messung, *f.* stoichiometry.

Element-gefäss, -glas, *n.* (*Elec.*) battery jar. -grösse, *f.* (*Elec.*) size of cell. -kohle, *f.* (*Elec.*) cell carbon. -schlamm, *m.* (*Elec.*) battery mud.

Elemi-harz, *n.* elemi, gum elemi. -öl, *n.* elemi oil. -säure, *f.* elemic acid.

Elen, *m.& n.* elk.

Elend, *n.* misery, distress, penury.

elend, *a.* miserable, pitiful, ill.

Elenfett, *n.* elk fat.

Elephanten-. see Elefanten-.

elf, *a.* eleven.

Elfenbein, *n.* ivory.—gebranntes —, burnt ivory, ivory black.—künstliches —, artificial ivory, specif. celluloid.

elfenbein-ähnlich, -artig, *a.* ivorylike, eburnean. -farbig, *a.* ivory-colored.

Elfenbein-gelb, *n.* ivory yellow. -küste, *f.* Ivory Coast. -nuss, *f.* ivory nut. -schwarz, *n.* ivory black. -substanz, *f.* dentine. -surrogat, *n.* ivory substitute, artificial ivory.

elfenbeinweiss, *a.* ivory-white.

elfte, *a.* eleventh.

eliminieren, *v.t.* eliminate.

Ellagengerbsäure, *f.* ellagic acid.

Ellagsäure, Ellagensäure, *f.* ellagic acid.

Ellbogen, *m.* elbow.

Elle, *f.* ell, yard; ulna.

Ellenbogen, *m.* elbow.

Ellenwaren, *f.pl.* dry goods, draper's goods.

Ellipsenbahn, *f.* elliptic orbit.

ellipsoidförmig, *a.* ellipsoidal.

elliptisch, *a.* elliptic, elliptical.

Else, *f.*, (*Bot.*) alder; shad. -beere, *f.* service berry.

Elsholtziasäure, *f.* elsholtzic acid.

elterlich, *a.* parental.

Eltern, *pl.* parents.

Eluat, *n.* extracted material, extract.

eluieren, *v.t.* elute, wash out, extract.

elutrieren, *v.t.* elutriate, wash.

Email, *n.* enamel. -belag, *m.* coating of enamel. -draht, *n.* enameled wire. -farbe, *f.* enamel color. -gefäss, *n.* enameled vessel. -glas, *n.* enamel glass, fusible glass. -lack, Emaillelack, *m.* enamel varnish.

Emaille, *f.* enamel.

emaillieren, *v.t.* enamel.

Emaillierofen, *m.* enameling furnace.

Emaillierung, *f.* enameling.

Emailschicht, *f.* coat of enamel.

Embeliasäure, *f.* embelic acid.

Emetäthylin, *n.* emetethyline.

emetisch, *a.* emetic.

Emissionsvermögen, *n.* emissive power.

emittieren, *v.t.* emit.

EMK., E.M.K., *abbrev.* (elektromotorische Kraft) electromotive force, E.M.F.

emollieren, *v.t.* soften.

empfahl, *pret.* of empfehlen.

Empfang, *m.* receipt; reception.

empfangen, *v.t.* receive; accept.—*v.i.* conceive.

Empfänger, *m.* receiver.

empfänglich, *a.* receptive, susceptible.

Empfängnis, *n.* conception.

Empfangs-. receiving.

empfehlen, *v.t.* recommend.—*v.r.* take leave, say goodby; pay one's respects; (impersonally) be proper, be well.

empfehlenswert, *a.* to be recommended, advisable; eligible.

empfiehlt, *pr. 3 sing.* of empfehlen.

empfindbar, *a.* sensible, perceptible; sensitive.

Empfindbarkeit, *f.* perceptibility; sensitiveness.

empfinden, *v.t.* experience, feel; perceive.

empfindlich, *a.* sensitive; susceptible; sensible; irritable; severe.— — machen, render sensitive, etc.; sensitize.

Empfindlichkeit, *f.* sensitiveness, etc. (see empfindlich).

Empfindung, *f.* sensation, feeling; sentiment.

empföhle, *pret. subj.* of empfehlen.

empfohlen, *p.p.* of empfehlen.

empirisch, *a.* empiric(al).

empor, *adv.* up, upward, on high.

emporblühen, *v.i.* grow, rise, prosper.

empören, *v.t.* stir up, excite; shock.

emporkommen, *v.i.* rise, emerge, mount, ascend; prosper.

empyreumatisch, *a.* empyreumatic.

emsig, *a.* diligent, industrious.

emulgieren, *v.t.* emulsify.

Emulgierung, *f.* emulsification.

emulsieren, *v.t.* emulsify, emulsionize.

Emulsierung, *f.* emulsification.

Emulsierungsmittel, *n.* emulsifying agent.

emulsionieren, *v.t.* emulsify, emulsionize.

Emulsionierung, *f.* emulsification.

Emulsionsbildung, *f.* formation of an emulsion.

emulsionsfähig, *a.* emulsifiable.

Emulsionsverfahren, *n.* emulsion process.

emulzieren, *v.t.* emulsify, emulsionize.

-en. (1) Case ending of certain nouns. (2) A suffix used like the English -en to form adjectives of material; as, *silbern*, of silver, *eichen*, oaken. (3) In *Org. Chem.*, the equivalent of the English -ene; as, *Propen*, propene.

Enantiotropie, *f.* enantiotropy, -tropism.

End-. final, terminal, end. -anzeiger, *m.* indicator. -ausbeute, *f.* final yield. -bahn, *f.* final path or orbit. -destillat, *n.* final distillate. -druck, *m.* final pressure.

Ende, *f.* end; limit, termination, purpose.

End-ecke, *f.*, -eck, *n.* terminal angle, summit.

enden, *v.t. & r.* end, terminate.

End-ergebnis, *n.* final result; final product. -fläche, *f.* terminal face, end face. -glied, *n.* terminal member, end member.

endgültig, *a.* final, conclusive, definitive.

endigen, *v.t. & r.* end, terminate.

End-lauge, *f.* final liquor; (*pl.*) foots. -laugenkalk, *m.* (*Agric.*) a product made by treating the mother liquor from potassium chloride manufacture with lime.

endlich, *a.* finite; final; late.—*adv.* finally; after all.

endlos, *a.* endless; infinite.

End-lösung, *f.* final solution. -niveau, *n.* final level. -nüance, *f.* final shade.

Endosmose, *f.* endosmosis.

endosmotisch, *a.* endosmotic.

endothermisch, *a.* endothermic.

End-produkt, *n.* final product, end product. -punkt, *m.* end point, final point; terminus. -quantenzahl, *f.* final quantum number. -resultat, *n.* final result. -silbe, *f.* final syllable, termination. -spannung, *f.* (*Elec.*) final voltage.

endständig, *a.* standing at the end, end, terminal.

**End-term,** *m.* final term. **-wert,** *m.* final value. **-zustand,** *m.* final state or condition.

**Energetik,** *f.* energetics.

**Energie-abnahme,** *f.* decrease in energy. **-änderung,** *f.* energy change. **-art,** *f.* form of energy. **-aufwand,** *m.* expenditure of energy. **-gleichung,** *f.* energy equation. **-inhalt,** *m.* energy content. **-niveau,** *n.* energy level. **-quant, -quantum,** *n.* energy quantum. **-quantelung,** *f.* energy quantization. **-quelle,** *f.* source of energy. **-stufe,** *f.* energy step or stage, energy level. **-umwandlung,** *f.* transformation of energy. **-verbrauch,** *m.* consumption of energy. **-verlust,** *m.* loss of energy. **-zufuhr,** *f.* addition of energy.

**energisch,** *a.* energetic.

**eng, enge,** *a.* narrow; close, tight.

**engbenachbart,** *a.* closely adjacent.

**Enge,** *f.* narrowness; closeness, tightness.

**Engel,** *m.* angel. **-rot,** *n.* colcothar. **-süss,** *n.* (*Pharm.*) polypody root. **-wurz, -wurzel,** *f.* (*Pharm.*) angelica.

**Enghalsflasche,** *f.* narrow-necked bottle.

**Englergrad,** *m.* Engler degree, Engler number.

**englisch,** *a.* English.—**englische Erde,** rotten stone.—**englisches Gewürz, englischer Piment,** pimento, allspice.—**englisches Leder,** moleskin.—**englisches Pflaster,** court-plaster.—**englisches Pulver,** powder of Algaroth (SbOCl).—**englisches Rot,** English red, colcothar.—**englisches Salz,** Epsom salt.

**Englisch-gelb,** *n.* patent yellow (lead oxychloride). **-leder,** *n.* moleskin. **-pflaster,** *n.* court-plaster. **-rot,** *n.* colcothar. **-salz,** *n.* Epsom salt.

**eng-lochig,** *a.* with small holes, fine-pored. **-maschig,** *a.* close-meshed, fine-meshed.

**Engobe,** *m.* engobe, slip.

**engobieren,** *v.t.* (*Ceram.*) coat with engobe, slip.

**en gros.** wholesale.

**enkaustisch,** *a.* encaustic.

**Enkel,** *m.* ankle; grandchild, grandson.

**Enlevage,** *f.* (*Dyeing*) discharge. **-druck,** *m.* discharge printing.

**Enolisierung,** *f.* enolization.

**enorm,** *a.* enormous.

**-ensäure.** -enoic acid (Geneva system).

**ent-.** A verbal prefix having the following principal meanings: (1) With nouns, deprive of, de-, dis-, di-, un-; as *entschwefeln,* desulfurize. (2) With verbs, away, out, dis-, de-, un-, in-, ex-, e-; as *entdecken,* discover; *entwickeln,* evolve. (3) With verbs, begin to, start; as *entflammen,* inflame; *entschlafen,* fall asleep.

**entaktivieren,** *v.t.* render inactive, deactivate.

**Entaktivierung,** *f.* deactivation.

**entalkoholisieren,** *v.t.* dealcoholize.

**entalkylieren,** *v.t.* dealkylate.

**entamidieren,** *v.t.* deprive of amidogen, deaminize, deamidize.

**entarretieren,** *v.t.* release; unlock.

**entarten,** *v.i.* degenerate, deteriorate.—*v.t.* render degenerate.—**entartet,** *p.a.* degenerate, debased.

**Entartung,** *f.* degeneration.

**Entartungsreaktion,** *f.* degeneration reaction.

**Entaschung,** *f.* ash removal.

**entbasten,** *v.t.* degum (silk).

**Entbastung,** *f.* degumming.

**Entbastungsmittel,** *n.* degumming agent.

**entbehren,** *v.t.* be without, lack; do without, dispense with.

**entbehrlich,** *a.* dispensable, unnecessary.

**entbinden,** *v.t.* disengage, set free, liberate, release; evolve (gases); (*Med.*) deliver.

**Entbindung,** *f.* disengagement, setting free, release; evolution (of gases); (*Med.*) delivery.

**Entbindungs-flasche,** *f.* generating flask (or bottle). **-rohr,** *n.* delivery tube.

**entbittern,** *v.t.* deprive of bitterness.

**entbleien,** *v.t.* deprive of lead.

**entblössen,** *v.t.* uncover, strip; deprive.

**entbrausen,** *v.i.* escape with effervescence.

**entbromen,** *v.t.* debrominate.

**entbunden,** *p.p.* of entbinden.

**Entchlorung,** *f.* dechlorination.

**entdampfen,** *v.t.* free from vapor.—*v.i.* escape as vapor.

**entdecken,** *v.t.* discover; disclose.

**Entdecker,** *m.* discoverer; detector.

**Entdeckung,** *f.* discovery; disclosure.

**entdenaturieren,** *v.t.* free from denaturants.

**entdunsten,** *v.t.* & *i.* = entdampfen.

**Ente,** *f.* duck; duck-shaped vessel (as one for catalytic hydrogenation); canard.

**entehren,** *v.t.* dishonor.

**enteisenen,** *v.t.* deprive of iron, deferrize.

**Enteisenung,** *f.* removal of iron, deferrization.

**entemulsionieren, entemulgieren,** *v.t.* deemulsify.

**Entenfuss,** *m.* podophyllum, duck's-foot.

**entfallen,** *v.i.* drop, slip, fall.

**entfalten,** *v.t.* unfold, display; evolve, develop.

**entfärbbar,** *a.* capable of being decolorized or bleached.

**entfärben,** *v.t.* decolorize, bleach; make pale. —*v.r.* fade; grow pale.

**Entfärbung,** *f.* decolorization, decoloration, bleaching; growing pale; paleness.

**Entfärbungs-kohle,** *f.* decolorizing carbon. **-messer,** *m.* decolorimeter. **-mittel,** *n.* decolorizing agent, decolorant.

**entfasern,** *v.t.* free of fibers, string (beans).

**entfernen,** *v.t.* remove.—*v.r.* withdraw, depart.

**Entfernung,** *f.* removal; distance; retirement; absence.

**entfetten,** *v.t.* remove fat, oil or grease from, degrease, ungrease, unoil, scour.

**Entfettung,** *f.* removal of fat, etc. (see entfetten).

**Entfettungsmittel,** *n.* scouring agent, degreasing agent; (*Med.*) remedy for obesity.

**Entfeuchter,** *m.* desiccator.

**entfilzen,** *v.t.* unfelt.

**entflammbar,** *a.* inflammable.

**Entflammbarkeit,** *f.* inflammability.

**entflammen,** *v.t.* inflame, kindle.—*v.r.* (of kerosene, etc.) flash.

**Entflammung,** *f.* inflammation; flash.

**Entflammungs-probe,** *f.* flash test. **-punkt,** *m.* flashing point, flash point. **-temperatur,** *f.* kindling temperature (of kerosene, etc.), flash point.

**entfleischen,** *v.t.* strip of flesh, flesh.

**entfliessen,** *v.i.* flow; emanate.

**entflocken,** *v.t. & i.* deflocculate.

**entfremden,** *v.t.* estrange; abandon; conceal.

**entführen,** *v.t.* carry off.

**entfuseln,** *v.t.* remove fusel oil from, rectify.

**entgasen,** *v.t.* extract gas from, degas, outgas.

**Entgasung,** *f.* degassing, outgassing; dry distillation.

**entgegen,** *prep.* against; opposite; toward.—*adv.* counter, oppositely. **-gehen,** *v.i.* go to meet, encounter, face. **-gesetzt,** *p.a.* opposite; opposed, contrary, inverse, reverse. **-halten,** *v.t.* contrast; oppose; offer. **-kommen,** *v.i.* come to meet, approach.

**entgegnen,** *v.t.* reply.

**entgehen,** *v.i.* escape, avoid.

**entgeisten,** *v.t.* deprive of spirit or alcohol, dealcoholize.

**entgelten,** *v.t.* pay for.

**entgerben,** *v.t.* detan.

**entgerbern,** *v.t.* wash (wool).

**entgiften,** *v.t.* deprive of poison, detoxicate.

**Entgiftung,** *f.* detoxication.

**Entgiftungsmittel,** *n.* detoxicating agent.

**entglasbar,** *a.* devitrifiable.

**entglasen,** *v.t* devitrify.

**Entglasung,** *f.* devitrification.

**entgolden,** *v.t.* extract the gold from; ungild.

**entgrannen,** *v.t.* awn, hummel (barley).

**entgummieren,** *v.t.* degum.

**enth.,** *abbrev.* (enthaltend) containing.

**enthaaren,** *v.t.* unhair, depilate.—**enthaarend,** *p.a.* depilatory.

**Enthaarung,** *f.* unhairing, depilation.

**Enthaarungsmittel,** *n.* depilatory.

**enthalogenisieren,** *v.t.* dehalogenate, dehalinate.

**enthalten,** *v.t.* contain; include.—*v.r.* abstain.

**enthaltsam,** *a.* abstemious, temperate.

**enthärten,** *v.t.* soften; (*Metal.*) anneal.

**Enthärtung,** *f.* softening; (*Metal*) annealing.

**entharzen,** *v.t.* deprive of resin.

**Entharzung,** *f.* freeing from resin, extraction of resin.

**enthäuten,** *v.t.* skin, flay.

**entheben,** *v.t.* exonerate, exempt; dismiss.

**Entholzung,** *f.* delignification.

**enthüllen,** *v.t.* unfold, unveil, disclose.

**enthülsen,** *v.t.* husk, hull, shell, peel, etc.

**enthydratisieren,** *v.t.* dehydrate.

**entionisieren,** *v.t.* de-ionize.

**Entionisierung,** *f.* de-ionization.

**entkalken, entkälken,** *v.t.* decalcify, delime, unlime, free from lime.

**Entkalkung,** *f.* decalcification, deliming.

**Entkalkungs-flüssigkeit,** *f.* decalcifying solution, deliming solution. **-mittel,** *n.* deliming agent.

**entkampfern,** *v.t.* decamphorate, deprive of camphor.

**entkarboxylieren,** *v.t.* deprive of carboxyl, decarboxylate.

**entkeimen,** *v.t.* degerminate.—*v.i.* germinate, sprout.

**Entkeimung,** *f.* removal of germs, degermination; germination.

**entkieseln,** *v.t.* desilicify.

**Entkieselung,** *f.* desilicification.

**entkleiden,** *v.t.* undress, strip.

**entkohlen,** *v.t.* decarbonize, decarburize.

**Entkohlung,** *f.* decarbonization, decarburization.

**entkörnen,** *v.t.* = auskörnen.

**entkräften,** *v.t.* exhaust; debilitate, weaken.

**entkupfern,** *v.t.* free from copper, decopper.

**entkuppeln,** *v.t.* uncouple, disconnect.

**entladen,** *v.t.* discharge; unload.—*v.r.* explode, go off.

**Entladestrom,** *m.* (*Elec.*) discharge current.

**Entladung,** *f.* discharge; exoneration.

**entlang,** *adv.* along.

**entlassen,** *v.t.* let go, dismiss, discharge.

**entlasten,** *v.t.* unload, discharge; release, disengage.

**entleeren,** *v.t.* empty, discharge.

**Entleerung,** *f.* emptying, discharging, discharge.

**Entleerungskammer,** *f.* discharging chamber.

**entlegen,** *a.* distant, remote.

**entlehnen,** *v.t.* borrow, take, derive.

**entleimen,** *v.t.* degum.

**entleuchten,** *v.t.* deprive of light, render nonluminous.—*v.i.* shine, radiate.

**entlüften,** *v.t.* deprive of air, deaerate.

**entmagnetisieren,** *v.t.* demagnetize.

**Entmanganung,** *f.* demanganization.

**Entmessingung,** *f.* debrassing.

**entmethylieren**, *v.t.* demethylate.

**entmischen**, *v.t.* separate into component parts, disintegrate, decompose, dissociate, segregate.

**Entmischung**, *f.* disintegration, etc. (see entmischen); (*Metal.*) coring.

**entmutigen**, *v.t.* discourage.

**Entnahme**, *f.* taking, etc. (see entnehmen).

**entnässen**, *v.t.* deprive of moisture, dry.

**entnebeln**, *v.t.* free from mist, fog, or fume.

**Entnebelung**, *f.* mist or fume dispersion.

**entnehmen**, *v.t.* take; take out, withdraw; draw, borrow; infer.

**entölen**, *v.t.* remove oil from, unoil.

**entpesten**, *v.t.* disinfect.

**entphosphoren**, *v.t.* dephosphorize.

**Entphosphorung**, *f.* dephosphorization.

**Entpolymerisierung**, *f.* depolymerization.

**entpressen**, *v.t.* press out, squeeze out; extort.

**Entquellung**, *f.* shrinkage (of gels), syneresis.

**entrahmen**, *v.t.* remove the cream from, skim.

**entraten**, *v.t.& i.* dispense (with).

**entreissen**, *v.t.* snatch or tear away; rescue.

**entrichten**, *v.t.* pay (debts).

**entrinden**, *v.t.* decorticate, bark.

**Entropie**, *f.* entropy.

**entrosten**, *v.t.* free from rust, clean the rust from.

**entröten**, *v.t.* free from red color.

**entsagen**, *v.t.* renounce, give up.

**entsalzen**, *v.t.* free from salt.

**Entsatz**, *m.* relief, rescue.

**entsäuern**, *v.t.* free from acid, deacidify; deoxidize.

**entschädigen**, *v.t.* indemnify, compensate for.

**entschälen**, *v.t.* shell, peel; (*Silk*) scour, degum.

**entschäumen**, *v.t.* skim, scum, despumate.—*v.i.* foam off, despumate.

**entscheiden**, *v.t.* decide.—**entscheidend**, *p.a.* decisive; final.—**entschieden**, *p.a.* decided, determined.

**Entscheidung**, *f.* decision; crisis.

**entscheinen**, *v.t.* debloom.

**Entscheinung**, *f.* deblooming.

**Entscheinungsmittel**, *n.* deblooming agent.

**entschlacken**, *v.t.* free from slag or dross.

**entschlagen**, *v.r.* divest oneself, forget.

**entschlammen**, *v.t.* free from mud or slime.

**entschleimen**, *v.t.* free from slime.

**entschlichten**, *v.t.* free from size, desize, undress (linen).

**Entschlichtungsmittel**, *n.* desizing agent.

**entschliessen**, *v.r.* resolve, decide.

**Entschlossenheit**, *f.* resolution, decision.

**Entschluss**, *m.* resolution.

**entschmelzen**, *v.i.* melt away.

**entschuldigen**, *v.t.* excuse.

**entschwefeln**, *v.t.* desulfurize.

**Entschwefelung**, *f.* desulfurization.

**Entschwefelungsmittel**, *n.* desulfurizing agent.

**entschweissen**, *v.t.* scour (wool).

**entschwinden**, *v.i.* disappear, vanish.

**entseifen**, *v.t.* free from soap, rinse.

**entsetzen**, *v.t.* displace, remove; relieve.—*v.r.* be horrified.

**entsetzlich**, *a.* terrible, atrocious.—*adv.* enormously, awfully.

**entseuchen**, *v.t.* disinfect.

**entsilbern**, *v.t.* desilver, desilverize.

**Entsilberung**, *f.* desilvering, desilverizing.

**entsinnen**, *v.r.* remember.

**entsintern**, *v.t.* desinter.

**entspannen**, *v.t.* = abspannen.

**Entspannung**, *f.* = Abspannung.

**entspr.**, *abbrev.* entsprechend.

**entsprechen**, *v.i.* correspond; answer.—**entsprechend**, *p.a.* corresponding; suitable.

**entspringen**, *v.i.* spring, arise; escape.

**entstählen**, *v.t.* (*Metal.*) soften.

**entstänkern**, *v.t.* deodorize.

**Entstänkerungspatrone**, *f.* deodorizing cartridge.

**entstauben**, *v.t.* free from dust; dust (off).

**Entstaubung**, *f.* dust removal.

**entstehen**, *v.i.* arise, originate; be formed; result.—**eben entstehend**, nascent; incipient.

**Entstehung**, *f.* origin, genesis, nascence.

**Entstehungs-art**, **-weise**, *f.* mode of origin. **-zustand**, *m.* nascent state.

**entstellen**, *v.t.* disfigure, distort.

**entströmen**, *v.i.* flow, stream, issue, escape (from).

**enttäuschen**, *v.t.* undeceive, disappoint.

**entteeren**, *v.t.* deprive of tar, detar.

**Entteerung**, *f.* tar removal.

**entw.**, *abbrev.* (entweder) either.

**Entw.**, *abbrev.* (Entwickelung) evolution, development.

**entwachsen**, *v.i.* outgrow.

**entwärmen**, *v.t.* deprive of heat.

**entwässerbar**, *a.* capable of being dehydrated, etc. (see entwässern).

**entwässern**, *v.t.* free from water, dehydrate; concentrate, rectify, (*Old Chem.*) dephlegmate; drain.—**entwässert**, *p.a.* freed from water, dehydrated, anhydrous; concentrated, rectified; drained.

**Entwässerung**, *f.* water removal, dehydration; desiccation; concentration; drainage; sewerage.

**Entwässerungs-mittel**, *n.* dehydrating agent. **-rohr**, *n.*, **-röhre**, *f.* drain pipe.

**entweder**, *conj.* either.

**entweichen**, *v.i.* escape; leak.

**Entweichung**, *f.* escaping, escape.

**Entweichungsventil**, *n.* escape valve, delivery valve.

**entwerfen,** *v.t.* trace out, design, plan.

**entwerten,** *v.t.* depreciate; cancel (stamps).

**entwickeln,** *v.t.* develop; evolve; disengage, generate (gases); unfold, display.—*v.r.* develop; be evolved.—**entwickelnd,** *p.a.* developing, etc.; nascent.

**Entwickelung,** *f.* developing, development; evolution; disengagement, generating (of gases); unfolding, explanation.

**Entwickelungsbad,** *n.* developing bath.

**entwickelungsfähig,** *a.* capable of being developed or evolved.

**Entwickelungs-flüssigkeit,** *f.* (*Photog.*) developing liquid, developer. **-gefäss,** *n.* generating vessel, generator (for gases). **-geschichte,** *f.* history of (the) development. **-kolben,** *m.* generating flask. **-mittel,** *n.* developer. **-rohr,** *n.,* **-röhre,** *f.* delivery tube or pipe. **-verfahren,** *n.* process of development or evolution.

**Entwickler,** *m.* generator (for gases); (*Photog. & Dyeing*) developer; evolver, etc. (see entwickeln).

**Entwicklung,** *f.* = Entwickelung.

**entwirren,** *v.t.* unravel, disentangle.

**entwöhnen,** *v.t.* disaccustom, wean.

**Entwurf,** *m.* sketch, outline, plan.

**entziehen,** *v.t.* abstract, extract; take away, withdraw, deprive.

**Entziehung,** *f.* abstraction, extraction; withdrawing; deprivation.

**entziffern,** *v.t.* decipher.

**entzinnen,** *v.t.* detin, untin.

**entzischen,** *v.i.* escape with hissing.

**entzücken,** *v.t.* ravish, charm.

**entzuckern,** *v.t.* extract sugar from, deprive of sugar.

**Entzuckerung,** *f.* extraction of sugar.

**entzündbar,** *a.* inflammable.

**Entzündbarkeit,** *f.* inflammability.

**entzünden,** *v.t.* ignite, kindle, inflame.—*v.r.* take fire, ignite.

**entzundern,** *v.t.* free from scale, scale.

**entzündlich,** *a.* inflammable; inflammatory.

**Entzündlichkeit,** *f.* inflammability.

**Entzündung,** *f.* ignition, inflammation; (*Med.*) (in combination) -itis.

**Entzündungs-gemisch,** *n.* ignition mixture. **-probe,** *f.* ignition test. **-punkt,** *m.* kindling point, ignition point; (of kerosene, etc.) burning point. **-rohr,** *n.,* **-röhre,** *f.* ignition tube.

**entzwei,** *adv.* in two, asunder.

**entzweit,** *p.a.* at variance.

**Enzian,** *m.* gentian. **-branntwein,** *m.* gentian spirit. **-wurzel,** *f.* gentian root.

**Enzyklopädie,** *f.* encyclopedia.

**enzymatisch,** *a.* enzymatic, enzymic.

**enzymisch,** *a.* enzymic.

**Enzymwirkung,** *f.* enzyme action.

**E.P.,** *abbrev.* (englisches Patent) English patent, British patent; (Erstarrungspunkt) freezing point.

**Epheu,** *m.* ivy.

**Epihydrinsäure,** *f.* epihydrinic acid.

**Epithelzelle,** *f.* epithelial cell.

**Epizuckersäure,** *f.* episaccharic acid.

**Eppich,** *m.* celery.

**Eprouvette,** *f.* cylinder (narrow cylindrical vessel), tube, specif. test tube.

**EPS,** *abbrev.* (effektive Pferdestärke) actual horsepower.

**Equisetsäure,** *f.* equisetic (aconitic) acid.

**er,** *pron.* he, it.

**er-,** a verbal prefix which, prefixed to verbs, signifies " out, forth," denoting either the perfecting of an action, as *erfinden,* find out, invent, or the commencement of an action or state, as *erscheinen,* shine forth, appear. With adjectives it signifies " make " or " become "; as, *ergänzen,* make whole, complete; *erkalten,* become cold, cool.

**-er.** (1) A plural ending of some nouns; as, *Männer,* men. (2) A suffix denoting agent, instrument, or some one in close relation, -er, -or, -ist; as, *Erfinder,* inventor; *Heber,* siphon (lifter); *Physiker,* physicist. (3) A suffix forming adjectives from names of cities, etc.; as, *Pariser,* Parisian, Paris.

**Er.,** *abbrev.* (Erstarrungspunkt) freezing point, solidification point.

**erachten,** *v.t.* consider, regard, deem.

**Erachten,** *n.* opinion, judgment.—**meines Erachtens,** in my opinion.

**erbarmen,** *v.r.* pity, have mercy.

**erbauen,** *v.t.* build, construct; edify.

**Erbauung,** *f.* building, foundation; edification.

**Erbe,** *m.* heir.—*n.* inheritance.

**erbeben,** *v.i.* shake, tremble.

**erben,** *v.t.* inherit.

**erbieten,** *v.r.* offer.

**Erbinerde,** *f.* erbia, erbium oxide.

**erbitten,** *v.t.* request; persuade.

**erbittern,** *v.t.* exasperate.

**erblasen,** *v.t.* (*Metal.*) subject to, or obtain by, the blast.

**erblassen,** *v.t.* fade; pale; die.

**erblich,** *a.* hereditary.

**erblicken,** *v.t.* behold, see.

**erbohren,** *v.t.* get by boring, bore.

**erbötig,** *a.* willing, ready.

**erbrechen,** *v.t.* break open; vomit.—*v.r.* vomit.

**erbreiten,** *v.i.* broaden.

**erbringen,** *v.t.* produce, adduce.

**Erbschaft,** *f.* inheritance.

**Erbse,** *f.* pea.

**Erbsen-baum,** *m.* Siberian acacia. **-erz,** *n.* pea ore (form of limonite).

**erbsen-förmig,** *a.* pealike, pisiform. **-gross,** *a.* of the size of a pea. **-grün,** *a.* pea-green.

**Erbsen-mehl,** *n.* pea flour, pea meal. **-stein,** *m.* peastone, pisolite (a granular limestone).

**Erbskohle,** *f.* pea coal.

**Erd-.** earth, earthy, terrestrial, mineral, ground, soil, geo-. **-ableitung,** *f.* (*Elec.*) earth connection, ground. **-achse,** *f.* axis of the earth.

**Erdalkali,** *n.* alkaline earth. **-halogen,** *n.* alkaline-earth halide. **-metall,** *n.* alkaline-earth metal. **-salze,** *n.pl.,* salts of the alkaline-earth metals.

**erdalkalisch,** *a.* alkaline-earth.

**Erdapfel,** *m.* potato; cyclamen; mandrake; truffle.

**erdartig,** *a.* earthy.

**Erd-asphalt,** *m.* earthy asphalt; native asphalt. **-ball,** *m.* terrestrial globe. **-balsam,** *m.* petroleum (old name). **-beben,** *n.* earthquake. **-beere,** *f.* strawberry. **-beschreibung,** *f.* geography. **-birne,** *f.* Jerusalem artichoke. **-boden,** *m.* ground, soil. **-bohrer,** *m.* soil borer. **-brot,** *n.* sow bread (*Cyclamen europaeum*). **-chlorid,** *n.* chloride of an earth metal.

**Erde,** *f.* earth; soil; ground.

**erdehaltig,** *a.* containing earth, earthy.

**Erdeichel,** *f.* earthnut (peanut, *Arachis hypogaea,* or heath pea, *Lathyrus tuberosus*).

**erden,** *v.t.* (*Elec.*) ground, earth.

**Erdenge,** *f.* isthmus.

**erdenken,** *v.t.* devise, invent.

**erdenklich,** *a.* conceivable.

**Erdfarbe,** *f.* earthy color, mineral color.

**erd-farbig, -farben,** *a.* earth-colored. **-feucht,** *a.* moist (like damp earth).

**Erd-flachs,** *m.* amianthus. **-forscher,** *m.* geologist. **-gang,** *m.* vein; tunnel, gallery. **-gas,** *n.* natural gas. **-gelb,** *n.* yellow ocher.

**erdgelb,** *a.* ocherous, ochery.

**Erd-gemisch,** *n.* mixture of earths. **-geruch,** *m.* earthy odor. **-geschmack,** *m.* earthy taste, flavor of the soil. **-geschoss,** *n.* = ground floor. **-glas,** *n.* selenite. **-grün,** *n.* = Berggrün; = grüne Erde. **-gürtel,** *m.* zone.

**Erdharz,** *n.* asphalt, bitumen; fossil resin. **-gelbes —,** amber.

**erdharz-ig, -artig, -haltig,** *a.* asphaltic, bituminous.

**erdichten,** *v.t.* invent, fabricate.

**erdig,** *a.* earthy; terrestrial. **—erdiges Wasser,** natural water containing calcium salts.

**Erd-innere,** *n.* interior of the earth. **-kalk,** *m.* marly limestone.

**Erdkobalt,** *m.* earthy cobalt, asbolite. **—grüner —,** nickel ocher (annabergite); **roter —,** cobalt crust (earthy erythrite); **roter strahliger —,** cobalt bloom (erythrite).

**Erd-kohle,** *f.* earthy coal, lignitic earth. **-körper,** *m.* terrestrial body. **-kruste,** *f.* earth's crust. **-kugel,** *f.* terrestrial globe. **-kunde,** *f.* geography; geology; geognosy. **-mandel,** *f.* chufa (*Cyperus esculentus*); chufa tuber. **-mehl,** *n.* = Kieselgur. **-messkunst,** *f.* geodesy.

**Erdmetall,** *n.* earth metal. **—alkalisches —,** alkaline-earth metal.

**Erdnuss,** *f.* earthnut, ground nut (most commonly the peanut, *Arachis hypogꞁea*). **-öl,** *n.* peanut oil, arachis oil. **-säure,** *f.* arachidic acid (old name).

**Erdoberfläche,** *f.* earth's surface.

**Erdöl,** *n.* petroleum. **-bearbeitung,** *f.* petroleum refining. **-industrie,** *f.* petroleum (or oil) industry. **-rückstand,** *m.* petroleum residue.

**Erd-oxyd,** *n.* oxide of an earth metal. **-pech,** *n.* mineral pitch, asphalt, bitumen.

**erdpech-artig,** *a.* asphaltic. **-haltig,** *a.* containing asphalt, asphaltic.

**Erd-probe,** *f.* soil sample; soil test. **-rauch,** *m.* fumitory (*Fumaria*). **-reich,** *n.* ground, earth, land. **-rinde,** *f.* earth's crust.

**erdrücken,** *v.t.* stifle, smother; repress; crush.

**Erd-salz,** *n.* rock salt; saline efflorescence on soil. **-scheibe,** *f.* = Erdbrot. **-schellack,** *m.* acaroid resin. **-schicht,** *f.* layer of earth, stratum. **-schierling,** *m.* hemlock (*Conium maculatum*). **-schlacke,** *f.* earthy slag. **-schluss,** *m.* (*Elec.*) earth connection, ground. **-scholle,** *f.* clod. **-schwamm,** *m.* mushroom. **-schwefel,** *n.* **-schwefelsamen,** *m.* lycopodium. **-seife,** *f.* mountain soap (species of clay). **-stein,** *m.* eaglestone, aetites. **-strom,** *m.* earth current. **-talg,** *m.* mineral tallow, hatchettite (or ozocerite). **-talk,** *m.* earthy talc. **-teer,** *m.* mineral tar, maltha, pissasphalt. **-teil,** *m.* part of the world, continent.

**erdulden,** *v.t.* suffer, endure.

**Erdung,** *f.* (*Elec.*) ground(ing), earth(ing).

**Erd-verbindung,** *f.* (*Elec.*) ground connection. **-wachs,** *n.* mineral wax, earth wax (ozocerite). **-wärme,** *f.* heat of the earth.

**-erei.** A suffix forming nouns of action, place, condition, etc., **-ing, -ery;** as, *Bäckerei,* bakery, baker's trade; *Stickerei,* embroidery.

**ereignen,** *v.r.* happen, occur.

**Ereignis,** *n.* event, occurrence.

**ereilen,** *v.t.* overtake.

**Eremakausie,** *f.* eremacausis (slow combustion).

erfahren, v.t. learn; hear; experience; undergo. —p.a. experienced; expert.

Erfahrung, f. experience; knowledge, practice.

erfahrungs-mässig, -gemäss, a. according to experience, empirical; usual.

erfassen, v.t. seize, grasp.

Erfassung, f. grasping; comprehension.

erfinden, v.t. invent; find out.

Erfinder, m. inventor; designer; author.

erfindsam, a. inventive, ingenious.

Erfindung, f. invention; discovery; device.

Erfolg, m. result; success.

erfolgen, v.i. follow, result; take place.

erfolg-los, a. unsuccessful, ineffective. -reich, a. successful, effective.

erforderlich, a. requisite, necessary.

erfordern, v.t. require, demand.

Erfordernis, n. exigency, necessity; requisite.

erforschen, v.t. investigate; explore; discover.

Erforscher, m. investigator; explorer; discoverer.

Erforschung, f. investigation, research; exploration; discovery.

erfragen, v.t. ascertain, inquire.

erfreuen, v.t. delight, rejoice.—v.r. be glad; be possessed.

erfreulich, a. delightful, gratifying.

erfreulicherweise, adv. happily, fortunately.

erfrieren, v.i. freeze; (Metal.) chill.

erfrischen, v.t. refrigerate; freshen, refresh. —erfrischendes Mittel, refrigerant.

Erfrischung, f. refrigeration; refreshing; refreshment.

Erfrischungsmittel, n. refrigerant; refreshment.

erfroren, p.p. of erfrieren.

erfüllen, v.t. impregnate; fill, fill up; fulfill.

ergänzen, v.t. supply, complete, make up, restore, replenish.—ergänzend, p.a. complementary, supplementary.

Ergänzung, f. completion, restoration; supplement; complement; supply, supplying; replenishment.

Ergänzungs-band, m. supplementary volume, supplement. -buch, n. supplemental volume, supplement. -farbe, f. complementary color. -nährstoff, m. accessory food factor, vitamin. -werk, n. supplement.

Erg.-Bd., abbrev. (Ergänzungsband) supplementary volume.

ergeben, v.t. yield; show.—v.r. result; appear; submit; devote oneself.—p.a. devoted; obedient; resigned.

ergebenst, a. most humble.—adv. yours truly.

Ergebnis, n. result; product; yield.

ergehen, v.i. be issued; happen; fare.

ergiebig, a. productive, plentiful, rich.

Ergiebigkeit, f. richness; productiveness; yield, return; plenty.

ergiessen, v.t.& i. pour forth, discharge.

erglühen, v.i. begin to glow, glow.—v.r. kindle.

Ergosterin, n. ergosterol, ergosterin.

ergreifen, v.t. seize, grasp; resort to; take up; affect, strike.

ergründen, v.t. investigate; discover; fathom.

Erguss, m. effusion, discharge, overflow. -gestein, n. effusive rock.

erh., abbrev. (erhitzt) heated.

Erh., abbrev. (Erhitzung) heating.

erhaben, a. raised, elevated; relief; convex (lens); high; sublime, grand, illustrious. —erhabene Arbeit, relief, rilievo.

Erhabenheit, f. elevation; convexity; prominence; relief; grandeur, eminence.

erhaltbar, a. preservable; obtainable.

erhalten, v.t. keep, preserve, maintain, support; receive, obtain, get, acquire.—v.r. keep; remain steady.

Erhaltung, f. conservation; preservation; maintenance; support.

Erhaltungs-mittel, n. preservative; antiseptic. -umsatz, m. basal metabolism.

erharten, v.i. harden, set (esp. harden, as distinguished from abbinden).

erhärten, v.t. harden; confirm, verify; aver.— v.i. =erharten.

Erhärtung, f. hardening; declaration.

erheben, v.t. raise.—v.r. rise.

erheblich, a. important, considerable.

Erhebung, f. raising; elevation; rising; collection.

erheischen, v.t. demand, require.

erheitern, v.t. brighten; cheer.—v.r. clear up; cheer up.

erhellen, v.t. light up, illuminate; brighten, lighten (colors); (Photog.) expose.—v.i. become clear, appear.

Erhellung, f. illumination; (Photog.) exposure.

erhitzen, v.t. heat.—v.r. grow hot; become angry.—erhitzend, p.a. heating; stimulating.

Erhitzung, f. heating; growing hot.

erhöhen, v.t. raise, erect, elevate; heighten, advance, increase.

Erhöhung, f. raising, etc. (see erhöhen); prominence.

erholen, v.r. breathe, come to, recover, amuse oneself.

Erholung, f. recovery; recreation, relaxation.

erhören, v.t. hear; grant.

erinnern, v.t. remind; state; admonish.—v.r. remember.

Erinnerung, f. memory, recollection; admonition.

Eriochromschwarz, n. eriochrome black.

**Erk.,** *abbrev.* (Erkennung) detection, recognition.

**erkalten,** *v.i.* cool, grow cold.

**erkälten,** *v.t.* cool, chill.—*v.r.* catch cold.

**Erkaltung,** *f.* cooling.

**Erkältung,** *f.* cold, catarrh.

**erkaufen,** *v.t.* purchase, buy; bribe, corrupt.

**erkennbar,** *a.* knowable, discernible, perceptible.

**erkennen,** *v.t.* detect, recognize, distinguish, know; acknowledge; (*Med.*) diagnose.—*v.i.* decide, pass sentence.

**erkenntlich,** *a.* grateful.

**Erkenntnis,** *f.* perception; knowledge; decision.

**Erkennung,** *f.* detection, recognition.

**Erkennungszeichen,** *n.* characteristic, distinctive mark.

**erklärbar,** *a.* explainable, explicable.

**erklären,** *v.t.* explain, illustrate; declare, announce.—*v.r.* explain; grow clear.

**erklärlich,** *a.* evident, obvious.

**Erklärung,** *f.* explanation, illustration; declaration.

**Erklärungsversuch,** *m.* explanatory experiment; attempted explanation.

**erkranken,** *v.i.* fall ill, sicken.

**Erkrankung,** *f.* illness, falling sick.

**erkundigen,** *v.r.* inquire.

**Erkundigung,** *f.* inquiry.

**erlangen,** *v.t.* reach, obtain, attain, acquire.

**Erlanger-blau,** *n.* Erlanger blue (a kind of Prussian blue). **-leder,** *n.* glove kid.

**Erlass,** *m.* order, decree, edict; reduction, allowance, remission.

**erlassen,** *v.t.* issue, proclaim; remit, exempt, let off.

**erlauben,** *v.t.* allow, permit.

**Erlaubnis,** *f.* permission; grant; license.

**erlaucht,** *a.* illustrious, noble.

**erläutern,** *v.t.* explain, illustrate.

**Erle,** *f.* alder.

**erleben,** *v.t.* experience, pass thru.

**Erlebnis,** *n.* occurrence, event; experience.

**erledigen,** *v.t.* dispose of, settle, arrange; vacate.

**erlegen,** *v.t.* lay down, pay; kill.—*p.p.* of erliegen.

**-erlei.** An adjective ending denoting "kinds,"; as, *zweierlei,* of two kinds.

**erleichtern,** *v.t.* make lighter or easier, facilitate.

**erleiden,** *v.t.* suffer; undergo.

**Erlen-baum,** *m.* alder (tree). **-holz,** *n.* alder wood. **-kohle,** *f.* alder charcoal.

**Erlenmeyerkolben,** *m.* Erlenmeyer flask, conical flask.

**erlesen,** *v.t.* choose, select.

**erleuchten,** *v.t.* illuminate, light.

**erliegen,** *v.i.* sink, succumb.

**erlitten,** *p.p.* of erleiden.

**erlogen,** *p.a.* fabricated, false.

**Erlös,** *m.* proceeds.

**erlöschen,** *v.i.* go out, be extinguished; grow dull or dim; (of lime) slake; expire, become extinct; be effaced.—**erloschen,** *p.a.* dull, dim, dead.

**erlösen,** *v.t.* redeem, save; realize (money).

**ermächtigen,** *v.t.* empower, authorize.

**ermahnen,** *v.t.* exhort, remind.

**Ermangelung, Ermanglung,** *f.* default, want.

**ermässigen,** *v.t.* moderate, reduce.

**ermatten,** *v.t.&. i.* tire.

**ermessen,** *v.t.* judge; conceive.

**Ermessen,** *n.* judgment.—**meines Ermessens,** in my judgment.

**ermitteln,** *v.t.* ascertain, find out.

**Ermittelung,** *f.* ascertaining, ascertainment, finding out, discovery; (*Analysis*) determination.

**ermöglichen,** *v.t.* make possible.

**ermüden,** *v.t.* tire, fatigue, exhaust.

**Ermüdung,** *f.* fatigue; tiring.

**Ermüdungs-festigkeit,** *f.* resistance to fatigue, fatigue strength. **-grenze,** *f.* endurance limit. **-stoff,** *m.* product of fatigue.

**ermuntern,** *v.t.* rouse, encourage, urge.

**-ern.** A suffix forming adjectives of material; as, *eisern,* of iron.

**ernähren,** *v.t.* nourish, feed; support.— **ernährend,** *p.a.* nourishing, nutritive.

**Ernährung,** *f.,* nutrition; alimentation; support.

**Ernährungs-bedürfnis,** *n.* food requirement. **-boden,** *m.* nutritive medium. **-flüssigkeit,** *f.* nutritive liquid. **-geschäft,** *n.* nutrition. **-kanal,** *m.* alimentary canal. **-kunde,** *f.* dietetics. **-stoff,** *n.,* **-substanz,** *f.* alimentary substance, food substance, nutrient. **-versuch,** *m.* experiment on nutrition. **-wert,** *m.* nutritive value.

**ernennen,** *v.t.* nominate, appoint.

**erneuen, erneuern,** *v.t.* renew; refresh (colors); regenerate (steam); repair.

**erniedrigen,** *v.t.* lower; humble.

**Erniedrigung,** *f.* lowering, depression; humiliation.

**ernst,** *a.* serious, earnest; severe.

**Ernst,** *m.* earnest, earnestness, seriousness; severity.

**Ernte,** *f.* harvest; crop; gathering. **-maschine,** *f.* harvester.

**ernten,** *v.t.* harvest, reap, gather.

**erobern,** *v.t.* conquer, win.

**erodieren,** *v.t.* erode.

**eröffnen,** *v.t.* open; discover, disclose; start. —**eröffnend,** *p.a.* opening, disclosing; (*Med.*) aperient.

Eröffnung, f. opening; beginning; communication; declaration.

erörtern, v.t. discuss; debate.

Erörterung, f. discussion; debate.

erproben, v.t. test, try.

erquicken, v.t. refresh, revive.

erraten, v.t. guess, solve.

erregbar, a. excitable, irritable, sensitive.

erregen, v.t. excite; stimulate; agitate, irritate. —erregend, p.a. exciting, stimulating, stimulant.—erregendes Mittel, stimulant.—erregt, p.a. excited; active.

Erreger, m. exciter, etc. (see erregen). -flüssigkeit, f. exciting fluid. -linie, f. exciting line. -salz, n. exciting salt (as ammonium chloride in the Leclanché cell). -strom, m. (Elec.) exciting current.

Erregung, f. excitation, etc. (see erregen).

Erregungsflüssigkeit, f. exciting fluid.

erreichbar, a. attainable.

erreichen, v.t. reach, attain, get.

erretten, v.t. save, rescue.

errichten, v.t. erect; establish.

erringen, v.t. obtain, achieve, win.

Errungenschaft, f. acquisition, achievement, improvement.

Ersatz, m. substitution, replacement; substitute; equivalent; compensation.

Ersatz-. equivalent; substitute; duplicate, extra, spare. -deckel, m. extra cover, spare cover. -elektron, n. equivalent or replacing electron. -fähigkeit, f. capability of replacement; equivalency. -gewicht, n. equivalent weight, equivalent. -leim, m. size substitute; glue substitute. -menge, f. equivalent amount, equivalent. -mittel, n. substitute, surrogate. -stoff, m. substitute. -stück, n., -teil, m. extra part, spare part. -waren, f.pl. substitutes.

ersaufen, v.i. drown; (of lime) overslake.

ersäufen, v.t. drown; flood.

erschaffen, v.t. create.

erschallen, v.i. sound, resound.

erscheinen, v.i. appear; be clear.

Erscheinung, f. phenomenon; appearance; vision.

Erscheinungsform, f. phase; state.

erschlaffen, v.t.&i. relax, slacken.

erschliessen, v.t. open; disclose; infer.

erschöpfen, v.t. exhaust.—erschöpfend, p.a. exhausting; exhaustive, thoro.

Erschöpfung, f. exhaustion.

erschrecken, v.t. frighten, startle.—v.i.& r. be frightened.

erschrocken, p.p. of erschrecken.

erschüttern, v.t. shake; thrill.—v.i. tremble.—erschütternd, p.a. concussive; thrilling.

Erschütterung, f. concussion; percussion; shaking; vibration; shock; commotion.

erschweren, v.t. weight (silk, etc.); reduce (dyes); make heavy (or difficult); aggravate.

Erschwerung, f. weighting, etc. (see erschweren).

erschwingen, v.t. afford.

ersehen, v.t. see, learn, find.

ersetzbar, a. replaceable, etc. (see ersetzen).

ersetzen, v.t. replace, substitute, displace; compensate; recover.

Ersetzung, f. replacement, substitution, etc. (see ersetzen).

ersichtlich, a. visible, evident.

ersinnen, v.t. devise, conceive.

ersoffen, p.p. of ersaufen.

ersparen, v.t. spare, save.

Ersparnis, f. saving(s), economy.

erspriesslich, a. useful, advantageous.

erst, adv. first; only; yet.— — recht, all the more.

erstarren, v.i. solidify, congeal, freeze; harden, set; coagulate; become stiff or torpid.

Erstarrung, f. solidification, congelation, etc. (see erstarren).

Erstarrungs-punkt, m. freezing point; solidification point; coagulation point. -wärme, f. heat evolved on solidification, heat of fusion.

erstatten, v.t. render, return, repay.

erstaunen, v.i. be surprised or astonished (at).

Erstaunen, n. astonishment.

erste, a. first, prime, head.—der (die, das) erstere, the former.—in erster Linie, first of all, primarily.

erstens, adv. in the first place.

erstgenannt, a. first named, first, former.

ersticken, v.t. suffocate, choke, stifle.

Erstmilch, f. colostrum.

Erstp., abbrev. (Erstarrungspunkt) freezing point.

erstreben, v.t. strive for; attain.

erstrebenswert, a. worthy of effort.

erstrecken, v.r. extend, amount, reach.

ersuchen, v.t. request, beseech.

ertappen, v.t. catch.

erteilen, v.t. give, impart, bestow, grant.

ertönen, v.i. sound, resound.

Ertrag, m. yield; produce; proceeds, profit.

ertragen, v.t. bear, endure.

erträglich, a. tolerable; middling, passable.

ertragsfähig, a. productive.

Ertragsfeststellung, f. determination of yield.

ertränken, v.t. drown.

ertrinken, v.i. drown.

ertrüben, v.i. become turbid.

erübrigen, v.i. remain (to say).—v.t. save, spare.

Erucasäure, f. erucic acid.

Eruptivgestein, n. eruptive rock.

**erw.,** *abbrev.* (erwärmt) warmed; (erwähnt) mentioned.

**erwachen,** *v.i.* wake, awake.

**erwachsen,** *p.a.* grown, adult.

**erwägen,** *v.t.* consider, weigh.

**erwählen,** *v.t.* choose; elect.

**erwähnen,** *v.t.* mention.

**erwärmen,** *v.t.* warm, heat.

**Erwärmung,** *f.* warming, heating.

**Erwärmungskraft,** *f.* heating power, calorific power.

**erwarten,** *v.t.* expect, await.

**erwecken,** *v.t.* waken; rouse, animate.

**erwehren,** *v.r.* keep off, restrain.

**erweichen,** *v.t.* soften; soak; mellow.—**erweichend,** *p.a.* softening; emollient, demulcent.

**Erweichung,** *f.* softening; mollification.

**Erweichungs-mittel,** *n.* softening agent; (*Pharm.*) emollient, demulcent. **-punkt,** *m.* softening point.

**Erweis,** *m.* proof, demonstration.

**erweisen,** *v.t.* prove; show.—*v.r.* prove, be found.

**erweitern,** *v.t.* widen, expand, extend, enlarge, distend, dilate.—*v.r.* expand, grow large, dilate.

**Erweiterung,** *f.* widening, etc. (see erweitern).

**Erwerb,** *m.* acquisition; gain, profit; industry.

**erwerben,** *v.t.* acquire; earn, gain.

**erwidern,** *v.t.* return; reply.

**erwünscht,** *p.a.* wished for, desired; agreeable.

**Erz,** *n.* ore; metal, esp. bronze.

**erz-.** (with adjectives) extremely.

**Erz-.** ore, metalliferous; bronze; arch-, chief, foremost, high. **-abfälle,** *m.pl.* tailings. **-ader,** *f.* ore vein, metalliferous vein.

**erzählen,** *v.t.* tell, relate, report.

**Erzarbeiter,** *m.* worker in bronze, metal worker.

**erzarm,** *a.* poor in metal, lean.

**Erz-aufbereitung,** *f.* ore dressing. **-brechmaschine,** *f.* ore crusher.

**erzdumm,** *a.* extremely stupid.

**Erzeisen,** *n.* mine iron (obtained from ore without addition of fluxes).

**erzeugen,** *v.t.* produce; generate (as gases); beget.

**Erzeuger,** *m.* producer; generator.

**Erzeugnis,** *f.* production, product; produce.

**Erzeugung,** *f.* production, etc. (see erzeugen).

**Erzeugungsort,** *m.* place of production.

**Erzfarbe,** *f.* bronze color.

**erz-farben, -farbig,** *a.* bronze-colored. **-führend,** *p.a.* ore-bearing.

**Erz-gang,** *m.* ore vein, lode. **-gestein,** *n.* ore in mass, rock composed of ore. **-gicht,** *f.* charge of ore. **-giesser,** *m.* bronze founder,

brass founder. **-giesserei,** *f.* bronze foundry, brass foundry. **-glühfrischen,** *n.* (*Iron*) refining with ore. **-graupe,** *f.* coarse grain of ore. **-grube,** *f.* mine, pit.

**erzhaltig,** *a.* containing ore, ore-bearing.

**Erzhütte,** *f.* smelting house.

**erziehen,** *v.t.* educate; bring up, rear.

**Erzieher,** *m.* educator; tutor.

**erziehlich,** *a.* educational.

**erzielen,** *v.t.* obtain, attain; produce, raise.

**Erz-kies,** *m.* metalliferous pyrites. **-kunde,** *f.* metallurgy. **-lager,** *n.* bed of ore, ore deposit. **-lagerstätte,** *f.* ore deposit. **-metalle,** *n.pl.* ore metals, heavy metals. **-mittel,** *n.* ore (as opposed to gangue). **-mühle,** *f.* ore mill. **-muster,** *n.* ore sample. **-mutter.** *f.* matrix. **-niere,** *f.* kidney-shaped ore. **-ofen,** *m.* ore furnace, smelting furnace. **-probe,** *f.* ore assay, ore assaying; ore sample.

**erzreich,** *a.* rich in ore.

**Erz-röster,** *m.* ore burner, calciner. **-scheider,** *m.* ore separator. **-schlamm,** *m.* ore slime. **-stahl,** *m.* ore steel, mine steel. Cf. Erzeisen. **-staub,** *m.* ore dust.

**erzürnen,** *v.t.* anger, provoke.—*v.r.* grow angry; quarrel.

**Erzverhüttung,** *f.* ore reduction.

**erzwingen,** *v.t.* force, enforce; extort.

**Erzzerkleinerung,** *f.* ore crushing.

**es,** *pron.* it.— **— gibt,** there is, there are.

**Esche,** *f.* ash, ash tree.

**Eschel,** *m.* zaffer; (*Founding*) black spot.

**Eschen-holz,** *n.* ash wood, ash. **-wurz,** *f.* (*Bot.*) fraxinella.

**Esdragol,** *n.* estragole.

**Esdragon,** *m.* tarragon.

**E.S.E.,** *abbrev.* (elektrostatische Einheit) electrostatic unit.

**Esel,** *m.* ass, donkey; (wooden) horse; (*Mach.*) ram, monkey; (*Brewing*) scooper.

**Eseresamen,** *m.* Calabar bean.

**Esparsette,** *f.* sainfoin.

**Espe,** *f.* aspen.

**essbar,** *a.* edible.

**Esse,** *f.* forge; hearth; chimney, stack.

**Esseisen,** *n.* (*Metal.*) tuyère, twyer.

**essen,** *v.t.* eat.

**Essen,** *n.* eating; meal; food; dish. **-klappe,** *f.* damper.

**essentiell,** *a.* essential.

**Essenz,** *f.* essence.

**Essig,** *m.* vinegar.

**Essig-.** vinegar; acetic, aceto-. **-aal,** *m.,* **-älchen,** *n.* vinegar eel.

**essigartig,** *a.* acetous, acetic; vinegar-like.

**Essig-äther,** *m.* acetic ether (ethyl acetate). **-bereitung,** *f.* vinegar making. **-bildung,** *f.* acetification. **-essenz,** *f.* vinegar essence (concentrated solution of acetic acid).

-ester, *m.* acetic ester (ethyl acetate).
-fabrik, *f.* vinegar factory. -gärung, *f.*
acetic fermentation. -geist, *m.* acetone.
-gut, *n.* alcoholic liquid for quick vinegar
process.

essighaltig, *a.* containing vinegar.

Essig-honig, *m.* oxymel. -messer, *m.* acetometer. -mutter, *f.* mother (of vinegar).
-naphta, *f.* ethyl acetate. -pilz, *m.* vinegar
plant, mother. -prüfer, -prober, *m.* vinegar
tester, acetimeter. -rose, *f.* French rose,
red rose. -salz, *n.* acetate.

essigsauer, *a.* of or combined with acetic acid,
acetate of; acetic, acetous; sour like vinegar.
—essigsaure Eisenflüssigkeit, (*Pharm.*)
solution of ferric acetate, liquor ferri
acetici. —essigsaures Salz, salt of acetic
acid, acetate.

Essigsäure, *f.* acetic acid. -anhydrid, *n.*
acetic anhydride. -äther, *m.* acetic ether
(ethyl acetate). -äthylester, -äthyläther,
*m.* ethyl acetate. -gärung, *f.* acetic fermentation.

essigsäurehaltig, *a.* containing acetic acid.

Essigsäure-messer, *m.* acetometer. -messung,
*f.* acetometry. -salz, *n.* salt of acetic acid,
acetate.

Essig-schaum, *m.* flower of vinegar. -sirup,
*m.* oxymel. -sprit, *m.* triple vinegar (10-12
per cent acetic acid). -ständer, *m.* vinegar
tun, graduator (in the quick vinegar
process). -stube, *f.* vinegar room (warm
room for the quick vinegar process).
-zucker, *m.* (*Pharm.*) oxysaccharum.

Ess-lust, *f.* appetite. -waren, *f.pl.* provisions,
eatables.

Ester, *m.* ester; specif., ethyl ester.

ester-ähnlich, *a.* resembling an ester. -artig,
*a.* ester-like; in the form of ester.

Esterbildung, *f.* ester formation, esterification.

esterifizieren, *v.t.* esterify.

Ester-säure, *f.* ester acid. -zahl, *f.* ester number.

Estragon, *m.* tarragon. -essig, *m.* tarragon
vinegar. -öl, *n.* tarragon oil.

Estrich, *m.* plaster floor; layer of mortar.
-gips, *m.* estrich gypsum, flooring plaster
(a form of anhydrous calcium sulfate similar
to Keene's cement). -stein, *m.* a kind of
paving brick.

Estrifikation, *f.* esterification.

estrifizieren, *v.t.* esterify.

Etablissement, *n.* establishment.

Etage, *f.* floor, story; stage.

Etagenofen, *m.* shelved oven or kiln.

Etagere, *f.* shelf, stand, support, rack.

Etat, *m.* (financial) statement. -jahr, Etats-
jahr, *n.* fiscal year.

Etikette, *f.*, Etikett, *n.* label; tag; etiquette.

etikettieren, *v.t.* label; tag.

etliche, *a.* some, several, a few.

Etui, *n.* case, box.

etw., *abbrev.* (etwas) something.

etwa, *adv.* perhaps; about; perchance.

etwaig, *a.* likely to be, contingent, possible.

etwas, *pron.* some, something, somewhat.

Eucalyptusöl, *n.* eucalyptus oil.

euch, *pron.* you, to you, yourselves.

Euchinin, *n.* (*Pharm.*) euquinine.

Euchlor, Euchlorin, *n.* euchlorine.

eudiometrisch, *a.* eudiometric.

euer, *pron.* of you, your, yours.

Eugensäure, *f.* eugenic acid (eugenol).

Euklas, *m.* (*Min.*) euclase.

Eule, *f.* owl.

eurig, *pron.* yours.

europäisch, *a.* European.

eustasisch, *a.* Eustachian.

Eutektikum, *n.* (*pl.* Eutektika) eutectic.

eutektisch, *a.* eutectic.

Euter, *n.* udder.

ev., *abbrev.* eventuell.

evakuieren, *v.t.* evacuate, empty, exhaust.

Evakuierungskessel, *m.* vacuum boiler, vacuum pan.

evaporieren, *v.t.& i.* evaporate.

event., *abbrev.* eventuell.

eventuell, *a.* eventual.—*adv.* eventually; if
necessary, perhaps, or, or in certain cases.

Everninsäure, *f.* everninic acid.

Evernsäure, *f.* evernic acid.

evolvieren, *v.t.* evolve.

evomieren, *v.t.* vomit.

evtl., *abbrev.* eventuell.

ewig, *a.* eternal, perpetual.—*adv.* ever, un-
ceasingly.

Ewigkeit, *f.* eternity; perpetuity.

Exaktheit, *f.* exactness.

Examen, *n.* examination.

Excenter, *m.* eccentric.

Excentricität, *f.* eccentricity.

excentrisch, *a.* eccentric.

Exemplar, *n.* specimen; sample; copy.

existenzfähig, *a.* capable of existence.

existieren, *v.i.* exist.

exkl., *abbrev.* exklusiv.

exklusiv, *a.* exclusive.—*adv.* exclusively.

exosmotisch, *a.* exosmotic.

exotherm, exothermisch, *a.* exothermic.

expandieren, *v.t.& r.* expand.

expedieren, *v.t.* dispatch, forward.

Expedition, *f.* expedition; office.

Experimentalchemie, *f.* experimental chemistry.

Experimentator, *m.* experimenter; experimen-
talist.

experimentell, *a.* experimental.

**experimentieren,** *v.i.* experiment.

**Expertist,** *f.* expert investigation or report.

**explodierbar,** *a.* explosive, explodable.

**Explodierbarkeit,** *f.* explodability.

**explodieren,** *v.i.* explode.—**explodierend,** *p.a.* exploding, explosive.

**explosibel,** *a.* explosive, explodable.

**Explosibilität,** *f.* explodability.

**explosionsartig,** *a.* explosive.

**Explosionsdruck,** *m.* explosion pressure.

**explosionsfähig,** *a.* explosive.

**Explosions-fähigkeit,** *f.* explosiveness, explosibility. **-gefahr,** *f.* danger of explosion. **-gemisch,** *n.* explosive mixture. **-grenze,** *f.* explosion limit, explosive limit. **-kraft,** *f.* explosive force or power.

**explosionssicher,** *a.* explosion-proof.

**Explosions-stoss,** *m.* explosive impact, explosion impulse. **-ursache,** *f.* cause of explosion. **-vorgang,** *m.* explosive process. **-wärme,** *f.* heat of explosion. **-welle,** *f.* explosion wave.

**Explosiv-geschoss,** *n.* explosive projectile. **-kraft,** *f.* explosive force or power. **-stoff,** *m.* explosive substance, explosive. **-stoffchemie,** *f.* chemistry of explosives. **-verbrennung,** *f.* explosive combustion.

**exponieren,** *v.t.* expose; expound.

**Exposition,** *f.* exposure; exposition.

**Expositions-dauer,** *f.* time or duration of exposure. **-zeit,** *f.* time of exposure.

**Exsiccator, Exsikkator,** *m.* exsiccator, desiccator.

**Exsudat,** *n.* exudate, exudation.

**extrahierbar,** *a.* extractable, extractible.

**extrahieren,** *v.t.* extract.

**Extrahierung,** *f.* extraction, extracting.

**Extraktbrühe,** *f.* extract liquor.

**Extrakteur,** *m.* extractor.

**Extraktgehalt,** *m.* extract content.

**Extraktions-apparat,** *m.* extraction apparatus. **-dauer,** *f.* time of extraction. **-flüssigkeit,** *f.* extraction liquid, liquid extract. **-gefäss,** *n.* extraction vessel. **-hülse,** *f.* extraction shell or thimble. **-kolben,** *m.* extraction flask. **-mittel,** *n.* extracting agent. **-mühle,** *f.* extraction mill. **-rückstand,** *m.* extraction residue.

**Extraktivstoff, Extraktstoff,** *m.* extractive substance or matter, extractive.

**Extraktwolle,** *f.* extract wool, extracted wool.

**extrapolatorisch,** *a.* pertaining to extrapolation.—*adv.* by extrapolation.

**extrapolieren,** *v.t.* extrapolate.

**Extremwert,** *m.* extreme value.

**Exzent-**. see **Excent-**.

**EZ.,** *abbrev.* (Esterzahl) ester number.

# F

**f.,** *abbrev.* (fest) solid; (fein) fine; (für) for; (folgende) following.

**F.,** *abbrev.* (Fusionspunkt) melting point, m.p., m.; Fahrenheit; (feinste Sorte) finest grade.

**f.a.B.,** *abbrev.* (frei an Bord) free on board, f.o.b.

**Fabel,** *f.* fable; fiction.

**fabelhaft,** *a.* fabulous.

**Fabellehre,** *f.* mythology.

**Fabrik,** *f.* factory, works, mill, plant, establishment. **-anlage,** *f.* manufacturing plant, factory; establishment of a factory.

**Fabrikant,** *m.* manufacturer, maker.

**Fabrikarbeit,** *f.* factory labor; manufactured article.

**Fabrikat,** *n.* manufacture, make; textile fabric.

**Fabrikation,** *f.* manufacturing, manufacture, production.

**Fabrikations-prozess,** *m.* manufacturing process. **-wasser,** *n.* water for manufacturing use.

**fabrikatorisch,** *a.* manufacturing, factory, industrial.

**Fabrikatur,** *f.* manufacture, make.

**Fabrik-betrieb,** *m.* factory management or practice. **-gold,** *n.* (strong) gold leaf. **-laboratorium,** *n.* factory laboratory, works laboratory. **-marke,** *f.* trademark.

**fabrikmässig,** *a. & adv.* by factory methods, on a factory scale, industrial(ly); by machinery.

**Fabrik-öl,** *n.* oil for manufacturing purposes, specif. an inferior grade of olive oil. **-preis,** *m.* factory price. **-ware,** *f.* manufactured article; factory quality. **-wesen,** *n.* manufacturing industry; factory system. **-zeichen,** *n.* manufacturer's mark, trademark.

**fabrizieren,** *v.t.* make, manufacture.

**Fäces,** *pl.* feces.

**facettiert,** *p.a.* faceted.

**-fach.** -fold; as, *hundertfach*, hundred-fold.

**Fach,** *n.* branch, department, line, profession, subject; division, compartment, cell; shelf.

**Fach-.** professional, technical, expert. **-arbeiter,** *m.* specialist, expert.

**fachartig,** *a.* cellular.

**Fach-ausdruck,** *m.* technical term or expression. **-bildung,** *f.* professional education, technical education. **-blatt,** *n.* = Fachzeitschrift.

**fächeln,** *v.t.* fan.

**Fächer,** *m.* fan; flapper. **-brenner,** *m.* fantail burner.

**fächerförmig,** *a.* fan-shaped.

**Fächergerste,** *f.* bearded barley.

**fächerig,** *a.* divided into compartments; locular.

**Fach-genosse,** *m.* professional colleague. **-literatur,** *f.* technical (or trade) literature. **-mann,** *m.* professional man, specialist, expert.

**fach-männisch,** *a.* professional, expert. **-mässig,** *a.* professional.

**Fach-ordnung,** *f.* classification. **-schule,** *f.* technical school, special school. **-sprache,** *f.* technical language, professional terminology. **-werk,** *n.* framework, bay-work. **-wissenschaft,** *f.* special branch of science, specialty. **-wörterbuch,** *n.* technical dictionary. **-zeitschrift,** *f.* special periodical, technical journal, trade journal.

**Facit,** *n.* sum, result, answer.

**Fackel,** *f.* torch. **-baum,** *m.* marsh elder. **-föhre,** *f.* Scotch pine (*Pinus sylvestris*). **-glanz,** *m.* (of wine) perfect clearness. **-kohle,** *f.* cannel coal. **-palme,** *f.* sago palm.

**Façon,** *f.* fashion; cut, style.

**façonnieren,** *v.t.* figure; fashion.

**Fädchen,** *n.* small thread, filament.

**fade,** *a.* insipid, flat, stale.

**Faden,** *m.* thread; filament, fiber; (of wood) grain; twine; fathom; (*Sugar*) string.

**faden-ähnlich, -artig, -förmig,** *a.* threadlike, filamentous, filiform.

**Faden-glas,** *n.* spun glass; filigree glass. **-holz,** *n.* cordwood. **-kreuz, -netz,** *n.* cross hairs. **-länge,** *f.* (*Dyeing*) length of fiber. **-nudeln,** *f.pl.* vermicelli. **-pilze,** *m.pl.* (*Bot.*) Hyphomycetes. **-zähler,** *m.* thread counter.

**fadenziehend,** *p.a.* ropy, stringy.

**fädig,** *a.* thready, filaceous.

**Fahamblätter,** *n.pl.* faham leaves (*Angraecum fragrans*).

**fähig,** *a.* capable; apt.

**-fähig.** capable of, -able, -ible.

**Fähigkeit,** *f.* capability, ability, capacity.

**fahl,** *a.* fallow (pale, pale yellow); fawn (light yellowish brown); dun (grayish brown); earth-colored; ashy; sallow; faded.

**Fahl-band,** *n.* (*Mining*) fahlband. **-erz,** *n.* fahlerz, fahlore (tetrahedrite-tennantite);

(**dunkles**) tetrahedrite; (**lichtes**) tennantite.

**fahl-gelb**, *a*. fallow, yellowish. **-grau**, *a*. grayish, ashy-gray.

**Fahlleder**, *n*. russet leather (for uppers).

**fahlrot**, *a*. fawn, pale yellowish brown.

**Fahlstein**, *m*. pale gray slate.

**Fahne**, *f*. flag, " policeman " (for precipitates); flag, standard; (of a dish) marli.

**Fahnenschraube**, *f*. wing nut, wing screw.

**fahrbar**, *a*. passable; transportable, movable.

**fahren**, *v.i*. go, travel, ride, drive.

**Fahr-geld**, *n*. fare; freight. **-karte**, *f*. ticket.

**fahrlässig**, *a*. negligent, careless.

**Fahr-rad**, *n*. bicycle. **-stuhl**, *m*. elevator, hoist; wheel chair.

**Fahrt**, *f*. passage, journey, trip, drive.

**Fährte**, *f*. trail, track.

**Fahr-weg**, *m*. carriage road. **-zeug**, *n*. vehicle; vessel.

**fäkal**, *a*. fecal.

**Fäkalien**, *n.pl*., feces.

**Fäkalstoff**, *m*. fecal substance.

**Faktis, Factis**, factice (rubber substitute).

**faktisch**, *a*. real, actual, *de facto*.

**Faktor**, *m*. factor; manager, agent.

**Faktorentabelle**, *f*. table of factors.

**Faktur, Faktura**, *f*. invoice.

**Fäkulenz**, *f*. feculence, sediment, dregs.

**falb**, *a*. pale yellow, pale, fallow.

**Fall**, *m*. fall, descent; case; event; yield.

**Fäll-apparat**, *m*. precipitation apparatus. **-bad**, *n*. precipitating bath.

**fällbar**, *a*. precipitable; fit to fell.

**Fäll-barkeit**, *f*. precipitability. **-bottich**, *m*. precipitating vat.

**Falle**, *f*. trap; valve; bolt.—*dative* of Fall.

**fallen**, *v.i*. separate, be deposited; fall, drop; (*Mining*) dip.— **—** **in** (**etwas**), verge on; strike.

**Fallen**, *n*. separating, etc. (see fallen); yield, produce.

**fällen**, *v.t*. precipitate; drop; fell; pass (judgment).

**Fäller**, *m*. precipitator.

**Fällflüssigkeit**, *f*. precipitating liquid.

**Fall-hammer**, *m*. drop hammer. **-höhe**, *f*. height of fall.

**fallieren**, *v.i*. fail.

**fällig**, *a*. due, payable.

**Fällkessel**, *m*. precipitating vessel.

**Fallkraut**, *n*. (*Bot*.) arnica.

**Fäll-methode**, *f*. precipitation method. **-mittel**, *n*. precipitating agent, precipitant.

**Fallrohr**, *n*. down pipe, waste pipe.

**falls**, *conj*. in case.

**Fall-schirm**, *m*. parachute. **-silber**, *n*. deposited silver. **-sucht**, *f*. epilepsy. **-tür**, *f*. trapdoor.

**Fällung**, *f*. precipitation, precipitating, etc. (see fällen).

**Fällungs-becherglas**, *n*. precipitation beaker. **-kraft**, *f*. precipitating power. **-mittel**, *n*. precipitant. **-reaktion**, *f*. precipitation reaction. **-vermögen**, *n*. precipitating power. **-wärme**, *f*. heat of precipitation. **-wert**, *m*. precipitation value.

**Fall-werk**, *n*. stamp; pile driver. **-winkel**, *m*. angle of inclination.

**falsch**, *a*. false, counterfeit, pseudo-; artificial; adulterated; wrong; deceitful. **-blau**, *a*. navy blue.

**fälschen**, *v.t*. falsify, adulterate, sophisticate, counterfeit; forge.

**Fälscher**, *m*. adulterator; adulterant; falsifier, forger.

**fälschlich**, *a*. false; erroneous. **-erweise**, *adv*. falsely; erroneously.

**Fälschung**, *f*. falsification, etc. (see fälschen); fraud.

**Fälschungs-mittel**, *n*., **-stoff**, *m*. adulterant. **-falt**. =-fältig.

**Falte**, *f*. fold, plait, crease; flexure, bend, turn; wrinkle.

**falten**, *v.t*. fold, plait; wrinkle.

**Faltenfilter**, *n*. plaited filter, folded filter.

**falten-frei, -los**, *a*. without folds (or wrinkles), creaseless, smooth.

**Falten-punkt**, *m*. (in a curve) point of sharp change of direction. **-werfen**, *n*. creasing, puckering, crimping.

**Falter**, *m*. folder, creaser; butterfly; third stomach of ruminants.

**faltig**, *a*. having folds, plaits or creases; wrinkled; puckered.

**-faltig, -fältig**. **-fold, -ple**; as, *vierfaltig*, fourfold, quadruple.

**Faltprobe**, *f*. folding test.

**Faltung**, *f*. folding, plaiting, plication, wrinkling.

**Faltungspunkt**, *m*. plait point, point of plication or folding.

**Falz**, *m*. fold; groove, flute, notch.

**falzen**, *v.t*. fold; groove, flute, rabbet; (*Leather*) pare.

**Falzziegel**, *m*. interlocking tile.

**Familie**, *f*. family.

**fand**, *pret*. of finden.

**Fang**, *m*. catch, capture; trap; collector; stab; fang; talon.

**fangen**, *v.t*. catch; capture, secure; soften (hides).

**Fänger**, *m*. catcher, trap.

**Fangstoff**, *m*. (*Paper*) stuff from the save-all.

**Faradaykäfig**, *m*. Faraday cage.

**Farb-abänderung**, *f*. change in color. **-an-**

strich, *m.* coat of color. -bad, *n.* dye bath. -band, *n.* typewriter ribbon.

färbbar, *a.* colorable, stainable.

Färbbarkeit, *f.* colorability, stainability.

Farb-becher, *m.* dye beaker (for dyeing tests). -bestimmung, *f.* color determination. -bier, *n.* dark beer for coloring. -brühe, *f.* dye liquor. -druck, *m.* color printing; color print.

Farbe, *f.* color; dye; pigment; stain; paint; hue, tint; (*Leather*) weak ooze, also a container for it.

Färbe, *f.* dyeing; staining; coloring. -artikel, *m.* (*Calico*) dyed style. -bad, *n.* dye bath. -becher, *m.* dye beaker, dye pot. -bier, *n.* dark beer for coloring. -brühe, *f.* dyeing liquor. -buch, *n.* dye book.

farbecht, *a.* of fast color.

färbefähig, *a.* capable of being colored, dyed or stained.

Färbe-fass, *n.* dye beck, dye tub. -flechte, *f.* archil, dyer's moss. -flotte, *f.* dye liquor, dye bath. -flüssigkeit, *f.* dyeing liquid, dye liquor; staining fluid. -ginster, *m.* = Färberginster. -grad, *m.* degree of coloring.

farbehaltend, *a.* holding color, fast.

Färbe-holz, *n.* dyewood. -kraft, *f.* dyeing power.

Färbekraut, *n.* dyer's weed.—gelbes —, yellowweed.

Färbe-kufe, -küpe, *f.* dyeing vat, dye vat. -lack, *m.* lac dye.

farbelos, *a.* colorless; achromatic.

Färbe-malz, *n.* = Farbmalz. -mittel, *n.* coloring agent, pigment, dye.

färben, *v.t.* color, dye, stain.—in der Wolle —, dye in grain.

Farben-abbeizmittel, *n.* paint remover. -abstreichmesser, *n.* (*Dyeing*) knife for removing excess dye, color doctor. -abstufung, *f.* color gradation. -abweichung, *f.* chromatic aberration. -änderung, *f.* alteration of color. -bild, *n.* colored image; colored spectrum. -bildung, *f.* color formation, coloration.

farbenblind, *a.* color-blind.

Farben-bogen, *m.* iris. -brechung, *f.* refraction of colors; color blending. -brühe, *f.* dyeing liquor, dye liquor. -buchdruck, *m.* color printing. -chemie, *f.* color chemistry.

farbenchemisch, *a.* relating to color chemistry or dye chemistry.

färbend, *p.a.* coloring, dyeing, staining.

Farben-distel, *f.* safflower (*Carthamus tinctorius*). -druck, *m.* color printing; color print. -erde, *f.* colored earth. -erscheinung, *f.* color phenomenon; appearance of color.

farbenerzeugend, *p.a.* color-producing, chromogenic.

Farben-erzeuger, *m.* chromogen. -erzeugung, *f.* production of colors. -fabrik, *f.* color factory, dye factory. -fabrikant, *m.* color maker, dye maker. -gebung, *f.* coloring, coloration. -glanz, *m.* brilliancy of color. -glas, *n.* colored glass, stained glass. -gleichheit, *f.* equality or sameness of color. -grund, *m.* ground color. -holz, *n.* dyewood. -industrie, *f.* color industry, specif. dye industry. -körper, *m.* coloring body; coloring matter. -körperchen, *n.* pigment granule. -lack, *m.* lake. -lehre, *f.* science of color, chromatics. -leiter, *m.* color scale.

farbenlos, *a.* = farblos.

Farben-malz, *n.* = Farbmalz. -mass, *n.*, -massstab, *m.* colorimeter. -messapparat, *m.* colorimeter. -messer, *m.* chromatometer; colorimeter; color knife. -messkunst, *f.* colorimetry. -messung, *f.* measurement of colors, chromatometry, colorimetry. -mischung, *f.* color mixing, color blending. -mühle, *f.* color mill. -ofen, *m.* enameling furnace. -probe, *f.* color test; dye test, dye trial. -rand, *m.* iris. -reaktion, *f.* color reaction. -reiben, *n.* color grinding. -reiber, *m.* color grinder.

farben-reich, *a.* richly colored. -rein, *a.* colorless.

Farbenschiller, *m.* play of colors, iridescence, schiller.

farbenschillernd, *a.* iridescent, chatoyant.

Farben-schimmer, *m.* = Farbenschiller. -schmelzofen, *m.* enameling furnace. -skala, *f.* color scale, color chart. -spektrum, *n.* colored spectrum, color spectrum, chromatic spectrum. -spiel, *n.*, -spielung, *f.* play of colors. -steindruck, *m.* chromolithography. -stift, *m.* colored pencil or crayon. -stoff, *m.* = Farbstoff. -strahl, *m.* colored ray. -stufe, *f.* color gradation, shade, tint. -stufenmesser, *m.* tintometer. -ton, *m.* color tone, hue. -umschlag, *m.* color change.

farbenverändernd, *a.* altering color or colors.

Farben-veränderung, *f.* discoloration; change in color. -waren, *f.pl.* = Farbwaren. -wechsel, *m.* play of colors, change of color. -wurzel, *f.* madder. -zerstreuung, *f.* (*Optics*) chromatic aberration, also dispersion.

Färbeprozess, *m.* dyeing process, dyeing; coloring process.

Färber, *m.* dyer. -baum, *m.* Venetian sumac (*Cotinus cotinus*). -blume, *f.* woodwaxen.

Färberde, *f.* (*Ceram.*) colored clay.

Färberdistel, *f.* safflower (*Carthamus tinctorius*); sawwort (*Serratula tinctoria*).

Färberei, *f.* dyeing; dye house, dye works.

Färber-eiche, *f.* dyer's oak, quercitron. -erde,

*f.* Armenian bole. -flechte, *f.* archil, dyer's moss. -flotte, *f.* dye liquor, dye bath. -ginster, *m.* dyer's broom (*Genista tinctoria*). -holz, *n.* dyer's wood, dyewood. -kraut, *n.* dyer's weed. -kreuzdorn, *m.* dyer's buckthorn, specif. *Rhamnus infectoria*. -küpe, *f.* dyer's vat, dye vat. -lack, *m.* lac dye. -maulbeerbaum, *m.* dyer's mulberry (*Morus tinctoria*). -meister, *m.* head dyer, foreman dyer. -moos, *n.* dyer's moss, archil. -ochsenzunge, *f.* dyer's alkanet (*Alkanna tinctoria*). -rinde, *f.* quercitron bark. -rot, *n.* alizarin. -röte, *f.* madder. -saflor, *m.* safflower.

**Farberscheinung,** *f.* = Farbenerscheinung.

**Färber-waid,** *m.* dyer's woad. -wau, *m.* yellowweed. -wurzel, *f.* madder.

**Färbe-sieb,** *n.* color strainer, color sieve. -stoff, *m.* coloring matter, pigment, dyestuff, dye. -trog, *m.* staining trough or box. -vermögen, *n.* coloring power, tinctorial power, dyeing value.

**Farbewaren,** *f.pl.* = Farbwaren.

**Färbe-weise,** *f.* method of dyeing, dye process. -wurzel, *f.* = Färberwurzel. -zwecke, *m.pl.* dyeing purposes.

**Färbfass,** *n.* dyeing vat, dye vat.

**farbfertig,** *a.* ready for dyeing (or coloring).

**Farb-flotte,** *f.* dye liquor, dye bath. -flüssigkeit, *f.* (*Micros.*) staining solution. -gehalt, *m.* content of dye or color. -glas, *n.* color glass, colored glass, stained glass. -gut, *n.* goods to be dyed. -holz, *n.* dyewood.

**farbig, farbicht,** *a.* colored; stained; chromatic.

**Farbigkeit,** *f.* color (the quality).

**Farb-kissen,** *n.* ink pad, inking pad. -kochapparat, *m.* color boiler, color kettle. -körper, *m.* coloring substance, coloring material. -kraft, *f.* coloring power, tinctorial power.

**farbkräftig,** *a.* of strong tinctorial or coloring power, (*Dyeing*) productive.

**Farbküche,** *f.* color shop, color house.

**farbl.,** *abbrev.* (farblos) colorless.

**Farblack,** *f.* color lake, lake.

**farblos,** *a.* colorless; achromatic.

**Farb-losigkeit,** *f.* colorlessness; achromatism. -lösung, *f.* (*Micros.*) staining solution. -malz, *n.* coloring malt, amber malt (darkened by roasting). -material, *n.* coloring material; dyeing material, dye, dyestuff.

**farbmessend,** *p.a.* colorimetric.

**Farb-messer,** *m.* colorimeter. -mine, *f.* colored lead (for pencils). -mischer, *m.* color mixer. -mittel, *n.* coloring agent. -muster, *n.* color pattern; color sample. -nuance, *f.* color shade, tint. -pflanze, *f.* dye plant. -reaktion, *f.* color reaction. -säure, *f.* color acid. -stärke, *f.* strength or depth of color,

shade. -stein, *m.* dyestone. -stift, *m.* colored pencil.

**Farbstoff,** *m.* dyestuff, dye; coloring matter; pigment; stain. -aufnahme, *f.* dye absorption. -bildung, *f.* dye or color formation; (*Biol.*) chromogenesis. -brühe, *f.* dye liquor.

**farbstofferzeugend,** *p.a.* chromogenic.

**Farbstofffabrik,** *f.* dye factory.

**farbstoffhaltig,** *a.* containing coloring matter, dye or pigment.

**Farbstofflösung,** *f.* dye solution, staining solution.

**Farb-stufe,** *f.* color gradation, tint, shade. -substanz, *f.* coloring substance, coloring matter. -tiefe, *f.* depth of color. -ton, *m.* color tone, tint. -trog, *m.* color vat, color bucket.

**Färbung,** *f.* dyeing, coloring, coloration, staining, pigmentation; hue, tinge; dye.

**färbungsfähig,** *a.* capable of being dyed, colored, or stained.

**Färbungsvermögen,** *n.* tinctorial power, coloring power.

**Farb-veränderung,** *f.* alteration of color. -wandel, *m.* color change. -waren, *f.pl.* coloring or dyeing materials, dyes, pigments, paints. -wechsel, *m.* color change, play of colors. -werk, *n.* dye factory, dye works. -wert, *m.* color value. -zelle, *f.* (*Biol.*) pigment cell. -zusatz, *m.* addition or admixture of color.

**Farin, -zucker,** *m.* brown sugar, muscovado.

**Farinade,** *f.* = Farin.

**Farn,** *m.,* -kraut, *n.* fern. -krautöl, *n.* fern oil. -wurzel, *f.* (*Pharm.*) aspidium.

**Farren,** *m.,* -kraut, *n.* fern.

**Fasel,** *f.* kidney bean.

**faseln,** *v.r.* unravel.—*v.i.* drivel.

**Faser,** *f.* fiber; filament; thread; string; (*Brewing*) pulp.

**Faser-.** fibrous, fibro-.

**faserähnlich,** *a.* fibroid.

**Faseralaun,** *m.* halotrichite.

**faserartig,** *a.* fibery, fibrous, filamentary.

**Faser-asche,** *f.* fiber ash. -blende, *f.* fibrous sphalerite.

**Fäserchen,** *n.* little fiber, fibril, filament.

**Faserfärbung,** *f.* coloration of the fiber.

**faserförmig,** *a.* fibrous, filiform.

**Faser-gehalt,** *m.* fiber content; (*Paper*) fiber yield. -gewebe, *n.* fibrous tissue; fibrous texture. -gips, *m.* fibrous gypsum. -haut, *f.* (*Anat.*) fibrous membrane.

**faserig,** *a.* fibrous, fibery, filamentous, stringy. -kristallinisch, *a.* fibrocrystalline.

**Faser-kalk,** *m.* fibrous calcite or aragonite. -kiesel, *m.* fibrolite. -kohle, *f.* fibrous coal.

**faserlos,** *a.* fiberless.

**fasern,** *v.r.& i.* feaze, fuzz; (*Paper*) assume a mottled appearance due to different absorptiveness of the fibers.

**Faser-richtung,** *f.* direction of the fiber or grain. **-rohstoff,** *m.* fibrous raw material. **-salz,** *n.* fibrous salt.

**Faserstoff,** *m.* fibrin; fibrous material.—**vegetabilischer —,** vegetable fibrin (gluten; cellulose); vegetable fiber.

**faserstoffartig, faserstoffig,** *a.* fibrinous.

**Faserung,** *f.* fibrillation.

**Faserzeolith,** *m.* natrolite.

**fasrig,** *a.* =faserig.

**Fass,** *n.* cask, barrel, keg; vat, tank, tub, tun; drum. **-bier,** *n.* draft beer.

**Fässchen,** *n.* small barrel, keg.

**fassen,** *v.t.* seize, grasp, take; put, mount, set; hold, contain, include; cask, tun (wine, etc.).—*v.i.* take, hold well; (of cement, etc.) set.—*v.r.* compose oneself; express oneself. —**gefasst,** *p.a.* seized, etc.; composed, calm; prepared.

**Fass-gärung,** *f.* cask fermentation. **-gärungs-system,** *n.* (*Brewing*) cleansing system. **-geläger,** *n.* cask deposit, bottoms. **-geschmack,** *m.* taste of the cask. **-hahn,** *m.* spigot, faucet, cock.

**fasslich,** *a.* comprehensible.

**Fass-pech,** *n.* cooper's pitch; pitch in casks. **-talg,** *m.* tallow in casks.

**Fassung,** *f.* seizing, etc. (see fassen); casing; frame; holder; wording; composure.

**Fassungs-raum,** *m.,* **-vermögen,** *n.* capacity, volume.

**Fass-waren,** *f.pl.* goods in casks or barrels. **-zwickel,** *m.* (*Brewing*) try cock.

**fast,** *adv.* almost, nearly.

**Fastage,** *f.* casks, cooperage, barrels and casks.

**fasten,** *v.i.* fast.

**Fastenzeit,** *f.* Lent.

**faul,** *a.* rotten, putrid, bad, decaying; lazy, slow; (*Metal.*) short, brittle.—**fauler Heinz,** (*Old Chem.*) athanor (kind of furnace).

**faulbar,** *a.* putrescible.

**Faul-baum,** *m.* alder buckthorn (*Rhamnus frangula*); bird cherry (*Prunus padus*). **-bruch,** *m.* shortness, brittleness.

**faulbrüchig,** *a.* short, brittle.

**Faul-butte, -bütte,** *f.* fermenting trough, rotting vat.

**Fäule,** *f.* rottenness; dry rot; blight; (*Mining*) rotten lode.

**faulen,** *v.i.* rot, putrefy; (*Tech.*) ferment.—**faulend,** *p.a.* rotting, putrescent, septic.

**fäulen,** *v.t.* cause to putrefy, rot.

**Faulenzer,** *m.* idler; book of tables, reckoner; (*Brewing*) Y connection.

**faulig, faulicht,** *a.* rotten, putrid, putrefactive, putrescent.

**Fäulnis,** *f.* putrefaction, putridness, rottenness, rot, sepsis. **-alkaloid,** *n.* ptomaine. **-bakterien,** *n.pl.* putrefactive bacteria. **-base,** *f.* ptomaine.

**fäulnis-befördernd, -bewirkend, -erregend,** *p.a.* septic; putrefactive.

**Fäulnisbeständigkeit,** *f.* resistance to rotting, imputrescibility.

**fäulniserregend,** *a.* putrefactive, septic.

**Fäulniserreger,** *m.* putrefactive agent.

**fäulnisfähig,** *a.* putrefiable, putrescible.

**Fäulnis-gärung,** *f.* putrefactive fermentation, putrefaction. **-geruch,** *m.* putrid or rotten odor. **-gift,** *n.* septic poison.

**fäulnis-hemmend, -hindernd,** *p.a.* antiseptic. **-sicher,** *a.* antifouling. **-unfähig,** *a.* unputrefiable, imputrescible. **-verhindernd, -verhütend,** *a.* antiseptic; antifouling. **-widrig,** *a.* antiseptic.

**Faulschlamm,** *m.* sapropel (decomposing slime at the bottom of stagnant waters).

**Faulung, Fäulung,** *f.* rotting, putrefaction, decay.

**Faulwerden,** *n.* =Faulung.

**Faum,** *m.* foam, froth.

**Faust,** *f.* fist; grasp. **-regel,** *f.* rule of thumb.

**Fäzes,** *f.pl.* feces.

**Fazies,** *f.* facies, face, aspect.

**fechten,** *v.i.* fight; fence.

**Feder,** *f.* feather; plume; pen; (*Mech.*) spring.

**federähnlich,** *a.* featherlike.

**Federalaun,** *m.* feather alum (halotrichite, alunogen or epsomite); amianthus.

**federartig,** *a.* feathery, plumaceous.

**Feder-barometer,** *m.* aneroid barometer. **-bart,** *m.* vane or web of a feather. **-busch,** *m.* plume; tuft, crest. **-chen,** *n.* little feather, pen, or spring; (*Bot.*) plumule. **-erz,** *n.* feather ore (form of jamesonite). **-fahne,** *f.* feather flag, trimmed feather for removing precipitates; = Federbart.

**federförmig,** *a.* feathered, feathery.

**Federgips,** *m.* fibrous gypsum.

**federhart,** *a.* springy, elastic.

**Federharz,** *n.* rubber, caoutchouc; elaterite.

**federicht,** *a.* feathered, feathery.

**federig,** *a.* feathery, plumose.

**Feder-kiel,** *m.* quill. **-kraft,** *f.* elasticity.

**federkräftig,** *a.* elastic, springy.

**federn,** *v.i.* be elastic, spring; lose feathers.

**Feder-salz,** *n.* feather salt (any of various fibrous or plumose mineral varieties). **-stahl,** *m.* spring steel. **-ventil,** *n.* spring valve. **-vieh,** *n.* poultry. **-wa(a)ge,** *f.* spring balance. **-weiss,** *n.* amianthus; French chalk; fibrous gypsum. **-zange,** *f.* spring pincers.

**Fege,** *f.* sieve, screen, riddle.

**fegen,** *v.t.* sweep; clean; winnow.

**Fege-salpeter,** *m.* saltpeter sweepings. **-sand,** *m.* scouring sand. **-schober,** *m.* (*Salt*) scum pan.

**Fegsel,** *n.* sweepings.

**Fehl-**. false, wrong, bad, vain, mis-, mal-.

**fehlbar,** *a.* fallible.

**Fehlbetrag,** *m.* deficit.

**fehlen,** *v.i.* fail; err; be missing, lack.

**Fehler,** *m.* error; mistake, fault, defect. **-ausgleichung,** *f.* equalization or compensation of errors.

**fehlerfrei,** *a.* faultless, sound, clear.

**Fehlergrenze,** *f.* limit of error.

**fehlerhaft,** *a.* faulty, defective.

**Fehlerquelle,** *f.* source of error.

**Fehlgeburt,** *f.* miscarriage.

**fehlgehen,** *v.i.* go wrong.

**Fehl-griff,** *m.* mistake, blunder. **-guss,** *m.* spoiled casting, waste.

**Fehlingsche Lösung.** Fehling('s) solution.

**Fehl-kochung,** *f.* defective boiling. **-schluss,** *m.* false inference. **-zündung,** *f.* misfire.

**feien,** *v.t.* make proof, charm (against).

**Feier,** *f.* holiday, festival, celebration; rest.

**feierlich,** *a.* festive; solemn.

**feiern,** *v.t.* celebrate, observe.—*v.i.* rest from work, strike, be idle.

**Feier-stunde,** *f.* leisure hour. **-tag,** *m.* holiday.

**feig,** *a.* rotten; cowardly.

**Feigbohne,** *f.* lupine.

**feige,** *a.* rotten; cowardly.

**Feige,** *f.* fig.

**Feigen-baum,** *m.* fig tree. **-wein,** *m.* fig wine.

**feil,** *a.* for sale; mercenary.

**Feile,** *f.* file; filings; polish.

**feilen,** *v.t.* file; polish.

**Feilicht,** *n.* filings.

**feilschen,** *v.i.* bargain.

**Feil-sel,** *n.,* **-späne,** *m.pl.,* **-staub,** *m.* filings. **-strich,** *m.* file mark, file cut.

**fein,** *a.* fine.—*adv.* finely.

**Fein-aufspaltung,** *f.* fine separation. **-bau,** *m.* fine structure.

**feinblasig,** *a.* having minute bubbles or blisters.

**Feinblech,** *n.* (*Metal.*) thin plate.

**feinbrennen,** *v.t.* refine (metals).

**Feinbrenner,** *m.* refiner.

**Feind,** *m.* enemy, foe.

**feindlich,** *a.* hostile, opposed.

**Feindschaft,** *f.* hostility, enmity.

**Feine,** *f.* fineness.

**Feineisen,** *n.* refined iron.

**feinen, feinern,** *v.t.* refine.

**feinfaserig,** *a.* fine-fibered, fine-grained.

**feinfein,** *a.* very fine.

**Fein-feuer,** *n.* refinery. **-gehalt,** *m.* fineness (of metals). **-gehaltsstempel,** *m.* hall mark.

**fein-gepulvert,** *p.a.* finely powdered. **-geteilt,** *p.a.* finely divided; finely graduated.

**Feingold,** *n.* fine gold.

**Feinheit,** *f.* fineness; fine detail; smartness.

**Feinheits-grad,** *m.* (degree of) fineness. **-grenze,** *f.* limit of fineness.

**Fein-kies,** *m.* fine ore, fines. **-kohle,** *f.* fine coal, slack. **-korneisen,** *n.* fine-grained iron.

**fein-körnig,** *a.* fine-grained. **-kristallinisch,** *a.* finely crystalline.

**Feinkupfer,** *n.* fine copper.

**fein-lochig,** *a.* fine-holed, fine-pored. **-machen,** *v.t.* refine. **-mahlen,** *v.t.* grind fine, triturate. **-maschig,** *a.* fine-meshed. **-mehlig,** *a.* finely powdered.

**Fein-metall,** *n.* fine metal. **-ofen,** *m.* refining furnace.

**feinporig,** *a.* finely porous.

**Fein-probe,** *f.* delicate test. **-prozess,** *m.* refining process. **-puddeln,** *n.* (*Metal.*) refining puddling.

**fein-pulvern,** *v.t.* powder fine, pulverize. **-pulvrig,** *a.* pulverulent.

**Feinschlacke,** *f.* refinery slag.

**fein-schleifen,** *v.t.* grind smooth. **-schmeckend,** *a.* delicate (in taste); savory.

**Fein-schmecker,** *m.* epicure. **-schrot,** *n.& m.* fine groats; (*Brewing*) finely crushed malt. **-silber,** *n.* fine silver, refined silver.

**feinstgepulvert,** *a.* very finely powdered.

**Fein-struktur,** *f.* fine structure. **-verschiebung,** *f.* fine displacement.

**feinverteilt,** *p.a.* finely divided.

**Feinwa(a)ge,** *f.* precision balance.

**fein-zellig,** *a.* fine-celled, finely cellular. **-zerkleinert,** *a.* finely divided, finely ground. **-zerrieben,** *a.* finely ground. **-zerteilt,** *p.a.* finely divided.

**Feinzeug,** *n.* (*Paper*) pulp, stuff. **-holländer,** *m.* (*Paper*) beater, beating engine.

**Fein-zinn,** *n.* grain tin. **-zucker,** *m.* refined sugar.

**feist,** *a.* fat; plump.

**Felbel,** *m.& f.* shag (the cloth or its nap).

**Feld,** *n.* field; land, ground; pane, panel, compartment. **-bau,** *m.* agriculture, farming. **-brand,** *m.* (*Ceram.*) clamp burning. **-dienst,** *m.* active (military) service.

**feldfrei,** *a.* field-free.

**Feld-frucht,** *f.* farm product. **-gerät,** *n.* agricultural implements; field equipage.

**feldgrau,** *a.* military gray, greenish-gray.

**Feld-kamille,** *f.* camomile (*Matricaria chamomilla*). **-klee,** *m.* white clover; rabbit-foot clover. **-kümmel,** *m.* wild caraway; wild thyme. **-messen,** *n.* land surveying. **-ofen,** *m.* (*Ceram.*) clamp kiln. **-rauch,** *m.,* **-raute,** *f.* fumitory (*Fumaria*).

**Feldspat,** *m.* feldspar.

feldspat-ähnlich, -artig, *a.* feldspathic.
Feldspatgestein, *n.* felspathic rock.
feldspat-naltig, -isch, *a.* felspathic.
Feld-stärke, *f.* field intensity. -stecher, *m.* field glass. -stein, *m.* compact feldspar; boulder; landmark. -thymian, *m.* wild thyme. -wirtschaft, *f.* agriculture. -ziegel, *m.* clamp brick (brick burnt in a clamp). -zug, *m.* campaign.
Felge, *f.* fallow; rim (of a wheel), felly.
Fell, *n.* skin, hide, pelt. -abfälle, *m.pl.* skin (or hide) parings or cuttings. -eisen, *n.* knapsack; valise; mail bag. -leim, *m.* hide glue. -schmitzer, *m.* dyer of skins. -späne, *m.pl.* hide parings.
Felpel, *m.& f.* = Felbel.
Fels, *m.* rock. -alaun, *m.* rock alum. -art, *f.* (kind or variety of) rock.
Felsen, *m.* rock. -ader, *f.* dike. -alaun, *m.* rock alum. -gebirge, *n.* Rocky Mountains. -glimmer, *m.* mica.
felsenhart, *a.* hard as rock, rocky.
Felsen-öl, *n.* rock oil (petroleum). -salz, *n.* saltpeter.
Felsglimmer, *m.* mica.
felsig, *a.* rocky, rocklike.
Felsöl, *n.* petroleum.
Fenchel, *m.* fennel. -geruch, *m.* fennel odor. -holz, *n.* sassafras wood. -öl, *n.* fennel oil. -wasser, *n.* (*Pharm.*) fennel water.
Fenchocamphersäure, *f.* fenchocamphoric acid.
Fenster, *n.* window. -glas, *n.* window glass. -kitt, *m.* glazier's putty. -scheibe, *f.* window pane.
Ferien, *f.pl.* holidays, vacation.
fermentieren, *v.i.* ferment.
Fermentierung, *f.* fermentation.
Fermentierungsvorgang, *m.* fermentation process.
Fermentwirkung, *f.* ferment action, fermentation.
fern, *a.* far, distant.
Fern-, far, distant, remote, tele-, perspective.
Fernambukholz, Fernambuk, *n.* Brazil wood.
Ferne, *f.* distance, remoteness.
ferner, *a.* farther, further.—*adv.* further, besides.
Fernewirkung, *f.* action at a distance.
Fernglas, *n.* telescope; spyglass.
fernhalten, *v.t.& i.* keep away.
Fern-hörer, *m.* telephone receiver. -photographie, *f.* telephotography.
Fernrohr, *n.* telescope; field glass. -lupe, *f.* telescopic magnifier.
Fern-schreiber, *m.* telegraph. -sehen, *n.* television. -sicht, *f.* perspective; vista. -sprecher, *m.* telephone. -zeichnung, *f.* perspective drawing.

Ferri-. ferric, ferri-. -acetat, *n.* ferric acetate. -ammonsulfat, *n.* ammonium ferric sulfate. -bromid, *n.* ferric bromide. -chlorid, *n.* ferric chloride. -chlorwasserstoff, -chlorwasserstoffsäure, *f.* ferrichloric acid. -cyan, *n.* ferricyanogen. -cyaneisen, *n.* ferrous ferricyanide (Turnbull's blue). -cyanid, *n.* ferric cyanide; ferricyanide.
Ferricyan-kalium, *n.* potassium ferricyanide. -natrium, *n.* sodium ferricyanide. -silber, *n.* silver ferricyanide. -verbindung, *f.* ferricyanide. -wasserstoff, *m.*, -wasserstoffsäure, *f.* ferricyanic acid.
Ferridcyankalium, *n.* potassium ferricyanide.
Ferrieisencyanür, *n.* = Ferriferrocyanid.
Ferriferro-cyanid, *n.* ferric ferrocyanide (Prussian blue). -jodid, *n.* ferrosoferric iodide. -oxyd, *n.* ferrosoferric oxide.
Ferri-hydroxyd, *n.* ferric hydroxide. -ion, *n.* ferric ion. -jodat, *n.* ferric iodate. -jodid, *n.* ferric iodide. -kaliumsulfat, *n.* ferric potassium sulfate. -nitrat, *n.* ferric nitrate. -oxyd, *n.* ferric oxide. -phosphat, *n.* ferric phosphate. -rhodanid, *n.* ferric thiocyanate (or sulfocyanate). -salz, *n.* ferric salt. -sulfat, *n.* ferric sulfate. -sulfid, *n.* ferric sulfide. -verbindung, *f.* ferric compound. -zyan, *n.* ferricyanogen.
Ferrizyan-. see Ferricyan-.
Ferro-. ferrous, ferro-, ferroso-. -ammonsulfat, *n.* ammonium ferrous sulfate. -bor, *n.* ferroboron. -bromid, *n.* ferrous bromide. -chlorid, *n.* ferrous chloride. -chrom, *n.* ferrochrome, ferrochromium.
Ferrocyan, *n.* ferrocyanogen. -eisen, *n.* ferric ferrocyanide (Prussian blue).
Ferrocyanid, *n.* ferrous cyanide; ferrocyanide.
Ferrocyan-kalium, *n.* potassium ferrocyanide. -kupfer, *n.* cupric ferrocyanide. -natrium, *n.* sodium ferrocyanide. -silber, *n.* silver ferrocyanide. -verbindung, *f.* ferrocyanide. -wasserstoff, *m.*, -wasserstoffsäure, *f.* ferrocyanic acid. -zink, *n.* zinc ferrocyanide.
Ferroferri-cyanid, *n.* ferrous ferricyanide. -oxyd, *n.* ferrosoferric oxide (Fe$_3$O$_4$).
Ferro-hydroxyd, *n.* ferrous hydroxide. -ion, *n.* ferrous ion. -jodid, *n.* ferrous iodide. -kaliumsulfat, *n.* ferrous potassium sulfate. -karbonat, *n.* ferrous carbonate. -legierung, *f.* ferro-alloy. -mangan, *n.* ferromanganese. -molybdän, *n.* ferromolybdenum. -nitrat, *n.* ferrous nitrate. -oxalat, *n.* ferrous oxalate. -oxyd, *n.* ferrous oxide. -phosphat, *n.* ferrous phosphate. -phosphor, *n.* ferrophosphorus. -salz, *n.* ferrous salt. -silizium, *n.* ferrosilicon. -sulfat, *n.* ferrous sulfate. -sulfid, *n.* ferrous sulfide. -titan, *n.* ferrotitanium. -verbindung, *f.* ferrous compound.

-wolfram, n. ferrotungsten. -zyan, n. ferro-cyanogen.

Ferrozyan- . see Ferrocyan- .

Ferse, f. heel.

fertig, a. ready; done, finished; ready-made; skilful; insolvent.

fertigen, v.t. make ready; make; manufacture; do.

Fertig-erzeugnis, f. finished product. -keit, f. readiness; skill, dexterity. -machen, n. finishing. -macher, m. finisher. -raffination, f. (Lead) refining. -stellen, n., -stellung, f. finishing.

Fertigung, f. making ready; making, manufacture; doing.

Ferulasäure, f. ferulic acid.

fesseln, v.t. fetter; captivate.

fest, a. solid; firm, compact, strong; fast, fixed, tight; stable; permanent; proof; steady.—adv. firmly, closely, strongly.

Fest, n. feast, festival, holiday.

-fest, proof, resistant.

festbacken, v.i. cake together (on heating), clinker.

Feste, f. compact rock; fortress.

fest-frieren, v.i. freeze solid, freeze hard. -geworden, p.a. solidified. -haften, v.i. cling tight, adhere strongly.

festhalten, v.t. hold fast, retain; fix; stop, arrest.—v.i. hold, adhere, cling.—festhaltend, p.a. tenacious, retentive.

festigen, v.t. make firm, consolidate.

Festigkeit, f. solidity, etc. (see fest); (of metals) tenacity; (Mech.) strength, resistance.

Festigkeitsgrenze, f. (Mech.) limit of resistance, breaking point.

fest-kitten, v.t. cement (or lute) tight. -kleben, v.t.& i. stick fast.

Festland, n. continent, mainland.

festlegen, v.t. fix; place; define; bed; moor.

Festlegung, f. fixation, etc. (see festlegen); convention, agreement.

festlich, a. festive; solemn.

festmachen, v.t. solidify; make fast, fasten; settle.

Festschrift, f. festival (or anniversary) publication.

festsetzen, v.t. establish, settle, fix.

Festsetzung, f. establishment, settlement, arrangement; appointment; imprisonment.

feststehen, v.i. stand fast, be fixed.—feststehend, p.a. stationary; stable; established, settled, fixed.

feststellen, v.t. establish, ascertain, determine; fix, fasten, stop.

Feststellung, f. establishing, etc. (see feststellen).

Festungsachat, m. fortification agate.

festweich, a. semi-solid.

Fest-werden, n. solidification; coagulation. -wert, m. fixed value, constant.

fett, a. fatty, oily; aliphatic; fat; rich, fertile, profitable.—fettes Puddeln, (Iron) pig boiling.

Fett, n. fat; grease. -abfall, m., -abfälle, m.pl. refuse fat. -abscheider, m. grease separator.

fett-arm, a. poor in fat. -aromatisch, a. aliphatic-aromatic. -artig, a. fat-like, fatty.

Fett-bedarf, m. fat requirement. -bestandteil, m. fatty constituent. -bestimmung, f. fat determination. -bildung, f. fat formation.

fettdicht, a. fat-tight.

Fettdruck, m. bold-faced type, boldface.

fettdrucken, v.t. print in boldface.

Fettdrüse, f. sebaceous gland.

Fette, f. fatness, greasiness.

fetten, v.t. oil, grease, lubricate; stuff (leather); fatten.

Fett-entziehung, f. fat extraction. -farbstoff, m. color for fats; (Micros.) fat stain; (Biochem.) lipochrome, lutein. -fleck, -flecken, m. grease spot.

fett-frei, a. fat-free, free from fat. -gar, a. (Leather) oil-tanned.

Fettgas, n. oil gas.

fettgebunden, p.a. united to an aliphatic compound or radical.

Fett-gehalt, m. fat content. -geruch, m. odor of grease. -geschmack, m. fatty taste, greasy taste. -gewebe, n. adipose tissue. -glanz, m. greasy luster.

fett-glänzend, a. having a greasy luster. -haltig, a. containing fat, fatty.

Fett-härtung, f. hardening of fat(s). -harz, n. oleoresin. -heit, f. fatness, etc. (see fett).

fettig, a. fatty, fat, greasy.

Fettigkeit, f. fattiness, fatness, greasiness.

Fett-industrie, f. fat industry. -kalk, m. fat lime. -kohle, f. fat coal, coal rich in volatile matter. -körper, m. fatty compound; fat; aliphatic compound; fatty or greasy matter. -kügelchen, n. fat globule.

fett-lösend, a. fat-dissolving. -löslich, a. soluble in fat.

Fett-lösungsmittel, n. solvent for fats. -noppe, f. grease spot (in fabrics). -ponceau, n. fat ponceau. -puddeln, n. (Iron) wet puddling, pig boiling. -quarz, m. greasy (lustered) quartz.

fettreich, a. rich in fat.

Fett-reihe, f. fatty series, aliphatic series. -reservemittel, n. fat resist, wax resist. -salbe, f. fatty ointment.

fettsauer, a. of or combined with fatty acid; (formerly) sebacate of.

Fett-säure, f. fatty acid; fat acid; (old name for) sebacic acid. -schicht, f. layer of fat or grease. **-schmiere,** *f.* (*Leather*) fat liquor. **-schmierung,** *f.* grease lubrication. **-schweiss,** *m.* yolk (of wool); fatty sweat. **-seife,** *f.* soap from fats; (*Soap*) lard soap. **-sein,** *n.* fatness, fattiness, greasiness; ropiness (of wine).

**fettspaltend,** *p.a.* fat-cleaving, lipolytic.

**Fett-spaltung,** *f.* cleavage of fat, lipolysis. **-spritze,** *f.* grease gun. **-stein,** *m.* eleolite. **-stift,** *m.* wax pencil, wax crayon. **-stoff,** *m.* fat; fatty matter; (formerly) adipocere. **-stoffwechsel,** *m.* fat metabolism. **-substanz,** *f.* fatty substance, fat. **-teilchen,** *n.* fat particle. **-ton,** *m.* fuller's earth.

**Fettung,** *f.* oiling, etc. (see fetten).

**Fett-verbindung,** *f.* fatty compound, aliphatic compound. **-verseifung,** *f.* saponification of fat. **-wachs,** *n.* adipocere. **-wolle,** *f.* wool in the yolk, grease wool.

**Fetzen,** *m.* shred, tatter, scrap; trifle.

**feucht,** *a.* moist; humid, damp; (of malt) slack.—**auf feuchtem Wege,** in the wet way, by wet process.

**Feuchte,** *f.* moistness, dampness. **-kammer,** *f.* moist chamber.

**feuchten,** *v.t.* moisten, dampen, wet.

**Feuchter,** *m.* moistener, damper, wetter.

**Feuchtheit,** *f.* moistness, dampness.

**Feuchtigkeit,** *f.* moisture; moistness, dampness, humidity; humor; phlegm.

**Feuchtigkeits-gehalt,** *m.* moisture content. **-grad,** *m.* degree of moisture or humidity. **-messer,** *m.* hygrometer. **-niederschlag,** *m.* deposit of moisture. **-prüfer,** *m.* moisture tester. **-zeiger,** *m.* hygroscope.

**Feuchtkammer,** *f.* moist chamber.

**feuchtlich,** *a.* slightly moist.

**Feuchtwalze,** *f.* dampening roller, damping roll.

**feuchtwarm,** *a.* moist and warm.

**Feuer,** *n.* fire; furnace, hearth, forge; light (as for a signal).

**feuerbeständig,** *a.* resistant to fire or heat; fireproof; refractory.

**Feuer-beständigkeit,** *f.* fire-resistant quality, fireproofness; refractoriness. **-bestattung,** *f.* cremation. **-blende,** *f.* fireblende, pyrostilpnite. **-brücke,** *f.* fire bridge. **-buchse, -büchse,** *f.* fire box.

**feuer-fangend,** *a.* inflammable. **-farbig,** *a.* flame-colored.

**feuerfest,** *a.* fireproof; refractory.—**feuerfester Ton,** fireclay.—**feuerfester Ziegel,** firebrick.

**Feuerfestigkeit,** *f.* fireproofness; refractoriness.

**feuerflüssig,** *a.* molten, fused; liquid at a high temperature.

**Feuer-führung,** *f.* firing. **-gas,** *n.* flue gas. **-gefahr,** *f.* danger of fire, fire hazard.

**feuergefährlich,** *a.* liable to take fire, inflammable.

**Feuer-gefährlichkeit,** *f.* inflammability. **-gradmesser,** *m.* pyrometer. **-gradmessung,** *f.* pyrometry. **-grube,** *f.* ash pit. **-haken,** *m.* fire hook, poker. **-holz,** *n.* firewood.

**feuerig,** *a.* = feurig.

**Feuer-kammer,** *f.* fire chamber, fire box. **-kitt,** *m.* fireproof cement. **-krücke,** *f.* furnace rake, rabble. **-kunst,** *f.* pyrotechnics. **-leitung,** *f.* priming, train.

**feuerlos,** *a.* fireless, lusterless.

**Feuer-löschapparat,** *m.* fire extinguisher. **-löschmittel,** *n.* fire-extinguishing substance. **-losigkeit,** *f.* lack of brilliance. **-luft,** *f.* furnace gas; (Scheele's name for) oxygen. **-material,** *n.* fuel, combustible. **-messer,** *m.* pyrometer. **-messung,** *f.* pyrometry.

**feuern,** *v.t.* fire, heat, burn; (*Wine*) sulfur. —*v.i.* fire, spark, glow.

**Feuer-porzellan,** *n.* refractory porcelain. **-probe,** *f.* fire test. **-punkt,** *m.* (*Optics*) focus; (*Mining*) hearth. **-raum,** *m.* fireplace, fire box, furnace, hearth. **-regen,** *m.* rain of fire, fiery rain. **-rohr,** *n.* fire tube, flue; firearm. **-rohrkessel,** *m.* fire-tube boiler, tubular boiler.

**feuerrot,** *a.* fiery red.

**Feuer-saft,** *m.* (*Iron*) slag bath. **-schutzmittel,** *n.* fireproofing agent. **-schwaden,** *m.* firedamp. **-schwamm,** *m.* tinder, punk.

**Feuersgefahr,** *f.* danger of fire, fire hazard.

**feuersicher,** *a.* fireproof.

**Feuerstein,** *m.* flint; fire brick.

**feuersteinartig,** *a.* flintlike, flinty.

**Feuer-stoff,** *m.* (*Old Physics*) caloric. **-ton,** *m.* fire clay.

**Feuerung,** *f.* firing, fire, heating; fuel; furnace; fireplace, hearth.

**Feuerungs-anlage,** *f.* furnace, hearth, fireplace. **-bedarf,** *m.* fuel requirement. **-gewölbe,** *n.* furnace arch. **-material,** *n.* fuel. **-öl,** *n.* fuel oil. **-raum,** *m.* = Feuerraum.

**feuerungstechnisch,** *a.* pyrotechnic.

**feuervergoldet,** *a.* fire-gilt.

**Feuer-vergoldung,** *f.* fire gilding. **-versicherung,** *f.* fire insurance. **-waffe,** *f.* firearm. **-werk,** *n.* firework, fireworks. **-werker,** *m.* pyrotechnist. **-werkerei,** *f.* pyrotechnics. **-werkerkunst,** *f.* pyrotechnics.

**feuerwiderstandsfähig,** *a.* resistant to fire.

**Feuer-zeug,** *n.* lighter. **-ziegel,** *m.* firebrick. **-zug,** *m.* flue, fire tube; train of explosives.

**feurig,** *a.* fiery; igneous; burning, hot, ardent, spirited; (of wine) generous; (of colors) bright, loud.—**feuriger Schwaden,** firedamp.

**feurig-flüssig,** *a.* igneous. **-rot,** *a.* fiery red; red-hot.

**ff.,** *abbrev.* (feinfein) very fine; (feuerfest) fireproof, refractory; (und folgende) and following, *et seq.*

**FF., Ff.,** *abbrev.* (Fusionspunkte) melting points.

**F.f.,** *abbrev.* (Fortsetzung folgt) to be continued.

**Fibel,** *f.* primer.

**Fibrille,** *f.* fibril.

**fibrinhaltig,** *a.* containing fibrin, fibrinous.

**fibrös,** *a.* fibrous.

**ficellieren,** *v.t.* wire (bottles).

**Fichte,** *f.* spruce (*Picea*); (loosely) pine, fir.

**Fichten-harz,** *n.* (strictly) spruce resin; (commonly) rosin. **-holz,** *n.* (strictly) spruce wood. **-nadelöl,** *n.* (commonly) oil from the needles of any of various conifers, " pine-needle oil." **-pech,** *n.* = Fichtenharz. **-säure,** *f.* pinic acid. **-span,** *m.* spruce (or loosely, pine) shaving, chip, or splint. **-wolle,** *f.* pine wool. **-zucker,** *m.* pinitol, pinite.

**-ficiren, ficirung.** = fizieren, -fizierung.

**F.i.D.,** *abbrev.* (Faden in Dampf) thread in vapor.

**Fieber,** *n.* fever.—**aussetzendes —,** intermittent fever.

**fieberartig,** *a.* feverish, febrile.

**Fieberarznei,** *f.* febrifuge, antipyretic.

**fieberfest,** *a.* immune to fever.

**Fieber-klee,** *m.* buck bean (*Menyanthes*). **-kraut,** *n.* feverfew. **-mittel,** *n.* febrifuge, antipyretic.

**fiebern,** *v.i.* have fever; rave.

**Fieber-pulver,** *n.* fever powder, ague powder (antimonial powder). **-rinde,** *f.* cinchona bark.

**fieber-vertreibend, -widrig,** *a.* febrifuge, antifebrile.

**Fieder,** *f.* leaflet; pinnule.

**fiel,** *pret.* of fallen.

**Figurendruck,** *m.* (*Calico*) topical printing. **-artikel,** *m.* (*Calico*) topical style.

**figurieren,** *v.t.* figure.

**figürlich,** *a.* figurative.

**fiktiv,** *a.* fictive, imaginary.

**Filial-.** branch; as, Filialanstalt, branch establishment.

**Filiasäure,** *f.* filicic acid.

**Filicinsäure,** *f.* filicinic acid.

**Filigran,** *n.* filigree.

**Filixsäure,** *f.* filicic acid.

**Filteranlage,** *f.* filtration plant.

**filterbar,** *a.* filterable.

**Filter-blatt,** *n.* filter, filter paper. **-dauer,** *f.* time of filtering. **-element,** *n.* filter cell. **-flasche,** *f.* filter flask. **-gaze,** *f.* filter gauze. **-gehäuse,** *n.* filter case, filter casing. **-ge-**stell, *n.* filter stand. **-gläschen,** *n.* small filter glass or tube. **-halter,** *m.* filter holder. **-kegel,** *m.* filter cone. **-kerze,** *f.* filter candle. **-konus,** *m.* filter cone. **-körper,** *m.* filtering material. **-kuchen,** *m.* filter cake. **-lage,** *f.* filter layer, filter bed. **-masse,** *f.* (*Brewing*) pulp, filter mass.

**filtern,** *v.t.* filter.

**Filter-papier,** *n.* filter paper. **-plättchen,** *n.* (small) filter plate. **-platte,** *f.* filter plate. **-rohr,** *n.*, **-röhre,** *f.* filter tube or pipe. **-rand,** *m.* edge of a filter. **-rückstand, -rest,** *m.* residue on the filter, filtration residue. **-schablone,** *f.* form for cutting filters. **-schale,** *f.* filter(ing) dish. **-schicht,** *f.* filter bed. **-schlauch,** *m.* filter hose. **-schoner,** *m.* filter cone. **-sieb,** *n.* filtering sieve, strainer. **-stativ,** *n.* filter stand. **-stein,** *m.* = Filtrierstein. **-stoff,** *m.* filter material. **-tiegel,** *m.* filtering crucible. **-träger,** *m.* filter holder, filter ring. **-trichter,** *m.* filter funnel. **-tuch,** *m.* filtering cloth. **-turm,** *m.* filter tower, filtering tower.

**Filterung,** *f.* filtering, filtration.

**Filterungsdauer,** *f.* time of filtering.

**Filter-wäger,** *m.* filter weigher. **-watte,** *f.* filter wadding.

**Filtrat,** *n.* filtrate.

**filtrationsfähig,** *a.* capable of filtration.

**Filtrier-apparat,** *m.* filtering apparatus. **-aufsatz,** *m.* filtering attachment.

**filtrierbar,** *a.* filterable.

**Filtrier-becher,** *m.* filtering beaker. **-beutel,** *m.* filtering bag, percolator. **-einlage,** *f.* (charge of) filtering material.

**filtrieren,** *v.t.* filter, strain.

**Filtrierer,** *m.* filterer, strainer.

**Filtrier-erde,** *f.* filtering earth. **-fläche,** *f.* filtering surface or area. **-flasche,** *f.* filtering flask. **-gestell,** *n.* filter stand. **-hut,** *m.* (paper) filtering funnel. **-kessel,** *m.* filtering boiler. **-konus,** *m.* filter cone. **-korb,** *m.* filtering basket. **-nutsche,** *f.* suction filter. **-papier,** *n.* filter paper. **-papierstreifen,** *m.* strip of filter paper. **-platte,** *f.* filter plate. **-presse,** *f.* filter press. **-pumpe,** *f.* filter pump. **-ring,** *m.* filter ring. **-rohr,** *n.*, **-röhre,** *f.* filter tube, filtering tube. **-sack,** *m.* filtering bag, bag filter. **-schale,** *f.* filtering dish (with perforated bottom). **-schicht,** *f.* filter bed. **-schwierigkeit,** *f.* difficulty in filtering. **-sieb,** *n.* filtering sieve, strainer. **-stativ,** *n.* filter stand. **-stein,** *m.* filter stone, filtering stone. **-stoff,** *m.* filtering material. **-stutzen,** *m.* filtering jar (a cylindrical jar with lip). **-tasse,** *f.* filtering cup (with perforated cover for holding a funnel). **-trichter,** *m.* filtering funnel. **-tuch,** *m.* filtering cloth; percolator.

**Filtrierung,** *f.* filtering, filtration.

**Filtrum,** *n.* filter.

**Filz,** *m.* felt; tomentum; felt hat; miser; (*Metal.*) slime ore.

**filzartig,** feltlike, felty.

**Filzbarkeit,** *f.* felting property.

**filzen,** *v.t.* felt.

**filzfähig,** *a.* capable of felting.

**Filz-fähigkeit,** *f.* felting property. **-falte,** *f.* (*Paper*) crease in the felt.

**filzig,** *a.* of felt, feltlike, tomentous; stingy.

**Filztuch,** *n.* felted cloth, felt; blanket.

**filzwollen,** *a.* of or like felted wool.

**Fimmel,** *m.* female hemp; (*Mining*) wedge.

**finden,** *v.t.* find; discover.—*v.r.* understand; be found, exist.

**Findling,** *m.* foundling; (*Geol.*) erratic block.

**fing,** *pret.* of fangen.

**Finger-futter,** *n.* finger stall. **-hut,** *m.* thimble; foxglove, digitalis. **-hutkraut,** *m.* foxglove, digitalis. **-ling,** *m.* finger stall. **-probe,** *f.* rule of thumb. **-stein,** *m.* belemnite. **-zeig,** *m.* pointing with the finger; hint, cue.

**fingieren,** *v.t.* simulate, invent.—**fingiert,** *p.a.* fictitious, imaginary.

**Finne,** *f.* pimple, pustule; stud, knot; fin.

**finster,** *a.* dark; obscure; gloomy.

**Finsternis,** *f.* darkness; obscurity; gloom; (*Astron.*) eclipse.

**Firma,** *f.* firm.

**firn,** *a.* of last year.

**Firn,** *m.* glacier snow, névé, firn. **-blau,** *n.* glacier blue.

**Firnis,** *m.* varnish.

**firnisartig,** *a.* varnishlike.

**Firnis-ersatz,** *m.* varnish substitute. **-fabrikant,** *m.* varnish maker. **-farbe,** *f.* varnish color. **-industrie,** *f.* varnish industry. **-papier,** *n.* glazed paper.

**firnissen,** *v.t.* varnish.

**Fisch,** *m.* fish. **-augenstein,** *m.* apophyllite. **-bein,** *n.* whalebone. **-blase,** *f.* fish bladder; sounds, isinglass. **-dünger,** *m.* fish manure; fish guano.

**fischen,** *v.t. & i.* fish.

**Fischerei,** *f.* fishing; fishery.

**fischig,** *a.* fishy.

**Fisch-körner,** *n.pl.* Indian berries (cocculus indicus). **-leim,** *m.* fish glue, isinglass, (*Pharm.*) ichthyocolla. **-leimgummi,** *n.* sarcocolla. **-mehl,** *n.* fish meal. **-öl,** *n.* fish oil; ichthyol. **-schwanz,** *m.* fish tail. **-speck,** *m.* fish blubber. **-tran,** *m.* fish oil, train oil. **-zucht,** *f.* fish culture, pisciculture.

**Fisetholz, Fisettholz,** *n.* young fustic (*Cotinus cotinus*).

**Fistel,** *f.* fistula; falsetto. **-holz,** *n.* = Fisetholz. **-kassie,** *f.* purging cassia, cassia fistula.

**fistulös,** *a.* fistular, fistulous.

**fix,** *a.* fixed; smart.—**fixe Luft,** fixed air (old name for carbon dioxide).

**Fixage,** *f.* fixing.

**Fix-bleiche,** *f.* bleaching with bleaching powder. **-färberei,** *f.* tipping (of plush), dyeing by staining; fast dyeing.

**Fixierbad,** *n.* fixing bath.

**fixierbar,** *a.* fixable.

**fixieren,** *v.t.* fix; harden; mordant (silk); stare at.

**Fixier-flüssigkeit,** *f.* fixing liquid or liquor. **-mittel,** *n.* fixing agent, fixative; hardening agent. **-natron,** *n.* sodium thiosulfate. **-salz,** *n.* fixing salt (specif. sodium thiosulfate, " hypo ").

**Fixierung,** *f.* fixing, fixation; hardening.

**Fixierungsmittel,** *n.* = Fixiermittel.

**Fix-punkt,** *m.* fixed point. **-stern,** *m.* fixed star.

**-fizieren.** **-fy** (as *esterifizieren*, esterify). **-fizierung.** **-fication**.

**fl.,** *abbrev.* (flüssig) liquid; (flüchtig) volatile.

**Fl.,** *abbrev.* (Flüssigkeit) liquid.

**flach,** *a.* flat; level, plain; shallow. **-bodig,** *a.* flat-bottomed.

**Flachbrenner,** *m.* flat-flame burner.

**Fläche,** *f.* surface, face; area; flatness; plain, plane; level; sheet.

**Flächen-anziehung,** *f.* surface attraction, adhesion. **-inhalt,** *m.* area. **-mass,** *n.* surface measure, square measure. **-raum,** *m.* area.

**flächenreich,** *a.* having many faces, polyhedral.

**Flachen-satz,** *m.,* theorem of conservation of areas. **-winkel,** *m.* plane angle. **-zahl,** *f.* number of faces; square number.

**flächenzentriert,** *a.* face-centered.

**flachgewunden,** *p.a.* planispiral.

**Flachheit,** *f.* flatness. (See flach.)

**-flächig.** **-faced, -hedral**.

**Flachkupfer,** *n.* flat copper.

**Flächner,** *m.* polyhedron.

**flachrund,** *a.* round and flat-bottomed.

**Flachs,** *m.* flax.

**Flachschnitt,** *m.* horizontal section.

**flächsen,** *a.* flaxen, of flax.

**flachsfarben,** *a.* flax-colored, flaxen.

**Flachs-samen,** *m.* flaxseed, linseed. **-samenöl,** *n.* flaxseed oil, linseed oil **-stein,** *m.* amianthus.

**Flachzange,** *f.* tongs with flat jaws, pliers.

**flackerig,** *a.* flaring, flickering.

**flackern,** *v.t.* flare, flicker.

**Flacon,** *n. & m.* small bottle, phial.

**Flader,** *f.* curl, speckle, streak; flaw.

**fladerig,** *a.* curled, etc. (see Flader).

**Flagge,** *f.* flag, colors.

**Flakon,** *n. & m.* small bottle.

**flambieren,** *v.t.* flame, singe.

**flämisch,** *a.* Flemish.

**Flamm-.** see also Flammen-.

**flammbar,** *a.* inflammable, flammable.

**Flämmchen,** *n.* flamelet, small flame.

**Flammdruck,** *m.* chiné printing.

**Flamme,** *f.* flame; light.

**flammen,** *v.t.* flame, blaze; singe; sear; water, cloud (fabric, etc.).—*v.i.* flame; burn, glow.

**Flammen-bogen,** *m.* flaming arc; electric arc. **-färbung,** *f.* flame coloration. **-feuer,** *n.* blazing fire. **-fläche,** *f.* flame surface. **-frischarbeit,** *f.* fining in a reverberatory furnace. **-höhe,** *f.* height of flame.

**flammenlos,** *a.* flameless.

**Flammen-ofen,** *m.* = Flammofen. **-opal,** *m.* fire opal. **-rohr,** *n.* -röhre, *f.* = Flammrohr.

**flammensicher,** *a.* flameproof.

**Flammenwerfer,** *m.* flame projector, flame thrower.

**flammfarbig,** *a.* flame-colored; rainbow-colored.

**Flamm-färbung,** *f.* flame coloration. **-gas,** *n.* flame gas.

**flammicht,** *a.* (of fabrics) watered; (of wood) veined, grained.

**flammieren,** *v.t.* = flammen, *v.t.*

**flammig,** *a.* flamelike, flaming; (of fabrics, etc.) watered.

**Flamm-kohle,** *f.* coal that burns with flame, open-burning coal. **-ofen,** *m.* flame furnace, reverberatory furnace. **-punkt,** *m.* flash point. **-punktprüfer,** *m.* flash-point tester. **-punkt(s)apparat,** *m.* flash-point apparatus. **-rohr,** *n.,* **-röhre,** *f.* fire tube, flue. **-rohrkessel,** *m.* fire-tube boiler.

**flandrisch,** *a.* Flanders, Flemish.

**Flanell,** *m.* flannel.

**flankieren,** *v.t.* flank.

**Flansch, Flantsch,** *m.,* **Flansche, Flantsche,** *f.* flange.

**Fläschchen,** *n.* small bottle or flask.

**Flasche,** *f.* bottle; flask; jar; (for gas) cylinder; (*Founding*) casting box, flask; (*Mech.*) block.

**Flaschen-abteilung,** *f.* (*Brewing*) bottlery. **-bier,** *n.* bottled beer. **-gestell,** *n.* bottle rack, flask rack. **-glas,** *n.* bottle glass.

**flaschengrün,** *a.* bottle-green.

**Flaschen-hals,** *m.* neck of a bottle or flask. **-inhalt,** *m.* contents of a bottle or flask or gas cylinder. **-kappe,** *f.* bottle cap. **-kürbis,** *m.* bottle gourd; calabash. **-schild,** *n.* bottle (flask, etc.) label. **-verschluss,** *m.* stopper fastener. **-zug,** *m.* set of pulleys, block and tackle.

**Flaser,** *f.* = Flader.

**flaserig,** *a.* curled, speckled, streaked.

**flattern,** *v.i.* flutter, flicker, wave; be flighty.

**Flatterruss,** *m.* lampblack.

**Flattierfeuer,** *n.* choked fire.

**flau,** *a.* faint, weak; dull, slack.

**flauen,** *v.t.* buddle.

**Flaum,** *m.* down, nap, fluff.

**flaumig,** *a.* downy, fluffy, pubescent.

**Flaus, Flausch,** *m.* tuft; pad; plug; pilot cloth.

**Flaveanwasserstoff,** *m.* old name for cyanothioformamide, $CNCSNH_2$.

**Flechse,** *f.* tendon, sinew.

**Flechte,** *f.* lichen; plait; twist; skin eruption.

**flechten,** *v.t.* plait, twist, braid, interweave.

**Flechten-farbstoff,** *m.* lichen coloring matter. **-rot,** *n.* orcein. **-säure,** *f.* fumaric acid (old name). **-stärkemehl,** *n.* lichenin, moss starch. **-stoffe,** *m.pl.* lichen substances.

**Fleck,** *m.* spot; speck, stain, blot, flaw, patch; *pl.* measles.

**flecken,** *v.t.* spot, stain, speckle, mottle; patch.—*v.i.* spot, stain, blot.

**Flecken,** *m.* spot, speck, stain, flaw, taint; small town.

**flecken-frei, -los,** *a.* stainless.

**Flecken-reiniger,** *m.* cleaner, scourer, spot (or stain) remover. **-reinigung,** *f.* stain (or spot) removal. **-wasser,** *n.* = Fleckwasser.

**Fleckfieber,** *n.* typhus.

**fleckig,** *a.* spotted, speckled, stained, flawy; freckled.— **— werden,** spot, stain.

**Fleck-schierling,** *m.* poison hemlock (*Conium maculatum*). **-seife,** *f.* scouring soap. **-stein,** *m.* scouring stone (clay for stain removal). **-storchschnabelwurzel,** *f.* (*Pharm.*) geranium, cranesbill. **-wasser,** *n.* scouring water, cleaning liquid (for removing spots).

**Fledermaus,** *f.* bat. **-brenner,** *m.* batswing burner.

**flehen,** *v.i.* make entreaty.—*v.t.* entreat.

**Fleisch,** *n.* flesh, meat; (of fruit) pulp.

**Fleisch-.** flesh, fleshy, meat, muscle, sarco-, sarcous. **-beschau,** *f.* meat inspection. **-brühe,** *f.* meat broth, bouillon.

**fleischen,** *v.t.* flesh.

**Fleischer,** *m.* butcher. **-talg,** *m.* unmelted tallow.

**Fleischfarbe,** *f.* flesh color.

**fleisch-farbig, -farben,** *a.* flesh-colored.

**Fleischfäulnis,** *f.* spoiling or putrefaction of meat.

**fleischfressend,** *p.a.* carnivorous.

**Fleisch-gift,** *n.* meat toxin, ptomaine. **-gummi,** *n.* sarcocolla.

**fleischig,** *a.* fleshy, fleshlike, pulpy.

**Fleisch-kohle,** *f.* animal charcoal. **-konserve,** *f.* preserved meat. **-leim,** *m.,* **-leimgummi,** *n.* sarcocolla. **-mehl,** *n.* meat meal. **-milchsäure,** *f.* sarcolactic acid.

fleischrot, *a.* flesh-colored.

Fleisch-saft, *m.* meat juice, extract of meat. -seite, *f.* flesh side. -waren, *f.pl.* meats, esp. dried meats. -wasser, *n.* meat broth. -zucker, *m.* inositol, inosite.

Fleiss, *m.* diligence, industry, purpose.

fleissig, *a.* diligent, industrious.

flicht, *pr. 3 sing.* of flechten.

flicken, *v.t.* patch, mend.

Flieder, *m.* elder; (spanischer) lilac. -blüte, *f.* elder blossom, elder flower.

Fliege, *f.* fly; sight (of a gun).

fliegen, *v.i.* fly.

Fliegen-gift, *n.* fly poison. -holz, *n.* quassia wood. -kobalt, *m.* = Fliegenstein. -papier, *n.* fly paper. -pilz, *m.* = Fliegenschwamm. -pulver, *n.* fly powder. -schwamm, *m.* fly agaric, fly amanita (*Amanita muscaria*). -stein, *m.* native arsenic.

Flieger, *m.* flier, specif. aviator.

fliehen, *v.t.& i.* flee.

Fliehkraft, *f.* centrifugal force.

Flies, Fliess, *n.* fleece.

Fliese, *f.* flag, floor tile, wall tile, paving brick.

Fliessdruck, *m.* flow pressure.

fliessen, *v.i.* flow; run; melt; blot; (of colors) run, bleed.—fliessend, *p.a.* flowing, running; fluid, liquid; fluent.—fliessende Hitze, melting heat.—fliessende Bindung, floating linkage.

Fliessen, *n.* flowing, flow, etc. (see fliessen).

Fliess-feder, *f.* fountain pen. -geschwindig-keit, *f.* velocity of flow. -glätte, *f.* wet litharge. -grenze, *f.* (*Metals*) flow limit, yield point. -harz, *n.* oleoresin, specif. tur-pentine. -ofen, *m.* pyrites kiln. -papier, *n.* blotting paper, absorbent paper. -wasser, *n.* running water; (*Physiol.*) lymph.

Flimmer, *m.* glitter; tinsel, spangle; mica.

Flimmer-. ciliated, ciliary, vibrating.

flimmern, *v.i.* glitter, glisten, sparkle, scintil-late.—flimmernd, *p.a.* glittering, etc; micaceous.

Flimmerschein, *m.* sparkling luster.

flink, *a.* agile, quick, alert.

flinken, *v.i.* shine, sparkle, glisten.

Flinte, *f.* gun, musket.

Flinten-lauf, *m.* gun barrel. -schrot, *n.* gun shot, small shot.

Flintstein, *m.* flintstone, flint.

Flinz, *m.* siderite.

Flitsch, *m.*, Flitsche, *f.*, Flitschenerz, *n.* = Flittererz.

Flitter, *m.* spangle, shining platelet; tinsel. -draht, *m.* tinsel wire. -erz, *n.* ore in glitter-ing laminas. -glas, *n.* pounded glass for frosting. -gold, *n.* Dutch metal, tombac (a kind of brass used for tinsel).

flittern, *v.i.* glitter, glisten, sparkle.

Flitter-sand, *m.* micaceous sand. -silber, *n.* silver-colored tinsel.

Fll., *abbrev.* (Flüssigkeiten) liquids.

flocht, *pret.* of flechten.

Flocke, *f.* flake, flock. ˈ]

flocken, *v.t.& i.* form flakes or flocks, flake, flocculate.

flockenartig, *a.* flakelike, flocculent.

Flocken-erz, *n.* mimetite. -graphit, *m.* flake graphite. -papier, *n.* flock paper. -reaktion, *f.* flocculation reaction. -salpeter, *m.* efflorescent saltpeter.

flockig, *a.* flocculent, flocky, flaky. -käsig, *a.* curdy.

Flockseide, *f.* floss silk, silk waste.

Flockung, *f.* flocculation.

Flockwolle, *f.* short wool, flock wool.

flog, *pret.* of fliegen.

floh, *pret.* of fliehen.

Floh, *m.* flea.

flohbraun, *a.* puce.

Floh-farbe, *f.* puce color. -kraut, *n.* fleabane. -samen, *m.* fleawort seed, psyllium seed.

Flor, *m.* bloom, blooming; gauze; nap, pile.

Florentiner Flasche. Florentine receiver (for essential oils).

Florettseide, *f.* floss silk.

Florida-bleicherde, -erde, *f.* Florida (bleach-ing) earth.

floss, *pret.* of fliessen.

Floss, *n.* (*Metal.*) pig; raft, float.—blumiges —, white pig with granular fracture.

Flosse, *f.* fin; blade; float; (*Metal.*) pig.

Flosseisen, *n.* white pig iron.

flössen, *v.t.* float; infuse; refine (tin).

Flossenbett, *n.* (*Metal*) pig mold.

Flossofen, *m.* flowing furnace.

flott, *a.* brisk (of a reaction), smooth; afloat; gay, flush.

Flotte, *f.* dye liquor, dye bath; fleet, navy.

Flotten-flüssigkeit, *f.* dye liquor. -gefäss, *n.* (*Dyeing*) color reservoir. -stand, *m.* (*Dye-ing*) height of the liquor.

Flott-seide, *f.* untwisted silk. -stahl, *m.* ingot steel, run steel.

Flötz, *n.* layer, stratum, bed, seam. -erz, *n.* ore in beds. -kalk, *m.* bedded limestone.

Flöz, *n.* = Flötz.

Fluch, *m.* curse.

Flucht, *f.* flight; line, row; play, swing. -ebene, *f.* vanishing plane.

flüchten, *v.t.* flee, escape.

Fluchtholz, *n.* rule, level.

flüchtig, *a.* volatile; fugitive; fleeting, fragile, fleet, fickle, hasty.—flüchtiges Laugensalz, ammonium carbonate.—flüchtiges Öl, vol-atile oil, essential oil.—flüchtige Salbᵗ, ammonia liniment, volatile liniment.

flüchtigen, v.t. volatilize.

Flüchtigkeit, f. volatility; fleetness, etc. (see flüchtig).

Flucht-linientafel, f. nomographic chart, nomogram. -punkt, m. vanishing point.

fluchtrecht, a. flush.

Flug, m. flight, flying; flock; swarm. -asche, f. light (or flying) ashes. -bahn, f. line of flight, trajectory. -blatt, n. fly sheet, handbill; pamphlet.

Flügel, m. wing; flap, lobe, vane, branch; casement (of a window); blade (of a screw propeller); grand piano.

flügelförmig, a. wing-shaped.

Flügel-gebläse, n. fan blower. -kühler, m. fan cooler. -mutter, f. (Mech.) wing nut, thumb nut.

flügeln, v.t. wing.—geflügelt, p.a. winged.

Flügel-rad, n. screw wheel, worm wheel; screw propeller; (Brewing) flighter. -schraube, f. wing screw, wing nut.

flügge, a. fledged.

Flug-linie, f. = Flugbahn. -mehl, n. mill dust.

flugs, adv. quickly, instantly.

Flug-sand, m. quicksand. -schrift, f. handbill; pamphlet. -staub, m. flue dust; (Metal.) smoke, fume; chimney soot; flying dust. -staubkammer, f. condensing chamber. -wesen, n. aviation. -zeug, n. airplane, flying machine. -zeuglack, m. airplane varnish.

Fluidität, f. fluidity.

Fluidum, n. fluid.

fluktuieren, v.i. fluctuate.

fluktuös, a. fluctuating.

Flunder, m. flounder.

Fluor, n. fluorine.

Fluor-. of or combined with fluorine, fluoro-, fluo-, fluoride of (see instances following). -ammonium, n. ammonium fluoride. -anthenchinon, n. fluoranthenequinone. -antimon, n. antimony fluoride. -arsen, n. arsenic fluoride. -baryum, n. barium fluoride. -benzol, n. fluorobenzene, fluobenzene. -bor, n. boron fluoride. -borsäure, f. fluoboric acid. -brom, n. bromine fluoride. -chrom, n. chromium fluoride. -eisen, n. iron fluoride.

Fluorescenz, Fluoreszenz, f. fluorescence. -farbe, f. fluorescence color.

fluorescieren, fluoreszieren, v.i. fluoresce.— fluoreszierend, p.a. fluorescent.

Fluorgehalt, m. fluorine content.

fluorhaltig, a. containing fluorine.

Fluorid, n. fluoride (esp. an -ic fluoride as contrasted with Fluorür).

Fluor-jod, n. iodine fluoride. -kalium, n. potassium fluoride. -kalzium, n. calcium fluoride. -kiesel, m. silicon fluoride. -kie-

selsäure, f. fluosilicic acid. -kohlenstoff, m. carbon fluoride. -lithium, n. lithium fluoride. -metall, n. metallic fluoride. -natrium, n. sodium fluoride. -phosphat, n. fluophosphate. -phosphor, m. phosphorus fluoride. -salz, n. fluoride. -schwefel, m. sulfur fluoride. -selen, n. selenium fluoride. -silber, n. silver fluoride. -silikat, n. fluosilicate. -silizium, n. silicon fluoride. -siliziumverbindung, f. fluosilicate. -tantalsäure, f. fluotantalic acid. -tellur, n. tellurium fluoride. -titan, n. titanium fluoride. -toluol, n. fluorotoluene, fluotoluene.

Fluorür, n. (-ous) fluoride. Cf. Chlorür.

Fluor-verbindung, f. fluorine compound. -wasserstoff, m. hydrogen fluoride; hydrofluoric acid.

fluorwasserstoffsauer, a. of or combined with hydrofluoric acid, fluoride or hydrofluoride of.

Fluor-wasserstoffsäure, f. hydrofluoric acid. -zink, m. & n. zinc fluoride. -zinn, n. tin fluoride.

Fluo-sulfosäure, f. fluosulfonic acid. -verbindung, f. fluorine compound.

Flur, f. field; floor; vestibule.

Fluss, m. flux; fluor spar; enamel; (Gems) paste; fusion; flow, flowing; (Soap) figging; river, stream; discharge; catarrh.

flüss., abbrev. (flüssig) liquid.

Fluss-bett, n. river bed. -eisen, n. ingot iron; ingot metal (including ingot iron and ingot steel). -erde, f. earthy fluorite. -gold, n. river gold. -harz, n. animé, gum animé.

flüssig, a. liquid; fluid.— — machen, liquefy. — — werdend, liquescent.—flüssiges Chlorzink (Pharm.) solution of zinc chloride (and so for similar names).—flüssiger Extrakt, fluidextract, fluid extract.

Flüssigkeit, f. liquid; liquidity; fluidity; fluid; liquor; (Physiol.) humor.

Flüssigkeits-druck, m. pressure of a liquid, hydrostatic pressure. -förderung, f. conveyance of liquids. -grad, m. degree of fluidity. -mass, n. liquid measure. -menge, f. amount of liquid. -oberfläche, f. liquid surface. -reibung, f. fluid friction. -säule, f. column of liquid. -spiegel, m. surface of a liquid. -spindel, f. hydrometer; float. -stand, m. level of a liquid. -verlust, m. loss or waste of liquid.

Flüssig-machen, n., -machung, f. liquefaction.

Fluss-kalkstein, m. limestone used as a flux. -kies, m. river gravel.

flusskieselsauer, a. of or combined with fluosilicic acid, fluosilicate of.

Fluss-kieselsäure, f. fluosilicic acid. -metall, n. liquid metal. -mittel, n. fluxing material; flux; antirheumatic. -ofen, m. flowing furnace. -pferd, n. hippopotamus. -pulver, n. flux powder, powdered flux. -punkt, m. melting point. -sand, m. river sand.

flusssauer, a. = fluorwasserstoffsauer.

Fluss-säure, f. hydrofluoric acid. -schmiedeeisen, n. ingot iron (as distinguished from ingot steel).

Flussspat, m. fluor spar, fluorite. -erde, f. earthy fluorite. -pulver, n. fluor spar powder. -säure, f. hydrofluoric acid.

Fluss-stahl, m. ingot steel. -stahldraht, m. ingot steel wire. -stein, m. compact fluorite. -ton, m. river clay. -wasser, n. river water. -wasserstoffsäure, f. hydrofluoric acid.

flüstern, v.t.& i. whisper.

Flut, Fluth, f. flood; (high) tide.

focht, pret. of fechten.

Föhre, f. Scotch pine or fir (Pinus sylvestris).

folg., abbrev. (folgend) following.

Folge, f. sequence, series, set; future; consequence, result; conclusion; compliance.

folgen, v.t. follow.

folgender-massen, -weise, adv. as follows.

folgenschwer, a. portentous, important.

Folgepunkte, m.pl. (Magnetism) consequent points (or poles).

folge-recht, -richtig, a. consequent; conclusive; logical.

folgern, v.t. conclude, infer.

Folgerung, f. conclusion, inference, induction.

Folgewirkung, f. resultant, consequence.

folglich, adv. consequently.

folgsam, a. obedient.

Folie, f. foil; film (as of viscose).

foliieren, v.t. cover with foil, silver; page (a book).

Follikel, m. follicle.

Fond, m. foundation, base, basis; capital, funds; (Dyeing) ground, bottom.

Fonziermaschine, f. (Paper) staining machine.

forcieren, v.t. force; overtax.

Forcierkrankheit, f. strain disease (of metals).

Förderband, n. conveyor belt.

Förderer, m. promoter; accelerator; conveyer.

Förderkohle, f. rough coal, coal directly from the mine, run-of-mine.

förderlich, a. serviceable; speedy.

Fördermenge, f. output.

fordern, v.t. demand, ask, require; summon; challenge.

fördern, v.t. further, promote, help; hasten, accelerate; raise, draw out, get out; convey.

Förder-quantum, n. (Mining) output. -schnecke, f. screw conveyer.

Forderung, f. demand, etc. (see fordern); claim.

Förderung, f. furthering, etc. (see fördern).

Förderungsmittel, n. (Pharm.) adjuvant.

Förderwirkung, f. promoting effect.

Forelle, f. trout.

Forelleneisen, n. mottled white pig iron.

forensisch, a. forensic.

Form, f. form; shape, cut, size; mold; tuyère; (Soap) frame. -änderung, f. change of form; deformation, strain.

formänderungsfähig, a. capable of deformation; specif. ductile.

Form-änderungsmesser, m. strainometer. -art, f. form species.

formbar, a. plastic, capable of being shaped.

Formbarkeit, f. plasticity.

Formel, f. formula. -bild, n. (structural) formula. -register, n. formula index.

formen, v.t. form, shape, fashion, mold, cast; (Soap) frame.

Formerde, f. molding clay, modeling clay.

Formerei, Förmerei, f. molding, forming; molding house.

Formerstoff, m. plastic material, plastic.

Form-gebung, f. fashioning, shaping. -gips, m. plaster of Paris (good grade).

formhaltend, a. retaining form or shape.

Formiat, n. formate.

formieren, v.t. form.

Formiersäure, f. (Elec.) forming acid. -förmig. -shaped, -formed, -form, -oid.

Formkörper, m. molded body.

förmlich, a. formal; plain; downright.

Förmling, m. molded article.

formlos, a. formless, amorphous.

Formopersäure, f. performic acid.

Form-sand, m. molding sand. -stein, m. (Lead) pipe stone. -ton, m. molding clay.

Formular, n. form, blank (to fill out).

formulieren, v.t. formulate.

Formulierung, f. formulation.

Formylsäure, f. formic acid.

forsch, a. vigorous; dashing.

forschen, v.i. investigate, search.

Forscher, m. investigator; inquirer; spy.

Forschung, f. investigation, research; inquiry.

Forschungs-anstalt, f. research institution. -gebiet, n. domain of research. -geist, m. spirit of research or inquiry.

Forst, m. forest.

Förster, m. forester.

Forst-kunde, f. forestry. -mann, m. forester.

fort, adv. on, along, forth, away, off.— — und —, on and on, forever.

fortan, adv. henceforth.

fortbestehen, v.i. continue.

Fortbewegung, f. locomotion, progression.

fortbringen, v.t. carry away, remove; convey; rear; support, maintain.

Fortdauer, f. permanence, duration.

fortdauern, v.i. continue, last.

**fortdiffundieren,** *v.t.* diffuse away.

**fortentwickeln,** *v.t.& r.* continue developing.

**fortfahren,** *v.i.* set off, depart; go on, continue.

**fortfallen,** *v.i.* be wanting, be omitted; cease.

**fortfliessen,** *v.i.* flow or run off or away.

**fortführen,** *v.t.* carry away, convey; continue, prosecute.

**Fortgang,** *m.* going away, etc. (see fortgehen); process; progress, advance.

**fortgehen,** *v.i.* go away, go off, go, depart; go on, proceed, continue.

**fortkochen,** *v.t.& i.* boil away, boil off.

**fortkommen,** *v.i.* get away; get on, progress.

**Fortkommen,** *n.* escape; getting on, success.

**fortlassen,** *v.t.* let go; leave out, omit.

**fortlaufend,** *p.a.* continuous, continual, successive.

**fortleiten,** *v.t.* carry off; transmit, conduct.

**fortoxydieren,** *v.t.& i.* oxidize away or off.

**fortpflanzen,** *v.t.* propagate, transmit, communicate.

**Fortpflanzung,** *f.* propagation, transmission, communication.

**Fortpflanzungsgeschwindigkeit,** *f.* velocity of propagation (or of transmission).

**fortrücken,** *v.t.* move away.—*v.i.* move on, advance.

**Fortsatz,** *m.* continuation; (*Med.*) process; (*Mach.*) catch, stop.

**fortschaffen,** *v.t.* take away, remove, get rid of, dismiss.

**fortschreiten,** *v.i.* step forward; progress. —**fortschreitend,** *p.a.* progressive; onward.

**Fortschritt,** *m.* advance, advancement, progress.

**fortsetzen,** *v.t.* continue, carry on; set away.

**Fortsetzung,** *f.* continuation; prosecution, pursuit.

**fortwährend,** *p.a.* continual, continuous, permanent, constant.—*adv.* continually.

**forzieren,** *v.t.* force; overtax.

**fossil,** *a.* fossil.—**fossiles Wachs,** fossil wax, ozocerite.

**fossilienhaltig,** *a.* fossiliferous.

**foto-chemisch,** *a.* photochemical. **-graphisch,** *a.* photographic.

**Fournier,** *n.* veneer.

**fournieren,** *v.t.* veneer, inlay.

**F.P.,** *abbrev.* (französisches Patent) French patent; (Fusionspunkt, Fliesspunkt) melting point, m.p.

**fr.,** *abbrev.* (frei) free.

**Fr.,** *abbrev.* (Franken) francs.

**Fracht,** *f.* freight; cargo, load, shipment. **-brief,** *m.* way bill, bill of lading.

**frachtfrei,** *a.* freight-free, carriage paid.

**Fracht-geld,** *n.* freight; cartage. **-gut,** *n.* freight. **-unkosten,** *f.pl.* freight charges.

**Frage,** *f.* question, problem; demand.—**in — kommen,** be in question, be concerned.

**fragen,** *v.t.& i.* ask.—**es fragt sich,** it is a question.

**Frage-stellung,** *f.* question. **-zeichen,** *n.* interrogation point.

**fraglich,** *a.* questionable, doubtful; in question, afore-mentioned.

**frakt.,** *abbrev.* (fraktioniert) fractionated.

**fraktionär,** *a.* fractional.

**Fraktionieraufsatz,** *m.* fractionating attachment, distilling tube.

**fraktionieren,** *v.t.* fractionate.—**fraktionierte Destillation,** fractional distillation.

**Fraktionier-kolben,** *m.* fractionating flask. **-rohr,** *n.,* **-röhre,** *f.* fractionating tube. **-röhrchen,** *n.* small fractionating tube.

**Fraktionierung,** *f.* fractionation.

**Fraktions-aufsatz,** *m.* fractionating attachment, distilling tube. **-hut,** *m.* a kind of receiver (for fractionating). **-kolben,** *m.* fractionating flask. **-rohr,** *n.,* **-röhre,** *f.* fractionating tube. **-vorlage,** *f.* receiver (for fractionating).

**Frankfurterschwarz,** *n.* Frankfort black.

**franko,** *adv.* postpaid, prepaid.

**Frankreich,** *n.* France.

**Franse,** *f.* fringe.

**Franz-band,** *m.* calf binding; calf-bound book. **-branntwein,** *m.* brandy, cognac. **-gold,** *n.* French leaf gold (pale, due to silver alloy).

**Franzose,** *m.* Frenchman; monkey wrench.

**Franzosen-harz,** *n.* guaiacum. **-holz,** *n.* guaiacum, lignum vitae.

**französisch,** *a.* French.—**französische Beeren,** Avignon berries.

**Franztopas,** *m.* smoky topaz.

**Fräs-.** (*Mach.*) milling.

**fräsen,** *v.t.* (*Mach.*) mill.

**frass,** *pret.* of fressen.

**Frass,** *m.* food, feed; corrosion.

**Frau,** *f.* woman; wife; lady; Mrs.

**Frauen-arzt,** *m.* gynecologist. **-distel,** *f.* Scotch thistle. **-eis,** *n.* (*Min.*) selenite.

**Frauenglas,** *n.* (*Min.*) selenite.—**russisches —,** muscovite.

**Frauenhaar,** *n.* (*Bot.*) maidenhair.

**frauenhaft,** *a.* womanlike, womanly.

**Frauen-heilkunde,** *f.* gynecology. **-milch,** *f.* human milk. **-spat,** *m.* (*Min.*) selenite. **-spiegel,** *m.* Venus's looking-glass.

**Fräulein,** *n.* young lady, single lady, Miss.

**frbl.,** *abbrev.* (farblos) colorless.

**frech,** *a.* bold, brazen.

**frei,** *a.* free; uncombined; liberal; bold; open; postpaid, prepaid.— **— werden,** be set free, be disengaged.

-frei. free (from), -less, an-; as, *wasserfrei*, free from water, anhydrous.

Frei-brief, *m.* license, charter, patent, permit. -couvert, *n.* stamped envelope.

freidrehen, *v.t.* (*Ceram.*) throw.

Frei-gabe, -gebung, *f.* release.

frei-gebig, *a.* generous; prodigal. -halten, *v.t.* pay for (someone).

Freiharzgehalt, *m.* content of free resin (or rosin).

freiharzreich, *a.* rich in free resin (or rosin).

Freiheit, *f.* freedom; degree of freedom; liberty; franchise. in — setzen, set free, liberate.

Freiheitsgrad, *m.* degree of freedom.

freilassen, *v.t.* set free, liberate.

Freileitung, *f.* (*Elec.*) open wire, overhead line.

frei-lich, *adv.* to be sure, indeed; of course. -machen, *v.t.* set free, liberate, disengage; prepay.

Frei-marke, *f.* postage stamp. -mut, *m.* frankness, sincerity. -sein, *n.* free state, freedom.

frei-sinnig, *a.* large-minded; liberal. -sprechen, *v.t.* acquit; dispense.

Frei-staat, *m.* republic. -werden, *n.* becoming free, liberation.

frei-werdend, *p.a.* (being) set free; nascent. -willig, *a.* spontaneous; voluntary; free.

Frei-williger, -willige, *m.* volunteer.

fremd, *a.* foreign; strange; exotic; belonging to others. -artig, *a.* heterogeneous; odd.

Fremde, *m.& f.* stranger; foreigner; visitor; (*f.*) foreign country.

fremdfarbig, *a.* artificially colored.

Fremdkörper, *m.* foreign substance; foreign body.

fremd-sprachig, -sprachlich, *a.* foreign-language.

Fremdstoff, *m.* foreign substance, impurity.

Frequenz, *f.* frequency; crowd; attendance; traffic. -wert, *m.* frequency value, frequency.

fressen, *v.t.* corrode; eat; (*Mach.*) bind, seize. —fressend, *p.a.* corrosive.

Fressen, *n.* food.

fressgierig, *a.* greedy, voracious.

Fresszelle, *f.* phagocyte.

Freude, *f.* joy, comfort, enjoyment.

freudig, *a.* joyful, glad, hearty.

freuen, *v.t.* make glad, rejoice.—*v.r.* be glad, rejoice.

Freund, *m.* friend; relation.

freundlich, *a.* friendly; kind, cheerful, pleasant.

Freundschaft, *f.* friendship; acquaintance; favor; friends, kindred.

Friede, *f.* peace.

friedfertig, *a.* peaceable.

friedlich, *a.* peaceful, peaceable.

frieren, *v.i.* freeze, congeal; feel cold.—gefroren, *p.a.* frozen, congealed.

Frieren, *n.* freezing; shivering; ague.

Frierpunkt, *m.* freezing point.

Friesel, *m.* miliary fever.

Friktionsmesser, *m.* tribometer.

frisch, *a.* fresh; green (hide); vigorous, gay. —*adv.* freshly; cheerily.

Frisch-arbeit, *f.* fining process, fining. -blei, *n.* refined lead. -dampf, *m.* live steam. -eisen, *n.* refined iron.

frischen, *v.t.* fine, refine; revive (litharge); reduce (lead); reclaim (as rubber or oil).

Frischer, *m.* finer, refiner.

Frischerei, *f.* finery, refinery; fining, refining. -roheisen, *n.* forge pig.

Frisch-esse, *f.* refining furnace, refinery. -feuer, *n.* refining fire, refinery. -feuereisen, *n.* refined iron.

frisch-gebrannt, *p.a.* freshly burned. -gefällt, *p.a.* freshly precipitated.

Frisch-glätte, *f.* a litharge containing silver. -herd, *m.* refining furnace; forge hearth. -lauge, *f.* fresh lye, fresh liquor; specif. (*Paper*) white liquor. -lech, *m.* crude matte. -ling, *m.* (*Metal.*) scoria; young boar. -luft, *f.* fresh air. -ofen, *m.* refining furnace, refinery. -prozess, *m.* (*Metal.*) fining (or refining) process. -roheisen, *n.* pig iron for fining. -schlacken, *f.pl.* refinery cinders. -stahl, *m.* steel made in a refinery, German steel, natural steel. -stück, *n.* (*Copper*) liquation cake.

Frischung, *f.* fining, etc. (see frischen).

Frisch-verfahren, *n.* (*Iron*) fining process. -wasser, *n.* fresh water. -wirkung, *f.* (*Metal.*) fining, refining.

frisst, *pr. 2 & 3 sing.* of fressen.

Frist, *f.* time, space of time, respite.

fristen, *v.t.* prolong, delay.

Fritte, *f.* frit.

fritten, *v.t.* frit, sinter.

Frittenporzellan, *n.* soft porcelain, frit porcelain.

Frittofen, *m.* frit kiln; (*Glass*) calcar.

Frittung, *f.* fritting, sintering.

froh, *a.* glad, joyful, cheerful, happy.

fröhlich, *a.* joyful, glad, merry.

Frohsinn, *m.* cheerfulness.

fromm, *a.* gentle; pious; brave.

frommen, *v.i.* avail.

fror, *pret.* of frieren.

Frosch, *m.* frog; (*Mach.*) cam, arm, etc. -arten, *f.pl.* batrachians. -laichpflaster, *n.* (*Pharm.*) lead plaster. -löffel, *m.* water plantain (*Alisma*).

Frost, *m.* frost, cold; chill.

frostbeständig, *a.* frostproof.

**Frost-beständigkeit,** *f.* resistance to frost. **-beule,** *f.* chilblain.

**frösteln,** *v.t.* chill.—*v.i.* feel chilly.

**frostempfindlich,** *a.* sensitive to frost.

**Frost-grad,** *m.* degree of frost, degree below 0° C. **-mischung,** *f.* freezing mixture. **-punkt,** *m.* freezing point. **-schnitt,** *m.* frozen section. **-schutzmittel,** *n.* antifreezing agent.

**frottieren,** *v.t.* rub; brush.

**Frucht,** *f.* fruit; grain; crop; fetus, embryo; profit, produce, product. **-abtreibungsmittel,** *n.* abortifacient.

**fruchtartig,** *a.* fruitlike, fruity.

**Fruchtäther,** *m.* fruit essence, specif. amyl acetate.

**fruchtbar,** *a.* fruitful, fertile, plenteous.

**Frucht-brand,** *m.* ergot. **-branntwein,** *m.* fruit brandy.

**fruchten,** *v.i.* have effect, be of use.

**Frucht-essig,** *m.* fruit vinegar. **-gelée,** *n.* jam. **-halter,** *m.* uterus. **-knoten,** *m.* (*Bot.*) ovary. **-konserve,** *f.* preserved fruit. **-saft,** *m.* fruit juice. **-säure,** *f.* fruit acid. **-wasser,** *n.* amniotic fluid. **-wechsel,** *m.* rotation of crops. **-zucker,** *m.* fruit sugar, levulose.

**frug,** *pret.* of fragen.

**früh,** *a.* early; premature.—*adv.* early, soon.

**Frühe,** *f.* earliness, early morning.

**früher,** *a.* earlier, former.—*adv.* formerly.

**Frühling,** *m.,* **Frühjahr,** *n.* spring.

**frühreif,** *a.* early-ripe; precocious.

**Frühstück,** *n.* breakfast.

**frühzeitig,** *a.* early; premature; precocious.

**Fuchs,** *m.* fox; trestle, jack; flue; sorrel horse; freshman; fluke; (*Metal.*) piece of iron that cannot be melted. **-brücke,** *f.* flue bridge. **-fett,** *n.* fox fat.

**fuchsig,** *a.* foxy (yellowish or reddish brown).

**fuchsinschweflige Säure.** Schiff's reagent.

**fuchsrot,** *a.* foxy, reddish brown.

**Fuchtel,** *f.* blade, sword, rod.

**Fuder,** *n.* cartload; large wine measure.

**Fug,** *m.* right, authority.

**Fugazität,** *f.* fugacity.

**Fuge,** *f.* joint; slit; groove; suture.

**fugen, fügen,** *v.t.* join, unite; add.

**füglich,** *a.* reasonably; well, easily.

**fügsam,** *a.* tractable, pliant.

**Fügung,** *f.* joining; jointing; resignation; degree.

**fühlbar,** *a.* sensible, palpable, perceptible.

**fühlen,** *v.t.,i.& r.* feel.

**Fühlen,** *n.* feeling, sensation, perception.

**Fühlung,** *f.* feeling, sensation; touch, contact.

**fuhr,** *pret.* of fahren.

**Fuhre,** *f.* carrying, carriage, cart, load.

**führen,** *v.t.* lead, guide; carry, convey; bear; wear; construct; carry on; run (a machine); cause.

**Fuhrmann,** *m.* carter, driver, carrier.

**Führung,** *f.* leading, etc. (see führen); conduct; guide.

**Führungsstange,** *f.* guide rod.

**Fuhrwerk,** *n.* vehicle.

**Füll-.** filling, bottling, feed, stuffing. **-apparat,** *m.* filling apparatus, bottling apparatus.

**Fülle,** *f.* filling; fulness, abundance; (of colors) body, depth.

**füllen,** *v.t.* fill, fill up; pour, put (in); load (paper, etc.); plump (leather); stuff.—*v.r.* fill.

**Füllen,** *n.* filling, etc. (see füllen); foal; colt.

**Füller,** *m.* filler; loader.

**Fullererde,** *f.* fuller's earth.

**Füll-flüssigkeit,** *f.* (*Micros.,* etc.) immersion liquid. **-haus,** *n.* filling house, filling room; (*Soap*) frame room. **-horn,** *n.* cornucopia. **-körper,** *m.* filling body, packing body. **-löffel,** *m.* filling ladle. **-masse,** *f.* filling material; (*Sugar*) fillmass, massecuite. **-material, -mittel,** *n.* filling material, filling, stuffing, filler; loading material. **-pulver,** *n.* filling powder, filling (for explosive shells). **-rohr,** *n.,* **-röhre,** *f.* filling tube, feed pipe, spout. **-saure,** *f.* electrolyte (for storage batteries). **-sel,** *n.* stuffing. **-stoff,** *m.=* Füllmaterial. **-strich,** *m.* filling mark, " full " mark. **-trichter,** *m.* filling funnel, funnel, hopper.

**Füllung,** *f.* filling, stuffing, packing; charge (as of a furnace); seal; panel.

**fulminant,** *a.* fulminating.

**fulminieren,** *v.i.* fulminate.

**fum.,** *abbrev.* fumaroid.

**Fumarsäure,** *f.* fumaric acid.

**Fund,** *m.* discovery; finding; find.

**Fundament,** *n.* foundation, base, basis; (*Metal.,* etc.) bottom plate, soleplate.

**fundieren,** *v.t.* found; fund.

**fündig,** *a.* ore-bearing.

**Fund-ort,** *m.,* **-stätte,** *f.* locality (where something is discovered), habitat. **-zettel,** *m.* (*Min.,* etc.) locality label.

**fünf,** *a.* five.

**fünf-, Fünf-.** five-, penta-, quinque-, quintuple.

**fünf-atomig,** *a.* pentatomic. **-basisch,** *a.* pentabasic.

**Fünfeck,** *n.* pentagon.

**fünfeckig,** *a.* pentagonal.

**fünffach,** *a.* fivefold, quintuple, penta-. — — **-Chlorphosphor,** phosphorus pentachloride.— — **- Schwefelantimon,** antimony pentasulfide.—**fünffaches Chlorid,** pentachloride.

**fünf-gliedrig,** *a.* five-membered. **-mal,** *adv.* five times.

**Fünfring,** *m.* five-membered ring.
**fünfseitig,** *a.* five-sided, pentahedral.
**fünfte,** *a.* fifth.
**Fünftel,** *n.* fifth, fifth part.
**fünfwertig,** *a.* quinquevalent, pentavalent.
**Fünfwertigkeit,** *f.* quinquevalence, pentavalence.
**fünfzig, funfzig,** *a.* fifty.
**fungieren,** *v.i.* function, act; officiate.
**Funke,** *f.,* **Funken,** *m.* spark; sparkle.
**funkelig,** *a.* sparkling, glittering.
**funkeln,** *v.i.* sparkle, scintillate; glitter.
**funkenähnlich,** *a.* sparklike.
**Funken-bildung,** *f.* sparkling. **-entladung,** *f.* spark discharge.
**funkenfrei,** *a.* free from sparks; (*Elec.*) nonarcking.
**Funken-geber,** *m.* sparking device, spark coil. **-holz,** *n.* touchwood.
**funkenlos,** *a.* sparkless.
**Funken-sammler,** *m.* spark condenser. **-spektrum,** *n.* spark spectrum. **-spiel,** *n.* play of sparks. **-sprühen,** *n.* emission of sparks, scintillation.
**funkensprühend,** *a.* emitting sparks; sparkling, scintillating.
**Funken-strecke,** *f.* spark gap. **-zündung,** *f.* spark ignition.
**funktionieren,** *v.i.* function.
**für,** *prep.* for.— — **sich,** of itself, *per se;* **was — ein,** what kind of.
**Fürbitte,** *f.* intercession.
**Furche,** *f.* furrow; groove, channel; wrinkle.
**furchen,** *v.t.* furrow; crease.
**Furchenspatel,** *f.* grooved spatula.
**Furcht,** *f.* fear; fright, horror.
**furchtbar,** *a.* fearful, terrible.
**fürchten,** *v.t.& r.* fear, be afraid.
**fürchterlich,** *a.* frightful, horrid; tremendous.
**furchtsam,** *a.* timid.
**Furchung,** *f.* furrowing; segmentation.
**Furnier,** *n.* veneer.
**furnieren,** *v.t.* veneer, inlay.
**Furoylierung,** *f.* furoylation.
**Fürsorge,** *f.* care, solicitude.
**Fürst,** *m.* prince.
**fürstenmässig,** *a.* princely.
**fürstlich,** *a.* princely.
**fürwahr,** *adv.* in truth, indeed.
**Fürwort,** *n.* pronoun.
**Fusel,** *m.* fusel oil; bad spirits, bad liquor. **-branntwein,** *m.* spirits containing fusel oil.
**fuselfrei,** *a.* free from fusel oil.

**Fusel-geruch,** *m.* odor of fusel oil. **-geschmack,** *m.* taste of fusel oil.
**fuselhaltig,** *a.* containing fusel oil.
**fuselig,** *a.* containing fusel oil; intoxicated.
**Fuselöl,** *n.* fusel oil.
**Fusionspunkt,** *m.* fusing point, melting point.
**Fuss,** *m.* foot (in various senses); base; establishment; standard; footing.
**Fuss-.** foot, pedal, ped-; low, bottom, base, inferior. **-blatt,** *n.* May apple (*Podophyllum peltatum*); sole (of the foot).
**Fussboden,** *m.* floor, flooring; ground. **-öl,** *n.* floor oil. **-platte,** *f.* floor tile. **-ziegel,** *m.* paving tile, paving brick.
**Fussbrett,** *n.* pedal.
**fussen,** *v.i.* stand; rely, depend.—*v.t.* found, base.—*v.r.* rely.
**fussfällig,** *a.* prostrate.
**Fuss-gänger,** *m.* pedestrian. **-gelenk,** *n.* ankle joint. **-gestell,** *n.* pedestal. **-glätte,** *f.* black, impure litharge. **-mehl,** *n.* the lowest grade of flour. **-note,** *f.* footnote. **-pfund,** *n.* foot pound. **-punkt,** *m.* (*Math.*) foot; (*Astron.*) nadir. **-teppich,** *m.* carpet, rug. **-wurzel,** *f.* tarsus. **-zehe,** *f.* toe. **-zylinder,** *m.* cylinder with a base.
**Fustage,** *f.* barrels, casks; package.
**Fustik, -holz,** *n.* fustic, specif. young fustic.
**Futter,** *n.* food, feed, fodder, forage; lining, casing, case, coating, covering; chuck (of a lathe).
**Futteral,** *n.* case, casing, box.
**Futter-bohne,** *f.* horse bean. **-erbse,** *f.* field pea (*Pisum arvense*). **-gerste,** *f.* winter barley. **-getreide,** *n.* grain for feeding. **-gewächse,** *n.pl.* forage plants, fodder plants. **-gras,** *n.* green fodder. **-kalk,** *m.* a calcium compound (esp. acid calcium phosphate) added to feed, "feed lime." **-klee,** *m.* red clover. **-korn,** *n.* grain for feeding. **-kräuter,** *n.pl.=* Futtergewächse. **-mehl,** *n.* low-grade flour or meal. **-mittel,** *n.=* Futterstoff.
**füttern, futtern,** *v.t.* feed; line, case, coat.
**Futter-pflanze,** *f.* forage plant. **-rübe,** *f.* common turnip (*Brassica rapa*). **-salz,** *n.* a salt added to feed, esp. CaHPO$_4$. **-stein,** *m.* lining brick. **-stoff,** *m.* feeding stuff; lining. **-stroh,** *n.* forage straw, feeding straw.
**Fütterung,** *f.* feeding; feed, food, fodder, forage; lining, casing, sheathing.
**Fütterungsversuch,** *m.* feeding experiment.
**Futter-wicke,** *f.* common vetch (*Vicia sativa*). **-wurzel,** *f.* forage root.

# G

G., *abbrev.* (Gewicht) weight; (Gesellschaft) society, company, Co.

gab, *pret.* of geben.

Gabanholz, *n.* camwood; (red) sandalwood.

Gabe, *f.* gift; dose; alms.

Gabel, *f.* fork; crotch; (*Bot.*) tendril.

gabel-artig, -förmig, *a.* forked, furcate, bifurcated.

Gabel-klammer, *f.* forked clamp. -mehl, *n.* superfine flour.

gabeln, *v.r.* fork, bifurcate.

Gabel-rohr, *n.*, -röhre, *f.* forked tube or pipe. -teilung, *f.* forking, bifurcation.

Gadolinerde, *f.* gadolinia, gadolinium oxide.

gaffen, *v.i.* gape; crack.

Gagat, *m.*, -kohle, *f.* jet.

Gähr-. see Gär-.

gähren, *v.i.* = gären.

Gais, *f.* = Geiss.

Galangawurzel, *f.* galangal.

Galanterie-arbeit, *f.*, -waren, *f.pl.* fancy goods, notions.

Galban, -harz, *n.* galbanum.

Galgant, *m.* galangal. -wurzel, *f.* galangal (root).

Galgen, *m.* gallows. -holz, *n.* rotten wood, touchwood.

Galizenstein, Galitzenstein, *m.* white vitriol (zinc sulfate); (blauer) blue vitriol.

galizisch, *a.* Galician.

gallabtreibend, *a.* cholagog.

Gallaminblau, *n.* gallamine blue.

Gallapfel, *m.* (nut) gall, gallnut.

Galläpfel-abkochung, *f.* nutgall decoction. -aufguss, *m.* infusion of nutgalls. -beize, *f.* (*Dyeing*) gall steep, galling. -säure, -gerbsäure, *f.* gallotannic (ordinary tannic) acid.

Gallat, *n.* gallate.

Gallbeize, *f.* (*Dyeing*) gall steep.

Galle, *f.* gall, bile; gall, protuberance; nutgall, gallnut; (*Min.*) nodule; flaw; (*Glass*) gall, sandiver; bubble, bleb, blister.

Galleiche, *f.* gall oak.

gallen, gällen, *v.t.* gall, treat with gallnuts; remove the gall from.

gallen-abführend, *p.a.* cholagog. -artig, *a.* biliary.

Gallen-behälter, *m.* gall bladder. -bitter, *n.* picromel.

gallenbitter, *a.* bitter as gall.

Gallen-blase, *f.* gall bladder. -blasenstein, *m.* = Gallenstein. -braun, *n.* bilirubin. -darm, *m.* duodenum. -farbstoff, *m.* bile pigment, biliary pigment. -fett, *n.* cholesterol. -fettsäure, *f.* bile acid. -fistel, *f.* biliary fistula. -gang, *m.* bile duct. -gelb, *n.* bilirubin. -grün, *n.* biliverdin. -salz, *n.* bile salt. -säure, *f.* bile acid. -seife, *f.* gall soap, ox-gall soap. -stein, *m.* gallstone, biliary calculus. -steinfett, *n.* cholesterol. -stoff, *m.* bile substance (or constituent); (formerly) bilin. -süss, *n.* picromel. -talg, *m.* cholesterol.

gallentreibend, *p.a.* cholagog.

Gallen-wachs, *n.* cholesterol. -zucker, *m.* picromel.

Gallert, *n.* jelly; gelatin; glue.

gallert-ähnlich, -artig, *a.* jellylike, gelatinous; colloidal.

Gallerte, *f.* = Gallert.

gallertig, *a.* jellylike, gelatinous.

Gallert-kapsel, *f.* gelatin capsule. -moos, *n.* Iceland moss; carrageen. -säure, *f.* pectic acid. -substanz, *f.* colloid substance, colloid.

Galletseide, *f.* silk waste.

Gallgerbsäure, *f.* gallotannic acid.

Galli-. gallic (relating to trivalent gallium). -chlorid, *n.* gallic chloride.

gallig, *a.* biliary, bilious; bitter like gall.

Galli-hydroxyd, *n.* gallic hydroxide. -oxyd, *n.* gallic oxide.

Gallipotharz, *n.* galipot.

Gallisalz, *n.* gallic salt.

gallisieren, *v.t.* (*Wine*) gallize.

Gallitzenstein, *m.* = Galizenstein.

Gallium-chlorid, *n.* gallium chloride, specif. gallic chloride. -chlorür, *n.* gallous chloride. -oxydul, *n.* gallous oxide, GaO.

Gallo-. gallous (relating to bivalent gallium). -chlorid, *n.* gallous chloride, GaCl$_2$. -oxyd, *n.* gallous oxide, GaO.

Gall-seife, *f.* = Gallenseife. -stoff, *m.* bile substance; bilin.

Gallus, *m.* nutgalls, gallnuts. -aldehyd, *n.* gallaldehyde. -gerbsäure, *f.* gallotannic acid, tannic acid (proper), tannin.

gallussauer, *a.* of or combined with gallic acid, gallate of.

Gallus-säure, *f.* gallic acid. -säuregärung, *f.* gallic fermentation. -tinte, *f.* nutgall ink.

gallieren, *v.t.* gall, treat with gallnut decoction.

**Galmei,** *m.* calamine (hydrous zinc silicate, also zinc carbonate).

**galt,** *pret.* of gelten.

**galvanisch,** *a.* galvanic.

**galvanisieren,** *v.t.* galvanize.

**Galvanis-ieren,** *n.,* **-ierung,** *f.* galvanization.

**Galvanismus,** *m.* galvanism.

**galvanometrisch,** *a.* galvanometric.

**Galvanoplastik,** *f.* galvanoplastics.

**galvanoplastisch,** *a.* galvanoplastic.

**Galvanostegie,** *f.* electroplating, electrodeposition.

**Gamander,** *m.* germander (*Teucrium*).

**Gambe,** *f.* (*Ceram.*) jamb.

**Gammastrahlen,** *m.pl.* gamma rays.

**Gang,** *m.* motion, action, working state; course, path, passage; (*Mining*) seam, vein, gallery; (*Mech.*) gear, thread; (*Med.*) duct, canal; going, gait, pace, walk; round, shift; progress; process; way. **-art,** *f.* gangue, matrix; gait.

**gangbar,** *a.* pervious; passable; current; in going condition; marketable; in regular demand; (*Pharm.*) officinal.

**Gang-erz,** *n.* vein ore. **-gestein,** *n.* (*Mining*) gangue. **-höhe,** *f.* pitch (of a screw). **-masse** *f.* (*Mining*) gangue. **-stein,** *m.* (*Mining*) gangue.

**Gans,** *f.* goose; (*Metal.*) pig; (*Salt*) lump of salt; (*Mining*) hard rock.

**Gänse-blume,** *f.* daisy. **-fett,** *n.* goose fat. **-füsschen,** *n.pl.* quotation marks. **-haut,** *f.* gooseflesh, creeps. **-leberpastete,** *f.* pâté de foie gras.

**Ganter,** *m.* support (for casks).

**ganz,** *a.* whole; all, full, perfect.—*adv.* wholly, entirely, all, quite, very.—**ganz und gar,** absolutely.—**im ganzen,** on the whole.

**Ganz,** *f.* (*Metal.*) pig.

**Ganze, Ganzes,** *n.* whole; whole number.

**Ganz-form,** *f.* pig mold, pig bed. **-holländer,** *m.* (*Paper*) beater, beating engine. **-holz,** *n.* unhewn timber; round timber. **-lederband,** *m.* (full) leather binding, (full) calf.

**gänzlich,** *a.* whole, full, complete.—*adv.* wholly, absolutely.

**Ganz-mahlen,** *n.* (*Paper*) beating. **-stoff,** *m.* = Ganzzeug. **-stoffholländer,** *m.* = Ganzholländer.

**ganzzahlig,** *a.* integral.

**Ganzzeug,** *n.* (*Paper*) whole stuff, stuff, pulp. **-holländer,** *m.* beating engine, beater, hollander. **-kasten,** *m.* (*Paper*) stuff chest.

**gar,** *a.* done; purified; (*Metal.*) refined; (*Leather*) tanned, also dressed.—*adv.* fully, quite, very, at all, even.— **machen,** finish; (*Metal.*) refine, bring to nature; (*Leather*) tan or dress.—**gar nicht,** not at all.

**Gar-.** finishing; dressing; (*Metal.*) refining, refined.

**Gär-.** fermenting, fermentation.

**Garaffel,** *f.* (*Bot.*) avens (*Geum*).

**Gäransteig,** *m.* the period during which enzyme action mounts to a maximum.

**garantieren,** *v.t.* guarantee, warrant.

**Gararbeit,** *f.* refining.

**Garaus,** *m.* finishing stroke, ruin.

**gärbar,** *a.* fermentable.

**Gärbarkeit,** *f.* fermentability.

**Garbe,** *f.* sheaf; (*Iron*) fagot, pile; caraway; yarrow (*Achillea*).

**gärben,** *v.t.* (*Iron*) pile and weld.

**Gärbottich,** *m.* fermenting vat or tub, fermenter.

**Garbrand,** *m.* (*Ceram.*) finishing burn.

**garbrennen,** *v.t.* (*Ceram.*) fire to maturity.

**Garbrühe,** *f.* finishing liquor, dressing liquor.

**Gärbstahl,** *m.* shear steel.

**Gär-bütte,** *f.* = Gärbottich. **-chemie,** *f.* = Gärungschemie. **-dauer,** *f.* duration of fermentation.

**Gardine,** *f.* curtain.

**Gär-druck,** *m.* fermentation pressure. **-dünger,** *m.* fermented manure.

**Gare,** *f.* refined state, finished state; (*Leather*) dressed state, dressing, hides dressed at one time, tawing paste; (of soil) friable state; refining; refinery.

**Gäre,** *f.* fermentation; yeast; (*Wine*) bouquet.

**Gareisen,** *n.* refined iron; trial rod (for testing melted copper).

**garen,** *v.t.* dress, refine, finish (any technical product).

**gären,** *v.i.* ferment.—**gegoren,** *p.a.* fermented.

**Garerz,** *n.* roasted ore.

**gärfähig,** *a.* fermentable.

**Gärfähigkeit,** *f.* fermentability.

**Garfass,** *n.* dressing vat or tub.

**Gär-fass,** *n.* fermenting cask, union. **-flüssigkeit,** *f.* fermentable liquid.

**garfrischen,** *v.t.* refine thoroly.

**Gärführung,** *f.* method of fermentation.

**Gargang,** *m.* (*Metal.*) good working order, normal working; thoro refining.

**Gärgefäss,** *n.* fermenting vessel.

**Gargekrätz,** *n.* refinery slag.

**Gärgeschirr,** *n.* fermenting vessel.

**Gar-heit,** *f.* finished state; (*Metal.*) refined state. **-herd,** *m.* refining hearth.

**Gär-kammer,** *f.,* fermenting room. **-kasten,** *m.* fermentation vat. **-keller,** *m.* fermenting cellar. **-kölbchen,** *n.* (*Urinalysis*) fermentation saccharimeter. **-kraft,** *f.* fermenting power.

**Gar-krätze,** *f.* refinery slag. **-kupfer,** *n.* refined copper. **-leder,** *n.* dressed leather.

**garmachen,** *v.t.* = gar machen, under gar.

Gär-messer, *m.* zymometer. -mittel, *n.* ferment.

Garn, *n.* yarn; thread, twine; net.

Garnele, Garneele, *f.* shrimp; prawn.

Garnfärberei, *f.* yarn dyeing.

garnieren, *v.t.* trim, garnish.

Garnitur, *f.* trimming(s), fitting(s), mounting(s), furniture; set.

Garnschlichtung, *f.* yarn sizing.

Gar-ofen, *m.* refining furnace. -probe, *f.* refining assay.

Gär-produkt, *n.* fermentation product. -raum, *m.* fermenting room.

Gar-rösten, *n.* (*Metal.*) finishing roast. -schaum, *m.* (*Iron*) kish. -scheibe, *f.* (*Copper*) disk of refined copper. -schlacke, *f.* refining slag, rich slag.

garschmelziges Eisen. low-silicon pig; open white pig.

Garspan, *m.* (*Copper*) coating of metal on the trial rod.

Gärstoff, *m.* ferment.

Garstück, *n.* lump of purified salt.

Gärtätigkeit, *f.* fermentative activity.

Garten, *m.* garden. -bau, *m.* -baukunst, *f.* horticulture. -distel, *f.* artichoke. -kunst, *f.* horticulture. -raute, *f.* garden rue, common rue.

Gärtner, *m.* gardener.

Gärtnerei, *f.* gardening, horticulture.

gärtüchtig, *a.* (of yeast) vital.

Gärung, *f.* fermentation.— — erregend, — erzeugend, fermentative.— — hemmend, — verhindernd, antifermentative.

Gärungs-alkohol, *m.* ethyl alcohol. -amylalkohol, *m.* amyl alcohol of fermentation (a mixture of 2- and 3- methylbutanol). -buttersäure, *f.* (ordinary) butyric acid. -chemie, *f.* fermentation chemistry, zymurgy.

gärungserregend, *p.a.* fermentative, zymogenic.

Gärungserreger, *m.* ferment.

gärungs-erzeugend, *a.* = gärungserregend. -fähig, *a.* fermentable.

Gärungs-fähigkeit, *f.* fermentability. -fuselöl, *n.* fusel oil. -gewerb(e), *n.* fermentation industry.

gärungshemmend, *a.* arresting fermentation.

Gärungs-kölbchen, *n.* fermentation tube. -kraft, *f.* fermentative power. -küpe, *f.* (*Dyeing*) steeping vat. -lehre, *f.* zymology. -messer, *m.* zymometer. -milchsäure, *f.* fermentation lactic acid. -mittel, *n.* ferment. -pilz, *m.* fermentation fungus. -probe, *f.* fermentation test. -stoff, *m.* ferment. -technik, *f.* zymotechnics.

gärungs-technisch, *a.* zymotechnic(al). -unfähig, *a.* unfermentable.

Gärungsverfahren, *n.* fermentation method or process.

gärungsverhindernd, *a.* antifermentative.

Gärungs-vermögen, *n.* fermentative power. -vorgang, *m.* fermentation process.

gärungswidrig, *a.* antizymotic, antifermentative.

Gärungszeit, *f.* time of fermentation; (*Gas*) coking period.

Gär-verfahren, *n.* = Gärungsverfahren. -vermögen, *n.* fermenting capacity. -vorgang, *m.* fermentation process.

Garwa(a)ge, *f.* (*Salt*) brine gage.

Gärwärme, *f.* heat of fermentation.

Gasableitungsrohr, *n.* gas delivery tube.

gasähnlich, *a.* resembling gas, gaseous.

Gasanalyse, *f.* gas analysis.

gasanalytisch, *a.* gas-analysis, gas-analytical.

Gas-angriff, *m.* gas attack. -anlage, *f.* gas plant, gas works. -ansammlung, *f.* accumulation of gas. -anstalt, *f.* gas plant, gas works. -anzünder, *m.* gas lighter.

gasarm, *a.* poor in gas, (of coals) lean.

Gasart, *f.* kind of gas.

gasartig, *a.* gasiform, gaseous.

Gas-artigkeit, *f.* gaseousness. -aufnahme, *f.* gas absorption. -aufsaugung, *f.* gas absorption. -behälter, *m.* gas holder, gasometer. -beleuchtung, *f.* gas lighting, illumination with gas. -bereitung, *f.* gas making.

gasbildend, *p.a.* gas-forming.

Gas-bildner, *m.* gas former, gas producer. -bildung, *f.* formation of gas, gasification. -blase, *f.* gas bubble. -bleiche, *f.* gas bleaching, (*Paper*) potching. -brenner, *m.* gas burner.

gäschen, *v.i.* foam, froth.

gasdicht, *a.* gas-tight.

Gas-dichte, *f.* gaseous density. -druck, *m.* gas pressure, gaseous pressure. -druckmesser, *m.* manometer. -durchlässigkeit, *f.* permeability for gas.

Gase, *f.* gauze; canvas.

Gaseinsteller, *m.* gas regulator.

gasen, *v.t.* gas.

Gasentbindung, *f.* generation of gas.

Gasentbindungs-flasche, *f.* gas-generating bottle or flask, gas generator. -rohr, *n.* gas delivery tube.

Gas-entweichung, *f.* escape of gas. -entwick(e)lung, *f.* evolution of gas. -entwick(e)lungsapparat, *m.* gas generator. -entwickler, *m.* gas generator.

gaserzeugend, *a.* gas-producing.

Gas-erzeuger, *m.* gas generator, gas producer. -erzeugung, *f.* production of gas, gasification.

gasf., *abbrev.* (gasförmig) gaseous.

Gas-fabrik, *f.* gas works. -fang, *m.* (*Metal.*)

gas take, gas catcher. -feuerung, f. gas heating; gas furnace. -flamme, f. gas flame. -flammkohle, f. = Flammkohle. -flasche, f. gas cylinder.

gasförmig, a. gaseous, gasiform.

Gas-förmigkeit, f. gaseousness. -frischen, n. (Metal.) gas puddling. -gebläse, n. gas blast; gas blast apparatus. -gehalt, m. gas content. -gemenge, -gemisch, n. gaseous mixture, gas mixture, mixture of gases. -geruch, m. odor of gas. -geschoss, n. gas projectile; specif., gas shell. -gesetz, n. gas law. -gestalt, f. gaseous form. -gewinnung, f. gas production. -gleichung, f. gas equation. -glühlicht, n. incandescent gas light. -glühlichtkörper, -glühlichtstrumpf, m. gas mantle. -granate, f. gas shell; gas grenade. -granatenangriff, m. gas shell attack. -halter, -hälter, m. = Gasbehälter.

gashaltig, a. containing gas.

Gasheizung, f. gas heating.

gasieren, v.t. gas.

gasig, a. gaseous.

Gas-kalk, m. gas lime. -kampfflasche, f. a small gas cylinder for cloud gas attacks. -kette, f. (Elec.) gas cell.

gaskinetisch, a. pertaining to the kinetics of gases.

Gas-kocher, m. gas burner (on which a vessel may be set), gas hot plate. -kohle, f. gas coal; gas-retort carbon. -koks, m. gas coke. -kraftmaschine, f. gas engine. -krieg, m. gas warfare. -leitung, f. gas conduction; gas pipe line, gas supply; flue. -leitungsröhre, f. gas-conducting tube, gas pipe. -licht, n. gaslight. -luftgemisch, n. mixture of gas and air. -maschine, f. = Gasmotor. -menge, f. amount of gas. -messer, m. gas meter. -messrohr, n., -messröhre, f. = Gasmessungsrohr. -messung, f. measurement of gases or of gas. -messungsrohr, n., -messungsröhre, f. gas-measuring tube; eudiometer. -mine, f. projector drum. -mischung, f. gas mixture; gas mixing. -motor, m. gas engine, gas motor, internal-combustion engine. -ofen, m. gas furnace; gas-fired kiln; gas stove. -öl, n. gas oil.

gasometrisch, a. gasometric, gasometrical.

gasös, a. gaseous.

Gas-pfeife, f. gas pipe. -pressung, f. gas pressure. -probe, f. gas test; gas testing; gas sample. -prüfer, m. gas tester; eudiometer. -quelle, f. gas well. -raum, m. gas volume, volume of gas.

gasreich, a. rich in gas, (of coals) fat.

Gas-reiniger, m. gas purifier. -reinigungsmasse, f. gas-purifying material. -rest, m. gas residue. -rohr, n., -röhre, f. gas tube;

gas pipe. -russ, m. gas soot, gas black. -sack, m. gas bag. -sammler, m. gas collector, gas tank. -sauger, m. gas exhauster. -schlauch, m. gas tubing, gas tube.

Gasschutz, m. protection against gas, gas defense. -dienst, m. gas defense service. -lager, n. gas defense depot.

Gasschweissen, n. gas welding.

Gasse, f. street, lane, alley; (Founding) channel.

Gas-spannung, f. gas pressure. -stoffwechsel, m. gaseous metabolism, gas exchange, respiration. -strahl, m. gas jet. -strom, m. current of gas, stream of gas. -strömung, f. gas flow, gas current. -sumpf, m. a dense, low-lying gas cloud.

Gast, m. guest; visitor, stranger, customer.

Gäst, f. yeast.

Gastechnik, f. gas engineering.

gastechnisch, a. relating to gas engineering.

Gas-teer, m. gas tar. -teilung, f. device (as a T-tube) for dividing a gas supply.

Gast-haus, n., -hof, m. inn, hotel. -mehl, n. banquet, feast.

Gas-trenner, m. gas separator. -trennung, f. separation of gas(es). -trockner, m. gas drier.

Gastrolle, f. star role, star part.

Gas-uhr, f. gas meter. -ventil, n. gas valve. -verbrauch, m. gas consumption. -verdichter, m. gas compressor. -verflüssigung, f. liquefaction of gas(es). -vergiftung, f. gas poisoning. -volumen, n. gas volume, volume of gas.

gasvolumetrisch, a. gasometric.

Gas-wa(a)ge, f. gas balance. -wanne, f. gas trough, pneumatic trough. -waschaufsatz, m. gas-washing attachment, washing tube. -wascher, m. gas washer.

Gaswasch-flasche, f. gas-washing bottle. -rohr, n. gas-washing tube. -turm, m. gas-washing tower, gas scrubber.

Gas-wasser, n. gas liquor. -wechsel, m. gas exchange; specif. (Physiol.) gaseous metabolism. -werfer, m. gas projector. -werferangriff, m. (gas) projector attack. -werk, n gas works. -wolke, f. gas wave, gas cloud. -wolkenangriff, m. gas wave attack, cloud gas attack. -zähler, m. gas meter. -zufuhr, f. gas supply. -zuleiter, m., -zuleitungsrohr, n., -zuleitungsröhre, f. gas inlet tube or pipe, gas conductor. -zünder, m. gas lighter. -zustand, m. gaseous condition.

Gatte, m. husband.

Gatter, n. grate, grating, lattice, railing.

gattern, v.t. refine (tin).

gattieren, v.t. mix; sort, classify.

Gattierung, f. mixing; mixture of ores; sorting

Gattin, f. wife.

**Gattung,** *f.* genus; kind, sort; family; race; gender.

**Gattungsname,** *m.* generic name.

**Gauchheil,** *n.* scarlet pimpernel (*Anagallis arvensis*); self-heal (*Prunella vulgaris*).

**gaufrieren,** *v.t.* goffer, emboss.

**gaukelhaft,** *a.* juggling, deceptive.

**gaukeln,** *v.i.* juggle; flit about.

**Gaumen,** *m.* palate.

**gautschen,** *v.t.* (*Paper*) couch.

**Gayerde,** *f.*, **Gaysalpeter,** *m.* native saltpeter earth, saltpeter sweepings.

**Gauze,** *f.* gauze; canvas.

**gbr.,** *abbrev.* (gebräuchlich) usual, usually; (gebraucht) used; (gebrannt) burned.

**ge-.** A prefix used in forming the past participle of most verbs, in forming collective nouns (as *Gerät*, apparatus, tools), and in various other ways.

**G.E.,** *abbrev.* (Gewichtseinheit) unit of weight.

**Geäder,** *n.* veins, veined structure; system of blood vessels.

**geb.,** *abbrev.* (gebunden) bound; (gebildet) formed, also educated; (geboren) born.

**Gebäck,** *n.* baking, batch; baker's wares, pastry.

**Gebälk,** *n.*, **Gebälke,** *f.* timber work.

**gebar,** *pret.* of gebären.

**Gebärde,** *f.* gesture; demeanor; mien.

**Gebaren,** *n.* behavior; appearance.

**gebären,** *v.t.* bear, bring forth.—**geboren,** *p.a.* born, native, nee.

**Gebären,** *n.* childbirth, parturition.

**Gebärmutter,** *f.* uterus, womb.

**Gebäude,** *n.* building, structure; mine; system.

**gebd.,** *abbrev.* (gebunden) bound.

**Gebein,** *n.* skeleton, bones; *pl.* remains.

**geben,** *v.t.* give; yield; emit, evolve; furnish; add; show; express.—*v.r.* give; abate; relent; prove; (of cloth) stretch.—**es gibt,** there is, there are; **nichts —,** to care nothing.

**Geber,** *m.* giver, donor; (*Teleg.*, etc.) transmitter, sender.

**Gebet,** *n.* prayer.—**ins — nehmen,** question closely.

**gebeten,** *p.p.* of bitten.

**gebiert,** *pr. 3 sing.* of gebären.

**Gebiet,** *n.* territory, region, area, district, department, domain, sphere.

**gebieten,** *v.t.* order, command.—*v.i.* rule.

**gebieterisch,** *a.* imperative, imperious.

**Gebilde, Gebild,** *n.* structure, organization, system; form; image; diaper; (*Geol.*) formation.

**Gebinde,** *n.* bundle; package; skein, hank; barrel, cask; range (of tiles); truss.

**Gebirge,** *n.* mountains, mountain system, highlands; rock; ground; (*Mining*) gangue.

**Gebirgs-art,** *f.* kind of stone or rock. **-bildung,** **-formation,** *f.* mountainous formation; rock formation. **-kunde, -lehre,** *f.* orology; geognosy.

**gebissen,** *p.p.* of beissen.

**Gebläse,** *n.* blast; bellows, blower, blast apparatus. **-lampe,** *f.* blast lamp. **-luft,** *f.* blast air. **-maschine,** *f.* blast engine, blower. **-messer,** *m.* blast meter. **-ofen,** *m.* blast furnace. **-röhre,** *f.* blast pipe, tuyère. **-vorrichtung,** *f.* blast apparatus, blowing apparatus. **-wind,** *m.* blast.

**geblättert,** *a.* foliated; foliate.

**geblichen, gebleicht,** *p.p.* of bleichen.

**geblieben,** *p.p.* of bleiben.

**Geblüt,** *n.* blood (entire blood in the body); blood, race.

**gebogen,** *p.p.* of biegen.

**geboren,** *p.p.* of gebären.

**geborgen,** *p.p.* of bergen.

**geborsten,** *p.p.* of bersten.

**Gebot,** *n.* bidding, bid; command, commandment.

**geboten,** *p.p.* of bieten and gebieten.

**gebr.,** *abbrev.* = gbr.

**Gebr.,** *abbrev.* (Gebrüder) brothers.

**gebracht,** *p.p.* of bringen.

**gebrannt,** *p.p.* of brennen.

**Gebräu,** *n.* brewing, brew, gyle.

**Gebrauch,** *m.* use; custom; fashion.

**gebrauchen,** *v.t.* use, employ, make use of. —**gebraucht,** *p.a.* used; second-hand; worn out.

**gebräuchlich,** *a.* usual, customary, ordinary, common.—**am gebräuchlichsten,** most commonly, usually.

**Gebrauchsanweisung,** *f.* directions for use.

**gebrauchs-fähig,** *a.* usable, serviceable. **-fertig,** *a.* ready for use.

**Gebrauchs-gegenstand,** *m.*, **-gut,** *n.* commodity. **-muster,** *n.* sample for experiments or tests; commercial sample; registered design (a kind of patent, good for a short term only). **-porzellan,** *n.* household porcelain. **-vorschrift,** *f.* directions (for use). **-wasser,** *n.* service water, tap water.

**gebraucht,** *p.p.* of brauchen and gebrauchen.

**Gebräude,** *f.* = Gebräu.

**gebrech,** *a.* brittle, soft.

**gebrechen,** *v.i.* be lacking.

**Gebrechen,** *n.* want, defect, infirmity.

**gebrochen,** *p.p.* of brechen.

**Gebrüder,** *m.pl.* brothers.

**Gebrüll,** *n.* roaring.

**Gebrumm,** *n.* humming, murmuring.

**Gebühr,** *f.* due, duty, charge, fee; decency.

**gebühren,** *v.i.* be due, belong.—*v.r.* be proper.

be fitting.—**gebührend,** *p.a.* due, fit, proper.
—*adv.* duly.

**Gebund, Gebünde,** *n.* bunch, bundle, skein.

**gebunden,** *p.p.* of binden.

**Geburt,** *f.* birth; labor; offspring; descent, race; origin.

**gebürtig,** *a.* native, born.

**Geburtshilfe,** *f.* obstetrics, midwifery.

**geburtshilflich,** *a.* obstetric.

**Geburts-kunde, -lehre,** *f.* obstetrics. **-not,** *f.* labor. **-tag,** *m.* birthday.

**Gebüsch,** *n.* bushes, thicket.

**gedacht,** *p.p.* of denken.

**Gedächtnis,** *n.* remembrance, memory, memorial. **-münze,** *f.* commemorative medal.

**Gedanke,** *m.* thought; opinion.

**Gedankenfolge,** *f.* train of thought.

**gedanklich,** *a.* intellectual.

**Gedärm,** *n.* intestines, entrails.

**Gedeck,** *n.* covering; cover (at table).

**gedeckelt,** *p.a.* see deckeln.

**gedeihen,** *v.i.* thrive, grow; proceed; (of slaking lime) swell.

**gedeihlich,** *a.* beneficial, favorable, profitable.

**gedenken,** *v.i.* think, be mindful.—*v.t.* intend.

**Gedenken,** *n.* memory.

**gedeucht,** *p.p.* of dünken.

**Gedicht,** *n.* poem.

**gediegen,** *a.* (*Min.*) native; pure, unmixed; (of elements) free; genuine, superior.

**Gediegenheit,** *f.* native state; purity; intrinsic worth.

**gedieh,** *pret.* of gedeihen.

**gediehen,** *p.p.* of gedeihen.

**Gedränge,** *n.* thronging, crowd; dilemma.

**gedrängt,** *p.p.& p. a.* see drängen.

**gedroschen,** *p.p.* of dreschen.

**gedrungen,** *p.p.* of dringen.

**Geduld,** *f.* patience; endurance.

**gedurft,** *p.p.* of dürfen.

**geeignet,** *p.a.* see eignen.

**gef.,** *abbrev.* (gefunden) found; (gefällig) kind; (gefälligst) please.

**Gefahr,** *f.* danger; risk.

**gefährden,** *v.t.* endanger.

**gefährlich,** *a.* dangerous.

**gefahrlos,** *a.* without danger, safe.

**Gefährte,** *m.* companion, associate.

**Gefäll, Gefälle,** *n.* fall; gradient, incline, slope; income; taxes; head (of water).

**gefallen,** *p.p.* of fallen and gefallen.

**gefallen,** *v.i.* please.

**Gefallen,** *n.* pleasure; favor.

**gefällig,** *a.* pleasing; obliging, kind.

**gefälligst,** *adv.* please, pray.

**gefällt,** *p.p.* of fällen; precipitated.

**Gefangene,** *m.& f.* prisoner.

**Gefängnis,** *n.* prison; confinement.

**gefärbt,** *p.p.* colored; dyed; stained.

**Gefäss,** *n.* vessel, receptacle; blood vessel; (of a sword) hilt.

**Gefäss-.** (*Med.*) vascular. **-barometer,** *n.* cistern barometer. **-bau,** *m.* vascular structure. **-einmündung,** *f.* anastomosis. **-haut,** *f.* vascular membrane.

**gefässig,** *a.* vascular.

**Gefäss-kunde,** *f.* ceramic art. **-ofen,** *m.* closed furnace. **-wand,** *f.* wall of a (or the) vessel.

**Gefecht,** *n.* fighting, fight.

**Gefieder,** *n.* feathering, plumage.

**gefl.,** *abbrev.* (gefällig) kind; (gefälligst) please.

**Geflecht,** *n.* plaited or woven work, network, netting; texture; plexus.

**geflissentlich,** *a.* willful, intentional.

**geflochten,** *p.p.* of flechten.

**geflogen,** *p.p.* of fliegen.

**geflohen,** *p.p.* of fliehen.

**geflossen,** *p.p.* of fliessen; molten.

**Geflügel,** *n.* fowls, poultry.

**gefochten,** *p.p.* of fechten.

**Gefolge,** *n.* train, attendants.

**Gef. P.,** *abbrev.* (Gefrierpunkt) freezing point.

**gefrässig,** *a.* voracious.

**Gefrierapparat,** *m.* freezing (or freezing-point) apparatus.

**gefrierbar,** *a.* congealable, freezable.

**Gefrierbarkeit,** *f.* congealability.

**gefrieren,** *v.i.* freeze, congeal.

**Gefrierer,** *m.* freezer, congealer.

**Gefrier-fleisch,** *n.* frozen meat. **-punkt,** *m.* freezing point. **-punktsbestimmung,** *f.* freezing-point determination. **-punkt(s)erniedrigung,** *f.* freezing-point lowering. **-salz,** *n.* freezing salt, specif. ammonium nitrate. **-versuch,** *m.* freezing experiment or test. **-vorrichtung,** *f.* freezing apparatus.

**gefroren,** *p.p.* of frieren and gefrieren.

**Gefrorene,** *n.* something frozen, ice cream, ice.

**Gefüge,** *n.* structure; texture; bed, stratum.

**gefügig,** *a.* pliable, pliant.

**Gefühl,** *n.* feeling; touch, sensation, sensitiveness.

**gefunden,** *p.p.* of finden.

**geg.,** *abbrev.* gegen.

**gegangen,** *p.p.* of gehen.

**gegast,** *p.p.* of gasen.—**gegaste Lauge,** (*Paper*) gassed liquor (tower liquor treated with gas from the cookers).

**gegebenenfalls,** *adv.* in an emergency, if necessary.

**gegen,** *prep.* toward, against, about, compared with, opposite.

**Gegen-.** counter-, contra-, anti-. **-arznei,** *f.* antidote. **-bewegung,** *f.* countermovement.

-beweis, *m.* counterevidence. -bild, *n.* counterpart, antitype.

Gegend, *f.* region, quarter.

Gegendruck, *m.* counter-pressure, back pressure, resistance.

gegen-einander, *adv.* toward (or against) each other or one another; reciprocally, mutually. -elektromotorisch, *a.* counter-electromotive, back-electromotive.

Gegen-email, *n.* counterenamel. -farbe, *f.* complementary color. -färbung, *f.* contrast staining. -flüssigkeit, *f.* counter-liquid (as in titration). -füssler, *m.pl.* antipodes. -gewicht, *n.* counter-weight, counterpoise. -gift, *n.* antidote; antivenin. -grund, *m.* contrary reason, objection. -kraft, *f.* opposing force, counter-force. -mittel, *n.* antidote, remedy. -probe, *f.* contrasting sample or test. -reizmittel, *n.* counter-irritant. -satz, *m.* opposition, opposite, contrast, return. -schein, *n.* reflection; counterglow; (*Astron.*) opposition. -schmelz, *m.* counterenamel. -seite, *f.* opposite side; (of a coin) reverse.

gegenseitig, *a.* mutual, reciprocal, common; opposite, adverse.

Gegen-sonne, *f.* mock sun, parhelion. -stand, *m.* object; matter, subject. -standsglas, *n.* object glass.

gegenstandslos, *a.* objectless, meaningless; annulled.

Gegen-stoff, *m.* antisubstance, antibody; antidote. -strahl, *m.* reflected ray, reflection. -strom, *m.* counter-current, inverse current. -stromkühler, *m.* countercurrent condenser or cooler. -stück, *n.* counterpart, match. -teil, *n.* contrary, opposite, converse.

gegenteilig, *a.* opposite, contrary.

gegenüber, *prep.* over against, opposite, in contrast with.—*adv.* opposite. -liegend, *p.a.* opposite.

Gegenversuch, *m.* control experiment.

Gegenwart, *f.* presence; present.

gegenwärtig, *a.* present.—*adv.* at present.

Gegen-welle, *f.* countershaft. -wert, *m.* equivalent.

gegenwirken, *v.i.* counteract, react.—gegenwirkend, *p.a.* counteractive, reactive; antagonistic.

Gegen-wirkung, *f.* counteraction, reaction. -zug, *m.* countermove.

gegessen, *p.p.* of essen.

geglichen, *p.p.* of gleichen.

geglitten, *p.p.* of gleiten.

geglommen, *p.p.* of glimmen.

Gegner, *m.* opponent, enemy.

gegolten, *p.p.* of gelten.

gegoren, *p.p.* of gären; fermented.

gegossen, *p.p.* of giessen.

gegr., *abbrev.* (gegründet) founded.

gegriffen, *p.p.* of greifen.

gehaben, *v.r.* behave, fare.

Gehalt, *m.* contents, content; capacity, extent, yield, standard (of coins), strength; salary, pay; value.

Gehaltsbestimmung, *f.* determination of content, analysis, assay.

Gehänge, *n.* slope; hanging, pendant.

Gehäuse, *n.* case, casing, box, shell.

geheftet, *p.a.* see heften.

geheim, *a.* secret, private, hidden.—geheime Tinte, sympathetic ink, invisible ink.

Geheimmittel, *n.* secret remedy, patent medicine, nostrum.

Geheimnis, *f.* secret, secrecy.

Geheimrat, *m.* privy councillor.

Geheiss, *n.* command, bidding.

gehen, *v.i.* go; walk, travel, pass; fare.—es geht um, it is a question of.—vor sich —, go on, take place.

Geheul, *n.* howling.

Gehilfe, *m.* helper, assistant.

Gehirn, *n.* brain.—kleines —, cerebellum.

Gehirn-. cerebral. -fett, *n.* cerebrin.

gehoben, *p.p.* of heben.

geholfen, *p.p.* of helfen.

Gehölz, *n.* wood, copse.

Gehör, *n.* hearing; ear.

Gehör-. auditory, acoustic.

gehorchen, *v.i.* obey.

gehören, *v.i.* belong.—*v.r.* be becoming, be proper.

gehörig, *a.* belonging; requisite; due, proper, appropriate.

Gehörlehre, *f.* acoustics.

gehorsam, *a.* obedient.

Gehorsam, *m.*, Gehorsamkeit, *f.*, obedience.

Gehre, Gehrung, *f.* bevel, miter.

Gehülfe, *m.* = Gehilfe.

Geier, *m.* vulture.

Geige, *f.* violin.

Geigenharz, *n.* rosin, colophony.

geil, *a.* luxuriant; rich; proud (flesh); lewd.

Geiss, *f.* (she) goat; doe. -bart, *m.*, -bartskraut, *n.* goatsbeard (*Spiraea aruncus*). -blatt, *n.* honeysuckle (*Lonicera*). -bock, *m.* he-goat.

Geissel, *f.* flagellum, cilium; whip, scourge.

Geissfuss, *m.* (*Bot.*) goatsfoot; (*Tech.*) any of various tools.

Geisslersches Rohr.  Geissler tube.

Geissraute, *f.* goat's-rue (*Galega officinalis*).

Geist, *m.* spirit; mind, ghost.

geistig, *a.* spirituous, alcoholic; (of wine, etc.) strong, generous; volatile; spiritual; mental.

Geistigkeit, *f.* spirituousness, etc. (see geistig).

**geist-lich,** *a.* spiritual; clerical. **-reich,** *a.* ingenious, clever; sprightly, smart, witty.

**Geiz,** *m.* avarice, stinginess.

**geizig,** *a.* avaricious; stingy; sparing (of).

**gekannt,** *p.p.* of kennen.

**geklommen,** *p.p.* of klimmen and klemmen.

**geklungen,** *p.p.* of klingen.

**gekniffen,** *p.p.* of kneifen.

**Geknister,** *n.* decrepitation; crunching.

**gekonnt,** *p.p.* of können.

**gekoren,** *p.p.* of küren.

**gekörnt,** *p.a.* see körnen.

**Gekrätz,** *n.* waste, refuse, dross, slag. **-ofen,** *m.* (*Metal.*) almond furnace.

**gekrischen,** *p.p.* of kreischen.

**gekrochen,** *p.p.* of kriechen.

**Gekrös-.** mesenteric.

**Gekröse,** *n.* mesentery; giblets.

**gel,** *abbrev.* (gelöst) dissolved.

**geladen,** *p.p.* of laden.

**Geläger,** *n.* deposits, dregs, bottoms.

**Gelände,** *n.* land, ground, country.

**Geländer,** *n.* railing, balustrade.

**gelang,** *pret.* of gelingen.

**gelangen,** *v.i.* arrive (at), reach (to), come.

**gelartig,** *a.* gel-like, of the nature of a gel.

**Gelass,** *m.* room, space.

**Gelatine,** *f.* gelatin.

**gelatineartig,** *a.* gelatinous.

**Gelatine-folie,** *f.* sheet gelatin. **-leim,** *m.* gelatin glue. **-lösung,** *f.* gelatin solution.

**gelatinieren,** *v.t.& i.* gelatinize.

**Gelatinierung,** *f.* gelatinization.

**Gelatinierungsmittel,** *n.* gelatinizing agent.

**gelatinisieren,** *v.t.& i.* gelatinize.

**gelatinös,** *a.* gelatinous.

**geläufig,** *a.* fluent, ready; familiar.

**gelaunt,** *a.* disposed.

**Geläut, Geläute,** *n.* ringing; chimes.

**gelb,** *a.* yellow.—gelbes Blutkraut, goldenseal (*Hydrastis canadensis*).—gelbes Blutlaugensalz, potassium ferrocyanide.—gelbe Erde, yellow ocher.—gelber Ingwer, turmeric.—gelbe Quecksilbersalbe, *f.* (*Pharm.*) ointment of mercuric nitrate.—gelbe Rübe, carrot.

**Gelb,** *n.* yellow. **-antimonerz,** *n.* cervantite. **-beeren,** *f.pl.* Avignon berries. **-beize,** *f.* (*Dyeing*) buff liquor. **-beizen,** *n.* (*Metal.*) yellowing.

**gelbblausauer,** *a.* of or pertaining to ferrocyanic acid, ferrocyanide of.

**Gelbbleierz,** *n.* wulfenite.

**gelb-braun, -bräunlich,** *a.* yellowish brown.

**Gelbbrenne,** *f.* pickle (for brass).

**gelbbrennen,** *v.t.* (*Metal.*) dip, pickle.

**Gelbbrennsäure,** *f.* pickling acid, pickle.

**Gelbe,** *n.* yellow (of an egg), yolk.

**Gelbeisen-erz,** *n.,* **-stein,** *m.* yellow clay iron-

stone; (okriges) yellow ocher; copiapite. **-kies,** *m.* pyrite.

**gelbeln,** *v.i.* turn yellowish.

**Gelb-erde,** *f.* yellow ocher. **-erz,** *n.* yellow ore, specif. (1) chalcopyrite, (2) limonite.

**gelbfarbig,** *a.* yellow.

**Gelbfärbung,** *f.* yellow coloration, yellow color; yellow dyeing.

**gelb-gar,** *a.* (*Leather*) tanned. **-giessen,** *v.t.* cast in brass.

**Gelb-giesserei,** *f.* brass foundry. **-glut,** *f.* yellow heat (about 1100°).

**gelb-grau,** *a.* yellowish-gray. **-grün,** *a.* yellowish green.

**Gelb-guss,** *m.* brass. **-heit,** *f.* yellowness. **-holz,** *n.* fustic, specif. old fustic.

**Gelbildung,** *f.* gel formation.

**Gelb-kali,** *n.* potassium ferrocyanide. **-kraut,** *n.* yellowweed, dyer's rocket (*Reseda luteola*).

**Gelbkreuz-geschoss,** *n.* (*Mil.*) "yellow cross" projectile or shell. **-kampfstoff, -stoff,** *m.* "yellow cross" shell filling (mustard gas or other vesicant).

**Gelbkupfer,** *n.* brass; crude copper. **-erz,** *n.* chalcopyrite.

**gelb-lich,** *a.* yellowish. **-rot,** *a.* yellowish-red.

**Gelbschoten,** *f.pl.* wongshy (pods of *Gardenia grandiflora*).

**gelbstichig,** *a.* yellow-tinged, yellowish.

**Gelbsucht,** *f.* jaundice.

**Gelb-wurz, -wurzel,** *f.* turmeric; yellowroot (*Xanthorrhiza*).

**Geld,** *n.* money. **-mittel,** *n.pl.* (pecuniary) means. **-münze,** *f.* coin. **-schrank,** *m.* safe. **-strafe,** *f.* fine. **-stück,** *n.* piece of money, coin. **-verschreibung,** *f.* promissory note. **-wesen,** *n.* monetary matters, finances.

**Gele,** *pl.* gels.

**Gelée,** *n.* jelly.

**gelegen,** *p.p.* of liegen.—*a.* situated; convenient, suitable; important.

**Gelegenheit,** *f.* occasion, opportunity; convenience; locality.

**gelegentlich,** *a.* occasional, accidental, incidental.—*adv.* occasionally; incidentally; second-hand; with regard (to), regarding.

**gelehrig,** *a.* teachable, docile.

**Gelehrsamkeit,** *f.* learning.

**Gelehrte, Gelehrter,** *m.* learned man, scholar, savant.

**Geleise,** *n.* track.

**geleiten,** *v.t.* accompany, conduct.

**Gelenk,** *n.* joint; link; hinge.

**Gelenk-.** articular. **-basalt,** *m.* flexible basalt. **-flüssigkeit,** *f.* synovial fluid.

**gelenkig,** *a.* flexible, pliable; supple; nimble.

**Gelenk-quarz,** *m.* flexible sandstone

itacolumite. -saft, *m.*, -schmiere, *f.* (*Anat.*)
synovia. -schwamm, *m.* white swelling.
-steifheit, *f.* ankylosis. -wasser, *n.* synovia,
synovial fluid.

Gelf, *m.* silver-bearing pyrites. -erz, -kupfer,
*n.* chalcopyrite.

geliehen, *p.p.* of leihen.

gelind, *a.* gentle; soft, mild.

gelingen, *v.i.* succeed.—gelungen, *p.a.* successful; excellent.

gelitten, *p.p.* of leiden.

geloben, *v.t.* promise, pledge.

gelogen, *p.p.* of lügen.

geloschen, gelöscht, *p.p.* of löschen

gelöst, *p.p.* of lösen; dissolved.

Gelsemien, *n.* gelsemium.

Gelseminsäure, Gelsemiensäure, *f.* gelsemic
acid.

Gelseminwurzel, *f.* gelsemium root.

gelt, *a.* (of cows) dry.

Gelte, *f.* pail, tub.

gelten, *v.i.* be worth; have weight; be current,
be valid; pass, be considered; apply; concern.

Geltung, *f.* value, validity, currency, importance.

gelungen, *p.p.* of gelingen.

Gelüst, *n.* desire, longing.

gem., *abbrev.* (gemein, gemeinsam) common;
(gemischt) mixed; (gemahlen) ground,
milled.

Gemach, *n.* chamber, room; closet.

gemächlich, *a.* slow, gentle, easy.

Gemahl, *m.* consort, husband.

gemahnen, *v.t.* remind.

Gemälde, *n.* picture, painting, drawing.
-firnis, *m.* painter's varnish.

gemäss, *prep.* (following its object). according
to, conformably to.—*a.* conformable, agreeable.

Gemäuer, *n.* masonry.

gemein, *a.* common; general, ordinary, vulgar.

Gemeinde, *f.* community; congregation.

Gemeinheit, *f.* commonness, meanness.

gemeinsam, *a.* common; mutual, joint.

Gemeinschaft, *f.* community; partnership;
society; intercourse.

gemein-schaftlich, *a.* common, mutual. -ver-
ständlich, *a.* popular.

Gemenganteil, *m.* ingredient of a mixture.

Gemenge, *n.* mixture; (*Glass*) frit; (*Petrog.*)
conglomerate. -asche, *f.* (*Assaying*) test
ash. -gestein, *n.* conglomerate. -stoff,
-teil, *m.* =Gemenganteil.

Gemeng-stoff, -teil, *m.* =Gemenganteil.

gemieden, *p.p.* of meiden.

Gemisch, *n.* mixture, mixing; admixture.

Gemme, *f.* gem, cameo.

gemocht, *p.p.* of mögen.

gemolken, *p.p.* of melken.

Gemse, Gems, *f.* chamois (goat).

Gemsenfett, *n.* chamois fat.

Gemsleder, *n.* chamois leather, chamois.

Gemüll, Gemülm, *n.* rubbish.

Gemüse, *n.* vegetables. -pflanzen, *f.pl.* culinary plants.

gemusst, *p.p.* of müssen.

gemustert, *p.p. & p.a.* figured, etc. (see mustern); fancy.

Gemüt, *n.* mind; heart, feeling.

gemütlich, *a.* good-hearted, genial, pleasant.

genannt, *p.p.* of nennen.

genas, *pret.* of genesen.

genau, *a.* accurate, exact; true, close, tight;
intimate.

Genauigkeit, *f.* accuracy, etc. (see genau).

Genauigkeitsgrad, *m.* degree of accuracy.

genehm, *a.* agreeable; acceptable.

genehmigen, *v.t.* approve of, assent to; allow.

geneigt, *p.a.* see neigen.

Geneigtheit, *f.* inclination; disposition.

General-nenner, *m.* common denominator.
-register, *n.* collective index.

Generator-betrieb, *m.* producer operation.
-gas, *n.* generator gas, producer gas.

generell, *a.* general.

generisch, *a.* generic.

genesen, *v.i.* recover, convalesce; be delivered.

genetisch, *a.* genetic.

Genever, *m.* geneva, Holland gin.

Genf, *n.* Geneva.

genial, *a.* gifted, of genius.

Genick, *n.* back of the neck.

Genie, *n.* genius; engineer corps. -corps, *n.*
engineer corps.

genieren, *v.t.* incommode, trouble.

geniessbar, *a.* palatable; edible, esculent.

geniessen, *v.t.* enjoy; take, taste (food or
drink).

genommen, *p.p.* of nehmen.

genoss, *pret.* of geniessen.

Genoss, Genosse, *m.* companion, associate,
partner, accomplice; (*pl.*) company.

genossen, *p.p.* of geniessen.

Genossenschaft, *f.* fellowship, partnership,
company, association.

Genre, *n.* kind, sort; (*Calico*) style.

genuesisch, *a.* Genoese, Genoa.

genug, *adv.* enough.

Genüge, *f.* sufficiency.—zur —, enough.

genügen, *v.i.* be enough, suffice; comply
(with).—genügend, *p.a.* sufficient; satisfactory.

genügsam, *a.* easily pleased, temperate.

Genugtuung, *f.* satisfaction.

Genuss, *m.* enjoyment, pleasure; taking (food
or drink); benefit, use. -mittel, *n.* any
substance used to heighten the enjoyment

of food (including condiments, beverages, etc.), food supplement.

**genusssüchtig,** *a.* pleasure-seeking.

**Genusszweck,** *m.* table purposes, food purposes.

**Geolog,** *m.* geologist.

**geologisch,** *a.* geological.

**geometrisch,** *a.* geometric(al).

**Georgine,** *f.* dahlia.

**Gepäck,** *n.* baggage, luggage.

**gepfiffen,** *p.p.* of pfeifen.

**gepflogen,** *p.p.* of pflegen.

**Gepflogenheit,** *f.* usage, custom, habit.

**Gepräge,** *n.* impression; stamp, coinage; character.

**gepriesen,** *p.p.* of preisen.

**gepulvert,** *p.p.* powdered, pulverized.

**gequollen,** *p.p.* of quellen.

**gerade,** *a.* straight; direct; even; upright.— *adv.* straightly, directly, exactly, just; plainly.

**Gerade,** *f.* straight line, right line.

**geradezu,** *adv.* straight on; immediately; absolutely.

**gerad-linig,** *a.* rectilinear. **-sichtig,** *a.* direct-vision. **-wandig,** *a.* straight-walled, with straight sides. **-wertig,** *a.* of even valence. **-zahlig,** *a.* even-numbered.

**Geranium-öl,** *n.* geranium oil. **-säure,** *f.* geranic acid.

**gerannt,** *p.p.* of rennen.

**Gerät,** *n.,* **Geräte,** *n.pl.* apparatus; instruments, implements, tools; utensils; plant; furniture, chattels.

**Geräteglas,** *n.* apparatus glass.

**geraten,** *p.p.* of geraten and raten.

**geraten,** *v.i.* come, fall, light, get; turn out, prosper.—*p.a.* prosperous, successful.

**Gerätschaft,** *f.* implement, instrument, apparatus, outfit.

**geraum,** *a.* ample, long.

**geräumig,** *a.* roomy, ample, large, spacious.

**Geräusch,** *n.* noise; murmur, clatter.

**geräusch-los,** *a.* noiseless. **-voll,** *a.* noisy.

**Gerb-anlage,** *f.* tannery. **-auszug,** *m.* tanning extract.

**gerbbar,** *a.* tannable, etc. (see gerben).

**Gerbbrühe, Gerbebrühe, Gerbeflüssigkeit,** *f.* tan liquor, tanner's liquor, ooze.

**Gerbe-methode,** *f.* tanning method. **-mittel,** *n.* tanning material, tan.

**gerben,** *v.t.* tan; hull (grain); polish (metal); tilt (steel).—**sämisch —,** chamois; **weiss —,** taw.

**Gerber,** *m.* tanner, currier. **-baum,** *m.* tanner's sumac.

**Gerberei,** *f.* tanning; tannery. **-abfälle,** *m.pl.* tanner's waste.

**Gerber-fett,** *n.* (*Leather*) dégras, stuff. **-hof,**

*m.* tan yard. **-kalk,** *m.* slaked lime; gas lime. **-lohe,** *f.* tanbark; tan liquor. **-strauch,** *m.* tanner's sumac (*Rhus coriaria*); ink plant (*Coriaria*). **-wolle,** *f.* skin wool.

**Gerbe-theorie,** *f.* theory of tanning. **-vermögen,** *n.* tanning power. **-versuch,** *m.* tanning experiment or trial.

**Gerb-extrakt,** *m.& n.* tanning extract. **-leim,** *m.* (*Paper*) size made from gelatin and sulfite liquor. **-lohe,** *f.* tanbark; tan liquor. **-material,** *n.* tanning material. **-pflanze,** *f.* tanniferous plant. **-prozess,** *m.* tanning process. **-rinde,** *f.* tanbark.

**gerbsauer,** *a.* of or combined with tannic acid, tannate of.

**Gerbsäure,** *f.* tannic acid. **-lösung,** *f.* tannic acid solution. **-messer,** *m.* tannometer.

**Gerbstahl,** *m.* tilted steel, weld steel; polishing steel, burnisher.

**Gerbstoff,** *m.* tanning principle, tanning matter, tan; specif., tannic acid, tannin. **-auszug,** *m.* tanning extract. **-bestimmung,** *f.* determination of tanning matter. **-extrakt,** *m.* tannin extract. **-gehalt,** *m.* tannin content.

**gerbstoffhaltig,** *a.* tanniferous.

**Gerbstoff-lösung,** *f.* tannin solution. **-rot,** *n.* phlobaphene.

**Gerbung,** *f.* tanning (or tannage), etc. (see gerben).

**gerecht,** *a.* right, just, legitimate; fit, skilled.

**Gerechtigkeit,** *f.* justice; law.

**Gerede,** *n.* talk, talking.

**Gereibe,** *n.* rubbing.

**gereichen,** *v.i.* turn out, redound.

**gereuen,** *v.t.* repent, regret.

**Gericht,** *n.* court; judgment; jurisdiction; dish.

**gerichtlich,** *a.* judicial, forensic, legal.

**Gerichts-.** judicial, forensic, legal. **-amt,** *n.* court, tribunal. **-amtmann,** *m.* judge. **-barkeit,** *f.* jurisdiction. **-chemie,** *f.* forensic chemistry. **-chemiker,** *m.* forensic chemist, legal chemist. **-hof,** *m.* court, tribunal. **-rat,** *m.* judge, counsellor.

**gerieben,** *p.p.* of reiben.

**gerieft,** *a.* grooved, channeled.

**geriet,** *imperfect* of geraten.

**gering,** *a.* small, slight, deficient, limited, inferior, low, base.

**geringer,** *a.* inferior, less.

**gering-fügig,** *a.* unimportant, trivial, petty. **-haltig,** *a.* poor, low, low-grade, lean.

**Geringhaltigkeit,** *f.* poor or low quality.

**geringste,** *a.* least, slightest.

**geringwertig,** *a.* of small or low value, poor.

**gerinnbar,** *a.* coagulable.

**Gerinnbarkeit,** *f.* coagulability.

**Gerinne,** *n.* running, flowing; channel, gutter.

gerinnen, *v.i.* coagulate, curd, curdle, congeal, jelly, gel; (*Cement*) set.

Gerinnsel, *n.* coagulum; curd, curds; clot.

Gerinnstoff, *m.* coagulant, coagulator.

Gerinnung, *f.* coagulation, etc. (see gerinnen); coagulum.

gerinnungsfähig, *a.* coagulable, etc. (see gerinnen).

Gerinnungs-fähigkeit, *f.* coagulability. -masse, *f.* coagulum; gel. -mittel, *n.* coagulant, coagulator.

Gerippe, *n.* skeleton; framework.

gerippt, *p.a.* see rippen.

gerissen, *p.p.* of reissen.

geritten, *p.p.* of reiten.

Germanium-fluorwasserstoffsäure, *f.* fluogermanic acid. -oxyd, *n.* germanium oxide, specif. germanic oxide. -oxydul, *n.* germanous oxide. -säure, *f.* germanic acid. -sulfid, *n.* germanium sulfide, specif. germanic sulfide. -sulfür, *n.* germanous sulfide. -wasserstoff, *m.* germanium hydride.

Germer, *m.* white hellebore (*Veratrum*). -wurzel, *f.* white hellebore root.

gern, gerne, *adv.* gladly, with pleasure.—ich möchte —, I should like.

gerochen, *p.p.* of riechen.

Geröll, Gerölle, *n.* gravel, shingle; rubbish.

geronnen, *p.p.* of rinnen and gerinnen.

Gerste, *f.* barley.

Gersten-graupen, *f.pl.*, pearl barley. -korn, *n.* barleycorn. -malz, *n.* barley malt. -mehl, *n.* barley flour. -schleim, *m.* barley water. -stärke, *f.* barley starch. -stoff, *m.* hordein. -wasser, *n.* barley water. -zucker, *m.* barley sugar.

Geruch, *m.* smell, odor, scent, savor.

geruchfrei, *c.* free from odor, odorless.

geruchlos, *c.* odorless, inodorous; savorless; unable to smell.— — machen, deodorize.

Geruchlos-igkeit, *f.* inodorousness. -machung, *f.* deodorization.

geruchreich, *a.* rich in odor, odorous, fragrant.

Geruchstoff, *m.* odorous substance.

Gerücht, *n.* report, rumor.

Gerümpel, *n.* lumber, trash.

gerungen, *p.p.* of ringen.

Gerüst, *n.* frame, framework; scaffold; crate.

ges., *abbrev.* (gesättigt) saturated; (gesetzlich) by law; (gesamt) total.

Ges., *abbrev.* (Gesellschaft) society, company.

gesalzen, *p.p.* of salzen; salted.

gesammelt, *p.a.* collected, assembled, accumulated.

gesamt, *a.* total, entire, whole, complete, general.

Gesamt-alkali, *n.* total alkali. -analyse, *f.* total analysis. -ansicht, *f.* general view. -brechung, *f.* (*Physics*) total refraction. -gebiet, *n.* entire territory, whole field. -gewicht, *n.* total weight. -härte, *f.* total hardness. -härtebestimmung, *f.* determination of total hardness. -heit, *f.* totality; generality; the whole. -lösliches, *n.* total soluble matter. -menge, *f.* total quantity. -rohfaser, *f.* total crude fiber. -rückstand, *m.* total residue. -säure, *f.* total acid. -schwefel, *m.* total sulfur. -spannung, *f.* (*Elec.*) total voltage. -stickstoff, *m.* total nitrogen. -strom, *m.* (*Elec.*) total current. -verhalten, *n.* general behavior. -volum, *n.* total volume. -wärme, *f.* total heat. -wassergehalt, *m.* total water content. -wert, *m.* total value. -widerstand, *m.* total resistance. -zahl, *f.* total number.

gesandt, *p.p.* of senden.

Gesandte, *m.* messenger; ambassador.

Gesang, *m.* singing; song; canto.

Gesäss, *n.* seat; floor.

Gesäss-. (*Anat.*) gluteal.

gesättigt, *p.p.* of sättigen; saturated.

Geschabsel, *n.* scrapings.

Geschäft, *n.* business; affair; trade, commerce; house, firm; bargain.

geschäftig, *a.* busy; fussy.

geschäftlich, *a.* business; business-like; professional.

Geschäftsbetrieb, *m.* management (of a business).

geschah, *pret.* of geschehen.

geschehen, *v.i.* happen, occur, be done.

Geschehnis, *n.* occurrence.

gescheit, *a.* sensible, clever.

Geschenk, *n.* present, gift.

Geschichte, *f.* history; tale; thing.

geschichtlich, *a.* historical.

Geschick, *n.* skill; order; fate, destiny.

Geschicklichkeit, *f.* skill, cleverness, art.

geschickt, *a.* skillful, skilled, qualified.

Geschiebe, *n.* rubble, boulder, detritus; shoving.

geschieden, *p.p.* of scheiden.

geschieht, *pr. 3 sing.* of geschehen.

geschienen, *p.p.* of scheinen.

Geschirr, *n.* vessel; vessels, ware; utensils, tools, apparatus, gear; harness; plant, mill; (*Leather*) vat. -leder, *n.* harness leather.

Geschlecht, *n.* sex; genus; kind, species, race, family, stock, generation; gender.

geschlechtlich, *a.* sexual; generic.

Geschlechts-. sexual; generic. -art, *f.* generic character, genus. -drüse, *f.* genital gland (ovary, testicle). -pflanze, *f.* phanerogam. -reife, *f.* puberty.

geschlechtsreizend, *p.a.* aphrodisiac.

geschlichen, *p.p.* of schleichen.

geschliffen, *p.p.* of schleifen.

geschlissen, *p.p.* of schleissen.

geschloffen, *p.p.* of schliefen.
geschlossen, *p.p.* of schliessen; closed.
Geschlossenheit, *f.* closeness.
geschlungen, *p.p.* of schlingen.
Geschmack, *m.* taste; flavor; liking.
geschmacklos, *a.* tasteless; insipid.
Geschmacklosigkeit, *f.* tastelessness.
Geschmeide, *n.* jewelry.
geschmeidig, *a.* pliable, flexible, supple; (of metals) soft, ductile, malleable; versatile.
geschmissen, *p.p.* of schmeissen.
geschmolzen, *p.p.* of schmelzen.
geschnitten, *p.p.* of schneiden.
geschoben, *p.p.* of schieben.
gescholten, *p.p.* of schelten.
Geschöpf, *n.* creature.
geschoren, *p.p.* of scheren.
Geschoss, *n.* projectile, missile; story, floor.
geschossen, *p.p.* of schiessen.
Geschossfüllung, *f.* shell filling.
geschosstreibend, *p.a.* ballistic.
Geschrei, *n.* cry, outcry; rumor; disrepute.
geschrieben, *p.p.* of schreiben.
geschrieen, *p.p.* of schreien.
geschritten, *p.p.* of schreiten.
geschroben, *p.p.* of schrauben.
geschunden, *p.p.* of schinden.
Geschür, *n.* (*Metal.*) dross, scoria.
Geschütz, *n.* gun, cannon; ordnance, artillery. -bronze, *f.*, -metall, *n.* gun metal. -rohr, *n.* cannon bore; gun barrel; gun, cannon.
geschützt, *p.p.* protected.
geschweigen, *v.t.* not mention.—geschweige denn, not to mention.
geschwiegen, *p.p.* of schweigen and geschweigen.
geschwind, *a.* fast, quick, immediate.
Geschwindigkeit, *f.* velocity, speed; quickness, despatch.
Geschwindigkeitsmesser, *m.* speed indicator.
Geschwister, *pl.* brother(s) and sister(s).
geschwollen, *p.p.* of schwellen.
geschwommen, *p.p.* of schwimmen.
geschworen, *p.p.* of schwären and schwören.
Geschwulst, *f.* swelling; tumor.
geschwunden, *p.p.* of schwinden.
geschwungen, *p.p.* of schwingen.
Geschwür, *n.* ulcer, abscess.
Gesell, Geselle, *m.* mate, comrade; journeyman.
gesellen, *v.t. & r.* join.
gesellig, *a.* social, sociable.
Gesellschaft, *f.* society; company, partnership; club; community; party.
Gesenk, *n.* slope; hollow; pit; sump; die, swage. -schmieden, *n.* drop forging.
gesessen, *p.p.* of sitzen.
Gesetz, *n.* law; rule; precept. -entwurf, *m.* (legislative) bill.

gesetzgebend, *p.a.* legislative.
Gesetzgebung, *f.* legislation.
gesetzlich, *a.* lawful, legal.—*adv.* lawfully, legally.— — geschützt, protected by law (patented, copyrighted, registered).
gesetzmässig, *a.* conformable to (natural) law, regular; lawful.
Gesetzmässigkeit, *f.* conformity to law, regularity; lawfulness.
gesetzt, *p.a.* see setzen.
Gesetzvorschlag, *m.* bill; motion.
ges. gesch., *abbrev.* (gesetzlich geschützt) protected by law, patented.
Gesicht, *n.* sight; face, countenance, look; vision.
Gesichts-. visual; facial. -achse, *f.* visual axis. -feld, *n.* field of vision, field of view. -krem, *m.* face cream. -linie, *f.* visual line; facial line. -puder, *m.* face powder. -punkt, *m.* visual point, point of sight; viewpoint. -strahl, *m.* visual ray. -winkel, *m.* visual angle, optic angle; facial angle.
Gesims, *n.* molding, cornice; shelf.
Gesinnung, *f.* mind, disposition, opinion.
gesittet, *a.* mannered, bred; polite; civilized; moral.
gesoffen, *p.p.* of saufen.
gesogen, *p.p.* of saugen.
gesonnen, *p.p.* of sinnen.
gesotten, *p.p.* of sieden; boiled.
Gespenst, *n.* specter, ghost.
gespieen, *p.p.* of speien.
Gespinst, *n.* spun yarn; spun goods; thread; (textile) fabric. -faser, *f.* textile fiber. -pflanze, *f.* textile plant; fiber plant.
gesplissen, *p.p.* of spleissen.
gesponnen, *p.p.* of spinnen.
Gespräch, *n.* talk, conversation.
gesprochen, *p.p.* of sprechen.
gesprossen, *p.p.* of spriessen.
gesprungen, *p.p.* of springen.
Gestade, *n.* shore, coast.
Gestalt, *f.* form; shape, figure; aspect; manner.
gestalten, *v.t.* form, shape, mold, fashion.
gestaltlos, *a.* amorphous, formless.
Gestaltlosigkeit, *f.* amorphousness, formlessness.
Gestaltung, *f.* configuration, formation, form, state.
Gestaltveränderung, *f.* change of form or shape.
gestanden, *p.p.* of stehen and gestehen.
Geständnis, *n.* confession, acknowledgment.
Gestänge, *n.* poles or rods (collectively).
Gestank, *m.* stench, stink, bad smell.
gestatten, *v.t.* permit, allow, consent to.
Geste, *f.* gesture.
gestehen, *v.i.* coagulate, congeal, clot.—*v.t.* confess, admit.

**Gestehungs-kosten,** *f.pl.* working costs. **-preis,** *m.* cost price.

**Gestein,** *n.* rock; stone. **-art,** *f.* (kind of) rock. **-kunde, -lehre,** *f.* petrology; mineralogy; geognosy.

**Gesteins-mantel,** *m.* (*Geol.*) lithosphere. **-rest,** *m.* (*Ceram.*) rock residue.

**Gestell,** *n.* frame, stand, support, rack.

**gestern,** *adv.* yesterday.

**Gestiebe,** *n.* dust, powder.

**gestiegen,** *p.p.* of steigen.

**Gestirn,** *n.* star; constellation.

**gestirnt,** *a.* starred, starry; browed.

**gestoben,** *p.p.* of stieben.

**Gestöber,** *n.* shower; snowstorm; dust storm.

**gestochen,** *p.p.* of stechen.

**gestohlen,** *p.p.* of stehlen.

**gestorben,** *p.p.* of sterben.

**gestrahlt,** *p.a.* see strahlen.

**Gesträuch,** *n.* bushes, shrubbery.

**gestrichen,** *p.p.* of streichen.

**gestrig,** *a.* of yesterday.

**gestritten,** *p.p.* of streiten.

**Gestrüpp,** *n.* thicket, underbrush.

**Gestübbe, Gestübe,** *m.* (*Metal.*) brasque; (*Coal*) culm, slack.

**gestunken,** *p.p.* of stinken.

**Gesuch,** *n.* request, demand; want ad.

**gesund,** *a.* sound, healthy, wholesome.

**Gesundbrunnen,** *m.* mineral spring; spa.

**gesunden,** *v.i.* recover.

**Gesundheit,** *f.* health, soundness, salubrity.

**gesundheitlich,** *a.* sanitary, hygienic.

**Gesundheits-amt,** *n.* board of health. **-pflege,** *f.* sanitation, hygiene. **-wesen,** *n.* sanitary affairs.

**gesungen,** *p.p.* of singen.

**gesunken,** *p.p.* of sinken.

**Getäfel,** *n.* wainscoting; inlaying.

**getan, gethan,** *p.p.* of tun, thun. See tun.

**Getränk,** *n.* beverage, drink, liquor.

**getrauen,** *v.t.* dare, venture.

**Getreide,** *n.* grain; cereals; crops. **-art,** *f.* kind of grain; (*pl.*) cereals. **-branntwein,** *m.* whisky from grain. **-brennerei,** *f.* grain distillery. **-frucht,** *f.* cereal. **-korn,** *n.* grain. **-kümmel,** *m.* kümmel (the spirit of which is made from grain). **-prüfer,** *m.* grain tester. **-schnaps,** *m.* whisky from grain. **-stein,** *m.* = Bierstein. **-stroh,** *n.* cereal straw, straw.

**getreu,** *a.* faithful, true.

**Getriebe,** *n.* driving, working; (driving) gear; pinion.

**getrieben,** *p.p.* of treiben.

**getrocknet,** *p.p.* of trocknen; dried.

**getroffen,** *p.p.* of treffen and triefen.

**getrogen,** *p p.* of trügen.

**getrost,** *a.* confident, courageous.

**getrübt,** *p.a.* see trüben.

**getrunken,** *p.p.* of trinken.

**Geviert, Gevierte,** *n.* square.

**gew.,** *abbrev.* (gewöhnlich) usual; usually.

**Gew.,** *abbrev.* (Gewicht) weight, gravity.

**Gew.-%,** *abbrev.* (Gewichtsprozent) per cent by weight.

**Gewächs,** *n.* plant; growth; growing; vintage.

**gewachsen,** *p.a.* see wachsen.

**Gewächs-haus,** *n.* greenhouse, conservatory. **-kunde, -lehre,** *f.* botany. **-reich,** *n.* vegetable kingdom.

**gewahr,** *a.* aware.

**Gewähr,** *f.* surety, security; guarantee.

**gewahren,** *v.t.* perceive.

**gewähren,** *v.t.* give, furnish, afford, grant.

**gewährleisten,** *v.t.* guarantee, warrant, vouch for, assure.

**Gewalt,** *f.* power, force, violence.

**gewaltig,** *a.* powerful, forcible; huge, vast.

**gewaltsam,** *a.* violent.

**Gewand,** *n.* garment, clothing.

**gewandt,** *p.p.* of wenden.

**gewann,** *pret.* of gewinnen.

**gewärtig,** *a.* expectant.

**gewaschen,** *p.p.* washed.

**Gewässer,** *n.* waters; (*pl.*) streams, running water.

**Gewebe,** *n.* tissue; texture; textile fabric; web.

**Gewebe-.** textile; tissue, histological, histo-. **-draht,** *m.* gauze wire. **-farbstoff,** *m.* histohematin. **-lehre,** *f.* histology.

**Gewebs-.** = Gewebe-. **-brei,** *m.* (*Bact.*) tissue pulp. **-lehre,** *f.* histology. **-waren,** *f.pl.* textile goods, textiles.

**Gewehr,** *n.* arms, gun, rifle. **-granate,** *f.* rifle grenade. **-pulver,** *n.* rifle powder.

**gewehrschusssicher,** *a.* bullet-proof.

**Geweih,** *n.* horns, antlers.

**gewellt,** *a.* wavy, undulated, corrugated.

**Gewerb, Gewerbe,** *n.* trade, occupation; industry.

**Gewerbe-ausstellung,** *f.* industrial exposition. **-museum,** *n.* industrial museum. **-salz,** *n.* industrial salt (common salt fit only for industrial use). **-schule,** *f.* technical school, industrial school.

**Gewerbetreibende(r),** *m.* artisan.

**Gewerb-fleiss,** *m.* industrial activity, industry. **-kunde,** *f.* technology.

**gewerb-kundlich,** *a.* technological. **-lich, -tätig,** *a.* industrial.

**Gewerk,** *n.* trade; factory; work. **-schaft,** *f.,* **-verein,** *m.* trade union.

**gewesen,** *p.p.* of sein.

**gewichen,** *p.p.* of weichen.

**Gewicht,** *n.* weight; gravity.

**gewichtig,** *a.* heavy; weighty.

**Gewichts-abgang,** *m.* deficiency in weight; loss

of weight. -abnahme, *f.* decrease in weight. -analyse, *f.* gravimetric analysis.

gewichtsanalytisch, *a.* gravimetric.—*adv.* gravimetrically.

Gewichts-änderung, *f.* change in weight. -bestimmung, *f.* determination of weight. -einheit, *f.* unit of weight. -konstanz, *n.* constancy of weight, °constant weight. -menge, *f.* amount by weight, weight. -prozent, *n.* per cent by weight.

gewichtsprozentig, *a.* per cent by weight, weight-per-cent.

Gewichts-satz, *m.* set of weights. -stück, *n.* weight. -teil, *m.* part by weight. -unterschied, *m.* difference in weight. -verhältnis, *n.* proportion by weight. -verlust, *m.* loss in weight. -verminderung, *f.* decrease in weight. -zunahme, *f.* increase in weight. -zusammensetzung, *f.* composition by weight.

gewiesen, *p.p.* of weisen.

gewillt, *a.* willing, inclined.

Gewinde, *n.* winding, coil; skein; thread (of a screw). -glas, *n.* glass tube with screw cap. -steigung, *f.* screw pitch.

gewinkelt, *a.* angled, angular.

Gewinn, *m.* yield; winning, gain, profit.

gewinnbar, *a.* obtainable.

gewinnen, *v.t.* obtain, get; extract, produce (metals, etc.); prepare (chemicals); win, gain, acquire.

Gewinnung, *f.* obtaining, etc. (see gewinnen); produce.

Gewinnungsweise, *f.* manner or way of obtaining, etc. (see gewinnen).

gewiss, *a.* sure, certain, fixed.—*adv.* certainly, indeed.

Gewissen, *n.* conscience.

gewissenhaft, *a.* conscientious.

gewissermassen, *adv.* in a certain degree, as it were.

Gewissheit, *f.* certainty; proof.

Gewitter, *n.* storm.

gewoben, *p.p.* of weben.

gewogen, *p.p.* of wägen and wiegen.

gewöhnen, *v.t.* accustom, habituate; domesticate.

Gewohnheit, *f.* custom, usage, habit, fashion.

gewöhnlich, *a.* usual, customary; common, ordinary; trivial.—*adv.* usually, etc.

Gewöhnung, *f.* habituation, etc. (see gewöhnen).

Gewölbe, *n.* vault, arch; crown (of a furnace); store, storehouse.

gewönne, *pret. subj.* of gewinnen.

gewonnen, *p.p.* of gewinnen.

geworben, *p.p.* of werben.

geworden, *p.p.* of werden.

geworfen, *p.p.* of werfen.

Gew. T., *abbrev.* (Gewichtsteil) part by weight.

Gewühl, *n.* crowd; turmoil.

gewunden, *p.p.* of winden.

Gewürm, *n.* worms, creeping things, vermin.

Gewürz, *n.* spice, spices, aromatics; condiment, seasoning.

gewürzartig, *a.* spicy, aromatic.

Gewürzessig, *m.* aromatic vinegar.

gewürzhaft, *a.* spicy, aromatic.

Gewürz-haftigkeit, *f.* spiciness, aromatic quality. -handel, *m.* spice trade, grocers' trade.

gewürzig, *a.* spicy, aromatic.

Gewürz-nelke, *f.* clove. -nelkenöl, *n.* oil of cloves, clove oil. -pulver, *n.* (*Pharm.*) aromatic powder. -stoff, *m.* aromatic.

gewürzt, *p.a.* see würzen.

Gewürz-tinktur, *f.* aromatic tincture. -waren, *f.pl.* spices, groceries. -wein, *m.* spiced wine.

gewusst, *p.p.* of wissen.

Gezäh, Gezähe, *n.* tools, implements.

Gezeit, *f.* tide.

Gezelt, *n.* pavilion, tent; sensorium.

Gezeug, *n.* utensils, tools, implements

geziehen, *p.p.* of zeihen.

geziemen, *v.i.& r.* become, befit.

gezogen, *p.p.* of ziehen.

gezweiteilt, *p.a.* bipartite.

gezwungen, *p.p.* of zwingen; forced.

gg., *abbrev.* (gegen) against, opposite.

Ggw., *abbrev.* (Gegenwart) presence.

Gheddasäure, *f.* gheddic acid.

gibt, *pr. 3 sing.* of geben.

Gicht, *f.* top, mouth, throat (of a furnace or crucible); charge (for a furnace); (*Med.*) gout.

gicht-artig, *a.* gouty, arthritic. -brüchig, *a.* paralytic.

Gicht-gas, *n.* gas from the top of a blast furnace, blast-furnace gas. -mittel, *n.* remedy for gout. -rauch, *m.* top smoke (of a blast furnace). -rose, *f.* peony; rhododendron. -rübe, *f.* bryony. -schwamm, *m.* (*Zinc*) tutty. -staub, *m.* blast-furnace dust.

Gichtung, *f.* charging (of a furnace).

gichtwidrig, *a.* antiarthritic.

giebt, *pr. 3 sing.* of geben.

Gier, *f.* avidity, eagerness.

gierig, *a.* greedy, covetous; eager (for).

giessbar, *a.* capable of being poured or cast.

Giessbecken-.

Giessbett, *n.* (*Metal.*) casting bed.

giessen, *v.t.* pour; cast, found, mold.

Giesser, *m.* founder, caster, molder; melter, smelter; pourer; a vessel for pouring, as a water jug or pot.

Giesserei, *f.* foundry, casting house; founding, casting. -eisen, *n.* foundry iron, foundry pig. -koks, *m.* foundry coke. -roh-eisen, *n.* foundry pig.

Giesserschwärze, *f.* (*Founding*) black wash.

giessfähig, *a.* capable of being poured or cast.

Giess-form, *f.* (casting) mold. -haus, *n.*, -hütte, *f.* foundry, casting house. -kanne, *f.* sprinkling can. -kasten, *m.* casting mold. -kelle, *f.* casting ladle. -koks, *m.* foundry coke. -kunst, *f.* founding. -mutter, *f.* matrix, mold. -ofen, *m.* founding furnace. -pfanne, *f.* casting ladle. -sand, *m.* molding sand. -topf, *m.* a pot or jar with a lip, for pouring. -zement, *m.* a quick-setting alumina cement.

Gift, *n.* poison; toxin; venom, virus; malice.

gift-abtreibend, *p.a.* antitoxic, antidotal. -artig, *a.* poisonous.

Gift-arznei, *f.* antidote. -erz, *n.* arsenic ore. -fang, *m.* = Giftturm.

gift-fest, *a.* immune to poison. -frei, *a.* free from poison, non-poisonous.

Giftgas, *n.* poison gas, toxic gas. -krieg, *m.* poison-gas warfare.

gifthaltig, *a.* containing poison, poisonous, toxic.

Gift-heber, *m.* siphon for poisons. -hütte, *f.* arsenic works.

giftig, *a.* poisonous; toxic; virulent; venomous; malicious.

Giftigkeit, *f.* poisonousness, toxicity.

Gift-jasmin, *m.* Carolina jasmine (*Gelsemium sempervirens*). -kies, *m.* arsenopyrite. -kunde, *f.* toxicology. -lattich, *m.* strong-scented lettuce (*Lactuca virosa*). -lehre, *f.* toxicology.

giftlos, *a.* non-poisonous.

Gift-mehl, *n.* crude powdered arsenic tri-oxide. -mittel, *n.* antidote. -pulver, *n.* = Giftmehl. -rauch, *m.* sublimed arsenic tri-oxide. -stein, *m.* white arsenic. -stoff, *m.* poisonous matter, poison. -sumach, *m.* poison ivy (*Rhus toxicodendron*). -turm, *m.* (*Metal.*) poison tower (for catching arsenic fumes). -wende, *f.* swallowwort (*Cynanchum vincetoxicum*).

giftwidrig, *a.* antitoxic; antidotal.

Gift-wirkung, *f.* poisonous action or effect. -wurzel, *f.* contrayerva; = Giftwende.

Gilbe, *f.* yellow or yellowish color; yellow substance; yellow ocher; dyer's rocket (*Reseda luteola*).

gilben, *v.i.* turn yellow, yellow.

gilbig, *a.* ocherous.

Gilb-kraut, *n.* yellowweed, dyer's rocket (*Reseda luteola*). -wurzel, *f.* turmeric.

gilt, *pr. 3 sing.* of gelten.

giltig, *a.* = gültig.

ging, *pret.* of gehen.

Ginster, *m.* (*Bot.*) broom (*Genista*).

Gipfel, *m.* top, summit; climax.

gipfeln, *v.i. & r.* culminate.

Gipfelung, *f.* culmination.

Gips, *m.* gypsum; calcium sulfate; plaster of Paris. -abdruck, -abguss, *m.* plaster cast. -arbeiter, *m.* plasterer.

gipsartig, *a.* gypseous.

Gips-brei, *m.* paste of plaster (Paris). -brennen, *n.* gypsum burning. -brennerei, *f.* calcination of gypsum; plaster kiln. -brenn-ofen, *m.* plaster kiln.

gipsen, *v.t.* plaster.—*a.* gypseous.

Gipser, *m.* plasterer.

Gips-erde, *f.*, -gu(h)r, *m.* earthy gypsum. -form, *f.* plaster (Paris) mold. -guss, *m.* plaster casting, plaster cast.

gipshaltig, *a.* containing gypsum or calcium sulfate, gypsiferous.

Gips-härte, *f.* hardness due to calcium sulfate. -kalk, *m.* plaster lime. -kitt, *m.* gypsum cement. -lösung, *f.* calcium sulfate solution. -mehl, *n.* powdered gypsum; powdered plaster. -mergel, *m.* gypseous marl. -mörtel, *m.* plaster, stucco. -niederschlag, *m.* calcium sulfate precipitate. -ofen, *m.* plaster kiln. -spat, *m.* sparry gypsum, selenite. -stein, *m.* gypseous stone, plaster stone; hard deposit of calcium sulfate. -teer, *m.* mixture of plaster of Paris and tar.

gischen, *v.i.* foam, froth; ferment.

Gischt, *m.* foam, froth; fermentation.

Gitter, *n.* grating; (as in *Cryst.*) lattice; (latticed) screen; grid.

gitter-artig, -förmig, *a.* lattice-like, latticed, grated.

Gitterfarbe, *f.* grating color.

gitterfremd, *a.* (*Cryst.*) foreign to the lattice.

Gitter-konstante, *f.* lattice constant; grating constant. -typus, *m.* lattice type.

Gl., *abbrev.* (Gleichung) equation.

Glacé-leder, *n.* glacé leather. -papier, *n.* glazed paper.

glacieren, *v.t.* gloss, glaze; freeze.

glandern, *v.t.* calender.

Glanz, *m.* luster; glitter, polish, gloss; glance (in names of minerals); brightness, brilliancy; (of diamonds, etc.) water.

Glanz-, shiny, glossy, polished, glazed, glazing, brilliant. -arsenikkies, *m.* löllingite. -blende, *f.* alabandite. -braunstein, *m.* hausmannite. -brenne, *f.* (*Metal.*) burnishing bath.

Glänze, *f.* polishing material; glaze, size.

Glanz-effekt, *m.* gloss, luster. -eisen, *n.* silvery iron. -eisenerz, *n.*, -eisenstein, *m.*, specular iron ore (hematite).

glänzen, *v.i.* shine, glisten, glitter.—*v.t.* gloss, glaze, polish, luster.—glänzend, *p.a.* shining, lustrous, glossy, glittering, brilliant.

**Glanz-erz,** *n.* argentite. **-farbe,** *f.* brilliant color; glazing varnish; gloss ink.

**glanzfein.** *a.* brilliant.

**Glanz-firnis,** *m.* glazing varnish. **-gold,** *n.* (*Ceram.*) brilliant gold; (imitation) gold foil. **-karton,** *m.* glazed (paste)board **-kattun,** *m.* glazed calico. **-kobalt,** *m.* glance cobalt, cobaltite; smaltite. **-kohle,** *f.* glance coal; lustrous carbon. **-kopf,** *m* hematite. **-lack,** *m.* glazing varnish; brilliant varnish. **-leder,** *n.* patent leather, enameled leather. **-leinwand,** *f.* glazed linen.

**glanzlos,** *a.* lusterless, dull, dim, dead, mat.

**Glanz-losigkeit,** *f.* lusterlessness, dullness. **-manganerz,** *n.* (*Min.*) manganite. **-messing,** *n.* polished brass. **-metall,** *n.* speculum metal. **-papier,** *n.* glazed paper. **-pappe,** *f.* glazed (paper) board. **-rot,** *n.* colcothar. **-russ,** *m.* a lustrous form of soot.

**glanzschleifen,** *v.t.* polish, burnish.

**Glanz-silber,** *n.* silver glance, argentite. **-stärke,** *f.* gloss starch. **-stoff,** *m.* trade name of a cuprammonium rayon; glazed or glossy fabric.

**glanzvoll,** *a.* brilliant, splendid.

**Glanzwichse,** *f.* polishing wax.

**Glas,** *n.* glass. **-abfall,** *m.* glass waste, cullet. **-achat,** *m.* obsidian.

**glas-ähnlich, -artig,** *a.* glasslike, glassy, vitreous.

**Glas-artigkeit,** *f.* glassiness, vitreousness. **-ätzkunst,** *f.* art of etching glass. **-ballon,** *m.* glass carboy; glass balloon flask. **-bereitung,** *f.* glassmaking. **-bildung,** *f.* formation of glass, vitrification. **-birne,** *f.* glass bulb or globe. **-blase,** *f.* bubble in glass. **-blasen,** *n.* glassblowing. **-bläser,** *m.* glassblower. **-bläserei,** *f.* glassblowing. **-bläserlampe,** *f.* glassblower's lamp. **-bläseröhre,** *f.* blowpipe, blow tube (for glass). **-brennen,** *n.* annealing of glass. **-brocken,** *m.pl.,* **-bruch,** *m.* glass waste, cullet.

**Gläschen,** *n.* little glass, small glass vessel or tube.

**Glas-dose,** *f.* glass box (esp. of flat cylindrical form). **-elektrizität,** *f.* vitreous (positive) electricity.

**Glaser,** *m.* glazier.

**Gläser,** *n.pl.* of Glas; glasses.

**Glaserde,** *f.* vitrifiable earth, siliceous earth.

**Glaserkitt,** *m.* (glazier's) putty.

**gläsern,** *a.* glass, of glass; glassy, vitreous.

**Gläsernheit,** *f.* glassiness, vitreousness.

**Glas-erz,** *n.* argentite. **-fabrik,** *f.* glassworks, glass factory. **-fabrikation,** *f.* glass manufacture, glass-making. **-faden,** *m.* glass thread; threadlike defect in glass. **-farbe,** *f.* glass color. **-farben,** *n.* glass staining.

**glasfarbig,** *a.* glassy, hyaline.

**Glas-feuchtigkeit,** *f.* vitreous humor. **-flasche,** *f.* glass bottle, glass flask. **-fluss,** *m.* glass flux; paste (for imitation of gems); enamel. **-flüssigkeit,** *f.* vitreous humor.

**glasförmig,** *a.* glasslike, vitriform.

**Glas-fritte,** *f.* glass frit. **-galle,** *f.* glass gall, sandiver. **-gefäss,** *n.* glass vessel. **-gerät,** *n.,* **-geräte,** *n.pl.* glass apparatus, glass utensils. **-gespinst,** *n.* spun glass; glass thread; glass cloth. **-glanz,** *m.* vitreous luster; pounded glass, frost.

**glasglänzend,** *p.a.* of vitreous luster, glassy.

**Glasglocke,** *f.* glass bell, bell glass, bell jar.

**glasgrün,** *a.* bottle-green.

**Glas-hafen,** *m.* glass pot. **-hahn,** *m.* glass cock.

**glashart,** *a.* hard as glass, brittle.

**Glas-härte,** *f.* glass hardness (highest temper of steel); chilling (of steel). **-härten,** *n.* tempering of glass. **-haut,** *f.* a product similar to cellophane.

**glashell,** *a.* clear as glass.

**Glashütte,** *f.* glass factory, glass house.

**glasicht,** *a.* = glasig.

**glasieren,** *v.t.* glaze; enamel; varnish.

**Glasierung,** *f.* glazing; enameling; varnishing; glaze; enamel; varnish.

**glasig,** *a.* glassy, vitreous, hyaline.

**Glas-isolator,** *m.* glass insulator. **-kalk,** *m.* glass gall. **-kasten,** *m.* glass box (of rectangular form), glass case. **-kattun,** *m.* glass cloth. **-kitt,** *m.* glass cement; putty. **-klotz,** *m.* glass block. **-kolben,** *m.* glass flask. **-kopf,** *m.* (roter, eigentlicher) hematite (fibrous or reniform); (brauner, gelber) limonite; (schwarzer) psilomelane; a kind of hard brick. **-körper,** *m.* vitreous humor. **-kraut,** *n.* wall pellitory (*Parietaria officinalis*); glasswort (*Salicornia herbacea*). **-kugel,** *f.* glass bulb. **-lack,** *m.* glass varnish. **-lava,** *f.* volcanic glass, specif. obsidian; hyalite. **-löffel,** *m.* glass spoon. **-machen,** *n.* glassmaking. **-macherseife,** *f.* glassmaker's soap (as manganese dioxide). **-malz,** *n.* brittle malt. **-masse,** *f.* (*Glass*) metal; (rohe) frit. **-mehl,** *n.* glass powder. **-messer,** *n.* glass knife, glass cutter. **-ofen,** *m.* glass furnace. **-opal,** *m.* hyalite. **-papier,** *n.* glass paper. **-pech,** *n.* hard pitch, stone pitch. **-perle,** *f.* glass bead; glass pearl. **-pinsel,** *m.* glass brush (for acids, etc.). **-platte,** *f.* glass plate. **-porzellan,** *n.* vitreous porcelain. **-pulver,** *n.* glass powder. **-quarz,** *m.* hyaline quartz, transparent quartz. **-rohr,** *n.,* **-röhre,** *f.* glass tube. **-röhrchen,** *n.* little glass tube. **-salz,** *n.* glass gall. **-satz,** *m.* glass composition, batch. **-schale,** *f.* glass dish. **-schaum,** *m.* glass gall, sandiver.

-scheibe, *f.* pane of glass. -scherben, *f.pl.* cullet. -schlacke, *f.* glass gall. -schliff, *m.* glass grinding; ground-glass joint. -schmelz, *m.* enamel. -schmelzofen, *m.* (*Glass*) ash furnace. -schmutz, *m.* glass gall. -schneider, *m.* glass cutter. -schörl, *m.* axinite. -schreibtinte, *f.* ink for writing on glass. -schweiss, *m.* glass gall. -seife, *f.* glass soap (as manganese dioxide). -spatel, *m.* glass spatula. -splitter, *m.* glass splinter or fragment. -stab, *m.,* -stange, *f.* glass rod. -staub, *m.* glass dust, powdered glass. -stein, *m.* axinite; paste (for imitating gems); glass brick. -stopfen, *n.* glass stopper. -stöpsel, *m.* glass stopper. -stöpselflasche, *f.* glass-stoppered bottle (or, less often, flask). -tiegel, *m.* glass crucible, glass pot. -träne, *f.* glass tear, Prince Rupert's drop. -trichter, *m.* glass funnel.

Glasur, *f.* glaze, glazing; varnish; frosting, icing; enamel; gloss (of leather). -blau, *n.* zaffer. -brand, *m.* (*Ceram.*) glaze baking.

glasuren, *v.t.* glaze; enamel.

Glasur-erz, *n.* alquifou. -farbe, *f.* overglaze color. -ofen, *m.* glaze kiln, glost oven. -stein, *m.* vitrified brick.

Glas-wanne, *f.* glass trough. -waren, *f.pl.* glassware. -wolle, *f.* glass wool, spun glass.

glatt, *a.* smooth; even, plain, flat; glossy, polished, glazed.—glatte Wurfmine, (*Mil.*) projector drum.

Glättanfrischen, *n.* reduction of litharge.

Glattbrand, *m.* (*Ceram.*) glost burn, glaze burn.

glattbrennen, *v.t.* subject to the glost burn.

Glatt-brennen, *n.* (*Ceram.*) firing on the glaze. -brennofen, *m.* (*Ceram.*) glaze kiln.

Glätte, *f.* smoothness, polish; litharge.

glätten, *v.t.* smooth; polish, burnish, plane, planish; glaze (paper, gunpowder); calender (cloth).

Glatt-färberei, *f.* plain dyeing. -feuer, *n.* (*Ceram.*) sharp fire, full fire.

Glättfrischen, *n.* reduction of litharge.

Glatt-ofen, *m.* (*Ceram.*) glost kiln, finishing kiln. -scherbe, *f.* potsherd. -wasser, *n.* (*Brewing*) last run of wort.

Glaube, *m.* belief, faith, credit.

glauben, *v.t.* believe; think.

Glaubersalz, *n.* Glauber's salt (sodium sulfate decahydrate).

gläubig, *a.* believing; credulous.

Gläubiger, *m.* creditor.

glauch, *a.* glaucous; (of ore, etc.) poor; clear, bright.

Glaucherz, *n.* poor ore.

glaukonitisch, *a.* glauconitic.

glazieren, *v.t.* glaze.

gleich, *a.* equal, like, alike, similar; same, constant.—*adv.* equally, like; directly, at once, quickly.

gleich-, Gleich-. *equal, like, similar, constant, iso-, homo-, equi-.*

gleichartig, *a.* of the same kind; similar; homogeneous.

Gleichartigkeit, *f.* similarity; homogeneity.

gleich-bedeutend, *p.a.* equivalent; synonymous. -berechtigt, *a.* of equal rights. -bleiben, *v.i.* remain constant. -bleibend, *p.a.* constant, invariable. -deutig, *a.* synonymous, equivalent.

gleichen, *v.i.* be equal; be like.—*v.t.* make like or alike, equalize, smooth, level; liken.

gleich-falls, *adv.* likewise, also. -farbig, *a.* of the same color, isochromatic. -förmig, *a.* uniform, even; conformable; similar; homogeneous; monotonous. -gekörnt, *a.* even-grained. -gerichtet, *a.* (*Elec.*) rectified. -gestaltet, -gestaltig, *a.* (*Cryst.*) isomorphous.

Gleichgewicht, *n.* equilibrium; balance.

Gleichgewichts-bedingung, *f.* condition of equilibrium. -gesetz, *n.* law of equilibrium. -lehre, *f.* statics. -störung, *f.* displacement of equilibrium. -verhältnis, *n.* equilibrium ratio. -verschiebung, *f.* displacement (or shifting) of equilibrium. -zustand, *m.* state or condition of equilibrium.

gleich-gross, *a.* equal. -gültig, *a.* indifferent; immaterial.

Gleich-gültigkeit, *f.* indifference. -heit, *f.* equality; likeness; sameness; constancy; uniformity.

gleich-ionig, *a.* of like ion (or ions), having a common ion. -kommen, *v.i.* be equal (to), equal. -laufend, *p.a.* parallel.

Gleich-machen, *n.,* -machung, *f.* equalization; leveling.

gleichmässig, *a.* proportionate, symmetrical, uniform, homogeneous, similar, equal, even.

Gleichmut, *m.* equanimity.

gleichnamig, *a.* of the same name or kind, like.

Gleichnis, *n.* simile; parable.

gleichrichten, *v.t.* arrange in the same way, unidirect; (*Elec.*) rectify.

Gleichrichtung, *f.* unidirection; (*Elec.*) rectifying.

gleich-sam, *adv.* so to say; as it were; almost. -schenkelig, *a.* (*Geom.*) isosceles. -schwer, *a.* of equal weight; equally difficult. -seitig, *a.* equilateral; (of fabrics) double-faced.

Gleichspannung, *f.* (*Elec.*) direct-current voltage.

Gleichstrom, *m.* (*Elec.*) continuous current, direct current. -leitung, *f.* direct-current line.

gleichteilig, *a.* homogeneous.

Gleichung, *f.* equation; equalization.

**gleich-verhaltend**, *p.a.* of similar properties or behavior. **-viel**, *adv.& a.* just as much, just as many, equally, all the same. **-weit**, *a.* of uniform width; equidistant. **-wertig**, *a.* equivalent.

**Gleichwertigkeit**, *f.* equivalence, equivalency.

**gleich-winklig**, *a.* equiangular. **-wohl**, *conj.* yet, however. **-zeitig**, *a.* simultaneous, contemporary, synchronous, isochronous. **-zusammengesetzt**, *p.a.* of like composition.

**Gleis**, *n.* track.

**Gleit-**, glide, gliding, slide, sliding. **-bahn**, *f.* slide, slide way, shoot.

**gleiten**, *v.i.* glide, slide, slip.

**Gleit-fläche**, *f.* gliding plane, slip plane; (*Mach.*) sliding surface, slide. **-lager**, *n.* slide bearing, plain bearing. **-linie**, *f.* (*Metal.*) slip band. **-modul**, *m.* modulus of elasticity in shear. **-schiene**, *f.* slide bar, slide rail. **-skale**, *f.* sliding scale.

**Gletscher**, *m.* glacier. **-salz**, *n.* Epsom salt.

**glich**, *pret.* of gleichen.

**Glied**, *n.* member; (*Math.*) term; limb, joint; link (of a chain); degree.

**-gliederig**, *a.* -membered; -limbed.

**gliedern**, *v.t.* organize, arrange, classify; articulate.

**Gliederung**, *f.* organization, etc. (see gliedern).

**Gliederzahl**, *f.* number of members.

**Glied-nummer**, *f.* number of a member (in a series). **-wasser**, *n.* synovial fluid.

**glimmen**, *v.i.* glimmer, glow feebly; smolder.

**Glimmentladung**, *f.* glow discharge.

**Glimmer**, *m.* mica.

**glimmerartig**, *a.* micaceous.

**Glimmergestein**, *n.* micaceous rock.

**glimmerhaltig**, *a.* micaceous.

**glimmern**, *v.i.* glimmer, glitter.

**Glimmerplatte**, *f.* mica plate.

**glimmerreich**, *a.* rich in mica.

**Glimmer-sand**, *m.* micaceous sand. **-schiefer**, *m.* micaceous schist, mica slate. **-ton**, *m.* micaceous clay.

**Glimmlicht**, *n.* faint light, glimmer.

**glimpflich**, *a.* moderate, gentle, mild.

**glitt**, *pret.* of gleiten.

**glitzern**, *v.i.* glisten, glitter.

**Gln.**, *abbrev.* (Gleichungen) equations.

**Glöckchen**, *n.* little bell or bell jar.

**Glocke**, *f.* bell; bell jar, bell glass; (of an air pump) receiver; clock.

**Glocken-bronze**, *f.*, **-erz**, *n.* bell metal. **-filter**, *n.* bell-jar filter.

**glocken-form**, **-förmig**, *a.* bell-shaped.

**Glocken-giesser**, *m.* bell founder. **-gut**, **-metall**, *n.*, **-speise**, *f.* bell metal. **-trichter**, *m.* bell funnel (as on a thistle tube). **-verfahren**, *n.* bell process, bell method.

**glomm**, *pret.* of glimmen.

**glotzen**, *v.i.* stare.

**Glover-säure**, *f.* Glover acid (acid from the Glover tower). **-turm**, *m.* Glover tower.

**Glucinerde**, *f.* glucina (beryllia).

**Glück**, *n.* happiness, good luck, fortune, success.

**glucken**, *v.i.* cluck; gurgle.

**glücken**, *v.i.* succeed, prosper.

**glücklich**, *a.* fortunate, lucky, happy.

**Glüh-asche**, *f.* glowing ashes, embers. **-behandlung**, *f.* (*Metal.*) annealing.

**glühbeständig**, *a.* stable at red heat.

**Glüh-birne**, *f.* incandescent bulb. **-draht**, *m.* glowing wire, hot wire; annealed wire.

**Glühe**, *f.* glowing, glow; (*Iron*) chafery.

**Glüheisen**, *n.* glowing iron, red-hot iron.

**glühen**, *v.i.* glow.—*v.t.* cause to glow, glow, ignite; calcine; anneal; mull (wine). —**glühend**, *p.a.* glowing, incandescent.

**Glühen**, *n.* glowing, etc. (see glühen); incandescence.

**Glüh-faden**, *m.* incandescent filament. **-farbe**, *f.* glowing-red color. **-frischen**, *n.* (*Iron*) malleableizing. **-hitze**, *f.* glowing heat, red (or white) heat. **-kasten**, *m.*, **-kiste**, *f.* annealing box. **-kolben**, *m.* retort. **-körper**, *m.* incandescent body; specif., incandescent mantle or filament. **-lampe**, *f.* incandescent lamp.

**Glühlicht**, *n.* incandescent light. **-brenner**, *m.* incandescent burner. **-körper**, **-strumpf**, *m.* incandescent mantle.

**Glüh-masse**, *f.* incandescing material, specif. crude strontium oxide. **-ofen**, *m.* glowing furnace, annealing furnace; (*Ceram.*) hardening-on kiln. **-ring**, *m.* ring support for ignitions. **-rohr**, **-röhrchen**, *n.* ignition tube. **-rückstand**, *m.* residue on ignition. **-sand**, *m.* refractory sand. **-schälchen**, *n.* igniting dish, incinerating capsule. **-schale**, *f.* roasting dish; cupel. **-schiffchen**, *n.* combustion boat. **-span**, *m.* iron scale. **-stoff**, *m.* incandescent material. **-strumpf**, *m.* incandescent mantle. **-topf**, *m.* (*Metal.*) annealing box.

**Glühung**, *f.* glowing, etc. (see glühen).

**Glüh-verlust**, *m.* loss on ignition. **-wachs**, *n.* gilder's wax. **-zone**, *f.* zone of incandescence.

**Glukonsäure**, *f.* gluconic acid.

**Glukosid**, *n.* glucoside.

**Glukosurie**, *f.* glucosuria, glycosuria.

**Glut**, *f.* glow, incandescence; (*Ceram.*) glow heat; (fig.) fire.

**Glutaminsäure**, *f.* glutamic acid.

**Glutarsäure**, *f.* glutaric acid.

**Glutasche**, *f.* embers.

**glutflüssig**, *a.* molten, fused (by high heat).

**Gluthitze**, *f.* glowing heat.

glutinös, a. glutinous.

Glutmesser, m. pyrometer.

glutrot, a. glowing red.

Gluzinsäure, f. glucic acid.

Glyc-. see also Glyk-, Glyz-.

Glycerinleim, m. glycerin jelly.

glycerinphosphorsauer, a. of or pertaining to glycerophosphoric acid, glycerophosphate of.

Glycerin-phosphorsäure, f. glycerophosphoric acid. -säure, f. glyceric acid. -seife, f. glycerin soap.

Glycin, n. glycine; glucina (beryllia). -erde, f. glucina (beryllia).

Glycium, n. beryllium, glucinum.

Glycosid, n. glucoside.

Glyk-. glyc-; gluc- (when referring to glucose or its derivatives).

Glyko-cholsäure, f. glycocholic acid. -gallussäure, f. glucogallic acid.

Glykol-säure, f. glycolic acid. -schwefelsäure, f. glycolsulfuric acid. -ursäure, f. glycoluric acid.

Glykolyse, f. glycolysis.

glykolytisch, a. glycolytic.

Glykosämie, f. glucemia.

Glykose, f. glucose.

Glykosid, n. glycoside.

Glykoson, n. glucosone.

Glykosurie, f. glycosuria, glucosuria.

Glykuronsäure, f. glucuronic acid.

Glyoxalsäure, f. glyoxalic acid.

Glyoxylsäure, f. glyoxylic (glyoxalic) acid.

Glyz-. = Glyc-.

Glyzerid, n. glyceride.

Glyzerin, n. glycerol, glycerin. (For compounds see Glycerin-.)

Glyzid, n. glycide. -säure, f. glycidic acid.

GM. abbrev. (Goldmark) gold mark.

G.m.b.H. abbrev. (Gesellschaft mit beschränkter Haftpflicht or Haftung) limited company.

Gnade, f. grace, mercy, pardon, favor.

Gnaden-geld, n. pension, allowance. -kraut, n. hedge hyssop (Gratiola). -stoss, m. finishing blow.

gnädig, a. gracious, merciful, favorable.

Gneis, m. gneiss; seborrhea.

gneisig, a. gneissic.

Gneist, m. (Leather) scud, scurf.

Goapulver, n. Goa powder.

gold-ähnlich, -artig, a. goldlike, golden.

Gold-anstrich, m. gilding. -äther, m. gold chloride in ether. -auflösung, f. gold solution -belag, -beleg, m. gold coating, gold plating; gold foil. -beryll, m. chrysoberyl. -blatt, n. gold leaf, gold foil. -blick, m. flash or "blick" of gold. -chlorid, n. gold chloride, specif. auric chloride. -chlorür, n.

aurous chloride. -chlorwasserstoff, m., -chlorwasserstoffsäure, f. chloroauric acid. -cyanid, n. gold cyanide, specif. auric cyanide. -cyanür, n. aurous cyanide. -doublé, n. rolled gold. -draht, m. gold wire. -erde, f. auriferous earth. -erz, n. gold ore. -farbe, f. gold color.

gold-farben, -farbig, a. gold-colored.

Gold-firnis, m. gold varnish. -folie, f. gold foil.

goldführend, a. gold-bearing, auriferous.

Goldgehalt, m. gold content.

goldgelb, a. golden-yellow.

Gold-gelbbraun, n. golden brown. -gewicht, n. gold weight; weight of gold; troy weight. -glanz, m. golden luster.

goldglänzend, a. shining like gold.

Gold-glätte, f. a kind of litharge. -glimmer, m. yellow mica. -grund, m. gold size.

gold-haltig, a. auriferous. -hell, a. bright as gold, bright-golden.

Gold-hydroxyd, n. gold hydroxide, specif. auric hydroxide. -jodid, n. gold iodide, specif. auric iodide. -jodür, n. aurous iodide. -käfer, m. gold beetle. -kaliumbromür, n. potassium aurobromide. -kaliumcyanür, n. potassium aurocyanide. -kalk, m. gold calx, gold oxide. -kies, m. auriferous pyrites; auriferous sand or gravel. -klee, m. yellow trefoil. -klumpen, m. gold nugget. -könig, m. regulus of gold. -krätze, f. gold dross, sweepings, etc. -kupfer, n. Mannheim gold (a form of brass). -lack, m. gold varnish; aventurine; wallflower (Cheiranthus cheiri). -legierung, f. gold alloy. -leim, m. gold size. -lösung, f. gold solution. -macherkunst, f. alchemy. -ocher, -ocker, m. finest yellow ocher.

Goldoxyd, n. gold oxide, specif. auric oxide. -ammoniak, n. fulminating gold. -salz, n. auric salt; aurate.

Goldoxydul, n. aurous oxide. -verbindung, f. aurous compound.

Gold-oxydverbindung, f. auric compound. -papier, n. gilt paper, gold paper.

goldplattiert, p.a. gold-plated.

Gold-plattierung, f. gold plating. -probe, f. gold assay, gold test; sample of gold. -purpur, m. gold purple, purple of Cassius. -quarz, m. auriferous quartz. -regen, m. laburnum.

goldreich, a. rich in gold.

Gold-rubinglas, n. ruby glass in which gold is used as a colorant. -rute, f. goldenrod. -salz, n. gold salt; specif. sodium chloroaurate.

goldsauer, a. of or combined with auric acid, aurate of.

Gold-säure, f. auric acid. -schale, f. gold

dish, gold cup; cupel. **-schaum**, *m.* gold leaf; imitation gold leaf, Dutch foil. **-scheiden**, *n.* gold parting, gold refining. **-scheider**, *m.* gold refiner, gold parter. **-scheidewasser**, *n.* aqua regia. **-scheidung**, *f.* gold parting, gold refining. **-schlag**, *m.* gold leaf, gold foil. **-schläger**, *m.* goldbeater. **-schlägerhaut**, *f.* goldbeater's skin. **-schlich**, *m.* gold slimes, gold schlich. **-schmied**, *m.* goldsmith. **-schnitt**, *m.* gilt edge. **-schwefel**, *m.* gold sulfide; golden sulfide of antimony ($Sb_2S_5$). **-siegellack**, *m.* gold sealing wax; aventurine. **-silber**, *n.* electrum. **-staub**, *m.* gold dust. **-stein**, *m.* auriferous stone; touchstone; goldstone (aventurine). **-streichen**, *n.* gold (streak) test. **-stück**, *n.* gold piece, gold coin. **-sulfür**, *n.* aurous sulfide. **-thioschwefelsäure**, *f.* aurothiosulfuric acid. **-tropfen**, *m.pl.* (*Pharm.*) ethereal tincture of ferric chloride. **-verbindung**, *f.* gold compound. **-vitriol**, *m.* gold sulfate. **-zahl**, *f.* gold number, gold figure. **-zyanid**, *n.* = Goldcyanid. **-zyanür**, *n.* aurous cyanide.

**Golf**, *m.* gulf.

**gölte**, *pret.subj.* of gelten.

**goniometrisch**, *a.* goniometric.

**gönnen**, *v.t.* wish; grant.

**Gönner**, *m.* well-wisher, patron.

**Goochtiegel**, *m.*, **Gooch'scher Tiegel**. Gooch crucible.

**gor**, *pret.* of gären.

**goss**, *pret.* of giessen.

**Goose**, *f.* gutter, drain.

**Gott**, *m.* God, god.

**Götter-baum**, *m.* tree of heaven (*Ailanthus glandulosus*). **-fabel**, **-lehre**, *f.* mythology. **-speise**, *f.* ambrosia. **-trank**, *m.* nectar.

**Gottesgnadenkraut**, *n.* hedge hyssop (*Gratiola officinalis*).

**Göttin**, *f.* goddess.

**Goudron**, *n.* a soft asphalt or mixture of asphalt with high-boiling mineral oil.

**gr.**, *abbrev.* (Gramm, Gramme) gram, grams, g.; (granuliert) granulated; (gross) large.

**Grab**, *n.* grave, tomb.

**graben**, *v.t.* dig; engrave, cut.

**Graben**, *n.* ditch, drain, trench. **-mörser**, *m.* trench mortar.

**Gräber**, *m.* digger.

**Grab-legung**, *f.* burying, interment. **-scheit**, *n.* spade, shovel. **-schrift**, *f.* epitaph. **-stichel**, *m.* graver, graving tool, chisel.

**Grad**, *m.* degree; grade, rank; order; stage; rate. **-abteilung**, *f.* graduation, scale. **-bogen**, *f.* graduated arc. **-einteilung**, *f.* graduation, scale.

**gradieren**, *v.t.* graduate; test with a hydrometer.

**Gradierhaus**, *n.* (*Salt*) graduation house.

**Gradierung**, *f.* graduation, etc. (see gradieren).

**Gradier-wa(a)ge**, *f.* brine gage. **-werk**, *n.* graduation apparatus or works (for concentrating a solution by exposing a large surface to the air).

**-gradig**, **-grädig**, *a.* having (certain) degrees.

**Gradigkeit**, **Grädigkeit**, *f.* number of degrees, concentration, density or the like (expressed in degrees); per cent purity (as of soda).

**Grad-messer**, *m.* graduator. **-teilung**, *f.* graduation, scale.

**graduieren**, *v.t.* graduate.

**Graduierung**, *f.* graduation.

**Gradverwandtschaft**, *f.* graduated affinity, degree of affinity.

**Graf**, *m.* count; (in England) earl.

**grafisch**, *a.* graphic.

**Grafit**, *n.* graphite.

**Grammäquivalent**, *n.* gram equivalent.

**Grammenflasche**, *f.* gram bottle, specific gravity bottle.

**Grammion**, *n.* gram ion.

**Grammmol**, *n.* mole, gram molecule.

**Grammmolekül-gewicht**, *n.* gram-molecular weight. **-volumen**, *n.* gram-molecular volume.

**Gran**, *n.& m.* grain.

**Granadilholz**, *n.* granadilla wood.

**Granalien**, *pl.* granulated metal.

**Granat**, *m.* garnet; (in combination) pomegranate. **-apfel**, *m.* pomegranate.

**granatartig**, *a.* garnetlike.

**Granat-baum**, *m.* pomegranate tree. **-dodekaeder**, *n.* rhombic dodecahedron.

**Granate**, *f.* grenade, shell; garnet; pomegranate.

**Granatgestein**, *n.* garnet rock.

**Granatill-holz**, *n.* granadilla wood. **-öl**, *n.* physic-nut oil. **-samen**, *n.* physic nut.

**Granatoeder**, *n.* = Granatdodekaeder.

**Granatrinde**, *f.* pomegranate bark.

**granatrot**, *a.* garnet-red, garnet.

**Granatwurzelrinde**, *f.* pomegranate root bark.

**Grand**, *m.* coarse sand or fine gravel; (*Brewing*) underback.

**granieren**, *v.t.* granulate, grain.

**granit-ähnlich**, *a.* granitoid. **-artig**, *a.* granitelike, granitic.

**graniten**, **granitisch**, *a.* granitic.

**granitfarbig**, *a.* granite-colored.

**Granit-fels**, **-felsen**, *m.* granitic rock.

**granitförmig**, *a.* granitiform.

**Granne**, *f.* awn, beard.

**granulieren**, *v.t.* granulate.

**Granulierung**, *f.* granulation.

**granulös**, *a.* granular.

Gränze, *f.* = Grenze.

Grapen, *m.* (iron) mixing pot, pot.

graphisch, *a.* graphic.

graphit-artig, -ähnlich, *a.* graphite-like, graphitoidal. -haltig, *a.* containing graphite, graphitic.

graphitieren, *v.t.* blacklead.

graphitisch, *a.* graphitic.

Graphit-kohle, *f.* graphitic carbon. -masse, *f.* graphite paste. -pulver, *n.* graphite powder. -säure, *f.* graphitic acid. -schmelztiegel, *m.* graphite crucible. -schmiermittel, *n.* graphite lubricant. -schmierung, *f.* graphite lubrication. -spitze, *f.* (of an arc lamp) carbon. -staub, *m.* graphite dust. -stein, *m.* graphite brick. -stift, *m.* lead pencil; pencil lead. -tiegel, *m.* graphite crucible.

Gras, *n.* grass.

grasen, *v.i.* graze.

Gräser, *n.pl.* grasses, (*Bot.*) Poaceae.

gras-fressend, *p.a.* graminiverous, herbiverous. -grün, *a.* grass-green.

grasig, *a.* grassy, grassgrown.

Gras-leinen, *n.* grass cloth. -öl, *n.* grass oil, specif. citronella oil.

grassieren, *v.i.* rage, spread.

Graswurzel, *f.* couch grass (*Agropyron repens*); (*Pharm.*) triticum; grass root.

Grat, *m.* edge, ridge, bur; groin (of a roof).

Gräte, *f.* fishbone; edge, ridge, spine.

grau, *a.* gray.—graue Quecksilbersalbe, *f.* mercurial ointment.

Grau, *n.* gray.

grau-blau, *a.* gray-blue. -braun, *a.* graybrown, dun.

Grau-braunstein, *m.* (*Min.*) manganite. -braunsteinerz, *n.* pyrolusite. -eisen, *n.* gray iron. -eisenerz, *n.* marcasite.

grauen, *v.i.* grow gray; dawn; be in dread.

Grauerz, *n.* galena.

grau-farben, -farbig, *a.* gray-colored. -gelb, *a.* grayish-yellow.

Grau-glanzoxydbad, *n.* a bath for coloring metals with a film of arsenic or antimony. -golderz, *n.* nagyagite.

graugrün, *a.* gray-green.

Grau-gültigerz, *n.* tetrahedrite. -guss, *m.* gray-iron casting. -kalk, *m.* gray lime (inferior in quality); gray chalk; crude calcium acetate. -kobalterz, *n.* gray cobalt ore, jaipurite. -kupfererz, *n.* chalcocite; tennantite; tetrahedrite.

graulich, gräulich, *a.* grayish.

Grau-manganerz, *n.* gray manganese ore, manganite; (lichtes) polianite. -metall, *n.* gray metal, specif. gray pewter.

Graumontsamen, *m.* pumpkin seed.

Graupe, *f.* peeled grain, esp. of barley; knot (in cotton); (*Min.*) grain.—*pl.* Graupen, pearl barley; groats.

graupeln, *v.i.* sleet.

Graupen-erz, *n.* granular ore. -kobalt, *m.* smaltite. -schleim, *m.* barley water. -schörl, *m.* aphrizite (a black tourmaline).

graupig, *a.* granular.

Graus, *m.* small fragments, smalls; horror; shudder.

grau-sam, *a.* horrible, inhuman, cruel. -schwarz, *a.* grayish-black.

Grau-spiegel, *m.* gray spiegeleisen. -spiessglanz, *m.*, -spiessglanzerz, -spiessglaserz, *n.* gray antimony ore, stibnite. -stein, *m.* (*Petrog.*) graystone.

grauviolett, *a.* gray-violet.

Grauwacke, *f.* (*Petrog.*) graywacke.

grauweiss, *a.* gray-white.

gravieren, *v.t.* engrave; aggravate.

gravimetrisch, *a.* gravimetric.

Grazie, *f.* grace, charm.

greifbar, *a.* graspable, tangible.

greifen, *v.t. & i.* grasp, seize, grip, catch.—*v.i.* mat, felt, cake.

Greifer, *m.* seizer, gripper, catcher, grab.

Greifzirkel, *m.* calipers.

greis, *a.* gray with age, old.

Greisen-. senile.

grell, *a.* bright, dazzling, glaring; shrill.—grelles Roheisen, white pig iron.

Grenadillholz, *n.* granadilla wood.

Grenz-. limit (in *Org. Chem.* designating saturated aliphatic compounds); limiting, terminal, marginal. -alkohol, *m.* limit alcohol, paraffin alcohol, saturated alcohol.

Grenze, *f.* limit, boundary, bound, end; limitation.

Grenzenlinie, *f.* boundary line.

grenzenlos, *a.* unlimited, infinite.

Grenz-fall, *m.* limiting case. -fläche, *f.* boundary surface, surface of contact, interface.

Grenzflächen-erscheinung, *f.* interfacial phenomenon. -katalyse, *f.* contact catalysis. -spannung, *f.* interfacial tension.

Grenz-gesetz, *n.* limit law (one which natural phenomena approximate but never actually fulfill). -kohlenwasserstoff, *m.* any hydrocarbon of the methane series, alkane, paraffin, limit hydrocarbon. -kurve, *f.* limiting curve, limit curve. -linie, *f.* boundary line. -scheide, *f.* boundary. -verbindung, *f.* terminal compound, end compound, end member; saturated aliphatic compound. -wert, *m.* limiting value, limit; (*Biol.*) threshold value. -winkel, *m.* critical angle. -zahl, *f.* limit value, limit figure. -zustand, *m.* limiting state.

greulich, *a.* abominable, detestable.

**Greze, Grezseide,** *f.* raw silk.

**Grieben,** *f.pl.* greaves, cracklings; residue (as from sifting sugar).

**Griechenland,** *n.* Greece.

**griechisch,** *a.* Greek.—**griechisches Heu,** fenugreek.

**Gries,** *m.* = Griess.

**grieselig, griesig,** *a.* gritty, gravelly.

**Griess,** *m.* grit, gravel, coarse sand; grits, groats, semolina; small coal; (*Med.*) gravel. **-holz,** *n.* (*Pharm.*) nephritic wood. **-kohle,** *f.* (*Coal*) smalls, small coal. **-mittel,** *n.* remedy for gravel. **-stein,** *m.* urinary calculus, gravel; jade. **-wurzel,** *f.* (*Pharm.*) pareira.

**griff,** *pret.* of greifen.

**Griff,** *m.* grip, grasp; handle, knob; touch, feel.

**Griffel,** *m.* style, stylus; slate pencil, pencil; (*Bot.*) style.

**griffelförmig,** *a.* styloid, styliform.

**Griffstopfen,** *m.* stopper with thumb piece.

**grignardieren,** *v.t.* subject to the Grignard reaction.

**Grille,** *f.* cricket; whim, crotchet.

**Grimmdarm,** *m.* (*Med.*) colon.

**grimmen,** *v.i.* gripe.

**Grind,** *m.* scab, scurf, crust. **-wurzel,** *f.* bitter-dock root.

**grinsen,** *v.i.* grin; (of colors) stare; (of metals) begin to melt.

**grob,** *a.* coarse; thick, heavy, rough; large, gross; ill-bred, rude.

**Grob-blech,** *n.* (*Metal.*) thick plate. **-eisen,** *n.* merchant iron.

**grob-fädig,** *a.* coarse-threaded. **-faserig,** *a.* coarse-fibered, coarse-grained. **-gepulvert,** *p.a.* coarsely powdered.

**Grob-gewicht,** *n.* gross weight. **-kalk,** *m.* coarse limestone. **-kies,** *m.* coarse gravel. **-keramik,** *f.* ordinary ceramic ware. **-kohle,** *f.* coarse or lump coal; open-burning coal. **-korn,** *n.* coarse grain, large grain. **-korneisen,** *n.* coarse-grained iron.

**grob-körnig,** *a.* coarse-grained, large-grained, coarsely granular. **-kristallinisch,** *a.* coarsely crystalline.

**gröblich,** *a.* rather coarse.—*adv.* coarsely, grossly.

**grobmechanisch,** *a.* macromechanical, large-scale.

**Grob-mörtel,** *m.* coarse mortar, concrete. **-sand,** *m.* coarse sand. **-schrot,** *n.& m.* coarse groats; (*Brewing*) coarsely ground malt. **-sieb,** *n.* coarse (wide-meshed) sieve. **-spiegel,** *m.* coarse spiegeleisen. **-zerkleinerung,** *f.* coarse division, coarse crushing.

**Grönland,** *n.* Greenland.

**gross,** *a.* great; large, tall; capital (letter). **—im grossen,** on a large scale; in bulk.—

**im grossen und ganzen,** on the whole, generally.

**grossartig,** *a.* grand, sublime.

**Grossbetrieb,** *m.* operation on a large scale; wholesale trade.

**gross-blätterig,** *a.* coarsely foliated or laminated; large-leaved. **-britannisch,** *a.* British.

**Grösse,** *f.* quantity; magnitude; amount, bulk, volume, size, largeness, greatness.

**Grössen-lehre,** *f.* mathematics; geometry. **-nummer,** *f.* size (expressed as a number). **-ordnung,** *f.* order of magnitude.

**grossenteils,** *adv.* in large part, mostly.

**Grossfabrikation,** *f.* large-scale manufacture.

**grossfaserig,** *a.* large-fibered, coarse-fibered.

**Gross-feuer,** *n.* conflagration; (*Ceram.*) full fire. **-gewerbe,** *n.* manufacture on a large scale. **-handel,** *m.* wholesale business. **-händler,** *m.* wholesaler.

**grossherzig,** *a.* magnanimous.

**Gross-hirn,** *n.* cerebrum. **-industrie,** *f.* = Grossgewerbe.

**gross-jährig,** *a.* of age. **-luckig,** *a.* coarsely porous; coarse-grained. **-mütig,** *a.* magnanimous, generous. **-stückig,** *a.* in large pieces.

**Grosstechnik,** *f.* large-scale technology or industry.

**grösstenteils,** *adv.* for the most part.

**grösstmöglich,** *a.* greatest possible.

**Grossverkauf,** *m.* wholesale.

**grosszügig,** *a.* large-scale.

**Grotte,** *f.* grotto.

**grub,** *pret.* of graben.

**Grübchen,** *n.* little hole or opening; dimple; (*Biol.*) lacuna.

**Grube,** *f.* mine; quarry; hole, cavity; pit; ditch.

**grübeln,** *v.i.* ponder, brood.

**Gruben-bau,** *m.* mine digging, underground working. **-betrieb,** *m.* mining. **-brand,** *m.* mine fire. **-dampf,** *m.* choke damp. **-feuchtigkeit,** *f.* pit moisture (in coal). **-gas,** *n.* marsh gas, methane; firedamp (explosive mixture of methane and air). **-gasanzeiger,** *m.* methanometer. **-gut,** *n.* (*Mining*) minerals. **-klein,** *n.* (*Mining*) smalls, slack. **-kohle,** *f.* pit coal, (mineral) coal; pit charcoal. **-lampe,** *f.,* miner's lamp. **-licht,** *n.* miner's lamp. **-pulver,** *n.* miner's powder, blasting powder. **-sand,** *m.* pit sand, dug sand. **-verkohlung,** *f.* pit burning (of charcoal). **-wasser,** *n.* pit water, mine water. **-wetter,** *n.* mine damp, specif. firedamp.

**Grude,** *f.* hot ashes, embers; = Grudekoks.

**Grudekoks,** *m.* a granular coke from lignite.

**grün,** *a.* green.—**grüne Erde** = Grünerde.

Grün, *n.* green.

grünblau, *a.* greenish-blue.

Grünbleierz, *n.* green lead ore, green pyromorphite (or green mimetite).

grünbraun, *a.* greenish-brown.

Grund, *m.* ground (in various senses); grounds, sediment; bottom; foundation, base, basis.—im Grunde, at bottom, on the whole, after all.—zu Grunde gehen, be ruined, fail.—zu Grunde legen, take as a basis, start out from.—zu Grunde liegen, be at the bottom of, be the basis of (or for).

Grund-. ground, bottom, foundation, fundamental, primary, elementary; (before *adjs.*, grund-) thoroly, radically. -anstrich, *m.* ground coat, priming coat. -bahn, *f.* ground orbit. -bau, *m.* foundation. -begriff, *m.* fundamental conception or notion, basic idea. -besitz, *m.* landed property, real estate. -bestandteil, *m.* elementary constituent, element. -einheit, *f.* fundamental unit.

gründen, *v.t.* ground, found, establish; groove.

Gründer, *m.* founder, establisher, promoter.

grund-falsch, *a.* radically false.

Grund-farbe, *f.* primary color; ground color, priming color; (*Dyeing*) bottom color. -feuchtigkeit, *f.* soil moisture. -firnis, *m.* priming varnish. -fläche, *f.* basal surface, base; area. -flüssigkeit, *f.* (*Colloids*) suspending liquid. -form, *f.* primary or fundamental form, type. -formel, *f.* fundamental formula. -gebirge, *n.* primitive rock. -gesetz, *n.* fundamental law. -gestein, *n.* primitive rock. -gleichung, *f.* fundamental equation. -heil, *n.* (*Pharm.*) mountain parsley (*Peucedanum oreoselinum*).

Grundierbad, *n.* bottoming bath.

grundieren, *v.t.* ground, prime; (*Gilding*) size; (*Paper*) stain; (*Dyeing*) bottom; (*Calico*) prepare.

Grundier-farbe, *f.* priming color. -firnis, -lack, *m.* filler. -salz, *n.* preparing salt (sodium stannate). -schicht, *f.* priming coat.

Grundierung, *f.* grounding, priming, etc. (see grundieren); (*Paper*) texture.

Grund-kapital, *n.* stock. -körper, *m.* fundamental or parent substance. -kraft, *f.* primary force, primitive force.

gründl., *abbrev.* gründlich.

Grundlage, *f.* foundation, groundwork, base; basis, principle; matrix; basement; (*Old Chem.*) radical base.

grundlegend, *a.* fundamental.

Grundlehre, *f.* fundamental doctrine.

gründlich, *a.* fundamental; profound; thoro. —*adv.* fundamentally; thoroly.

Grundlinie, *f.* ground line, base line, basis.

grundlos, *a.* groundless, baseless.

Grund-mass, *n.* fundamental unit of measurement. -masse, *f.* groundmass; (*Anat.*) stroma. -mörtel, *m.* concrete. -niveau, *n.* ground level. -platte, *f.* base plate, bed plate. -problem, *n.* fundamental problem. -regel, *f.* principle, axiom. -riss, *m.* ground plan; sketch, outline. -satz, *m.* principle, axiom.

grundsätzlich, *a.* fundamental, based on principles.

Grund-schicht, *f.* primary layer, fundamental layer; ground course. -stein, *m.* foundation stone, cornerstone; lower (mill) stone. -stock, *m.* matrix. -stoff, *m.* element; raw material; base. -strich, *m.* first coat, priming; down stroke. -stück, *n.* premises, (real) property. -substanz, *f.* element; (*Anat.*) ground substance. -teilchen, *n.* fundamental particle. -ton, *m.* fundamental tone, primary tone. -umsatz, *m.* (*Biol.*) basal metabolism.

Gründung, *f.* foundation; first coat, priming.

Grün-düngen, *n.* (*Agric.*) green manuring. -dünger, *m.* (*Agric.*) green manure.

Grund-versuch, *m.* fundamental experiment. -wasser, *n.* ground water. -wasserspiegel, *m.* ground-water level. -zahl, *f.* unit; base number, base; cardinal number. -zug, *m.* leading feature, characteristic; (*pl.*) outline.

Grüne, *f.* green, greenness.

Grüneisen-erde, *f.*, -erz, -stein, *m.* green iron ore, dufrenite.

grünen, *v.r.& i.* become green, green.

Grün-erde, *f.* green earth (glauconite, also celadonite). -feuer, *n.* green fire.

grün-gelb, *a.* greenish-yellow. -grau, *a.* greenish gray.

Grün-kalk, *m.* gas lime. -kreuzkampfstoff, *m.* "green cross" shell filling (trichloromethyl chloroformate or other lung irritant).

grünlich, *a.* greenish. -blau, *a.* greenish-blue. -gelb, *a.* greenish-yellow. -grau, *a.* greenish-gray. -weiss, *a.* greenish-white.

Grün-malz, *n.* green malt. -mist, *m.* green manure. -öl, *n.* green oil (anthracene oil). -rost, *m.* verdigris.

grünrostig, *a.* aeruginous.

Grünsand, -stein, *m.* (*Geol.*) greensand.

grünschwarz, *a.* greenish-black.

Grünspan, *m.* verdigris. -blumen, *f.pl.* crystals of verdigris. -essig, -geist, -spiritus, *m.* = Kupfergeist.

Grün-spat, *m.* a variety of diopside. -star, *m.* glaucoma. -stein, *m.* (*Geol.*) greenstone. -sucht, *f.* chlorosis.

Gruppe, *f.* group; cluster, set.

Gruppen-geschwindigkeit, *f.* group velocity. -reagens, *n.* group reagent.

gruppenweise, *adv.* in groups.

gruppieren, *v.t.* group.

Gruppierung, *f.* grouping.

Grus, *m.* & *n.* small fragments, smalls; specif., small coal, slack; fine gravel; débris. -kakao, *m.* cacao husks. -kohle, *f.* small coal, slack.

Gruss, *m.* greeting, salutation.

grüssen, *v.t.* greet, salute.

Grütz-. of or like grits, pulpy, (*Med.*) sebaceous, atheromatous. -brei, *m.* porridge, mush.

Grütze, *f.* grits, groats.

Grützschleim, *m.* gruel.

G-Säure, *f.* G-acid (2-naphthol-6,8-disulfonic acid).

G.T., *abbrev.* (Gewichtsteil) part by weight.

Guaj-. guai-.

Guajac, Guajac-. = Guajak, Guajak-.

Guajadol, *n.* guaiadol.

Guajak, *m.* guaiacum. -blau, *n.* guaiacum blue. -gelb, *n.* guaiacum yellow. -harz, *n.* guaiacum resin, guaiacum. -harzsäure, *f.* guaiaretic acid. -holz, *n.* guaiacum wood. -insäure, *f.* guaiacinic acid. -ol, *n.* guaiacol. -onsäure, *f.* guaiaconic acid. -säure, *f.* guaiacic acid. -seife, *f.* guaiac soap.

Guajen, *n.* guaiene. -chinon, *n.* guaiene-quinone.

Guajol, *n.* guaiol.

Guäthol, *n.* guethol.

gucken, *v.i.* look, peep.

Guckloch, *n.* peep hole.

Guhr, *f.* = Gur.

Gulden, *m.* gulden, florin.

guldig, güldig, *a.* golden; auriferous.

Gülle, *f.* liquid manure (esp. a kind formed by the decomposition of animal refuse).

gültig, *a.* valid, binding, good, current; applicable; (*Mining*) specif., auriferous.

Gültigkeit, *f.* validity, binding force, availability.

Gummi, *n.* gum; (India) rubber. (For compounds see also under Kautschuk-.) -abfälle, *m.pl.* scrap rubber. arabicum, gum arabic. -art, *f.* variety of gum, gum.

gummiartig, *a.* gumlike, gummous, gummy.

Gummi-auflösung, *f.* = Gummilösung. -band, *n.* rubber band; elastic. -baum, *m.* gum tree; rubber tree. -blase, *f.* rubber bulb.

gummicht, *a.* gummy, gummous.

Gummi elasticum. rubber.

gummieren, *v.t.* gum; (*Gilding*) size.

Gummi-ersatzstoff, *m.* rubber substitute. -erz, *n.* (*Min.*) gummite. -fahne, *f.* rubber flag (for precipitates). -fichte, *f.* balsam fir. -finger, *m.* rubber finger stall. -flasche, *f.* rubber bottle.

gummig, *a.* gummy, gummous.

Gummi-gärung, *f.* mucous fermentation. -gebläse, *n.* rubber bellows, rubber bulb. -gut, -gutt, *n.* gamboge.

gummihaltig, *a.* containing gum, gummy.

Gummi-handschuh, *m.* rubber glove. -harz, *n.* gum resin; rubber resin.

gummiharzig, *a.* of or pertaining to a gum resin.

Gummi-hütchen, *n.* (small) rubber cap. -isolierung, *f.* rubber insulation. -käppchen, *n.* (small) rubber cap. -kappe, *f.* rubber cap. -lack, *m.* gum-lac; rubber varnish. -lösung, *f.* gum solution; rubber solution. -packung, *f.* rubber packing. -papier, *n.* gummed paper. -pfropf, -pfropfen, *m.* rubber stopper or plug. -platte, *f.* rubber plate. -ring, *m.* rubber ring. -rohr, *n.*, -röhre, *f.* rubber tube. -sauger, *m.* rubber suction bulb. -säure, *f.* gummic acid (arabic acid). -scheibe, *f.* rubber disk. -schicht, *f.* layer of rubber. -schlauch, *m.* rubber tube, rubber tubing, rubber hose. -schleim, *m.* mucilage (made from gum), (*Pharm.*) mucilage of acacia. -sirup, *m.* (*Pharm.*) sirup of acacia. -stein, *m.* hyalite. -stempel, *m.* rubber stamp. -stoff, *m.* gum substance; gummy matter; rubber cloth; (*Min.*) gummite. -stopfen, -stöpsel, *m.* rubber stopper. -tragant, *m.* gum tragacanth. -verbindung, *f.* rubber connection. -waren, *f.pl.* rubber goods. -wasser, *n.* gum water. -wischer, *m.* rubber wiper, rubber policeman. -zahl, *f.* (*Paper*) gum number. -zucker, *m.* arabinose.

gummös, *a.* gummous, gummy.

Gundelrebe, *f.*, Gundermann, *m.* ground ivy (*Glecoma hederacea*).

Gunst, *f.* favor, kindness.—zu Gunsten or zu gunsten, in favor (of), for the benefit (of).

günstig, *a.* favorable; convenient; propitious.

Gur, *f.* guhr (pulverulent mineral deposit); specif., kieselguhr; fermentation.

Guranuss, *f.* guru nut, cola nut.

Gurdynamit, *m.* & *n.* guhr dynamite.

Gurgel, *f.* throat, gullet. -ader, *f.* jugular vein. -mittel, *n.* gargle.

gurgeln, *v.t.* & *i.* gargle; gurgle.

Gurgelwasser, *n.* (*Pharm.*) gargle.

Gurke, *f.* cucumber.

Gurkenkraut, *n.* borage.

Gurt, *m.* girdle, belt, girth.

Gürtel, *m.* belt, girdle, band; zone.

gürten, *v.t.* gird, girdle.

Gurtförderer, *m.* belt conveyor.

Guss, *m.* casting, founding; cast iron; gate (of a mold); gutter; pouring; jet (of liquid); font (of type); (*Brewing*) mash liquor, mash water.

gussbar, *a.* =giessbar.

Guss-beton, *m.* cast (or poured) concrete. -blase, *f.* flaw in a casting, blowhole. -blei, *n.* cast lead. -block, *m.* ingot. -bruch, *m.* broken castings, cast-metal scrap.

Gusseisen, *n.* cast iron; pig iron. -rohr, *n.* -röhre, *f.* cast-iron pipe.

gusseisern, *a.* cast-iron.

Guss-fehler, *m.* casting flaw. -flasche, *f.* molding flask. -form, *f.* (casting) mold; (*Soap*) frame. -kasten, *m.* casting box, molding box. -messing, *n.* cast brass. -metall, *n.* cast metal. -mörtel, *m.* concrete, cement. -naht, *f.* (*Founding*) burr, seam. -pfanne, *f.* (*Metal.*) ladle. -rohr, *n.*, -röhre, *f.* cast-iron pipe. -schlicker, *m.* (*Ceram.*) casting slip. -späne, *m.pl.* cast-iron chips or borings. -stahl, *m.* cast steel. -stahltiegel, *m.* cast-steel crucible. -stein, *m.* sink; drain. -stück, *n.* cast, casting. -wachs, *n.* casting wax. -waren, *f.pl.* castings, foundry goods. -zink, *m.& n.* cast zinc.

gut, *a.* good.—*adv.* well.

Gut, *n.* good; (valuable or useful) material, possession, property, goods, ware; estate; (in combination) goods or material to be treated; as, *Farbgut*, goods to be dyed. —*pl.* Güter, goods, wares, commodities.

Gutachten, *n.* expert opinion, judgment; decision, verdict.

gutartig, *a.* good-natured; mild.

Güte, *f.* goodness, worth, quality. -grad, *m.* quality; efficiency. -messer, *m.* eudiometer.

Güter, *n.pl.* see Gut. -zug, *m.*, freight train, goods train.

Güteverhältnis, *n.* efficiency.

Gut-gewicht, *n.* fair weight; allowance. -haben, *n.* balance, credit.

gütig, *a.* good, kind, gracious.

gut-sagen, *v.i.* be responsible (for). -schliessend, *a.* (of corks, etc.) tight-fitting.

Gut-schmecker, *m.* gastronomist, epicure. -schrift, *f.* credit.

Gutti, *n.* gamboge.

gut-willig, *a.* willing, obliging; voluntary. -ziehend, *p.a.* well-drawing, with a good draft.

Gymnasium, *n.* (German) gymnasium, a classical school preparing for the universities.

Gynocard-insäure, *f.* gynocardinic acid. -säure, *f.* gynocardic acid (chaulmoogric acid).

Gyps, Gyps-. see Gips, Gips-.

# H

**h.,** *abbrev.* (hochschmelzend) high-melting; (heiss) hot; (hoch) high, great; (heilig) holy, sacred.

**H.,** *abbrev.* (Härte) hardness; (Höhe) altitude; (Haben) credit; (Hoheit) Highness.

**Haar,** *n.* hair.

**Haar-.** capillary. **-alaun,** *m.* capillary alum.

**haarartig,** *a.* hairlike, capillary.

**Haar-balg,** *m.* hair follicle. **-beize,** *f.* depilatory.

**haardünn,** *a.* hair-thin, capillary.

**Haar-erz,** *n.* capillary ore. **-farbe,** *f.*, **-färbemittel, -färbungsmittel,** *n.* hair dye.

**haar-faserig,** *a.* filamentous. **-fein,** *a.* fine as a hair. **-förmig,** *a.* capillary, hair-shaped.

**Haargefäss,** *n.* capillary vessel.

**haarig,** *a.* hairy; pilose.

**Haar-kies,** *m.* capillary pyrites, millerite. **-kraft,** *f.* capillarity. **-kupfer,** *n.* capillary copper.

**Haarlemer Öl.** (*Pharm.*) Dutch drops.

**haarlos,** *a.* hairless, bald; (of fabrics) napless.

**Haar-nadel,** *f.* hairpin. **-riss,** *m.* hair crack, craze.

**haarrissig,** *a.* crazed. — **werden,** craze.

**Haar-rohr, -röhrchen,** *n.*, **-röhre,** *f.* capillary tube. **-röhrenanziehung,** *f.* capillary attraction. **-säckchen,** *n.* hair follicle. **-salbe,** *f.* pomade, pomatum. **-salz,** *n.* hair salt (fibrous form of alunogen, halotrichite or epsomite).

**haarscharf,** *a.* very sharp; extremely precise or accurate.

**Haar-schärfe,** *f.* extreme precision. **-schwefel,** *m.* capillary sulfur. **-schweif,** *m.* coma (of a comet). **-seite,** *f.* hair side, grain side. **-silber,** *n.* capillary silver. **-strang,** *m.* (*Bot. & Pharm.*) peucedanum; hair cord. **-vertilgungsmittel,** *n.* depilatory. **-vitriol,** *m.* capillary epsomite. **-waschmittel, -wasser,** *n.* hair wash.

**Habe,** *f.* property.

**haben,** *v.t.* have.

**Haben,** *n.* (*Com.*) credit; creditor.

**Haberverfahren,** *n.* Haber process.

**Habicht,** *m.* hawk.

**Habichtskraut,** *n.* hawkweed (*Hieracium*).

**Habilitationsschrift,** *f.* inaugural dissertation.

**habituell,** *a.* habitual, chronic.

**Habitus,** *m.* habit.

**Habsucht,** *f.* avidity.

**Hacke,** *f.* hoe; mattock; pick.

**hacken,** *v.t.* hack, chop; mince.

**Hacken,** *m.* heel.

**Hack-fleisch,** *m.* chopped meat, minced meat. **-früchte,** *f. pl.* potatoes, turnips and cabbage. **-salz,** *n.* salt for minced meat.

**Häcksel,** *m.& n.* chopped straw.

**Hackspan,** *m.* chip.

**Hader,** *m.* rag.

**haderig, hadrig,** *a.* (of iron) short.

**Hadernlade,** *f.* rag chest.

**Hafen,** *m.* pot; harbor, port. **-ofen,** *m.* (*Glass*) pot furnace.

**Hafer,** *m.* oats. **-mehl,** *n.* oatmeal. **-schleim,** *m.* oat gruel. **-stärke,** *f.* oat starch.

**Hafner,** *m.* potter. **-erz,** *n.* potter's ore (fine galena).

**-haft.** partaking of the nature of, -ish, -ous, -ose, -y, -ly, -ful; as, *schmerzhaft*, painful, grievous.

**haftbar,** *a.* liable, responsible.

**Haftdruck,** *m.* solution pressure.

**haften,** *v.i.* adhere, cling, stick; be liable.

**Haften,** *n.* adhering, adhesion, etc. (see haften). **-bleiben,** *n.* adherence, adhesion.

**Haft-festigkeit,** *f.* adhesiveness; tenacity; firmness of attachment. **-fläche,** *f.* surface of adhesion. **-intensität,** *f.* intensity of adhesion; solution pressure; affinity. **-mittel,** *n.* adhesive. **-pflicht,** *f.* liability.

**Haftung,** *f.* adhesion; liability.

**Haftvermögen,** *n.* adhesive power.

**Hag,** *m.* hedge; clamp, pile (of tiles or bricks); bush; grove; meadow.

**Hage-buche,** *f.* hornbeam. **-butte,** *f.* hip (rosebush pseudocarp). **-dorn,** *m.* hawthorn.

**Hagel,** *m.* hail; small shot.

**hageln,** *v.i.* hail.

**hager,** *a.* haggard, thin; (of soils) lean, unproductive.

**Hahn,** *m.* cock, stopcock; tap, faucet; cock, rooster.

**Hahnenfuss,** *m.* lit., cock's foot; (*Ceram.*) cockspur; (*Bot.*) crowfoot, ranunculus.

**Hahnstopfen,** *n.* cock stopper.

**Hai, Haifisch,** *m.* shark.

**Haifisch-leder,** *n.* shark leather. **-tran,** *m.* shark-liver oil.

**Hain,** *m.* grove, wood.

**Häkchen,** *n.* little hook, clasp.

**Häkelgarn,** *n.* crochet thread.

**häkeln,** *v.t.* crochet; hook.

**Haken,** *m.* hook; clasp, catch; (*Puddling*) rabble.

**hakenförmig,** *a.* hooked, unciform.

**Hakenprobe,** *f.* (*Sugar*) hook test.

**hakig,** *a.* hooked; hackly (fracture).

**halb,** *a.& adv.* half.

**Halb-, halb-.** half, semi-, hemi-, demi-, sub-.

**Halb-acetal,** *n.* hemiacetal. **-alaun,** *m.* impure alum. **-aldehyd,** *m.& n.* semialdehyde. **-anthrazit,** *m.* semianthracite. **-art,** *f.* subspecies. **-bleiche,** *f.* half bleach; cream color. **-chlorschwefel,** *m.* sulfur subchloride (monochloride).

**halbcylindrisch,** *a.* semicylindrical.

**Halbdunkel,** *n.* twilight.

**halbdurchlässig,** *a.* semipermeable.

**Halbdurchmesser,** *m.* semidiameter, radius.

**halbdurchsichtig,** *a.* semitransparent.

**Halb-durchsichtigkeit,** *f.* semitransparency. **-edelstein,** *m.* semiprecious stone.

**halbeirund,** *a.* semioval.

**halber, halben,** *prep.* (following its object). in behalf of, on account of.

**Halb-erzeugnis, -fabrikat,** *n.* intermediate product, semi-manufacture.

**halb-fest,** *a.* semisolid. **-fett,** *a.* (*Coal*) semibituminous. **-flächig,** *a.* (*Cryst.*) hemihedral.

**Halb-flächner,** *m.* hemihedron. **-flügler,** *m.pl.* Hemiptera.

**halbflüssig,** *a.* semiliquid, semifluid.

**Halbfranzband,** *m.* half-calf binding; volume bound in half calf.

**halb-geleimt,** *p.a.* half-sized. **-gesättigt,** *a.* half-saturated. **-gesäuert,** *a.* semiacidified.

**Halb-gold,** *n.* imitation gold (as similor). **-gut,** *n.* (*Metal.*) tin containing much lead. **-harz,** *n.* crude resin; resinoid. **-heit,** *f.* imperfection; indecision. **-holländer,** *m.* (*Paper*) washing engine.

**halbieren,** *v.t.* halve; bisect; mottle.

**Halbinsel,** *f.* peninsula.

**halbjährlich,** *a.* semiannual.

**Halb-kochen,** *n.* partial boiling, parboiling. **-koks,** *m.* semicoke. **-kolloid,** *n.* semicolloid. **-kreis,** *m.* semicircle.

**halbkreis-förmig, -rund,** *a.* semicircular.

**halbkristallisiert,** *a.* semicrystalline.

**Halbkugel,** *f.* hemisphere.

**halbkugelig,** *a.* hemispherical.

**Halb-lederband,** *m.* half-leather binding (or a volume so bound). **-leinen,** *n.,* **-leinwand,** *f.* half-linen; half-cloth (binding). **-leiter,** *m.* (*Elec.*) semiconductor. **-literkolben,** *m.* half-liter flask. **-mahlen,** *n.* breaking in. **-mattglasur,** *f.* (*Ceram.*) semi-mat glaze. **-messer,** *m.* radius. **-metall,** *n.* semimetal. **-metallglanz,** *m.* submetallic luster.

**halbmetallisch,** *a.* semimetallic.

**Halbmikro-.** semimicro-.

**halbmonatlich,** *a.* semimonthly.

**Halb-mond,** *m.* half-moon, crescent. **-nitril,** *n.* seminitrile.

**halbnormal,** *a.* half-normal, seminormal.

**Halb-opal,** *m.* semiopal. **-orthooxalsäure,** *f.* semiortho-oxalic acid. **-porzellan,** *n.* semiporcelain. **-prisma,** *n.* (*Cryst.*) hemiprism.

**halbracemisch,** *a.* semiracemic.

**Halbreduktion,** *f.* semireduction, partial reduction.

**halb-rund,** *a.* half-round, semicircular; hemispherical. **-sauer,** *a.* semiacid.

**Halb-schatten,** *m.* half-shade, half-shadow. **-schwefeleisen,** *n.* iron hemisulfide (supposedly $Fe_2S$). **-schwefelkupfer,** *n.* cuprous sulfide. **-seide,** *f.* half-silk.

**halb-seitig,** *a.* relating to one side or half, unilateral; half-page. **-selbsttätig,** *a.* semiautomatic.

**Halbstahl,** *m.* semisteel.

**Halbstoff,** *m.* (*Paper*) half stuff. **-erzeugung,** *f.* half-stuff production. **-holländer,** *m.* breaker. **-werk,** *n.* half-stuff mill.

**halb-tief,** *a.* of half the depth, shallow. **-trocken,** *a.* half-dry, semi-dry.

**Halbvitriolblei,** *n.* lanarkite ($Pb_2SO_5$).

**halbwalzig,** *a.* hemicylindrical.

**Halbwassergas,** *n.* semiwater gas.

**halbweich,** *a.* half-soft, partly soft.

**Halb-wertdruck,** *m.* half-value pressure. **-wertsbreite,** *f.* width at half of maximum intensity (of a spectral line or band). **-wertzeit,** *f.* half-life period.

**halbzahlig,** *a.* half-integral.

**Halb-zeit,** *f.* half-life period. **-zeitkonstante,** *f.* half-life constant. **-zellstoff,** *n.* hemicellulose. **-zeug,** *n.* half-finished product; (*Paper*) half stuff. **-zinn,** *n.* = Halbgut. **-zirkel,** *m.* semicircle.

**Halde,** *f.* heap (of refuse), dump.

**Halden-erz,** *n.* waste-heap ore. **-schlacke,** *f.* discarded slag.

**half,** *pret.* of helfen.

**Halfa,** *f.* esparto.

**Hälfte,** *f.* half.

**Hälftflächner,** *m.* (*Cryst.*) hemihedron.

**Hall,** *m.* sound, peal; resonance.

**Halle,** *f.* hall; porch.

**hallen,** *v.i.* sound, resound.

**Halm,** *m.* blade, stalk; straw. **-früchte,** *f.pl.* cereals.

**Halochemie,** *f.* chemistry of salts, halochemistry.

**halochemisch,** *a.* halochemical.

**Halogen-.** halogen, halo- (as in *Halogenbenzoesäure, Halogenpyridin,* etc.), halide of (as in *Halogensilber,* silver halide). **-alkyl,** *n.* alkyl halide. **-aryl,** *n.* aryl halide.

**Halogenid,** *n.* halide.

**halogenierbar,** *a.* capable of being halogenated.

**halogenieren,** *v.t.* halogenate, halogenize.

**Halogenierung,** *f.* halogenation.

**Halogen-kohlenstoff,** *m.* carbon halide. **-metall,** *n.* metallic halide. **-quecksilber,** *n.* mercury halide. **-säure,** *f.* halogen acid. **-schwefel,** *m.* sulfur halide. **-silber,** *n.* silver halide.

**halogensubstituiert,** *p.a.* halogen-substituted or, better, halo- (as, *halogensubstituierte Chinone,* haloquinones).

**Halogen-überträger,** *m.* halogen carrier. **-ür,** *n.* (ous) halide. *Cf.* Chlorür. **-verbindung,** *f.* halogen compound.

**Halogenwasserstoff,** *m.* hydrogen halide. **-säure,** *f.* halogen hydracid, hydrohalic acid (general name for hydrochloric acid, hydrobromic acid, etc.). **-verbindung,** *f.* hydrogen halide.

**Haloid, -salz,** *n.* halide, haloid, haloid salt. **-wasserstoff,** *m.* hydrogen halide.

**Hals,** *m.* neck; throat; stem (of a thermometer, etc.).

**Hals-.** (*Anat.*) cervical. **-band,** *n.* neck ribbon; necklace; collar. **-bein,** *n.* collar bone. **-bräune,** *f.* throat affection (applied to various diseases, as diphtheria, croup, etc.). **-mandel,** *f.* tonsil. **-röhre,** *f.* trachea.

**Halt,** *m.* hold, holding; halt, stop; firmness; yield.— **— machen,** stop, halt.

**hält,** *pr. 3 sing.* of halten.

**haltbar,** *a.* stable; lasting, durable; fast, permanent (colors).

**Haltbar-keit,** *f.* stability, etc. (see haltbar); keeping quality. **-machen,** *n.* making stable, etc. (see haltbar); stabilizing; preserving, conserving.

**halten,** *v.t.* hold; keep; consider; take (a journal); give (a talk).—*v.r.* hold on, remain; keep, last.—*v.i.* hold, keep, last; stop, halt.

**Haltepunkt,** *m.* halting point, (in a curve) break.

**Halter,** *m.* holder; support; handle; hold; keeper.

**Hälter,** *m.* holder; reservoir.

**Halterarm,** *m.* supporting arm, support.

**Haltezeit,** *f.* halt, pause.

**haltig, hältig,** *a.* rich (ore); (as a suffix) containing, holding, yielding, bearing, **-ferous,** as *zinnhaltig,* containing tin, stanniferous.

**haltlos,** *a.* unstable, unsteady, infirm, loose; (of paper) tender.

**Haltung,** *f.* holding, etc. (see halten); attitude, bearing, state, position; harmony; principle.

**Häm-.** hem-, haem-. **-alaun,** *m.* (*Micros.*) hemalum (a hematoxylin-alum stain).

**Hämatin,** *n.* hematin, haematin.

**Hämatit,** *m.* hematite. **-eisen,** *n.* hematite iron.

**Hamburgerweiss,** *n.* Hamburg white.

**Hämin,** *n.* hemin, haemin.

**Hammatsch.** (*Brewing*) sodium bicarbonate.

**Hammel,** *m.* wether, (male) sheep; mutton. **-fett,** *n.* mutton fat. **-fleisch,** *n.* mutton. **-talg,** *m.* mutton tallow.

**hämmerbar,** *a.* malleable.

**Hämmerbarkeit,** *f.* malleability.

**Hämmereisen,** *n.* wrought iron.

**hammergar,** *a.* (*Copper*) tough-pitch, tough.

**hämmern,** *v.t.* hammer, forge.

**Hammer-schlacke,** *f.* hammer scale. **-schlag,** *m.* hammer scale; hammer blow.

**Hämo-chininsäure,** *f.* hemoquinic acid. **-lyse,** *f.* hemolysis, hemolysis.

**hämolytisch,** *a.* hemolytic, haemolytic.

**Hämopyrrol,** *n.* hemopyrrole.

**Hand-arbeit,** *f.* hand work; manual labor; handiwork. **-ausgabe,** *f.* pocket edition. **-betrieb,** *m.* hand drive or operation. **-buch,** *n.* manual, handbook, compendium.

**Handel,** *m.* commerce, trade; business, affair; quarrel.

**handeln,** *v.i.* act; trade.— **— um,** treat, be about.—**es handelt sich um. . . ,** the question is as to . . .

**Handels-.** commercial. **-amt,** *n.* board of trade. **-analyse,** *f.* commercial analysis. **-artikel,** *m.* article of commerce, commodity. **-benzol,** *n.* commercial benzene, benzol. **-betrieb,** *m.* traffic. **-chemiker,** *m.* commercial chemist, (commercial) analytical chemist. **-eisen,** *n.* merchant iron.

**handelsgängig,** *a.* of commerce, commercial.

**Handels-gesellschaft,** *f.* (trading) company. **-gewicht,** *n.* commercial weight. **-harz,** *n.* commercial rosin (or resin). **-harzleim,** *m.* commercial rosin size. **-kautschuk,** *m.* commercial rubber. **-laboratorium,** *n.* commercial laboratory. **-leute,** *pl.* tradespeople, tradesmen. **-mann,** *m.* tradesman. **-öl,** *n.* commercial oil. **-silber,** *n.* commercial silver (containing impurities). **-sorte,** *f.* commercial form or variety.

**handelsüblich,** *a.* customary in commerce or trade, commercial.

**Handels-verein,** *m.* commercial association, commercial union. **-ware,** *f.* commercial article, article of commerce, merchandise. **-wert,** *m.* commercial value. **-zeichen,** *n.* trademark. **-zink,** *n.* commercial zinc, spelter.

**Hand-fertigkeit,** *f.* manual skill or dexterity. **-gebläse,** *n.* hand blowpipe. **-gebrauch,** *m.* daily use. **-gelenk,** *n.* wrist, wrist joint. **-granate,** *f.* hand grenade.

**handgreiflich,** *a.* obvious, palpable, downright.

**Hand-griff,** *m.* handle; grasp; knack, trick; manipulation. **-habe,** *f.* handle; hold, grip; means.

**handhaben,** *v.t.* handle; manipulate; operate.

**Handhabung,** *f.* handling; manipulation; operation.

**handheiss,** *a.* of the temperature of the hand, lukewarm.

**Händler,** *m.* dealer, retailer.

**Handlexikon,** *n.* abridged lexicon.

**handlich,** *a.* handy, manageable.

**Handlichkeit,** *f.* handiness.

**Handlung,** *f.* trade, commerce; (commercial) establishment; action; plot.

**handpuddeln,** *v.t.* puddle by hand.

**Hand-reibe,** *f.* hand grater. **-scheidung,** *f.* separation (or sorting) by hand. **-schmierung,** *f.* hand lubrication. **-schrift,** *f.* handwriting; manuscript. **-schuh,** *m.* glove. **-strich,** *m.* (*Ceram.*) hand molding. **-stück,** *n.* specimen (of ore or the like, of a size conveniently held in the hand), hand specimen. **-tuch,** *n.* towel. **-verkauf,** *m.* retail. **-voll,** *f.* handful. **-wa(a)ge,** *f.* hand balance. **-wärme,** *f.* heat (or warmth) of the hand. **-werk,** *n.* handicraft, trade; guild. **-werker,** *m.* mechanic, artisan, workman.

**handwerksmässig,** *a.* workmanlike; mechanical.

**Hand-werkszeug,** *n.* tools, instruments. **-wörterbuch,** *n.* abridged dictionary. **-wurzel,** *f.* wrist; carpus; wrist joint.

**Hanf,** *m.* hemp.

**hanfartig,** *a.* hemplike, hempen.

**Hanf-faden,** *m.* hemp fiber; hemp twine. **-korn,** *n.* hemp seed.

**hanfkorngross,** *a.* of the size of hempseed.

**Hanf-nessel,** *f.,* **-nesselkraut,** *n.,* hemp nettle (*Galeopsis*). **-öl,** *n.* hemp (seed) oil. **-samen,** *n.,* **-saat,** *f.* hempseed. **-säure,** *f.* linoleic acid. **-seil,** *n.* hemp rope, hemp cord.

**Hang,** *m.* slope, declivity; inclination, propensity, bent.

**Hänge,** *f.* place where things are hung to dry, drying house, loft; (*Dyeing*) ager.

**Hänge-.** hanging, suspension, suspended. **-farbe,** *f.* (*Leather*) suspender.

**hängen, hangen,** *v.i.* hang; cling, adhere; (in a furnace) scaffold.—**hängend, hangend,** *p.a.* hanging, suspended, pendent.

**hängen,** *v.t.* hang, suspend; attach.

**Hängenbleiben,** *n.* (in a furnace) scaffolding.

**Hängetropfen,** *m.* hanging drop.

**Hansel,** *m.* (*Brewing*) return wort.

**Hantel,** *f.* dumb-bell.

**hantieren,** *v.t.* work, handle, manipulate; manage.—*v.i.* be busy, be occupied.

**Hantierung,** *f.* manipulation, etc. (see hantieren); occupation.

**Härchen,** *n.* little hair; cilium.

**Harfe,** *f.* harp.

**Häring,** *m.* = Hering.

**Harke,** *f.* rake.

**harken,** *v.t.* rake.

**Harn,** *m.* urine. **-absatz,** *m.* urinary sediment. **-absonderung,** *f.* urinary secretion.

**harnabtreibend,** *a.* diuretic.

**Harnanalyse,** *f.* urine analysis, urinalysis.

**harnartig,** *a.* urinous, urinose.

**Harn-benzoesäure,** *f.* hippuric acid. **-blase,** *f.* (urinary) bladder.

**Harnblasen-.** (*Anat.*) vesical, vesico-.

**Harnblau,** *n.* (*Biochem.*) indican.

**harnen,** *v.i.* urinate.

**harnfähig,** *a.* (*Biochem.*) capable of passage into the urine.

**Harn-farbstoff,** *m.* urinary pigment. **-geist,** *m.* ammonium chloride (old name).

**harnig,** *a.* uric; urinous, urinose.

**Harn-kolloid,** *n.* urinary colloid. **-kraut,** *n.* a diuretic plant, specif. (1) dyer's rocket (*Reseda luteola*), (2) *Herniaria* species. **-lehre,** *f.* urinology. **-leiter,** *m.* ureter; catheter. **-messer,** *m.* urinometer. **-mittel,** *n.* diuretic. **-niederschlag,** *m.* urinary deposit. **-oxyd,** *n.* xanthic oxide (xanthine). **-phosphor,** *m.* urinary phosphorus. **-probe,** *f.* test for urine; sample of urine. **-prüfung,** *f.* testing of urine, urine analysis. **-röhre,** *f.* urethra.

**Harnröhren-.** urethral, urethro-.

**Harn-rosa,** *f.* urorosein. **-ruhr,** *f.* diabetes. **-salz,** *n.* microcosmic salt; (any) salt found in urine. **-sand,** *m.* (urinary) gravel. **-satz,** *m.* urinary deposit.

**harnsauer,** *a.* of or combined with uric acid, urate of.

**Harn-säure,** *f.* uric acid. **-säurestein,** *m.* uric-acid calculus. **-stein,** *m.* urinary calculus. **-stoff,** *m.* urea.

**harntreibend,** *p.a.* diuretic.

**Harn-untersuchung,** *f.* investigation of urine, urinalysis. **-wa(a)ge,** *f.* urinometer. **-zucker,** *m.* sugar in urine.

**harren,** *v.i.* wait, stay.

**hart,** *a.* hard; hardy; (*Mining*) refractory. —*adv.* hardly, hard.— **an,** close by.

**härtbar,** *a.* capable of being hardened.

**Hart-blei,** *n.* hard lead (applied to crude lead hardened by antimony and other impurities, and to an alloy of lead and antimony). **-borst,** *m.,* **-borste,** *f.* (*Steel*) crack formed during hardening. **-brandstein,** *m.* hard-burned brick. **-braunstein,** *m.* braunite.

**Härte,** *f.* hardness; hardening; tempering; hardiness. **-bad,** *n.* (*Metal.*) tempering bath. -bestimmung, f. determination of hardness. -bildner, m. (Water) a salt causing hardness. -flüssigkeit, f. tempering liquid. -grad, m. degree of hardness; temper (of steel).

Harteisen, n. hard iron.

Härte-messer, m. hardness gage. -messung, f. measurement of hardness. -mittel, n. hardening or tempering agent.

härten, v.t. harden; —v.i.& r. harden.

Härte-ofen, m. tempering furnace, hardening furnace. -probe, f. hardness test. -prüfung, f. hardness test(ing). -pulver, n. (Metal.) cementing powder. -riss, m. = Hartborst. -skala, f. scale of hardness. -tiefe, f. depth of hardening. -trog, m. hardening trough. -verfahren, n. hardening (or tempering) process. -wasser, n. hardening water, tempering water.

Hart-feuerporzellan, n. hard porcelain. -filter, m. hard filter, hardened filter. -floss, n. spiegeleisen. -flügler, m.pl. Coleoptera.

hart-gebrannt, a. hard-burned. -gefroren, a. hard-frozen. -gelötet, p.p. of hartlöten. -gesotten, a. hard-boiled. -giessen, v.t. chill-cast.

Hart-glas, n. hard glass. -glasbecher, m. hard-glass beaker. -gummi, n. hard rubber. -guss, m. chill casting; chilled casting. -harz, n. hard resin, solid resin. -heu, n. St.-John's-wort. -holz, n. hard wood, hardwood. -kautschuk, m. & n. hard rubber. -kies, m., -kobalterz, n., -kobaltkies, m. skutterudite. -kupfer, n. hard copper.

hartleibig, a. costive.

Härtling, m. (Metal.) hard slag.

Hartlot, n. hard solder.

hartlöten, v.t. hard-solder, braze.

Hart-machen, n. hardening. -manganerz, n. psilomelane; braunite. -metall, n. hard metal, hard pewter. -pech, n. hard pitch, dry pitch. -porzellan, n. hard porcelain. -riegel, m. privet (Ligustrum vulgare); cornel; dogwood. -salz, n. hard salt (an impure sylvite). -spat, m. andalusite. -spiritus, m. solid alcohol. -stahl, m. hard steel. -steingut, n. (Ceram.) hard white ware, feldspathic ware. -trockenöl, n. hard-drying oil.

Härtung, f. hardening.

Härtungs-kohle, f. hardening carbon. -mittel, n. hardening agent. -verfahren, n. hardening process.

Hart-vernickelung, f. hard nickel plating. -waren, f.pl. hardware. -werden, n. hardening. -zerkleinerung, f. crushing of hard material. -zinn, n. (hard) pewter.

Harz, n. resin; rosin.

harz-ähnlich, -artig, a. resinlike, resinous, rosiny.

Harz-alkohol, m. resin alcohol. -baum, m. pitch tree (applied to various conifers). -cerat, n. (Pharm.) rosin cerate. -elektrizität, f. resinous (negative) electricity.

harzen, v.i. be resinous or sticky; gather resin.—v.t. resin; extract resin from.

Harz-essenz, f. rosin essence. -fichte, f. pitch pine. -firnis, m. resin varnish. -fleck, m. (Paper) resin (or rosin) spot. -fluss, m. resinous exudation, oleoresin.

harz-förmig, a. resiniform, resinous. -frei, a. free from resin (or rosin).

Harz-galle, f. resin deposit (in wood). -gas, n. resin gas.

harzgebend, p.a. yielding resin, resiniferous.

Harz-gehalt, m. resin (or rosin) content. -geist, m. rosin spirit, pinolin. -glanz, m. resinous luster.

harzhaltig, a. containing resin, resiniferous.

harzig, harzicht, a. resinous, resiny.— machen, resinify.

Harz-karbollösung, f. (Paper) solution of rosin in carbolic acid. -kitt, m. resinous cement. -kohle, f. bituminous coal. -lack, m. resin lake; resin varnish. -leim, m. (Paper) rosin size. -masse, f. resinous mass or composition. -milch, f. a suspension of resin or rosin. -naphta, f. resin oil. -öl, n. rosin oil. -pech, n. resinous pitch, rosin.

harzreich, a. rich in resin or rosin.

Harz-röhre, f. resin duct. -saft, m. resinous juice. -salbe, f. (Pharm.) rosin cerate. -salz, n. resinate.

harzsauer, a. of or combined with a resinic acid, resinate of.

Harz-säure, f. resin acid, resinic acid. -seife, f. resin soap; rosin soap. -spiritus, m. rosin spirit. -spur, f. trace of resin or rosin. -stippe, f. (Paper) rosin speck, rosin spot. -stoff, m. resinous substance. -talgseife, f. tallow-rosin soap. -tanne, f. pitch fir. -teer, m. resinous tar. -zahl, f. resin number; rosin number. -zement, m. resinous cement.

haschen, v.t.& i. catch, seize.

haschieren, v.t. hatch.

Haschisch, n. hashish.

Hase, m. hare; coward.

Hasel, f. hazel; dace. -nuss, f. hazelnut. -wurz, f. asarum, asarabacca.

Hasen-klee, m. rabbit-foot clover, hare's-foot trefoil. -kohl, m. wood sorrel. -öhrlein, n. hare's-ear (Bupleurum). -schwanz, m. hare's-tail grass.

Haspe, Häspe, f. hasp, staple; clamp; cramp.

Haspel, m. reel; spool; windlass.

haspeln, v.t. reel, wind.

**Hass,** *m.* hate, hatred.

**hassen,** *v.t.* hate.

**Hast,** *f.* haste, hurry.

**hastig,** *a.* hasty.

**hat,** *pr. 3 sing.* of haben.

**hatte,** *pret.* of haben.

**Hau,** *m.* cut, cutting, hewing.

**Haube,** *f.* hood, cap, bonnet; dome.

**Haubenlerche,** *f.* crested lark; (*Ceram.*) cone protector.

**Haubitze,** *f.* (*Mil.*) howitzer.

**Haubitzzünder,** *m.* howitzer fuse.

**Hauch,** *m.* breath, breathing; condensed moisture; tinge.

**hauchen,** *v.t.& i.* breathe.

**Haue,** *f.* hoe; mattock; pick.

**hauen,** *v.t.* hew, chop; cut; strike (with a stick or the like).

**Hauer,** *m.* hewer, cutter; pickman.

**Häufchen,** *n.* little heap; little mass, clump.

**Haufe, Haufen,** *m.* heap; pile; great amount or number, mass; (*Brewing*) couch, piece, floor, batch; (*Biol.*) agglomeration, clump, cluster.

**häufen,** *v.t.* heap; pile; accumulate, amass. —*v.r.* increase.

**Haufen-führen,** *n.* (*Brewing*) couching, flooring. **-röstung,** *f.* (*Metal.*) heap roasting. **-verkohlung,** *f.* charcoal burning in long rectangular piles.

**häufig,** *a.* frequent; numerous; abundant.— *adv.* frequently, often; abundantly.

**Häufigkeit,** *f.* frequency; abundance.

**Häufung,** *f.* heaping, etc. (see häufen); congestion.

**Haufwerk,** *n.* aggregate; run of mine, mine run.

**Hauhechel,** *f.* rest-harrow (*Ononis*).

**Haupt,** *n.* head; chief.

**Haupt-.** principal, chief, main, primary; cephalic. **-achse,** *f.* principal axis. **-agens,** *n.* principal agent. **-anteil,** *m.* chief or principal constituent; main or principal portion. **-bedingung,** *f.* chief condition. **-bestandteil,** *m.* chief constituent. **-bindung,** *f.* principal union or bond, linkage of the first order. **-brennpunkt,** *m.* principal focus. **-brennweite,** *f.* principal focal distance (or length). **-erzeugnis,** *n.* principal product. **-farbe,** *f.* primary color; principal color. **-form,** *f.* chief or principal form; master mold. **-gärung,** *f.* principal or primary fermentation. **-gesetz,** *n.* fundamental law. **-kette,** *f.* principal chain. **-klasse,** *f.* principal or chief class. **-linie,** *f.* principal line. **-mann,** *m.* captain; chieftain. **-nenner,** *m.* common denominator. **-ölbad,** *n.* (*Dyeing*) white steeping. **-pflaster,** *n.* (*Pharm.*) opium plaster. **-platz,** *m.* principal place, center, seat. **-postamt,** *n.* general post-office. **-quantenzahl,** *f.* principal or total quantum number. **-quelle,** *f.* chief source. **-reaktion,** *f.* principal reaction. **-redakteur,** *m.* chief editor. **-register,** *n.* general index. **-rohr,** *n.* main tube or pipe, main.

**Hauptsache,** *f.* chief matter, main point. —**in der —,** mainly, chiefly.

**hauptsächlich,** *a.* chief, main, principal.— *adv.* chiefly, principally, especially.

**Haupt-satz,** *m.* fundamental principle or law; (*Math.*) axiom. **-schlüssel,** *m.* master key. **-schwingung,** *f.* principal vibration. **-serie,** *f.* principal series. **-sicherung,** *f.* (*Elec.*) main fuse, main cutout. **-spule, -spirale,** *f.* primary coil. **-stadt,** *f.* metropolis, capital. **-strom,** *m.* (*Elec.*) primary current. **-stück,** *n.,* **-teil,** *m.* principal part, body. **-typus,** *m.* principal type. **-ursache,** *f.* chief cause, principal reason. **-valenz,** *f.* chief valence, principal valence, primary valence. **-vorkommen,** *n.* principal occurrence. **-würze,** *f.* (*Brewing*) first wort. **-zahl,** *f.* cardinal number. **-zug,** *m.* main or principal feature.

**Haus,** *n.* house; home; family. **-arznei,** *f.* domestic remedy. **-besitzer,** *m.* house owner, landlord. **-brand,** *m.* domestic use (of fuels).

**hausen,** *v.i.* reside; keep house; behave badly.

**Hausen,** *m.* sturgeon. **-blase,** *f.* isinglass.

**Haus-gerät,** *n.* household furniture or utensils. **-halt,** *m.* household; housekeeping. **-hälter,** *m.* housekeeper, steward; economist. **-lauch,** **-lauf,** *m.* houseleek.

**häuslich,** *a.* domestic.

**Haus-mittel,** *n.* household remedy. **-müll,** *n.* household refuse. **-schwamm,** *m.* dry rot. **-seife,** *f.* household soap, specif. common curd soap; home-made soap.

**Haustein,** *m.* ashlar.

**Haus-wanze,** *f.* bedbug. **-wurz,** *f.* houseleek.

**Haut,** *f.* skin; hide; membrane; film; crust. —**durchsichtige —,** cornea.—**harte —,** sclerotic coat.

**Haut-.** cutaneous, membranous. **-bräune,** *f.* croup.

**Häutchen,** *n.* thin skin, film, pellicle, membrane.

**häuten,** *v.t.* skin.—*v.r.* cast the skin.

**häutig,** *a.* cutaneous, membranous; skinny.

**Haut-krankheit,** *f.* skin disease. **-krebs,** *m.* cancer of the skin, epithelioma. **-lehre,** *f.* dermatology. **-leim,** *m.* glue (or size) from hides. **-pulver,** *n.* hide powder.

**hautreinigend,** *p.a.* skin-cleansing.

**Hautreiz,** *m.* skin irritant; skin irritation.

**hautreizend,** *a.* irritating to the skin.

**Haut-salbe,** *f.* sebaceous matter; skin ointment. -substanz, *f.* hide substance. -talg, *m.* sebaceous matter.

Häutung, *f.* skinning; shedding of the skin, desquamation.

H.D., *abbrev.* (Hochdruck) high pressure.

hebärztlich, *a.* obstetric.

Hebe-. lifting, raising, hoisting. -arm, *m.* lever. -baum, lever, crowbar. -daumen, *m.* cam. -eisen, *n.* crowbar.

Hebel, *m.* lever. -kraft, *f.* leverage. -wa(a)ge, *f.* lever scale, beam scale.

heben, *v.t.* lift, raise, elevate; further; remove; (*Math.*) reduce.—*v.r.* rise; go; cancel.

Hebe-pumpe, *f.* lift pump, lifting pump. -punkt, *m.* fulcrum.

Heber, *m.* siphon; pipette; syringe; lifter; lever; (*Anat.*) levator. -barometer, *m.* siphon barometer. -haarrohr, *n.* capillary siphon.

hebern, *v.t.* siphon; pipette.

Heber-pumpe, *f.* siphon pump. -rohr, *n.* siphon tube, siphon. -säuremesser, *m.* syringe hydrometer for acids.

Hebe-vorrichtung, *f.* lifting apparatus; lever. -werk, -zeug, *n.* lifting apparatus, hoisting device, gin, whim, screw jack, etc.

Hebung, *f.* lifting, etc. (see heben).

hecheln, *v.t.* comb, hatchel, heckle; criticize.

Hecht, *m.* pike (fish).

Hecke, *f.* hedge; hatch, brood.

Hede, *f.* tow.

Hederich, *m.* hedge mustard, specif. *Sisymbrium officinale.*

Heer, *n.* army; host.

Heeresgerät, *n.* army material.

Heerstrasse, *f.* highway; military road.

Hefe, *f.* yeast; (*Brewing*) barm; lees, dregs, sediment. -apparat, *m.* (*Brewing*) yeast propagator. -bier, *n.* rest beer. -ernte, *f.* crop of yeast. -gabe, *f.* (*Brewing*) quantity of yeast for a pitching. -geben, *n.* (*Brewing*) adding yeast to the wort, pitching. -mehl, *n.* yeast powder.

hefenähnlich, *a.* yeastlike, yeasty.

Hefenahrung, *f.* yeast food.

Hefenart, *f.* variety of yeast.

hefenartig, *a.* yeastlike, yeasty.

Hefenartigkeit *f.* yeastiness.

Hefen-keim, *m.* yeast germ. -pflanze, *f.* yeast plant. -pilz, *m.* = Hefepilz. -pulver, *n.* yeast powder; baking powder.

hefentrüb, *a.* yeasty, muddy (from yeast).

Hefe-nukleinsäure, *f.* nucleic acid of yeast. -pilz, *m.* yeast fungus; yeast plant. -rasse, *f.* race, breed or type of yeast. -reinzucht, *f.* pure yeast culture. -trieb, *m.* (*Brewing*) yeasty head. -wanne, *f.* yeast trough. -zelle, *f.* yeast cell.

hefig, *a.* yeasty, yeastlike; dreggy.

Hefnerkerze, *f.* Hefner candle.

Heft, *n.* part, number (of a book or periodical); stitched book; handle, hilt.

heften, *v.t.* fasten, hook, pin; stitch, sew.— geheftet, *p.a.* (of printed matter) stitched but not bound (or only in paper).

heftig, *a.* violent, severe; vigorous, lively.

Heftigkeit, *f.* violence; intensity; ardor.

Heftpflaster, *n.* adhesive plaster.

heftweise, *adv.* in parts or numbers, serially.

hegen, *v.t.* enclose; cherish; entertain, feel.

Hehl, *n.* secrecy.

hehlen, *v.t.* conceal.

hehr, *a.* sublime, grand.

Heide, *f.* heath; heather.—*m.* heathen, pagan.

heideähnlich, *a.* (*Bot.*) ericaceous.

Heidekorn, *n.* buckwheat (*Fagopyrum*).

Heidelbeere, *f.* whortleberry; bilberry.

Heidetorf, *m.* peat.

heikel, *a.* critical; delicate.

he'l, *a.* whole, sound.— — werden, heal.

Heil, *n.* welfare, safety.

Heil-. healing, curative, medical. -anstalt, *f.* hospital, sanatorium.

heilbar, *a.* curable.

Heilbrunnen, *m.* mineral spring or well.

Heilbutt, *m.* halibut.

heilen, *v.t.* heal, cure.

heilfähig, *a.* curable.

Heilformel, *f.* (*Med.*) prescription.

heilig, *a.* holy; solemn, sacred.

heiligen, *v.t.* hallow, sanctify; consecrate.

Heiligen-harz, *n.* guaiacum (resin). -holz, *n.* holy wood (a variety of lignum vitae). -stein, *m.* (*Pharm.*) lapis divinus, cuprum aluminatum.

Heilkraft, *f.* curative power.

heilkräftig, *a.* curative, healing, therapeutic.

Heil-kraut, *n.* officinal plant, medicinal herb. -kunde, -kunst, *f.* medicine, therapeutics, "healing art." -mittel, *n.* remedy, medicament. -mittellehre, *f.* pharmacology, pharmacy. -pflanze, *f.* officinal or medicinal plant.

Heilpflaster, *n.* healing plaster.—englisches —, court-plaster.

Heil-quell, *m.*, -quelle, *f.* medicinal spring or well, mineral spring or well. -salbe, *f.* healing ointment.

heilsam, *a.* wholesome.

Heil-serum, *n.* antitoxic serum. -stoff, *m.* curative, remedy. -stofflehre, *f.* pharmacology, pharmacy. -wasser, *n.* curative water, mineral water. -wert, *m.* therapeutic value. -wesen, *n.* medical affairs. -wirkung, *f.* curative effect. -wissenschaft, *f.* medical science.

Heim, *n.* home, dwelling.

Heimat, *f.* native place or country; habitat.

**heimisch,** *a.* native, domestic, indigenous.

**heimlich,** *a.* secret; private.

**Heirat,** *f.* marriage, wedding, match.

**heiraten,** *v.t.& i.* marry, wed.

**heischen,** *v.t.* demand, require.

**heiser,** *a.* hoarse, husky.

**heiss,** *a.* hot; ardent, burning; torrid. **-blütig,** *a.* warm-blooded; hot-blooded. **-brüchig,** *a.* hot-short.

**Heissdampf,** *m.* superheated steam.

**Heisse,** *f.* (*Metal.*) charge.

**heissen,** *v.t.* call; bid, order.—*v.i.* be called; mean, be.—**es heisst,** it says, they say.

**heiss-gar,** *a.* (*Metal.*) too hot; (of iron) kishy. **-grädig,** *a.* (of ores) difficultly fusible.

**Heisskühlung,** *f.* cooling by evaporation.

**heisslaufen,** *v.i.* (*Mach.*) heat, overheat.

**Heissluft-.** hot-air. **-bad,** *n.* hot-air bath. **-trichter,** *m.* hot-air funnel. **-trocknung,** *f.* hot-air drying.

**Heisswasser-behälter,** *m.* hot-water tank or container. **-heizung,** *f.* hot-water heating. **-trichter,** *m.* hot-water funnel.

**Heisswerden,** *n.* becoming hot, heating.

**-heit.** A suffix attached to adjectives to form abstract nouns (as Trocken*heit*, dryness), and to nouns to form collectives (as Menschh*eit*, mankind); -hood, -ness, -dom.

**heiter,** *a.* clear, fair; cheerful, bright.

**Heiz-.** heating, calorific. **-apparat,** *m.* heating apparatus. **-bad,** *n.* heating bath. **-band,** *n.* heating tape, heating band. **-draht,** *m.* heating wire.

**Heize,** *f.* (*Steel*) charge of pig.

**Heizeffekt,** *m.* heating effect.

**heizen,** *v.t.& i.* heat; fire, stoke.

**Heizer,** *m.* fireman, stoker.

**Heiz-faden,** *m.* heating filament. **-fähigkeit,** *f.* heating capacity. **-fläche,** *f.* heating surface. **-gas,** *n.* gas for heating, fuel gas. **-gerät,** *n.* heating apparatus. **-kammer,** *f.* heating chamber; fire box. **-kessel,** *m.* kettle, boiler, cauldron. **-körper,** *m.* heating body, heater, radiator. **-kraft,** *f.* heating power, calorific power. **-kranz,** *m.* ring burner. **-loch,** *n.* fire door, stoke hole. **-luftmotor,** *m.* hot-air motor. **-mantel,** *m.* heating jacket. **-material,** *n.* fuel. **-oberfläche,** *f.* heating surface. **-ofen,** *m.* heating furnace or oven. **-öl,** *n.* fuel oil. **-platte,** *f.* hot plate. **-raum,** *m.* heating space; fire place. **-rohr,** *n.,* **-röhre,** *f.,* heating tube; fire tube. **-röhrenkessel,** *m.* fire-tube boiler. **-schlange,** *f.* heating coil. **-schrank,** *m.* heating chamber. **-spule,** *f.* heating coil. **-stoff,** *m.* fuel. **-strom,** *m.* (*Elec.*) heating current. **-tisch,** *m.* (*Micros.*) heating stage, warm stage.

**Heizung,** *f.* heating, firing; fuel.

**Heizungs-anlage,** *f.* heating plant. **-vorrichtung,** *f.* heating apparatus or contrivance.

**Heiz-verlust,** *m.* loss of heat. **-vorgang,** *m.* heating process. **-vorrichtung,** *f.* heating apparatus, heating device.

**Heizwert,** *m.* heating value, calorific power. **-bestimmung,** *f.* determination of heating value. **-messer,** *m.* calorimeter. **-untersuchung,** *f.* calorimetric investigation.

**Heiz-wirkung,** *f.* heating effect. **-zug,** *m.* heating flue. **-zweck,** *m.* heating purpose(s).

**Held,** *m.* hero.

**helfen,** *v.i.* help, assist; be of use, avail.

**Helfer,** *m.* helper, assistant.

**Helioechtrot,** *n.* (*Dyes*) helio fast red.

**Heliumgehalt,** *m.* helium content.

**hell,** *a.* bright, brilliant; light, pale; clear, transparent, limpid; loud, shrill. **-blau,** *a.* light blue. **-bläulich,** *a.* light bluish. **-braun,** *a.* light brown.

**Helle,** *f.* brightness, luminosity; clearness, transparency; vermeil (the varnish).

**hellen,** *v.t.* make clear, clarify; treat with vermeil.

**Heller,** *m.* heller ($\frac{1}{100}$ krone); farthing.

**hellfarbig,** *a.* light-colored.

**Hellfeldbeleuchtung,** *f.* bright-field illumination.

**hell-gelb,** *a.* light yellow, bright yellow. **-grau,** *a.* light gray. **-grün,** *a.* light green.

**Helligkeit,** *f.* brightness, luminosity; clearness, transparency.

**hellrot,** *a.* bright red; light red.

**Hellrotglut,** *f.* bright red heat (about 950°).

**hellrotwarm,** *a.* bright-red-hot.

**Helltran,** *m.* a clear, light yellow cod oil.

**hellweiss,** *a.* clear white, bright white.

**Helm,** *m.* helmet; helm; (of a still) head. **-kolben,** *m.* distilling flask. **-rohr,** *n.,* **-schnabel,** *m.* (of a still) beak, nose.

**Hemd,** *n.* shirt; chemise; (of a blast furnace) shell.

**Hemellit(h)säure,** *f.* hemellitic acid.

**Hemi-eder,** *n.* hemihedron, hemihedral form or crystal. **-edrie,** *f.* hemihedrism.

**hemiedrisch,** *a.* hemihedral.

**Hemimellit(h)säure,** *f.* hemimellitic acid.

**hemitrop,** *a.* (*Cryst.*) hemitrope, twinned.

**hemmen,** *v.t.* stop, check, arrest; brake; clog.

**Hemmnis,** *n.* obstruction, check.

**Hemmung,** *f.* stopping; hindrance, restraint; check, arrest; escapement.

**Heneikosan,** *n.* heneicosane.

**Hengst,** *m.* stallion; jack; (*Brewing*) old piece.

**Henkel,** *m.* handle, lug, ear. **-schale,** *f.* casserole.

**Henne,** *f.* hen.

**hepatisch,** *a.* hepatic.

**heptacarbocyclisch,** *a.* heptacarbocyclic.

**Heptanaphten,** *n.* heptanaphthene.

**her,** *adv.* here, hither; since, ago.—**von je —,** always.

**herab,** *adv.* down, downwards. **-drücken,** *v.t.* press down, depress. **-lassen,** *v.t.* let down, lower.—*v.r.* condescend. **-liessen,** *v.i.* flow down, run down. **-mindern,** *v.t.* diminish, lessen. **-rieseln,** *v.i.* trickle down. **-setzen,** *v.t.* degrade; disparage; reduce.

**Herabsetzung,** *f.* lowering; degradation; undervaluation.

**herab-transformieren,** *v.t.* (*Elec.*) step down. **-tropfen,** *v.i.* drop down, drip down.

**Heraldik,** *f.* heraldry.

**heran,** *adv.* on, up, near, along (side). **-bilden,** *v.t.* bring up, educate. **-wachsen,** *v.t.* grow up. **-ziehen,** *v.t.* draw on; call upon; refer to, consult.—*v.i.* draw near.

**herauf,** *adv.* up, up here.

**heraus,** *adv.* out, out here, forth. **-bekommen,** *v.t.* get back; get out, elicit, solve. **-bringen,** *v.t.* get out, turn out, draw out; perplex. **-fordern,** *v.t.* challenge; provoke.

**Herausgabe,** *f.* editing, edition, editorship; publication; issue; giving up.

**herausgeben,** *v.t.* edit; publish, issue; give out or up; give back (change).

**Herausgeber,** *m.* editor; publisher.

**heraus-greifen,** *v.t.* single out, choose at random. **-kommen,** *v.i.* come out, get out, be edited, be published, result, amount. **-lösen,** *v.t.* dissolve out. **-nehmbar,** *a.* removable. **-nehmen,** *v.t.* take out, remove; choose. **-oxydieren,** *v.t.* oxidize off. **-pipettieren,** *v.t.* remove with a pipette, pipette out. **-ragen,** *v.i.* project. **-schlagen,** *v.t.* beat out; strike (sparks); make (money). **-schleudern,** *v.t.* throw out, fling out; spatter. **-spritzen,** *v.i.* spurt out, spout out. **-stellen,** *v.r.* turn out, prove. **-treiben,** *v.t.* drive out, expel. **-treten,** *v.i.* protrude; emerge; step out. **-ziehen,** *v.t.* draw out, pull out, extract.

**herb, herbe,** *a.* harsh, sharp, tart, rough, raw.

**herbei,** *adv.* here, hither, near, on. **-führen,** *v.t.* bring; bring about, cause. **-schaffen,** *v.t.* bring up, collect, procure, furnish.

**Herberge,** *f.* inn; shelter.

**herblich,** *a.* sourish, subacid; somewhat harsh.

**Herbst,** *m.* autumn. **-rose,** *f.* hollyhock. **-zeitlose,** *f.* meadow saffron.

**Herd,** *m.* hearth; center, focus, seat; (*Mining*) buddle.

**Herd-.** (*Med.*) focal, localized. **-asche,** *f.* hearth ashes. **-blei,** *n.* furnace lead. **-brücke,** *f.* fire bridge.

**Herde,** *f.* herd, flock, drove; crowd.

**Herdformerei,** *f.* open sand molding.

**Herdfrisch-arbeit,** *f.* (*Iron*) refinery process.

**-eisen,** *n.* iron treated by the refinery process.

**Herdfrischen,** *n.* (*Lead*) reduction of litharge; (*Iron*) refining in hearths, refinery process.

**Herdfrisch-prozess,** *m.* (*Iron*) refinery process. **-roheisen,** *n.* pig iron for refining. **-schlacke,** *f.* refinery cinder (or slag). **-stahl,** *m.* fined steel.

**Herd-glas,** *n.* glass that has run down from the pot into the hearth. **-guss,** *m.* open sand casting. **-ofen,** *m.* hearth furnace. **-raum,** *m.* heating chamber. **-schlacke,** *f.* (*Metal.*) hearth cinder. **-sohle,** *f.* hearth bottom, hearth bed, sole. **-stahl,** *m.* fined steel.

**herein,** *adv.* in; come in. **-ziehen,** *v.t.* draw in.

**herführen,** *v.t.* lead on; refresh (yeast); usher in.

**Hergang,** *m.* affair, circumstances.

**hergeben,** *v.t.* deliver, yield.

**hergebracht,** *p.a.* established, conventional.

**herhalten,** *v.t.* hold out; suffer, pay.

**Hering,** *m.* herring.

**Herings-öl,** *n.,* **-tran,** *m.* herring oil.

**herkommen,** *v.i.* come; come here, come on.

**Herkommen,** *n.* origin, descent; usage, custom.

**Herkunft,** *f.* origin, source; arrival.

**herleiten,** *v.t.* derive; deduce; conduct.

**Hermelin,** *n.* ermine.

**Hermesfinger,** *m.* (*Pharm.*) hermodactyl.

**hermetisch,** *a.* hermetic.—**hermetische Wissenschaft,** hermetic science, alchemy.

**hernach,** *adv.* afterwards, hereafter, then.

**Herr,** *m.* master, lord; gentleman; Mr.

**herrichten,** *v.t.* prepare, arrange, adjust; season (wood).

**herrlich,** *a.* magnificent, grand, excellent.

**Herrlichkeit,** *f.* grandeur, splendor, excellence.

**herrschen,** *v.i.* rule, reign; prevail.

**herrühren,** *v.i.* proceed, be due (to), come (from).

**hersagen,** *v.t.* recite, repeat.

**herschieben,** *v.t.* shove along, snove this way.

**Herst.,** *abbrev.* (Herstellung) production.

**herstellbar,** *a.* capable of being produced, etc. (see herstellen).

**herstellen,** *v.t.* produce, prepare, make, manufacture; restore.

**Hersteller,** *m.* producer, maker, manufacturer.

**Herstellung,** *f.* production, preparation, manufacture; restoration, recovery.

**Herstellungs-mittel,** *n.* restorative. **-verfahren,** *n.* method of production, manufacturing process.

**herüber,** *adv.* over (here).

**herum,** *adv.* round, about. **-spritzen,** *v.i. & t.* squirt (spurt, spatter, etc.) about.

**herunter,** *adv.* down (here); low. **-drücken,** *v.t.*

lower, depress. **-kommen,** *v.i.* come down; decay. **-kühlen,** *v.t.* cool down. **-lassen,** *v.t.* let down, lower; (*Brewing*) strike out (wort). **-schwemmen,** *v.t.* wash down. **-setzen,** *v.t.* reduce; undervalue. **-trocknen,** *v.t.* dry down, reduce by drying.

**hervor,** *adv.* forth, forward, out. **-bringen,** *v.t.* produce, cause; bring forth. **-gehen,** *v.i.* arise, result; go forth. **-heben,** *v.t.* make prominent, emphasize; raise. **-ragen,** *v.i.* project; stand out, be prominent. **-ragend,** *p.a.* projecting; outstanding, signal, prominent. **-rufen,** *v.t.* call forth, bring about, produce; develop (a photographic image). **-stehend,** *p.a.* prominent, projecting, standing out. **-treten,** *v.i.* step forward; stand out, be prominent. **-tun,** *v.r.* distinguish oneself.

**Herz,** *n.* heart; core, kernel, etc.

**Herz-.** heart, cardiac. **-beutel,** *m.* pericardium. **-bräune,** *f.* angina pectoris.

**Herzens-.** cardiac; of the heart; darling; inmost.

**Herzfell,** *n.* pericardium.

**herzförmig,** *a.* heart-shaped, cordate.

**Herz-gekröse,** *n.* mesocardium. **-gespann,** *n.* motherwort (*Leonurus cardiaca*). **-gift,** *n.* cardiac poison.

**herzhaft,** *a.* hearty; brave; strong (taste).

**Herzhaut,** *f.* (äussere) pericardium; (innere) endocardium.

**herzig,** *a.* hearty; dear, lovely.

**Herz-kammer,** *f.* ventricle. **-klappe,** *f.* cardiac valve. **-kurve,** *f.* (*Math.*) cardioid.

**herzlich,** *a.* heartfelt, hearty; loving.—*adv.* heartily; extremely.

**Herzog,** *m.* duke.

**Herzreiz,** *m.* cardiac stimulant or irritant.

**herzu,** *adv.* here, hither, near.

**Herz-vorhof,** *m.,* **-vorkammer,** *f.* auricle. **-wasser,** *n.* pericardial fluid.

**hessisch,** *a.* Hessian.

**Hessischpurpur,** *n.* (*Dyes*) Hessian purple.

**hetero-atomig,** *a.* heteratomic. **-cyclisch,** *a.* heterocyclic. **-gen,** *a.* heterogeneous.

**Heterogenität,** *f.* heterogeneity.

**heterolog,** *a.* heterologous.

**Hetero-polysäure,** *f.* heteropolyacid. **-ringbildung,** *f.* formation of a ring (or rings) composed of atoms of different kinds. **-zimtsäure,** *f.* heterocinnamic acid

**heterozyklisch,** *a.* heterocyclic.

**Heterozyklus,** *m.* heterocycle.

**Heu,** *n.* hay.

**heuer,** *adv.* this year, this season.

**heuern,** *v.t.* hire.

**heulen,** *v.i.* howl, yell, roar.

**Heu-pferd,** *n.* grasshopper. **-schrecke,** *f.* locust. **-schreckenbaum,** *m.* locust tree.

**heute,** *adv.* to-day.— **— abend,** this evening; **— nacht,** to-night.

**heutig,** *a.* of to-day; present; modern.

**heutzutage,** *adv.* at present, nowadays.

**Heveabaum,** *m.* hevea tree, rubber tree.

**hexacyclisch,** *a.* hexacyclic.

**Hexaeder,** *n.* hexahedron.

**hexaedrisch,** *a.* hexahedral.

**Hexa-naphten,** *n.* hexanaphthene (cyclohexane). **-vanadinsäure,** *f.* hexavanadic acid.

**hexazyklisch,** *a.* hexacyclic.

**Hexe,** *f.* witch; hag.

**Hexen-kraut,** *n.* mandragora, mandrake; enchanter's nightshade (*Circaea*). **-mehl,** **-pulver,** *n.* lycopodium, witch meal. **-meister,** *m.* sorcerer, wizard. **-schuss,** *m.* lumbago.

**Hexonsäure,** *f.* hexonic acid.

**Hg-Bogen,** *m.* mercury arc.

**Hg-Druck,** *m.* mercurial pressure.

**hieb,** *pret.* of hauen.

**Hieb,** *m.* stroke, cut, slash.

**hiebei,** *adv.* = hierbei.

**hielt,** *pret.* of halten.

**hier,** *adv.* here.

**hieran,** *adv.* hereon, hereat, at this, on this.

**hierauf,** *adv.* hereupon, upon this.

**hieraus,** *adv.* from this, hence.

**hierbei,** *adv.* hereby, herewith, herein.

**hierdurch,** *adv.* through here; by this means, hereby, thus; herewith, inclosed.

**hierfür,** *adv.* for this, for it.

**hierher,** *adv.* hither, here, now.

**hierhin,** *adv.* hither, this way.

**hiermit,** *adv.* herewith, with it.

**hiernach,** *adv.* hereafter, according to this.

**Hiersein,** *n.* presence.

**hierüber,** *adv.* over here, regarding this, on this account.

**hierum,** *adv.* hereabout, concerning this.

**hierzu,** *adv.* hereto, to this, moreover.

**hiesig,** *a.* of this place, in this place.

**hiess,** *pret.* of heissen.

**Hilfe,** *f.* help; relief; remedy.

**hilf-los,** *a.* helpless. **-reich,** *a.* helpful.

**Hilfs-.** assistant, auxiliary, subsidiary, accessory. **-arbeiter,** *m.* assistant, helper. **-beize,** *f.* (*Dyeing*) assistant. **-buch,** *n.* manual, primer, textbook. **-dünger,** *m.* auxiliary fertilizer. **-elektrode,** *f.* auxiliary electrode. **-geld,** *n.* subsidy. **-grösse,** *f.* (*Math.*) auxiliary or subsidiary quantity, auxiliary. **-kondensator,** *m.* auxiliary condenser. **-leitung,** *f.* auxiliary line (piping, conduit, circuit, etc.). **-mittel,** *n.* help, aid, expedient; (*Med.*) adjuvant. **-quelle,** *f.* resource, expedient. **-stativ,** *n.* auxiliary stand or support. **-stoff,** *m.* adjuvant substance,

auxiliary or accessory material or agent.
-strom, *m.* (*Elec.*) auxiliary current.
-teilung, *f.* auxiliary graduation. -vorrichtung, *f.* auxiliary contrivance or appliance.

Himbeere, *f.* raspberry.

Himbeer-essig, *m.* raspberry vinegar. -spat, *m.* rhodochrosite. -wein, *m.* raspberry wine.

Himmel, *m.* sky; heaven; canopy.

himmelblau, *a.* sky-blue, azure.

Himmel-blau, *n.* cerulean blue, ceruleum. -brot, *n.* manna.

Himmels-gegend, *f.* quarter of the heavens, point of the compass. -gerste, *f.,* -korn, *n.* naked barley. -körper, *m.* celestial body. -kunde, *f.* astronomy. -luft, *f.* ether. -mehl, *n.* earthy gypsum. -schlüssel, *m.* primrose. -strich, *m.* zone, climate.

himmlisch, *a.* celestial, heavenly.

hin, *adv.* there, thither, away, out, along, gone. — — und her, hither and thither, to and fro, back and forth.— — und wieder, now and again.

hinab, *adv.* down there, down.

hinauf, *adv.* up.

hinaufsetzen, *v.t.* set up, put up; superscribe. —hinaufgesetzter Index, superscript.

hinauftransformieren, *v.t.* (*Elec.*) step up.

hinaus, *adv.* out; beyond. -schieben, *v.t.* push out, expel. -waschen, *v.t.* wash out.

Hinblick, *m.* look, view, regard.

hinbringen, *v.t.* carry; pass (time).

hinderlich, *a.* obstructive, troublesome.

Hindernis, *n.* hindrance, obstacle.

Hinderung, *f.* hindrance, hindering.

hindeuten, *v.i.* point (at or to).

hindurch, *adv.* thru, thruout. -leiten, *v.t.* lead thru, conduct thru. -saugen, *v.t.* suck thru, draw thru.

hinein, *adv.* in, inside. -bringen, *v.t.* bring in, take in. -dringen, *v.i.* penetrate. -ziehen, *v.t.* draw in, drag in; incorporate; implicate; involve.

hinfahren, *v.i.* go, drive (away or along); pass away, depart.

hinfällig, *a.* decaying, perishable, weak.

hinfliessen, *v.i.* flow (in or toward).

hinfort, *adv.* henceforth.

hing, *pret.* of hängen.

hingeben, *v.t.* give up.

hingegen, *adv.* on the contrary.

hingehen, *v.i.* go, pass.—hin- und hergehen, (*Mech.*) reciprocate.

hinhalten, *v.t.* hold out, hold off.

hinken, *v.i.* limp, be lame; be imperfect.

hinlänglich, *a.* sufficient, adequate.

hinreichen, *v.i.* suffice, do.—hinreichend, *p.a.* sufficient.

hinreissen, *v.t.* tear away, carry away.

hinrichten, *v.t.* turn, direct; execute; spoil.

hinschreiben, *v.t.* write, write down.

Hinsicht, *f.* respect, regard, view.

hinsichtlich, *adv.* with regard to.

hinstellen, *v.t.* put down; put or bring forward.

hintan, *adv.* behind, after, back.

hinten, *adv.* behind, after, in the rear.

hinter, *prep.* behind, after.—*adv.* behind, back.

Hinter-. hind, posterior, back. -bliebene, *m.& f.* survivor.

hinterbringen, *v.t.* give information of.

Hinterdarm, *m.* rectum.

hintereinander, *adv.* one after another, in succession; (*Elec.*) in series.

Hinter-einanderschaltung, *f.* (*Elec.*) connection in series. -grund, *m.* background. -halt, *m.* reserve; ambush. -haupt, *n.* occiput (back part of head).

Hinterhaupts-. occipital.

hinterher, *adv.* behind, after, afterward.

Hinterkopf, *m.* occiput.

hinter-lassen, *v.t.* leave behind, leave. -legen, *v.t.* deposit, consign.

Hinterleib, *m.* hind quarters; back, dorsum.

hinterst, *a.* hindmost, last.

hinüber, *adv.* over, across, beyond. -reissen, *v.t.* carry over (as in distillation).

hinunter, *adv.* down (there), below.

hinuntersetzen, *v.t.* put down, put below.— hinuntergesetzter Index, subscript.

hinweg, *adv.* off, away.

Hinweg, *m.* way there.

Hinweis, *m.* hint; reference.

hinweisen, *v.t.* refer, direct.—*v.i.* point (to).

hinwerfen, *v.t.* throw, throw down; jot down; drop (remarks).

hinziehen, *v.t.* draw, draw along; draw out, protract; attract.—*v.i.* go.

hinzu, *adv.* besides, to it, towards, near. -addieren, *v.t.* add, add further. -fügen, *v.t.* add.

Hinzufügung, *f.* addition.

hinzu-geben, *v.t.* add. -kommen, *v.i.* come to, come toward, be added.— -kommend, *p.a.* additional, adventitious. -setzen, *v.t.* add. -träufeln, *v.t.* add by dropping.

Hinzutritt, *m.* approach; appearance; accession.

hinzu-tropfen, *v.t.* drop (on or in), add by dropping. -tun, *v.t.* add.

hippursauer, *a.* of or combined with hippuric acid, hippurate of.

Hippursäure, *f.* hippuric acid.

Hirn, *n.* brain.

Hirn-. cerebral; (of wood) crosscut. -fett, *n.* cerebrin. -holz, *n.* wood cut across the grain. -mark, *n.* medullary brain substance. -säure, *f.* cerebric acid. -schädel, *m.,* -schale, *f.* skull, cranium.

Hirsch, *m.* stag, deer. **-dorn,** *m.* buckthorn (*Rhamnus cathartica*).

Hirschhorn, *n.* hartshorn. **-geist,** *m.* spirits of hartshorn (aqua ammoniae). **-salz,** *n.* salt of hartshorn (commercial ammonium carbonate). **-schwarz,** *n.* hartshorn black (fine boneblack). **-spiritus,** *m.* = Hirschhorngeist.

Hirsch-leder, *n.* buckskin. **-zunge,** *f.* (*Bot.*) hart's-tongue.

Hirse, *f.* millet. **-erz,** *n.* oölitic hematite. **-fieber,** *n.* miliaria. **-korn,** Hirsenkorn, *n.* millet seed.

Hirsen-eisenstein, *m.,* **-erz,** *n.,* Hirsestein, *m.* oölitic hematite.

Hirt, Hirte, *m.* shepherd, herdsman.

Hirten-tasche, *f.,* **-täschchen, -täschlein,** *n.* shepherd's purse (*Bursa bursa-pastoris*).

Histochemie, *f.* histochemistry (chemistry of the tissues).

histologisch, *a.* histological.

Hitzdraht, *m.* (*Elec.*) hot wire.

Hitze, *f.* heat; hotness; ardor, passion.

hitzebeständig, *a.* stable on heating, heat-resistant; (*Biochem.*) thermostable; (of colors) fast to ironing or hot-pressing.

Hitzeeinwirkung, *f.* action or influence of heat.

hitze-empfindlich, *a.* sensitive to heat. **-fest,** *a.* resistant to heat.

Hitzegrad, *m.* degree of heat. **-messer,** *m.* pyrometer. **-messung,** *f.* pyrometry.

Hitze-messer, *m.* pyrometer. **-messung,** *f.* pyrometry.

hitzempfindlich, *a.* sensitive to heat.

hitzen, *v.t.* heat.—hitzend, *p.a.* heating, calorific.

hitzig, *a.* hot; heating; inflammatory; acute; passionate.

Hk., HK., *abbrev.* (Hefnerkerze, -en) Hefner candle(s).

Hl., *abbrev.* (Halbleder) half-leather.

Hlw., *abbrev.* (Halbleinwand) half-cloth.

hob, *pret.* of heben.

Hobel, *m.* plane.

hobeln, *v.t.* plane; smooth.

Hobelspäne, *m.pl.* shavings.

hoch, *a.* high; tall; (of colors) intense, bright, deep; great, sublime.—*adv.* highly, high, deeply, greatly. **-angeregt,** *p.a.* highly excited. **-atomig,** *a.* containing a large number of atoms.

Hoch-ätzung, *f.* relief engraving. **-bild,** *n.* relief.

hoch-bildsam, *a.* highly plastic; highly flexible. **-blau,** *a.* bright blue. **-bleichbar,** *a.* highly bleachable. **-dispers,** *a.* highly dispersed.

Hochdruck, *m.* high pressure; relief printing. **-dampf,** *m.* high-pressure steam. **-dampf-kocher,** *m.* high-pressure steam cooker.

**-kessel,** *m.* high-pressure boiler. **-rohr,** *n.,* **-röhre,** *f.* high-pressure tube or pipe.

Hoch-ebene, *f.* tableland. **-email,** *n.* embossed enamel. **-empfindlichkeit,** *f.* great sensitiveness.

hoch-erhitzt, *a.* highly heated. **-evakuiert,** *a.* highly evacuated. **-farbig,** *a.* high-colored, intensely colored. **-fein,** *a.* superfine, choice. **-feuerfest,** *a.* highly fireproof; highly refractory. **-flüchtig,** *a.* highly volatile.

Hochfrequenz-grenze, *f.* high frequency limit. **-strom,** *m.* (*Elec.*) high-frequency current.

hoch-geladen, *p.a.* (*Elec.*) highly charged. **-gespannt,** *p.a.* at high tension, highly superheated, etc. (see spannen).

Hochglanz, *m.* high polish or luster, brilliancy.

hoch-gradig, **-grädig,** *a.* in or of high degree; high-grade; (of acids, etc.) concentrated; intense. **-grün,** *a.* bright green. **-haltig,** *a.* of high content, high-grade. **-herzig,** *a.* noble-minded, high-spirited.

Hochkante, *f.* edge (of a brick or the like).

hochkantig, *a.& adv.* on edge, edgewise.

hochkonz., *abbrev.* hochkonzentriert.

hochkonzentriert, *a.* highly concentrated, high-concentration.

Hochleistungs-. (*Mach.*) high-capacity, heavy-duty.

hoch-molekular, *a.* of high molecular weight. **-mütig,** *a.* haughty, proud; arrogant, insolent.

Hochofen, *m.* blast furnace. **-anlage,** *f.* blast-furnace plant. **-betrieb,** *m.* blast-furnace operation. **-gas,** *n.* blast-furnace gas. **-guss,** *m.* blast-furnace cast iron. **-schlacke,** *f.* blast-furnace slag. **-schmelze,** *f.* blast-furnace smelting.

hoch-orange, *a.* bright or deep orange. **-phosphorhaltig,** *a.* high in phosphorus. **-plastisch,** *a.* highly plastic. **-prozentig,** *a.* high-per-cent, high-percentage. **-quantig,** *a.* of high quantum number. **-rot,** *a.* bright red. **-rund,** *a.* convex.

Hochscharlach, *m.* cochineal scarlet.

hochschmelzend, *p.a.* high-melting.

Hochschule, *f.* a German higher school (college, institution, etc.; *not* high school as used in U. S. A.).

hoch-selig, *a.* late, deceased. **-sensibel,** *a.* highly sensible (or sensitive). **-siedend,** *p.a.* high-boiling. **-siliziert,** *a.* high in silicon.

Hochspannung, *f.* high tension.

Hochspannungs-leitung, *f.* (*Elec.*) high-tention line or circuit. **-strom,** *m.* (*Elec.*) high-tension (or high-voltage) current.

höchst, *a.* highest; maximum; utmost.—*adv.* most highly, extremely.

Höchst-besetzungszahl, *f.* maximum number

of electrons in a shell. **-betrag,** m. maximum amount. **-druck,** m. highest pressure, maximum pressure.

**höchstempfindlich,** a. extremely sensitive.

**höchstens,** adv. at most, at best.

**Höchst-fall,** m. maximum case. **-last,** f. maximum load. **-leistung,** f. maximum performance or output.

**höchst-prozentig,** a. highest-percentage, of or at the maximum per cent. **-siedend,** a. highest-boiling.

**Höchst-spannung,** f. maximum tension. **-temperatur,** f. highest temperature, maximum temperature. **-wert,** m. highest value, maximum value. **-zahl,** f. highest number, maximum number.

**hoch-trabend,** p.a. pompous, bombastic. **-treiben,** v.t. drive or raise high, work or refine highly, etc. (see treiben).

**Hochvakuum,** n. high vacuum.

**hochvergärend,** p.a. (of yeast) high-attenuating; (also of yeast) top-fermenting.

**Hochvergärung,** f. high attenuation (of wort); top fermentation.

**hochviskos,** a. highly viscous.

**Hochwald,** m. forest.

**hoch-weiss,** a. very white. **-wertig,** a. of high value or quality, high-grade; of high valence.

**Hochzeit,** f. wedding.

**Höcker,** m. hump, bump, protuberance; huckster.

**höckerig,** a. knotty, knobby, rough, humpy.

**Hode,** f., **Hoden,** m., **Hodendrüse,** f. testicle.

**Hodensack,** m. scrotum.

**Hof,** m. areola; halo; court; yard; farm; residence.

**hoffen,** v.t.& i. hope for, hope.

**hoffentlich,** adv. it is to be hoped, as I hope.

**Hoffnung,** f. hope.

**höflich,** a. civil, courteous.

**hohe, hoher,** etc. case forms of hoch, a.

**Höhe,** f. height, altitude; head (of water); intensity (of color); amount; summit; latitude.—**in der** —, on high.—**in die** —, up.

**Hoheit,** f. highness; greatness.

**höhensymmetrisch,** a. (Cryst.) symmetrical about the vertical axis.

**Höhepunkt,** m. high point, maximum.

**höher,** a. higher; superior. **-quantig,** a. of higher quantum number. **-wertig,** a. of higher valence, multivalent.

**hohl,** a. hollow; concave.

**Hohldrüse,** f. (Anat.) follicle.

**Höhle,** f. cave, cavern; hole, cavity.

**höhlen,** v.t. hollow, excavate.

**hohl-erhaben,** a. concavo-convex. **-geschliffen,** p.a. hollow-ground, concave.

**Hohl-glas,** n. hollow glassware (bottles, tumblers, etc.); concave glass. **-granate,** f.

hollow shell. **-guss,** m. hollow casting, cored work. **-hand,** f. palm (of the hand).

**höhlig,** a. containing cavities, honeycombed, blebby.

**Hohl-körper,** m. hollow body or piece. **-linse,** f. concave lens. **-mass,** n. measure of capacity. **-prisma,** n. hollow prism. **-raum,** m. hollow space, empty space, cavity. **-rührer,** m. hollow stirrer.

**hohlrund,** a. concave.

**Hohl-schicht,** f. air space. **-spat,** m. chiastolite. **-spiegel,** m. concave mirror.

**Höhlung,** f. cavity, hollow, excavation.

**Hohl-welle,** f. hollow shaft. **-zahn,** m. (Bot.) hemp nettle. **-ziegel,** m. hollow brick (or tile). **-zirkel,** m. inside calipers. **-zylinder,** m. hollow cylinder.

**hold,** a. kind, friendly, lovely, charming.

**Holder,** m. = Holunder.

**holen,** v.t. fetch, go for, get.

**holl.,** abbrev. (holländisch) Dutch.

**Holländer,** m. (Paper, etc.) hollander, engine.

**holländern,** v.t. beat in a hollander.

**Holländerweiss,** n. Dutch white.

**holländisch,** a. Dutch.—**holländisches Geschirr,** (Paper) hollander.—**holländisches Öl,** holländische Flüssigkeit, ethylene chloride.

**Hölle,** f. hell.

**Höllen-öl,** n. curcas oil (from Jatropha curcas); castor oil; worst grade of olive oil. **-stein,** m. lapis infernalis, lunar caustic (silver nitrate).

**Hollunder,** m. = Holunder.

**Holo-eder,** n. holohedral form or crystal. **-edrie,** f. holohedrism.

**holoedrisch,** a. holohedral.

**holperig, holprig,** a. uneven, rough.

**Holunder,** m. elder.—**spanischer** (or türkischer) —, lilac.

**Holunder-beere,** f. elderberry. **-blüte,** f. elder blossom. **-wein,** m. elder(berry) wine.

**Holz,** n. wood; timber; forest; thicket. **-abfall,** m., **-abfälle,** m.pl. wood waste.

**holzähnlich,** a. wood-like, ligneous.

**Holz-alkohol,** m. wood alcohol. **-amiant,** m. ligneous asbestos. **-apfel,** m. crab apple. **-apfelwein,** m. crab cider. **-art,** f. kind of species of wood.

**holzartig,** a. woody, ligneous, xyloid.

**Holz-asbest,** m. ligneous asbestos. **-asche,** f. wood ashes. **-aschenlauge,** f. lye from wood ashes.

**Holzäther,** m. methyl ether.—**essigsaurer** —, methyl acetate.

**Holz-beize,** f. mordant for staining wood. **-beizen,** n. wood staining. **-branntwein,** m. wood spirit. **-büchse,** f. wooden box or case.

-cassie, *f.* = Holzkassie. -chemie, *f.* chemistry of wood.

Hölzchen, *n.* splinter, splint; match.

Holz-deckel, *m.* wooden cover or lid. -destillation, *f.* wood distillation. -destillieranlage, *f.* wood-distilling plant.

hölzern, *a.* wooden; ligneous.

Holzessig, *m.*, -säure, *f.* wood vinegar, pyroligneous acid. -geist, *m.* = Holzgeist.

holzessigsauer, *a.* of or combined with pyroligneous acid, pyrolignite of.—holzessigsaures Eisen, iron liquor.

holzfarbig, *a.* of the color of wood.

Holzfaser, *f.* wood fiber, ligneous fiber; wood pulp; = Holzfaserstoff. -papier, *n.* wood-pulp paper. -stoff, *m.* lignin; cellulose; lignocellulose.

Holz-fäule, -fäulnis, *f.* dry rot. -feuer, *n.* wood fire. -firnis, *m.* wood varnish.

holzfrei, *a.* (*Paper*) without wood (pulp).

Holz-fuss, *m.* wooden base or foot; wooden stand. -gas, *n.* wood gas. -gattung, *f.* kind of wood. -geist, *m.* wood spirit, wood alcohol.

holzgeistig, *a.* containing wood alcohol.

Holz-gestell, *n.* wooden stand, wooden frame. -gewächs, *n.* woody plant. -griff, *m.* wooden handle. -gummi, *n.* wood gum, xylan.

holzicht, holzig, *a.* woody, ligneous.

Holz-kalk, *m.* pyrolignite of lime. -kassie, *f.* cassia lignea, coarse cassia bark. -kasten, *m.* wooden box, case or vat. -kirche, *f.* wild cherry. -kistchen, *n.* wooden box. -kitt, *m.* wood cement, joiner's putty. -klotz, *m.* wooden block, wood block. -kohle, *f.* charcoal (from wood).

Holzkohlen-brennofen, *m.* charcoal furnace. -eisen, *n.* charcoal iron. -feuer, *n.* charcoal fire. -klein, *n.*, -lösche, *f.* charcoal dust, charcoal smalls. -meiler, *m.* charcoal mound (*cf.* Meiler). -ofen, *m.* charcoal oven. -pulver, *n.* powdered charcoal. -roheisen, *n.* charcoal pig iron. -staub, *m.* charcoal dust.

Holz-konservierung, *f.* wood preservation. -konservierungsmittel, *n.* wood preservative. -körper, *m.* woody tissue, xylem. -kugel, *f.* wooden ball. -kupfer, -kupfererz, *n.* wood copper (fibrous olivenite). -lack, *m.* stick-lac. -mangold, *m.* (*Bot.*) pyrola. -masse, *f.* wood paste. -mehl, *n.* wood powder, wood meal, wood flour. -melasse, *f.* wood molasses. -naphta, *n.* wood naphtha, (crude) wood spirit. -öl, *n.* wood oil (any of various oils found in certain woods, also an oil obtained by destructive distillation). -opal, *m.* wood opal. -papier, *n.* paper from wood pulp, wood paper. -pappe, *f.* (*Paper*) board made from wood

pulp. -pech, *n.* wood pitch. -pflanze, *f.* woody plant. -pulver, *n.* = Holzmehl. -reif, -reifen, *m.* wooden ring, wooden hoop. -rot, *n.* redwood extract. -russ, *m.* wood soot.

holzsauer, *a.* = holzessigsauer.

Holz-säure, *f.* pyroligneous acid. -schleifer, *m.* (*Paper*) wood-pulp grinder. -schliff, *m.* mechanical wood pulp. -schnitt, *m.* wood engraving, woodcut. -schutzmittel, *n.* wood preservative. -span, *m.* wood shaving, chip or boring. -spiritus, *m.* wood spirit, wood alcohol. -stein, *m.* petrified wood. -steinkohle, *f.* lignite. -stich, *m.* wood engraving, woodcut. -stoff, *m.* (*Paper*) wood pulp; specif. mechanical wood pulp; lignin (*obs.?*).

holzstoff-frei, *a.* (*Paper*) free from wood pulp. -haltig, *a.* (*Paper*) containing wood pulp.

Holz-stoffmasse, *f.* wood pulp. -tafel, *f.* board. -tee, *m.* (*Pharm.*) wood drink.

Holzteer, *m.* wood tar. -öl, *n.* wood-tar oil. -pech, *n.* wood-tar pitch.

Holz-trank, *m.* (*Pharm.*) wood drink. -tränkung, *f.* wood pickling. -vergasung, *f.* wood distillation. -verkohlung, *f.* carbonization of wood, charcoal burning. -wolle, -watte, *f.* wood wool. -zellstoff, *m.* chemical wood pulp. -zeug, *n.* wood pulp. -zimt, *m.* = Holzkassie. -zinn, -zinnerz, *n.* wood tin (fibrous cassiterite). -zucker, *n.* wood sugar.

Homo-brenzcatechin, *n.* homopyrocatechol. -campher, *m.* homocamphor. -camphersäure, *f.* homocamphoric acid.

homo-chrom, *a.* of uniform color, homochromous; (*Dyeing*) monogenetic. -edrisch, *a.* (*Cryst.*) homohedral.

Homogallusaldehyd, *n.* homogallaldehyde.

homogen, *a.* homogeneous.

homogenisieren, *v.t.* homogenize.

Homogenität, Homogeneität, *f.* homogeneity.

Homogen-kohle, *f.* solid carbon. -stahl, *m.* homogeneous steel.

Homo-kaffeesäure, *f.* homocaffeic acid. -kamphersäure, *f.* homocamphoric acid.

homolog, *a.* homologous.

Homologie, *f.* homology.

homöomorph, *a.* homeomorphous.

Homöomorphie, *f.* (*Cryst.*) homeomorphism.

homöopolar, *a.* homopolar.

Homo-phtalsäure, *f.* homophthalic acid. -pinocamphersäure, *f.* homopinocamphoric acid. -veratrumaldehyd, *n.* homoveratraldehyde. -veratrumsäure, *f.* homoveratric acid.

Honig, *m.* honey.

honig-ähnlich, -artig, *a.* honeylike, melleous.

Honigessig, *m.* oxymel.

honig-farbig, *a.* honey-colored. -gelb, *a.* honey-yellow.

Honig-geruch, *m.* odor of honey. -geschmack, *m.* taste of honey.

honighaltig, *a.* containing honey, honeyed.

Honig-harnruhr, *f.* diabetes mellitus. -kuchen, *m.* gingerbread. -saft, *m.* nectar. -säure, *f.* (*Pharm.*) oxymel; mellitic acid. -scheibe, *f.* honeycomb. -seim, *m.* liquid honey. -stein, *m.* honeystone, mellite. -steinsäure, *f.* mellitic acid.

honigsüss, *a.* honey-sweet.

Honig-trank, *m.* mead. -wasser, *n.* hydromel. -wein, *m.* mead; mulse.

hopfen, *v.t.* hop, add hops to.

Hopfen, *m.* hop, hops.

Hopfenabkochung, *f.* hop decoction.

hopfen-ähnlich, -artig, *a.* like hops.

Hopfen-aufguss, *m.* infusion of hops. -baum, *m.* hop tree (*Ptelea trifoliata*). -bitter, *n.*, -bittersäure, *f.*, -bitterstoff, *m.* lupulin. -darre, *f.*, -darrofen, *m.* hop kiln. -drüsen, *f.pl.* (*Bot.*) lupulin. -harz, *n.* hop resin. -mehl, *n.* lupulin, hop dust. -mehltau, *m.* hop blight, -öl, *n.* hop oil; (spanisches) origanum oil. -staub, *m.* hop dust, lupulin. -stopfen, *n.* (*Brewing*) dry hopping. -treber, *pl.* spent hops. -trieb, *m.* (*Brewing*) frothy head, first stage of fermentation.

hörbar, *a.* audible.

horchen, *v.i.* listen, hearken; eavesdrop.

Horde, *f.* hurdle.

hören, *v.t.& i.* hear.

Hörer, *m.* hearer; (telephone) receiver.

Horizont, *m.* horizon; level.

Horizontale, *f.* horizontal (line).

Hornabfall, *m.* horn waste (chippings, etc.).

horn-ähnlich, -artig, *a.* hornlike, horny.

Horn-blatt, *n.* horn blade (for cleaning mortars); horn sheet. -blei, -bleierz, *n.* phosgenite. -chlorsilber, *n.* horn silver (cerargyrite).

hörnern, *a.* of horn, horny.

Hörnerv, *m.* auditory nerve.

Horn-erz, *n.* horn silver (cerargyrite). -gewebe, -gebilde, *n.* horny tissue. -gummi, *n.* hard rubber. -haut, *f.* cornea; horny layer of the skin.

Hornhaut-. corneal; horny, callous.

hornig, *a.* hornlike, horny, callous.

hornisieren, *v.t.* hornify; vulcanize.

Hornisse, Hornis, *f.* hornet.

Horn-kobalt, *n.* asbolite. -löffel, *m.* horn spoon. -mohn, *m.* poppy (*Glaucium glaucium*). -quecksilber, *n.* horn quicksilver (native mercurous chloride). -schicht, *f.* horny layer, specif. epidermis. -silber, *n.* horn silver (cerargyrite). -spatel, *m.* horn spatula. -stein, *m.* hornstone (variety of quartz). -stoff, *m.*, -substanz, *f.* keratin; horny substance.

Hörsaal, *m.* lecture room, auditorium.

Hortensienblau, *n.* Prussian blue.

Hosenrohr, *n.* siphon pipe (of a hot-blast oven).

h.s.l., *abbrev.* (heiss sehr löslich) very soluble hot.

Huaco, *m.* (*Bot.*) guaco.

Huano, *m.* guano.

hub, *pret.* of heben.

Hub, *m.* lift, lifting; (*Mach.*) stroke.

Hübel, *m.* hillock, mound.

hübsch, *a.* pretty, handsome.

Hubwerk, *n.* (*Mach.*) hoisting gear.

Huf, *m.* hoof. -eisen, *n.* horseshoe. -fett, *n.* neat's-foot oil; hoof ointment. -lattich, -lattig, *m.* coltsfoot. -nagel, *m.* horseshoe nail; hobnail. -schlag, *m.* hoof beat; horseshoeing.

Hüftbein, *n.* hip bone.

Hüfte, *f.* hip; haunch.

Hüft-loch, *n.* obturator foramen. -nerv, *m.* sciatic nerve.

Hügel, *m.* hill, hillock; knob, nodule.

Huhn, *n.* hen; fowl.

Hühnchen, *n.* chicken, pullet.

Hühner-auge, *n.* corn (the callosity). -eiweiss, *n.* white of egg.

hühnereiweissartig, *a.* like white of egg, albuminous.

Hühnerfett, *n.* chicken fat.

Huld, *f.* grace; kindness, favor.

huldigen, *v.i.* pay homage, devote oneself.

Hülfe, etc. see Hilfe, etc.

Hülle, *f.* cover, covering, case, casing, wrapper, envelope, sheath, integument.

hüllen, *v.t.* cover, wrap.

Hüllrohr, *n.* encasing tube, jacket.

Hülse, *f.* hull, husk, pod, shell; case; (*Mach.*) socket, collar, sleeve, etc.

hülsenartig, *a.* like a hull, socket, etc. (see Hülse); leguminous.

Hülsen-baum, *m.* locust tree. -frucht, *f.* legume.

hülsen-fruchtartig, -früchtig, *a.* leguminous.

Hülsen-früchtler, *m.pl.* (*Bot.*) Leguminosae. -gewächs, *n.*, -pflanze, *f.*, -träger, *m.* leguminous plant, legume.

Humin-säure, *f.* humic acid. -stoff, *m.*, -substanz, *f.* humic (or humous) substance.

Hummel, *f.* bumblebee.

Hummer, *m.* lobster.

humpeln, *v.i.* hobble.

Humulo-chinon, *n.* humuloquinone. -hydrochinon, *n.* humulohydroquinone.

humusreich, *a.* rich in humus.

Humus-säure, *f.* humic acid. -schicht, *f.* layer of humus. -stoff, *m.* humus substance.

Hund, *m.* dog; hound; (*Mach.*) rammer, monkey; (*Mining*) car.

Hundekot, *m.* canine feces, album graecum.

hundert, *a.* hundred.

Hundertel, *n.* hundredth.

hundertgradig, *a.* centigrade.

Hundertstel, *n.* hundredth.

hundertteilig, *a.* centesimal, centigrade.

Hundezahnspat, *m.* dogtooth spar (variety of calcite).

Hunds-kamille, *f.* dog's camomile, mayweed (*Anthemis cotula*). -zahnspat, *m.* = Hundezahnspat. -zunge, *f.*, -zungenkraut, *n.* hound's-tongue (*Cynoglossum*).

Hungerkorn, *n.* ergot.

Hungersnot, *f.* famine.

Hunger-stein, *m.* salt-pan scale (sulfates of calcium and sodium, etc.). -stoffwechsel, *m.* starvation metabolism.

hungrig, *a.* hungry.

Hupe, *f.* horn, trumpet.

Hürdentrockner, *m.* tray drier.

hurtig, *a.* quick, nimble, speedy.

husten, *v.i.* cough.

Hustenmittel, *n.* cough remedy.

Hut, *m.* hat; cap, cover, lid, top; loaf (of sugar); scum (of wine); layer of spent tanbark.—*f.* guard; pasture.

Hütchen, *n.* cap; capsule; (*Bot.*) pileus.

hüten, *v.t.* watch, guard, keep.—*v.r.* take care.

Hut-filz, *m.* hatter's felt. -pilz, *m.* pileate fungus, agaricaceous fungus, mushroom.

Hütte, *f.* (metallurgical or glass) works, mill, smelting house, foundry; hut, cabin, cottage, shed.

Hütten-abfall, *m.* (*Metal.*) waste. -after, *m.* residue or refuse from a foundry or the like. -arbeit, *f.* smelting, founding; foundry work (distinguished from blast-lamp work, in glass). -glas, *n.* (*Glass*) pot metal. -herr, *m.* owner of a smeltery or the like. -katze, *f.* lead colic. -koks, -kok, *m.* metallurgical coke. -kunde, *f.* metallurgy. -kundiger, *m.* metallurgist. -mann, *m.* metallurgist; smelter, founder, etc.

hüttenmännisch, *a.* metallurgical.

Hütten-mehl, *n.* white-arsenic powder. -nichts, *n.* nihilum album, white tutty (impure zinc oxide). -probierkunst, *f.* metallurgical assaying. -produkt, *n.* metallurgical product. -prozess, *m.* metallurgical process. -prüfer, *m.* metallurgical assayer. -rauch, *m.* smelter smoke; flue dust; white arsenic. -reise, *f.* (*Metal.*) campaign. -speise, *f.* material to be smelted. -trichter, *m.* conical funnel (the common form). -werk, *n.* smelting works, foundry, mill, plant, works (where smelting, founding, rolling, etc. are carried on). -wesen, *n.* smelting, metallurgy. -zinn, *n.* (*Metal.*) grain tin.

Hutzucker, *m.* loaf sugar.

h.w.l., *abbrev.* (heiss wenig löslich) not very soluble hot.

Hyacinthgranat, *m.* essonite.

Hyänasäure, *f.* hyenic acid.

Hyäne, *f.* hyena.

Hydantoinsäure, *f.* hydantoic acid.

Hydnocarpussäure, *f.* hydnocarpic acid.

Hydrat, *n.* hydrate; hydroxide.

Hydratation, *f.* hydration.

Hydratationswärme, *f.* heat of hydration.

Hydratbildung, *f.* hydrate formation, hydration.

hydrathaltig, *a.* hydrated.

hydratieren, *v.t.* hydrate.

Hydrationswärme, *f.* heat of hydration.

hydratisch, *a.* hydrated.

hydratisieren, *v.t.* hydrate.—*v.r.* become hydrated.

Hydratisierung, *f.* hydration.

Hydratisierungsgrad, *m.* degree of hydration.

Hydratropa-aldehyd, *n.* hydratropaldehyde. -alkohol, *m.* hydratropic alcohol. -säure, *f.* hydratropic acid.

Hydratwasser, *n.* water of hydration.

hydratwasserhaltig, *a.* containing water of hydration.

Hydrat-zellulose, *f.* hydrate cellulose. -zustand, *m.* state of hydration.

Hydraulik, *f.* hydraulics.

hydraulisch, *a.* hydraulic.

Hydrazo-benzol, *n.* hydrazobenzene. -körper, *m.*, -verbindung, *f.* hydrazo compound.

Hydrid, *n.* hydride, esp. a higher hydride, as contrasted with Hydrür.

hydrieren, *v.t.* hydrogenize, hydrogenate.

Hydrierung, *f.* hydrogenation.

hydroaromatisch, *a.* hydroaromatic.

Hydrobromsäure, *f.* hydrobromic acid.

Hydrochin-. hydroquin-.

Hydro-chinon, *n.* hydroquinone. -chinoxalin, *n.* hydroquinoxaline. -chlorsäure, *f.* hydrochloric acid. -cumaron, *n.* hydrocoumarone, hydrocumarone. -cumarsäure, *f.* hydrocoumaric (or -cumaric) acid. -cyansäure, *f.* hydrocyanic acid.

hydroelektrisch, *a.* hydroelectric.

hydrogenieren, *v.t.* hydrogenize, hydrogenate.

Hydrogenisation, *f.* hydrogenation.

hydrogenisieren, *v.t.* = hydrogenieren.

Hydrogenschwefel, *m.* hydrogen sulfide.

Hydro-jodid, *n.* hydriodide. -jodsäure, *f.* hydriodic acid. -kaffeesäure, *f.* hydrocaffeic acid. -kautschuk, *m.* hydrorubber -kette, *f.* (*Elec.*) hydrocell, hydroelement.

hydrolis-. see hydrolys-.

Hydrolyse, *f.* hydrolysis.

hydrolysierbar, *a.* hydrolyzable.

hydrolysieren, *v.t.* hydrolyze.

Hydrolysierzahl, *f.* hydrolyzation number.

hydro-lytisch, *a.* hydrolytic. -metrisch, *a.* hydrometric.

Hydro-peroxyd, *n.* hydrogen peroxide. -persulfid, *n.* hydrogen persulfide. -phtalsäure, *f.* hydrophthalic acid. -polysulfid, *n.* hydrogen polysulfide.

hydro-schweflig, *a.* hydrosulfurous. -statisch, *a.* hydrostatic.

Hydro-thionsäure, *f.* hydrosulfuric acid, hydrogen sulfide. -verbindung, *f.* hydro compound (compound formed by the addition of hydrogen).

Hydroxyd, *n.* hydroxide.

Hydroxydul, *n.* (-ous) hydroxide.

hydroxylhaltig, *a.* containing hydroxyl.

hydroxylieren, *v.t.* hydroxylate.

Hydrozellulose, *f.* hydrocellulose.

Hydrozimt-, Hydrozimmt-. hydrocinnamic. -säure, *f.* hydrocinnamic acid.

Hydrür, *n.* hydride, specif. a lower hydride as contrasted with Hydrid.

Hygienik, *f.* hygienics, hygiene.

hygienisch, *a.* hygienic.

hygro-metrisch, *a.* hygrometric. -skopisch, *a.* hygroscopic.

Hygroskopizität, *f.* hygroscopicity.

Hyperbel, *f.* hyperbola. -bahn, *f.* hyperbolic orbit or path.

Hyper-chlorat, *n.* perchlorate. -chlorid, *n.* perchloride. -chlorsäure, *f.* perchloric acid. -glukämie, *f.* hyperglycemia. -jodat, *n.* periodate. -jodsäure, *f.* periodic acid.

hypermangansauer, *a.* = übermangansauer.

Hyper-mangansäure, *f.* permanganic acid. -oxyd, *n.* hyperoxide (peroxide).

Hypo-chloritlauge, *f.* hypochlorite liquor, hypochlorite solution. -gäasäure, *f.* hypogeic acid. -hirnsäure, *f.* hypocerebric acid. -jodit, *n.* hypoiodite.

hypophosphorig, *a.* hypophosphorous.

Hypophyse, *f.* (*Anat.*) hypophysis, pituitary body.

Hypothek, *f.* mortgage, security.

Hypothese, *f.* hypothesis.

hypothetisch, *a.* hypothetical.

H.Z., *abbrev.* (Hydrolysierzahl) hydrolyzation number.

**I**

i., *abbrev.* (in) in; (im) in the; (ist) is; (imido) imino, imido.

i.A., *abbrev.* (im Allgemeinen) in general; (im Auftrag) by, per (in signatures).

Ia., *abbrev.* (prima) first-class, prime.

i. allg., *abbrev.* (im allgemeinen) in general.

Iatro-chemie, *f.* iatrochemistry. -chemiker, *m.* iatrochemist.

iatrochemisch, *a.* iatrochemical.

i.B.auf, *abbrev.* (in Bezug auf) in relation to, referred to.

ich, *pron.* I.

-icht. a suffix used with verb roots to form collective nouns (as Fei*licht*, filings, from f*eilen*) and with nouns to form adjectives of quality, as öl*icht*, oily. In the latter sense the ending -*ig* is more common. See -*ig*, and adjectives ending in -ig.

Ichthyolseife, *f.* ichthyol soap.

i.D., *abbrev.* (in Dampf) in steam; (in Dampf-form) in vapor form; (im Durchschnitt) on the average; (im Dunkeln) in the dark.

-id. -ide. (There is American authority for chlor*id*, am*id*, etc., but these spellings are not used by the American or London chemical societies. Translation should be uniform, not -ide for some compounds and -id for others.)

Idee, *f.* idea, notion, conception.

identifizieren, *v.t.* identify.

identisch, *a.* identical.

Identität, *f.* identity.

Idit, *n.* iditol, idite.

Idozuckersäure, *f.* idosaccharic acid.

I.E., *abbrev.* (Immunisierungseinheit) immunization unit.

-ieren. -ate, -ize, etc. (the infinitive ending of a large number of verbs, mostly of non-German origin, the meaning of which can often be easily guessed).

-ierung, *f.* -ation, -ization, etc. Cf. -ieren.

-ig. an adjective suffix denoting quality or relation; -y, -ous, -ed, -ful; as, öl*ig*, oily; flücht*ig*, volatile, flying; zweiseit*ig*, two-sided; 5%*ig*, 5 per cent; specif., in names of chemical compounds, -ous; as, schwefl*ig*, sulfurous.

-igen. a termination of causative verbs formed from adjectives and nouns; as, rein*igen* (make pure) from rein; end*igen* (make an end of) from Ende.

Ignatiusbohne, *f.* St.-Ignatius's-bean.

ihn, *pron.* him, it.—ihnen, to them.

Ihnen, *pron.* to you.

ihr, *pron.* you; to her; her; their.

Ihr, *pron.* your.

ihrer, *pron.* of her; of them; hers; theirs.

Ihrer, *pron.* of you.

ihrerseits, *adv.* for its, her, or their part, in turn, again.

ihresgleichen, *pron.* their like, its like, her like.

ihrige, *pron.* hers; theirs.

Ihrige, *pron.* yours.

i.J., *abbrev.* (im Jahre) in the year.

I.K., *abbrev.* (Immunkörper) immune body.

Ikositetraeder, *n.* icositetrahedron.

i.L., *abbrev.* (in Liter) in a liter, per liter.

-il. (*Org. Chem.*) -il; as, an*il*, carbostyr*il*, etc. Nitril (translated nitrile) is an exception.

illuminieren, *v.t.* illuminate.

illustrieren, *v.t.* illustrate.

Iltis, *m.* polecat, fitchet (*Putorius*).

im, *abbrev.* (in dem) in the.

imaginär, *a.* imaginary.

im allg., im allgem., *abbrev.* (im allgemeinen) in general.

Imber, *m.* ginger. See Ingwer.

imbibieren, *v.t.* imbibe.

Imbiss, *m.* light meal, lunch.

Imido-. imido-, imino- (should be translated imido- only when the compound is of imide nature, otherwise imino-). -äther, *m.* imido ester. -gruppe, *f.* imido group; imino group. -säure, *f.* imido acid. -sulfonsäure, *f.* imidosulfonic acid (disulfamic acid). -thioäther, *m.* imido thio ester.

Immedialschwarz, *n.* immedial black.

immer, *adv.* always, ever.— — noch, still.

immer-fort, *adv.* always, constantly. -grün, *a.* evergreen.

Immergrün, *n.* periwinkle (*Vinca*).

immer-hin, *adv.* still, after all. -während, *p.a.* everlasting, perpetual. -zu, *adv.* always; go on!

immunisieren, *v.t.* immunize.

Immunisierung, *f.* immunization.

Immunität, *f.* immunity.

Immunkörper, *m.* immune body.

Immunochemie, *f.* immunochemistry.

Impf-. inoculation, vaccination.

impfbar, *a.* inoculable.

impfen, *v.t.* inoculate; vaccinate; (of plants) graft.

Impf-flüssigkeit, *f.* inoculation lymph, vaccine

lymph. -kristall, *m.* seed crystal. -mittel, *n.* inoculating agent, inoculum; vaccine. -stift, *m.* inoculating pencil. -stoff, *m.* inoculating material, inoculum; vaccine.

Impfung, *f.* inoculation, vaccination.

Impfversuch, *m.* inoculation experiment.

imponieren, *v.i.* impose, impress.

imprägnierbar, *a.* impregnable.

imprägnieren, *v.t.* impregnate.

Imprägniermittel, *n.* impregnating agent.

Imprägnierung, *f.* impregnation.

Imprägnierverfahren, *n.* impregnation process or method.

Impulssatz, *m.* momentum principle.

imstande, *a.* able.

in, *prep.* in, at; into, to. |

-in. a suffix used to form a feminine; as, Wirt*in*, host*ess*, land*lady*.

-in. (as a chemical ending) -ine when the compound is a base, -in when it is not. Names of alcohols and phenols are preferably translated so as to end in -ol; as, Resorc*in*, resorcinol.

inaktiv, *a.* inactive.

Inaktivität, *f.* inactivity.

inaktivieren, *v.t.* inactivate.

Inaktivierung, *f.* inactivation.

Inanspruchnahme, *f.* requisition, claim.

Inaug. Diss., *abbrev.* inaugural dissertation.

Inbegriff, *m.* total, sum, inclusion; summary.

inbegriffen, *p.a.* included; implied.

Inbetriebsetzung, *f.* setting in motion, starting.

incarnat, *a.* flesh-colored.

Indanthren-blau, *n.* indanthrene blue. -gelb, *n.* indanthrene yellow.

indem, *conj.* while, when, as; since, because. (*Indem* is often conveniently translated *by* or *on*, with a participial construction, e.g. *indem man behandelt*, by treating, on treating.)

indessen, indes, *adv.* meanwhile; however.

indianisch, *a.* Indian (usually, American Indian).

Indien, *n.* India.

Indig, *m.* indigo. -blau, *n.* indigo blue. -blauschwefelsäure, *f.* = Indigoblauschwefelsäure.

indigen, *a.* indigenous.

Indigkraut, *n.* indigo plant.

indigoartig, *a.* indigoid.

Indigo-auszug, *m.* indigo extract. -blau, *n.* indigo blue. -blauschwefelsäure, *f.* indigosulfuric acid, sulfindigotic acid (indigosulfonic or indigodisulfonic acid). -druck, *m.* indigo printing. -farbstoff, *m.* indigo blue, indigotin. -küpe, *f.* indigo vat, blue vat (solution of indigo white). -leim, *m.* indigo gelatin, indigo gluten. -lösung, *f.* indigo solution. -messung, *f.* indigometry. -purpur, *m.* indigo purple. -rot, *n.* indigo red (indirubin). -salz, *n.* indigo salt, indigotate. -säure, *f.* indigotic acid. -schwefelsäure, *f.* = Indigoblauschwefelsäure. -stein, *m.* = Indigstein. -stoff, *m.* indigo blue, indigotin. -sulfosäure, *f.* indigosulfonic acid. -weiss, *n.* indigo white.

Indig-rot, *n.* = Indigorot. -stein, *m.* indicolite (blue tourmaline). -weiss, *n.* indigo white.

Indikator-lösung, *f.* indicator solution. -papier, *n.* indicator paper.

Indioxyd, *n.* indium oxide, $In_2O_3$.

indisch, *a.* (East) Indian.—indische Bohne, St.-Ignatius's-bean.—indische Feige, prickly pear.—indischer Balsam, balsam of Peru.—indischer Flachs, jute.

Indisch-gelb, *n.* Indian yellow. -hanftinktur, *f.* tincture of Indian hemp. -rot, *n.* Indian red.

Indisulfid, Indiumsulfid, *n.* indium (sesqui)sulfide ($In_2S_3$).

Indiumsulfür, *n.* indium monosulfide.

Individuum, *n.* (*pl.* Individuen). individual.

Indizes, *m.pl.* indices.

indizieren, *v.t.* indicate.

Indochinolin, *n.* indoquinoline.

Indol-gruppe, *f.* indole group. -körper, *m.* indole substance, member of the indole group.

Indoxylschwefelsäure, *f.* indoxylsulfuric acid.

Induktions-rolle, -spule, *f.* induction coil. -strom, *m.* induction current. -vermögen, *n.* inductive capacity.

indurieren, *v.t.* indurate, harden.

Industrie-abfallstoff, *m.* industrial waste material. -abwasser, *n.* industrial waste water or waste liquor. -gas, *n.* industrial gas.

Industrielle(r), *m.* industrial, manufacturer.

Industrie-ofen, *m.* industrial furnace. -wasser, *n.* industrial water. -zweig, *m.* branch of industry.

induzieren, *v.t.* induce.

ineinander, *adv.* into each other, into one another. -fliessen, *v.i.* flow or run into one another. -passen, *v.i.* fit into each other, fit together.

Inertie, *f.* inertia; inertness.

Infektionskrankheit, *f.* infectious disease.

infektionswidrig, *a.* opposing infection.

infiltrieren, *v.t.& i.* infiltrate.

infizieren, *v.'.* infect; inoculate (with crystals).

Infizierung, *f.* infection; (crystal) inoculation.

infökund, *a.* sterile.

infolge, *prep.* on account of, owing to.— — dessen, consequently.

infrarot, *a.* infra-red.

Infundier-apparat, *m.* infusion apparatus. -büchse, *f.* infusion vessel, digester.

**infundieren**, *v.t.* infuse.
**Infusionstierchen**, *n.pl.* infusoria.
**Infusorienerde**, *f.* infusorial earth (kieselguhr).
**Ing.**, *abbrev.* (Ingenieur) engineer.
**Ingangsetzung**, *f.* (*Mach.*) starting.
**Ingber**, *m.* ginger. See Ingwer.
**Ingebrauchnahme**, *f.* putting into operation or use.
**Ingenieur, Ingeniör**, *m.* engineer. **-Chemiker**, *m.* chemical engineer (graduate in chemistry of a Technikum). **-wesen**, *n.* engineering.
**Ingotstahl**, *m.* ingot steel.
**Ingrediens**, *n.*, **Ingredienz**, *f.* ingredient.
**Inguss**, *m.* ingot; ingot mold.
**Ingwer**, *m.* ginger; (gelber) turmeric.
**ingwerartig**, *a.* like ginger, gingery.
**Ingwer-bier**, *n.* ginger beer. **-gewürz**, *n.* ginger (the spice). **-gras**, *n.* ginger grass. **-öl**, *n.* ginger oil.
**Inh.**, *abbrev.* Inhalt; Inhaber.
**Inhaber**, *m.* holder, owner.
**inhalieren**, *v.t.* inhale.
**Inhalt**, *m.* content, contents; (of a surface) area; (of a body) volume; (of a vessel) capacity; index.
**Inhalts-angabe, -übersicht**, *f.* table of contents; summary. **-verzeichnis**, *n.* table of contents.
**inhomogen**, *a.* inhomogeneous.
**Inhomogenität**, *f.* inhomogeneity.
**Initial-explosivstoff, -sprengstoff**, *m.* priming explosive, primer, priming.
**initiieren**, *v.t.* initiate; (*Explosives*) explode.
**injizieren**, *v.t.* inject.
**inkl.**, *abbrev.* (inklusive) inclusive(ly).—**bis inkl.**, up to and including.
**Inkohärens**, *f.* incoherence.
**Inkohlung**, *f.* conversion into coal, coalification.
**Inkompressibilität**, *f.* incompressibility.
**inkrustieren**, *v.t.* incrust.—*v.i.* become incrusted.
**Inkrustierung**, *f.* incrustation.
**Inländer**, *m.* inlander; native.
**inländisch**, *a.* native, indigenous; internal, domestic; inland.
**inliegend**, *a.* enclosed, inclosed.
**inmitten**, *adv.* in the midst.
**inne**, *adv.* in. **-haben**, *v.t.* hold, occupy, keep. **-halten**, *v.t.* keep within; keep in.—*v.i.* stop; pause.
**innen**, *adv.* within, in, inside; at home.
**Innen-**. internal, interior, inside, inner. **-druck**, *m.* internal pressure. **-durchmesser**, *m.* inside diameter. **-feuerung**, *f.* internal furnace. **-fläche**, *f.* inner surface. **-haut**, *f.* inner or internal membrane or skin. **-heizung**, *f.* internal heating. **-leitung**, *f.* interior wiring, piping, etc.; inner circuit.

**-mass**, *n.* inside measure. **-raum**, *m.* interior space, interior. **-rinde**, *f.* inner rind, bark, or crust. **-wandung**, *f.* inner wall. **-weite**, *f.* inside diameter.
**inner**, *a.* internal; interior, inward, inner; intrinsic.—**innere Reibung**, internal friction.
**inner-atomar**, *a.* intra-atomic. **-halb**, *adv. & prep.* within. **-lich**, *a.* inward, internal, interior; profound, sincere. **-molekular**, *a.* intramolecular.
**innewohnend**, *p.a.* inherent.
**innig**, *a.* intimate; cordial, earnest, sincere.
**inokulieren**, *v.t.* inoculate.
**Inosinsäure**, *f.* inosic acid.
**Inosit**, *n.* inositol, inosite.
**in praxi**. in practice.
**Insass, Insasse**, *m.* inhabitant; inmate.
**insbesondere**, *adv.* especially, particularly.
**Inschrift**, *f.* inscription.
**Insekten-kunde, -lehre**, *f.* entomology. **-pulver**, *n.* insect powder. **-vertilgungsmittel**, *n.* insecticide. **-vertreibungsmittel**, *n.* insectifuge. **-wachs**, *n.* insect wax.
**Insel**, *f.* island.
**Inserat**, *n.* advertisement; insertion.
**Insgesamt**, *adv.* all together, collectively.
**insofern**, *conj.* so far as, inasmuch as.
**instabil**, *a.* unstable.
**Instandhaltung**, *f.* maintenance.
**inständig**, *a.* earnest, urgent.
**Instandsetzung**, *f.* reconditioning, repairing.
**instruieren**, *v.t.* instruct.
**Instrumentenkunde**, *f.* knowledge of instruments.
**Integralrechnung**, *f.* integral calculus.
**integrieren**, *v.t.* integrate.—**integrierend**, *p.a.* integrating, integrant.
**Intensität**, *f.* intensity.
**Interesse**, *f.* interest.
**Interessent**, *m.* person interested (or concerned).
**Interesterifizierung**, *f.* inter-esterification.
**Interferenzbild**, *n.* interference figure.
**inter-mediär**, *a.* intermediary, intermediate. **-mittierend**, *p.a.* intermittent. **-polieren**, *v.t.* interpolate. **-ponieren**, *v.t.* insert, interpolate. **-punktieren**, *v.t.* punctuate.
**intim**, *a.* intimate.
**intraatomar**, *a.* intra-atomic.
**Inventar**, *n.* inventory.
**invertieren**, *v.t.* invert.
**Invertierung**, *f.* inversion.
**Invertzucker**, *m.* invert sugar.
**inwärts**, *adv.* inwards.
**inwendig**, *a.* inward, interior, internal.
**inwiefern**, *adv.* in what respect.
**inwohnend**, *p.a.* inherent.
**inzwischen**, *adv.* meantime.

**Iod,** etc. see **Jod,** etc.

**Ionen-art,** *f.* kind of ion. **-beweglichkeit,** *f.* ionic mobility. **-bildung,** *f.* formation of ions. **-dichte,** *f.* ionic density. **-geschwindigkeit,** *f.* ionic velocity. **-gleichung,** *f.* ionic equation. **-reaktion,** *f.* ionic reaction. **-reibung,** *f.* ionic friction. **-reihe,** *f.* ionic series. **-spaltung,** *f.* ionic cleavage, ionization. **-theorie,** *f.* ionic theory. **-wanderung,** *f.* ionic migration. **-zustand,** *m.* ionic state.

**Ionisationswärme,** *f.* heat of ionization.

**ionisch,** *a.* ionic.

**ionisierbar,** *a.* ionizable.

**ionisieren,** *v.t.* ionize.

**Ionisierung,** *f.* ionization.

**Ionisierungs-mittel,** *n.* ionizing agent. **-wärme,** *f.* heat of ionization.

**I.P.,** *abbrev.* (italienisches Patent) Italian patent.

**Ipecacuanhasäure,** *f.* ipecacuanhic acid.

**I.P.S.,** *abbrev.* (indizierte Pferdestärke) indicated horsepower.

**Ipser Tiegel.** a kind of graphite crucible.

**irden,** *a.* earthen.—*irdenes Geschirr*, earthenware.

**Irdenware,** *f.* earthenware.

**irdisch,** *a.* terrestrial; earthly; perishable.

**-iren.** = -ieren.

**irgend,** *adv.* any, at all, some. **-welcher,** *pron.* someone, anyone, some, any. **-wie,** *adv.* anyhow, somehow. **-wo,** *adv.* anywhere, somewhere.

**iridisieren,** *v.t.& i.* = irisieren.

**iridisierend,** *p.a.* iridescent.

**Irisblende,** *f.* iris diaphragm.

**irisieren,** *v.t.* irisate, iridize.—*v.i.* iridesce. —irisierend, *p.a.* iridescent.

**Irisierung,** *f.,* **Irisieren,** *n.* iridescence.

**Irisöl,** *n.* iris oil, orris oil.

**Irland,** *n.* Ireland.

**irländisch,** *a.* Irish.

**Iron,** *n.* irone.

**irre,** *a.& adv.* astray, wrong.

**Irre,** *f.* wandering; labyrinth.—*m. & f.* lunatic.

**irreführend,** *p.a.* misleading.

**irren,** *v.i.* err, be wrong; be insane or delirious. —*v.r.* be mistaken.—*v.t.* mislead; puzzle; disturb.

**Irrenarzt,** *m.* alienist.

**Irresein,** *n.* insanity.

**irreversibel,** *a.* irreversible.

**Irr-fahrt,** *f.* wandering, vagary. **-gang, -garten,** *m.* labyrinth.

**irrig,** *a.* erroneous, false.

**Irr-lehre,** *f.* false teaching, heresy. **-licht,** *n.* will-o'-the-wisp. **-sinn,** *m.* insanity; delirium. **-strom,** *m.* (*Elec.*) stray current. **-tum,** *m.* error; mistake, fault.

**irrtümlich,** *a.* erroneous.—*adv.* erroneously. **-erweise,** *adv.* erroneously.

**isabellen, -farbig,** *a.* cream-colored, light buff.

**Isäthionsäure,** *f.* isethionic acid.

**Isatropasäure,** *f.* isatropic acid.

**-isch.** an adjective suffix equivalent to -ish (as weib*isch*, womanish) and also used to form adjectives from proper names and foreign words (as Schiff'*sche* Basen, Schiff bases; chem*isch*, chemical).

**isentrop, -tropisch,** *a.* isentropic.

**-isieren, -ize.** (infinitive verb ending).

**isländisch,** *a.* Iceland, Icelandic.

**Iso-bernsteinsäure,** *f.* isosuccinic acid. **-buttersäure,** *f.* isobutyric acid. **-chinolin,** *n.* isoquinoline.

**iso-chrom, -chromatisch,** *a.* isochromatic. **-chron,** *a.* isochronal, isochronous.

**Iso-crotonsäure,** *f.* isocrotonic acid. **-cumarin,** *n.* isocoumarin, isocumarin. **-cyansäure,** *f.* isocyanic acid. **-cyanursäure,** *f.* isocyanuric acid.

**iso-cyclisch,** *a.* isocyclic. **-elektrisch,** *a.* isoelectric.

**Isoferulasäure,** *f.* isoferulic acid.

**isohydrisch,** *a.* isohydric.

**Isokamphersäure,** *f.* isocamphoric acid.

**Isolation,** *f.* isolation; insulation.

**Isolations-fehler,** *m.* defect in insulation. **-hülle,** *f.* insulating covering. **-material,** *n.* = Isolationsstoff. **-mittel,** *n.* insulating agent. **-schicht,** *f.* insulating layer. **-stoff,** *m.* insulating material. **-vermögen,** *n.* insulating power. **-zustand,** *m.* state of isolation or of insulation.

**Isolator,** *m.* (*Elec.*) insulator.

**Isolier-anstrich,** *m.* insulating paint, varnish, or coat. **-band,** *n.* insulating tape.

**isolierbar,** *a.* capable of being isolated or insulated.

**isolieren,** *v.t.* isolate; (*Elec.*) insulate.—*isolierte Färbung*, (*Micros.*) differential staining.

**Isolier-farbe,** *f.* insulating paint. **-firnis,** *m.* insulating varnish. **-flasche,** *f.* insulating bottle, vacuum flask. **-flüssigkeit,** *f.* insulating liquid. **-gewebe,** *n.* insulating fabric. **-hülle,** *f.* insulating covering. **-kitt,** *m.* insulating cement. **-lack,** *m.* insulating varnish. **-masse,** *f.,* **-material,** *n.* insulating material. **-mittel,** *n.* insulating agent, insulator. **-rohr,** *n.,* **-röhre,** *f.* (*Elec.*) insulating tube or pipe, conduit. **-schicht,** *f.* insulating layer. **-stoff,** *m.* insulating substance.

**Isolierung,** *f.* isolation; insulation.

**isolog,** *a.* isologous.

**isomer,** *a.* isomeric.

**Isomerie,** *f.* isomerism. **-fall,** *m.* case of isomerism. -**möglichkeit,** *f.* possibility of isomerism.

**isomerisch,** *a.* isomeric.

**isomerisieren,** *v.t.* isomerize.

**Isomerisierung,** *f.* isomerization.

**Isomerismus,** *m.* isomerism.

**iso-metrisch,** *a.* isometric. -**morph,** *a.* isomorphous.

**Iso-morphie,** *f.*, -**morphismus,** *m.* isomorphism. -**ölsäure,** *f.* isoöleic acid.

**Isop,** *m.* hyssop.

**Iso-phtalsäure,** *f.* isophthalic acid. -**pikrinsäure,** *f.* isopicric acid.

**Isopöl,** *n.* hyssop oil.

**Iso-polysäure,** *f.* isopolyacid. -**purpurinsäure,** *f.* isopurpuric acid. -**saccharinsäure,** *f.* isosaccharinic acid.

**isosmotisch,** *a.* isosmotic.

**iso-therm, -thermisch,** *a.* isothermal.

**Iso-therme,** *f.* isotherm. -**thiocyansäure,** *f.* isothiocyanic acid. -**tonie,** *f.* isotonicity.

**iso-tonisch,** *a.* isotonic. -**top,** *a.* isotopic. -**trop,** *a.* isotropic.

**Isotropie,** *f.* isotropy, isotropism.

**Iso-valeriansäure,** *f.* isovaleric acid. -**xylol,** *n.* isoxylene. -**xylylsäure,** *f.* isoxylic acid. -**zimmtsäure,** *f.* isocinnamic acid. -**zuckersäure,** *f.* isosaccharic acid.

**isozyklisch,** *a.* isocyclic.

**isst,** *pr.2 & 3 sing.* of essen.

**ist,** *pr.3 sing.* of sein.

**Istrien,** *n.* Istria.

-**it.** -ite. (When it seems desirable to retain the exact spelling of a German name ending in -*it*, quotation marks should be used; as, thermite or " thermit " (or Thermit). Names of alcohols ending in -*it* are preferably translated so as to end in -*ol*; as, mannitol.)

**Itaconsäure,** *f.* itaconic acid.

**Italien,** *n.* Italy.

**italienisch,** *a.* Italian.

-**ität.** a suffix used to form abstract nouns from adjectives; -ity, -ness.

**i.V.,** *abbrev.* (im Vakuum) in vacuo; (in Vertretung) by, per.

**Iva-kraut,** *n.* iva (*Achillea moschata*). -**öl,** *n.* iva oil.

**i.W.,** *abbrev.* (innere Weite) inside diameter; (in Worten) in words.

# J

**J.** symbol for iodine, I.

**J.,** *abbrev.* Jahresbericht der Chemie; (Jahr) year.

**ja,** *adv.* yes; indeed; certainly, by all means.

**Jagarazucker,** *m.* jaggery.

**Jagd,** *f.* chase, hunt, hunting; huntsmen; game; hubbub. **-pulver,** *n.* sporting powder.

**jagen,** *v.t.* hunt, chase; drive.—*v.i.* hunt; rush.

**Jäger,** *m.* hunter, sportsman; chasseur.

**jäh,** *a.* steep, abrupt; hasty, sudden.

**jählings,** *adv.* headlong; abruptly.

**Jahr,** *n.* year. **-buch,** *n.* yearbook; almanac; annal.

**Jahres-bericht,** *m.* annual report. **-frist,** *f.* space of a year. **-schrift,** *f.* annual publication. **-tag,** *m.* anniversary; birthday. **-wechsel,** *m.* new year. **-zeit,** *f.* season.

**Jahrg.,** *abbrev.* Jahrgang.

**Jahr-gang,** *m.* year's course, year's set, year; vintage. **-hundert,** *n.* century.

**jährlich,** *a.* yearly, annual.

**Jahr-tausend,** *n.* millennium, a thousand years. **-zehnt,** *n.* decade.

**Jakobskraut,** *n.* groundsel (*Senecio*).

**Jalape, Jalappe,** *f.* jalap.

**Jalap-enharz,** *n.* jalap resin, jalapin. **-insäure,** *f.* jalapic acid.

**jämmern,** *v.i.* lament.—*v.t.* move to pity.

**Janusgrün,** *n.* Janus green.

**Japanholz,** *n.* sapanwood.

**japanieren,** *v.t.* japan.

**japanisch,** *a.* Japanese, Japan.

**Japan-lack,** *m.* Japan lacquer, Japan varnish. **-säure,** *f.* japonic acid. **-wachs, -talg,** *n.* Japan wax.

**Jasmin,** *m.* jasmine, jessamine.—**gemeiner —, wilder —,** syringa.

**Jasmin-blütenöl,** *n.* jasmine-flower oil. **-öl,** *n.* jasmine oil.

**Jaspachat,** *m.* jasper agate, jasper.

**Jaspis,** *m.* jasper. **-gut,** *n.* jasper ware. **-porzellan,** *n.* jasperated china. **-steingut,** *n.* jasper ware.

**Jaspopal,** *m.* jasper opal.

**jäten,** *v.t.* weed.

**jatro-, Jatro-.** see Iatro-.

**Jauche,** *f.* dung water, liquid manure; (*Med.*) ichor.

**Javazimt,** *m.* Java cinnamon.

**Javelle'sche Lauge.** Javelle water.

**jawohl,** *adv.* yes indeed.

**je,** *adv.* always, ever; every; apiece.— **— nach,** according to.— **— . . . —,** the . . . the.— **— . . . um so, the . . . the.**

**jedenfalls,** *adv.* in any case, by all means.

**jeder,** *pron.* every, each, any; everyone, everybody, each. **-zeit,** *adv.* at any time, always.

**jedesmal,** *adv.* every time.

**jedoch,** *adv.* however, yet, nevertheless.

**jeglicher,** *pron.* every, any, everything.

**jeher,** *adv.*—**von —,** ever since, all along.

**jemals,** *adv.* ever, at any time.

**jemand,** *pron.* somebody, someone, anybody, anyone.

**Jenaer Glas.** Jena glass.

**jenaisch, jenesisch,** *a.* Jena, of Jena.

**jener,** *pron.* that, the other; that one, that person, the former.

**jenseit, jenseits,** *prep.* beyond, on the other side of.

**Jesuitenrinde,** *f.* Jesuit bark (cinchona bark).

**jettschwarz,** *a.* jet-black.

**jetzig,** *a.* present.

**jetzt,** *adv.* now, at present.

**Jetzt-wert,** *m.* present value. **-zeit,** *f.* present time.

**jeweilig,** *a.* for the time being; respective, particular, under consideration.

**jeweils,** *adv.* for the time being; at times.

**Jg.,** *abbrev.* (Jahrgang) year's set, year.

**Joch,** *n.* yoke; section. **-baum,** *m.* hornbeam.

**Jod,** *n.* iodine.

**Jod-.** iodine, iodide of, iodo-, iodated. **-alkyl,** *n.* alkyl iodide. **-allyl,** *n.* allyl iodide. **-ammonium,** *n.* ammonium iodide. **-amylum,** *n.* starch iodide. **-antimon,** *n.* antimony iodide. **-arsen,** *n.,* **-arsenik,** *m.* arsenic iodide.

**jodartig,** *a.* iodine-like.

**Jodat,** *n.* iodate.

**Jod-äther,** *m.* iodo ether. **-äthyl,** *n.* ethyl iodide, iodoethane.

**Jodation,** *f.* iodination.—*n.* iodate ion.

**Jod-azid,** *n.* iodine azide. **-baryum,** *n.* barium iodide. **-benzoesäure,** *f.* iodobenzoic acid. **-benzol,** *n.* iodobenzene ($C_6H_5I$, or in general, any iodine derivative of benzene; cf. Jodobenzol). **-blei,** *n.* lead iodide. **-bromchlorsilber,** *n.* (*Min.*) iodobromite. **-bromid,** *n.* iodine bromide. **-bromür,** *n.* iodine monobromide. **-cadmium,** *n.* cadmium iodide. **-calcium,** *n.* calcium iodide. **-chinolin,** *n.* iodoquinoline. **-chlor,** *n.* iodine chloride. **-chlorid,** *n.* iodine chloride, esp. iodine trichloride. **-chlorür,** *n.* iodine monochloride. **-cyan,** *n.* cyanogen iodide. **-dampf,** *m.* iodine vapor. **-eisen,** *n.* iron iodide. **-eiweiss,** *n.* (*Pharm.*) iodated albumen. **-essigester,** *m.* iodoacetic ester. **-gehalt,** *m.* iodine content. **-gold,** *n.* gold iodide. **-grün,** *n.* iodine green.

**jod-haltend, -haltig,** *a.* containing iodine, iodiferous.

**Jod-hydrat,** *n.* hydriodide. **-hydrin,** *n.* iodohydrin.

**Jodid,** *n.* iodide (esp. an -ic iodide, as contrasted with Jodür). **-chlorid,** *n.* iodochloride.

**jodierbar,** *a.* capable of being iodinated or iodized.

**jodieren,** *v.t.* iodinate; iodize, iodate.

**jodig,** *a.* iodous.

**Jodijodat,** *n.* iodine iodate.

**jodimetrisch,** *a.* iodometric.

**Jod-ion,** *n.* iodine ion. **-ismus,** *m.* iodism.

**Jodit,** *m.* iodite (iodyrite, AgI).

**Jodiverbindung,** *f.* iodic compound.

**Jod-jodkaliumlösung,** *f.* solution of iodine in aqueous potassium iodide. **-kadmium,** *n.* cadmium iodide. **-kali,** *n.* potassium iodide. **-kaliumlösung,** *f.* potassium iodide solution. **-kaliumstärkepapier,** *n.* potassium-iodide-starch paper. **-kalzium,** *n.* calcium iodide. **-kohlenstoff,** *m.* carbon (tetra)iodide. **-kupfer,** *n.* copper iodide. **-lebertran,** *m.* iodated cod-liver oil. **-lithium,** *n.* lithium iodide. **-lösung,** *f.* iodine solution. **-magnesium,** *n.* magnesium iodide. **-mangan,** *n.* manganese iodide. **-menge,** *f.* amount of iodine. **-messung,** *f.* iodometry. **-metall,** *n.* metallic iodide. **-methode,** *f.* iodine method. **-methyl,** *n.* methyl iodide, iodomethane. **-methylat,** *n.* methiodide. **-mittel,** *n.* iodiferous remedy. **-natrium,** *n.* sodium iodide. **-natron,** *n.* sodium hypoiodite.

**Jodo-.** iodoxy- (IO$_2$); iodo-. **-benzoesäure,** *f.* iodoxybenzoic acid. **-benzol,** *n.* iodoxybenzene (C$_6$H$_5$IO$_2$). **-form,** *n.* iodoform. **-formprobe,** *f.* iodoform test.

**Jodol,** *n.* iodol.

**Jodometrie,** *f.* iodometry.

**jodometrisch,** *a.* iodometric.

**Jodonaphtalin,** *n.* iodoxynaphthalene.

**Jodonium,** *n.* iodonium.

**Jodoso-.** iodoso-. **-benzol,** *n.* iodosobenzene (C$_6$H$_5$IO).

**Jodoxy-.** iodohydroxy-. **-naphtochinon,** *n.* hydroxyiodonaphthoquinone, C$_{10}$H$_4$O$_2$(OH)I.

**Jod-phosphonium,** *n.* phosphonium iodide. **-phosphor,** *m.* phosphorus iodide. **-phtal-**

**-säure,** *f.* iodophthalic acid. **-präparat,** *n.* iodine preparation. **-probe,** *f.* iodine test. **-quecksilber,** *n.* mercury (esp. mercuric) iodide. **-radium,** *n.* radium iodide. **-salbe,** *f.* iodine ointment. **-salz,** *n.* iodine salt, specif. iodide.

**jodsauer,** *a.* of or combined with iodic acid, iodate of.

**Jod-säure,** *f.* iodic acid. **-schwefel,** *m.* sulfur iodide. **-silber,** *n.* silver iodide. **-silizium,** *n.* silicon iodide. **-stärke,** *f.* starch iodide, iodized starch. **-stickstoff,** *m.* nitrogen iodide. **-thymol,** *n.* (*Pharm.*) thymol iodide. **-tinktur,** *f.* tincture of iodine. **-toluol,** *n.* iodotoluene. **-überträger,** *m.* iodine carrier.

**Jodür,** *n.* (-ous) iodide. Cf. Chlorür.

**Jod-verbindung,** *f.* iodine compound. **-vergiftung,** *f.* iodine poisoning, iodism. **-wasser,** *n.* iodine water.

**Jodwasserstoff,** *m.* hydrogen iodide; hydriodic acid. **-äther,** *m.* ethyl iodide. **-säure,** *f.* hydriodic acid.

**Jodwismut,** *m.& n.* bismuth iodide.

**Jodyrit,** *m.* iodyrite.

**Jod-zahl,** *f.* iodine number. **-zim(m)tsäure,** *f.* iodocinnamic acid. **-zink,** *n.* zinc iodide. **-zinn,** *n.* tin iodide. **-zinnober,** *m.* red mercuric iodide.

**Joghurt,** *n.* yoghurt (a fermented milk).

**Johannis-beere,** *f.* currant. **-beerwein,** *m.* currant wine. **-brot,** *n.* St.-John's-bread (carob bean). **-kraut,** *n.* St.-John's-wort. **-wurzel,** *f.* male fern, (*Pharm.*) aspidium.

**Jon,** *n.* ion (for compounds see Ion-).

**Jonan,** *n.* ionan.

**Jonen,** *n.* ionene.—*n.pl.* ions.

**Jonidin,** *n.* ionidine.

**Jonium,** *n.* ionium.

**Jonol,** *n.* ionol.

**Jonon,** *n.* ionone. **-säure,** *f.* iononic acid.

**Jubel,** *m.* jubilation; jubilee. **-band,** *m.* jubilee volume. **-feier,** *f.,* **-fest,** *n.* jubilee.

**Jubiläum,** *n.* jubilee.

**Jucht, Juchten, Juchtenleder,** *n.* Russia leather.

**Juchten-öl,** *n.* birch-tar oil, birch oil. **-rot,** *n.* Janus red.

**jucken,** *v.t.& i.* itch.—*v.r.* scratch, rub.

**Jucken,** *n.* itching, pruritus.

**Jude,** *m.* Jew.

**Juden,** *m.pl.* Jews; (*Metal.*) refinery scraps. **-dornbeere,** *f.* jujube, zizyphus. **-harz,** *n.* = Judenpech. **-kirsche,** *f.* alkekengi (*Physalis*). **-pech,** *n.* Jew's pitch (asphalt). **-pilz,** *m.* a species of *Boletus.* **-schwamm,** *m.* a species of *Boletus.*

**jüdisch,** *a.* Jewish.

**Jugend,** *f.* youth; adolescence.

**jugendlich,** *a.* youthful, young, juvenile.

**Jugoslawien**, *n.* Jugoslavia.

**Juli**, *m.* July.

**jung**, *a.* young; fresh, early; new (wine or beer); overpoled (copper).

**Jungbier**, *n.* new beer.

**Junge**, *m.* boy, lad, youth; apprentice; young (of animals), cub, etc.

**Jünger**, *m.* disciple, follower, votary.

**Jungfer**, *f.* virgin, maid; iron ladle; rammer.

**Jungfern-, Jungfer-.** virgin; native.

**Jungfern-blei**, *n.* first lead from a furnace. **-erde,** *f.* virgin soil. **-glas**, *n.* selenite (transparent gypsum). **-metall**, *n.* native metal. **-öl**, *n.* virgin oil. **-pergament**, *n.* vellum. **-quecksilber**, *n.* native mercury. **-schwefel,** *m.* virgin sulfur, native sulfur. **-wachs,** *n.* virgin wax. **-wein,** *m.* wine from un-pressed grapes. **-zeugung,** *f.* parthenogenesis.

**Jungfrau**, *f.* virgin, maid; (*Geog.*) Jungfrau.

**jüngst**, *a.* youngest, last, latest.—*adv.* lately, recently.

**Juni**, *m.* June.

**justieren**, *v.t.* adjust; justify (type).

**Justiertisch**, *m.* adjusting table.

**Justierung**, *f.* adjustment; justification.

**Justiz**, *f.* justice. **-wesen**, *n.* the law, legal affairs.

**Jute-faden**, *m.* jute fiber; jute twine. **-faser,** *f.* jute fiber.

**Juwel**, *n.* jewel.

**Juwelier**, *m.* jeweler. **-arbeiten**, *f.pl.* jewelry. **-borax,** *m.* octahedral borax.

**Jux**, *m.* filth; spree, lark.

**J.Z.,** *abbrev.* (Jodzahl) iodine number.

# K

**k.,** *abbrev.* (kalt) cold; (kaiserlich) imperial; (königlich) royal; (as symbol, no period) Γ constant.

**-k.,** *abbrev.* (-keit) -ness.

**K.,** *abbrev.* (elektrische Dissociationskonstante) electric dissociation constant; (kaiserlich) imperial; (königlich) royal.

**Kabel,** *n.* cable. **-ausgussmasse,** *f.* cable compound.

**Kabeljau,** *m.* cod, codfish. **-lebertran, Kabliaulebertran,** *m.* cod-liver oil.

**Kabelwachs,** *n.* cable wax.

**Kachel,** *f.* (Dutch) tile.

**Kaddig, Kaddich,** *m.* cade (*Juniperus oxycedrus*).

**Kaddigöl,** *n.* oil of cade.

**Kadeöl, Kadinöl, Kadiöl,** *n.* oil of cade.

**Kadmium,** *n.* cadmium. **-gehalt,** *m.* cadmium content. **-gelb,** *n.* cadmium yellow.

**kadmiumhaltig,** *a.* containing cadmium, cadmiferous.

**Kadmium-jodid,** *n.* cadmium iodide. **-legierung,** *f.* cadmium alloy. **-salz,** *n.* cadmium salt.

**Käfer,** *m.* beetle, coleopter.

**käferartig,** *a.* coleopterous.

**Kaffalsäure,** *f.* coffalic acid, caffalic acid.

**Kaffee,** *m.* coffee.

**kaffeeähnlich,** *a.* coffee-like.

**Kaffee-auszug,** *m.* coffee extract. **-baum,** *m.* coffee tree. **-bohne,** *f.* coffee bean.

**kaffeebraun,** *a.* coffee-brown, coffee-colored.

**Kaffee-ersatzstoff,** *m.* coffee substitute. **-gerbsäure,** *f.* caffetannic acid. **-kanne,** *f.* coffee pot. **-öl,** *n.* coffee oil. **-satz,** *m.* coffee grounds. **-säure,** *f.* caffeic acid. **-surrogat,** *n.* coffee substitute.

**Kaffein,** *n.* caffeine.

**Käfig,** *m.* cage, birdcage.

**Kahinkawurzel,** *f.* cahinca root.

**kahl,** *a.* bald; bare; barren; (of fabrics) napless; mere, poor. **— gehen,** (*Metal.*) need no flux.

**Kahm,** *m.* mold (on wine, etc.).

**kahmen,** *v.i.* mold.

**Kahmhaut,** *f.* pellicle of mold.

**kahmig,** *a.* moldy, stale, (of wine) ropy.

**Kahn,** *m.* boat.

**kahnförmig,** *a.* boat-shaped, scaphoid.

**Kai,** *m.* quay, wharf.

**Kaïnkawurzel,** *f.* cahinca root.

**Kaiser,** *m.* emperor.

**Kaiser-.** imperial; Caesarean. **-blau,** *n.* smalt. **-gelb,** *n.* mineral yellow. **-grün,** *n.* imperial green (Paris green).

**kaiserlich,** *a.* imperial.

**Kaiser-öl,** *n.* a kind of kerosene. **-reich,** *n.* empire. **-rot,** *n.* colcothar; imperial red (a dye). **-wasser,** *n.* aqua regia. **-wurz,** *f.* masterwort (specif. *Imperatoria ostruthium*).

**Kajaputöl, Kajeputöl,** *n.* cajuput oil.

**Kakao,** *m.* cacao; cocoa. **-baum,** *m.* cacao, cacao tree. **-bohne,** *f.* cacao bean, cocoa bean. **-butter,** *f.* cacao butter, cocoa butter. **-masse,** *f.* cocoa paste. **-öl,** *n.* cocoa (cacao) oil or butter. **-pulver,** *n.* cocoa powder.

**Kakaorin,** *n.* cacaorine.

**Kakaorot,** *n.* cocoa red.

**Kakodyl,** *.* cacodyl. **-säure,** *f.* cacodylic acid. **-wasserstoff,** *m.* cacodyl hydride.

**Kakothelin,** *n.* cacotheline.

**Kakoxen,** *n.* (*Min.*) cacoxene, cacoxenite.

**Kaktus,** *m.* cactus.

**Kal.,** *abbrev.* (Kalorie) large or kilogram calorie, al.

**Kalabarbohne,** *f.* Calabar bean.

**Kalamin,** *m.* calamine.

**Kalander,** *m.* calender.

**kalandern,** *v.t.* calender.

**Kalb,** *n.* calf.

**Kälber-lab,** *n.,* **-magen,** *m.* rennet.

**Kalb-fell,** *n.* calfskin. **-fleisch,** *n.* veal. **-leder,** *n.* calf (leather).

**Kalbs-m gen,** *m.* rennet; calf's stomach. **-pergament,** *n.* vellum.

**kalcinieren,** *v.t.* calcine.

**Kalcinierung,** *f.* calcination.

**Kalcit,** *m.* calcite.

**Kalcium,** *n.* calcium. See Calcium-.

**Kaldaune,** *f.* tripe; (*pl.*) guts.

**Kalender,** *m.* calendar; almanac.

**Kaleszenz,** *f.* calescence.

**kalfatern,** *v.t.* calk.

**Kali,** *n.* (caustic) potash, potassium hydroxide; potash (K2O; equivalent in old names of salts to potassium; as, *chlorsaures Kali,* chlorate of potash, potassium chlorate); saltwort (*Salsola kali*). **-alaun,** *n.* potash alum. **-ammonsalpeter,** *m.* a material made by mixing potassium chloride and ammonium nitrate. **-apparat,** *m.* potash apparatus.

**Kaliaturholz,** *n.* caliatour wood.

**Kali-bergwerk,** *n.* potash mine. **-blau,** *n.*

Prussian blue. -bleiglas, *n.* potash lead glass.

**kalibrieren,** *v.t.* calibrate; groove (a roll).

**Kali-düngemittel,** *n.,* -dünger, *m.* potash manure, potash fertilizer. -düngesalz, *n.* potassium salt for fertilizing. -eisenalaun, *m.* potash iron alum. -eisencyanür, *m.* potassium ferrocyanide. -feldspat, *m.* potash feldspar. -form, *f.* potash mold.

**kalifornisch,** *a.* California.

**kalifrei,** *a.* potash-free.

**Kali-glas,** *n.* pota h glass. -glimmer, *m.* potash mica.

**kalihaltig,** *a.* containing potash.

**Kali-hydrat,** *n.* potassium hydroxide. -kalk, *m.* potash lime.

**Kalikodruck,** *m.* calico printing.

**Kali-kugel,** *f.* potash bulb. -lauge, *f.* potash lye, caustic potash solution. -lösung, *f.* potash solution. -metall, *n.* (metallic) potassium. -rohsalz, *n.* crude potassium salt. -salpeter, *m.* saltpeter, potassium nitrate. -salz, *n.* potash salt, potassium salt. -salzlager, *n.* bed or deposit of potash salts. -schmelze, *f.* potash fusion; potash melt. -schwefelleber, *f.* (*Pharm.*) sulfurated potassa, liver of sulfur. -seife, *f.* potash soap. -siederei, *f.* potash works. -sulfat, *n.* potassium sulfate. -tonerde, *f.* potassium aluminate.

**Kalium,** *n.* potassium. -alaun, *m.* potassium alum. -azetat, *n.* potassium acetate. -brechweinstein, *m.* antimonyl potassium tartrate. **bromatum.** (*Pharm.*) potassium bromide. -bromid, *n.* potassium bromide. **chloratum.** (*Pharm.*) potassium chloride. **chloricum.** (*Pharm.*) potassium chlorate. -chlorid, *n.* potassium chloride. -eisencyanid, *n.* potassium ferricyanide. -eisencyanür, *n.* potassium ferrocyanide. -ferrisulfat, *n.* ferric potassium sulfate. -gehalt, *m.* potassium content. -goldbromür, *n.* potassium bromoaurate. -goldchlorid, *n.* potassium chloroaurate. -goldcyanid, *n.* potassium cyanoaurate, potassium auricyanide. -goldcyanür, *n.* potassium cyanoaurite, potassium aurocyanide. -halogen, *n.* potassium halide.

**kaliumhaltig,** *a.* containing potassium.

**Kalium-hydrat,** *n.* potassium hydroxide. -hydrid, *n.* potassium hydride (KH). -hydroxyd, *n.* potassium hydroxide. -hydrür, *n.* potassium subhydride ($K_2H$ or $K_4H_2$). -iridichlorid, *n.* potassium chloroiridate. -jodat, *n.* potassium iodate. **jodatum.** (*Pharm.*) potassium iodide. -jodid, *n.* potassium iodide. -jodidlösung, *f.* potassium iodide solution. -jodidstärke, *f.* potassium iodide starch. -kobaltnitrit, *n.* potas-

sium cobaltinitrite. -kohlenoxyd, *n.* potassium carboxide, potassium hexacarbonyl. -nitrat, *n.* potassium nitrate. **nitricum.** (*Pharm.*) potassium nitrate. **nitrosum.** (*Pharm.*) potassium nitrite. -oxydhydrat, *n.* potassium hydroxide. -permanganat, *n.* potassium permanganate. -platinchlorid, *n.* potassium platinichloride (potassium chloroplatinate). -platinchlorür, *n.* potassium platinochloride (potassium chloroplatinite). -platincyanür, *n.* potassium platinocyanide (cyanoplatinite). -platinochlorid, *n.* potassium platinochloride (chloroplatinite). -rhodanat, -rhodanid, *n.* potassium thiocyanate (or sulfocyanate). -salz, *n.* potassium salt. -seife, *f.* potassium soap. -sulfat, *n.* potassium sulfate. -sulfhydrat, *n.* potassium sulfhydrate (potassium hydrosulfide.) -verbindung, *f.* potassium compound. -wasserstoff, *m.* potassium hydride. -zyanid, *n.* potassium cyanide.

**Kali-verbindung,** *f.* potash compound. -wasserglas, *n.* potash water glass. -werk, *n.* potash works.

**Kalk,** *m.* lime (equivalent, in old names of salts, to calcium; as, *phosphorsaurer Kalk*); phosphate of lime, calcium phosphate); limestone; (*Old Chem.*) calx.—gelöschter —, slaked lime.—gebrannter —, quicklime.

**Kalk-.** lime, calc-, calci-, calcareous, calcium, limestone. -ablagerung, *f.* lime deposit, calcareous deposit. -anlagerung, *f.* (*Physiol.*) calcification. -anstrich, *m.* whitewash.

**kalk-arm,** *a.* deficient in lime. -artig, *a.* calcareous, limy.

**Kalk-artigkeit,** *f.* calcareousness. -äscher, *m.* (*Soap*) lixiviated ashes, soap waste; (*Leather*) lime pit. -back, *m.* (*Sugar*) lime back. -bad, *n.* lime bath. -baryt, *m.* (*Min.*) calcareous barite. -bestimmung, *f.* determination of lime. -beton, *m.* lime concrete. -beuche, *f.* (*Bleaching*) lime boil. -bewurf, *m.* coat of plaster, plastering. -blau, *n.* blue verditer. -boden, *m.* lime soil, calcareous soil. -borat, *n.* calcium borate. -brei, *m.* lime paste, lime cream. -brennen, *n.* lime burning. -brennerei, *f.* lime kiln; lime burning. -bruch, *m.* limestone quarry. -brühe, *f.* milk of lime; whitewash. -düngung, *f.* manuring with lime.

**Kälke,** *f.* (*Leather*) lime.

**kalkecht,** *a.* fast to lime.

**Kalk-einlagerung,** *f.* calcareous deposit. -eisenstein, *m.* ferruginous limestone.

**kalken, kälken,** *v.t.* lime.

**Kalkerde,** *f.* lime, calcium oxide; calcareous earth.

**kalkerdig,** *a.* calcareous.

Kalk-fällung, f. precipitation of lime. -farbe, f. lime color, lime paint. -fass, n. (Leather) lime pit. -feldspat, m. lime feldspar.

kalk-frei, a. free from lime. -führend, a. lime-bearing, calciferous.

Kalk-gehalt, m. lime content. -glas, n. lime glass. -glimmer, m. (Min.) margarite. -granat, m. lime garnet (grossularite). -grube, f. lime pit. -guss, m. thin lime mortar, grout.

kalk-haft, a. limy, calcareous. -haltig, a. containing lime, calcareous.

Kalk-haltigkeit, f. calcareousness. -härte, f. hardness due to lime. -hütte, f. lime kiln. -hydrat, n. hydrate of lime (calcium hydroxide).

kalkig, a. limy, calcareous.

Kalk-kitt, m. lime cement, calcareous cement. -körperchen, n. (Physiol.) calcareous body. -lager, n. lime deposit, calcareous deposit. -lauge, f. lime lye (calcium hydroxide solution). -licht, n. lime light, calcium light. -löschen, n. lime slaking. -lösung, f. solution of lime (calcium hydroxide). -mangel, m. lack or deficiency of lime. -mehl, n. lime powder (air-slaked lime). -menge, f. amount of lime. -mergel, m. lime marl, calcareous marl. -messer, m. calcimeter (for determination of carbon dioxide in limestone, etc.). -milch, f. milk of lime. -mörtel, m. lime mortar. -niederschlag, m. lime precipitate. -ofen, m. lime kiln. -pulver, n. lime powder. -rahm, m. cream of lime.

kalkreich, a. rich in lime.

Kalk-salpeter, m. calcium nitrate. -salz, n. lime salt, calcium salt.. -sand, m. lime sand, calcareous sand. -sandstein, m. calcareous sandstone; (Ceram.) sand-lime brick. -sandziegel, m. sand-lime brick. -sauerbad, m. (Bleaching) lime sour. -schaum, m. lime froth or scum. -schiefer, m. calcareous slate (or schist). -schlamm, m. lime sludge, lime mud. -schwefelleber, f. (Pharm.) sulfurated lime, lime hepar. -seife, f. lime soap, calcium soap. -sinter, m. calcareous sinter. -spat, m. calc-spar, calcite. -stein, m. limestone. -steingut, n. (Ceram.) calcareous white ware. -steinzuschlag, m. limestone flux. -stickstoff, m. (crude) calcium cyanamide, "lime-nitrogen." -sulfat, n. sulfate of lime (calcium sulfate). -talkspat, m. dolomite. -tiegel, m. lime crucible. -tropfstein, m. calcareous dripstone. -tuff, m. calcareous tufa. -tünche, f. (lime) whitewash.

kalkulieren, v.t. & i. calculate.

Kalk-verbindung, f. lime compound, calcium compound. -verseifung, f. saponification with lime. -wasser, n. limewater. -weinstein, m. calcareous tartar. -werk, n. lime works.

-zementmörtel, m. lime-cement mortar. -zuschlag, m. lime(stone) flux.

Kalmie, f. mountain laurel (Kalmia latifolia).

Kalmus, m. calamus. -öl, n. calamus oil. -wurzel, f., calamus root.

Kalorifer, m. heater, radiator.

Kalorimetrie, f. calorimetry.

kalorimetrisch, a. calorimetric.

kalorisch, a. caloric.

kalt, a. cold; cool.—kalter Satz, (Brewing) cold-water extract of malt.

Kaltbad, n. cold bath.

kaltbläsig, a. (Metal.) refractory.

Kaltbruch, m. cold-shortness.

kaltbrüchig, a. cold-short.

Kälte, f. cold, coldness. -anlage, f. refrigerating plant.

kältebeständig, a. resistant to cold; antifreezing, antifreeze.

Kältebeständigkeit, f. resistance to cold.

kälte-empfindlich, a. sensitive to cold. -erzeugend, p.a. frigorific.

Kälte-erzeugung, f. production of cold, refrigeration. -grad, m. degree of cold, degree below zero. -leistung, f. refrigerating capacity. -maschine, f. refrigerating machine. -mischung, f. freezing mixture. -mittel, n. refrigerating agent.

kälten, v.t. chill, refrigerate.

Kälte-probe, f. cold test. -punkt, m. (Oils) solidifying point. -schutzmittel, n. protective agent against cold. -träger, m. cooling medium.

Kalt-färben, n. cold-dyeing. -gebläse, n. cold blast.

kalt-gewalzt, p.a. cold-rolled. -gezogen, p.a. cold-drawn. -giessen, v.t. cast cold. -gründig, a. (of soil) cold.

Kaltguss, m. spoiled casting.

kalthämmern, v.t. cold-hammer, cold-forge.

Kalt-hefe, f. wild yeast. -lagerung, f. cold storage.

kaltlegen, v.t. blow out, stop (a furnace).

Kaltleim, m. cold glue.

kalt-liegen, v.i. (Metal.) be out of operation. -walzen, v.t. cold-roll.

Kaltwasser-bad, n. cold-water bath. -farbe, f. cold-water color or paint.

Kaltwerden, n. becoming cold, cooling.

kalz., abbrev. (kalziniert) calcined.

Kalzi-, kalzi-, calci-.

kalzinieren, v.t. calcine.

Kalzit, n. calcite.

Kalzium, n. calcium. (For compounds see Calcium-.)

kam, pret. of kommen.

Kambaholz, Kambalholz, n. camwood.

Kambodscha, n. Cambodia.

kambrisch, a. Cambrian.

**Kamel,** *n.* camel.

**Kamelie,** *f.* camellia.

**Kamerad,** *m.* comrade, fellow.

**Kamfer,** *m.* camphor.  See Kampher-.

**Kamholz,** *n.* camwood.

**Kamille,** *f.* camomile.

**Kamillenöl,** *n.* camomile oil.

**Kamin,** *m.* chimney, stack; fireplace. **-brenner,** *m.* burner with a chimney. **-russ,** *m.* chimney soot.

**Kamm,** *m.* comb; cog (of a wheel); cam; ridge. **-abfall,** *m.* combings.

**kämmen,** *v.t.* comb; card; notch.

**Kammer,** *f.* chamber; room; ventricle (of the heart).

**Kämmerchen,** *n.* little chamber, closet.

**Kämmerei,** *f.* board of finances, exchequer.

**Kammer-kristall,** *m.* chamber crystal. **-prozess,** *m.* chamber process. **-säure,** *f.* chamber acid. **-schlamm,** *m.* chamber sludge. **-sohle,** *f.* chamber floor. **-tuch,** *n.* cambric. **-wasser,** *n.* (*Anat.*) aqueous humor. **-wesen,** *n.* finances.

**Kammfett,** *n.* horse grease.

**kammförmig,** *a.* comb-shaped.

**Kamm-garn,** *n.* worsted (yarn). **-gras,** *n.* dog's-tail. **-kies,** *m.* cockscomb pyrites (variety of marcasite). **-muschel,** *f.* scallop. **-rad,** *n.* cog wheel. **-wolle,** *f.* carded wool.

**Kamomille,** *f.* camomile.

**Kampagne,** *f.* campaign, (working) season.

**Kampane,** *f.* bell jar.

**Kampescheholz,** *n.* campeachy wood (logwood).

**Kampf,** *m.* combat, conflict, battle, fight.

**Kampfen,** *n.* camphene.

**kämpfen,** *v.i.* battle, contend, fight.

**Kampfer,** *m.* camphor.  (For compounds see Kampher-.)

**Kämpfer,** *m.* combatant, fighter.

**Kämpferid,** *n.* kaempferide.

**Kämpferin,** *n.* kaempferin.

**Kämpferol,** *m.* kaempferol.

**Kampfgas,** *n.* gas used in warfare, war gas.

**Kampfor,** *m.* camphor.  See Kampher-.

**Kampf-platz,** *m.* field of battle, arena. **-stoff,** *m.* war material, esp. a chemical used in war. **-wagen,** *m.* (*Mil.*) tank.

**Kampher,** *m.* camphor. **-art,** *f.* (variety of) camphor.

**kampherartig,** *a.* camphorlike, camphoraceous.

**Kampher-chinon,** *n.* camphorquinone. **-essig,** *m.* camphorated vinegar. **-geist,** *m.* spirit of camphor.

**kampher-haltig,** *a.* containing camphor, camphorated, **-ieren,** *v.t.* camphorate.

**kamphern,** *v.t.* camphorate.

**Kampher-öl,** *n.* camphor oil; (*Pharm.*) camphorated oil. **-phoron,** *n.* camphorphorone. **-säure,** *f.* camphoric acid. **-spiritus,** *m.* spirit of camphor. **-wein,** *m.* camphorated wine.

**Kamphorsäure,** *f.* camphoric acid.

**kanadisch,** *a.* Canadian, Canada.

**Kanadischbalsam,** *m.* Canada balsam.

**Kanal,** *m.* canal; channel; conduit; sewer. **-gas,** *n.* sewer gas.

**Kanalisations-rohr,** *n.,* **-röhre,** *f.* sewer pipe, water pipe, gas pipe, or electric conduit.

**Kanal-jauche,** *f.* (liquid) sewage. **-ofen,** *m.* tunn l kiln. **-strahl,** *m.* canal ray. **-wasser,** *n.* sewage.

**Kanarien-.** canary. **-farbe,** *f.* canary color; canarin.

**kanariengelb,** *a.* canary-yellow.

**kandeln,** *v.t.* channel, flute, groove.

**kandieren,** *v.t.* candy.

**Kandis,** **-zucker,** *m.* sugar candy. **-störzel,** *m.* mother liquor from sugar candy.

**Kanditen-.** candy.

**Kaneel,** **Kanel,** *m.* cinnamon; (weisser) canella; clove cassia; (brauner) Ceylon cinnamon. **-bruch,** *m.* broken cinnamon. **-granat,** **-stein,** *m.* cinnamon stone (essonite).

**Kanellarinde,** *f.* canella bark.

**Kanevas,** *m.* canvas.

**Känguruh,** *n.* kangaroo. **-leder,** *n.* kangaroo leather.

**Kaninchen,** *n.* rabbit.

**kann,** *pr.1 & 3 sing.* of können; can.

**Kännchen,** *n.* small can.

**Kanne,** *f.* can; jug, pot, liter.

**kannelieren,** *v.t.* channel, flute, groove.

**Kannelierung,** *f.* channeling, fluting.

**Kannelkohle,** *f.* cannel coal.

**Kannenzinn,** *n.* pewter.

**kannte,** *pret.* of kennen.

**Kanone,** *f.* cannon, gun.

**Kanonen-gut,** **-metall,** *n.* gun metal. **-ofen,** *m.* bomb furnace. **-pulver,** *n.* cannon powder. **-rohr,** *n.,* **-röhre,** *f.* bomb-furnace tube.

**Kante,** *f.* edge; border, brim; lace.

**kanten,** *v.t.* edge, border; square (stones); cant, tilt. **-weise,** *adv.* edgewise, on edge.

**Kanthar-.** see Canthar-.

**Kantholz,** *n.* squared timber.

**kantig,** *a.* edged, angular.

**Kanzleitinte,** *f.* record ink.

**kaolinisieren,** *v.t.* kaolinize.

**Kaolinisierung,** *f.* kaolinization.

**Kaoutschuk,** *m.* caoutchouc, rubber.  See Kautschuk-.

**Kap.,** *abbrev.* (Kapitel) chapter.

**Kapaun,** *m.* capon.

**Kapazität,** *f.* capacity.

**Kapelle,** *f.* cupel; sand bath; subliming dish; capsule; priming cap; chapel; band.

**Kapellen-asche,** *f.* bone ash. **-form,** *f.* cupel mold. **-gold,** *n.* fine gold. **-kläre,** *f.* = Kapellenpulver. **-ofen,** *m.* cupelling furnace, assay furnace; sublimation furnace. **-probe,** *f.* cupel test, cupellation. **-pulver,** *n.* cupel dust, bone ash. **-raub,** *m.* loss in cupellation. **-silber,** *n.* fine silver. **-träger,** *m.* cupel holder. **-zug,** *m.* = Kapellenraub.

**kapellieren,** *v.t.* cupel.

**kapillar,** *a.* capillary.

**Kapillar,** *n.* capillary. **-affinität,** *f.* capillary affinity.

**kapillaraktiv,** *a.* active in lowering surface tension.

**Kapillar-analyse,** *f.* capillary analysis. **-chemie,** *f.* capillary chemistry. **-druck,** *m.* capillary pressure.

**Kapillare,** *f.* capillary.

**Kapillar-flasche,** *f.* capillary bottle or flask. **-fläschchen,** *n.* small capillary bot.'e or flask.

**kapillarförmig,** *a.* capillary, capillaceous.

**Kapillargefäss,** *n.* capillary vessel.

**kapillar-inaktiv,** *a.* not lowering surface tension. **-isieren,** *v.t.* investigate by capillary analysis.

**Kapillarität,** *f.* capillarity.

**Kapillaritätsanziehung,** *f.* capillary attraction.

**Kapillar-kraft,** *f.* capillary force. **-rohr,** **-röhrchen,** *n.,* **-röhre,** *f.* capillary tube. **-spannung,** *f.* capillary tension. **-wirkung,** *f.* capillary action.

**Kapir,** *m.* kefir.

**Kapitel,** *n.* chapter.

**Kapocköl,** *n.* kapok oil.

**Kappe,** *f.* cap; hood; top, dome, crown, etc.

**kappeln,** *v.t.* top.

**kappen,** *v.t.* top (trees); cut; caponize.

**Kappen-flasche,** *f.* bottle with cap. **-pfeffer,** *m.* Guinea pepper.

**Kaprinsäure,** etc. see Caprinsäure, etc.

**Kapsel,** *f.* capsule; case, box; (priming) cap; (*Founding*) chill, mold; (*Ceram.*) sagger.

**kapsel-artig, -förmig,** *a.* capsular.

**Kapsel-guss,** *m.* casting in chills; chilled work. **-ton,** *m.* sagger clay.

**Kapuziner,** *m.* Capuchin. **-kresse,** *f.* Indian cress, nasturtium.

**Kapwein,** *m.* Cape wine.

**Kapyr,** *n.* kefir.

**Karaghenmoos,** *n.* carrageen, Irish moss.

**karaibisch,** *a.* Caribbean.

**karamelisieren,** *v.t.* caramelize.

**Karapöl,** *n.* carap oil, carapa oil.

**Karat-gewicht,** *n.* troy weight. **-gold,** *n.* alloyed gold.

**karatieren,** *v.t.* alloy (gold or silver).

**Karatierung,** *f.* alloying (of gold or silver).

**-karatig, -karätig,** *a.* -carat (as, achtzehn-*karatig,* eighteen-carat).

**Karb-.** see Carb-.

**Kardamom,** *m.* cardamom. **-öl,** *n.* cardamom oil.

**Kardobenedikt,** *m.* blessed thistle.

**Karfunkel,** *m.* carbuncle. **-stein,** *m.* garnet, esp. almandite.

**karg,** *a.* stingy, close; poor (soil).

**kargen,** *v.i.* be sparing.

**kärglich,** *a.* sparing, spare, scanty.

**karibisch,** *a.* Caribbean.

**Kariteöl,** *n.* karite oil, shea butter.

**Karmalaun,** *m.* (*Micros.*) carmalum.

**Karmelitergeist,** *m.* Carmelite water (an old toilet water made from balm mint).

**karmesin,** *a.* crimson.

**Karmesinbeeren,** *f.pl.* kermes berries, kermes.

**karmesin-farbig,** *a.* crimson-colored. **-rot,** *a.* crimson-red, crimson.

**Karmin,** *m.* carmine. **-blau,** *n.* indigo carmine. **-farbe,** *f.* carmine color, carmine.

**karminfarben,** *a.* carmine.

**Karminlack,** *m.* carmine lake.

**Karminochinon,** *n.* carminoquinone.

**karminrot,** *a.* carmine-red, carmine.

**Karmin-rot,** *n.* carmine red. **-säure,** *f.* carminic acid. **-spat,** *m.* (*Min.*) carminite. **-stoff,** *m.* carminic acid.

**karmoisin,** *a.* crimson.

**Karmoisin,** *n.* carmoisin (a dye).

**Karnallit,** *m.* carnallite.

**Karnauba-.** = Carnauba-.

**Karneol,** *m.* carnelian.

**kärntisch, kärntnerisch,** *a.* Carinthian.

**Karo,** *n.* check, checker, square.

**Karobe,** *f.* carob, carob bean.

**Karotin,** *n.* carotene, (formerly) carotin.

**Karotte,** *f.* carrot.

**Karpfen,** *m.,* **Karpfe,** *f.* carp.

**Karraghenmoos,** *n.* carrageen, Irish moss.

**Karre,** *f.* wheelbarrow; cart.

**Karren,** *m.* cart; wheelbarrow; truck; car.

**Karst,** *m.* mattock, hoe; (*Geog.*) Karst, karst.

**Kartäuser-likör,** *m.* chartreuse. **-pulver,** *n.* Carthusian powder (kermes mineral).

**Karte,** *f.* card; ticket; map; chart; menu; charter.

**Kartei,** *f.* card index. **-karte,** *f.* index card. **-wesen,** *n.* card indexing, card indexes.

**Karten-blatt,** *n.* card. **-papier,** *n.* cardboard.

**Karthäuser-.** = Kartäuser-.

**Kartoffel,** *f.* potato. **-branntwein,** *m.* potato spirits. **-brei,** *m.* mashed potatoes. **-fuselöl,** *n.* fusel oil from potatoes. **-mehl,** *n.* potato flour. **-spiritus,** *m.* potato spirits. **-stärke,** *f.* potato starch. **-zucker,** *m.* potato sugar (glucose from potato starch).

**Karton,** *m.* carton, (paste)board; carton, pasteboard box.

**Kartonage,** *f.* = Kartonnage.

**kartonieren,** *v.t.* bind in boards.

**Kartonnage,** *f.* paper board, pasteboard, cardboard; paper-board box, carton.

**Kartonnagen-fabrikation,** *f.* paper-board making; carton making. **-leim,** *m.* boxmakers' glue.

**Kartonpapier,** *n.* paper board.

**Kartothek,** *f.* card collection, card catalog or index.

**Kartusche,** *f.* cartridge; cartouche.

**Karub,** *m.,* **Karube,** *f.* carob.

**Karzinom,** *n.* (*Med.*) carcinoma.

**Kaschmir,** *m.* cashmere.

**Kaschu,** *n.* catechu, cutch.

**kaschutieren,** *v.t.* dye with catechu or cutch.

**Käse,** *m.* cheese; cheese-shaped object, as a disk of fireclay used as a crucible stand.

**käseartig,** *a.* cheesy, caseous.

**Käse-bildung,** *f.* cheese formation; caseation. **-firnis,** *m.* (*Med.*) vernix caseosa.

**Kasein,** *n.* casein. (See Casein-.)

**Käse-lab,** *n.* rennet. **-leim,** *m.* casein glue.

**käsen,** *v.i.* curd, curdle.

**Käse-pappel,** *f.* wild mallow (*Malva sylvestris*). **-säure,** *f.* lactic acid. **-stoff,** *m.* casein. **-wasser,** *n.* whey.

**käsig,** *a.* cheesy, caseous, curdy.

**Kaskarillenrinde,** *f.* cascarilla bark.

**kaspisch,** *a.* Caspian.

**Kassaunzucker,** *m.* raw or muscovado sugar, cassonade.

**Kassawa,** *f.* cassava. **-mehl,** *n.* cassava starch, cassava.

**Kasse,** *f.* (money) box, chest, safe; cash; pay office, ticket office, etc.

**Kasseler Braun, Kassler Braun.** Cassel brown.

**Kasseler Erde.** Cassel earth.

**Kasseler-gelb,** *n.* Cassel yellow. **-grün,** *n.* Cassel green.

**Kasserolle,** *f.* casserole.

**Kassette,** *f.* sagger; casket, coffer; box.

**Kassia, Kassie,** *f.* cassia.

**Kassien-blüten,** *f.pl.* cassia buds. **-rinde,** *f.* cassia bark.

**Kassierer,** *m.* cashier, treasurer, ticket agent.

**Kassiuspurpur,** *m.* purple of Cassius.

**Kastanie,** *f.* chestnut.

**Kastanienauszug,** *m.* chestnut extract.

**kastanienbraun,** *a.* chestnut-brown, chestnut.

**Kästchen,** *n.* little chest, casket; alveolus.

**Kasten,** *m.* chest, box, case, trunk, frame; vat, back, beck; crucible (of a furnace); (*Founding*) flask; (*Ceram.*) sagger; (*Jewelry*) collet. **-blau,** *n.* pencil blue (indigo blue produced by vat dyeing).

**Kastoröl,** *n.* castor oil.

**katalonisch,** *a.* Catalan.

**Katalysator,** *m.* catalyst.

**katalysatorisch,** *a.* catalytic.

**Katalyse, Katalysis,** *f.* catalysis.

**katalysieren,** *v.t.* catalyze.

**katalytisch,** *a.* catalytic.

**Kataphorese,** *f.* cataphoresis.

**Katechinsäure,** *f.* catechuic acid (catechol).

**Katechu-gerbsäure,** *f.* catechutannic acid. **-säure,** *f.* catechuic acid (catechol).

**kathartisch,** *a.* cathartic.

**Kathoden-dichte,** *f.* cathode density. **-fläche,** *f.* cathode surface. **-raum,** *m.* cathode space, space around the cathode. **-strahl,** *m.* cathode ray.

**kathodisch,** *a.* cathodic.

**kathodochemisch,** *a.* cathodochemical.

**Katholyt,** *n.* catholyte.

**Kation,** *n.* cation, kation.

**Kattun,** *m.* calico, cotton (cloth). **-druck,** *m.* calico printing. **-druckerei,** *f.* calico printing; calico printery. **-fabrik,** *f.* calico factory, cotton mill. **-färberei,** *f.* cotton (cloth) dyeing or dye works. **-presse,** *f.* calico press.

**Kätzchen,** *n.* kitten; catkin.

**Katze,** *f.* cat; (*Paper*) thread in the stuff.

**Katzen-auge,** *n.* cat's-eye. **-baldrian,** *m.* (common) valerian. **-darm,** *m.* catgut. **-glimmer,** *m.,* **-gold,** *n.* cat gold (yellow mica). **-kraut,** *n.* cat thyme. **-minze,** *f.* catnip. **-münze,** *f.* catnip. **-minzöl,** *n.* catnip oil. **-silber,** *n.* cat silver (colorless mica).

**kaubar,** *a.* masticable.

**kauen,** *v.t.& i.* chew, masticate.

**Kauf,** *m.* purchase; bargain. **-blei,** *n.* merchant lead, commercial lead.

**kaufen,** *v.t.* buy, purchase.

**Käufer,** *m.* buyer, purchaser, customer.

**Kauf-gut,** . merchandise. **-handel,** *m.* trade, commerce. **-laden,** *m.* store, shop. **-leute,** *pl.* merchants, tradesmen.

**käufl.,** *abbrev.* käuflich.

**käuflich,** *a.* commercial, of commerce; merchantable, purchasable.

**Kaufmann,** *m.* merchant, tradesman.

**kaufmännisch,** *a.* mercantile, commercial, businesslike.

**Kauf-muster,** *n.* commercial sample. **-zink,** *n.* commercial zinc.

**Kaugummi,** *n.* chewing gum.

**kaum,** *adv.* scarcely, hardly.

**Kau-mittel,** *n.* masticatory. **-pfeffer,** *m.* betel.

**Kaupren,** *n.* cauprene.

**Kauprobe,** *f.* mastication test.

**Kauri-harz,** *n.* kauri resin, kauri. **-öl,** *n.* kauri oil.

**kaustifizieren,** *v.t.* causticize.

**Kaustifizierung,** *f.* causticizing, -cization.

**kaustisch,** *a.* caustic.

kaustizieren, v.t. causticize.
Kaustizierung, f. causticization.
Kaustizität, f. causticity.
Kautabak, m. chewing tobacco.
Kautel, f. precaution.
Kauter, m. (Med.) cautery.
Kauterien, n.pl. (Med.) cauteries.
kauterisieren, v.t. cauterize.
kautschen, v.t. couch.
Kautschin, n. caoutchene (dipentene).
Kautschuk, m.& n. caoutchouc, rubber. (For compounds see also Gummi-.) -feigenbaum, m. rubber fig (Ficus elastica). -firnis, m. rubber varnish. -kitt, m. rubber cement. -milch, -saft, m. rubber latex.
Kaverne, f. cavity.
Kawa-pfeffer, m. kava. -säure, f. kavaic acid.
keck, a. bold.
Kegel, m. cone; pin, skittle.
Kegel-. conical. -fläche, f. conical surface. -flasche, f. conical flask (as an Erlenmeyer flask).
kegelförmig, a. cone-shaped, conical, coniform.
Kegelglas, n. conical glass; conical flask.
kegelig, a. conical, cone-shaped.
Kegel-rad, n. bevel wheel; cone wheel. -schnitt, m. conic section.
Kehl-ader, f. jugular vein. -deckel, m. epiglottis. -drüse, f. thyroid gland.
Kehle, f. throat, larynx; channel, flute, groove.
kehlen, v.t. groove, channel, flute.
Kehlkopf, m. larynx.
Kehlkopf-. laryngeal.
Kehre, f. turn, turning; direction.
kehren, v.t. sweep, brush; turn.—v.r.& i. turn.
Kehricht, m.& n. sweepings, rubbish.
Kehr-salpeter, f. saltpeter sweepings. -salz, n. salt sweepings.
Keil, m. wedge; cuneus; key, cotter.
keil-ähnlich, -artig, a. wedge-shaped, cuneiform, sphenoid.
Keilbein, n. sphenoid bone; cuneiform bone.
keilen, v.t. wedge; key.
keilförmig, a.= keilähnlich.
Keilpaar, n. pair of wedges, double wedge.
Keim, m. germ; embryo; (of crystallization) nucleus.
Keim-. embryonic, germinal, germinating. -apparat, m. germinating apparatus.
keimbar, a. germinable.
Keimblatt, n. cotyledon; germinal layer.
keim-blätterig, a. cotyledonous. -blattlos, a. acotyledonous.
keimen, v.i. germinate.
Keimentwickelung, f. development of the germ.
keimfähig, a. capable of germinating, germinable.

Keimfähigkeit, f. capability of germinating, germinating power.
keimfrei, a. free from germs (or from nuclei), sterile.
Keimgift, n. poison from germs, bacterial toxin; poison for germs.
keimhaltig, a. containing germs (or nuclei).
Keim-haut, f. blastoderm. -kraft, f. germinating power. -kristall, m. nucleus crystal, crystal nucleus. -ling, n. germ, embryo. -prüfung, f. germination test. -stoff, m., -substanz, f. germinal matter, blastema.
keimtötend, p.a. germicidal.—keimtötendes Mittel, germicide.
keimunfähig, a. incapable of germinating.
Keimung, f. germination.
keimvoll, a. full of germs (or of nuclei).
Keim-wirkung, f. germ action; (of crystallization) action of nuclei. -zelle, f. germ cell.
kein, a. no, not a.
keiner, pron. no one, none, neither.
keinerlei, a. of no sort, not any.
keinesfalls, dv. in no case.
keineswegs, adv. by no means.
keinmal, adv. not once, never.
-keit. a suffix used like -heit (which see); -ness, -hood, -dom.
Keks, Kek, m. small cake, cookie.
Kelch, m. cup; calyx; infundibulum. -blatt, n. sepal.
kelchförmig, a. cup-shaped.
Kelch-glas, n. cup-shaped test glass. -mensur, f. measuring cup.
Kelen, n. (Pharm.) kelene (ethyl chloride).
Kelle, f. ladle; scoop; trowel.
kellen, v.t. ladle.
Keller, m. cellar.
Kellerei, f. cellarage; brewery.
Keller-geschoss, n. basement. -hals, m. mezereon (Daphne mezereum).
Kelter, f. winepress.
keltern, v.t. press (grapes).
Kelterwein, n. wine from expressed juice.
Keltium, n. celtium.
Kenn-. characteristic, distinctive, indicative.
kennbar, a. knowable, distinguishable; remarkable.
kennen, v.t. know.
Kenner, m. connoisseur, professional.
Kenn-linie, f. characteristic line. -marke, f. identification mark.
kenntlich, a. knowable, distinguishable; distinctive; distinct, clear.— — machen, make known, characterize.
Kenntnis, f. knowledge; information, notice.
Kenn-wort, n. (Com.) code word. -zeichen, n. mark, sign, indication; characteristic; criterion; symptom.

**kennzeichnen**, *v.t.* mark, denote; distinguish; characterize.

**Kennziffer**, *f.* characteristic (of a logarithm); code number.

**Keph-. ceph-.**

**Keramik**, *f.* ceramics.

**keramisch**, *a.* ceramic.

**Kerargyrit**, *m.*, **Kerat**, *n.* cerargyrite.

**Kerbe**, *f.*, **Kerb**, *m.* notch, nick, groove, slit, slot.

**Kerbel**, *m.* (*Bot.*) chervil.

**kerben**, *v.t.* notch, indent, groove.

**kerbig**, *a.* notched, indented; grooved.

**Kerb-tier**, *n.* insect. **-tierkunde**, *f.* entomology. **-zähigkeit**, *f.* (*Metal.*) impact resistance or strength (in notched-bar test).

**Kerf**, *m.* insect;= Kerbe. **-kunde**, *f.* entomology.

**Kermes-beeren**, *f.pl.* kermes berries, kermes; (vegetabilische) pokeberries. **-körner**, *n.pl.* kermes grains, kermes.

**kermesrot**, *a.* scarlet.

**Kermesschildlaus**, *f.* kermes insect.

**Kern**, *m.* nucleus; kernel, pip, stone; pith; core; heart; gist; (*Soap*) curd.

**Kern-**. nuclear; pithy, choice. **-abstand**, *m.* nuclear distance. **-aufbau**, *m.* nuclear structure; nuclear synthesis. **-bewegung**, *f.* nuclear motion.

**kernchloriert**, *a.* chlorinated in the nucleus.

**Kern-eisen**, *n.* mottled white pig iron; (*Elec.*) core iron. **-farbe**, *f.*, **-färbemittel**, *n.*, **-farbstoff**, *m.* nuclear stain. **-färbung**, *f.* (*Micros.*) nuclear staining.

**kern-faul**, *a.* rotten at the core or heart. **-frisch**, *a.* quite fresh. **-gebunden**, *p.a.* united to a (or the) nucleus.

**Kern-gehäuse**, *n.* core. **-guss**, *m.* (*Founding*) cored work.

**kernhaltig**, *a.* containing a nucleus or kernel, nucleate(d).

**Kern-hefe**, *f.* seed yeast. **-holz**, *n.* heart wood.

**kernig**, *a.* strong, stout, solid, vigorous; (of liquors) full; (of leather) compact; kernelly; pithy.

**-kernig**. **-nuclear**.

**Kernigkeit**, *f.* (*Leather*) fullness, body.

**Kern-isomerie**, *f.* nucleus (or nuclear) isomerism. **-körper**, *m.*, **-körperchen**, *n.* nucleolus. **-ladung**, *f.* nuclear charge. **-ladungszahl**, *f.* nuclear-charge number. **-leder**, *n.* bend leather.

**kernlos**, *a.* without a nucleus, anucleate.

**Kern-mehl**, *n.* best grade of flour, firsts. **-membran**, *f.* nuclear membrane. **-milch**, *f.* buttermilk.

**kernnah**, *a.* close to the nucleus.

**Kern-obst**, *n.* stone fruit. **-öl**, *n.* kernel oil, specif. palm kernel oil. **-physik**, *f.* nuclear

physics. **-polymerie**, *f.* nuclear polymerism. **-salz**, *n.* rock salt. **-sand**, *m.* core sand. **-schatten**, *m.* complete shadow, umbra. **-schwarz**, *n.* a carbon black from fruit kernels; (*Micros.*) nucleus black. **-schwingung**, *f.* nuclear vibration. **-seife**, *f.* curd soap, grain soap. **-spin**, *m.* nuclear spin. **-synthese**, *f.* nuclear synthesis. **-teilung**, *f.* nuclear division. **-theorie**, *f.* nucleus theory.

**kerntrocken**, *a.* thoroly dry.

**Kern-wolle**, *f.* prime wool. **-zerfall**, *m.* nuclear disintegration.

**Kerze**, *f.* candle; (*Mach.*) spark plug.

**Kerzenstärke**, *f.* candle power.

**Kessel**, *m.* kettle, cauldron, copper; boiler; basin, reservoir; kennel. **-blech**, *n.* boiler plate, boiler iron. **-druck**, *m.* boiler pressure. **-fabrik**, *f.* boiler factory.

**kesselförmig**, *a.* kettle-shaped.

**Kessel-gas**, *n.* boiler flue gas. **-haus**, *n.* boiler house. **-hausbetrieb**, *m.* boiler-house operation or management. **-kohle**, *f.* boiler coal, steam coal. **-niederschlag**, *m.* deposit in a kettle, boiler or reservoir. **-spannung**, *f.* boiler pressure. **-speisewasser**, *n.* boiler feed water. **-speisung**, *f.* boiler feeding, boiler feed.

**Kesselstein**, *m.* boiler scale; compass brick. **-ablagerung**, *f.* deposit(ion) of boiler scale. **-beseitigung**, *f.* removal of boiler scale. **-beseitigungsmittel**, *n.* (boiler) scale remover, disincrustant. **-bilder**, **-bildner**, *m.* (boiler) scale former. **-kruste**, *f.* incrustation of boiler scale. **-lösemittel**, **-lösungsmittel**, *n.* (boiler) scale solvent, disincrustant. **-mittel**, *n.* boiler compound, disincrustant. **-schicht**, *f.* layer of (boiler) scale. **-verhütung**, *f.* (boiler) scale prevention. **-verhütungsmittel**, *n.* boiler compound, anti-incrustant.

**Kessel-wagen**, *m.* tank car; tank wagon. **-wand**, *f.* boiler wall. **-wasser**, *n.* boiler water.

**Ketogruppe**, *f.* keto group.

**Keton**, *n.* ketone.

**ketonartig**, *a.* ketonic: ketonelike.

**Keton-säure**, *f.* ketonic acid, keto acid. **-spaltung**, *f.* ketonic cleavage. **-zucker**, *m.* ketonic sugar.

**Ketoverbindung**, *f.* keto compound, ketonic compound.

**Kette**, *f.* chain; train, series; warp (of a fabric); bondage; (*Elec.*) cell, element (also, circuit).

**ketten**, *v.t.* link, join, connect; chain. **-artig**, *a.* of the nature of a chain, chainlike.

**Ketten-bruch**, *m.* (*Math.*) continued fraction. **-druck**, *m.* warp printing.

**kettenförmig**, *a.* having the form of a chain, chain.

**Ketten-glied**, *n.* link (or member) of a chain.

-isomerie, f. chain isomerism. -rad, n. sprocket wheel. -reaktion, f. chain reaction.

keuchen, v.i. gasp, pant.

Keuchhusten, m. whooping cough.

Keule, f. pestle; club; leg, joint (of meat).

keulenförmig, a. club-shaped, clavate, claviform.

kgl., abbrev. (königlich) royal.

Khakifarbe, f. khaki color.

khakifarben, a. khaki-colored.

Kicher, -erbse, f. chick-pea.

Kiefer, m. jawbone, jaw, maxilla.

Kiefer, f. pine, esp. Scotch pine (Pinus sylvestris.)

Kiefer-. maxillary.

Kiefer-, Kiefern-. pine. -harz, n. pine resin, rosin. -holz, n. pine(wood). -nadel, f. pine needle. -nadelöl, n. pine-needle oil.

Kiel, m. quill; keel.

Kieme, f. gill, branchia.

Kiemen-. branchial.

Kien, m. resinous pine. -apfel, m. pine cone. -baum, m. pine tree. -harz, m. pine resin, rosin. -holz, n. (resinous) pine wood, pine. -holzöl, n. pine wood oil.

kienig, a. piny, resinous.

Kien-öl, n. pine oil, oil of turpentine. -russ, m. pine soot (form of lampblack). -stock, m. (Metal.) carcass. -teer, m. pine tar.

Kies, m. pyrites; gravel; shingle. -abbrand, m. roasted pyrites.

kies-ähnlich, a. pyritous; gravelly. -artig, a. pyritic; gravelly.

Kiesbrenner, m. pyrites burner.

Kiesel, m. flint; silica, silex.

Kiesel-. siliceous; silica.

kieselartig, a. flinty, siliceous.

Kiesel-chlorid, n. silicon (tetra)chloride. -erde, f. silica.

kieselerdehaltig, a. siliceous, siliciferous.

Kiesel-erdehydrat, n. hydrated silica. -fluorbaryum, n. barium fluosilicate. -fluorblei, n. lead fluosilicate. -fluorid, n. silicon (tetra)fluoride. -fluorkalium, n. potassium fluosilicate. -fluornatrium, n. sodium fluosilicate. -fluorsalz, n. fluosilicate. -fluorsäure, f. fluosilicic acid. -fluorverbindung, f. fluosilicate. -fluorwasserstoff, m., -fluorwasserstoffsäure, f. fluosilicic acid. -fluss, m. siliceous flux. -flusssäure, f. fluosilicic acid. -galmei, m. siliceous calamine (hydrous zinc silicate). -gips, m. vulpinite (variety of anhydrite). -glas, n. flint glass; siliceous calamine. -gur, -guhr, m. diatomaceous earth, kieselguhr. -gurstein, m. kieselguhr brick.

kiesel-haltig, a. siliceous, siliciferous. -hart, a. hard as flint.

Kieselhärte, f. hardness of flint.

kieselig, a. siliceous; flinty; pebbly.

Kieselkalk, m. siliceous limestone. -eisen, n. ilvaite.

kieselkalkhaltig, a. silicilcalcareous.

Kiesel-kalkspat, m. wollastonite. -körper, m. siliceous body. -kreide, f. siliceous chalk. -kristall, m. crystal of silica, rock crystal. -kupfer, n. chrysocolla. -mangan, n. rhodonite. -metall, n. silicon. -papier, n. flint paper. -pulver, n. pebble powder.

kieselreich, a. siliceous; pebbly.

Kieselsandstein, m. siliceous sandstone.

kieselsauer, a. of or combined with silicic acid, silicate of.

Kieselsäure, f. silicic acid. -anhydrid, n. silicic anhydride, silicon dioxide. -gallerte, f. silica jelly, silica gel. -gehalt, m. silicic acid content, silica content. -gel, n. silica gel.

kieselsäure-haltig, a. containing silicic acid, siliceous. -reich, a. rich in silicic acid.

Kieselsäure-salz, n. silicate. -seife, f. silicated soap.

Kiesel-schiefer, m. siliceous schist. -sinter, m. siliceous sinter. -spat, m. albite. -stein, m. pebble, gravelstone, flint. -tuff, m. siliceous sinter. -verbindung, f. silicate. -wasserstoff, m. hydrogen silicide. -wasserstoffsäure, f. hydrosilicic acid. -wismut, m. bismuth silicate. -wolframsäure, f. silicotungstic acid. -zinkerz, n., -zinkspat, m. siliceous calamine; willemite. -zuschlag, m. siliceous flux.

Kiesfilter, n. gravel filter.

kieshaltig, a. pyritiferous; gravelly.

kiesig, a. gravelly, gritty; pyritic.

Kies-ofen, m. pyrites burner, pyrites kiln. -sand, m. gravelly sand.

Kiff, m. tan, tanbark.

Kilowattstunde, f. (Elec.) kilowatt-hour.

Kind, n. child.

Kinder-balsam, m. soothing syrup. -mehl, n. (powdered) infant food. -nährmittel, n. infant food. -pech, n. meconium.

Kinder-pulver, n. (Pharm.) compound powder of rhubarb. -schleim, m., -schmiere, f. vernix caseosa.

Kindespech, n. meconium.

Kindeswasser, n. amniotic fluid.

Kindheit, f. childhood, infancy.

Kindspech, n. meconium.

Kinetik, f. kinetics.

kinetisch, a. kinetic.

Kinn, n. chin. -backen, m. jaw, jawbone. -lade, f. jaw.

Kino, n. motion pictures, cinema; kino. -gerbsäure, f. kinotannic acid.

Kipp-. tilting, tipping, dumping.

Kippe, f. tilt; hinge. —auf der —, atilt; on the verge of disaster.

**kippen,** *v.t.* tilt, tip, tip over.

**Kipper,** *m.* tipping device, tipper.

**Kippofen,** *m.* tilting furnace.

**Kipp'scher Apparat.** Kipp apparatus.

**Kirche,** *f.* church.

**kirr, kirre,** *a.* tame.

**Kirsch-baum,** *m.* cherry tree. **-branntwein,** *m.* kirsch (see Kirschwasser); cherry brandy.

**Kirsche,** *f.* cherry; small bulb.

**Kirsch-farben, -farbig,** *a.* cherry-colored.

**Kirsch-geist,** *m.* kirsch (see Kirschwasser). **-glut,** *f.* cherry-red heat. **-gummi, -harz,** *n.* cherry gum. **-kernöl,** *n.* cherry-kernel oil. **-lorbeer,** *m.* cherry laurel.

**kirschrot,** *a.* cherry-red.

**Kirschrotglut,** *f.* cherry-red heat (about 850°).

**kirschrotwarm,** *a.* cherry-red (hot).

**Kirsch-saft,** *m.* cherry juice. **-wasser,** *n.* kirsch, kirschwasser (a liquor distilled from fermented cherry juice); bitter-almond water. **-wurzelkraut,** *n.* athamanta (*Peucedanum oreoselinum*).

**Kissen,** *n.* cushion; pillow, bolster; pad.

**Kistchen,** *n.* small chest, box or case.

**Kiste,** *f.* chest, box, case.

**Kistenzucker,** *m.* muscovado.

**Kitt,** *m.* cement; lute; mastic; putty.

**kitt-artig,** *a.* cementlike; puttylike. **-bar,** *a.* capable of being cemented or luted.

**kitten,** *v.t.* cement; lute, putty, glue.

**Kitt-erde,** *f.* luting clay; pozzuolana. **-masse,** *f.* cementing composition; (*Anat.*) cement substance. **-öl,** *n.* putty oil. **-substanz,** *f.* cement substance, cement.

**Kitzel,** *m.* tickling; itching; longing, desire.

**kitzeln,** *v.t.* tickle.

**Kjeldahlkolben,** *m.* Kjeldahl flask.

**K.K., k.k.,** *abbrev.* (kaiserlich-königlich) imperial-royal.

**k.kal.,** *abbrev.* (kleine Kalorie) small calorie.

**kl.,** *abbrev.* (kaum löslich) scarcely soluble; (klein) small.

**Kl.,** *abbrev.* (Klasse) class.

**Kladstein,** *m.* place brick (brick not fully burned).

**klaffen,** *v.i.* gape, yawn; split.

**kläffen,** *v.i.* bark; clamor.

**Klafter,** *f.* cord (of wood); fathom.

**Klage,** *f.* complaint, grievance; claim; suit, accusation; lament.

**klagen,** *v.i.* lament; complain; sue.

**Klai,** *m.* clay.

**klamm,** *a.* tight, close, narrow; clammy.

**Klammer,** *f.* clamp, clasp, cramp; parenthesis; (eckige) bracket; brace.

**klammern,** *v.t.* cramp, clamp, rivet, fasten.

**Klampe,** *f.* clamp, cramp, clasp; cleat.

**klang,** *pret.* of klingen.

**Klang,** *m.* sound, ring, clang; timbre. **-zinn,** *n.* fine tin, sonorous tin.

**Klapp-.** hinged, folding, tilting, swinging.

**klappbar,** *a.* hinged.

**Klappe,** *f.* flap, trap, lid; damper; (clack) valve; stop.

**klappen,** *v.t.* clap, flap.—*v.i.* clap, strike, clatter.

**Klappen-.** valvular. **-ventil,** *n.* clack valve, flap valve.

**klappern,** *v.i.* rattle, clatter, chatter.

**Klapper-rose,** *f.* corn poppy. **-schlange,** *f.* rattlesnake. **-stein,** *m.* eaglestone (nodular clay ironstone).

**klapsen,** *v.t.* clap, smack, slap.

**klar,** *a.* clear.

**Klär-.** clearing, clarifying, fining, settling. **-anlage,** *f.* (*Sewage*) purification plant. **-apparat,** *n.* settling or clarifying apparatus. **-bassin,** *n.* settling tank or reservoir. **-becken,** *n.* settling basin or vessel. **-behälter,** *m.* settling tank or vessel. **-bottich,** *m.* clearing tub, settling vat.

**Klare,** *f.* clear liquid.

**Kläre,** *f.* clarifier; clear (clarified) liquid; coal dust; boneash.

**klären,** *v.t.* clear, clarify, purify, defecate.— *v.r.* clear, clear up.

**Klären,** *n.* = Klärung.

**Klär-fass,** *n.* clearing cask or tub, clarifier, settler; (*Brewing*) cleansing cask; (*Vinegar*) fining tun. **-filter,** *n.* filter. **-flasche,** *f.* decanting bottle (or flask). **-gefäss,** *n.* (*Sugar*) clarifier.

**Klarheit,** *f.* clearness, clarity.

**klarieren,** *v.t.* (*Sugar*) clear, purge.

**Klär-kasten,** *m.* (*Paper*) settler. **-kessel,** *m.* (*Sugar*, etc.) clarifier.

**klarkochen,** *v.t.* boil till clear.

**Klär-mittel,** *n.* clarifying or clearing agent, clarifier, fining. **-pfanne,** *f.* (*Sugar*) clearing pan, clarifier, defecating pan.

**klarschleifen,** *v.t.* grind smooth.

**Klär-sel,** *n.* (*Sugar*) clear(ing) liquor, fine liquor, clear, clairce. **-staub,** *m.* boneash.

**Klärung,** *f.* clarification, clarifying, clearing.

**Klärungs-fass,** *n.* = Klärfass. **-mittel,** *n.* = Klärmittel. **-prozess,** *m.* clarification process.

**Klarwerden,** *n.* clearing up, becoming clear.

**Klasse,** *f.* class.

**Klassenordnung,** *f.* classification.

**klassieren,** *v.t.* classify (as ore).

**klassifizieren,** *v.t.* classify.

**Klassiker,** *m.* classic.

**klassisch,** *a.* classic, classical.

**klastisch,** *a.* clastic.

**Klatsch,** *m.* clap, pop, slap, dab, etc.; gossip.

**klatschen,** *v.i.* clap, pop, flap, etc.; chat, gossip.

**Klatsch-präparat,** *n.* (*Micros.*) a smear prepara

tion made by pressing the material between two cover glasses and sliding them apart. -rose, *f.* corn poppy.

**klauben**, *v.t.* pick, sort.

**Klaue**, *f.* claw; paw; hoof; clutch, grasp.

**Klauen-fett**, *n.*, -öl, *n.* oil from the feet of animals, specif. neat's-foot oil. -mehl, *n.* hoof meal.

**Klause**, *f.* cell; closet; sink.

**Klaviatur**, *f.* keys, keyboard.

**Klavier**, *n.* piano. -draht, *m.* piano wire.

**Kleb-, Klebe-**, adhesive, adherent, sticking.

**Klebäther**, *m.* collodion.

**Klebe**, *f.* dodder.

**Klebe-korn**, *n.* (*Biol.*) microsome. -material, *n.* adhesive material. -mittel, *n.* adhesive, agglutinant.

**kleben**, *v.i.* stick, adhere.—*v.t.* stick, glue, gum, paste.—**klebend**, *p.a.* adherent, adhesive, glutinative, agglutinant.

**Klebepflaster**, *n.* adhesive plaster.

**Kleber**, *m.* gluten; adhesive; sticker, gluer. -brot, *n.* gluten bread.

**kleber-haltig**, *a.* containing gluten.

**kleberig**, *a.* sticky, adhesive, viscid, glutinous.

**Kleberigkeit**, *f.* viscidity, viscosity.

**Kleber-leim**, *m.* gluten glue. -mehl, *n.* aleurone.

**Kleberolle**, *f.* (roll of) gummed tape or adhesive tape.

**Kleber-protein**, *n.* gluten protein. -schicht, *f.* (*Bot.*) aleurone layer.

**Klebe-stoff**, *m.* adhesive substance, cement; adhesive. -wachs, *n.* adhesive wax, sticking wax.

**klebfähig**, *a.* adhesive.

**Kleb-fähigkeit**, *f.* adhesiveness. -kraft, *f.* adhesive power. -kraut, *n.* cleavers (*Galium*). -mittel, *n.* adhesive, agglutinant.

**klebrig, klebricht**, *a.* = kleberig.

**Klebrigkeit**, *f.* stickiness, viscidity.

**Kleb-sand**, *m.* (*Ceram.*) luting sand, daubing sand. -schmutz, *m.* adhering dirt. -stoff, *m.* = Klebestoff. -wachs, *n.* adhesive wax, sticking wax. -zwecken, *m.pl.* adhesive purposes.

**klecken**, *v.i.* blot; blur; daub.

**Klecks**, *m.* blot, splotch.

**Klee**, *m.* clover, trefoil.—ewiger —, Luzerner —, alfalfa, lucern.—spanischer —, türkischer —, sainfoin.

**Kleebaum**, *m.* = Hopfenbaum.

**kleerot**, *a.* clover-red, purplish-red.

**Klee-salz**, *n.* salt of sorrel (acid potassium oxalate). -samenöl, *n.* cloverseed oil.

**kleesauer**, *a.* of or combined with oxalic acid, oxalate of.

**Klee-säure**, *f.* oxalic acid. -seide, *f.* dodder.

**Klei**, *m.* clay; clay soil. -absudbad, *n.* (*Dyeing*) bran decoction.

**Kleid**, *n.* garment, dress, clothing, garb.

**kleiden**, *v.t.* dress, clothe; fit.

**Kleiderstoff**, *m.* garment material.

**Kleidung**, *f.* clothing, dressing, costume.

**Kleie**, *f.* bran.

**kleienartig**, *a.* branny, furfuraceous.

**Kleien-bad**, *n.*, -beize, *f.* bran drench, bran steep. -brot, *n.* bran bread. -essig, *m.* bran vinegar. -mehl, *n.* pollard. -wasser, *n.* bran water.

**Kleierde**, *f.* clay earth.

**kleiig**, *a.* clayey.

**klein**, *a.* small, little; short.—kleinstes Lebewesen, microörganism.

**Klein**, *n.* (*Mining*) smalls. -asien, *n.* Asia Minor. -bessemerei, *f.* small Bessemer plant; small-scale Bessemerizing. -betrieb, *m.* work on a small scale; small business.

**kleinen**, *v.t.* pulverize, comminute.

**Klein-färber**, *m.* clothes dyer. -gärmethode, *f.* micro fermentation method. -gefüge, *n.* fine structure, microstructure.

**kleingepulvert**, *a.* finely powdered.

**Klein-handel**, *m.* retail trade. -heit, *f.* smallness, minuteness. -hirn, *n.* cerebellum. -igkeit, *f.* trifle.

**klein-körnig**, *a.* small-grained, fine-grained. -kristallinisch, *a.* finely crystalline, in small crystals.

**Kleinlebewesen**, *n.* microörganism.

**kleinlich**, *a.* petty, paltry, mean.

**Kleinlichtbildkunst**, *f.* photomicrography.

**kleinluckig**, *a.* finely porous; close-grained.

**Kleinmühle**, *f.* pulverizing mill.

**Kleinod**, *n.* jewel, gem, ornament.

**kleinstädtisch**, *a.* provincial.

**Kleinverkauf**, *m.* retailing, retail.

**Kleister**, *m.* paste; size (thin paste). -bildung, *f.* formation of paste.

**kleisterig**, *a.* pasty, sticky.

**kleistern**, *v.t.* paste; size (with paste).

**Kleisterzähigkeit**, *f.* viscidity (or glutinousness) of starch.

**kleistrig**, *a.* pasty, sticky.

**Klemmbacke**, *f.* (*Mach.*) jaw.

**Klemme**, *f.* clamp; clip; nippers, tongs, forceps; (*Elec.*) terminal; dilemma.

**klemmen**, *v.t.* pinch, squeeze, bind, jam.

**Klemmenspannung**, *f.* (*Elec.*) terminal voltage.

**Klemmer**, *m.* pinchcock; nose glasses.

**Klemm-schraube**, *f.* binding screw, set screw. -verbindung, *f.* clamp connection; screw fastening.

**Klette**, *f.* bur; burdock.

**Klettenwurzel**, *f.* (*Pharm.*) lappa, burdock root.

**klettern**, *v.i.* climb.

**Klima**, *n.* climate.

**klimatisch**, *a.* climatic.

**klimmen**, *v.i.* climb.

klimpern, *v.i.* jingle, tinkle, strum.

Klinge, *f.* blade; sword.

Klingel, *f.* (small) bell.

klingeln, *v.i.* ring; tinkle, jingle.

klingen, *v.i.* sound, ring, clink.

Kling-glas, *n.* flint glass. -stein, *m.* clinkstone (phonolite).

Klinke, *f.* latch; (door) handle.

Klinker, *m.* clinker, (hard) brick.

Klino-achse, *f.* (*Cryst.*) clino axis. -edrit, *n.* (*Min.*) clinohedrite. -klas, *m.* clinoclase, clinoclasite.

Klippe, *f.* cliff, rock, crag.

klirren, *v.i.* clink, clatter.

Klischee, *n.* engraved plate, stereotype, cliché, electrotype, electro.

klischieren, *v.t.* stereotype; electrotype.

Klistier, *n.* enema.

Kloake, *f.* cloaca, sewer; sink; cesspool.

Kloaken-gas, *n.* sewer gas. -wasser, *n.* sewage.

Kloben, *m.* pulley, block; vise; pincers; log.

klomm, *pret.* of klimmen.

klonisch, *a.* (*Med.*) clonic.

klopfen, *v.t.& i.* beat, knock, tap; scale (a boiler); drive (a nail); break (stone).

klopffest, *a.* knockproof, antiknock.

Klopf-festigkeit, *f.* resistance to knocking. -holz, *n.* mallet, beater. -sieb, *n.* shaking or tapping sieve.

Klöppel, *m.* beater, knocker, clapper, etc.; (lace) bobbin.

Kloss, *m.* clod; dumpling.

Kloster, *n.* cloister.

Klotz, *m.* block, log, stump.

klotzen, *v.t.* (*Calico*) slop-pad.

Klotzschwarz, *n.* (*Dyeing*) slop-padded black.

Kluft, *f.* cleft, fissure; chasm; tongs.

klüften, *v.t.* cleave.

klüftig, *a.* split, cracked, creviced.

Klüftung, *f.* cleaving, segmentation.

klug, *a.* clever, knowing, wise, skilful.

Klümpchen, *n.* little lump, etc. (see Klumpen).

Klumpen, *m.* lump, mass; ingot; bloom; nugget; clot; clump; clod. -bildung, *f.* formation of lumps, clots, clumps, etc. (see Klumpen).

klumpig, klümperig, klümprig, *a.* clotted, clotty; lumpy.

Kluppe, *f.* pincers, tongs; diestock.

Kluppzange, *f.* forceps.

Klystier, *n.* enema.

k.M., *abbrev.* (kommenden Monats) of the coming month, of next month.

Knabbelkoks, *m.* crushed coke.

knabbern, *v.t.& i.* gnaw, nibble.

Knabe, *m.* boy.

knacken, *v.i.* crack; crackle, crepitate; click. —*v.t.* crack.

Knagge, *f.* cam, catch, tappet.

Knall, *m.* detonation; explosion, report, crack, pop.

Knall-, detonating; fulminating, fulminate of. -blei, *n.* fulminating lead.

knallen, *v.i.* detonate, fulminate; crack, pop, go off.

Knall-erbse, *f.* (*Fireworks*) torpedo. -flamme, *f.* oxyhydrogen flame.

Knallgas, *n.* detonating gas, specif. an explosive mixture of hydrogen and oxygen, oxyhydrogen gas. -flamme, *f.* oxyhydrogen flame. -gebläse, *n.* oxyhydrogen blowpipe. -licht, *n.* oxyhydrogen light. -lötapparat, *m.* oxyhydrogen blowpipe.

Knall-gebläse, *n.* oxyhydrogen blast. -glas, *n.* Rupert's drop; anaclastic glass. -gold, *n.* fulminating gold. -kraft, *f.* explosive force or power. -luft, *f.* detonating gas. -pulver, *n.* detonating powder. -pyrometer, *n.* explosion pyrometer -quecksilber, *n.* fulminating mercury (mercuric fulminate). -salpeter, *m.* ammonium nitrate. -satz, *m.* detonating composition.

knallsauer, *a.* of or combined with fulminic acid, fulminate of.

Knall-säure, *f.* fulminic acid. -silber, *n.* fulminating silver. -zucker, *m.* (*Expl.*) nitrosaccharose. -zünder, *m.* detonator. -zündmittel, *n.* detonating priming.

knapp, *a.* close, tight, narrow; scanty; exact.

Knappheit, *f.* tightness; conciseness; scarcity.

knarren, *v.i.* crackle, rattle, creak, squeak.

Knast, *m.* knot (in wood).

knattern, *v.i.* rattle, crackle; (*Motors*) knock.

Knäuel, Knauel, *m.* ball, coil (of thread, etc.); convolution. -drüse, *f.* sweat gland.

knäuelförmig, *a.* convoluted.

Knauf, *m.* knob, stud; capital.

Knäulchen, *n.* little (wound) ball or coil.

Knebel, *m.* stick; crossbar; (*Bot.*) slip.

Knecht, *m.* (man) servant; trestle, horse

kneifen, *v.t.* nip, squeeze, pinch, gripe.

Kneifzange, *f.* nippers.

Kneipe, *f.* pincers, nippers; beer party; tavern.

kneipen, *v.t.* nip, pinch, squeeze, gripe; drink (beer).

knetbar, *a.* kneadable, plastic.

kneten, *v.t.* knead; (*Ceram.*) pug.

Knetmaschine, *f.* kneading machine, malaxator; (*Ceram.*) pug mill.

Knick, *m.* break (in curves, etc.); sharp bend; crack, flaw.

knicken, *v.t.& i.* crack; break; buckle; collapse.

Knick-festigkeit, *f.* breaking strength; (of metals) buckling strength. -punkt, *m.* (in a curve) break.

Knie, *n.* knee; angle, elbow; sharp bend.

knieen, *v.i.* kneel.

knieförmig, *a.* knee-shaped, geniculate.

Knie-kehle, *f.* popliteal space. -rohr, *n.*, -röhre, *f.* elbow tube (or pipe), bent tube. -scheibe, *f.* kneepan, patella. -stück, *n.* (*Mach.*) elbow; knee, angle.

kniff, *pret.* of kneifen.

Kniff, *m.* pinch; crease; trick, device.

knirschen, *v.i.* crackle, grate, crunch, rustle.

Knirschpulver, *n.* a kind of coarse gunpowder.

Knistergold, *n.* Dutch metal, Dutch gold.

knistern, *v.i.* crackle, decrepitate, crepitate; (of silk) rustle.

Knistersalz, *n.* decrepitating salt.

Knitter, *m.* crease. -gold, *n.* = Knistergold.

knitterig, knittrig, *a.* creased, crumpled; crackling.

knittern, *v.i.* crackle; crumple.

Knoblauch, *m.* garlic.

knoblauchartig, *a.* garlic-like, garlicky.

Knoblauch-erz, *n.* (*Min.*) scorodite. -gamander, *m.* water germander. -öl, *n.* garlic oil.

Knöchel, *m.* knuckle; angle; (*pl.*) dice.

Knochen, *m.* bone.

Knochen-. bone, bony, osseous, osteo-. -abfall, *m.* bone waste, waste bone.

knochenähnlich, *a.* bonelike, osseous.

Knochenasche, *f.* bone ash.

knochenbildend, *p.a.* bone-forming.

Knochen-bruch, *m.* (bone) fracture. -dämpfapparat, *m.* bone steamer. -dünger, *m.* bone manure. -dungmehl, *n.* (*Agric.*) bone meal. -düngung, *f.* manuring with bone. -erde, *f.* bone earth (bone ash). -fett, *n.* bone fat, bone grease. -gallerte, *f.* bone gelatin; ossein. -geist, *m.* bone spirit. -gewebe, *f.* bony tissue. -haut, *f.* periosteum. -kohle, *f.* boneblack. -kohleglühofen, *m.* boneblack furnace. -leim, *n.* bone glue, osteocolla. -mark, *n.* bone marrow. -masse, *f.* osseous material. -mehl, *n.* bone meal, bone dust. -öl, *n.* bone oil, Dippel's oil. -porzellan, *n.* bone porcelain, bone china. -säure, *f.* phosphoric acid. -schrot, *n.& m.* crushed bone. -schwarz, *n.* boneblack. -teeröl, *n.* bone oil.

knöchern, *a.* of bone, bony, osseous.

knochig, *a.* bony, osseous.

Knöllchen, *n.* nodule, little knob.

Knolle, *f.*, Knollen, *m.* lump, knob, nodule; tuber; tubercle; tumor.

knollig, *a.* knobby, knotty, bulbous; immense.

Knopf, *m.* button; stud, head, knob; knot. -deckel, *m.* knobbed cover.

Knopper, *f.* (nut)gall, gallnut.

Knorpel, *m.* cartilage, gristle.

knorpelartig, *a.* cartilaginous.

Knorpelhaut, *f.* (*Anat.*) perichondrium.

knorpelig, *a.* cartilaginous, gristly.

Knorpel-leim, *m.* chondrin. -tang, *m.* carrageen, (*Pharm.*) chondrus.

knorplich, *a.* cartilaginous.

Knorren, *n.* protuberance, excrescence, knot, gnarl, snag.

Knospe, *f.* bud.

knospen, *v.i.* bud.

Knötchen, *n.* little knot; nodule; tubercle; pimple.

Knoten, *m.* knot; node; nodule; tubercle; ganglion; knob; plot.

knoten, *v.t.* knot, tie in knots.

Knoten-linie, *f.* nodal line. -punkt, *m.* nodal point; junction. -wurz, *f.* figwort, (*Pharm.*) scrophularia. -zahl, *f.* nodal number; number of nodes.

Knöterich, *m.* knotgrass (*Polygonum* sp.).

knotig, *a.* knotty, nodular, tubercular, nobby; caddish.

knüpfen, *v.t.* knit, tie, unite, attach.

Knüppel, *m.* billet; cudgel, club.

knurren, *v.i.* snarl, growl, rumble.

knusperig, *a.* crisp.

Koagulationswärme, *f.* heat of coagulation.

koagulierbar, *a.* coagulable.

koagulieren, *v.t.& i.* coagulate.

Koagulierung, *f.* coagulation.

koagulierungsfähig, *a.* coagulable.

Koagulierungs-fähigkeit, *f.* coagulability. -flüssigkeit, *f.* coagulating liquid. -mittel, *n.* coagulating agent, coagulant.

Kobalt, *m.* cobalt. -ammin, -amin, *n.* cobaltammine. -bad, *n.* cobalt bath. -beschlag, *m.* (*Min.*) cobalt bloom, erythrite. -blau, *n.* cobalt blue. -bleierz, *n.*, -bleiglanz, *m.*(*Min.*) clausthalite. -blüte, -blume, *f.* cobalt bloom (erythrite). -chlorür, *n.* cobaltous chloride. -erz, *n.* cobalt ore. -farbe, *f.* powder blue. -flasche, *f.* cobaltglass bottle. -gehalt, *m.* cobalt content. -gelb, *n.* cobalt yellow. -glanz, *m.* cobalt glance (cobaltite). -grün, *n.* cobalt green.

kobalthaltig, *a.* cobaltiferous.

Kobalti-. cobaltic, cobalti-.

Kobaltiak, *n.* cobaltiac, cobaltammine. -salz, *n.* cobaltiac salt, cobaltammine salt.

Kobalti-chlorid, *n.* cobaltic chloride. -cyankalium, *n.* potassium cobalticyanide. -cyanwasserstoff, *m.*, -cyanwasserstoffsäure, *f.* cobalticyanic acid.

kobaltieren, *v.t.* coat or plate with cobalt.

Kobalti-kaliumnitrit, *n.* potassium cobaltinitrite. -oxyd, *n.* cobaltic oxide. -verbindung, *f.* cobaltic compound.

Kobalt-kies, *m.* cobalt pyrites (linnaeite). -manganerz, *n.* asbolite. -nickelkies, *m.* (*Min.*) linnaeite.

Kobalto-. cobaltous, cobalto-. -chlorid, *n.* cobaltous chloride. -cyanwasserstoff, *m.*, -cyanwasserstoffsäure, *f.* cobaltocyanic acid. -nitrat, *n.* cobaltous nitrate. -oxyd,

*n.* cobaltous oxide. **-salz,** *n.* cobaltous salt.
**-sulfat,** *n.* cobaltous sulfate. **-verbindung,**
*f.* cobaltous compound.

**Kobaltoxyd,** *n.* cobalt oxide, specif. cobaltic
oxide. **-oxydul,** *n.* cobaltocobaltic oxide.

**Kobaltoxydul,** *n.* cobaltous oxide. **-oxyd,** *n.*
cobaltocobaltic oxide. **-verbindung,** *f.*
cobaltous compound.

**Kobalt-oxydverbindung,** *f.* cobaltic compound. **-salz,** *n.* cobalt salt. **-spat,** *m.*
(*Min.*) sphaerocobaltite. **-speise,** *f.* cobalt
speiss. **-verbindung,** *f.* cobalt compound.
**-vitriol,** *m.* cobalt vitriol (cobaltous sulfate).

**Kober,** *m.* basket.

**Koch,** *m.* cook. **-abschnitt,** *m.* period of
boiling or cooking. **-apparat,** *m.* cooking
apparatus. **-becher,** *m.* beaker.

**kochbeständig,** *a.* stable on boiling or cooking; (of dyes) fast to boiling.

**Koch-brenner,** *m.* boiling (or cooking) burner.
**-dauer,** *f.* duration of boiling.

**kochecht,** *a.* fast to boiling (in water).

**kochen,** *v.t.* boil; cook.—*v.i.* boil.

**Kochen,** *n.* boiling, ebullition; cooking, cookery.

**Kocher,** *m.* boiler, cooker, digester; hot plate.
**-ausbeute,** *f.* cooker yield, yield on cooking
or boiling.

**Kocherei,** *f.* boiling; cooking.

**Kocherlauge,** *f.* cooking liquor, cooker liquor.

**Koch-flasche,** *f.* boiling flask. **-flüssigkeit,** *f.*
liquid for boiling, cooking liquor. **-gefäss,**
*n.* boiling vessel, boiler; cooking vessel;
(*Paper*, etc.) bucking keir. **-gerät,** *n.* boiling
or cooking apparatus.

**kochheiss,** *a.* boiling hot.

**Koch-hitze,** *f.* boiling heat. **-kessel,** *m.* boiling
kettle, boiler; (*Paper*) pulp boiler, pulp
digester. **-kläre,** *f.* (*Sugar*) filtered liquor
(or sirup). **-kölbchen,** *n.* small boiling
flask, fractional distillation flask. **-kolben,**
*m.* boiling flask. **-lauge,** *f.* boiling lye.
**-platte,** *f.* cooking plate, hot plate. **-probe,**
*f.* boiling test. **-prozess,** *n.* boiling process.
**-puddeln,** *n.* slag puddling, pig boiling.
**-punkt,** *m.* boiling point. **-rohr,** *n.,* **-röhre,**
*f.* boiling tube, distilling tube.

**Kochsalz,** *n.* common salt (sodium chloride).
**-bad,** *n.* (common) salt bath; brine bath.

**kochsalzhaltig,** *a.* containing (common) salt,
salted.

**Kochsalz-lauge,** *f.* brine (of common salt).
**-lösung,** *f.* (common) salt solution. **-säure,**
*f.* hydrochloric acid.

**Koch-stadium,** *n.* stage of boiling or cooking.
**-topf,** *m.* boiler; cooker.

**Kochung,** *f.* boiling; cooking.

**Koch-vergütung,** *f.* (*Metal.*) artificial aging.

**-wasser,** *n.* boiling water. **-zeit,** *f.* period
of boiling or cooking. **-zucker,** *m.* brown
sugar; powdered sugar.

**Kockels-beere,** *f.,* **-korn,** *n.* cocculus indicus.

**Kodäthylin,** *n.* codethyline.

**Kodein,** *n.* codeine.

**Kodöl,** *n.* cod-liver oil; rosin oil.

**Koeffizient,** *m.* coefficient.

**Koenzym,** *n.* coenzyme.

**koerzibel,** *a.* coercible.

**Koerzitivkraft,** *f.* coercive force.

**koexistieren,** *v.i.* coexist.

**Koffein,** *n.* caffeine.

**Koffer,** *m.* trunk, coffer, box.

**Kognak,** *m.* cognac.

**kohärent,** *a.* coherent.

**Kohärenz,** *f.* coherence, coherency.

**kohärieren,** *v.i.* cohere.

**Kohäsion,** *f.* cohesion.

**kohäsiv,** *a.* cohesive.

**Kohl,** *m.* cabbage.

**Kohle,** *f.* coal; charcoal; carbon. **-fadenlampe,**
*f.* carbon-filament lamp. **-feuerung,** *f.* heating with coal; coal furnace. **-hydrat,** *n.*
carbohydrate. **-klemme,** *f.* (*Elec.*) carbon
terminal. **-lampe,** *f.* carbon lamp.

**kohlen,** *v.t.* char; carbonize, carburize.—*v.i.*
char.

**Kohlenabbrand,** *m.* (*Elec.*) carbon loss.

**kohlen-ähnlich, -artig,** *a.* coal-like, carbon-
like, carbonaceous.

**Kohlen-asche,** *f.* coal ash, coal ashes. **-benzin,**
*n.* benzene, benzol. **-bergbau,** *m.* coal mining. **-beule,** *f.* (*Med.*) carbuncle. **-bleispat,**
*m.* cerussite. **-bleivitriolspat,** *m.* lanarkite.
**-blende,** *f.* anthracite. **-bogenlampe,** *f.*
carbon arc lamp. **-bohrer,** *m.* charcoal
borer. **-brennen,** *n.* charcoal burning; coal
burning. **-brennerei,** *f.* charcoal works.
**-dampf,** *m.* gases from burning coal.
**-dioxyd,** *n.* carbon dioxide. **-dioxydstrom,**
*m.* current of carbon dioxide. **-disulfid,** *n.*
carbon disulfide. **-dithiolsäure,** *f.* dithiolcarbonic acid. **-dunst,** *m.* vapor from coals
(containing carbon monoxide as a poisonous
ingredient). **-eisen,** *n.* iron carbide. **-eisen-
stein,** *m.* blackband (carbonaceous iron carbonate). **-faden,** *m.* carbon filament. **-filter,**
*n.* charcoal filter; boneblack filter. **-flöz,** *n.*
coal seam, coal measure. **-futter,** *n.* carbonaceous lining. **-gas,** *n.* coal gas. **-ge-
stübbe,** *n.* coal slack; brasque. **-griess,** *m.*
small coal, slack. **-grube,** *f.* coal mine.
**-grus,** *m.* small coal, slack.

**kohlenhaltig,** *a.* carbonaceous, carboniferous.

**Kohlenhaufe(n),** *m.* coal pile, coal heap.

**Kohlenhydrat,** *n.* carbohydrate. **-stoffwech-
sel,** *m.* carbohydrate metabolism.

**Kohlenkalk,** *m.* carboniferous limestone.

-spat, *m.* anthraconite. -stein, *m.* carboniferous limestone.

Kohlen-karbonit, *n.* kohlencarbonite (trade name of an explosive). -klein, *n.* small coal. -klemme, *f.* (*Elec.*) carbon terminal. -licht, *n.* carbon light. -lösche, *f.* coal dust or slack. -meiler, *m.* charcoal pile. -monoxyd, *n.* carbon monoxide. -mulm, *m.* coal dust, slack; charcoal dust. -ölsäure, *f.* carbolic acid. -oxychlorid, *n.* carbon oxychloride, carbonyl chloride.

Kohlenoxyd, *n.* carbon monoxide. -eisen, *n.* iron carbonyl. -gas, *n.* carbon monoxide gas. -Hämoglobin, *n.* carbohemoglobin. -kalium, *n.* potassium carboxide, potassium hexacarbonyl. -knallgas, *n.* explosive mixture of carbon monoxide and oxygen. -nickel, *m.& n.* nickel carbonyl.

kohlenoxydreich, *a.* rich in carbon monoxide.

Kohlen-oxydvergiftung, *f.* carbon monoxide poisoning. -oxysulfid, *n.* carbon oxysulfide. -papier, *n.* carbon paper. -pulver, *n.* coal powder, powdered coal; charcoal powder, powdered charcoal. -sandstein, *m.* carboniferous sandstone.

kohlensauer, *a.* of or combined with carbonic acid, carbonate of.

Kohlensäure, *f.* carbonic acid. -anhydrid, *n.* carbonic anhydride (carbon dioxide). -bestimmer, *m.* apparatus for determining carbon dioxide. -brot, *n.* aerated bread. -chlorid, *n.* carbonyl chloride. -entwickelung, *f.* evolution of carbonic acid. -ester, *m.* carbonic ester. -gas, *n.* carbonic acid gas (carbon dioxide).

kohlensäurehaltig, *a.* containing carbonic acid, carbonated.

Kohlensäure-messer, *m.* instrument or apparatus for measuring carbon dioxide, anthracometer, carbonometer. -salz, *n.* carbonate. -schnee, *m.* carbon dioxide snow. -strom, *m.* stream or current of carbon dioxide. -verlust, *m.* loss (or escape) of carbon dioxide. -wasser, *n.* carbonated water, soda water.

Kohlen-schiefer, *m.* bituminous shale; coal-bearing shale. -schlacke, *f.* cinder, clinker. -schlichte, *f.* (*Founding*) black wash. -schwarz, *n.* carbon black; charcoal black. -schwefelwasserstoffsäure, *f.* (tri)thiocarbonic acid ($H_2CS_3$). -spat, *m.* anthraconite; whewellite. -spitze, *f.* carbon point. -staub, *m.* coal dust; charcoal dust. -stickstoff, *m.* cyanogen. -stickstoffsäure, *f.* carbazotic acid (picric acid). -stoff, *m.* carbon.

kohlenstoffarm, *a.* poor in carbon, low-carbon,

Kohlenstoff-art, *f.* variety of carbon. -ausscheidung, *f.* separation of carbon. -bestimmung, *f.* carbon determination. -bin-

dung, *f.* carbon linkage. -eisen, *n.* iron carbide. -entziehung, *f.* removal of carbon, decarbonization. -gehalt, *m.* carbon content. -gerüst, *n.* carbon skeleton.

kohlenstoffhaltig, *a.* carbonaceous, carboniferous.

Kohlenstoff-kalium, *n.* potassium carbide. -kern, *m.* carbon nucleus. -kette, *f.* carbon chain. -legierung, *f.* carbon alloy. -metall, *n.* carbide.

kohlenstoffreich, *a.* rich in carbon.

Kohlenstoff-silicium, *n.* carbon silicide. -skelett, *n.* carbon skeleton. -stahl, *m.* carbon steel. -stein, *m.* carbon brick. -stickstofftitan, *n.* titanium carbonitride. -sulfid, *n.* carbon disulfide. -verbindung, *f.* carbon compound.

Kohlen-suboxyd, *n.* carbon suboxide. -sulfid, *n.* carbon disulfide. -sulfidsalz, *n.* thiocarbonate, sulfocarbonate. -teer, *m.* coal tar. -teerfarbe, *f.* coal-tar color. -tiegel, *m.* carbon crucible; charcoal crucible; crucible with carbonaceous lining. -verbrauch, *m.* coal consumption. -vergasung, *f.* gasification of coal.

Kohlenwasserstoff, *m.* hydrocarbon. -gas, *n.* hydrocarbon gas; (leichtes) methane; (schweres) ethylene. -gemisch, *n.* hydrocarbon mixture.

kohlenwasserstoffhaltig, *a.* containing hydrocarbons, hydrocarbonaceous.

Kohlen-wasserstoffverbindung, *f.* hydrocarbon. -ziegel, *m.* coal briquet.

Kohlepapier, *n.* carbon paper.

Köhler, *m.* charcoal burner.

Köhlerei, *f.* charcoal burning; charcoal works.

Kohle-schwelung, *f.* coal distillation. -staub, *m.* coal dust; charcoal dust.

kohlig, *a.* like coal, coaly, coal-bearing.

Kohl-palme, *f.* cabbage palm. -palmöl, *n.* cabbage-palm oil. -raps, *m.* rape, rapeseed, -rübe, *f.* rutabaga. -saat, *f.* colza, rapeseed. -saatöl, *n.* colza oil, rape oil.

kohlschwarz, *a.* coal-black.

Kohlsprossen, *f.pl.* Brussels sprouts.

Kohlung, *f.* charring; carbonization, carburization.

Kohlungsmittel, *n.* carbonizing (or carburizing) agent.

kohobieren, *v.t.* cohobate, distill repeatedly.

Kohunennuss, *f.* cohune nut.

koinzidieren, *v.i.* coincide.

Kok, *m.* coke.

Koka, *f.* coca.

Kokaïn, *n.* cocaine.

Koke, *m.& f.* coke.

Koken, *m.* sagger.

Kokerei, *f.* coke plant, coke works. -gas, *n.* coke-oven gas.

Kokes-. see Koks-.

Kokille, *f.* ingot mold; (*Founding*) chill, chill mold.

Kokillenguss, *m.* chill casting.

Kokkelskorn, *n.* cocculus indicus.

Kokken, *m.pl.* (*Bact.*) cocci. **-ketten**, *f.pl.* (*Bact.*) streptococci.

Kokon, *m.* cocoon.

Kokos, **-baum**, *m.*, coco, coco palm, coconut tree. **-butter**, *f.* coconut butter (coconut oil). **-faser**, *f.* coco fiber, coir (fiber from the husk of the coconut). **-fett**, *n.* coconut oil. **-garn**, *n.* coir yarn.

Kokosnuss, *f.* coconut. **-milch**, *f.* coconut milk. **-öl, Kokosöl**, *n.* coconut oil.

Kokos-ölseife, *f.* coconut-oil soap. **-palme**, *f.* coco palm. **-seife**, *f.* coconut-oil soap. **-talg**, *m.* coconut oil. **-talgsäure**, *f.* cocinic acid (formerly supposed to exist in coconut oil).

Koks, *m.& m.pl.* coke. **-abfall**, *m.* refuse coke.

koksähnlich, *a.* cokelike.

Koks-ausbeute, *f.* yield of coke. **-bereitung**, *f.* coke making, coking. **-brennen**, *n.* coke burning, coking. **-erzeugung**, *f.* coke production. **-filter**, *m.* coke filter. **-gas**, *n.* coke gas. **-gicht**, *f.* charge of coke. **-heizung**, *f.* heating with coke. **-hochofen**, *m.* coke blast furnace. **-klein**, *n.* small coke, coke breeze, coke dust. **-kohle**, *f.* coking coal. **-lösche**, *f.* coke dust. **-ofen**, *m.* coke oven. **-roheisen**, *n.* coke pig iron. **-schicht**, *f.* layer of coke. **-staub**, *m.* coke dust.

Kolanuss, *f.* cola nut.

Kolatorium, *n.* colatorium, strainer.

Kölbchen, *n.* little flask, etc. (see Kolben).

Kolben, *m.* flask; butt, butt end; (*Mach.*) piston; soldering iron; (*Metal.*) bloom; (*Old Chem.*) bolthead, matrass, cucurbit; (*Bot.*) head, spike; club. **-hals**, *m.* neck of a flask. **-schimmel**, *m.* club mold (*Aspergillus* sp.). **-stange**, *f.* piston rod. **-träger**, *m.* flask support, flask stand.

kolbig, *a.* knobby, clubby, knotty; club-shaped.

Kolibazillus, *m.* colon bacillus.

kolieren, *v.t.* filter, percolate.

Kolier-rahmen, *m.* filtering frame. **-tuch**, *n.* filtering cloth.

Kolleg, *n.* (course of) lectures; college.

Kollege, *m.* colleague.

Kollegium, *n.* board, council, staff.

Kollektor, *m.* (*Elec.*) commutator.

Koller-gang, *m.*, **-mühle**, *f.* edge mill.

kollern, *v.i.* rumble; gobble; rave; roll.

Kolli, *m.* = Kollo.

kollidieren, *v.i.* collide.

Kollidin, *n.* collidine.

kolligativ, *a.* colligative.

Kollo, *n.* parcel, bale, bundle.

kollodisieren, *v.t.* collodionize.

Kollodium, *n.* collodion. **-ersatz**, *m.* collodion substitute. **-lösung**, *f.* collodion solution. **-seide**, *f.* collodion silk. **-überzug**, *m.* coat or skin of collodion. **-verfahren**, *n.* collodion process or method. **-wolle**, *f.* collodion cotton, soluble guncotton, pyroxylin.

kolloid, kolloidal, *a.* colloid, colloidal.

Kolloidalzustand, *m.* colloidal state.

Kolloidchemie, *f.* colloid chemistry, chemistry of colloids.

kolloidchemisch, *a.* colloidochemical.

Kolloidität, *f.* colloidal quality.

Kolloid-stoff, *m.*, **-substanz**, *f.* colloid substance, colloid.

kölner, kölnisch, *a.* Cologne.

Kölnerwasser, *n.* cologne, Cologne water.

Kölnischbraun, *n.* Cologne brown.

Kolombowurzel, *f.* calumba root, calumba.

Kolonialzucker, *m.* muscovado; cane sugar.

Kolonie, *f.* colony.

Kolonne, *f.* column.

Kolonnenapparat, *m.* column apparatus.

Kolophoneisenerz, *m.* pitticite.

Kolophonium, *n.* colophony, rosin.

Kolophonsäure, *f.* colophonic acid.

Koloquinte, *f.* colocynth.

Koloquintin, *n.* colocynthin.

kolorieren, *v.t.* color.

Kolorimetrie, *f.* colorimetry.

kolorimetrisch, *a.* colorimetric.

Kolorit, *n.* coloring, color, hue.

Kolumbin, *n.* columbin.

Kolumbowurzel, *f.* = Kolombowurzel.

Kolzaöl, *n.* colza oil, rape oil.

Komansäure, *f.* comanic acid.

kombinieren, *v.t.& i.* combine.

Komensäure, *f.* comenic acid.

komisch, *a.* comic, funny.

kommen, *v.i.* come; happen; be, come out.

Kommerz, *m.* commerce.

Kommis, *m.* clerk.

Kömmling, *m.* new product; newcomer.

kommunizieren, *v.i.* communicate.

kommutieren, *v.t.* commute.

Komödie, *f.* comedy.

Kompendium, *n.* compendium, abridgment, summary.

kompensieren, *v.t.* compensate.

komplementär, *a.* complementary.

Komplementbindung, *f.* complement fixation.

komplett, *a.* complete.

komplettieren, *v.t.* complete.

Komplexverbindung, *f.* complex compound.

kompliziert, *p.a.* complicated.

Komposition, *f.* composition; (*Dyeing*) tin composition (solution of tin in aqua regia); hard lead.

**Kompostdünger,** m. (*Agric.*) compost.

**Kompott,** n. compote (preserved or stewed fruit).

**kompressibel,** a. compressible.

**Kompressibilität,** f. compressibility.

**Kompressionswelle,** f. compression wave.

**komprimierbar,** a. compressible.

**komprimieren,** v.t. compress.

**Konchylien,** f.pl. shells, shellfish.

**Kondensat,** n. condensate.

**Kondensations-apparat,** m. condensing apparatus, condenser. **-druck,** m. condensation pressure. **-ergebnis,** n. condensation product. **-gefäss,** n. condensation vessel, receiver. **-kammer,** f. condensing chamber. **-raum,** m. condensation space, condensing chamber. **-rohr,** n., **-röhre,** f. condensing tube; adapter. **-turm,** m. condensing tower. **-verlust,** m. loss from condensation. **-wärme,** f. heat of condensation. **-wasser,** n. = Kondenswasser.

**Kondensator,** m. condenser.

**kondensierbar,** a. condensable.

**kondensieren,** v.t. & i. condense.

**Kondensierung,** f. condensation.

**Kondens-topf,** m. condensing pot; steam trap. **-wasser,** n. condensation water, condensed water, condensing water.

**konditionieren,** v.t. condition.

**Konditor,** m. confectioner.

**Konditorei,** f. confectionery.

**Konfekt,** n. confectionery.

**Konfitüren,** pl. confectionery, sweets.

**kongelieren,** v.i. congeal.

**Kongo-.** see Congo-.

**Konifere,** f. conifer.

**König,** m. regulus; king.

**Königin,** f. queen. **-metall,** n. queen's metal (a tin alloy).

**königlich,** a. kingly, regal.

**König-reich,** n. kingdom, realm. **-salbe,** f. (*Pharm.*) rosin cerate, basilicon ointment.

**Königs-blau,** n. king's blue (a name for cobalt blue and for smalt). **-chinarinde,** f. calisaya bark, (yellow) cinchona. **-farbe,** f. = Königsblau. **-gelb,** n. king's yellow (As₂S₃); chrome yellow; massicot. **-grün,** n. Paris green. **-kerze,** f. (common) mullen. **-krankheit,** f. king's evil, scrofula. **-pulver,** n. perfuming powder. **-salbe,** f. basilicon, resin ointment. **-säure,** f. aqua regia. **-wasser,** n. aqua regia.

**Koniin,** n. conine, coniine.

**konisch,** a. conic, conical, coniform.

**Konizität,** f. conicity, angle of taper.

**konjugiert,** p.a. conjugate.

**konkav,** a. concave.

**Konkrement,** n. concrement, concretion.

**Konkurrenz,** f. competition.

**konkurrieren,** v.i. compete.

**Konkurs,** m. bankruptcy, failure; assignment.

**Konkussionszünder,** m. concussion fuse.

**können,** v.t. be able, can; may.

**konnte,** pret. of können.

**konsequent,** a. consequent; consistent.

**Konserve,** f. preserved food (as canned fruit or meat, preserves, pickles); (*Pharm.*) confection, electuary.

**Konserven-büchse,** f. can, tin (for food). **-fabrik,** f. cannery, preserve factory, etc.

**konservieren,** v.t. preserve.

**Konservierung,** f. preservation; conservation.

**Konservierungs-firnis,** m. preserving varnish. **-mittel,** n. preservative. **-verfahren,** n. preserving process or method.

**Konsistenz,** f. consistency. **-messer,** m. viscosimeter.

**Konsole,** f. bracket, console.

**Konsortium,** n. syndicate (properly, a less permanent combination than Syndikat).

**konst.,** abbrev. (konstant) constant.

**Konstante,** f. constant.

**Konstant(er)haltung,** f. keeping constant.

**Konstanz,** f. constancy.

**konstatieren,** v.t. ascertain, establish, verify.

**Konstitutions-formel,** f. constitutional formula. **-wasser,** n. water of constitution.

**konstruieren,** v.t. construct.

**Konsum,** m. consumption.

**Kontakt-fläche,** f. surface of contact. **-gift,** n. contact poison. **-mittel,** n. contact agent, catalyst. **-substanz,** f. contact substance, catalyst. **-verfahren,** n. contact process. **-wirkung,** f. contact action, catalysis.

**kontinuierlich,** a. continuous.

**Kontinuität,** f. continuity.

**Konto,** n. account.

**kontrahieren,** v.i. & t. contract.

**kontrainsulär,** a. opposing the action of insulin.

**kontrapolarisieren,** v.t. counterpolarize.

**Kontrastfärbung,** f. contrast staining.

**Kontravalenz,** f. contravalence.

**Kontroll-bestimmung,** f. control determination. **-gerät,** n. control apparatus, controlling device. **-kolben,** m. control flask. **-versuch,** m. control test, control experiment.

**Kontur,** f. outline, contour.

**Konus,** m. cone. **-spülung,** f. conical rinsing.

**Konvektionsstrom,** m. convection current.

**konventionell,** a. conventional.

**konvergieren,** v.i. converge.—**konvergierend,** p.a. convergent.

**Konversionssalpeter,** m. converted saltpeter (sodium nitrate converted into potassium nitrate by double decomposition with potassium chloride).

**Konverter-birne,** *f.* (*Metal.*) converter. **-futter,** *n.* converter lining.

**konvertierbar,** *a.* convertible.

**konvertieren,** *v.t.* convert.

**Konvertierung,** *f.* conversion.

**konz.,** *abbrev.* (konzentriert) concentrated.

**Konzentrations-änderung,** *f.* change in concentration. **-apparat,** *m.* concentrating apparatus, concentrator. **-stein,** *m.* (*Copper*) white metal. **-verhältnis,** *f.* ratio of concentration.

**konzentrieren,** *v.t.* concentrate.

**konzentriert,** *p.a.* concentrated.—**konzentrierter Alaun,** concentrated alum (aluminum sulfate).

**Konzentrierung,** *f.* concentration.

**konzentrisch,** *a.* concentric.

**Koordinations-lehre,** *f.* coördination theory. **-zahl,** *f.* coördination number.

**Kopaiva-.** see Copaiva-.

**Kopal-firnis,** *m.* copal varnish. **-harz, -gummi,** *n.* copal resin, copal. **-insäure,** *f.* copalinic acid. **-lack,** *m.* copal varnish. **-säure,** *f.* copalic acid.

**köpern,** *v.t.* twill.

**Kopf,** *m.* head (in various senses); top.

**Kopf-.** head; top; main, principal; cephalic; mental. **-decke,** *f.* scalp. **-drüse,** *f.* cephalic gland. **-düngung,** *f.* (*Agric.*) top-dressing.

**köpfen,** *v.t.* top; behead.

**Kopfhaut,** *f.* scalp.

**-köpfig.** -headed.

**Kopfkissen,** *n.* pillow.

**kopflos,** *a.* headless, acephalous; silly.

**Kopf-ring,** *m.* (*Zinc*) nozzle block. **-rose,** *f.* erysipelas. **-salat,** *m.* head lettuce. **-schimmel,** *m.* any mold of the genus *Mucor.* **-schmerz,** *m.* headache. **-steuer,** *f.* poll tax. **-titel,** *m.* main title, main heading. **-überschrift,** *f.* principal heading. **-wasser,** *n.* hair wash; head wash. **-wassersucht,** *f.* hydrocephalus. **-weh,** *n.* headache.

**Kopie,** *f.* copy.

**kopieren,** *v.t.* copy.

**Kopier-farbe,** *f.* copying ink. **-mine,** *f.* copying lead (for pencils). **-presse,** *f.* copying press. **-tinte,** *f.* copying ink.

**koppeln,** *v.t.* couple.

**köppeln,** *v.i.* (*Brewing*) froth in after-fermentation.

**Koppelung,** *f.* coupling.

**Koppelwirtschaft,** *f.* rotation of crops.

**Kopra-öl, -fett,** *n.* coconut oil.

**Koprolith,** *m.* coprolite.

**Koprosterin,** *n.* coprosterol.

**Kopsfärbung,** *f.* cop dyeing.

**kor,** *pret.* of küren.

**Koralle,** *f.* coral.

**korallenartig,** *a.* coral-like, coralloid.

**Korallenwurzel,** *f.* (*Pharm.*) polypody root.

**Korb,** *m.* basket; hamper, crate, canister; (*Mining*) corf, cage. **-flasche,** *f.* carboy; demijohn.

**Kordel,** *f.* twine, string.

**Kordit,** *n.* cordite.

**Korduan,** *n.* cordovan, Cordovan leather.

**Korinthe,** *f.* (dried) currant.

**kork-ähnlich,** *a.* corklike, suberose. **-artig,** *a.* of the nature of cork, corky.

**Kork-asbest,** *m.* mountain cork, rock cork. **-baum,** *m.* cork tree. **-bohrer,** *m.* cork borer. **-bohrerschärfer,** *m.* cork borer sharpener.

**korken,** *v.t.* cork.

**Korken,** *m.* cork, cork stopper.

**korkig,** *a.* corky, of the nature of cork.

**Kork-isolation,** *f.* cork insulation. **-kohle,** *f.* cork charcoal, burnt cork. **-mehl,** *n.* cork powder. **-messer,** *n.* cork knife. **-propfen,** *m.* cork stopper, cork. **-säure,** *f.* suberic acid. **-schwarz,** *n.* cork black. **-spund,** *m.* cork stopper, cork. **-stein,** *m.* cork board; cork brick. **-stoff,** *m.* suberin. **-stopfen, -stöpsel,** *m.* cork stopper, cork. **-substanz,** *f.* suberin. **-teppich,** *n.* linoleum. **-verbindung,** *f.* cork connection. **-wachs,** *säure,** *f.* (*Org. Chem.*) ceric acid. **-zieher,** *m.* corkscrew.

**Korn,** *n.* grain; fineness, standard (of coins); corn; (of flax) boon; (*Assaying*) button. **-alkohol,** *m.* grain alcohol. **-art,** *f.* (kind of) grain. **-bildung,** *f.* (*Sugar*) granulation, crystallization. **-bildungspunkt,** *m.* (*Sugar*) granulating point.

**kornblau,** *a.* cornflower-blue.

**Korn-blei,** *n.* grain lead (finely granulated lead for use in assaying). **-blume,** *f.* bluebottle, cornflower (*Centaurea cyanus*). **-branntwein,** *m.* grain spirits, whisky. **-bürste,** *f.* (*Assaying*) button brush.

**Körnchen,** *n.* little grain, granule.

**Korneisen,** *n.* iron of granular fracture.

**Kornelkirsche,** *f.* cornelian cherry.

**körneln,** *v.t.* granulate.

**Körnelung,** *f.* granulation.

**körnen,** *v.t.* granulate; grain; corn (gunpowder).—**gekörnt,** *p.a.* granulated, granular.

**Körner,** *n.pl.* of Korn (which see); grain, corn (collectively); kermes.—*m.* center.

**Körner-.** granular, grained, in grains. **-asant,** *m.* asafetida in grains. **-frucht,** *f.* cereal, grain. **-lack,** *m.* seed-lac. **-leder,** *n.* grained leather. **-spitze,** *f.* (*Mach.*) dead center. **-zinn,** *n.* grain tin, granular tin.

**kornförmig,** *a.* in the form of grains, granular.

**Korn-fuselöl,** *n.* fusel oil from grain. **-grösse,** *f.* grain size, particle size.

**Körnhaus,** *n.* (*Explosives*) corning house, granulating house.

**körnig,** *a.* granular, granulated; grainy, gritty; grained, showing a grain; brittle (malt).

**Körnigkeit,** *f.* granularity.

**körnigkristallinisch,** *a.* granular-crystalline.

**Korn-käfer,** *m.* grain weevil. **-kluft,** *f.* assayer's tongs. **-kochen,** *n.* (*Sugar*) boiling to grain. **-kupfer, Körnkupfer,** *n.* granulated copper.

**Korn-mutter,** *f.* ergot. **-prüfer,** *m.* grain tester. **-puddeln,** *n.* puddling of fine-grained iron. **-pulver,** *n.* granulated powder, powder in grains. **-schnaps,** *m.* grain spirits, whisky. **-sieb,** *n.* granulating sieve; grain sieve. **-stahl,** *m.* granulated steel.

**Körnung,** *f.* granulation; graining; grain; pitting.

**Korn-wa(a)ge,** *f.* button balance, assay balance; grain scales. **-zange,** *f.* assayer's tongs. **-zinn,** *n.* (*Metal.*) grain tin. **-zucker,** *m.* granulated sugar.

**Körper,** *m.* body; substance; compound. (Careful modern usage avoids the translation "body" for chemical substances.)

**Körper-.** body, bodily, corpor(e)al, physical; solid. **-bau,** *m.* bodily structure, build. **-beschaffenheit,** *f.* constitution. **-chen,** *n.* corpuscle; particle. **-farbe,** *f.* body color. **-flüssigkeit,** *f.* body fluid. **-fülle,** *f.* corpulence. **-gruppe,** *f.* group of substances (or bodies). **-klasse,** *f.* class of substances (or bodies).

**körperlich,** *a.* bodily, corporeal, material; corpuscular; solid.

**Körper-mass,** *n.* solid measure, cubic measure. **-pflegemittel,** *n.* cosmetic. **-schaft,** *f.* corporation. **-stoff,** *m.* organic matter; matter. **-teilchen,** *n.* particle, specif. molecule. **-wärme,** *f.* body heat.

**korr.,** *abbrev.* (korrigiert) corrected.

**Korrektivmittel,** *n.* corrigent.

**Korrektur,** *f.* correction; proof.

**Korrelat,** *n.* correlative.

**korrigieren,** *v.t.* correct.

**korrodieren,** *v.t. & i.* corrode.

**Korrosionsmittel,** *n.* corrosive.

**Korund,** *m.* corundum.

**Koschenille,** *f.* cochineal.

**Kosekante,** *f.* cosecant.

**Kosinus,** *m.* cosine.

**kosmetisch,** *a.* cosmetic.

**Kosoblüten,** *f.pl.* (*Pharm.*) cusso.

**Kost,** *f.* food, fare, diet, board.

**kostbar,** *a.* costly, expensive, precious.

**kosten,** *v.i.* cost.—*v.t.* taste.

**Kosten,** *f.pl.* costs, expenses, charges. **-anschlag,** *m.* estimate (of cost).

**kosten-frei, -los,** *a.* free of charge, free.

**köstlich,** *a.* costly, dainty, excellent.

**kostspielig,** *a.* expensive.

**Kot,** *m.* feces, excrement; mud; sludge; dirt.

**Kot-.** fecal. **-abgang,** *m.* defecation.

**kot-artig,** *a.* fecal, feculent, excremental. **-ausführend, -ausleerend,** *p.a.* purgative, cathartic.

**Kotbad,** *n.* dung bath.

**koten,** *v.t.* dung.

**Kotgeruch,** *m.* fecal odor.

**kotig,** *a.* fecal, stercoraceous; dirty, filthy.

**kotonisieren,** *v.t.* cottonize; degum (silk).

**Kotorinde,** *f.* coto bark.

**Kot-porphyrin,** *n.* coproporphyrin. **-stein,** *m.* fecal concretion.

**Kouvert,** *n.* envelope; cover.

**Kovolum, Kovolumen,** *n.* covolume.

**Kp.,** *abbrev.* (Kochpunkt) boiling point, b.p.

**kpl.,** *abbrev.* (komplett) complete.

**Krabbe,** *f.* crab.

**krabbecht,** *a.* fast to crabbing.

**krabbeln,** *v.t.* tickle.—*v.i.* itch; crawl.

**Krach,** *m.* crack, crash.

**krachen,** *v.i.* crack, crash, crackle; (of silk) rustle.

**Krackverfahren,** *n.* cracking (process).

**kraft,** *prep.* on the strength of, by virtue of.

**Kraft,** *f.* force; power; strength, vigor, energy. **-anlage,** *f.* power plant, power station. **-bedarf,** *m.* power demand.

**kräftefrei,** *a.* force-free.

**Kraft-einheit,** *f.* unit of force. **-erzeugung,** *f.* power production. **-feld,** *n.* (*Physics*) field of force. **-futter, -futtermittel,** *n.* concentrated feed.

**Kraftgas,** *n.* power gas, fuel gas, esp. producer gas. **-anlage,** *f.* power gas plant; gas producer. **-erzeuger,** *m.* gas producer.

**kräftig,** *a.* strong; vigorous; effective; valid; nourishing; (of hides) plump.

**Kraft-leitung,** *f.* (*Elec.*) power circuit. **-linie,** *f.* line of force.

**kraftlos,** *a.* forceless, powerless, feeble.

**Kraft-mehl,** *n.* starch, amylum. **-messer,** *m.* dynamometer. **-mittel,** *n.* forceful means; powerful remedy; tonic. **-quelle,** *f.* source of power. **-sammler,** *m.* accumulator. **-spiritus,** *m.* motor spirit. **-stoff,** *m.* fuel. **-übertragung,** *f.* power transmission. **-verbrauch,** *m.* power consumption. **-wagen,** *m.* automobile, motor car. **-wagenlack,** *m.* automobile varnish. **-wechsel,** *m.* energy exchange. **-werk,** *n.,* **-zentrale,** *f.* power station. **-wirkung,** *f.* effect, action (of a force).

**Kragen,** *m.* collar; cape; flange.

**Krähe,** *f.* crow.

**Krähenaugen,** *pl.* (*Pharm.*) nux vomica.

**Krahle,** *f.* rake, rabble.

**Krahn,** *m.* = Kran.

**Kralle,** *f.* claw.

**Kram,** *m.* retail; store, shop; retail articles; stuff, lot.

**Krämer,** *m.* retailer, storekeeper, tradesman. **-gewicht,** *n.* avoirdupois.

**Krampe,** *f.* cramp, cramp iron.

**Krampf,** *m.* cramp, spasm, convulsion. **-ader,** *f.* varicose vein. **-arznei,** *f.* antispasmo lic. **-gift,** *n.* convulsive poison.

**krampfhaft,** *a.* spasmodic, convulsive.

**Krampf-mittel,** *n.* antispasmodic. **-wurzel,** *f.* valerian root.

**Kran,** *m.* cock, faucet; crane.

**Kranewitbeere,** *f.* juniper berry.

**Kranich,** *m.* crane.

**krank,** *a.* ill, sick.

**kränkeln,** *v.i.* be ailing, be sickly.

**Kranken-anstalt,** *f.* hospital. **-haus,** *n.* hospital. **-heilanstalt,** *f.* sanatorium, hospital.

**krankhaft,** *a.* diseased; morbid.

**Krankheit,** *f.* disease; illness, sickness.

**krankheitserregend,** *a.* disease-producing, pathogenic.

**Krankheitserreger,** *m.* excitant of disease.

**krankheitserzeugend,** *p.a.* pathogenic.

**Krankeits-keim,** *m.* disease germ. **-kunde, -lehre,** *f.* pathology.

**kränklich,** *a.* sickly, in poor health.

**Kranz,** *m.* wreath; crown; corona; ring; border, rim, brim; lid (of a furnace).

**Kranz-.** (*Anat.*) coronary, coronal. **-brenner,** *m.* ring burner, crown burner.

**Kränzchen,** *n.* little wreath; (social) circle.

**Krapp,** *m.* madder. **-farbe,** *f.* madder color, madder dye. **-färben,** *n.* madder dyeing. **-farbstoff, -färbestoff,** *m.* alizarin. **-gelb,** *n.* madder yellow, xanthin. **-lack,** *m.* madder lake. **-rot,** *n.* madder red, alizarin. **-stoff,** *m.* alizarin. **-wurzel,** *f.* madder root.

**Krätzblei,** *n.* slag lead.

**Kratzbürste,** *f.* stiff brush, scraper; cross person.

**Kratze,** *f.* scraper; rabble; rake; scrapings.

**Krätze,** *f.* waste metal (dross, cuttings, sweepings, etc.); (*Med.*) itch.

**kratzen,** *v.t.* scrape, scratch; card (wool, etc.); (*Metal.*) rabble.—*v.i.* scratch, grate; be harsh (in taste).—**kratzend,** *p.a.* harsh, irritating (of taste).

**Kratzer, Krätzer,** *m.* scraper, scratcher, rake, raker.

**Krätzfrischen,** *n.* (*Metal.*) refining of waste.

**krätzig,** *a.* itchy; (*Glass*) fibrous.

**Krätz-kupfer,** *n.* copper from waste. **-messing,** *n.* brass cuttings. **-wurzel,** *f.* white hellebore (root).

**kraus,** *a.* crisp; curly, curled; nappy.

**kräuseln,** *v.t.* curl, crisp, crimp; mill (coins).

**Krauseminze,** *f.* curled mint (*Mentha crispa*); spearmint (*Mentha spicata*).

**Kräusen,** *f.pl.* (*Brewing*) head, specif. rocky head.

**Kraus-gummi,** *n.* crêpe rubber. **-putz,** *m.* rough plaster, rough cast. **-tabak,** *m.* shag.

**Kraut,** *n.* (*pl.* **Kräuter**). herb, plant; weed; top (of beets, etc.); cabbage.

**krautartig,** *a.* herbaceous.

**Kräuter-essig,** *m.* aromatic vinegar. **-mittel,** *n.* vegetable remedy. **-salz,** *n.* vegetable salt. **-tee,** *m.* herb tea. **-wein,** *m.* medicated wine. **-zucker,** *m.* (*Pharm.*) conserve, confection.

**Kreatin,** *n.* creatine.

**Kreatinin,** *n.* creatinine.

**Krebs,** *m.* cancer; crayfish; grain, hard particle (in clay, etc.); knot (in ore, etc.); canker; crab.

**krebsartig,** *a.* cancerous; crablike; crustaceous.

**Krebs-milch,** *f.* (*Med.*) cancer juice. **-wurz,** *f.* beechdrops (*Leptamnium virginianum*). **-wurzel,** *f.* bistort; squawroot (*Conopholis americana*).

**Kreide,** *f.* chalk.

**kreideartig,** *a.* chalky, cretaceous.

**Kreidegur,** *f.* = Bergmilch.

**kreidehaltig,** *a.* containing chalk, cretaceous.

**Kreidemehl,** *n.* powdered chalk.

**kreiden,** *v.t.* chalk.

**Kreide-papier,** *n.* enameled paper. **-paste,** *f.* a cement of chalk and glue. **-pulver,** *n.* chalk powder. **-stein,** *m.* chalkstone. **-stift,** *m.* crayon.

**kreidig,** *a.* chalky, cretaceous.

**Kreis,** *m.* circle; circuit; orbit; district; range. **-ausschnitt,** *m.* sector. **-bahn,** *f.* circular path; orbit. **-bewegung,** *f.* rotary motion, rotation. **-bogen,** *m.* arc of a circle; circular arch.

**kreischen,** *v.i.* shriek, scream, (of fat) sizzle, (of bending tin) cry.

**Kreisel,** *m.* top; gyroscope. **-bewegung,** *f.* motion of a top, gyroscopic motion. **-elektron,** *n.* spinning electron. **-molekül,** *n.* spinning molecule.

**kreiseln,** *v.i.&r.* spin like a top, rotate with precession.

**Kreiselrad,** *n.* turbine.

**kreisen,** *v.i.* circle, revolve, circulate.

**Kreisfläche,** *f.* circular area.

**kreisförmig,** *a.* circular; round.

**Kreis-frequenz,** *f.* angular velocity. **-gang,** *m.* revolution. **-lauf,** *m.* cycle; circulation (of liquid or gas); circular course, circuit; revolution; rotation.

**kreislaufend,** *p.a.* circulatory.

**Kreis-linie,** *f.* circular line, circumference. **-ordnung,** *f.* district regulation. **-prozess,** *m.* cyclic process, cycle. **-pumpe,** *f.* circulating pump.

kreisrund, a. circular.

Kreis-schicht, f. circular layer, (of a tree) annual ring. -umfang, m. circumference, periphery.

Krem, m. cream. -farbe, f. cream color.

Kremnitzerweiss, n. Kremnitz white.

krempeln, v.t. card.

Kremserweiss, n. Kremnitz white.

Krensäure, f. crenic acid.

Kreo-sol, n. creosol. -sot, n. creosote.

kreosotieren, v.t. creosote.

Kreosotöl, n. creosote oil.

krepieren, v.i. burst.—v.t. vex.

krepitieren, v.i. crepitate, crackle.

Krepp, m. crêpe.

Kresol, n. cresol. -natron, n. sodium cresylate. -seife, f. cresol soap.

Kresorcin, n. cresorcinol.

Kresotinsäure, f. cresotic acid, cresotinic acid.

Kresse, f. cress.

Kresyl, n. cresyl ($HOC_6H_4CH_2$ or $CH_3C_6H_4$; in the latter case better translated tolyl). -säure, f. cresylic acid (cresol).

Kreuz, n. cross; loins; rump. -beeren, f.pl. = Kreuzdornbeeren. -bein, n. sacrum. -blume, f. milkwort (Polygala). -blütler, m. (Bot.) crucifer. -dorn, m. buckthorn (Rhamnus). -dornbeeren, f.pl. buckthorn berries, Persian berries.

kreuzen, v.t. cross.

kreuzförmig, a. cross-shaped, cruciform, cruciate.

Kreuz-gitter, n. cross grating; surface lattice. -hahn, m. four-way cock. -kopf, m. (Mach.) crosshead. -kraut, n. groundsel (Senecio). -kümmel, m. cumin. -schmerz, m. lumbago. -stein, m. cross-stone (chiastolite, harmotome, staurolite). -tisch, m. mechanical stage.

Kreuzung, f. crossing.

Kreuzungspunkt, m. intersection.

kreuzweise, adv. crosswise.

kribbeln, kriebeln, v.t. tickle, irritate.

kriechen, v.i. creep, crawl.

Krieg, m. war.

kriegen, v.t. seize, get.—v.i. make war.

Kriegführung, f. warfare.

Kriegs-ersatzstoff, m. war substitute, wartime substitute. -gerät, n. war material. -mittel, n. warfare agent, war material.

krimpen, v.t. shrink (cloth).

Krimpfähigkeit, f. property of shrinking; (of wool) felting property.

Kringel, m. cracknel.

Krippe, f. crib, manger.

krisch, pret. of kreischen.

Krise, f. crisis.

krispelig, a. grained, pebbled; blistered.

krispeln, v.t. grain, pebble (leather).

krist., abbrev. of kristallisiert, kristallinisch.

Krist., abbrev. of Kristalle, Kristallisation.

Kristall, m. crystal. -achse, f. crystal axis, crystallographic axis.

kristallähnlich, a. crystal-like, crystalloid.

Kristallanschuss, m. crop of crystals.

kristallartig, a. crystal-like, crystalline.

Kristall-ausscheidung, f. separation of crystals. -bau, m. crystal structure. -benzol, n. benzene of crystallization. -bildung, f. formation of crystals, crystallization, (Sugar) granulation. -bildungspunkt, m. (Sugar) granulating pitch.

Kriställchen, n. little crystal.

Kristall-chloroform, n. chloroform of crystallization. -ecke, f. (solid) crystal angle.

kristallen, a. crystalline.

Kristall-fabrik, f. glass works. -feuchtigkeit, f. crystalline humor (vitreous humor). -fläche, f. crystal face.

kristallförmig, a. crystalline, crystalloid.

Kristall-gitter, n. crystal lattice. -glasur, f. (Ceram.) crystalline glaze.

kristallhaltig, a. containing crystals, crystalliferous.

Kristall-haut, f. crystalline crust. -häutchen, n. crystalline film.

kristallhell, a. crystal-clear, transparent.

Kristallierschale, f. crystallizing dish or basin.

kristallinisch, a. crystalline.

Kristallinität, f. crystallinity.

Kristallinse, f. (Anat.) crystalline lens.

Kristallisationsbassin, n. crystallizing basin, tank, or cistern.

kristallisationsfähig, a. crystallizable.

Kristallisationsfähigkeit, f. crystallizability.

kristallisationsfreudig, a. readily crystallizable.

Kristallisations-gefäss, n. crystallizing vessel, crystallizer. -schale, f. crystallizing dish. -wärme, f. heat of crystallization.

kristallisch, a. crystalline.

kristallisierbar, a. crystallizable.

Kristallisier-barkeit, f. crystallizability. -behälter, m. crystallizing receptacle, crystallizing tank.

kristallisieren, v.t. & i. crystallize.

Kristallisier-gefäss, n. crystallizing vessel, crystallizer. -schale, f. crystallizing dish or basin.

Kristallisierung, f. crystallization, crystallizing.

Kristallisierungsgefäss, n. crystallization vessel.

Kristall-kante, f. crystal edge. -keim, m. crystal nucleus, seed crystal. -kern, m. nucleus of crystallization. -lehre, f. crystallography. -linse, f. (Anat.) crystalline lens. -mehl, m. crystal powder; crystal sand. -messung, f. crystallometry. -oberfläche, f. crystal surface. -nädelchen, n. crystal needle, acicular crystal.

kristallogenisch, a. crystallogenic.

Kristallographie, f. crystallography.

kristallographisch, a. crystallographic.

Kristall-pulver, n. crystal powder. -säure, f. fuming sulfuric acid of high strength, forming a crystalline solid. -soda, f. soda crystals ($Na_2CO_3 \cdot 10H_2O$). -stein, m. rock crystal. -waren, f.pl. (crystal) glassware. -wasser, n. crystal water, water of crystallization.

kristallwasser-frei, a. free from water of crystallization. -haltig, a. containing crystal water.

Kristallzucker, m. refined sugar in crystals.

Kristfm., abbrev. (Kristallform) crystal form.

Kriterium, n. criterion.

Kritik, f. criticism.

kritisch, a. critical.

kritteln, v.i. carp at, criticize.

kritzeln, v.i. scribble; scratch.

kroch, pret. of kriechen.

Krokonsäure, f. croconic acid.

Krone, f. crown; corolla; corona; wreath; crest, top.

kronenartig, a. like a crown, coronal; (Anat.) coronary.

Kronen-aufsatz, m. column (of a still). -brenner, m. crown burner, ring burner. -gold, n. crown gold.

Kron-glas, n. crown glass. -kümmel, m. cumin.

Kropf, m. goiter; craw, crop; bend; (Paper) breasting.

kröpfen, v.t. bend at right angles, bend.

Kropf-rohr, m., -röhre, f. bent tube, bent pipe. -wurz, f. = Knotenwurz. -wurzel, f. polypody root. -zylinder, m. a glass cylinder with a wider upper part, hydrometer jar.

kröseln, v.t. crumble (glass); groove.

Kröte, f. toad.

Kroton-öl, n. croton oil. -säure, f. crotonic acid.

Krücke, f. crutch; rake, rabble, scraper, etc. (of crutch shape).

Krug, m. pitcher; jug, mug; jar, pot.

Kruke, f. earthenware pot, jar or pitcher.

krüllen, v.t. crumple.

Krulltabak, m. shag.

Krume, f. crumb, bit; black earth.

krümelig, a. crumbly, crumbling, friable.

krümeln, v.i. crumble, crumb.—v.a. crumble.

Krümelzucker, m. (dextro)glucose, dextrose.

krumm, a. crooked, curved, bent. -blätterig, a. in curved or bent leaflets; (Bot.) curvifoliate.

Krummdarm, m. ileum.

krümmen, v.t. curve, bend, crook.—v.r. bend; warp.

Krümmer, m. bent piece, bend, elbow.

Krummholz, n. crooked or curved piece of wood; = Krummholzbaum. -baum, m., -fichte, -kiefer, f. knee pine (Pinus montana pumilio). -öl, n. templin oil (from knee pine).

krummlinig, a. curvilinear.

Krümmung, f. curvature; curve, bend, turn, sinuosity; crookedness.

Krummzirkel, m. calipers.

krumös, a. friable, crumbly.

krümpeln, v.t. crumple, pucker, crinkle.

Krupp, m. croup.

Kruste, f. crust, incrustation.

krustenartig, a. crustlike, crusty.

Krusten-bildung, f. crust formation, incrustation. -tier, n. crustacean.

krustieren, v.t. crust, incrust.

krustig, a. crusty, crusted.

kryohydratisch, a. cryohydric.

Kryo-lith, m. cryolite. -phor, n. cryophorus. -skopie, f. cryoscopy.

Krystall, m. crystal (for compounds see Kristall-).

k.s.l., abbrev. (kalt sehr löslich) very soluble cold.

Kubaholz, n. Cuba wood (fustic).

Kubebe, f. cubeb.

Kübel, m. vat, tub, pail, bucket.

kubieren, v.t. cube.

Kubik-inhalt, m. cubic contents. -wurzel, f. cube root. -zahl, f. cube.

kubisch, a. cubic, cubical. -zentriert, a. (Cryst.) body-centered.

kubizieren, v.t. calculate the volume of.

Kubus, m. cube.

Küche, f. kitchen; cooking, cookery.

Kuchen, m. cake.

kuchenbildend, a. cake-forming, caking.

Küchen-gewächs, n. kitchen herb. -salz, n. common salt. -schelle, f. pasque flower (Pulsatilla).

Kufe, f. vat, tun, tub.

Kugel, f. bulb; ball, sphere, globe; shot.

Kugel-, spherical, ball, globular, bulb.

kugelähnlich, a. spheroidal; ball-like.

Kugelapparat, m. bulb apparatus (e.g., potash bulbs).

Kügelchen, n. small bulb; globule; pellet; small ball.

Kugel-diorit, m. globular diorite. -fläche, f. spherical surface. -flasche, f. balloon flask, spherical flask.

kugelförmig, a. globular, spherical, globose.

Kugel-funktion, f. spherical harmonic. -gelenk, n. ball-and-socket joint. -hahn-

**pipette**, *f.*, **-hahnstechheber**, *m.* pipette with globe stopcock.

**kugelig**, *a.* globular, spherical, globose.

**Kugel-kühler**, *m.* ball condenser, spherical condenser. **-lack**, *m.* lac or lake in balls. **-lager**, *n.* ball bearing. **-linse**, *f.* spherical lens. **-mühle**, *f.* ball mill.

**kugeln**, *v.t.& i.* roll; form into a ball.

**Kugel-rohr**, *n.*, **-röhre**, *f.* bulb tube (tube with one or more bulbar enlargements). **-rührer**, *m.* bulb (or ball) stirrer. **-schale**, *f.* spherical shell. **-schliff**, *m.* ground ball-and-socket joint. **-spiegel**, *m.* spherical mirror. **-stopfen**, *m.* bulb stopper, globular stopper. **-symmetrie**, *f.* spherical symmetry.

**kugelsymmetrisch**, *a.* spherosymmetric.

**Kugel-tee**, *m.* gunpowder tea. **-ventil**, *n.* ball valve. **-vorlage**, *f.* spherical (or globular) receiver. **-welle**, *f.* spherical wave.

**Kuh**, *f.* cow. **-dünger**, **-kot**, *m.* cow dung. **-euter**, *n.* cow udder; Bredt adapter for vacuum distillation. **-kotbad**, *n.* cow-dung bath.

**kuhkoten**, *v.t.* dung (with cow dung).

**kühl**, *a.* cool.

**Kühl-anlage**, *f.* cooling plant, refrigerating plant. **-apparat**, *m.* cooling apparatus; cooler; refrigerator; condenser. **-bottich**, *m.* cooling tub, cooler.

**Kühle**, *f.* coolness; cooler.

**kühlen**, *v.t.* cool, chill, refrigerate; (*Glass*) anneal.

**Kühler**, *m.* condenser; cooler; refrigerator; (of an automobile) radiator. **-gestell**, *n.* condenser stand, condenser support. **-halter**, *m.* condenser holder or clamp. **-mantel**, *m.* condenser jacket. **-retorte**, *f.* condenser retort. **-stativ**, *n.* condenser stand or support.

**Kühl-fass**, *n.* cooling vessel, cooling vat, cooling tub. **-fläche**, *f.* cooling surface. **-flüssigkeit**, *f.* cooling liquid. **-gefäss**, *m.* cooling vessel, cooler; refrigerator; condenser. **-geläger**, *n.* (*Brewing*) wort sediment, dregs. **-kammer**, *f.* cooling chamber. **-kasten**, *m.* cooling box, cooler. **-mantel**, *m.* cooling jacket or mantle. **-maschine**, *f.* refrigerating machine, refrigerator. **-mittel**, *n.* refrigerant. **-ofen**, *m.* cooling oven, annealing furnace. **-pfanne**, *f.* cooling pan, cooler; (*Glass*) leer pan. **-rohr**, *n.*, **-röhre**, *f.* cooling tube or pipe; condenser tube. **-salz**, *n.* refrigerating salt. **-schiff**, *n.* (*Brewing*) cooling back, cooler. **-schlange**, **-schnecke**, *f.* worm (for distilling), cooling coil, condenser coil. **-schrank**, *m.* refrigerator. **-tasche**, *f.* cooling chamber. **-turm**, *n.* cooling tower.

**Kühlung**, *f.* cooling, refrigeration.

**Kühlungsgrad**, *m.* degree of cooling; rate of cooling.

**Kühl-verfahren**, *n.* cooling or refrigerating method or process. **-vorrichtung**, *f.* cooling or refrigerating device or apparatus. **-wagen**, *m.* refrigerator car (truck, etc.). **-wasser**, *n.* cooling water; (*Pharm.*) lead water. **-werk**, *n.* cooling or refrigerating plant or apparatus. **-wirkung**, *f.* cooling effect. **-zylinder**, *m.* condenser; cooling cylinder.

**Kuh-milch** *f.* cow's milk. **-mist**, *m.* cow dung.

**kühn**, *a.* bold.

**Kuhpockengift**, *n.* vaccine virus.

**Kukabrühe**, *f.* (*abbrev.* for *Kupfer-Kalk-Brühe*) Bordeaux mixture.

**Kukuruz**, *m.* corn, maize.

**Küken**, *n.* stopcock plug; stopcock; chicken.

**Külbchen**, *n.* (*Glass*) ball, piece, lump.

**Kulilawanöl**, *n.* culilawan oil.

**kulinarisch**, *a.* culinary.

**Kulisse**, *f.* coulisse (something that slides).

**kultivieren**, *v.t.* cultivate.

**Kultur**, *f.* civilization; culture; cultivation. **-flasche**, *f.* culture flask. **-hefe**, *f.* culture yeast. **-kolben**, *m.* culture flask. **-pflanze**, *f.* cultivated plant. **-röhre**, *f.* culture tube. **-schale**, *f.* culture dish. **-staat**, *m.* civilized state (or nation). **-stufe**, *f.* stage of civilization. **-versuch**, *m.* cultivation experiment.

**Kumar-**. coumar- (or cumar-). See Cumar-.

**Kuminsäure**, *f.* cumic acid, cuminic acid.

**Kümmel**, *m.* caraway; (*römischer*) cumin; kümmel (the liqueur). **-branntwein**, **-likör**, *m.* kümmel (the liqueur). **-öl**, *n.* caraway oil; cumin oil; (*Org. Chem.*) carvone.

**Kummer**, *m.* sorrow, trouble.

**kümmern**, *v.t.* trouble, concern.

**Kumol**, *n.* cumene.

**Kumpe**, *f.* (*Dyeing*) basin, vessel.

**kümpeln**, *v.t.* dish, flange.

**kumulieren**, *v.t.* accumulate.

**Kumys**, *m.* kumiss.

**kund**, *a.* known, public.— **— und zu wissen sei**, be it known, take notice.

**Kunde**, *f.* knowledge, information, science; news.—*m.* customer; client.

**kundgeben**, *v.t.* make known, manifest, declare.

**kundig**, *a.* learned, expert, skilful, intelligent.

**kündigen**, *v.t.* give notice of; recall.

**Kündigung**, *f.* notice, warning.

**Kundschaft**, *f.* notice, information, knowledge; custom, patronage.

**künftig**, *a.* future, coming, to be.

**Kunst**, *f.* art; profession; skill; work (of art).

**Kunst-**. artificial; technical; art. **-ausdruck**, *m.* technical term. **-bronze**, *f.* art bronze.

-butter, *f.* artificial butter, oleomargarine. -druckpapier, *n.* paper for art printing. -dünger, *m.* artificial manure, fertilizer. -eis, *n.* artificial ice. -faden, *m.* artificial fiber. -fertigkeit, *f.* technical skill. -fett, *n.* artificial fat (or grease). -feuerwerkerei, *f.* pyrotechnics. -fleiss, *m.* industry. -gärtnerei, *f.* horticulture; nursery. -gewerbe, *n.* useful art, applied art. -gewerbeschule, *f.* polytechnic school. -glanz, *m.* artificial luster. -griff, *m.* artifice, trick, device. -harz, *n.* artificial resin. -hefe, *f.* artificial yeast. -heilmittel, *n.* artificial remedy, synthetic remedy. -holz, *n.* artificial wood. -honig, *m.* artificial honey. -keramik, *f.* art ceramics. -kohle, *f.* artificial coal. -leder, *n.* artificial leather. -lehre, *f.* technology, technics.

Künstler, *m.* artist; artificer. -farbe, *f.* artist's color.

künstlerisch, *a.* artistic.

künstlich, *a.* artificial; artful, ingenious.

Kunst-mittel, *n.* artificial means. -produkt, *n.* artificial product. -richter, *m.* critic. -schmalz, *n.* artificial lard, compound lard. -seide, *f.* artificial silk. -sprache, *f.* technical language. -stein, *m.* artificial stone. -stoff, *n.* artificial substance or material. -stück, *n.* feat, trick. -werk, *n.* work of art. -wolle, *f.* artificial wool; shoddy. -wort, *n.* technical word, technical term.

kunterbunt, *a.* party-colored; topsy-turvy.

Küpe, *f.* vat; boiler, copper.

kupellieren, *v.t.* cupel.

küpen, *v.t.* vat-dye, vat.

Küpen-artikel, *m.* (*Calico*) vat style. -bad, *n.* dye liquor. -blau, *n.* vat blue, indigo blue. -färber, *m.* vat dyer. -färberei, *f.* vat dyeing. -farbstoff, *m.* vat dye. -färbung, *f.* vat dyeing.

Kupfer, *n.* copper. -abfall, *m.* waste copper. -alaun, *m.* (*Pharm.*) cuprum aluminatum, lapis divinus. -ammonium, *n.* cupr(o)ammonium, Schweitzer's reagent. -antimonglanz, *m.* chalcostibite.

kupferartig, *a.* = kupferig.

Kupfer-asche, *f.* copper scale. -azetat, *n.* copper acetate. -azetylen, *n.* copper acetylide. -bad, *n.* copper bath. -barre, *f.* copper bar; copper ingot. -blatt, *n.* copper foil. -blau, *n.* blue verditer, azurite. -blech, *n.* sheet copper, copper foil. -blei, *n.* copper-lead alloy. -bleiglanz, *m.* (*Min.*) cuproplumbite. -bleivitriol, *m.* linarite. -blende, *f.* tennantite. -blüte, *f.* copper bloom (capillary cuprite). -braun, *n.* tile ore (earthy ferruginous cuprite). -bromid, *n.* copper (specif. cupric) bromide. -bromür, *n.* cuprous bromide. -chlorid, *n.* copper

(specif. cupric) chloride. -chlorür, *n.* cuprous chloride. -cyanid, *n.* copper cyanide, specif. cupric cyanide. -cyanür, *n.* cuprous cyanide. -dorn, *m.* slag from liquated copper. -draht, *m.* copper wire. -drahtnetz, *n.* copper gauze. -drehspäne, *m.pl.* copper turnings. -druck, *m.* copperplate. -eisenvitriol, *n.* copper iron sulfate; specif., pisanite. -elektrode, *f.* copper electrode. -erz, *n.* copper ore. -fahlerz, *n.* tetrahedrite; tennantite. -farbe, *f.* copper color.

kupfer-farben, -farbig, *a.* copper-colored.

Kupfer-federerz, *n.* = Kupferblüte. -feilicht, *n.* copper filings. -folie, *f.* copper foil.

kupferführend, *a.* copper-bearing, cupriferous.

Kupfer-gare, *f.*, -garmachen, *n.* copper refining. -gefäss, *n.* copper vessel. -gehalt, *m.* copper content. -geist, *m.* spirit of verdigris (mixture of acetic acid and acetone obtained by distilling verdigris). -gewebe, *n.* copper gauze. -gewinnung, *f.* extraction of copper. -giesserei, *f.* copper foundry; copper founding. -glanz, *m.* copper glance (chalcocite). -glas, -glaserz, *n.* (*Min.*) chalcocite. -glimmer, *m.* chalcophyllite; micaceous copper (copper made brittle by the presence of foreign oxides, formed in refining). -glühspan, *m.* copper scale. -gold, *n.* a copper alloy imitating gold, as Mannheim gold or similar. -grün, *n.* copper green (verditer; verdigris).

kupferhaltig, *a.* containing copper, cupriferous, cupreous.

Kupfer-hammerschlag, *m.* copper scale. -hydrat, *n.* copper hydroxide. -hydroxyd, *n.* copper hydroxide, specif. cupric hydroxide. -hydroxydul, *n.* cuprous hydroxide.

kupferig, *a.* coppery, copperlike, cupreous.

Kupfer-indig, -indigo, *m.* indigo copper (covellite). -jodid, *n.* copper (specif. cupric) oxide. -jodür, *n.* cuprous iodide. -kalk, *m.* copper calx, copper oxide. -kalkbrühe, *f.* (*Agric.*) Bordeaux mixture.

Kupferkies, *m.* copper pyrites (chalcopyrite). —bunter —, bornite.

kupferkieshaltig, *a.* containing copper pyrites.

Kupfer-kohle, *f.* coppered carbon. -könig, *m.* copper regulus. -lasur, *f.* azurite. -legierung, *f.* copper alloy. -lösung, *f.* copper solution. -lot, *n.* copper solder. -mangan, *n.* cupromanganese. -münze, *f.* copper coin.

kupfern, *v.t.* treat with copper, copper.—*a.* copper, coppery, copper-colored.

Kupfer-nickel, *m.* copper-nickel (niccolite). -niederschlag, *m.* copper precipitate or deposit. -ocher, -ocker, *m.* = Kupferbraun.

**Kupferoxyd,** *n.* cupric oxide. **-ammoniak,** *n.* ammoniacal copper oxide. **-hydrat,** *n.* cupric hydroxide. **-salz,** *n.* cupric salt.

**Kupferoxydul,** *n.* cuprous oxide. **-hydrat,** *n.* cuprous hydroxide. **-salz,** *n.* cuprous salt. **-verbindung,** *f.* cuprous compound.

**Kupfer-oxydverbindung,** *f.* cupric compound. **-pecherz,** *n.* = Kupferbraun. **-platte,** *f.* copper plate, copperplate. **-pol,** *m.* (*Elec.*) copper pole (positive pole). **-probe,** *f.* copper assay, test for copper. **-raffination,** *f.* copper refining. **-rauch,** *m.* copper smoke, copper fumes; white vitriol. **-regen,** *m.* = Streukupfer. **-reinigung,** *f.* copper refining. **-rhodanat, -rhodanid,** *n.* copper thiocyanate, specif. cupric thiocyanate. **-rhodanür,** *n.* cuprous thiocyanate. **-rohr,** *n.,* **-röhre,** *f.* copper tube, copper pipe. **-rohstein,** *m.* raw copper matte. **-rost,** *m.* copper rust, verdigris (greenish coating on exposed copper).

**kupferrot,** *a.* copper-red, copper-colored.

**Kupfer-rot,** *n.* red copper (cuprite). **-salz,** *n.* copper salt. **-sammeterz, -samterz,** *n.* velvet copper ore (cyanotrichite). **-säure,** *f.* cupric acid. **-schaum,** *m.* (*Metal.*) copper scum; (*Min.*) tyrolite. **-scheibe,** *f.* copper disk. **-schlacke,** *f.* copper slag. **-schlag,** *m.* copper scale. **-schlange,** *f.* copper coil. **-schwamm,** *m.* copper sponge; (*Min.*) tyrolite. **-schwärze,** *f.* black copper (melaconite). **-schwefel,** *m.* copper sulfide. **-seide,** *f.* cuprammonium silk, cuprammonium rayon. **-silberglanz,** *m.* stromeyerite. **-sinter,** *m.* copper scale; copper pyrites. **-smaragd,** *m.* emerald copper (dioptase). **-spiritus,** *m.* = Kupfergeist. **-stahl,** *m.* copper steel. **-stechen,** *n.* copper engraving.

**Kupferstein,** *m.* copper matte.—**blasiger —,** pimple metal.

**Kupfer-stich,** *m.* copper engraving. **-sulfat,** *n.* copper sulfate, cupric sulfate. **-sulfid,** *n.* copper (specif. cupric) sulfide. **-sulfür,** *n.* cuprous sulfide. **-überzug,** *m.* copper coating or covering. **-verbindung,** *f.* copper compound. **-vergiftung,** *f.* copper poisoning. **-verhüttung,** *f.* copper smelting. **-vitriol,** *m.* blue vitriol, copper sulfate. **-wasser,** *n.* copperas (*Obs.*); (*Mining*) copper water, cement water. **-wasserstoff,** *m.* copper hydride. **-wismuterz,** *n.* klaprotholite; wittichenite. **-wismutglanz,** *m.* emplectite. **-zahl,** *f.* copper number, copper value. **-ziegelerz,** *n.* = Kupferbraun. **-zuschlag,** *m.* copper flux. **-zyanid,** *n.* = Kupfercyanid. **-zyanür,** *n.* cuprous cyanide.

**kupfrig,** *a.* copperlike, coppery.

**Kupol-hochofen,** *m.* cupola blast furnace. **-ofen,** *m.* cupola furnace or kiln, cupola.

**Kuppe,** *f.* top, summit, tip, head; meniscus.

**Kuppel,** *f.* cupola, dome.

**kuppeln,** *v.t.& i.* couple; (*Dyeing*) develop; (*Mach.*) engage, connect.

**Kuppelofen,** *m.* = Kupolofen.

**Kuppelung,** *f.* coupling; (*Dyeing*) developing; (of an automobile) clutch.

**Kuppelungs-bad,** *n.* (*Dyeing*) developing bath. **-flotte,** *f.* (*Dyeing*) developing liquor.

**Kuppler,** *m.* coupler; (*Dyeing*) developer.

**Kupplung,** *f.* = Kuppelung.

**Kupri-.** see Cupri-.

**Kuprit,** *m.* cuprite.

**Kupro-.** see Cupro-.

**Kur,** *f.* cure, treatment.

**Kurbel,** *f.* crank, winch.

**Kürbis,** *m.* gourd; pumpkin. **-baum,** *m.* gourd tree, calabash tree. **-gewächse,** *n.pl.* Cucurbitaceae. **-korn,** *n.,* **-kern, -samen,** *m.* pumpkin seed; gourd seed.

**küren,** *v.t.* choose, elect.

**Kurkuma,** *f.* curcuma, turmeric. **-gelb,** *n.* curcumin. **-papier,** *n.* turmeric paper. **-säure,** *f.* curcumic acid. **-wurzel,** *f.* turmeric.

**Kuromojiöl,** *n.* curomoji oil.

**Kurort,** *m.* health resort.

**Kurrent-buchstaben,** *m.pl.,* **-schrift,** *f.* script.

**Kurs,** *m.* exchange; circulation; course.

**Kürschner,** *m.* furrier.

**kursieren,** *v.i.* be current.

**kursiv,** *a.* italic.

**Kursivschrift,** *f.* italics.

**Kursus,** *m.* course.

**Kurswert,** *m.* exchange value.

**Kurve,** *f.,* **Kurvenbild,** *n.* curve.

**K rven-ast,** *m.* branch of a (or the) curve. **-eck,** *n.* angle in a curve. **-schar,** *f.* group or system of curves. **-zacke,** *f.* jag (sharp change in direction) in a curve. **-zug,** *m.* curve.

**kurz,** *a.* short, brief.—**binnen kurzem,** within a short time.—**kurze Flotte,** concentrated dye liquor.—**vor kurzem,** recently.

**k rz-armig,** *a.* short-armed, short-arm, short-beam (balance). **-brüchig,** *a.* short, brittle. **-dauernd,** *a.* short(lived), brief, transient.

**Kürze,** *f.* shortness, brevity.

**kürzen,** *v.t.* shorten; abridge.

**kurz-flammig,** *a.* short-flame, short-flaming. **-gefasst,** *a.* brief, concise, compendious. **-haarig,** *a.* short-haired; (of wool) short-staple. **-halsig,** *a.* short-necked. **-lebig,** *a.* short-lived.

**kürzlich,** *a.* late, recent.

**kurzschliessen,** *v.t.* (*Elec.*) short-circuit.

**Kurzschliffhalskolben,** *m.* flask with short ground neck.

**Kurzschluss,** *m.* (*Elec.*) short circuit. **-ofen,**

*m.* short-circuit furnace. **-strom,** *m.* short-circuit current.

**Kurzschrift,** *f.* shorthand, stenography.

**kurz-sichtig,** *a.* near-sighted, short-sighted. **-skalig,** *a.* short-scale(d).

**Kurzstäbchen,** *n.* bacillus.

**kurzum,** *adv.* in short, in brief.

**Kurzwaren,** *f.pl.* small wares.

**kurzwellig,** *a.* of short wave length, short-wave.

**küssen,** *v.t.* kiss.

**Kussin,** *n.* kosin.

**Kusso,** *m.* (*Pharm. & Bot.*) cusso.

**Küste,** *f.* coast, shore.

**Kustos,** *m.* keeper, custodian.

**Kutsche,** *f.* coach, carriage.

**Kuvert,** *n.* envelope; cover.

**Kuvette, Küvette,** *f.* bulb; cell, vessel.

**k.w.l.,** *abbrev.* (kalt wenig löslich) not very soluble cold.

**Kwst.,** *abbrev.* (Kilowattstunde) kilowatt-hour.

**KW-stoff,** *abbrev.* (Kohlenwasserstoff) hydro-carbon.

**Kyanäthin,** *n.* cyanethine, kyanethine.

**Kyanidin,** *n.* cyanidine, kyanidine.

**kyanisieren,** *v.t.* kyanize.

**Kyanisierung,** *f.* kyanizing, kyanization.

**Kyaphenin,** *n.* cyaphenine, kyaphenine.

**Kynurensäure,** *f.* kynurenic acid.

**Kyste,** *f.* cyst.

**KZ.,** *abbrev.* (Kernzahl) number of (crystal) nuclei.

# L

1., *abbrev.* (löslich) soluble; (lies) read; liter; (linksdrehend) levorotatory.

L., *abbrev.* lira, lire.

-l., *abbrev.* -lich. See -lich.

Lab, Laab, *n.* rennet.

lab., *abbrev.* (labil) labile.

Labdanharz, *n.* labdanum, ladanum.

Labdrüse, *f.* peptic gland.

laben, *v.t.* curdle with rennet; refresh.

Laberdan, *m.* salted codfish.

Labessenz, *f.* rennet extract, rennet.

labil, *a.* labile, unstable.

Labkraut, *n.* galium.

Laborant, *m.* (male) laboratory helper. -in, *f.* (female) laboratory helper.

Laborationstaxe, *f.* tax on chemists.

Laboratorien, *n.pl.* laboratories.

Laboratorium, *n.* laboratory.

laborieren, *v.i.* practice chemistry; labor.

Labpulver, *n.* rennet powder.

Labrador-isieren, *n.* play of colors (as on labradorite). -stein, *m.* Labrador stone, labradorite.

lächeln, *v.i.* smile.

lachen, *v.i.* laugh.

lächerlich, *a.* laughable, ludicrous.

Lachgas, *n.* laughing gas.

Lachs, *m.* salmon.

lachs-farben, -farbig, *a.* salmon-colored.

Lachsöl, *n.* salmon oil.

Lacht, *m.* slag.

Lack, *m.* lac; lake; lacquer, japan; varnish. -abbeizmittel, -auflösungsmittel, *n.* varnish remover. -anstrich, *m.* coat of lacquer or varnish. -bildner, *m.* lake former. -farbe, *f.* lake; lac dye; varnish color, color varnish.

lackfarbig, *a.* lake-colored, laky, laked.

Lack-firnis, *m.* lac varnish, lacquer; lake varnish. -firnislack, *m.* lac lake. -harz, *n.* varnishing resin, esp. copal.

lackieren, *v.t.* lacquer, japan; varnish.

Lack-ierung, *f.* lacquering; varnishing; dope paint. -lack, *m.* lac lake. -lasurfarbe, *f.* transparent varnish color. -leder, *n.* japanned leather, patent leather.

Lackmus, *m.* litmus. -farbstoff, *m.* litmus. -flechte, *f.* litmus lichen, archil. -lösung, *f.* litmus solution. -papier, *n.* litmus paper. -tinktur, *f.* litmus tincture.

Lack-säure, *f.* laccaic acid. -überzug, *m.* = Lackanstrich.

Lacmus, *m.* litmus. See Lackmus-.

Lactar-insäure, *f.* lactarinic acid. -säure, *f.* lactaric acid (stearic acid).

Lacton-bindung, *f.* lactonic linkage. -säure, *f.* lactonic acid, lactone acid (a compound which is both an acid and a lactone); lactonic acid, *d*-galactonic acid.

Ladangummi, *n.* labdanum, ladanum.

Lade, *f.* chest, box, case; (*Founding*) flask.

laden, *v.t.* load, charge; summon, invite; (*Elec.*) charge.

Laden, *m.* store, shop; shutter; plank.

Ladenburgkolben, *m.* Ladenburg flask.

Ladenpreis, *m.* retail price.

Lader, *m.* loader, charger, filler.

Lade-raum, *m.* exploding chamber; loading space. -strom, *m.* charging current.

lädieren, *v.t.* hurt, injure, damage.

Ladung, *f.* charge; load; cargo; charging, loading.

Ladungs-dichte, *f.* density of charge, charge density. -flasche, *f.* Leyden jar. -sinn, *m.* (*Elec.*) nature of a charge, sign. -wolke, *f.* charge cloud.

lag, *pret.* of liegen.

Lage, *f.* layer, stratum, bed; coat, coating; state, position, situation, location; condition; attitude; quire (of paper); (*Textiles*) lap.—in — sein, be in a position, be able.

Lägel, *n.* barrel, keg.

lagenweise, *adv.* in layers or beds.

Lager, *n.* bed, layer, stratum; store, stock; storehouse; sediment; camp; bed, couch; lair; stand (for casks); (*Mech.*) bearing, bush. -bestand, *m.* stock, inventory. -bock, *m.* (*Mach.*) pedestal. -buchse, -büchse, *f.* (*Mach.*) bush, bushing.

lagerecht, *a.* fast to storing.

Lager-fass, *n.* storage vat or cask. -festigkeit, *f.* stability in storage. -haus, *n.* warehouse, storehouse. -keller, *m.* storage cellar. -metall, *n.* bush metal, bearing metal.

lagern, *v.i.& r.* lie stored; be deposited; lie, remain; lie down; camp.—*v.t.* store; lay down, deposit; season.

Lager-platz, *m.* storage place, depot. -prozess, *m.* storage process. -raum, *m.* store room, warehouse room.

lagerreif, *a.* aged.

Lager-schale, *f.* (*Mach.*) bush, bushing. -stätte, *f.* deposit, bed.

211

**Lagerung,** *f.* arrangement; stratification, bedding; bed; grain (of a stone); storage; lying down; encampment.

**Lagerwein,** *m.* wine seasoned by storage.

**lageweise,** *adv.* in layers, in strata.

**lahm,** *a.* lame.

**lähmen,** *v.t.* paralyze, cripple, lame.

**Lähmung,** *f.* lameness, paralysis.

**Lahn,** *m.* flattened wire; tinsel.

**Laib,** *m.* loaf.

**Laich,** *m.* spawn.

**Laie,** *m.* layman; novice.

**Lake,** *f.* brine, pickle.

**Laken,** *n.* linen; cloth; sheet.

**Lakmus,** *m.* litmus. See Lackmus-.

**Lakritze,** *f.*, **Lakritz, Lakriz,** *m.* licorice.

**Lakritzensaft,** *m.* extract of licorice.

**Laktat,** *n.* lactate.

**Lakton,** *n.* lactone.

**Lambertsnuss,** *f.* filbert.

**Lamelle,** *f.* lamella; lamina.

**lamellieren,** *v.t.* laminate.

**laminieren,** *v.t.* laminate; (*Spinning*) draw.

**Lamm,** *n.* lamb.

**Lämmerwolle,** *f.* lamb's wool.

**Lampe,** *f.* lamp.

**Lampen-arbeit,** *f.* (*Glass*) blast-lamp work, as distinguished from foundry work. **-brennstunde,** *f.* lamp hour. **-docht,** *m.* lamp wick. **-russ,** *m.*, **-schwarz,** *n.* lampblack. **-säure,** *f.* lampic acid. *Obs.*

**Land,** *n.* land; country.

**Land-.** land, country, rural, agricultural, provincial; (*Med.*) epidemic, also endemic. **-bau,** *m.* agriculture. **-enge,** *f.* isthmus.

**Landes-.** state, national, of a country; native, home; land; agricultural. **-erzeugnis,** *n.* agricultural product; native product.

**Land-gut,** *n.* estate. **-karte,** *f.* map. **-krankheit,** *f.* epidemic or endemic disease.

**land-kundig,** *a.* notorious. **-läufig,** *a.* customary, current.

**ländlich,** *a.* rural; rustic.

**Land-mann,** *m.* farmer, countryman. **-messer,** *m.* surveyor. **-polizei,** *f.* rural police. **-schaft,** *f.* province, state; landscape. **-see,** *m.* lake. **-seuche,** *f.* epidemic. **-stadt,** *f.* inland town, country town. **-strasse,** *f.* highway. **-strich,** *m.* district; climate. **-sturm,** *m.* general levy, levy in mass. **-tag,** *m.* diet, legislature. **-vogt,** *m.* governor.

**landw.,** *abbrev.* landwirtschaftlich.

**Land-wehr,** *f.* first home reserve, militia. **-wirt,** *m.* farmer. **-wirtschaft,** *f.* agriculture.

**landwirtschaftlich,** *a.* agricultural.

**lang,** *a.* long; tall; (of wine, etc.) ropy.—**lange Flotte,** dilute dye liquor.—**seit langem,** for a long time.

**lang-brennweitig,** *a.* long-focus. **-dauernd,** *a.* long-continued.

**lange,** *adv.* long; far.

**Länge,** *f.* length; longitude; tallness. **-bruch,** *m.* longitudinal fracture.

**langeiförmig,** *a.* of extended oval shape.

**langen,** *v.i.* suffice; reach.—*v.t.* seize, take.

**Längen-.** longitudinal; linear. **-ausdehnung,** *f.* linear expansion. **-bruch,** *m.* longitudinal fracture. **-durchschnitt,** *m.* longitudinal section. **-grad,** *m.* degree of longitude. **-mass,** *n.* linear measure.

**länger,** *a.* longer, etc. (see lang).

**Langerhanssche Inseln.** (*Anat.*) islands of Langerhans.

**längern,** *v.t.* = verlängern.

**lang-flammig,** *a.* long-flame, long-flaming. **-fristig,** *a.* long-time. **-gestielt,** *p.a.* long-handled. **-gestreckt,** *p.a.* extended, elongated. **-haarig,** *a.* long-haired; flossy (silk); long-staple (wool). **-halsig,** *a.* long-necked.

**langj.,** *abbrev.* langjährig.

**lang-jährig,** *a.* of many years. **-lebig,** *a.* long-lived. **länglich,** *a.* elongated; oblong. **-rund,** *a.* elliptical; oval.

**Lang-loch,** *n.* oblong hole, slot. **-mut,** *f.* patience, forbearance.

**langrund,** *a.* oval.

**längs,** *prep.* along.

**Längs-.** longitudinal. **-achse,** *f.* longitudinal axis.

**langsam,** *a.* slow.

**Langsam-binder,** *m.* slow-setting cement. **-keit,** *f.* slowness.

**Langschliff,** *m.* long-fibered mechanical pulp.

**Längs-durchschnitt,** *m.* longitudinal section. **-ebene,** *f.* longitudinal plane.

**Langsein,** *n.* (of wine) ropiness.

**Längs-faser,** *f.* longitudinal fiber. **-schnitt,** *m.* longitudinal section. **-streifen,** *m.* longitudinal stripe or stria.

**längst,** *a.* longest.—*adv.* long ago.

**Langstäbchen,** *n.* bacillus.

**langstapelig,** *a.* long-staple.

**längstens,** *adv.* at the longest.

**lang-stielig,** *a.* long-stemmed; long-handled. **-weilen,** *v.t.* tire, bore. **-wellig,** *a.* of long wave length, long-wave. **-wierig,** *a.* protracted, wearisome.

**Lanthan,** *n.* lanthanum. **-salz,** *n.* lanthanum salt. **-schwefelsäure,** *f.* lanthanumsulfuric acid (lanthanum hydrogen sulfate).

**Lanze,** *f.* lance.

**Lapisdruck,** *m.* (*Calico*) lapis style.

**Läppchen,** *n.* lobe; flap, rag.

**Lappen,** *m.* flap; tab; flange; rag; lobe.

**lappig,** *a.* lobed, lobate; flabby, flaccid.

**Lärche,** *f.* larch.

**Lärchen-baum,** *m.* larch. **-baumharz, -harz,** *n.* larch resin, Venetian turpentine. **-holzöl,** *n.* larch-wood oil. **-pilz, -schwamm,** *m.* purging agaric (*Polyporus officinalis*). **-stoff,** *m.* coniferin. **-terpentin,** *m.* larch turpentine, Venetian turpentine.

**Lardöl,** *n.* lard oil.

**Laricinsäure,** *f.* laricinic acid, maltol.

**Larixinsäure,** *f.* larixinic acid, laricic acid.

**Larve,** *f.* larva; mask.

**larvizid,** *a.* larvicidal.

**las,** *pret.* of lesen.

**Lasche,** *f.* (*Mech.*) fish, fishplate.

**lasieren,** *v.t.* glaze.

**Lasierfarbe,** *f.* glazing color, glazing.

**Läsion,** *f.* lesion.

**lassen,** *v.t.* let, leave, yield, allow; cause, have (something done).—*v.i.* desist; look, suit.—**gelassen,** *p.a.* patient, calm.—**es lässt sich sehen,** it can be seen.

**lässig,** *a.* negligent, lazy.

**lässt,** *pr. 2 & 3 sing.* of lassen.

**Last,** *f.* load, burden, weight.

**lasten,** *v.i.* weigh.—*v.t.* load, burden.

**lästig,** *a.* burdensome, irksome, troublesome.

**Lastwagen,** *m.* truck, lorry; freight car.

**Lasur,** *f.* azure; azurite; glazing.—*m.* lapis lazuli.

**lasurblau,** *a.* azure, sky-blue.

**Lasur-blau,** *n.* ultramarine. **-farbe,** *f.* azure; glazing color; ultramarine.

**lasurfarben,** *a.* azure, sky-blue.

**Lasurit,** *m.* azurite; lapis lazuli.

**Lasur-lack,** *m.* transparent varnish. **-spat,** *m.* lazulite.

**Lasurstein,** *m.* lapis lazuli.—**unechter —,** false lapis lazuli, chessylite.

**lateinisch,** *a.* Latin; roman (letters).

**Latenz,** *f.* latency. **-zeit,** *f.* latent period.

**Laterne,** *f.* lantern; lamp.

**Latsche, Latschen-kiefer,** *f.* knee pine (*Pinus montana pumilio*). **-öl,** *n.* templin oil.

**Latte,** *f.* lath.

**Lattich,** *m.* lettuce. **-säure,** *f.* lactucic acid.

**Latwerge,** *f.* (*Pharm.*) electuary, confection.

**lau,** *a.* tepid, lukewarm; mild.

**Laub,** *n.* foliage, leaves.

**Laube,** *f.* arbor, bower; hall.

**Laub-erde,** *f.* leaf mold. **-grün,** *n.* a kind of chrome green. **-holz,** *n.* leaved trees, deciduous trees; wood of deciduous trees, hardwood. **-holzkohle,** *f.* hardwood charcoal.

**Lauch,** *m.* leek.

**lauch-artig,** *a.* like or of the nature of leeks. **-grün,** *a.* leek-green.

**laudieren,** *v.t.* gloss (cloth).

**Lauer,** *m.* (*Distilling*) low wine, singlings.

**Lauf,** *m.* course, path, running, run, race, current; (gun) barrel. **-bahn,** *f.* tract, runway, run; career; racecourse.

**laufen,** *v.i.* run; go, move, turn; leak.—**laufend,** *p.a.* running, current; consecutive (numbers).—**laufendes Bad,** (*Dyeing*) standing bath.

**Läufer,** *m.* runner; muller; rammer; slider; rotor. **-gewicht,** *n.* sliding weight. **-mühle,** *f.* edge mill.

**Lauf-fläche,** *f.* bearing surface; (*Mach.*) journal. **-gewicht,** *n.* sliding weight. **-glasur,** *f.* (*Ceram.*) flow glaze. **-kran,** *m.* traveling crane. **-pass,** *m.* dismissal. **-pfanne,** *f.* (*Sugar*) cooler. **-rolle,** *f.* (*Mach.*) roller, roll. **-term,** *m.* variable term. **-zahl,** *f.* variable number, running variable.

**Lauge,** *f.* lye; (in many technical phrases) liquor; (*Metal.*, etc.) leach; (*Bleaching*) buck. **-anlage,** *f.* lixiviation plant, leaching plant. **-bottich,** *m.* leaching vat, tub or tank.

**laugen,** *v.t.* lye, steep in lye; buck; leach, lixiviate.—**gelaugte Säure,** (*Paper*) tower liquor to which has been added liquor from the cookers (in the sulfite process).

**laugenartig,** *a.* of, the nature of, or resembling, lye, alkaline, (*Old Chem.*) lixivial.

**Laugen-asche,** *f.* leached ashes. **-bad,** *n.* lye bath, lye, liquor.

**laugenecht,** *a.* fast to (caustic) lye.

**Laugen-essenz,** *f.* caustic soda (or potash) solution. **-fass,** *n.* lye vat, leaching tub, etc. **-flüssigkeit,** *f.* liquor.

**laugenhaft,** *a.* like lye, alkaline.

**Laugenmesser,** *m.* alkalimeter.

**Laugensalz,** *n.* (*Old Chem.*) alkaline salt, lixivial salt.—**flüchtiges —,** sal volatile (commercial ammonium carbonate).—**mineralisches —,** sodium carbonate.—**vegetabilisches —,** potassium carbonate.—**bernsteinsaures —,** potassium succinate.

**laugensalzig,** *a.* (*Old Chem.*) alkaline, lixivial.

**Laugen-wa(a)ge,** *f.* lye or liquor hydrometer; (*Salt*) brine gage. **-wasser,** *n.* weak lye or liquor. **-zusatz,** *m.* addition of lye or liquor.

**Laugerei,** *f.* lixiviation.

**Laugerückstand,** *m.* residue from lixiviation or extraction.

**Laugflüssigkeit,** *f.* (*Metal.*, etc.) liquor.

**laugig,** *a.* = laugenartig.

**Laugrückstand,** *m.* = Laugerückstand.

**Laugung,** *f.* lyeing, bucking; leaching.

**Laune,** *f.* humor, temper.

**Laurin-fett,** *n.* laurin. **-säure,** *f.* lauric acid.

**Laus,** *f.* louse; (*Tech.*) a fault of some kind, as a knot in wool or a light spot on a dyed fabric.

**lauschen,** *v.i.* listen.

**Läuse-körner**, *n.pl.* stavesacre seed; cocculus indicus; sabadilla seed. **-pulver**, *n.* insect powder. **-samen**, *m.pl.*= Läusekörner.

**laut**, *a.* loud; public.—*prep.* according to, in accordance with.

**Laut**, *m.* sound; tone.

**lautbar**, *a.* audible; public; notorious.

**Laute**, *f.* lute; (*Dyeing*) crutch.

**lauten**, *v.i.* sound; run, read

**läuten**, *v.t.& i.* ring.

**lauter**, *a.* pure; clear; genuine, unalloyed; mere, only.

**Läuter**, *m.*= Lauer. **-batterie**, *f.* (*Brewing*) underlet.

**Lauterbeize**, *f.* (in turkey red dyeing) white liquor.

**Läuter-boden**, *m.* (*Brewing*) false bottom, strainer. **-bottich**, *m.* (*Brewing*) straining vat, clarifying tub. **-feuer**, *n.* refining fire.

**Lautermaische**, *f.* (*Brewing*) liquid part of mash.

**läutern**, *v.t.* purify, refine, clear, clarify, rectify, defecate; wash (hides).

**Läuter-ofen**, *m.* refining furnace (or kiln). **-pfanne**, *f.* clearing pan, clarifier; defecator.

**Läuterung**, *f.* purification, etc. (see läutern).

**Läuterungsmittel**, *n.* purifying agent.

**Läutervorrichtung**, *f.* purifying apparatus.

**Lautstärke**, *f.* loudness, sound intensity.

**lauwarm**, *a.* lukewarm.

**Lavendel**, *m.* lavender. **-blüte**, *f.* lavender flower. **-farbe**, *f.* lavender color, lavender.

**lavendelfarben**, *a.* lavender-colored, lavender.

**Lavendelöl**, *n.* lavender oil.

**Lavezstein**, *m.* potstone.

**Lävo-**. levo-, laevo-. **-glukosan**, *n.* levoglucosan.

**lävogyr**, *a.* levorotatory.

**Lavör**, *m.* washer.

**Lävulin**, *n.* levulin. **-säure**, *f.* levulinic acid.

**Lävulose**, *f.* levulose.

**Lawine**, *f.* avalanche.

**Laxanz**, *f.* laxative.

**laxieren**, *v.t.* purge.—**laxierend**, *p.a.* purging, laxative.

**Laxiermittel**, *n.* laxative, purgative.

**Laxiersalz**, *n.* purging or laxative salt.— **englisches ——**, Epsom salt.

**Lazarett**, *n.* hospital.

**Lazur, Lazur-**.= Lasur, Lasur-.

**Leben**, *n.* life.

**leben**, *v.i.* live.—**lebender Kalk**, quicklime.

**lebendig**, *a.* living, live.—**lebendige Kraft**, vis viva.—**lebendiger Kalk**, quicklime.

**Lebens-**. life, vital, biological, bio-. **-art**, *f.* way of living, life; (*pl.*) behavior, manners. **-baum**, *m.* arbor-vitae. **-dauer**, *f.* life period; life, lifetime.

**lebensfähig**, *a.* capable of living; (*Med.*) viable.

**Lebens-fähigkeit**, *f.* capacity for living, vitality; viability. **-holz**, *n.* lignum-vitae. **-kraft**, *f.* vital force; vitality. **-lehre**, *f.* biology. **-luft**, *f.* (*Old Chem.*) vital air (oxygen). **-luftmesser**, *m.* eudiometer.

**Lebensmittel**, *n.pl.* provisions, victuals; food; nourishment, sustenance. **-gewerb(e)**, *n.* foodstuff industry. **-untersuchung**, *f.* investigation of foods, food research.

**Lebens-ordnung**, *f.* regimen, diet. **-prozess**, *m.* vital process. **-saft**, *m.* vital fluid; (*Bot.*) latex. **-unterhalt**, *m.* living, subsistence. **-verrichtung**, *f.* vital function. **-versicherung**, *f.* life insurance. **-vorgang**, *m.* vital process. **-wandel**, *m.* life, conduct. **-wasser**, *n.* aqua vitae (spirits). **-weise**, *f.* mode of life.

**Leber**, *f.* liver; hepar.

**Leber-**. hepatic. **-blende**, *f.* reniform sphalerite. **-blume**, *f.* **-blümchen**, *n.* hepatica, liverwort.

**leberbraun**, *a.* liver-brown, liver-colored.

**Leber-eisenerz**, *n.* pyrrhotite. **-erz**, *n.* hepatic ore, esp. hepatic cinnabar (liver-brown cinnabar). **-farbe**, *f.* liver color.

**leberfarben**, *a.* liver-colored, liver-brown.

**Leber-galle**, *f.* hepatic bile. **-kies**, *m.* pyrrhotite. **-klette**, *f.* agrimony (*Agrimonia eupatoria*). **-kraut**, *n.* liverwort; hepatica. **-mittel**, *n.* liver remedy. **-nucleinsäure**, *f.* nucleic acid of liver. **-opal**, *m.* menilite (brown opaque opal). **-schwefel**, *m.* liver of sulfur, hepar. **-stärke**, *f.* glycogen. **-stein**, *m.* hepatite (fetid variety of barite); biliary calculus, gallstone. **-tran**, *m.* fish-liver oil, specif. cod-liver oil.

**Lebe-wesen**, *n.* living being, organism. **-wohl**, *n.* farewell.

**leb-haft**, *a.* lively, brisk, active; vivacious; bright, vivid, gay (colors). **-los**, *a.* lifeless, inanimate; inactive, dull.

**Lecanorsäure**, *f.* lecanoric acid.

**Lech**, *m.* (*Metal.*) regulus, matte, metal.

**Leck**, *m.& n.* leak.

**Leckage**, ;., **Lecken**, *n.* leaking, leakage.

**lecken**, *v.i.* leak, drop out, trickle out.—*v.t. & i.* lick.

**lecker**, *a.* dainty, nice.

**Leckerei**, *f.* dainty, sweetmeat; daintiness.

**Leder**, *n.* leather. **-abfall**, *m.* leather waste, leather cuttings.

**leder-ähnlich, -artig**, *a.* leatherlike, leathery, coriaceous.

**Leder-band**, *m.* leather binding. **-etui**, *n.* leather case. **-farbe**, *f.* leather color.

**lederfarben**, *a.* leather-colored.

**Lederfett**, *n.* leather grease.

ledergelb, *a.* buff.

Leder-gummi, *n.*= Lederharz. -handel, *m.* leather trade. -harz, *n.* (India) rubber. -haut, *n.* true skin, corium. -kohle, *f.* charcoal from leather. -lack, *m.* leather varnish. -leim, *m.* glue from leather waste. -mehl, *n.* leather powder, ground leather.

ledern, *a.* of leather, leathern.

Leder-öl, *n.* oil for dressing leather. -pappe, *f.* leather board. -schmiere, *f.* (*Leather*) dégras, dubbing. -wichse, *f.* leather polish. -zucker, *m.* marshmallow paste; (brauner) licorice paste.

ledig, *a.* exempt; devoid; vacant; unmarried.

lediglich, *adv.* only, solely, merely, entirely.

leer, *a.* empty; blank; void; vacant.—leerer Raum, empty space, vacuum.

Leerdarm, *m.* jejunum.

Leere, *f.* vacuum; emptiness; vacancy; gage, pattern.

leeren, *v.t.* empty, evacuate.

Leer-fass, *n.* (*Paper*) emptying vat. -gang, -lauf, *m.* (*Mach.*) idle motion, running without load. -gewicht, *n.* weight empty, tare.

Leerung, *f.* emptying, evacuation.

Leerversuch, *m.* blank experiment or test.

Lefze, *f.* lip.

lege artis. (Latin) by the rules of art.

legen, *v.t.* lay; put, place, plant.—*v.r.* lie down; abate; devote oneself.

legierbar, *a.* alloyable.

Legierbarkeit, *f.* alloyability.

legieren, *v.t.* alloy.

Legierung, *f.* alloy; alloying.

Legierungsstahl, *m.* alloy steel.

Leguminose, *f.* legume; pea meal.

Lehm, *m.* loam; clay; mud. -formguss, *m.* loam casting. -grube, *f.* loam pit, clay pit. -guss, *m.* loam casting.

lehmig, *a.* loamy; clayey, argillaceous.

Lehm-kalk, *m.* argillocalcite (argillaceous limestone). -kern, *m.* loam core. -kitt, *m.* loam lute, clay lute. -mergel, *m.* loamy marl; clay marl. -stein, *m.* unburnt brick, adobe.

Lehne, *f.* slope; support; back (of a chair); railing.

lehnen, *v.i.* lean.

Lehr-anstalt, *f.* educational institution. -buch, *n.* textbook.

Lehre, *f.* teaching, instruction, doctrine, theory, science, -ology; lesson; apprenticeship; pattern; gage; balance; centering.

lehren, *v.t.* teach, instruct.—gelehrt, *p.a.* learned.

Lehrer, *m.* teacher.

Lehr-fach, *n.* teaching; branch of study. -kursus, *m.* course of study. -ling, *m.*

apprentice. -mittel, *n.* instruction material, means of instruction.

lehrreich, *a.* instructive.

Lehr-satz, *m.* theorem; doctrine. -stelle, *f.* teaching position.

Leib, *m.* body; belly; waist.

Leibesfrucht, *f.* fetus.

leiblich, *a.* bodily, corporal; (*Med.*) somatic. —*adv.* corporally; personally, in person.

Leichdorn, *m.* corn (callosity).

Leiche, *f.* corpse, cadaver.

Leichen-alkaloid, *n.* putrefactive alkaloid, ptomaine. -base, *f.* putrefactive base, ptomaine. -fett, *n.* adipocere. -gift, *n.* cadaveric poison, ptomaine. -verbrennung, *f.* cremation. -wachs, *n.* adipocere.

Leichnam, *m.* corpse, cadaver.

leicht, *a.* light; easy; slight.—*adv.* easily, readily, lightly, slightly. -aschig, *a.* (*Coal*) giving a light ash.

Leichtbenzin, *n.* light benzine (boiling under 80–100° C.), light petrol.

leichtbeweglich, *a.* (of liquids) very mobile.

Leichtbrennstoff, *m.* light fuel.

leicht-entzündlich, *a.* easily inflammable. -flüchtig, *a.* readily volatile. -flüssig, *a.* easily fusible; easily liquefiable; mobile.

Leicht-flüssigkeit, *f.* easy fusibility; easy liquefiability; mobility. -frucht, *f.* light grain (as oats, emmer).

leichtgläubig, *a.* credulous.

Leichtigkeit, *f.* lightness; facility, ease.

leichtl., *abbrev.* leichtlöslich.

leichtlöslich, *a.* easily soluble.

Leicht-metall, *n.* light metal (of sp. gr. less than 5; sometimes, specif., an alkali or alkaline-earth metal). -öl, *n.* light oil.

leicht-schmelzbar, *a.* easily fusible. -siedend, *a.* low-boiling.

Leid, *n.* sorrow, pain; wrong, harm; mourning.

leiden, *v.t.* suffer; undergo.—*v.i.* suffer.

Leiden, *n.* suffering, distress; ailment, disease. -schaft, *f.* passion.

leider, *adv.* unfortunately; alas.

leidig, *a.* fatal; evil; tiresome.

leidlich, *a.* tolerable, passable, fair.

leihen, *v.t.* lend; borrow.

Leim, *m.* glue; size.—farbloser —, weisser —, gelatin.—pflanzlicher —, gluten.

leimartig, *a.* gluey, glutinous, gelatinous.

Leimaufstrich, *m.* coat of glue or size.

leimen, *v.t.* glue; size.—leimend, *p.a.* adhesive, agglutinative.—ganz — (*Paper*) hard-size.

Leim-farbe, *f.* distemper; (*Paper*) size color. -fass, *n.* (*Paper*) size tank, glue tank. -festigkeit, *f.* (*Paper*) resistance (imperviousness) due to sizing. -flüssigkeit, *f.* size. -galle, *f.* (*Paper*) a dark precipitate from rosin size.

**leimgebend**, *p.a.* yielding glue, gelatigenous.

**Leim-gewebe**, *n.* (*Bot.*) collenchyma. **-glanz**, *m.* (*Leather*) size. **-gut**, *n.* material for making glue, glue stock.

**leimig**, *a.* gluey, glutinous.

**Leim-kitt**, *m.* joiner's cement. **-küche**, *f.* glue cooking. **-leder**, *n.* leather scraps for making glue. **-lösung**, *f.* glue solution. **-niederschlag**, *m.* (*Soap*) = Leimsiederniederschlag. **-pflaster**, *n.* adhesive plaster. **-prober**, *m.* glue tester. **-pulver**, *n.* glue powder, powdered glue. **-rohstoff**, *m.* = Leimgut. **-seife**, *f.* filled soap (in which the glycerin and lye are allowed to remain). **-sieder**, *m.* glue boiler. **-siederniederschlag**, *m.* the solution of soap in salt lye which forms as an under layer in making curd soap. **-stoff**, *m.* sizing material; gluten. **-substanz**, *f.* gelatigenous substance. **-süss**, *n.* glycine, glycocoll. **-trog**, *m.* (*Paper*) sizing vat.

**Leimung**, *f.* gluing; sizing.— **in der Masse**, (*Paper*) engine sizing.

**Leim-wasser**, *n.* glue water; size. **-werk**, *n.* glue factory. **-zucker**, *m.* glycine, glycocoll.

**-lein**, little, small, -let, -kin.

**Lein**, *m.* flax; linseed. **-dotter**, *f.* gold-of-pleasure, dodder seed (*Camelina sativa*, the seeds of which yield an oil); sometimes, dodder (*Cuscuta*). **-dotteröl**, *n.* cameline oil.

**Leine**, *f.* line, cord.

**leinen**, *a.* linen.

**Leinen**, *n.* linen. **-faden**, *m.* linen fiber; linen thread.

**Lein-firnis**, *m.* linseed varnish (thickened linseed oil). **-kraut**, *n.* toadflax. **-kuchen**, *m.* linseed cake, oil cake. **-mehl**, *m.* linseed meal.

**Leinöl**, *n.* linseed oil. **-ersatz**, *m.* linseed-oil substitute. **-firnis**, *m.* linseed oil varnish, boiled linseed oil. **-kuchen**, *m.* linseed cake, oil cake.

**leinölsauer**, *a.* linoleate of.

**Leinöl-säure**, *f.* linoleic acid. **-trockenprozess**, *m.* drying of linseed oil.

**Lein-pflanze**, *f.* flax. **-saat**, *f.* linseed.

**Leinsamen**, *m.* flaxseed, linseed. **-abkochung**, *f.* decoction of linseed. **-mehl**, *n.* flaxseed meal, linseed meal. **-öl**, *n.* linseed oil. **-schleim**, *m.* linseed (or flaxseed) mucilage.

**Leinwand**, *f.* linen; cloth; (painter's) canvas. **-band**, *m.* cloth binding.

**leise**, *a.* low, soft; slight.—*adv.* low, softly.

**Leiste**, *f.* ledge, border; ridge; list, selvage; (*Anat.*) groin.

**leisten**, *v.t.* do, perform, accomplish, effect; render, pay, give.

**Leisten-**. (*Anat.*) inguinal.

**Leistung**, *f.* work, performance, output;

capacity; (mechanical, etc.) power; service; doing, rendering.

**Leistungsfähigkeit**, *f.* serviceability, power, ability; capacity; (*Mech.*) efficiency.

**leiten**, *v.t.* conduct; lead; guide; govern; preside over.

**Leiter**, *m.* conductor; leader, guide, director, etc.—*f.* ladder.

**Leitfaden**, *m.* clue; guide, manual.

**leitfähig**, *a.* conducting, conductive.

**Leit-fähigkeit**, *f.* conductivity. **-linie**, *f.* directrix. **-rohr**, *m.* **-röhre**, *f.* = Leitungsrohr. **-salz**, *n.* conducting salt. **-satz**, *m.* rule, guiding principle. **-stern**, *m.* polestar; guiding star. **-strahl**, *m.* (*Math.*) radius vector.

**Leitung**, *f.* conduction, conducting, transmission (as of electricity); (electric) circuit; (electric) wire, cable, lead; conduit, piping, tubing, line, supply (as of gas or water); leading, direction; guide.

**Leitungsdraht**, *m.* conducting wire.

**leitungsfähig**, *a.* conducting, conductive.

**Leitungs-fähigkeit**, *f.* conductivity. **-kraft**, *f.* conducting power. **-messer**, *m.* conductometer. **-netz**, *n.* network of piping or wiring (for gas, etc., or electricity), distribution system. **-rohr**, *m.*, **-röhre**, *f.* conducting tube or pipe; (for gases) delivery tube; conduit pipe, conduit. **-vermögen**, *n.* = Leitvermögen. **-wärme**, *f.* heat of conduction. **-wasser**, *n.* tap water. **-widerstand**, *m.* (*Elec.*) resistance, specif. line resistance.

**Leitvermögen**, *n.* conducting power, (*Elec.*) conductance; conductivity.

**Lekanorsäure**, *f.* lecanoric acid.

**Lektion**, *f.* lesson.

**Lektüre**, *f.* reading.

**Lemnische Erde.** Lemnian earth.

**Lemongrasöl**, *n.* lemon-grass oil.

**Lende**, *f.* loin; haunch.

**Lenden-**. lumbar.

**lenken**, *v.t.* guide, direct, drive, steer.

**Lenz**, *m.* spring.

**Lenzin**, *n.* a white pigment (ground gypsum).

**Leonecopal-insäure**, *f.* leonecopalinic acid. **-säure**, *f.* leonecopalic acid.

**Lerche**, *f.* lark; larch.

**lernen**, *v.t.* learn.—**kennen —**, become acquainted with.

**Lesart**, *f.* reading.

**lesbar**, *a.* legible, readable.

**Lesbarkeit**, *f.* legibility, readability.

**Lese**, *f.* vintage; gathering.

**Lese-buch**, *n.* reader. **-glas**, *n.* reading glass. **-lupe**, *f.* reading lens.

**lesen**, *v.t.* read; gather; cull.—*v.i.* read; lecture.

**leserlich,** *a.* legible.

**Lesestein,** *m.* bog iron ore (form of limonite); boulder.

**letal,** *a.* lethal, fatal.

**Letten,** *m.* potter's clay.

**Letter,** *f.* letter, character, type.

**Lettern-gut, -metall,** *n.* type metal.

**lettig,** *a.* clayish, clayey, loamy.

**letzte,** *a.* last; latest; lowest.—**der (die, das) letztere,** the latter.—**in letzter Zeit,** recently, lately.

**letztgenannt,** *p.a.* last-named, latter.

**Leuchämie,** *f.* leukemia.

**Leucht-.** illuminating, lighting, luminous. **-bakterien,** *n.pl.* photogenic bacteria. **-brenner,** *m.* illuminating burner.

**Leuchte,** *f.* light; lamp.

**Leuchtelektron,** *n.* emitting electron, optical electron.

**leuchten,** *v.i.* give light, shine, glow.—**leuchtend,** *p.a.* luminous, bright, shining.

**leuchtfähig,** *a.* capable of luminescence.

**Leuchtfarbe,** *f.* luminous paint or color.

**Leuchtgas,** *n.* illuminating gas. **-anstalt,** *f.* illuminating-gas plant. **-erzeugung,** *f.* production of illuminating gas.

**Leucht-hülle,** *f.* luminous envelope, (of the sun) photosphere. **-käfer,** *m.* firefly, glow-worm. **-kraft,** *f.* illuminating power, luminosity. **-kraftbestimmung, -kraftmessung,** *f.* photometry. **-masse,** *f.* luminescent mass or composition. **-mittel,** *n.* illuminant. **-öl,** *n.* illuminating oil. **-petroleum,** *n.* kerosene. **-rohr,** *n.* illuminating tube; radiating tube. **-schirm,** *m.* luminescent screen. **-stein,** *m.* phosphorescent stone. **-stoff,** *m.* luminous substance. **-vermögen,** *n.* illuminating power. **-wert,** *m.* illuminating value. **-wurm,** *m.* glowworm.

**leugnen,** *v.t.* deny; retract.

**Leuk-, Leuko-.** leuc-, leuco-.

**Leukämie,** *f.* leukemia.

**Leuko-phan,** *m.* leucophane. **-verbindung,** *f.* leuco compound. **-zyt,** *n.* (*Physiol.*) leucocyte.

**Leunasalpeter,** *m.* Leuna saltpeter (ammonium sulfate nitrate).

**Leute,** *pl.* people; persons, men, the world, hands, servants.

**leutselig,** *a.* humane, affable, popular, kind.

**Leuzit,** *m.* (*Min.*) leucite.

**ievantisch,** *a.* Levantine.

**levigieren,** *v.t.* levigate.

**Levkoje,** *f.* stock, gillyflower.

**lexikalisch,** *a.* lexical, lexicographic.

**Lexikon,** *n.* dictionary, lexicon.

**Leydner Flasche.** Leyden jar.

**Lezithin,** *n.* lecithin.

**lfd.,** *abbrev.* (laufend) running, current, consecutive.

**lfd. Nr.,** *abbrev.* (laufende Nummer) serial number, running number.

**lg.,** *abbrev.* (lang) long.

**Lg.,** *abbrev.* Ligroin.

**Libelle,** *f.* (water or spirit) level.

**-lich.** a suffix forming adjectives from nouns (-ly, -ful, -ous), from verb roots (-able, -ible), and from adjectives (-ly, -ish); as, *schädlich,* harmful, *möglich,* possible, *süsslich,* sweetish.

**licht,** *a.* light, pale; bright, luminous; clear; (of widths) in the clear, interior, inside.

**Licht,** *n.* light; candle.

**Licht-.** light, photo-, luminous, lighting; candle. **-abschluss,** *m.* exclusion of light. **-art,** *f.* kind of light. **-äther,** *m.* luminiferous ether. **-ausschluss,** *m.* exclusion of light. **-bedürfnis,** *n.* light requirement.

**lichtbeständig,** *a.* stable in light; (of colors) fast to light.

**Lichtbild,** *n.* photograph. **-kunst,** *f.* photography.

**lichtbildlich,** *a.* photographic.—*adv.* photographically.

**Lichtbildung,** *f.* production of light, photogenesis.

**lichtblau,** *a.* light blue.

**Lichtbogen,** *m.* luminous arc, (electric) arc. **-ofen,** *m.* (electric) arc furnace. **-schweissung,** *f.* arc welding.

**licht-braun,** *a.* light brown. **-brechend,** *p.a.* refracting, refractive.

**Lichtbrechung,** *f.* refraction of light, optical refraction.

**Lichtbrechungsvermögen,** *n.* (optical) refractive power, refractivity.

**licht-chemisch,** *a.* photochemical. **-dicht,** *a.* light-tight.

**Lichtdruck,** *m.* photomechanical printing; photographic printing.

**lichtdurchlässig,** *a.* transmitting light.

**Lichtdurchlässigkeit,** *f.* permeability to light, transparency or translucency.

**lichtecht,** *a.* fast to light.

**Licht-echtheit,** *f.* fastness to light. **-effekt,** *m.* luminous effect. **-eindruck,** *m.* luminous impression. **-einwirkung,** *f.* action or effect of light.

**lichtelektrisch,** *a.* photoelectric.

**Lichtelektron,** *n.* photoelectron.

**lichtempfindlich,** *a.* sensitive to light, optically sensitive.

**lichten,** *v.t.* clear, thin; weigh (anchor).

**lichtentwickelnd,** *a.* emitting light, photogenic.

**Lichtentwick(e)lung,** *f.* evolution of light, photogenesis.

Lichterfabrik, *f.* candle factory.

lichterloh, *a.* blazing.—*adv.* ablaze.

Lichterscheinung, *f.* luminous phenomenon; optical phenomenon.

licht-erzeugend, *p.a.* producing light, photogenic. -farben, -farbig, *a.* light-colored.

Licht-farbendruck, *m.* photomechanical color printing. -filter, *n.* light filter, color filter. -form, *f.* candle mold. -fortpflanzung, *f.* transmission of light.

licht-gebend, *p.a.* giving light, luminous. -gelb, *a.* light yellow.

Licht-geschwindigkeit, *f.* velocity of light. -giessen, *n.* candle molding. -glanz, *m.* brilliant luster, brilliance.

licht-grün, *a.* light green. -hoffrei, *a.* (*Photog.*) free from halo.

Licht-kegel, *m.* cone of light, luminous cone. -kohle, *f.* (electric-)light carbon. -kreis, *m.* circle of light, halo. -lehre, *f.* optics. -leimdruck, *m.* collotypy; collotype. -leitung, *f.* (*Elec.*) lighting circuit. -loch, *n.* opening for light; pupil (of the eye). -messer, *m.* photometer. -messkunst, -messung, *f.* photometry. -pause, *f.* photographic tracing. -pauspapier, *n.* photographic paper for blueprints or the like. -punkt, *m.* luminous point, bright spot; focus. -quant, -quantum, *n.* light quantum. -quelle, *f.* light source, source of light. -schein, *m.* gleam, shine, glow.

licht-schluckend, *p.a.* light-absorbing, (optically) absorptive. -schwach, *a.* (*Optics*) of small intensity.

Lichtspiegler, *m.* reflector (of light).

lichtstark, *a.* (*Optics*) of strong intensity.

Licht-stärke, *f.* intensity of light. -stärkemesser, *m.* photometer. -steindruck, *m.* photolithography. -strahl, *m.* light ray, ray of light, luminous ray. -strahlung, *f.* light radiation. -talg, *m.* candle tallow.

licht-undurchlässig, *a.* opaque to light. -unempfindlich, *a.* insensitive to light. -voll, *a.* luminous, lucid.

Licht-welle, *f.* light wave. -wirkung, *f.* action of light; luminous effect. -zerstreuung, *f.* di persion of light.

Lid, *n.* lid, esp. of the eye.

Liderung, *f.* packing.

lieb, *a.* dear, beloved; agreeable.

Liebe, *f.* love; favor.

lieben, *v.t.* love; like.

Liebenswürdigkeit, *f.* amiability, kindness.

lieber, *adv.* rather, sooner, better.

Liebhaber, *m.* lover; amateur; buyer.

Liebig'scher Kühler. Liebig condenser.

lieblich, *a.* lovely, sweet, charming.

Lieb-stöckel, -stock, *m.* lovage (*Levisticum*).

Lied, *n.* song.

liederlich, *a.* careless, disorderly, dissolute.

lief, *pret.* of laufen.

Lieferant, Lieferer, *m.* purveyor, contractor.

liefern, *v.t.* yield, produce; furnish, supply, afford; deliver.

Lieferung, *f.* supply; providing; delivery; (of books, etc.) issue, number, part.

lieferungsweise, *adv.* in parts or numbers.

liegen, *v.i.* lie; be (situated); matter, signify.— liegend, *p.a.* extended, horizontal.—liegende Schrift, italics.—gelegen, *p.a.* situated; convenient; important.—es liegt auf der Hand, it is plain (or obvious).—es liegt nahe, it is natural, it suggests itself.

lieh, *pret.* of leihen.

liess, *pret.* of lassen.

liest, *pr. 2 & 3 sing.* of lesen.

Ligand, *n.* attached atom or group.

lignin-haltig, *a.* containing lignin. -reich, *a.* rich in lignin.

Lignocerinalkohol, *m.* lignoceric alcohol.

Likariol, *n.* licareol (*l*-linalool).

Likör, *m.* liqueur.

likörartig, *a.* liqueurlike.

Likörwein, *m.* liqueur wine.

lila, *a.* lilac, lilac-colored.

Lila, Lilak, *m.* lilac.

lilablau, *a.* lilac-blue.

Lila-farbe, *f.* lilac color. -öl, *n.* lilac oil.

Lilie, *f.* lily.

Limaholz, *n.* Lima wood (a dyewood).

Limes, *m.* limit.

Limette, *f.* lime (the fruit).

Limettenessenz, *f.* lime juice.

Limettöl, *n.* lime oil.

Limone, *f.* citron; (süsse) lime; (saure, eigentliche) lemon.

Limonen, *n.* limonene.—*f.pl.* of Limone. -öl, *n.* lemon oil.

Limongras, *n.* lemon grass. -öl, *n.* lemongrass oil.

Linaloëöl, *n.* linaloa oil.

lind, linde, *a.* soft, mild; (of silk) scoured.

Linde, *f.* linden, lime (the tree).

Linden-blüte, *f.* linden flower. -holz, *n.* linden wood, basswood. -kohle, *f.* linden charcoal.

lindern, *v.t.* alleviate, soften, relieve.—lindernd, *p.a.* soothing, palliative.

Linderungsmittel, *n.* palliative, lenitive.

Lineal, *n.* straight edge, rule.

-ling, a suffix used to denote a person or thing described, or connected with the idea conveyed, by the original word (as, Abkömm*ling*, derivative, descendant; Jüng*ling*, youth).

Linie, *f.* line.

linienförmig, *a.* linear.

Linien-gebild(e), *n.* system of lines. -kern, *m.* nucleus (central part) of a line. -mitte, *f.* middle of a line. **-paar,** *n.* pair of lines.

**linienreich,** *a.* rich in lines.

**Linien-spannung,** *f.* (*Elec.*) line tension, line voltage. **-spektrum,** *n.* line spectrum. **-verschiebung,** *f.* displacement of lines. **-zahl,** *f.* number of lines. **-zug,** *m.* line, trace (in a graph).

**linieren, liniieren,** *v.t.* rule.

**Linierfarbe,** *f.* ruling ink.

**link,** *a.* left; wrong.

**linkisch,** *a.* awkward, clumsy.

**links,** *adv.* to the left, on the left, left.

**links-.** to the left, levo-, counterclockwise.

**linksdr.,** *abbrev.* linksdrehend.

**linksdrehend,** *p.a.* levorotatory.

**Links-drehung,** *f.* levorotation, left-handed polarization. **-lauf,** *m.* motion to the left, counterclockwise motion.

**linksläufig,** *a.* to the left, counterclockwise.

**Links-milchsäure,** *f.* levolactic acid. **-polarisation,** *f.* = Linksdrehung. **-säure,** *f.* levo acid. **-schraube,** *f.* left-handed screw. **-weinsäure,** *f.* levotartaric acid.

**Linolensäure,** *f.* linolenic acid.

**Linolsäure,** *f.* linoleic acid.

**Linse,** *f.* lens; lentil; bob (of a pendulum).

**Linsen-.** lenticular.

**linsen-ähnlich,-artig,** *a.* lenticular lens-shaped.

**Linsenerz,** *n.* oölitic limonite.

**linsenförmig,** *a.* lens-shaped, lenticular.

**Linsenglas,** *n.* lens.

**linsengross,** *a.* lentil-sized.

**Lipolyse,** *f.* lipolysis.

**lipolytisch,** *a.* lipolytic.

**Lippe,** *f.* lip.

**Lippen-.** labial.

**Liquatsalz,** *n.* an aluminum salt solution used as a disinfectant and astringent.

**liqueszieren,** *v.i.* liquefy, melt.

**liquidieren,** *v.t.* liquidate, settle.

**lischt,** *pr. 2 & 3 sing.* of löschen.

**List,** *f.* device, artifice, trick, cunning.

**Liste,** *f.* list, register, catalog.

**Listenpreis,** *m.* list price, catalog price.

**Liter-kolben,** *m.* liter flask. **-messkolben,** *m.* liter measuring flask.

**Lithargyrum,** *n.* litharge.

**Lithion,** *n.* lithia. **-glimmer,** *m.* lithia mica.

**lithiumhaltig,** *a.* containing lithium.

**Lithium-jodid,** *n.* lithium iodide. **-salz,** *n.* lithium salt.

**litt,** *pret.* of leiden.

**Litze,** *f.* braid, lace, cord, string; strand.

**Lixiv,** *n.* lixivium; lye.

**Lizenz,** *f.* license.

**ll.,** *abbrev.* (leicht löslich) readily soluble.

**Loangocopal-insäure,** *f.* loangocopalinic acid. **-säure,** *f.* loangocopalic acid.

**Lob,** *n.* praise; fame.

**Lobelie,** *f.* lobelia.

**loben,** *v.t.* praise.

**löblich,** *a.* praiseworthy; estimable.

**Lobrede,** *f.* eulogy.

**Loch,** *n.* hole, opening; eye; pore; (billiard) pocket; prison. **-blende,** *f.* perforated screen or diaphragm.

**lochen,** *v.t.* perforate, punch, pierce.

**löcherig,** *a.* full of holes, perforated, porous.

**Loch-frass,** *m.* pitting (as of metals). **-kultur,** *f.* (*Bact.*) stab culture.

**Lochung,** *f.* perforation, punching.

**Lochweite,** *f.* width of opening, inside diameter.

**locken,** *v.t.* entice, induce, attract; curl.

**locker,** *a.* loose; incompact, spongy, porous.

**lockern,** *v.t.* loosen, make loose; release.—*v.r.* slacken, relax.

**Lockerung,** *f.* loosening.

**Lode,** *f.,* shoot, sprig; rag; tuft.

**Loden,** *m.* coarse cloth; tuft.

**lodern,** *v.i.* blaze, flame.

**Löffel,** *m.* spoon; ladle; (*Surgery*) curette. **-kraut,** *n.* scurvy grass (*Cochlearia officinalis*). **-stiel,** *m.* spoon handle.

**log,** *pret.* of lügen.

**logisch,** *a.* logical. **-erweise,** *adv.* logically.

**loh,** *a.* blazing, burning.

**Loh-beize,** *f.* tan liquor; tanning. **-brühe,** *f.* (*Leather*) bark liquor, ooze. **-brühleder,** *n.* ooze leather.

**Lohe,** *f.* tanbark; tan liquor, ooze; flame, blaze.

**loheartig,** *a.* tan-like.

**Loheiche,** *f.* tanbark oak.

**lohen,** *v.t.* tan, steep in tan liquor.—*v.i.* blaze, flame.

**Lohfarbe,** *f.* tan color.

**loh-farbig, -farben,** *a.* tan-colored, tan, tawny.

**Lohfass,** *n.* tan vat.

**lohgar,** *a.* (bark-)tanned.

**Loh-gare,** *f.* (bark) tanning; dressing. **-gerber,** *m.* (bark) tanner. **-gerberei,** *f.* tanning, bark tanning; tannery. **-grube,** *f.* tan pit. **-messer,** *m.* barkometer.

**Lohn,** *m.* reward; wages, pay. **-arbeiter,** *m.* common workman.

**lohnen,** *v.t.* pay, recompense, reward.—*v.i. & r.* pay.

**Lohnfärber,** *m.* job dyer.

**Lohnung, Löhnung,** *f.* pay, payment.

**Loh-probe,** *f.* (*Leather*) bark test. **-prüfer, -prober,** *m.* barkometer. **-pulver,** *n.* tan powder. **-rinde,** *f.* tan bark.

**Lohschmidt'sche Zahl.** Lohschmidt number.

**Lokal,** *n.* locality, place; tavern. **-farbe,** *f.* natural color.

**lokalisieren,** *v.t.* localize.

**Lokalwirkung,** *f.* local action or effect.

**Lorbeer,** *m.* laurel, bay. **-blatt,** *n.* laurel leaf, bay leaf. **-kampher,** *m.* laurin. **-öl,** *n.* laurel oil, bay oil. **-rose,** *f.* oleander. **-spiritus,** *m.* bay rum.

**los,** *a.* loose, free.—*adv.* on, up.

**Los,** *n.* lot; share; fate; prize.

**los-.** loose, free, off, un-, de-, dis-.

**-los.** destitute of, -less.

**Lös.,** *abbrev.* (Lösung) solution.

**lösbar,** *a.* soluble; dissoluble, resolvable.

**Lösbarkeit,** *f.* solubility; dissolubility; (*Math.*) resolvability.

**losblättern,** *v.i.* exfoliate.

**losch,** *pret.* of löschen.

**Lösch-arbeit,** *f.* (*Metal.*) charcoal process. **-blatt,** *n.* sheet of blotting paper.

**Lösche,** *f.* charcoal dust, charcoal bed; coal dust, slack, or culm; coke dust; cinder; clinker; quenching tub or trough; quenching material, quench. **-beton,** *m.* cinder concrete.

**löschen,** *v.t.* extinguish, quench; slake (lime); blot; cancel; discharge; unload.—*v.i.* be extinguished, go out; blot.

**Löscher,** *m.* extinguisher; quencher; slaker; blotter.

**Lösch-kalk,** *m.* quicklime; slaked lime. **-karton,** *m.* thick blotting paper. **-kohle,** *f.* quenched charcoal. **-papier,** *n.* blotting paper. **-turm,** *m.* quenching tower.

**Löschung,** *f.* extinguishing, etc. (see löschen).

**Löschwasser,** *n.* quenching water, tempering water.

**losdrücken,** *v.t.* push off; fire off.

**lose,** *a.* loose.—*a lv.* loosely.

**Lösegefäss,** *n.* dissolving vessel.

**lösekräftig,** *a.* strongly solvent.

**Lösemittel,** *n.* solvent.

**lösen,** *v.t.* dissolve; solve; loosen, untie, release; redeem; fire (a gun); make (money). —*v.r.* dissolve; get loose.—*lösend,* *p.a.* dissolving, solvent; expectorant; purgative.

**Löse-verlust,** *m.* loss on solution. **-vermögen,** *n.* dissolving power. **-wirkung,** *f.* dissolving action, solvent effect.

**los-gehen,** *v.i.* become loose, come off, go off. **-kitten,** *v.t.* unlute, unseal, etc.

**lösl.,** *abbrev.* löslich.

**Lösl.,** *abbrev.* Löslichkeit.

**löslich,** *a.* soluble.

**Löslichkeit,** *f.* solubility.

**Löslichkeits-bestimmung,** *f.* solubility determination. **-druck,** *m.* solubility pressure. **-produkt,** *n.* solubility product. **-verminderung,** *f.* decrease of solubility.

**Löslichmachung,** *f.* rendering soluble, solubilization.

**los-lösen,** *v.t.* set free, liberate, separate, de-

tach, untie. **-löten,** *v.t.* unsolder. **-platzen,** *v.i.* explode; burst out. **-reissen,** *v.t.* tear off or away, tear loose.

**Löss,** *m.* loess.

**los-sagen;** *v.t.* renounce. **-sprechen,** *v.t.* release; acquit. **-sprengen,** *v.t.* blast loose, burst off. **-trennen,** *v.t.* separate; tear apart; unstitch.

**Losung,** *f.* casting of lots; excrement; watchword.

**Lösung,** *f.* solution; discharge (of a gun); loosening.

**Lösungs-benzol,** *n.* solvent naphtha (a coaltar distillate containing alkylated benzenes). **-druck,** *m.* solution pressure. **-erscheinung,** *f.* phenomenon of solution.

**lösungsfähig,** *a.* capable of solution.

**Lösungs-fähigkeit,** *f.* dissolving capacity. **-flüssigkeit,** *f.* solvent liquid, solvent. **-mittel,** *n.* solvent. **-stärke,** *f.* strength of solution. **-tension,** *f.* solution tension, solution pressure. **-theorie,** *f.* theory of solution. **-vermögen,** *n.* dissolving power. **-wärme,** *f.* heat of solution. **-wasser,** *n.* solvent water.

**Lot,** *n.* solder; plummet, plumb; a weight (now 10 grams); perpendicular.

**Lötapparat,** *m.* soldering apparatus.

**lötbar,** *a.* solderable.

**Löt-blei,** *n.* lead solder. **-brenner,** *m.* gas blowpipe.

**Löte,** *f.* solder, soldering.

**loten,** *v.t.* plumb.—*v.i.* sound.

**löten,** *v.t.* solder; braze; agglutinate.

**Löten,** *n.* soldering; brazing.

**Lötflamme,** *f.* blowpipe flame.

**Loth, löthen,** etc. = Lot, löten, etc.

**lötig,** *a.* weighing 10 grams; (of ore) containing 10 grams silver per hundredweight; (of silver) fine, pure; (in combination) so many sixteenths fine (as, *dreizehnlötiges Silber,* silver $\frac{13}{16}$ fine); (in combination) per cent.

**Lötigkeit,** *f.* fineness (of silver).

**Löt-kolben,** *m.* soldering bit. **-material,** *n.* soldering material. **-metall,** *n.* soldering metal. **-mittel,** *n.* solder. **-probe,** *f.* blowpipe test.

**lotrecht,** *a.* perpendicular, vertical.

**Lötrohr,** *n.* blowpipe. **-analyse,** *f.* blowpipe analysis. **-beschlag,** *m.* coating before the blowpipe.

**Lötröhre,** *f.* blowpipe.

**Lötrohr-flamme,** *f.* blowpipe flame. **-fluss,** *m.* blowpipe flux. **-gebläse,** *n.* blast lamp. **-kohle,** *f.* blowpipe charcoal. **-probe,** *f.* blowpipe test. **-prüfgerätschaft,** *f.* apparatus for blowpipe testing. **-reagens,** *n.* blowpipe reagent. **-versuch,** *m.* blowpipe experiment or test.

Löt-salz, n. soldering salt. -säure, f. soldering acid. -stelle, f. junction (of a thermocouple).

Lotte, f. (Iron) ball, bloom.

Lötung, f. soldering; agglutination; adhesion.

Löt-versuch, m. blowpipe test; soldering test. -wasser, n. soldering fluid. -zinn, n. soldering tin.

Loupe, f. magnifying glass.

Löwe, m. lion.

Löwenmaul, n. toadflax; snapdragon.

Löwenzahn, m. dandelion. -bitter, n. taraxacin. -wurzel, f. dandelion root.

Loxachina, f. loxa bark, loxa bark.

Lsg., abbrev. (Lösung) solution.

Lsgg., abbrev. (Lösungen) solutions.

lt., abbrev. (laut) in accordance with.

Lucke, f. (Metal.) blister.

Lücke, f. gap, void, space, blank, deficiency.

Lückenbindung, n. unsaturated linkage.

lückenhaft, a. having gaps, defective, interrupted, incomplete.

luckig, a. (Metal.) porous, honeycombed.

lud, pret. of laden.

Luder, n. carrion.

Luft, f. air; atmosphere. -ablass, m. escape of air; air outlet -abschluss, m. exclusion of air. -abzug, m. air exhaust, air exhauster.

luft-ähnlich, -artig, a. gaseous, aeriform.

Luft-aufnehmer, m. air receiver. -ausdehnungsmaschine, f. hot-air engine. -ausschluss, m. exclusion of air. -bad, n. air bath. -befeuchter, m. air moistener. -behälter, m. air holder, air chamber; lungs. -beschaffenheit, f. condition of the air.

luftbeständig, a. stable in air, not affected by the air.

Luft-beständigkeit, f. stability in air. -bestandteil, m. constituent of air. -bläschen, n. (small) air bubble. -blase, f. air bubble; air bladder. -bleiche, f. open-air bleaching. -bombe, f. aerial bomb.

luftdicht, a. airtight.—adv. hermetically.

Luft-dichtheit, f. air-tightness, impermeability to air. -dichtigkeit, f. atmospheric density.

luftdichtschliessend, a. forming an airtight seal, hermetic.

Luftdruck, m. atmospheric pressure; air pressure, pneumatic pressure.

Luftdruck-. pneumatic. -messer, m. barometer; manometer. -pumpe, f. pneumatic pump, air compressor. -unterschied, m. difference in air pressure.

luftecht, a. fast to air (atmospheric influences).

Luft-eintritt, m. entrance of air; air inlet. -einwirkung, f. action or effect of air. -elektrizität, f. atmospheric electricity.

luftempfindlich, a. sensitive to air.

lüften, v.t. air; aerate; ventilate; weather; raise.

luftentzündlich, a. inflammable in contact with air, pyrophoric.

Lüfter, m. ventilator.

Luft-erhärtung, f. air hardening. -erhitzer, m. air heater. -erscheinung, f. atmospheric phenomenon. -erscheinungslehre, f. meteorology. -fahrt, f. aeronautics; balloon ascent. -fahrzeug, n. aircraft. -feuchtigkeit, f. atmospheric moisture. -filter, n. air filter.

luft-förmig, a. gaseous, aeriform. -frei, a. free from air.

Luft-gas, n. air gas. -gehalt, m. air content.

luftgekühlt, a. air-cooled.

Luft-gütemesser, m. eudiometer. -gütemessung, f. eudiometry. -hahn, m. air cock.

lufthaltig, a. containing air.

Luft-heizung, f. hot-air heating. -hülle, f. atmosphere.

luftig, a. light, voluminous; aerial, airy, windy, flighty.

Luft-ion, n. atmospheric ion. -kalk, m. airhardening lime. -kanal, m. air duct. -kessel, m. air chamber or reservoir. -kraftmaschine, f. hot-air engine. -kreis, m. atmosphere. -kühler, m. air cooler. -kühlung, f. air cooling. -lack, m. air-proof varnish.

luftleer, a. exhausted (of air), void.—luftleerer Raum, vacuum.

Luftleere, f. vacuum; exhaustion (of air). -messer, m. vacuometer, vacuum gage.

luftleitend, a. air-conducting.

Luft-leitung, f. air piping. -loch, n. air hole, vent hole. -malz, n. air-dried malt. -mangel, n. lack of air. -mantel, m. air mantle, air jacket. -menge, f. amount of air. -messer, m. aerometer. -messung, f. aerometry. -mörtel, m. air mortar, lime mortar (requiring air to harden it). -nitrit, n. nitrite from atmospheric nitrogen. -prüfer, m. air tester. -pumpe, f. air pump, pneumatic pump. -raum, m. air space; atmosphere.

luftreinigend, a. purifying the air.

Luft-reiniger, m. air purifier. -röhre, f. air tube, air pipe; windpipe, trachea.

Lufttröhren-. tracheal; bronchial. -entzündung, f. bronchitis.

Luft-rückstand, m. air residue, residual atmosphere. -salpetersäure, f. nitric acid from atmospheric nitrogen. -sättigung, f. saturation of the air. -sauerstoff, m. atmospheric oxygen. -saugapparat, -sauger, m. aspirator. -säule, f. air column. -säure, f. carbonic acid. -schicht, f. layer or film of air. -schiff, n. airship. -schiffer, m. aeronaut. -schlag, m. (Pyro.) petard.

-schöpfen, n. respiration. -schwärmer, m. (*Pyro.*) serpent. -seide, f. (literally, air silk) a kind of hollow-tubular rayon. -spiegelung, f. mirage. -stählung, f. air hardening. -stickstoff, m. atmospheric nitrogen. -strom, m., -strömung, f. air current. -trennung, f. separation of air.

lufttrocken, a. air-dry, air-dried.

Lufttrocken-gewicht, n. weight when dried by exposure to the air. -schrank, m. air drying closet.

lufttrocknen, v.t. dry in air, air-dry.

Luft-trocknung, f. air drying. -überschuss, m. excess of air.

Lüftung, f. airing, etc. (see lüften).

Luft-verdichter, m. air condenser or compressor. -verdichtung, f. air condensation or compression.

luftverdorben, a. damaged by air; weathered.

Luft-verdrängung, f. displacement of air. -verdünnung, f. rarefaction of air; vacuum. verdünnungsmesser, m. vacuum gage. -wa(a)ge, f. aerometer. -wechsel, m. ventilation. -weg, m. airway, air passage. -welle, f. air wave. -widerstand, m. air resistance, atmospheric resistance. -wirkung, f. action of the air, atmospheric effect. -ziegel, m. air-dried brick. -zufuhr, f. air supply. -zuführung, f. air supply; air duct. -zug, m. draft, current (of air); air duct. -zünder, m. pyrophorus (substance inflaming spontaneously in air).

Luftzutritt, m. access of air, admission of air. —unter —, with access of air, in a stream of air.

Luftzwischenraum, m. air gap.

lugen, v.i. look out.

lügen, v.i. lie (speak falsely); deceive; be affected.

lullen, v.t. lull.

Lumineszenz, f. luminescence.

Lumpen, m. rag; tißler (coarse sugar loaf). -auskohlung, f. carbonization of rags. -bleiche, f. rag bleaching. -brei, m. (*Paper*) first stuff, (first) pulp from rags. -bütte, -butte, f. (*Paper*) rag tub. -kocher, m. rag boiler. -papier, n. rag paper. -wolf, m. rag-

tearing machine, devil. -wolle, f. shoddy. -zucker, m. titlers (sugar in coarse loaves).

Lunge, f. lung, lungs.

Lungen-. pulmonary. -entzündung, f. pneumonia. -kraut, n. lungwort. -schützer, m. respirator. -stein, m. pulmonary concretion. -sucht, f. (pulmonary) consumption.

lungern, v.i. (*Iron*) pipe.

Lunker, n. pipe, cavity (in metals). -bildung, f. piping (in metals).

lunkern, v.i. develop cavities, pipe.

Lunte, f. slow match.

Lupe, f. magnifying glass, lens.

Lupenlinse, f. magnifying lens.

Luppe, f. (*Metal.*) bloom, loop, lump.

Luppen-frischhütte, f. bloomery. -stahl, m. bloom steel, steel in blooms.

Lupulinsäure, f. lupulic acid, lupulinic acid.

Lust, f. pleasure, joy, mirth; desire, inclination; lust. -gas, n. laughing gas (nitrous oxide).

lustig, a. merry, jolly; funny.

lustrieren, v.t. luster.

Lust-seuche, f. syphilis. -spiel, n. comedy.

Luteo-kobaltchlorid, n. luteocobaltic chloride. -verbindung, f. luteo compound.

Lutidinsäure, f. lutidinic acid.

lutieren, v.t. lute.

Lutter, m. (*Distilling*) low wine, singlings. -blase, f. low-wine still.

luttern, v.i. distill low wine.

Lutterprober, m. low-wine tester.

Luxus, m. luxury.

Luxus-. fancy, fine, de luxe, luxury. -konsumption, f. (*Foods*) excess consumption.

Luzerne, f. Luzernerklee, m. lucern, alfalfa.

l.W., abbrev. (lichte Weite) internal diameter.

Lw., abbrev. (Leinwand) linen, cloth.

lydischer Stein. Lydian stone (touchstone).

Lymphdrüse, f. lymphatic gland.

Lymphe, f. lymph.

Lymphgefäss, n. lymphatic vessel.

lyo-phil, a. lyophile, lyophil(ic). -phob, a. lyophobe, lyophobic. -trop, a. lyotrope, lyotropic.

Lyse, f. lysis.

lytisch, a. lytic.

# M

**m.,** *abbrev.* (mit) with; (mein, meine, meines) my, of my.

**M.,** *abbrev.* (Masse) mass; (Monat) month; (Mittelsorte) medium grade; Monatshefte für Chemie; (Mark) mark, marks.

**Maal,** *n.* mole, mark.

**Maass, Maass-.** see Mass, Mass-.

**macerieren,** *v.t.* macerate.

**Maceriergefäss,** *n.* macerater.

**Mache,** *f.* making, make, workmanship.

**machen,** *v.t.* make; do; cause.—*v.r.* make oneself; procure, get.—*v.i.* deal, trade.

**Macherei,** *f.* making; make.

**Macht,** *f.* might, power, force.

**mächtig,** *a.* mighty, powerful, strong, huge, big, thick; in command (of something).

**Mächtigkeit,** *f.* mightiness, etc. (see mächtig); (*Tech.*) thickness, size, power, etc.

**machtlos,** *a.* powerless, impotent.

**Machwerk,** *n.* poor work; hack work.

**Macis,** *f.* mace. **-öl,** *n.* mace oil, oil of mace.

**Madarwurzel,** *f.* mudar root.

**Mädchen,** *n.* girl; maid.

**Made,** *f.* maggot, mite.

**mafurische Butter.** mafura tallow.

**mag,** *pr. 1 & 3 sing.* of mögen.

**Magdalarot,** *n.* Magdala red.

**Magen,** *m.* stomach; maw.

**Magen-.** gastric, gastro-, stomach. **-arznei,** *f.* stomachic. **-brei,** *m.* chyme.

**Magendarm-.** gastro-intestinal.

**Magen-drüse,** *f.* gastric gland, peptic gland. **-entzündung,** *f.* gastritis. **-flüssigkeit,** *f.* gastric fluid, gastric juice. **-haut,** *f.* lining or coat of the stomach. **-inhalt,** *m.* stomach contents. **-lab,** *n.* rennet. **-mittel,** *n.* stomachic. **-pförtner,** *m.* pylorus. **-saft,** *m.* gastric juice. **-schlund,** *m.* esophagus. **-schwäche,** *f.* dyspepsia.

**magenstärkend,** *p.a.* stomachic.

**Magen-stärkungsmittel,** *n.* stomachic. **-stein,** *m.* gastric concretion. **-wand,** *f.* wall or coat of the stomach.

**mager,** *a.* lean; slender, thin, meager.— **magerer Kalk,** lime that does not slake easily.—**mageres Öl,** mineral oil (as distinguished from a fatty oil).

**Mager-kalk,** *m.* = magerer Kalk. **-keit,** *f.* leanness, thinness. **-keitsanzeiger,** *m.* (*Soils*) indicator of lime exhaustion. **-kohle,** *f.* lean coal. **-milch,** *f.* skim milk.

**magern,** *v.t.& i.* make or grow lean or poor;

specif. (*Ceram.*) diminish the plasticity of, shorten.

**Magerungsmittel,** *n.* leaning material.

**Magisterium,** *n.* magistery.

**Magnesia-gehalt,** *m.* magnesia content. **-glimmer,** *m.* magnesium mica (biotite).

**magnesiahaltig,** *a.* containing magnesia, magnesian.

**Magnesia-härte,** *f.* hardness due to magnesia. **-hydrat,** *n.* magnesium hydroxide. **-kalk,** *m.* magnesian limestone. **-milch,** *f.* milk of magnesia. **-mischung, -mixtur,** *f.* magnesia mixture. **-salz,** *n.* magnesia salt (magnesium salt). **-seife,** *f.* magnesia soap. **-zement,** *m.* magnesia cement.

**Magnesit-spat,** *m.* magnesite. **-stein,** *m.* magnesite brick.

**Magnesium-draht,** *m.* magnesium wire. **-gehalt,** *m.* magnesium content.

**magnesiumhaltig,** *a.* containing magnesium.

**Magnesium-jodid,** *n.* magnesium iodide. **-legierung,** *f.* magnesium alloy. **-licht,** *n.* magnesium light.

**magnesiumorganisch,** *a.* magnesium-organic, organomagnesium.

**Magnesium-pulver,** *n.* magnesium powder. **-salz,** *n.* magnesium salt. **-verbindung,** *f.* magnesium compound.

**Magnet-eisen, -eisenerz,** *n.***, -eisenstein,** *m.* magnetic iron ore (magnetite). **-feld,** *n.* magnetic field.

**magnethaltig,** *a.* magnetic.

**magnetisch,** *a.* magnetic.

**magnetisierbar,** *a.* magnetizable.

**Magnetisierbarkeit,** *f.* magnetizability.

**magnetisieren,** *v.t.* magnetize.

**magnetisierfähig,** *a.* magnetizable.

**Magnetisierfähigkeit,** *f.* magnetizability.

**Magnetisierung,** *f.* magnetizing, magnetization.

**Magnetismus,** *m.* magnetism.

**Magnet-kies,** *m.* magnetic pyrites (pyrrhotite). **-nadel,** *f.* magnetic needle. **-stab,** *m.* magnetic bar, bar magnet. **-stahl,** *m.* magnet steel. **-stein,** *m.* magnetic iron ore (magnetite).

**Magsamen,** *m.* poppy seed.

**Mahagoni,** *n.* mahogany.

**mahagonibraun,** *a.* mahogany-brown.

**Mahagoni-holzöl,** *n.* mahogany wood oil. **-nuss,** *f.* cashew nut.

**mähen,** *v.t.* mow.

**Mahl**, *n.* meal; banquet; mark; mole.

**Mahlanlage**, *f.* grinding or milling plant.

**mahlen**, *v.t.* grind, mill.

**Mahl-feinheit**, *f.* fineness of grinding. **-gut**, *n.* material to be ground or milled; (less often) ground material. **-korn**, *n.* grist. **-rückstand**, *m.* grinding residue.

**Mahlung**, *f.* grinding, milling.

**Mahl-zahn**, *m.* molar. **-zeit**, *f.* meal, repast.

**mahnen**, *v.t.* remind, urge; dun.

**Mai**, *m.* May. **-baum**, *m.* birch. **-blume**, *f.* lily of the valley. **-fisch**, *m.* shad.

**Mais**, *m.* maize, (Indian) corn. **-branntwein**, *m.* corn whisky, whisky from maize.

**Maisch**, *m.* = Maische. **-apparat**, *m.* mashing apparatus, mash machine. **-bottich**, *m.* mash tub, mashing tun.

**Maische**, *f.* mash; grape juice, grape must.—**weingare** — (*Distilling*) wash.—**zweite —**, aftermash.

**maischen**, *v.t.* mash.

**Maisch-gitter**, *n.* (*Brewing*) stirrer, rake. **-gut**, *n.* (*Brewing*) mash goods, mash. **-kessel**, *m.* mash copper. **-pfanne**, *f.* mash copper. **-prozess**, *m.* mashing process.

**Maischung**, *f.* mashing; mash.

**Maisch-ventil**, *f.* (*Brewing*) grains valve, trap. **-wasser**, *n.* mash liquor. **-würze**, *f.* mash wort, grain wash.

**Mais-geist**, *m.* = Maisspiritus. **-kolben**, *m.* corncob. **-krankheit**, *f.* pellagra. **-mehl**, *n.* Indian meal, corn meal. **-mehlkleber**, *m.* zein. **-öl**, *n.* maize oil, corn oil. **-pistille**, *n.pl.* cornsilk, (*Pharm.*) zea. **-spiritus**, *m.* spirits from maize, corn spirit. **-stärke**, *f.* maize starch, cornstarch. **-stroh**, *n.* maize straw, corn fodder.

**Mai-wein, -trank**, *m.* white wine flavored with woodruff. **-weinessenz**, *f.* an alcoholic solution of coumarin used for flavoring.

**Majoran**, *m.* marjoram. **-öl**, *n.* marjoram oil.

**majorenn**, *a.* of age.

**Makel**, *m.* spot, blemish, flaw.

**Maker**, *m.* maul, sledge.

**Makler, Mäkler**, *m.* broker, jobber; faultfinder.

**Makrele**, *f.* mackerel.

**Makro-achse**, *f.* (*Cryst.*) macro axis. **-analyse**, *f.* macroanalysis. **-elementaranalyse**, *f.* elementary macroanalysis. **-mechanik**, *f.* macromechanics.

**Makrone**, *f.* macaroon.

**makroskopisch**, *a.* macroscopic.

**Makulatur**, *f.* (*Printing*) waste sheets.

**mal**, *adv.* times, time; once, just.

**Mal**, *n.* time; mark, spot, mole; sign, token; (*Biol.*) stigma.

**mal.**, *abbrev.* maleinoid.

**Malachit-grün**, *n.* malachite green. **-kiesel**, *m.* chrysocolla.

**malaiisch**, *a.* Malay, Malayan.

**Malakkanuss**, *f.* Malacca nut, marking nut.

**malaxieren**, *v.t.* malax, malaxate.

**Malayenstaaten**, *m.pl.* Malay States.

**Malein-aldehyd**, *n.* maleic aldehyde, maleal-dehyde. **-amidsäure**, *f.* maleamic acid. **-anilsäure**, *f.* maleanilic acid. **-säure**, *f.* maleic acid.

**malen**, *v.t.* paint; depict.

**Maler**, *m.* painter, artist.

**Malerei**, *f.* (artistic) painting.

**Maler-email**, *n.* painter's enamel. **-farbe**, *f.* painter's color, artist's color. **-firnis**, *m.* painter's varnish. **-gold**, *n.* painter's gold, ormolu. **-grundierung**, *f.* painter's priming.

**malerisch**, *a.* picturesque.

**Maler-kolik, -krankheit**, *f.* painter's colic, plumbism. **-silber**, *n.* painter's silver, silver powder. **-tuch**, *n.* canvas.

**Malonester**, *m.* malonic ester.

**Malonitril**, *n.* malonitrile, malic nitrile; (improperly but commonly) malononitrile, malonic nitrile.

**malonsauer**, *a.* of or combined with malonic acid, malonate of.

**Malonsäure**, *f.* malonic acid. **-äthylester**, *m.* ethyl malonate.

**Malve, Malwe**, *f.* Malvenkraut, *n.* mallow.

**Malvenfarbe**, *f.* mauve.

**Malz**, *n.* malt. **-aufguss**, *m.* infusion of malt, wort. **-auszug**, *m.* malt extract; wort. **-bottich**, *m.* malt vat, malt tub. **-darre**, *f.* malt kiln. **-eiweiss**, *n.* diastase.

**malzen, mälzen**, *v.t.* malt.

**Malzer, Mälzer**, *m.* maltster, maltman.

**Mälzerei**, *f.* malting; malt house.

**Malz-essig**, *m.* malt vinegar. **-fabrik**, *f.* malt house, malting. **-fabrikation**, *f.* malt manufacture. **-gerste**, *f.* malting barley. **-häufen**, *n.* couching. **-haus**, *n.* malt house. **-probe**, *f.* malt test, malt testing. **-schrot**, *n.* crushed malt, malt grist. **-surrogat**, *n.* malt substitute. **-tenne**, *f.* malt floor. **-treber**, *pl.* spent malt, brewer's grains, spent grains, malt husks.

**Mälzung**, *f.* malting.

**Mälzungsschwand**, *m.* loss in malting, malting shrinkage.

**Malzzucker**, *m.* malt sugar, maltose.

**man**, *pron.* one, a person, somebody, they, people, we, you.

**manch**, *pron.* many a.

**mancher**, *pron.* many a one, many a thing, many a.

**mancherlei**, *a.* many, various.

**manchmal**, *adv.* often, sometimes.

**Mandarindruck**, *m.* (*Calico*) mandarining.
**Mandarine**, *f.* mandarin orange, mandarin (*Citrus nobilis*).
**Mandarinen-öl**, *n.* mandarin oil. **-schalenöl**, *n.* oil of mandarin peel.
**Mandaringelb**, *n.* mandarin yellow.
**Mandel**, *f.* almond; tonsil; fifteen; shock; (*Geol.*) geode.
**mandelartig**, *a.* almond-like, amygdaline.
**Mandel-blüte**, *f.* almond blossom. **-drüse**, *f.* tonsil. **-entzündung**, *f.* tonsillitis.
**mandelförmig**, *a.* almond-shaped, amygdaloid.
**Mandel-kern**, *m.* almond kernel. **-milch**, *f.* almond milk, (*Pharm.*) emulsion of almond. **-öl**, *n.* almond oil. **-säure**, *f.* mandelic acid. **-säureamid**, *n.* mandelamide. **-seife**, *f.* almond soap. **-stein**, *m.* amygdaloid; tonsillar concretion.
**mandelsteinartig**, *a.* amygdaloidal.
**Mandel-stoff**, *m.* amygdalin. **-storax**, *m.* amygdaloid storax.
**Mandschurei**, *f.* Manchuria.
**Mangan**, *n.* manganese. **-alaun**, *m.* manganese alum. **-bister**, *m.* manganese bister, manganese brown. **-blende**, *f.* alabandite. **-braun**, *n.* manganese brown. **-chlorid**, *n.* manganese chloride, specif. manganic chloride. **-chlorür**, *n.* manganous chloride. **-dioxyd**, *n.* manganese dioxide. **-eisen**, *n.* ferromanganese. **-eisenstein**, *m.* triplite.
**Manganerz**, *n.* manganese ore.—graues —, manganite; pyrolusite.—schwarzes —, hausmannite.
**Mangan-gehalt**, *m.* manganese content. **-glanz**, *m.* (*Min.*) alabandite. **-granat**, *m.* manganese garnet, spessartite.
**manganhaltig**, *a.* containing manganese, manganiferous.
**Mangan-hydroxyd**, *n.* manganic hydroxide. **-hydroxydul**, *n.* manganous hydroxide. **-hyperoxyd**, *n.* manganese peroxide (dioxide).
**Mangani-**. manganic. **-chlorid**, *n.* manganic chloride. **-cyanwasserstoffsäure**, *f.* manganicyanic acid.
**manganig**, *a.* manganous. **-sauer**, *a.* of or combined with manganous acid, manganite of.
**Manganigsäure**, *f.* manganous acid.
**Mangani-hydroxyd**, *n.* manganic hydroxide. **-salz**, *n.* manganic salt. **-sulfat**, *n.* manganic sulfate. **-verbindung**, *f.* manganic compound.
**Mangan-jodür**, *n.* manganous iodide. **-karbid**, *n.* manganese carbide. **-kiesel**, *m.* rhodonite. **-kupfer**, *n.* cupromanganese. **-legierung**, *f.* manganese alloy. **-menge**, *f.* amount of manganese.

**Mangano-**. manganous, mangano-. **-azetat**, *n.* manganous acetate. **-chlorid**, *n.* manganous chloride. **-cyanwasserstoffsäure**, *f.* manganocyanic acid. **-ferrum**, *n.* ferromanganese. **-hydroxyd**, *n.* manganous hydroxide. **-ion**, *n.* manganous ion. **-karbonat**, *n.* manganous carbonate. **-oxyd**, *n.*manganous oxide. **-phosphat**, *n.* manganous phosphate. **-salz**, *n.* manganous salt. **-sulfat**, *n.* manganous sulfate. **-verbindung**, *f.* manganous compound.
**Manganoxyd**, *n.* manganese oxide, specif. manganic oxide.—rotes —, mangano-manganic oxide.
**Manganoxyd-hydrat**, *n.* manganic hydroxide. **-oxydul**, *n.* mangano-manganic oxide. **-salz**, *n.* manganic salt.
**Manganoxydul**, *n.* manganous oxide.—schwefelsaures —, manganous sulfate.
**Manganoxydul-hydrat**, *n.* manganous hydroxide. **-oxyd**, *n.* mangano-manganic oxide. **-salz**, *n.* manganous salt. **-verbindung**, *f.* manganous compound.
**Mangan-oxydverbindung**, *f.* manganic compound. **-pecherz**, *n.* triplite. **-peroxyd**, *n.* manganese peroxide (dioxide). **-salz**, *n.* manganese salt.
**mangansauer**, *a.* of or combined with manganic acid, manganate of.
**Mangan-säure**, *f.* manganic acid. **-säureanhydrid**, *n.* manganic anhydride, manganese trioxide. **-schaum**, *m.* bog manganese; wad. **-schlamm**, *m.* Weldon mud (regenerated slime in the Weldon process). **-schwarz**, *n.* manganese black. **-spat**, *m.* rhodochrosite. **-stahl**, *m.* manganese steel. **-sulfat**, *n.* manganese sulfate. **-sulfür**, *n.* manganous sulfide. **-superoxyd**, *n.* manganese peroxide (dioxide). **-verbindung**, *f.* manganese compound. **-vitriol**, *m.* manganese vitriol (manganese sulfate).
**Mangel**, *m.* lack, want, deficiency; fault, defect; distress, want.
**mangelhaft**, *a.* deficient, defective, imperfect.
**mangeln**, *v.i.* be wanting, lack.—*v.t.* mangle.
**mangels**, *prep.* for want of, failing.
**Mangfutter**, *n.* mixed grain.
**Manie**, *f.* mania.
**Manier**, *f.* manner.
**manipulieren**, *v.t. & i.* manipulate.
**Manko**, *n.* shortage, deficiency, deficit.
**Mann**, *m.* man; husband.
**Manna-zucker**, **-stoff**, *m.* manna sugar, mannitol.
**Männchen**, *n.* little man, mannikin; male.
**Mannesreife**, *f.* puberty.
**mannig-fach**, **-faltig**, *a.* manifold, various, varied.

**Mannigfaltigkeit,** *f.* manifoldness, variety, multiplicity.

**Mannit,** *m.* mannitol, mannite.

**männlich,** *a.* male; masculine; manly.

**Mannloch,** *n.* manhole.

**Manno-heptit,** *n.* mannoheptitol. **-zucker-säure,** *f.* mannosaccharic acid.

**Mannschaft,** *f.* men, forces, crew.

**manometrisch,** *a.* manometric.

**Manschette,** *f.* cuff; (*Tech.*) flap, collar.

**Mantel,** *m.* mantle; casing, jacket, case, shell; (*Math.*) surface, nappe, sheet. **-kühlung,** *f.* jacket cooling. **-schicht,** *f.* covering layer, protective layer. **-tier,** *n.* (*Zoöl.*) tunicate.

**Manufaktur,** *f.* manufacture; manufactory.

**Mappe,** *f.* portfolio; case (for paper, etc.).

**Marantastärke,** *f.* arrowroot.

**Märchen,** *n.* (fairy) tale, story.

**märchenhaft,** *a.* fabulous, legendary, fictitious.

**Märe,** *f.* news, report, story, tradition.

**Margarinekäse,** *m.* margarine cheese.

**margarinsauer,** *a.* of or combined with margaric acid, margarate of.

**Margarinsäure,** *f.* margaric acid.

**Marien-bad,** *n.* water bath. **-distel,** *f.* milk thistle (*Silybum marianum*). **-glas,** *n.* selenite; (russisches) mica. **-käfer,** *m.* lady-bird. **-körner,** *n.pl.* milk-thistle seeds.

**Marine,** *f.* navy. **-leim,** *m.* marine glue.

**marienieren,** *v.t.* marinate, pickle.

**Mark,** *n.* marrow; pith; pulp; medulla.—*f.* mark (the money); boundary.

**Mark-.** medullary.

**markartig,** *a.* marrowlike, myeloid; pithlike.

**Markasit,** *m.* marcasite. **-glanz,** *m.* tetradymite.

**Markbildung,** *f.* (*Physiol.*) myelinization.

**Marke,** *f.* mark; stamp; brand; quality, sort.

**Markette,** *f.* virgin wax in cake form.

**Markflüssigkeit,** *f.* spinal fluid.

**markieren,** *v.t.* mark, brand.

**Mark-knopf,** *m.* (*Anat.*) medulla oblongata. **-lager,** *n.* medullary layer. **-masse,** *f.* medullary substance. **-saft,** *m.* medullary sap. **-scheide,** *f.* boundary, limit. **-stoff,** *m.* medullary substance. **-strahl,** *m.* medullary ray. **-substanz,** *f.* medullary substance.

**Markt,** *m.* market, mart, fair.

**markten,** *v.i.* market; bargain.

**marktgängig,** *a.* market, current.

**Marktpreis,** *m.* market price.

**marktreif,** *a.* ready for market, marketable.

**Marktzettel,** *m.* market report.

**Marmor,** *m.* marble.

**marmor-ähnlich, -artig,** *a.* marblelike, marmoraceous, marmoreal.

**marmorieren,** *v.t.* marble, vein, mottle.

**Marmor-kalk,** *m.* lime from marble. **-kiesel,** *m.* a kind of hornstone. **-mehl,** *n.* marble dust. **-papier,** *n.* marbled paper. **-weiss,** *n.* whiting (as a pigment). **-zement,** *m.* marble cement; specif., Keene's cement.

**marode,** *a.* tired, exhausted.

**marokkanisch,** *a.* Moroccan, Morocco.

**Marokko,** *n.* Morocco.

**Marone,** *f.* chestnut, marron.

**Maroquin,** *m.* morocco.

**Marsch,** *f.* marsh.—*m.* march. **-boden,** *m.* marsh land, marshy soil.

**Marseillerseife,** *f.* Marseilles soap.

**Marshische Probe.** Marsh test, Marsh's test.

**Martin-.** (*Iron*) Martin, open-hearth. **-ofen,** *m.* Martin furnace. **-stahl,** *m.* Martin steel (open-hearth steel).

**Martiusgelb,** *n.* Martius yellow.

**März,** *m.* March.

**Masche,** *f.* mesh, stitch; compartment.

**Maschen-grösse,** *f.* size of mesh. **-weite,** *f.* width of mesh. **-werk,** *n.* network.

**maschig,** *a.* meshed, netted, reticulated.

**Maschine,** *f.* machine; engine. **-lehre,** *f.* engineering.

**maschinell,** *a.* mechanical.

**Maschinen-bauer,** *m.* machine (or engine) builder, machinist, millwright. **-element,** *n.* machine part, engine part. **-fett,** *n.* machine grease, lubricating grease. **-gewehr,** *n.* machine gun. **-guss,** *m.* machine casting. **-kunde,** *f.* mechanical science. **-lack,** *m.* machine varnish, engine varnish. **-lager,** *n.* (*Mach.*) bearing. **-lageröl,** *n.* bearing oil.

**maschinenmässig,** *a.* machinelike, mechanical.

**Maschinen-mischung,** *f.* machine mixing, mechanical mixing. **-öl,** *n.* machine oil. **-schmiere,** *f.* lubricating grease. **-schrift,** *f.* typewriting. **-strom,** *m.* (*Elec.*) generator current. **-torf,** *m.* machine-cut peat. **-werk,** *n.* machinery.

**Masel,** *f.* mark, spot, scar.

**Maser,** *f.* speckle, spot, mark; (*pl.*) measles.

**maserig,** *a.* speckled, streaked, grained.

**Maserpapier,** *n.* speckled (or grained) paper.

**Maserung,** *f.* speckling, streaking, graining.

**Maske,** *f.* mask.

**maskieren,** *v.t.* mask, disguise.

**mass,** *pret.* of messen.

**Mass,** *n.* measure; dimension; proportion; degree; manner. **-analyse,** *f.* volumetric analysis.

**massanalytisch,** *a.* volumetric.

**Massbürette,** *f.* measuring burette.

**Masse,** *f.* mass; substance; composition; bulk; stock; assets; (*Founding*) dry sand; (*Ceram.*) paste; (*Paper*) pulp; (= Mass) measure, manner.

**Masseinheit,** *f.* unit of measure.

**Massel,** *f.* (*Metal.*) pig; slab, bloom. **-bett,** *n.* (*Metal.*) pig bed. **-eisen,** *n.* pig iron.

**Massen-bewegung,** *f.* mass motion. **-einheit,** *f.* unit of mass. **-erzeugung,** *f.* mass production. **-gesteine,** *n.pl.* unstratified rocks. **-guss,** *m.* dry-sand casting.

**massenhaft,** *a.* massive, massy; numerous, abundant.—*adv.* abundantly; in a lump; wholesale.

**Massen-moment,** *n.* moment of inertia. **-punkt,** *m.* mass point, center of mass. **-teilchen,** *n.* corpuscle. **-wirkung,** *f.* mass action. **-wirkungsgesetz,** *n.* law of mass action.

**Masse-schlamm,** *m.* (*Ceram.*) body slip. **-schlicker,** *m.* (*Ceram.*) body paste.

**Mass-flasche,** *f.* measuring flask. **-flüssigkeit,** *f.* standard solution. **-formel,** *f.* (*Pharm.*) standard formula. **-gabe,** *f.* measure, proportion.

**massgebend,** *p.a.* determinative, decisive, authoritative, conclusive.

**Mass-gefäss,** *n.* measuring vessel; graduate. **-holder,** *m.* (field) maple.

**massig,** *a.* massy, massive.

**mässig,** *a.* moderate; temperate; reasonable (in cost).

**-mässig.** an adjective suffix signifying " in the manner of"; as, verhältnismässig, proportional.

**mässigen,** *v.t.* moderate, temper.—**gemässigt,** *p.a.* temperate, moderate.

**Mässigkeit,** *f.* moderation; temperance.

**Mässigung,** *f.* moderation.

**massiv,** *a.* massive; unalloyed; clumsy.

**Mass-nahme,** *f.* mode of action; precaution. **-regel,** *f.* measure, step, expedient. **-röhre,** *f.* measuring tube, graduated tube, burette. **-stab,** *m.* scale; rule, measure. **-system,** *n.* system of measurement. **-teil,** *m.* part by measure.

**Mast,** *f.* feeding, fattening; mast, nuts. **-darm,** *m.* rectum.

**Mastdarm-.** rectal, recto-.

**masten,** *v.t. & i.* fatten, feed well.

**mästen,** *v.t.* feed, fatten.

**Mastix,** *m.* mastic (the resin), gum mastic. **-branntwein,** *m.* mastic (the liquor). **-firnis,** *v.* mastic varnish. **-harz,** *n.* mastic (resin). **-kitt,** *m.* mastic (cement).

**mastizieren,** *v.t.* masticate.

**Masut,** *n.* mazut, masut.

**Material,** *n.* material, matter.—**Materialien,** *pl.* material(s); groceries; drugs.

**Material-behälter,** *m.* receptacle for material, container. **-eigenschaft,** *f.* property of materials.

**Materialien,** *n.pl.* See **Material.**

**Material-prüfung,** *f.* testing of materials.

**-prüfungsamt,** *n.* bureau for testing materials (often not translated). **-überhitzung,** *f.* overheating of materials. **-untersuchung,** *f.* investigation of materials. **-waren,** *f.pl.* groceries; drugs.

**Materie,** *f.* matter.

**materiell,** *a.* material.

**Materienofen,** *m.* (*Glass*) calcar.

**materieren,** *v.i.* suppurate.

**Mathematik,** *f.* mathematics.

**mathematisch,** *a.* mathematical.

**Matratze,** *f.* mattress.

**matrisieren,** *v.t.* damp (paper).

**Matrize,** *f.* matrix; mold.

**Matsch,** *m.* pulp, mash; slush, mire.

**matt,** *a.* dull, dead, mat; (of glass) ground; faint, feeble, weak, dull; insipid, flat; (*Metal.*) pasty.

**Matt,** *n.* dullness, deadness of surface. **-beize,** *f.* pickle for giving a dull surface. **-brenne,** *f.,* **-brennen,** *n.* dull pickling.

**Matte,** *f.* mat; meadow.

**Matt-eisen,** *n.* white pig iron. **-farbe,** *f.* deadening color.

**matt-gelb,** *a.* pale-yellow, cream. **-geschliffen,** *p.a.* ground, frosted.

**Matt-glanz,** *m.* dull finish. **-glas,** *n.* ground glass, frosted glass. **-glasur,** *f.* (*Ceram.*) mat glaze. **-gold,** *n.* dead gold. **-heit,** *f.* dullness, etc. (see matt).

**mattierbar,** *a.* (of metals) tarnishable.

**mattieren,** *v.t.* deaden, dull, tarnish; give a mat surface to; grind (glass).

**Mattkohle,** *f.* dull coal.

**mattrot,** *a.* dull red.

**Mattscheibe,** *f.* ground-glass plate.

**mattschleifen,** *v.t.* grind, frost (glass).

**Matt-schwarz,** *n.* dead black. **-sein,** *n.* dullness, deadness, dimness. **-vergoldung,** *f.* dead-gilding.

**mattweiss,** *a.* dull white, dead white.

**Mauer,** *f.* wall. **-gelb,** *n.* yellow badigeon. **-kalk,** *m.* mortar. **-kraut,** *n.* wall pellitory.

**mauern,** *v.t.* build of masonry; wall in or up.

**Mauer-pfeffer,** *m.* stonecrop (*Sedum acre*). **-salpeter,** *m.,* **-salz,** *n.* wall saltpeter (calcium nitrate). **-stein,** *m.* (building) stone; (building) brick.

**Mauerung,** *f.,* **Mauerwerk,** *n.* masonry, walling.

**Mauerziegel,** *m.* (building) brick.

**Mauken,** *n.* (*Ceram.*) fermenting, aging.

**Maul,** *n.* mouth; jaws.

**Maulbeere,** *f.* mulberry.

**Maul-esel,** *m.* mule. **-sperre,** *f.* lockjaw. **-wurf,** *m.* mole (the animal).

**Maurer,** *m.* mason, bricklayer.

**maurisch,** *a.* Moorish.

**Maus,** *f.* mouse.

**Mäuse-dreck,** *m.* mouse dung. **-gift,** *n.* ratsbane, (white) arsenic.

**Mauser,** *f.* molting.

**mausern,** *v.r.* molt.

**maus-fahl, -farben, -grau,** *a.* mouse-colored, mouse-gray.

**maximal,** *a.* maximum, maximal.

**Maximal-spannung,** *f.* (*Elec.*) maximum voltage. **-strom.** *m.* (*Elec.*) maximum current. **-wert,** *m.* maximum value. **-wertigkeit,** *f.* maximum valence.

**Maxivalenz,** *f.* maximum valence.

**mazerieren,** *v.t.* macerate. See Macerier-.

**m.b.H.,** *abbrev.* (mit beschränkter Haftung, or Haftpflicht) with limited liability, Limited, Ltd.

**M.D.,** *abbrev.* (Mitteldruck) medium pressure.

**m.E.,** *abbrev.* (meines Erachtens) in my opinion.

**M.E.,** *abbrev.* (Mache-Einheit) Mache unit; (*Biol.*) (Mäuse-Einheit) mouse unit.

**Mechanik,** *f.* mechanics; mechanism.

**Mechaniker,** *m.* mechanician.

**mechanisch,** *a.* mechanical, mechanic.—*adv.* mechanically.—**mechanisches Gemenge,** mechanical mixture.

**Meconsäure,** *f.* meconic acid.

**med.,** *abbrev.* (medizinisch) medical, medicinal.

**Medaille,** *f.* medal.

**Medien,** *n.pl.* mediums, media.

**Medizin,** *f.* medicine.

**Medizinal-rinde,** *f.* officinal bark. **-ware,** *f.* drug.

**Mediziner,** *m.* medical man or student.

**mediziniert,** *p.a.* medicated.

**medizinisch,** *a.* medicinal; medical. **-chemisch,** *a.* medico-chemical.

**Meer,** *n.* sea, ocean.

**meer-bewohnend,** *a.* marine. **-blau,** *a.* greenish-blue, glaucous.

**Meeres-boden,** *m.* sea bottom. **-fläche,** *f.* sea level; surface of the sea. **-grund,** *m.* sea bottom. **-leuchten,** *n.* = Meerleuchten. **-niveau,** *n.* sea level. **-oberfläche,** *f.*, **-spiegel,** *m.* sea level; surface of the sea.

**Meer-farbe,** *f.*, **-grün,** *n.* sea green. **-kohl,** *m.* sea kale. **-leuchten,** *n.* phosphorescence of the sea. **-rettich, -rettig,** *m.* horseradish. **-salz,** *n.* sea salt. **-sand,** *m.* sea sand. **-schaum,** *m.* meerschaum; sea foam. **-schlamm,** *m.* sea ooze. **-schwein,** *n.* porpoise. **-schweinchen,** *n.* guinea pig. **-schweintran,** *m.* porpoise oil. **-torf,** *m.* sea peat. **-wasser,** *n.* sea water.

**meerwasserecht,** *a.* fast to sea water.

**Meerzwiebel,** *f.* squill.

**Megerkraut,** *n.* yellow bedstraw (*Galium verum*).

**Mehl,** *n.* meal; flour; dust, powder.

**mehlartig,** *a.* like meal or flour, farinaceous.

**Mehl-beere,** *f.* haw. **-beutel,** *m.* bolter, sifter. **-fälschung,** *f.* adulteration of flour or meal. **-früchte,** *f.pl.* cereals. **-gips,** *m.* (*Min.*) earthy gypsum.

**mehlhaltig,** *a.* containing flour, farinaceous.

**mehlig,** *a.* mealy, floury, farinaceous.

**Mehl-kleister,** *m.* flour paste. **-körper,** *m.* endosperm (of grains). **-kreide,** *f.* earthy calcite; kieselguhr. **-prüfer,** *m.* flour tester; specif., aleurometer. **-pulver,** *n.* meal powder. **-speise,** *f.* farinaceous food. **-stoff,** *m.* farinaceous substance. **-tau,** *m.* mildew. **-zucker,** *m.* brown sugar; powdered sugar.

**mehr,** *a.& adv.* more.

**mehr-, Mehr-.** poly-, multi-, many-; excess of; additional.

**mehratomig,** *a.* polyatomic.

**Mehrbasigkeit,** *f.* polybasicity.

**mehr-basisch, -basig,** *a.* polybasic.

**Mehr-betrag,** *m.* increased amount; surplus. **-deutigkeit,** *f.* ambiguity.

**mehrdimensional,** *a.* many-dimensional, multidimensional.

**Mehrdrehung,** *f.* multirotation.

**mehren,** *v.t.* increase, multiply.

**mehrere,** *a.* several.

**mehr-fach, -fältig,** *a.* manifold, multiple, multiplex, repeated. **-farbig,** *a.* polychromatic; pleochroic.

**Mehrfarbigkeit,** *f.* polychromatism; pleochroism; (*Art*) polychromy.

**mehrflammig,** *a.* having more than one flame.

**Mehr-gehalt,** *m.* excess content. **-gewicht,** *n.* excess weight, overweight.

**mehrgliedrig,** *a.* having several, or more, members.

**Mehrheit,** *f.* majority; plural.

**mehrkernig,** *a.* polynuclear, having more than one nucleus.

**Mehrlinienspektrum,** *n.* many-line spectrum.

**mehr-malig,** *a.* repeated. **-mals,** *adv.* several times, repeatedly.

**Mehrphasen-.** polyphase, multiphase. **-strom,** *m.* (*Elec.*) polyphase current.

**mehr-phasig,** *a.* polyphase, multiphase. **-polig,** *a.* multipolar. **-säurig,** *a.* polyacid. **-schichtig,** *a.* many-layered, multilayered. **-stündig,** *a.* lasting for hours, of several hours' duration. **-tägig,** *a.* of several days' duration. **-wertig,** *a.* multivalent, polyvalent.

**Mehrzahl,** *f.* majority; plural.

**mehrzellig,** *a.* multicellular.

**meiden,** *v.t.* avoid, shun.

**Meierei,** *f.* farm, dairy farm.

**Meile,** *f.* mile.

**Meiler,** *m.* circular pile (esp. that used in

charcoal burning), mound, stack; (*Brick*) clamp. -kohle, *f.* charcoal. -verfahren, *n.*, -verkohlung, *f.* pile charring. -verkokung, *f.* pile coking.

mein, *pron.* my, mine.

meinen, *v.t.& i.* think; mean.

meinet-halben, -wegen, *adv.* for my sake; for my part.

Meinung, *f.* opinion, idea; meaning, intention.

Meiran, *m.* marjoram. -öl, *n.* marjoram oil.

Meisch, *m.* mash; (unfermented) grape juice, grape must.

Meissel, *m.* chisel; cutting tool; (*Med.*) pledget.

meisselförmig, *a.* chisel-shaped.

Meisselstahl, *m.* chisel steel.

meist, *a.* most.—*adv.* mostly.—am meisten, for the most part, mostly.

meistens, meistenteils, *adv.* for the most part, generally.

Meister, *m.* master; foreman.

meisterhaft, *a.* masterly.

Meister-stück, *n.* masterpiece; master stroke. -wurz, -wurzel, *f.* masterwort (imperatoria), or its rhizome.

Mekoninsäure, *f.* meconinic acid.

Mekonsäure, *f.* meconic acid.

Melangallussäure, *f.* melanogallic acid, metagallic acid.

Melange, *f.* mixture.

melangieren, *v.t.* mix.

Melan-glanz, *m.* (*Min.*) stephanite. -glimmer, *m.* stilpnomelane (in part).

Melasse, *f.* molasses.

Melassen-säure, *f.* melassic acid. -spiritus, *m.* molasses spirit.

Melasse-schlempe, *f.* molasses residue. -sprit, *m.* molasses spirit.

Melde-. registration, recording, record, intelligence; alarm, signal.

melden, *v.t.* announce, inform, mention.—*v.r.* present oneself, apply.

Meldolablau, *n.* Meldola blue.

melieren, *v.t.* mix; mottle.

Melier-fasern, *f.pl.* (*Paper*) mottling fibers. -papier, *n.* mottled paper.

Melilote, *f.*, Melilotenklee, *m.* melilot.

Melilotsäure, *f.* melilotic acid.

Melis, -zucker, *m.* titlers (coarse loaf sugar).

Melisse, *f.*, Melissen-kraut, *n.* balm, balm mint. -geist, *m.*= Karmelitergeist. -öl, *n.* balm mint oil. -spiritus, *m.*, -wasser, *n.* = Karmelitergeist.

Melissinsäure, *f.* melissic acid.

melken, *v.t.* milk.

Mellit(h)säure, *f.* mellitic acid.

Mellonwasserstoffsäure, *f.* hydromellonic acid.

Melone, *f.* melon.

Melonenöl, *n.* melon (seed) oil.

Meltau, *m.* mildew.

Membran, *f.* membrane; diaphragm.

Meng-. mixing.

mengbar, *a.* capable of being mixed, miscible.

Menge, *f.* quantity, amount; multitude, crowd; abundance, plenty. -einheit, *f.* unit of quantity.

mengen, *v.t.* mix; blend.

Mengenbestimmung, *f.* quantitative determination.

mengenmässig, *a.* quantitative.

Mengen-untersuchung, *f.* quantitative examination. -verhältnis, *n.* quantitative relation, proportion, composition.

Meng-gestein, *n.* conglomerate. -kapsel, *f.* mixing capsule. -spatel, *m.* mixing spatula. -teil, *m.* ingredient of a mixture.

Mengung, *f.* mixing, mixture; blending, blend; hybridization.

Mengungsverhältnis, *n.* proportion of ingredients.

Menhadenöl, *n.* menhaden oil.

Mennig, *m.*, Mennige, *f.* minium, red lead.

mennigen, *v.t.* paint with minium, miniate.

mennig-farbig, -rot, *a.* minium-colored, miniaceous.

Mensch, *m.* man, human being, person.

Menschen-. human. -alter, *n.* generation. -fett, *n.* human fat. -freund, *m.* philanthropist. -körper, *m.* human body. -lehre, *f.* anthropology; human teaching. -pocken, *f.pl.* smallpox.

Menschheit, *f.* mankind, human race.

menschlich, *a.* human; humane.

Mensur, *f.* measure, measuring vessel; duel. -glas, *n.* measuring glass, graduated glass.

Menthakampher, *m.* mint camphor, menthol.

mephitisch, *a.* mephitic.

Mercerisationsgrad, *m.* degree of mercerization.

mercerisieren, *v.t.* mercerize.

Mercur, Mercur-. see Merkur, Merkur-.

Mergel, *m.* marl. -art, *f.* (kind or variety of) marl.

mergelartig, *a.* marly.

Mergel-düngung, *f.* (*Agric.*) marling. -erde, *f.* earthy marl.

mergelhaltig, *a.* containing marl, marly.

mergelig, *a.* marly.

Mergelkalk, *m.* marly limestone.

mergeln, *v.t.* marl.

Merinorot, *n.* (*Dyeing*) Turkey red.

merkbar, *a.* perceptible, noticeable.

merken, *v.t.* mark, notice, perceive.

merklich, *a.* perceptible, appreciable.

Merkmal, *n.* characteristic, mark, sign, indication, index, criterion.

**Merkmalsträger,** *m.* (*Biol.*) gene.

**Merktinte,** *f.* marking ink.

**Merkur,** *m.* mercury. **-blende,** *f.* (*Min.*) cinnabar. **-chlorid,** *n.* mercury chloride, specif. mercuric chloride. **-chlorür,** *n.* mercurous chloride.

**merkurhaltig,** *a.* containing mercury, mercurial.

**Merkurhornerz,** *n.* (*Min.*) horn quicksilver, calomel.

**Merkuri-.** mercuric, mercuri-.

**Merkurialien,** *pl.* (*Pharm.*) mercurials.

**Merkurialmittel,** *n.* (*Pharm.*) mercurial.

**Merkuri-ammoniumchlorid,** *n.* mercuriammonium chloride. **-azetat,** *n.* mercuric acetate. **-chlorid,** *n.* mercuric chloride. **-cyanid,** *n.* mercuric cyanide. **-cyanwasserstoffsäure,** *f.* mercuricyanic acid.

**merkurieren,** *v.t.* mercurize, combine with mercury.

**Merkurierung,** *f.* mercurization.

**Merkuri-jodid,** *n.* mercuric iodide. **-nitrat,** *n.* mercuric nitrate. **-oxyd,** *n.* mercuric oxide. **-rhodanid,** *n.* mercuric thiocyanate. **-salz,** *n.* mercuric salt. **-sulfat,** *n.* mercuric sulfate. **-sulfid,** *n.* mercuric sulfide. **-verbindung,** *f.* mercuric compound.

**Merkurjodid,** *n.* mercury iodide.

**Merkuro-.** mercurous. **-azetat,** *n.* mercurous acetate. **-chlorid,** *n.* mercurous chloride. **-chrom,** *n.* (*Pharm.*) mercurochrome. **-jodid,** *n.* mercurous iodide. **-nitrat,** *n.* mercurous nitrate. **-oxyd,** *n.* mercurous oxide. **-salz,** *n.* mercurous salt. **-sulfat,** *n.* mercurous sulfate. **-sulfid,** *n.* mercurous sulfide. **-verbindung,** *f.* mercurous compound.

**Merkur-oxyd,** *n.* mercury oxide, specif. mercuric oxide. **-silber,** *n.* silver amalgam. **-sulfid,** *n.* mercury sulfide, specif. mercuric sulfide.

**merkwürdig,** *a.* noteworthy, remarkable. **-erweise,** *adv.* strange to say.

**Merkzeichen,** *n.* mark, sign.

**Mero-chinen,** *n.* meroquinene. **-tropie,** *f.* merotropism, merotropy.

**Merzerisation,** *f.* mercerization.

**merzerisieren,** *v.t.* mercerize.

**Mesoweinsäure,** *f.* mesotartaric acid.

**Mesoxalsäure,** *f.* mesoxalic acid.

**Mess-.** measuring. **-analyse,** *f.* volumetric analysis. **-apparat,** *m.* measuring apparatus. **-band,** *n.* tape measure.

**messbar,** *a.* measurable.

**Mess-bereich,** *m.* measuring range. **-einteilung,** *f.* graduation.

**messen,** *v.t.* measure; survey; contain.—**gemessen,** *p.a.* measured, etc.; strict; formal.

**Messer,** *m.* measurer, meter.—*n.* knife; cutter.

**Messergebnis,** *n.* result of measurement.

**Messer-klinge,** *f.* knife blade. **-spitze,** *f.* knife point. **-stahl,** *m.* knife steel.

**Mess-fehler,** *m.* error in measurement. **-flasche,** *f.* measuring bottle (or flask). **-flüssigkeit,** *f.* measuring liquid, (frequently) titrating solution. **-gefäss,** *n.* measuring vessel, measure. **-genauigkeit,** *f.* accuracy of measurement. **-geräte,** *n.pl.* measuring apparatus. **-glas,** *n.* measuring glass, graduated glass vessel. **-grenze,** *f.* limit of measurement. **-heber,** *m.* measuring pipette.

**Messing,** *n.* brass. **-abstrich, -abzug,** *m.* brass scum.

**messingartig,** *a.* like brass, brassy.

**Messing-artigkeit,** *n.* brassiness. **-blatt,** *n.* brass foil. **-blech,** *n.* sheet brass, brass plate. **-blüte,** *f.* aurichalcite. **-brennen,** *n.* brass making. **-draht,** *m.* brass wire.

**messingen,** *a.* of brass, brass.

**messingfarben,** *a.* brass-colored.

**Messing-fassung,** *f.* brass casing or mounting. **-folie,** *f.* brass foil. **-gewicht,** *n.* brass weight. **-giesser,** *m.* brass founder. **-lot,** *n.* brass solder, hard solder. **-netz,** *n.* brass netting, brass gauze. **-rohr,** *n.,* **-röhre,** *f.* brass tube or pipe. **-schlaglot,** *n.* brass solder, hard solder. **-späne,** *m.pl.* brass shavings, brass turnings.

**Mess-instrument,** *n.* measuring instrument. **-keil,** *m.* measuring wedge (inside caliper for tubing). **-kelch,** *m.* measuring cup. **-kölbchen,** *n.* little measuring flask. **-kolben,** *m.* measuring flask. **-länge,** *f.* gage length. **-mittel,** *n.* means of measuring, measuring instrument. **-okular,** *n.* micrometric eyepiece. **-pipette,** *f.* graduated pipette, scale pipette. Cf. Vollpipette. **-reihe,** *f.* series of measurements. **-rohr,** *m.,* **-röhre,** *f.* measuring tube; specif. burette. **-röhrenklemme,** *f.* burette clamp. **-serie,** *f.* series of measurements. **-stab,** *m.* measuring rod; (for casks) liquor gage. **-trichter,** *m.* measuring funnel or hopper.

**Messung,** *f.* measuring, measurement, mensuration.

**Mess-verfahren,** *n.* method or process of measurement. **-vorrichtung,** *f.* measuring device. **-zylinder,** *m.* measuring cylinder. **-zylinderchen,** *n.* small measuring cylinder.

**Met,** *m.* mead.

**metaantimonig,** *a.* metantimonious.

**Metaantimonsäure,** *f.* metantimonic acid.

**metaarsenig,** *a.* metarsenious.

**Meta-arsensäure,** *f.* metarsenic acid. **-bleisäure,** *f.* metaplumbic acid.

**Metabolie,** *f.* metabolism.

**metabolisch,** *ä.* metabolic.

**Metabolismus,** *m.* metabolism.
**Meta-borsäure,** *f.* metaboric acid. **-cer,** *n.* metacerium. **-cymol,** *n.* metacymene, *m*-cymene. **-eisenoxyd,** *n.* metaferric oxide. **-ferrihydrat,** *n.* metaferric hydroxide. **-gallussäure,** *f.* metagallic acid. **-kieselsäure,** *f.* metasilicic acid. **-kohlensäure,** *f.* metacarbonic acid (ordinary carbonic acid, $H_2CO_3$).
**Metall,** *n.* metal.
**Metall-.** metallic, metal. **-abfall,** *m.* metal waste, waste metal. **-ader,** *f.* metallic vein, metalliferous vein.
**metall-ähnlich, -artig,** *a.* metallic, metalline.
**Metallamid,** *n.* metallic amide.
**metall-arm,** *a.* poor in metal. **-artig,** *a.* metallic, metalline.
**Metall-artigkeit,** *f.* metallicity. **-asche,** *f.* metallic ash. **-auftrag,** *m.* metallic coating or plating. **-azid,** *n.* metallic azide. **-bad,** *n.* metallic bath or solution. **-bau,** *m.* metal construction. **-bearbeitung,** *f.* metal working. **-beschreibung,** *f.* metallography. **-beschwerung,** *f.* (*Textiles*) loading with metallic salts. **-blatt,** *n.* (thin) sheet of metal. **-carbid,** *n.* metallic carbide. **-chemie,** *f.* the chemistry of metals. **-chlorid,** *n.* metallic chloride. **-chlorwasserstoffsäure,** *f.* an acid composed of hydrogen, chlorine and a metal. **-cyanid,** *n.* metal(lic) cyanide. **-dampf,** *m.* metallic vapor. **-eigenschaft,** *f.* metallic property.
**metallen,** *a.* metallic, metalline.
**Metall-erz,** *n.* metallic ore. **-faden,** *m.* metal thread, metal filament. **-farbe,** *f.* metallic color; bronze color.
**metallfarbig,** *a.* metal-colored.
**Metall-färbung,** *f.* coloring of metal (specif. metallochrome); metallic coloring. **-fassung,** *f.* metal casing or mounting. **-folie,** *f.* metal foil.
**metall-förmig,** *a.* metalliform. **-führend,** *a.* metalliferous.
**Metall-gefäss,** *n.* metal(lic) vessel. **-gehalt,** *m.* metal(lic) content. **-gekrätz,** *n.* metal waste, dross. **-gemisch,** *n.* metallic mixture, alloy. **-gewebe,** *n.* wire gauze, wire cloth. **-gewinnung,** *f.* extraction of metals, metallurgy. **-gift,** *n.* metallic poison. **-glanz,** *m.* metallic luster.
**metallglänzend,** *p.a.* having metallic luster.
**Metall-glas,** *n.* enamel. **-gold,** *n.* Dutch gold, Dutch foil. **-guss,** *m.* metal founding, metal casting.
**metallhaltig,** *a.* containing metal, metalliferous.
**Metall-hütte,** *f.* smeltery (for metals other than iron). **-hydroxyd,** *n.* metallic hydroxide.

**metallisch,** *a.* metallic.
**metallisieren,** *v.t.* metallize.
**Metallität,** *f.* metallic nature.
**Metall-kalk,** *m.* metallic calx (oxide). **-karbid,** *n.* metallic carbide. **-karbonyl,** *n.* compound of a metal with carbonyl. **-komplexsäure,** *f.* complex metallic acid. **-könig,** *m.* metallic regulus or button. **-korn,** *n.* metal grain; *pl.*, granulated metal. **-kühler,** *m.* metallic condenser or cooler. **-kunde,** *f.* science of metals; metallography. **-lack,** *m.* metal lacquer or varnish. **-legierung,** *f.* metallic alloy. **-lösung,** *f.* metallic solution. **-membran,** *f.* metal diaphragm. **-mischung,** *f.* metal mixture, alloy; alloying. **-mischungswa(a)ge,** *f.* alloy balance. **-mohr,** *m.* metallic moiré; = Mineralmohr. **-mutter,** *f.* matrix (of ores). **-nebel,** *m.* metallic fog, metal fog. **-niederschlag,** *m.* metallic precipitate or deposit.
**Metallo-chemie,** *f.* = Metallchemie. **-graphie,** *f.* metallography.
**metallographisch,** *a.* metallographic.
**metallorganisch,** *a.* organometallic, metallo-organic.
**Metall-oxyd,** *n.* metallic oxide. **-oxydhydrat,** *n.* metal(lic) hydroxide. **-probe,** *f.* test for metal, assay. **-rohr,** *n.,* **-röhre,** *f.* metal tube or pipe. **-röhrchen,** *n.* (small) metal tube or pipe. **-safran,** *m.* crocus of antimony. **-salz,** *n.* metallic salt. **-salzlösung,** *f.* metallic-salt solution. **-säure,** *f.* metallic acid (as $HMnO_4$). **-schlacke,** *f.* metal slag. **-schlauch,** *m.* (flexible) metallic tube, metallic hose. **-schmelze,** *f.* metallic fusion; fused metal. **-schwamm,** *m.* metallic sponge. **-seife,** *f.* soap for metals, metal soap. **-silber,** *n.* imitation silver foil. **-späne,** *m.pl.* metal shavings, turnings or chips. **-spektrum,** *n.* spectrum of a metal. **-spiegel,** *m.* metallic mirror. **-spritzverfahren,** *n.* metallization. **-staub,** *m.* metal(lic) dust. **-sulfid,** *n.* metallic sulfide. **-teil,** *m.* metal part, metallic part. **-tuch,** *n.* wire cloth. **-überziehung,** *f.* metalplating. **-überzug,** *m.* metallic coating, plating, wash.
**Metallurg,** *m.* metallurgist.
**Metallurgie,** *f.* metallurgy.
**metallurgisch,** *a.* metallurgic, metallurgical.
**Metall-verarbeitung,** *f.* metal working. **-verbindung,** *f.* metallic compound. **-vergiftung,** *f.* metal(lic) poisoning. **-verlust,** *m.* loss of metal. **-versetzung,** *f.* alloying, alloy. **-waren,** *f.pl.* metal wares, hardware. **-wolle,** *f.* metal wool.
**metamer,** *a.* metameric.
**Metamerie,** *f.* metamerism, metamery.
**metamerisch,** *a.* metameric.

**Metamerismus,** *m.* metamerism.

**metamorphisch,** *a.* metamorphic.

**Metanilgelb,** *n.* metanil yellow, metaniline yellow.

**metantimonig,** *a.* metantimonious.

**Metantimonsäure,** *f.* metantimonic acid.

**meta-phosphorig,** *a.* metaphosphorous. **-phosphorsauer,** *a.* of or combined with metaphosphoric acid, metaphosphate of.

**Meta-phosphorsäure,** *f.* metaphosphoric acid. **-säure,** *f.* meta acid.

**meta-stabil,** *a.* metastable. **-ständig,** *a.* in the meta position.

**Meta-stellung,** *f.* meta position. **-styrol,** *n.* metastyrene. **-vanadinsäure,** *f.* metavanadic acid. **-verbindung,** *f.* meta compound. **-weinsäure,** *f.* metatartaric acid. **-wolframsäure,** *f.* metatungstic acid. **-xylol,** *n.* metaxylene, *m*-xylene. **-zinnober,** *m.* (*Min.*) metacinnabarite. **-zinnsäure,** *f.* metastannic acid. **-zirkonsäure,** *f.* metazirconic acid. **-zuckersäure,** *f.* metasaccharic acid.

**Meteoreisen,** *n.* meteoric iron.

**meteorisch,** *a.* meteoric; (*Med.*) meteoristic.

**meteorologisch,** *a.* meteorological.

**Meteor-stahl,** *m.* meteoric steel. **-staub,** *m.* meteoric dust. **-stein,** *m.* meteoric stone, aerolite.

**Meterkerze,** *f.* (*Optics*) meter candle.

**Methacrylsäure, Methakrylsäure,** *f.* methacrylic acid.

**Methämoglobin,** *n.* methemoglobin.

**Methan,** *n.* methane. **-säure,** *f.* methanoic (formic) acid.

**Methen,** *n.* methene (methylene).

**Methode,** *f.* method.

**Methodik,** *f.* methodics, methodology.

**methodisch,** *a.* methodical.

**Methoxylgruppe,** *f.* methoxyl (or methoxy) group.

**methylalkoholisch,** *a.* methyl-alcoholic, methanolic.

**Methyl-arsonsäure,** *f.* methylarsonic (methanearsonic) acid. **-äther,** *m.* methyl ether. **-blau,** *n.* methyl blue. **-chlorid, -chlorür,** *n.* methyl chloride.

**Methylen-blau,** *n.* methylene blue. **-gruppe,** *f.* methylene group. **-jodid,** *n.* methylene iodide.

**Methyl-gallusäthersäure,** *f.* *O*-methylgallic acid, methyl ether of gallic acid. **-grün,** *n.* methyl green. **-hydrür,** *n.* methyl hydride, methane.

**methylierbar,** *a.* capable of being methylated.

**methylieren,** *v.t.* methylate.

**Methyl-ierung,** *f.* methylation. **-jodid,** *n.* methyl iodide, iodomethane. **-kautschuk,** *m.* methyl rubber.

**Methylostärke,** *f.* methylstarch.

**Methyl-oxydhydrat,** *n.* methyl hydroxide (methanol). **-rot,** *n.* methyl red. **-verbindung,** *f.* methyl compound. **-wasserstoff,** *m.* methyl hydride, methane. **-zahl,** *f.* methyl number, methyl value. **-zinnsäure,** *f.* methylstannic acid.

**Metochinon,** *n.* metoquinone.

**metrisch,** *a.* metric, metrical.

**Metze,** *f.* peck.

**Metzelsuppe,** *f.* meat broth.

**mexikanisch,** *a.* Mexican.

**m.G.,** *abbrev.* (mit Goldschnitt) with gilt edges.

**M.G.,** *abbrev.* (Molekulargewicht) molecular weight.

**mich,** *pron.* me, myself.

**mied,** *pret.* of meiden.

**Miene,** *f.* mien, look, air, feature.

**Miesmuschel,** *f.* (edible) mussel.

**Miete,** *f.* hiring, hire; lease; rent; stack, shock; (*Zoöl.*) mite.

**mieten,** *v.t.* hire, rent, lease.

**Migräne,** *f.* migraine, (sick) headache.

**Mikro-analyse,** *f.* microanalysis. **-analytiker,** *m.* microanalyst. **-arbeit,** *f.* micro work, work on a minute scale. **-becher,** *m.* micro beaker. **-bestimmung,** *f.* microdetermination. **-brenner,** *m.* micro burner. **-chemie,** *f.* microchemistry. **-chemiker,** *m.* microchemist.

**mikrochemisch,** *a.* microchemical.

**Mikro-dampfbad,** *n.* micro steam bath. **-elementaranalyse,** *f.* elementary microanalysis. **-gasbrenner,** *m.* micro gas burner. **-graphie,** *f.* micrography. **-klin,** *n.* microcline.

**mikro-kosmisch,** *a.* microcosmic. **-kristallinisch,** *a.* microcrystalline.

**Mikromechanik,** *f.* micromechanics.

**mikrometrisch,** *a.* micrometric.

**Mikro-nutsche,** *f.* micro suction filter, esp micro Büchner funnel. **-organismen,** *m. pl.* microörganisms. **-probe,** *f.* micro test; micro sample. **-schnellbestimmung,** *f.* rapid microdetermination.

**mikroskopieren,** *v.t.* examine with the microscope.

**Mikroskopiker,** *m.* microscopist.

**mikroskopisch,** *a.* microscopic, microscopical.

**Mikro-spatel,** *m.* micro spatula. **-stativ,** *n.* micro stand. **-trichter,** *m.* micro funnel. **-verbrennung,** *f.* microcombustion.

**mikrovolumetrisch,** *a.* microvolumetric.

**Mikro-wage, -waage,** *f.* microbalance.

**mikrurgisch,** *a.* micrurgic(al).

**Milbe,** *f.* mite.

**Milch,** *f.* milk; milt (of fishes).

**Milch-.** milk, lacteal, lacto-, galacto-.

**milch-abscheidend, -absondernd,** *a.* milk-secreting. **-abtreibend,** *p.a.* antigalactic.

**Milch-achat,** *m.* milk-white agate. **-ader,** *f.* lacteal vessel.

**milch-ähnlich,** *a.* milklike, milky. **-artig,** *a.* milky, lacteal.

**Milch-bestandteil,** *m.* constituent of milk. **-bier,** *n.* kumiss. **-drüse,** *f.* mammary gland; lacteal gland. **-fälschung,** *f.* adulteration of milk. **-farbe,** *f.* milk color, milk white. **-fett,** *n.* milk fat.

**milchführend,** *a.* lactiferous.

**Milch-gärung,** *f.* fermentation of milk. **-glas,** *n.* milk glass; breast glass. **-grad,** *m.* milk degree (degree on the galactometer). **-güte,** *f.* quality of milk. **-harnen,** *n.,* **-harnfluss,** *m.* chyluria.

**milchig, milchicht,** *a.* milky, lacteal.

**Milch-kanal,** *m.* lactiferous duct. **-konserve,** *f.* preserved milk (any kind). **-kraut,** *n.* sea milkwort. **-kügelchen,** *n.* milk globule, fat globule in milk. **-lab,** *n.* rennet. **-messer,** *m.* galactometer; lactometer. **-porzellan,** *n.* milk glass, glass porcelain. **-prober, -prüfer,** *m.* milk tester (specif. lactometer). **-prüfung,** *f.* milk testing. **-pulver,** *n.* milk powder. **-quarz,** *m.* milky quartz. **-rahm,** *m.* cream. **-saft,** *m.* milky juice; (*Bot.*) latex; (*Physiol.*) chyle.

**milch-saftig,** *a.* chylous. **-sauer,** *a.* of or combined with lactic acid, lactate of.

**Milchsäure,** *f.* lactic acid. **-gärung,** *f.* lactic fermentation. **-pilz,** *m.* lactic-acid bacillus. **-salz,** *n.* lactate.

**Milch-strasse,** *f.* Milky Way. **-untersuchung,** *f.* examination of milk, milk analysis. **-verfälschung,** *f.* adulteration of milk.

**milch-vermehrend,** *p.a.* galactagog. **-vertreibend,** *p.a.* antigalactic.

**Milch-wa(a)ge,** *f.* lactometer. **-wein,** *m.* kumiss.

**milchweiss,** *a.* milk-white.

**Milchwirtschaft,** *f.* dairy.

**milchwirtschaftlich,** *a.* dairy, dairying.

**Milchwurz,** *f.* milkwort.

**Milchz.,** *abbrev.* Milchzucker.

**Milchzucker,** *m.* milk sugar, lactose. **-säure,** *f.* saccholactic acid (mucic acid).

**mild, milde,** *a.* mild, soft, tender; mellow; gentle, kind.

**mildern,** *v.t.* temper, mitigate, moderate, soften; correct (acidity).—**mildernd,** *p.a.* (*Pharm.*) mitigant, lenitive.

**Milderung,** *n.* tempering, etc. (see mildern).

**Milderungsmittel,** *n.* mitigant, demulcent, lenitive; corrective.

**Militär-.** military.

**millionstel,** *a.* millionth (part of), micro-.

**Miloriblau,** *n.* milori blue (Prussian blue).

**Milz,** *f.* spleen.

**Milz-.** splenic. **-brand,** *m.* anthrax. **-drüse,** *f.* spleen.

**Mimosengummi,** *n.* gum arabic, esp. a fine variety.

**minder,** *a.* less, smaller, inferior, minor.—*adv.* less.

**Minder-druck,** *m.* diminished pressure. **-ertrag,** *m.* decreased yield. **-gewicht,** *n.* underweight.

**minderhaltig,** *a.* inferior, low-grade.

**Minderheit,** *f.* minority.

**minderjährig,** *a.* under age, minor.

**mindern,** *v.t.& i.* diminish, lessen, decrease.

**Minderwert,** *m.* inferior value.

**minderwertig,** *a.* of lower valence; of inferior quality.

**Minder-wertigkeit,** *f.* lower valence; inferior quality. **-zahl,** *f.* minority.

**Mindest-.** least, minimum, lowest.

**mindestens,** *adv.,* **zum mindesten.** at least, at the least.

**Mindestwert,** *m.* least value, minimum value.

**Mine,** *f.* mine; lead (for pencils).

**Minen-gas,** *n.* mine gas. **-pulver,** *n.* blasting powder.

**Mineral-analyse,** *f.* mineral analysis. **-bad,** *n.* mineral bath. **-beize,** *f.* (*Dyeing*) mineral mordant. **-bestandteil,** *m.* mineral (inorganic) constituent. **-bildner,** *m.* mineral former, mineralizer. **-blau,** *n.* mineral blue. **-brunnen,** *m.* mineral spring (or well). **-chemie,** *f.* mineral chemistry, inorganic chemistry. **-farbe,** *f.* mineral color; mineral dye. **-farbstoff,** *m.* mineral coloring matter. **-fett,** *n.* mineral fat or grease, specif. vaseline or petroleum jelly, also ozocerite. **-fettwachs,** *n.* = Mineraltalg. **-gelb,** *n.* mineral yellow. **-gerbung,** *f.* mineral tannage. **-grün,** *n.* mineral green.

**Mineralienkunde,** *f.* mineralogy.

**mineralisch,** *a.* mineral. — **mineralisches Leichenwachs,** ozocerite.

**Mineral-kermes,** *m.* kermes mineral. **-laugensalz,** *n.* (*Old Chem.*) sodium carbonate. **-mohr,** *m.* ethiops mineral (essentially amorphous HgS).

**Mineralog, Mineraloge,** *m.* mineralogist.

**Mineralogie,** *f.* mineralogy.

**mineralogisch,** *a.* mineralogical.

**Mineral-öl,** *n.* mineral oil; specif., petroleum. **-pech,** *n.* mineral pitch, asphalt. **-quelle,** *f.* mineral spring or well. **-reich,** *n.* mineral kingdom. **-rot,** *n.* cinnabar. **-salz,** *n.* mineral salt. **-säure,** *f.* mineral acid. **-schmiermittel,** *n.* mineral lubricant. **-schmieröl,** *n.* mineral lubricating oil. **-schwarz,** *n.* mineral black (ground graphite or graphitic slate). **-seife,** *f.* mineral soap.

**Mineralstoff,** *m.* mineral substance, mineral matter. **-gehalt,** *m.* mineral content. **-wechsel,** *m.* mineral (or inorganic) metabolism. **-zusammensetzung,** *f.* composition of mineral matter.

**Mineral-talg,** *m.* mineral tallow (hatchettite or ozocerite). **-teer,** *m.* mineral tar, maltha. **-trennung,** *f.* separation of minerals. **-turpeth,** *m.* turpeth mineral (basic mercuric sulfate). **-vorkommen,** *n.* mineral occurrence or deposit. **-wachs,** *n.* mineral wax, ozocerite. **-wasser,** *n.* mineral water. **-wasserfabrikant,** *m.* mineral water manufacturer. **-weiss,** *n.* mineral white. **-wolle,** *f.* mineral wool.

**Minimal-.** lowest, minimum. **-betrag,** *m.* lowest amount; lowest rate. **-gehalt,** *m.* minimum content. **-wert,** *m.* minimum value.

**Minimiformel,** *f.* empirical formula.

**Ministerium,** *n.* ministry; administration.

**Minivalenz,** *f.* minimum valence.

**Minuszeichen,** *n.* minus sign.

**Minze,** *f.* mint.

**mir,** *pron.* to me, me.

**Mirban-essenz,** *f.* essence of mirbane (nitrobenzene). **-öl,** *n.* oil of mirbane (nitrobenzene).

**Mirrhe,** *f.* myrrh.

**Mirte,** *f.* myrtle.

**Misch-.** mixed; mixing. **-apparat,** *m.* mixing apparatus, mixer.

**mischbar,** *a.* miscible, mixable.

**Misch-barkeit,** *f.* miscibility. **-bleichen,** *n.* mixed bleaching. **-bottich,** *m.* mixing tub or trough. **-dünger,** *m.* mixed fertilizer; compost. **-element,** *n.* mixed element (a mixture of isotopes).

**mischen,** *v.t.& r.* mix; mingle, blend; adulterate; alloy (metals); (*Metal.*) fettle; (*Old Chem.*) combine.

**Mischer,** *m.* mixer; mixing vessel; (*Dyeing*) color mixer.

**Mischfarbe,** *f.* mixed color, combination color.

**misch-farben, -farbig,** *a.* of mixed color.

**Misch-färbung,** *f.* (*Micros.*) mixed staining. **-flasche,** *f.* mixing bottle. **-gärung,** *f.* mixed fermentation. **-gas,** *n.* mixed gas; specif., semi-water gas. **-gefäss,** *n.* mixing vessel. **-glas,** *n.* mixing glass. **-hefe,** *f.* composite yeast. **-infektion,** *f.* mixed infection. **-kessel,** *m.* mixing kettle. **-kristall,** *m.* mixed crystal, crystalline solid solution. **-ling,** *m.* hybrid, crossbreed. **-maschine,** *f.* mixing machine, mixer. **-metall,** *n.* mixed metal, alloy; specif., "misch metal" (an alloy of cerium, lanthanum, etc.). **-molekül,** *n.* mixed molecule (loosely bound union of molecules). **-mühle,** *f.* mixing mill, incorporating mill. **-öl,** *n.* mixed oil. **-pipette,**

*f.* mixing pipette. **-raum,** *m.* mixing space or chamber. **-rohr,** *n.* mixing tube. **-salz,** *n.* mixed salt. **-säure,** *f.* mixed acid. **-spektrum,** *n.* mixed spectrum.

**Mischung,** *f.* mixture; mixing; composition; blend; adulteration; (*Old Chem.*) combination, compound.

**Mischungsbestandteil,** *m.* ingredient of a mixture.

**mischungsfähig,** *a.* miscible.

**Mischungs-gewicht,** *n.* (*Old Chem.*) combining weight. **-kohle,** *f.* (*Soda*) mixing coal. **-lücke,** *f.* miscibility gap. **-probe,** *f.* test or sample of a mixture; mixing test. **-rechnung,** *f.* (*Math.*) alligation. **-regel,** *f.* rule or law of mixtures. **-verhältnis,** *f.* mixing proportion. **-wärme,** *f.* heat of mixing, heat of mixture.

**Misch-ventil,** *n.* mixing valve. **-walzwerk,** *n.* (set of) mixing rollers. **-zement,** *m.& n.* mixed cement. **-zylinder,** *m.* mixing cylinder.

**Mispel,** *f.* medlar.

**miss-, Miss-.** mis-, dis-, mal-, de-, ill-.

**miss-achten,** *v.t.* disregard; disdain. **-arten,** *v.i.* degenerate.

**Missbildung,** *f.* malformation; deformity.

**missbilligen,** *v.t.* disapprove of, oppose.

**Missbrauch,** *m.* misuse, abuse.

**missen,** *v.t.* miss; dispense with.

**Miss-erfolg,** *m.* failure. **-ernte,** *f.* crop failure.

**miss-fallen,** *v.i.* be displeasing. **-farbig,** *a.* discolored; inharmonious in color.

**Miss-färbung,** *f.* discoloration. **-geschick,** *n.* misfortune; mishap.

**missgestaltet,** *a.* deformed, misshapen.

**Missgriff,** *m.* mistake, blunder.

**miss-handeln,** *v.t.* maltreat. **-lang,** *pret.* of misslingen. **-lich,** *a.* doubtful, embarrassing, precarious. **-lingen,** *v.i.* fail, miscarry. **-lungen,** *p.p.* of misslingen. **-raten,** *v.i.=* misslingen.

**Missstand,** *m.* improper state, inconvenience, nuisance, abuse, grievance.

**misst,** *pr. 2 & 3 sing.* of messen.

**misstrauen,** *v.i.* distrust, mistrust.

**Miss-verhältnis,** *n.* disproportion, asymmetry; disparity; inadequacy. **-verständnis,** *n.* misunderstanding.

**missverstehen,** *v.t.* misunderstand.

**Misswachs,** *m.* crop failure.

**Mist,** *m.* manure, dung. **-bad,** *n.* dung bath. **-beet,** *n.* hotbed. **-beize,** *f.* (*Leather*) dung bate.

**Mistel,** *f.* mistletoe.

**misten,** *v.t.* manure, dung.

**Mist-jauche,** *f.* liquid manure, dung water. **-pulver,** *n.* powdered manure; specif., poudrette.

**mit,** *prep.* with; by, in, at.—*adv.* together, jointly, along, also.

**Mit-.** fellow, joint, common, co-, com-, sym-. -arbeiter, *m.* fellow worker, coworker, collaborator, contributor, assistant.

**mit-begreifen,** *v.t.* include. -bewegt, *a.* (of the atomic nucleus) in relative motion, moving.

**Mit-bewegung,** *f.* associated movement, co-movement; relative motion (as of the atomic nucleus). -bewerber, *m.* competitor.

**mit-einander,** *adv.* with one another, together. -führbar, *a.* capable of being carried along or entrained. -führen, *v.t.* carry along, take along, entrain.

**Mitgefühl,** *n.* sympathy.

**mitgerissen,** *p.p.* of mitreissen.

**Mitglied,** *n.* member; fellow. -schaft, *f.* membership.

**mithin,** *conj.* therefore; of course.

**Mitisgrün,** *n.* Mitis green.

**mit-machen,** *v.t.* join in, take part in, conform to. -nehmen, *v.t.* take along, take, share; weaken, exhaust, wear; maltreat, criticize.

**Mitnehmer,** *m.* (*Mach.*) driver.

**Mitnehmer-.** (*Mach.*) driving, carrying, pushing.

**mit-niederreissen,** *v.t.* carry down. -reissen, -schleppen, *v.t.* carry over (in distillation, etc.); carry, pull or drag along. -schwingen, *v.t.* covibrate.

**Mitschwingen,** *n.* covibration.

**Mitt.,** *abbrev.* (Mitteilung) communication.

**Mittag,** *m.* midday, noon; south.

**Mittags-essen,** *n.* noon meal. -kreis, *m.*, -linie, *f.* meridian.

**Mitte,** *f.* middle, midst, center; mean.

**mitteilen,** *v.t.* communicate, impart, give.

**Mitteilung,** *f.* communication, etc. (see mitteilen).

**mittel,** *a.* middle, central, mean, median, medium, intermediate, middling.

**Mittel,** *n.* middle; medium; means, agent; (*Pharm.*) remedy; (*Math.*) mean; (*Mining*) mass; average; means, capital; mediation.

**Mittel-.** middle, etc. (see mittel); meso-.

**mittel-alterlich,** *a.* medieval. -bar, *a.* indirect, mediate.

**Mittel-bauchgegend,** *f.* mesogastric region. -benzin, *n.* medium benzine (boiling about 80–120° C.) -binder, *m.* medium-setting cement. -ding, *n.* intermediate, cross. -druck, *m.* medium pressure. -eck, *n.*, -ecke, *f.* (*Cryst.*) lateral summit. -erz, *n.* ore of medium value. -farbe, *f.* intermediate color; secondary color. -fehler, *m.* average error, mean error. -fell, *n.* mediastinum. -fleisch, *n.* perineum.

**mittelflüssig,** *a.* semifluid.

**Mittel-fuss,** *m.* metatarsus. -gehirn, *n.* midbrain, mesencephalon. -glied, *n.* intermediate member (of a series); (*Anat.*) middle phalanx.

**mittelgross,** *a.* medium-sized.

**Mittel-grösse,** *f.* medium size. -hand, *f.* metacarpus.

**mittelhart,** *a.* medium-hard, moderately hard.

**Mittel-haut,** *f.* middle coat, tunica media. -hirn, *n.* mid-brain, mesencephalon. -keim, *m.* (*Zoöl.*) mesoblast. -kraft, *f.* resultant force. -lage, *f.* middle position.

**mittellang,** *a.* of medium length.

**Mittel-lauf,** *m.* (in distillation) middle fraction. -lauge, *f.* weak lye. -linie, *f.* median line; axis; equator.

**mittel-los,** *a.* without means. -mässig, *a.* middling, mediocre, average.

**Mittel-meer,** *n.* Mediterranean Sea. -öl, *n.* middle oil. -punkt, *m.* center, central point.

**mittels,** *prep.* by means of.

**Mittel-salz,** *n.* neutral salt. -schicht, *f.* middle or intermediate layer.

**mittelschwer,** *a.* medium heavy; half-weighted.

**mittelst,** *prep.* by means of.

**Mittelstand,** *m.* middle class.

**mittel-ständig,** *a.* occupying a middle position, middle. -stark, *a.* moderately strong.

**Mittel-strasse,** *f.* middle course. -stück, *n.* middle piece, central portion. -wand, *f.* middle wall; (*Anat.*) mediastinum.

**mittelweich,** *a.* medium-soft, moderately soft.

**Mittel-wert,** *m.* mean value. -zahl, *f.* mean. -zeug, *n.* (*Paper*) middle stuff, second stuff.

**mitten,** *adv.* in the middle or midst; midway. —*v.t.* center.

**Mitternacht,** *f.* midnight; north.

**mittler,** *a.* middle, central, etc. (see mittel). -weile, *adv.* meanwhile.

**Mitwoch,** *m.* Wednesday.

**mitunter,** *adv.* occasionally.

**Mitwelt,** *f.* present age, contemporaries.

**mitwirken,** *v.i.* coöperate, take part, assist.

**Mitwirkung,** *f.* coöperation, assistance.

**mk.,** *abbrev.* (mikroskopisch) microscopic(al).

**Mk.,** *abbrev.* (Mark, Marken) mark, marks.

**MK.,** *abbrev.* (Meterkerze) meter candle.

**mkr.,** *abbrev.* (mikroskopisch) microscopic.

**Möbel,** *n.* piece of furniture. -politur, *f.* furniture polish.

**mobil,** *a.* mobile; quick, active.

**mobilisieren,** *v.t.* mobilize.

**Mobilität,** *f.* mobility.

**möblieren,** *v.t.* furnish, fit up.

**mochte,** *pret.* of mögen.

**Mock, -stahl,** *m.* German steel (made by direct refining of cast iron).

**Mode,** *f.* fashion, mode.

Mode-. fancy, fashionable. -gewürz, n. allspice, pimento.

Model, m. modulus; mold.

Modell, n. model; (*Founding*) pattern.

modellieren, v.t. model, mold.

Modellier-holz, n. (wooden) modeling tool. -ton, m. modeling clay. -wachs, n. modeling wax.

modellmässig, a. according to a model, in terms of a model.

modeln, v.t. model, mold.

Moder, m. mold; putridity, decay. -duft, -geruch, m. musty or moldy smell; smell of decay.

moderhaft, a. moldy, musty, moldering, molded.

moderieren, v.t. moderate, regulate.

moderig, a. musty, moldy; decayed.

modern, v.i. molder, decay.

modern, a. modern; fashionable.

Moderstein, m. rottenstone.

modifizieren, v.t. modify.

Modul, m. modulus.

mögen, v.i. be able, may; like, choose.

mögl., abbrev. möglich.

möglich, a. possible; potential; feasible. -erweise, adv. possibly; as far as possible.

Möglichkeit, f. possibility; practicability. —nach —, as far as possible.

möglichst, adv. (as much) as possible.

Mohn, m. poppy. -kapsel, f., -kopf, m. poppy capsule, poppy head. -öl, n. poppy-seed oil. -saft, m. poppy juice, opium. -samen, m. poppy seed. -säure, f. meconic acid. -stoff, m. narcotine.

Mohr, m. (*Old Chem.*) black, ethiops; watered fabric, moiré; watered effect, moiré; Moor; negro.—mineralischer —, = Mineralmohr.

Möhre, f. carrot.

Möhrenfarbstoff, m. carotene.

Mohrenhirse, f. Kafir corn, durra.

Möhrenöl, n. carrot oil.

Mohrrübe, f. carrot.

Mohrrübenfarbstoff, m. carotene.

Mohrsches Salz. Mohr's salt (ammonium ferrous sulfate).

moirieren, v.t. water, cloud (fabrics)

mol., abbrev. (molekular) molecular.

Mol, n. mole, mol.

Mol-. molar.

Molargewicht, n. molar weight.

Molarität, f. molarity.

Molch, m. salamander.

Molekelgewicht, n. molecular weight.

Molekül, Molekel, n. molecule.

Molekular-abstossung, f. molecular repulsion. -anziehung, f. molecular attraction. -bewegung, f. molecular motion or movement. -brechung, f. molecular refraction.

-drehung, f. molecular rotation. -druck, m. molecular pressure. -formel, f. molecular formula. -gewicht, n. molecular weight.

Molekulargewichts-bestimmung, f. molecularweight determination. -bestimmungsmethode, f. method for determining molecular weights.

Molekular-grösse, f. molecular magnitude; molecular weight. -kraft, f. molecular force. -reibung, f. molecular friction. -störung, f. molecular disturbance. -verbindung, f. molecular compound. -wärme, f. molecular heat. -wirkung, f. molecular action (or effect). -zustand, m. molecular state or condition, molecularity.

Molekül-bau, m. molecular structure. -schicht, f. layer of molecules. -sieb, n. microfilter. -umlagerung, f. molecular rearrangement. -verbindung, f. molecular compound.

Molenverhältnis, n. mole ratio.

Mol.-Gew., abbrev. (Molekulargewicht) molecular weight.

Mol-gewicht, n. molar weight, gram-molecular weight; inexactly, molecular weight. -grösse, f. molar magnitude. -ion, n. mole ion. -isierung, f. molization (union of ions to form a molecule).

molk, pret. of melken.

Molke, f., Molken, f.pl. whey.

Molken-eiweiss, n. whey protein. -säure, f. lactic acid. -wesen, n., -wirtschaft, Molkerei, f. dairy.

molkig, molkicht, a. wheyey, wheyish.

Möller, m. mixture (of ores and fluxes for smelting).

möllern, v.t. (*Metal.*) mix (the ores and fluxes for the charge).

Möllerung, f. (*Metal.*) mixture (of ores and fluxes), charge.

mollig, a. cosy, snug; soft; (of leather) plump.

Mol.-Refr., abbrev. Molekularrefraktion.

Mol-refraktion, f. molar refraction. -verhältnis, n. molar ratio. -volum, -volumen, n. molar volume.

Molybdän, n. molybdenum. -blau, n. molybdenum blue. -bleispat, m., -blei, n. (*Min.*) wulfenite. -eisen, n. ferromolybdenum. -erz, n. molybdenum ore. -glanz, m. molybdenite.

molybdänhaltig, a. molybdeniferous.

Molybdänit, n. molybdenite.

Molybdän-kies, m. molybdenite. -ocker, m. molybdic ocher, molybdite. -oxyd, n. molybdenum oxide (specif. one higher than $Mo_2O_3$). -oxydul, n. molybdous oxide (MoO, also $Mo_2O_3$).

molybdänsauer, a. of or combined with molybdic acid, molybdate of.

**Molybdän-säure**, *f.* molybdic acid. **-stahl**, *m.* molybdenum steel.

**Molzustand**, *m.* molecular condition.

**Moment**, *n.* moment; momentum; reason, motive.

**momentan**, *a.* momentary; instantaneous.

**Moment-aufnahme**, *f.*, **-bild**, *n.* instantaneous photograph. **-klemme**, *f.* instantaneous clamp.

**Mon.**, *abbrev.* (Monographie) monograph; (Monat) month.

**monalkyliert**, *p.a.* having one alkyl group introduced, monoalkylated.

**Monat**, *m.* month.

**monatelang**, *a.* of months' duration, for months.

**Monats-bericht**, *m.* monthly report. **-fluss**, *m.* menses, menstruation. **-heft**, *n.* monthly part or number. **-schrift**, *f.* monthly publication.

**Mönch**, *m.* monk.

**Mönchs-kappe**, *f.* monkshood, aconite. **-pfeffer**, *m.* (*Bot.*) agnus castus.

**Mond**, *m.* moon.

**Mondamin**, *n.* a kind of corn starch (maize flour).

**mondförmig**, *a.* crescent-shaped, lunate.

**Mond-gas**, *n.* Mond gas (named from its inventor). **-glas**, *n.* crown glass. **-milch**, *f.* agaric mineral. **-stein**, *m.* moonstone.

**Mono-carbonsäure**, *f.* monocarboxylic acid. **-chloressigsäure**, *f.* monochloroacetic acid. **-chlorhydrat**, *n.* monohydrochloride.

**monocyclisch**, *a.* monocyclic.

**Monographie**, *f.* monograph.

**mono-heteroatomig**, *a.* monoheteroatomic. **-hydratisch**, *a.* monohydric.

**Monokalium-**. monopotassium.

**mono-klin**, **-klinisch**, *a.* monoclinic.

**Mononatrium-**. monosodium.

**Monooxy-**. (usually) monohydroxy-; monoxy-.

**monophasisch**, *a.* monophase, single-phase.

**Monosulfosäure**, *f.* monosulfonic acid.

**monoton**, *a.* monotonous.

**Monoxyd**, *n.* monoxide.

**monozyklisch**, *a.* monocyclic.

**Montag**, *m.* Monday.

**Montage**, *f.* mounting, setting up, erection, assemblage.

**Montan-**. mountain; mining; montanic, montan. **-alkohol**, *m.* montanic alcohol. **-industrie**, *f.* mining industry. **-säure**, *f.* montanic acid. **-wachs**, *n.* montan wax.

**montieren**, *v.t.* mount; set up, erect; assemble; adjust.

**Moor-boden**, *m.* marshy soil. **-erde**, *f.* bog earth, peaty soil, muck soil. **-lauge**, *f.* extract from bog earth or peat. **-salz**, *n.* salt from peaty soil. **-wasser**, *n.* peat water.

**Moos**, *n.* moss. **-achat**, *m.* moss agate.

**moosartig**, *a.* mosslike, mossy.

**Moos-beere**, *f.* cranberry; whortleberry; (schwarze) crowberry (*Empetrum nigrum*). **-grün**, *n.* moss green. **-pulver**, *n.* lycopodium powder. **-stärke**, *f.* lichen starch, lichenin. **-tierchen**, *n.* (*Zoöl.*) polyzoan. **-torf**, *m.* peat, peat turf.

**Morast**, *m.* bog, marsh, swamp, morass.

**Morasterz**, *n.* bog ore.

**Morchel**, *f.* morel.

**Mord**, *m.* murder.

**mordanzieren**, *v.t.* mordant.

**morgen**, *adv.* tomorrow.

**Morgen**, *m.* morning; East, Orient; acre. **-brot**, *n.* breakfast.

**morgend**, *a.* of tomorrow.

**Morgenland**, *n.* East, Orient.

**morgenländisch**, *a.* oriental.

**Moringagerbsäure**, **Moringerbsäure**, *f.* moringatannic acid (maclurin).

**Morphium**, *n.* morphine.

**morphotropisch**, *a.* morphotropic.

**morsch**, *a.* rotten, decayed; tender, fragile.

**morschen**, *v.i.* rot, decay.

**Morschheit**, *f.* rottenness, decay.

**Morselle**, *f.* lozenge.

**Mörser**, *m.* mortar (the vessel and the cannon). **-keule**, *f.* pestle.

**Mörtel**, *m.* mortar (the material). **-wäsche**, *f.* thin mortar, grout.

**mosaisch**, *a.* mosaic.

**Moschus**, *m.* musk. **-korn**, *n.* musk seed (from abelmosk). **-kraut**, *n.* cat thyme. **-wurzel**, *f.* musk root (specif. the root of *Ferula sumbul*).

**Moskovade**, *f.* muscovado.

**Most**, *m.* must. **-messer**, *m.* must gage.

**Mostrich**, *m.* mustard.

**Most-sirup**, *m.* arrope (boiled-down must). **-wa(a)ge**, *f.* must hydrometer. **-wein**, *m.* a lightly fermented fruit juice.

**Motoren-betriebsstoff**, *m.* motor fuel. **-öl**, *n.* motor oil.

**Motorrad**, *n.* motorcycle.

**Motte**, *f.* moth.

**Motten-pulver**, *n.* moth powder, insect powder. **-schutzmittel**, *n.* moth preventive.

**Motze**, *f.* (*Glass*) marver.

**moussieren**, *v.i.* effervesce, sparkle, fizz.

**Movrægen-insäure**, *f.* mowrageninic acid. **-säure**, *f.* mowragenic acid.

**Movrasäure**, *f.* mowric acid.

**müde**, *a.* tired, weary, fatigued.

**Müdigkeit**, *f.* fatigue, weariness.

**Muff**, *m.*, **Muffe**, *f.* muff; (*Tech.*) sleeve, socket joint, clamp, coupling box.

Muffel, f. muffle. -farbe, f. muffle color. -ofen, m. muffle furnace.

Muffenrohr, n. socket pipe.

muffig, müffig, a. musty, moldy.

Mühe, f. pains, trouble.

mühelos, a. without trouble, effortless, easy.

mühen, v.r. trouble, take pains.

mühevoll, a. troublesome, laborious.

Mühle, f. mill.

Mühlenstaub, m. mill dust.

Mühlstein, m. millstone.

Mühsal, n. difficulty, trouble.

mühsam, a. troublesome, toilsome, hard.

Mulde, f. trough; basin; bowl; (Metal.) pig mold, pig.

Muldenblei, n. pig lead.

Müll, Mull, n.& m. dust, dry mold; refuse.

Müller, m. miller.

Mull-erde, f. humus, mold. -krapp, m. mull madder.

Mulm, m. ore dust, earthy ore; mold, humus; decay.

mulmen, v.t. pulverize.—v.i. fall to powder.

mulmig, a. dusty; earthy; decayed.

multiplizieren, v.t. multiply.

Mumie, f. mummy.

Mumienbildung, f. mummification.

mumifizieren, v.t. mummify.

Mumme, f. mum (a strong beer).

München, n. Munich.

Münchener, a. Munich, of Munich.

Mund, m. mouth; opening, muzzle, vent, etc. -art, f. dialect; idiom. -drüse, f. oral gland, buccal gland.

munden, v.i. taste well.

münden, v.i. discharge, empty, open.

Mundhöhle, f. oral cavity.

mündig, a. of age.

Mund-klemme, f. lockjaw. -leim, m. mouth glue (to be moistened with the mouth).

mündlich, a. oral, verbal.

Mundstück, n. mouthpiece.

Mündung, f. mouth; aperture, orifice, etc.; terminus (of a railway).

Mundwasser, n. gargle, mouth wash.

munter, a. live, lively, cheerful, vigorous.

Münz-anstalt, f. mint. -beschickung, f. alloyage.

Münze, f. coin; money; medal; mint (for coining); mint (the herb).

münzen, v.t. mint, coin. -ähnlich, -förmig, a. coin-shaped, nummular, nummiform.

Münz-gehalt, m. fineness (of coins). -kenner, m. numismatist. -wesen, n. coinage, minting. -zusatz, m. alloy (in coins).

mürbe, a. mellow, tender, soft; brittle, friable; (Metal.) short.

Mürbigkeit, f. mellowness, etc. (see mürbe).

muriatisch, a. muriatic (hydrochloric).

murmeln, v.i. murmur.

Mus, n. pulp; jam, marmalade, (fruit) sauce.

musartig, a. pulpy, thick.

Muschel, f. (mussel) shell; mussel; external ear. -gold, n. ormolu.

muschelig, a. conchoidal; shelly.

Muschel-kalk, m. shell lime; shell limestone. -kalkstein, m. shell limestone. -marmor, m. shell marble, lumachel. -mergel, m. shell marl.

Musiker, m. musician.

Musiv-. mosaic. -arbeit, f. mosaic work, mosaic. -gold, n. mosaic gold. -silber, n. mosaic silver.

Muskat-balsam, m. nutmeg butter. -birne, f. musk pear. -blüte, f. mace. -blütöl, n. oil of mace, mace oil. -butter, f. nutmeg butter.

Muskate, f. nutmeg.

Muskateller, m. muscatel.

Muskatenblüte, f. mace.

Muskat-fett, n. nutmeg butter. -nuss, f. nutmeg. -nussöl, -öl, n. nutmeg oil.

Muskel, m. muscle.

Muskel-. muscular, myo-. -eiweiss, n. myosin. -farbstoff, m. muscle pigment. -faser, f. muscular fiber. -fleisch, n. muscular substance. -gewebe, n. muscular tissue. -gift, n. muscle poison. -lehre, f. myology. -masse, f. muscular substance. -stoff, m. sarcosine. -zucker, m. inositol.

muss, pr. 1 & 3 sing. of müssen.

Muss, n.= Mus; necessity.

Musse, f. leisure.

Musselin, m. muslin.

müssen, v.i. must, be obliged, ought.

mussieren, v.i. effervesce, sparkle, fizz.

müssig, a. idle.

musste, pret. of müssen.

Muster, n. pattern; sample, specimen; model, type; standard; example; design. -flasche, f. sample bottle.

muster-gültig, a. model, standard, ideal, classic. -haft, a. standard, typical; exemplary.

Musterkarte, f. pattern card, sample card.

mustermässig, a. standard, typical.

mustern, v.t. figure (fabrics); emboss (paper); muster; (Dyeing) bring to shade.—gemustert, p.a. figured, fancy.

Muster-sammlung, f. specimen collection. -schutz, m. registered pattern. -zeichnung, f. design.

Mut, m. courage, spirit; humor, mood; anger.

Muter, m. claimant, petitioner, applicant.

mutig, a. spirited, courageous.

mut-massen, v.t. guess, suppose, conjecture. -masslich, a. supposed, conjectural.

**Mutmassung**, *f.* conjecture, supposition.

**Mutter**, *f.* mother; matrix; uterus; nut, female screw.

**Mutter-**. mother, maternal; parent; uterine. **-boden**, *m.* (*Biol.*) parent tissue; (*Agric.*) native soil. **-erde**, *f.* garden mold; native soil. **-essig**, *m.* mother of vinegar. **-fass**, *n.* (*Vinegar*) mother vat. **-form**, *f.* (*Ceram.*) master mold; (*Biol.*) parent form. **-gestein**, *n.* gangue, matrix. **-gewebe**, *n.* mother tissue, matrix; uterine tissue. **-gummi**, **-harz**, *n.* galbanum.

**Mutterkorn**, *n.* ergot. **-säure**, *f.* ergotic acid. **-vergiftung**, *f.* ergotism.

**Mutter-kraut**, *n.* feverfew. **-kuchen**, *m.* placenta. **-kümmel**, *m.* cumin. **-lauge**, *f.* mother liquor. **-leib**, *m.* womb, uterus. **-nelke**, *f.* mother clove. **-pech**, *n.* (*Med.*) meconium. **-schlüssel**, *m.* nut wrench. **-stoff**, *m.*, **-substanz**, *f.* mother substance, parent substance; matrix. **-zelle**, *f.* mother cell, parent cell. **-zimt**, *m.* cassia.

**Mutung**, *f.* claim, demand, concession.

**mützenförmig**, *a.* cap-shaped.

**m.W.**, *abbrev.* (meines Wissens) so far as I know.

**mydriatisch**, *a.* mydriatic.

**Mydriatikum**, *n.* mycosterol.

**Mykosterin**, *n.* mycosterol.

**Myrikawachs**, *n.* myrtle wax.

**Myristicinsäure**, *f.* myristicic acid

**Myristinsäure**, *f.* myristic acid.

**Myronsäure**, *f.* myronic acid.

**Myrrhe**, *f.*, **Myrrhenharz**, *n.*, myrrh.

**Myrte**, *f.* myrtle.

**Myrtenwachs**, *n.* myrtle wax.

**Myzel**, *n.* mycelium.

# N

**n,** *symbol.* (Nutzeffect) efficiency.

**n.,** *abbrev.* normal; (nördlich) northern; (netto) net; (nach) after.

**N.,** *abbrev.* (nachmittags) afternoon, P.M.; (nachts) at night; (Nord, Norden) north.

**Nabe,** *f.* (*Mach.*) hub, nave, boss.

**Nabel,** *m.* navel; (*Bot.*) hilum.

**Nabel-.** umbilical, navel. **-kraut,** *n.* navelwort.

**nach,** *prep.* (sometimes following its object). to, toward, after, according to, (smell, taste) of.—*adv.* behind, after.— — **und —,** little by little, gradually, by degrees.

**Nach-, nach-.** (with nouns) after, post-, subsequent, additional, supplementary, secondary, second, counter-; (with verbs) after, again, re-, post-.

**nachahmen,** *v.t.& i.* imitate, counterfeit, adulterate.—**nachgeahmt,** *p.a.* imitation, counterfeit, fictitious.

**Nachbar,** *m.* neighbor.

**Nachbar-.** neighboring, adjoining, adjacent, vicinal. **-linie,** *f.* adjacent line, neighboring line. **-schaft,** *f.* neighborhood, vicinity. **-stellung,** *f.* neighboring position.

**Nachbehandlung,** *f.* after-treatment.

**nachbeizen,** *v.t.* (*Dyeing*) redye, also sadden.

**Nachbeschickung,** *f.* (*Metal.*) aftercharging, aftercharge.

**nachbessern,** *v.t.* improve upon, touch up, retouch, repair.

**Nachbild,** *n.* after-image; copy, imitation.

**nach-bilden,** *v.t.* copy, reproduce, imitate, counterfeit. **-bleichen,** *v.t.* bleach again.

**Nachbrand,** *m.* second burning, second fire.

**nach-brauen,** *v.t.* brew again. **-brennen,** *v.i.* smolder.—*v.t.* burn again, etc. (see brennen). **-chromieren,** *v.t.* (*Dyeing*) afterchrome, back-chrome.

**Nachdampf,** *m.* (*Mining*) afterdamp, choke damp.

**nachdem,** *adv.* afterward, hereafter.—*conj.* after, according as.

**nachdenken,** *v.i.* meditate, reflect.

**Nachdruck,** *m.* energy, emphasis; reprinting.

**nachdunkeln,** *v.t.& i.* darken; (*Dyeing*) sadden.

**Nacheifer,** *m.* emulation.

**nach-eilen,** *v.i.* lag, retard; follow. **-einander,** *adv.* one after another, successively.

**Nachen,** *m.* boat.

**Nachf.,** *abbrev.* (Nachfolger) successor, successors.

**nachfärben,** *v.t.* dye again, counterstain.

**Nachfilter,** *m.* second filter.

**nach-filtern,** *v.t.* filter again, refilter. **-fixieren,** *v.t.* afterfix.

**nachfolgen,** *v.i.* follow, succeed.—**nachfolgend,** *p.a.* following, subsequent; continuous, consecutive.

**Nachfolger,** *m.* successor; imitator.

**nachforschen,** *v.i.* search, make search, investigate.

**Nach-forschung,** *f.* research, investigation, search, scrutiny. **-frage,** *f.* inquiry; (*Com.*) demand.

**nach-füllen,** *v.t.* fill up, replenish, add to. **-gären,** *v.i.* undergo after-fermentation.

**Nachgärfass,** *n.* (*Brewing*) cleansing cask.

**Nachgärung,** *f.* after-fermentation, secondary fermentation.

**Nachgärungsfass,** *n.* (*Brewing*) cleansing vat.

**nach-geahmt,** *p.a.* see nachahmen. **-geben,** *v.i.* give way, yield.

**Nachgeburt,** *f.* afterbirth.

**Nachgeburts-.** placental.

**nach-gemacht,** *p.a.* see nachmachen. **-gerben,** *v.t.* tan again, retan.

**Nach-geruch,** *m.* aftersmell. **-geschmack,** *m.* aftertaste.

**nach-giebig,** *a.* flexible, pliable; compliant. **-giessen,** *v.t.* pour again, add more; refill, replenish. **-glühen,** *v.t.& i.* glow again; anneal.

**Nach-guss,** *m.* second pouring, refilling; (*Brewing*) after-mash, second wort, also sparging water and sparging. **-hall,** *m.* reverberation; resonance, echo.

**nachhaltig,** *a.* lasting, enduring; persevering.

**Nachhaltigkeit,** *f.* durability; perseverance.

**nachher,** *adv.* afterward, hereafter, later.

**nachherig,** *a.* subsequent.

**Nachhirn,** *n.* afterbrain, metencephalon.

**nachholen,** *v.t.* recover, make up.

**Nach-hut,** *f.* rear, rear guard. **-impfung,** *f.* reinoculation.

**nachkochen,** *v.t.* continue boiling, boil again.

**Nachkomme,** *m.* descendant, successor.

**nachkommen,** *v.i.* follow, overtake, comply with, perform.

**Nachkondensator,** *m.* secondary condenser.

**nachkühlen,** *v.t.* cool again, recool.

Nach-kühler, *m.* aftercooler, recooler. -küh-lung, *f.* aftercooling, recooling.

nachkupfern, *v.t.* after-treat with copper or a copper compound.

Nach-ladung, *f.* additional charge, recharge. -lass, *m.* relaxation, intermission; diminution; deduction; legacy.

nachlassen, *v.t.* temper, anneal (glass or metals); slacken, relax; allow (gases) to expand; abate, deduct; leave behind, leave. —*v.i.* slacken, subside.

nachlässig, *a.* negligent, remiss.

Nachlauf, *m.* last runnings, faints.

nachleuchten, *v.i.* shine afterward, phosphoresce.

Nachleuchten, *n.* afterglow, phosphorescence.

nachliefern, *v.t.* furnish subsequently; supplement.

Nachluft, *f.* additional air.

nachmachen, *v.t.* imitate, counterfeit.—nach-gemacht, *p.a.* imitation, counterfeit, artificial.

Nachmaische, *f.* after-mash.

nachmalig, *a.* subsequent.

Nach-mittag, *m.* afternoon. -mühlenöl, *n.* inferior olive oil from the marc.

Nachnahme, *f.* reimbursement.—unter —, C.O.D.

nachnuancieren, *v.t.* shade (colors).

Nach-öl, *n.* an inferior olive oil. -oxydation, *f.* after-oxidation. -presse, *f.* re-pressing machine; (*Paper*) press rolls.

nach-pressen, *v.t.* re-press. -prüfen, *v.t.* re-examine, check. -putzen, *v.t.* repolish, finish off.

Nach-reifen, *n.* subsequent or secondary ripening or maturing. -reiniger, *m.* repurifier. -reinigung, *f.* after-purification.

Nachricht, *f.* news; information, notice.

nach-salzen, *v.t.* salt again, resalt. -schlagen, *v.t.* look up, refer to.

Nachschlagewerk, *n.* reference work.

nachschleifen, *v.t.* regrind, resharpen.

Nachschlüssel, *m.* master key; skeleton key.

nach-schmecken, *v.i.* to leave an aftertaste. -schmieren, *v.t.* relubricate.

Nach-schrift, *f.* postscript. -schwaden, *m.* afterdamp, choke damp.

nach-schwelen, *v.i.* continue to smolder. -sehen, *v.i.* look, search, see (to).—*v.t.* look after, look over, overhaul; overlook, excuse. -seigern, *v.t.* (*Metal.*) liquate again. -setzen, *v.t.* add; put after; postpone.

Nach-setzlöffel, *m.* spoon or ladle for adding something, as ore. -sicht, *f.* inspection; forbearance, indulgence.

nachspülen, *v.t.* rinse out (the last parts of).

nächst, *adv.& prep.* next.

nächste, *a.* next, nearest.

Nachstechbier, *n.* feed beer.

nach-stechen, *v.t.* (*Brewing*) top up. -stehen, *v.i.* follow; be inferior.— -stehend, *p.a.* following, below. -stellbar, *a.* regulable, adjustable. -stellen, *v.t.* regulate.

nächstens, *adv.* next time, shortly.

nächst-höher, *a.* next higher. -niedrig, *a.* next lower.

Nachsud, *m.* second boiling, afterboiling, etc. (see Sud).

Nacht, *f.* night. -blau, *n.* night blue.

Nachteil, *m.* disadvantage, detriment, damage.

nachteilig, *a.* disadvantageous, detrimental.

Nachtgrün, *n.* night green.

Nachtigall, *f.* nightingale.

Nachtisch, *m.* dessert.

Nacht-kerze, *f.* night light; evening primrose (*Oenothera*). -mahl, *n.* supper.

Nachtrag, *m.* supplement, addendum.

nach-tragen, *v.t.* add, append. -träglich, *a.* supplementary, additional; extra; subsequent, later.

Nachtripper, *m.* (*Med.*) gleet.

Nachtschatten, *m.* nightshade.

nachverdampfen, *v.t.* evaporate again, re-evaporate.

Nach-verdampfung, *f.* re-evaporation. -ver-gasung, *f.* after-gasification.

nach-waschen, *v.t.* wash (after some operation); rewash. -weichen, *v.t.* (*Brewing*) couch.

Nach-weichen, *n.*, -weiche, *f.* (*Brewing*) couching.

Nachweis, *m.* detection; proof; information; index.

nachweisbar, *a.* detectable; demonstrable; evident.

nachweisen, *v.t.* detect; prove, demonstrate, establish; identify; point out, refer to.

nachweislich, *a.* = nachweisbar.

Nachweismittel, *n.* means of detection or proof, agent for detection.

Nachweisung, *f.* detection; proof, demonstration; identification; information; reference.

Nachweisungsmittel, *n.* = Nachweismittel.

Nach-welt, *f.* posterity. -wert, *m.* later value, future value.

nachwiegen, *v.t.* weigh again, reweigh.

Nach-wirkung, *f.* after-effect, secondary effect. -würze, *f.* second wort. -zündung, *f.* (*Mach.*) retarded ignition.

Nacken, *m.* neck, nape.

Nacken-. cervical. -drüse, *f.* cervical gland.

nackt, *a.* naked, bare; plain; open.

Nadel, *f.* needle; pin.

nadelartig, *a.* needle-like, acicular.

Nadelblatt, *n.* (*Bot.*) needle.

Nädelchen, *n.* little needle (or pin).

**Nadel-eisenerz,** n., **-eisenstein,** m. needle iron ore (göthite in acicular crystals). **-erz,** n. needle ore (aikinite in acicular crystals).

**nadelförmig,** a. needle-shaped, acicular.

**Nadel-holz,** n. conifers (collectively), esp. pines and firs; wood of conifers, soft wood. **-holzkohle,** f. soft-wood charcoal. **-punktierung,** f. acupuncture. **-stein,** m. needlestone (natrolite). **-zeolith,** m. needle zeolite (natrolite). **-zinnerz,** n. acicular cassiterite.

**Nafta,** f. naphtha.

**Naftalin,** n. naphthalene.

**Nagel,** m. nail.

**Nägelein,** n. little nail; tack; clove; pink. **-öl,** n. clove oil. **-pfeffer,** m. allspice, pimento. **-rinde,** f., **-zimt,** m. clove bark, clove cinnamon.

**nageln,** v.t. nail.

**nagelneu,** a. brand-new.

**nagen,** v.t.& i. gnaw.

**Nager,** m., **Nagetier,** n. rodent.

**Näglein, Näglein-.** = Nägelein, Nägelein-.

**Näh-.** sewing.

**nahe,** a. near, adjacent; imminent.—adv. near, close.—— **legen,** make plain, bring home.

**Nähe,** f. nearness, closeness; vicinity; presence.

**nahe-liegen,** v.i. be near, border (on); be natural, be obvious, suggest itself. **-liegend,** a. nearby, adjacent; neighboring; obvious.

**nahen,** v.i. approach.

**nähen,** v.t. sew.

**näher,** a. nearer, closer.

**nähern,** v.t. bring near.—v.r. draw near.

**Näherung,** f. approach; approximation.

**Näherungs-formel,** f. approximation formula. **-wert,** m. approximate value.

**nahe-stehend,** p.a. closely related or connected; standing near. **-zu,** adv. almost, well-nigh.

**nahm,** pret. of nehmen.

**Nähnadel,** f. sewing needle.

**Nähr-.** nutritive, nutrient, alimentary. **-agar,** m. nutrient agar. **-äquivalent,** n. nutritive equivalent or value. **-blatt,** n. (Bot.) storage leaf. **-boden,** m. nutrient medium, nutrient substratum, culture medium. **-bouillon, -brühe,** f. nutrient broth.

**nähren,** v.t. feed; nourish; support.—nährend, p.a. nourishing, nutritive, nutritious, nutrient.

**Nähr-flüssigkeit,** f. nutrient (or nutritive) liquid or fluid. **-gang,** m. alimentary canal; nutrient duct. **-geschäft,** n. nutrition.

**nahrhaft,** a. nutritive, nourishing, nutritious; productive; lucrative.

**Nahrhaftigkeit,** f. nutritiousness; productiveness.

**Nähr-hefe,** f. nutrient yeast. **-kraft,** f. nutritive power.

**nährkräftig,** a. nutritious.

**Nähr-lösung,** f. nutrient (or nutritive) solution. **-mittel,** n. food; nutriment, nutrient. **-plasma,** f. (Biol.) trophoplasm. **-präparat,** n. food preparation. **-saft,** m. nutrient juice; chyle; sap. **-salz,** n. nutrient salt (salt required for proper nutrition). **-stoff,** m. nutritive substance, nutrient; nutritive material, foodstuff, food.

**nährstoffarm,** a. poor in food material.

**Nähr-stoffgehalt,** m. nutrient content, food content. **-substanz,** f. nutrient (or nutritive) substance. **-substrat,** n. nutrient substratum, nutrient base, nutrient medium.

**Nahrung,** f. nourishment, nutriment, food; subsistence; (Leather) tawing paste.

**Nahrungs-aufnahme,** f. reception or absorption of food. **-bedarf,** m. food requirement. **-brei,** m. chyme. **-dotter,** m. (Biol.) food yolk, deutoplasm. **-flüssigkeit,** f. nutritive liquid; chyle. **-kanal,** m. alimentary canal. **-milch,** f. (Physiol.) chyle.

**Nahrungsmittel,** n. food, foodstuff. **-chemie,** f. food chemistry. **-chemiker,** m. food chemist. **-fälschung,** f. food adulteration. **-kunde,** f. (science of) nutrition. **-untersuchung,** f. examination or investigation of food; food research. **-verfälschung,** f. food adulteration.

**Nahrungs-rohr,** n., **-röhre,** f. alimentary canal. **-saft,** m. nutrient juice; specif.: (Med.) chyle, (Bot.) sap. **-stoff,** m. nutritive substance, nourishment, food. **-teilchen,** n. nutritive element. **-vergiftung,** f. food poisoning. **-wert,** m. nutritive value.

**Nähr-vorrat,** m. reserve food. **-wasser,** n. nutrient solution. **-wert,** m. nutritive value, food value.

**Naht,** f. seam; joint; suture.

**nahtlos,** a. seamless.

**Nähwachs,** n. sewing wax.

**Name, Namen,** m. name; denomination; title.

**Namen-gebung,** f. naming; nomenclature. **-register, -verzeichnis,** n. name index, specif. author index; list of names.

**namentlich,** adv. by name, namely, especially.

**namhaft,** a. named; famous, well known; considerable.

**nämlich,** a. identical.—adv. namely, that is.

**Nancysäure,** f. (ordinary) lactic acid.

**nannte,** pret. of nennen.

**Nanziger Säure,** (ordinary) lactic acid.

**Napf,** m. bowl, basin, pan.

**Näpfchen,** n. cup; little bowl or basin. **-kobalt,** m. flaky metallic arsenic.

**napfförmig,** a. bowl-shaped.

**Napht-.** naphth-.

**Naphta**, *f.* naphtha; petroleum.

**Naphtacen**, *n.* naphthacene. **-chinon**, *n.* naphthacenequinone.

**Naphtafeld**, *n.* oil field.

**Naphtaldehyd**, *n.* naphthaldehyde.

**Naphtalin**, *n.* naphthalene. **-farbe**, *f.* naphthalene dye. **-gelb**, *n.* naphthalene yellow. **-rosa**, *n.* naphthalene pink (Magdala red). **-rot**, *n.* naphthalene red (Magdala red). **-säure**, *f.* naphthalenic acid. **-sulfosäure**, *f.* naphthalenesulfonic acid.

**Naphtalsäure**, *f.* naphthalic acid, $C_{10}H_6-(CO_2H)_2$.

**Naphtanthrachinon**, *n.* naphthanthraquinone.

**Naphtaquelle**, *f.* oil well.

**Napht-azarin**, *n.* naphthazarin. **-azen**, *n.* naphthacene. **-azin**, *n.* naphthazine.

**Naphten**, *n.* naphthene.

**Naphth-**. see Napht-.

**Naphtidin**, *n.* naphthidine.

**Naphtionsäure**, *f.* naphthionic acid.

**Naphto-**. naphtho-. **-brenzcatechin**, *n.* naphthopyrocatechol. **-chinaldin**, *n.* naphthoquinaldine. **-chinhydron**, *n.* naphthoquinhydrone. **-chinolin**, *·n.* naphthoquinoline. **-chinon**, *n.* naphthoquinone. **-cumarin**, *n.* naphthocoumarin (or -cumarin).

**Naphtoe-aldehyd**, *n.* naphthaldehyde, naphthoic aldehyde. **-säure**, *f.* naphthoic acid.

**Naphtohydrochinon**, *n.* naphthohydroquinone.

**Naphtol**, *n.* naphthol. **-blau**, *n.* naphthol blue. **-gelb**, *n.* naphthol yellow.

**naphtol-ieren**, *v.t.* naphtholize, naphtholate. **-sauer**, *a.* naphtholsulfonate of.

**Naphtolschwarz**, *n.* naphthol black.

**Naphtoyl**, *n.* naphthoyl.

**Napht-sultam**, *n.* naphthosultam, naphsultam. **-sulton**, *n.* naphthosultone, naphsultone.

**Naphtyl**, *n.* naphthyl. **-amin**, *n.* naphthylamine. **-blau**, *n.* naphthyl blue.

**Naphtyridin**, *n.* naphthyridine.

**Narbe**, *f.* scar; seam; (of leather and paper) grain.

**narben**, *v.t.* grain (leather, paper, etc.).—*v.i.* scar.

**Narben**, *m.* (*Leather*, etc.) grain. **-bindegewebe**, **-gewebe**, *n.* scar tissue. **-leder**, *n.* grain leather. **-seite**, *f.* grain side.

**narbig**, *a.* scarred, scarry; grained (leather).

**Narde**, *f.* spikenard, nard.

**Narkose**, *f.* narcosis. **-äther**, *m.* ether for anesthesia.

**narkotisch**, *a.* narcotic.—**narkotische Mittel**, narcotic.

**narkotisieren**, *v.t.* narcotize.

**Narkotisierung**, *f.* narcotization.

**närrisch**, *a.* foolish; crazy; odd; merry, funny.

**Narzisse**, *f.* narcissus.

**nascierend**, *p.a.* nascent.

**Nase**, *f.* nose; (projection) beak, cam, tappet, lug, etc.; spout, nozzle.

**näseln**, *v.i.* nasalize.

**Nasen-**. (*Physiol.*) nasal, naso-. **-loch**, *n.*, **-öffnung**, *f.* nostril. **-schlacke**, *f.* (*Metal.*) tuyère (twyer) slag.

**Nashorn**, *n.* rhinoceros.

**nass**, *a.* wet; moist, humid, damp.—**nasser Weg**, wet way, wet process.

**Nass-beize**, *f.* liquid (or soak) disinfectant or disinfection. **-beizmittel**, *n.* liquid (or soak) disinfectant. **-bleiche**, *f.* wet bleach. **-dampf**, *m.* wet steam, moist steam.

**Nässe**, *f.* wetness, moisture, humidity.

**nässen**, *v.t.* wet, soak, moisten; ooze, discharge.—*v.i.* ooze, discharge, run.

**Nässgehalt, Nass-gehalt**, *m.* moisture content. **-messer**, *m.* hygrometer. **-probe**, *f.* wet test.

**Nässprobe**, *f.* moisture test or determination.

**Nass-reinigung**, *f.* wet purification. **-verfahren**, *n.* wet process.

**nasz.**, *abbrev.* (naszierend) nascent.

**naszierend**, *p.a.* nascent.

**Nativpräparat**, *n.* (*Micros.*) untreated specimen.

**Natr-acetessigester**, *m.* sodioacetoacetic ester. **-amid**, *n.* sodamide, sodium amide.

**Natrium**, *n.* sodium. **-alaun**, *m.* sodium alum. **-amid**, *n.* sodium amide, sodamide. **-arseniat**, *n.* sodium arsen(i)ate. **-äthylat**, *n.* sodium ethylate. **-benzoat**, *n.* sodium benzoate. **-brechweinstein**, *m.* antimonyl sodium tartrate. **bromatum.** (*Pharm.*) sodium bromide. **-bromid**, *n.* sodium bromide. **chloratum.** (*Pharm.*) sodium chloride. **chloricum.** (*Pharm.*) sodium chlorate. **-chlorid**, *n.* sodium chloride. **-dampf**, *m.* sodium vapor. **-draht**, *m.* sodium wire. **-flamme**, *f.* sodium flame. **-formiat**, *n.* sodium formate. **-gehalt**, *m.* sodium content. **-goldchlorid**, *n.* sodium chloroaurate. **-hydrat**, *n.* sodium hydroxide. **-hydroxyd**, *n.* sodium hydroxide. **-hyperjodat**, *n.* sodium periodate. **-hyperoxyd**, *n.* sodium peroxide. **-jodat**, *n.* sodium iodate. **jodatum.** (*Pharm.*) sodium iodide. **-jodid**, *n.* sodium iodide. **-kaliumtartrat**, *n.* sodium potassium tartrate. **-karbonat**, *n.* sodium carbonate. **-kieselfluorid**, *n.* sodium fluosilicate. **-löffel**, *m.* sodium spoon. **-metall**, *n.* sodium metal, metallic sodium. **-nitrat**, *n.* sodium nitrate. **-oxyd**, *n.* sodium oxide. **-oxydhydrat**, *n.* sodium hydroxide. **-phosphat**, *n.* sodium phosphate. **-platinchlorid**, *n.* sodium chloroplatinate. **-presse**, *f.* sodium press. **-salz**, *n.* sodium salt. **-seife**, *f.* sodium soap. **-sulfat**, *n.* sodium sulfate. **-sulfhydrat**, *n.* sodium hydrosulfide. **-superoxyd**, *n.* sodium superoxide (sodium peroxide). **-ver-**

bindung, *f.* sodium compound. **-wasser-stoff,** *m.* sodium hydride. **-zange,** *f.* sodium tongs. **-zyanamid,** *n.* sodium cyanamide.

**Natron,** *n.* (caustic) soda, sodium hydroxide; soda (Na$_2$O, cf. Kali). **-alaun,** *m.* soda alum. **-ätzlauge,** *f.* caustic soda solution. **-cellulose,** *f.* (*Paper*) soda pulp. **-feldspat,** *m.* soda feldspar. **-glas,** *n.* soda glass.

**natronhaltig,** *a.* containing soda.

**Natron-hydrat,** *n.* sodium hydroxide. **-hydratlösung,** *f.* sodium hydroxide solution. **-hyperoxyd,** *n.* sodium peroxide. **-kalk,** *m.* soda lime. **-kalkglas,** *n.* soda-lime glass. **-lauge,** *f.* soda lye, solution of caustic soda. **-metall,** *n.* (metallic) sodium. **-pastille,** *f.* (*Pharm.*) troche of sodium bicarbonate. **-präparat,** *n.* soda preparation. **-salpeter,** *m.* soda saltpeter, Chile saltpeter (NaNO$_3$). **-salz,** *n.* soda salt, sodium salt. **-schwefelleber,** *f.* soda liver of sulfur (essentially Na$_2$S). **-see,** *m.* soda lake. **-seife,** *f.* soda soap. **-stoff,** *m.* (*Paper*) soda pulp. **-wasserglas,** *n.* soda water glass, sodium silicate. **-weinstein,** *m.* sodium tartrate, or sodium potassium tartrate. **-zellstoff,** *m.* (*Paper*) soda pulp. **-zellstoff(f)fabrikation,** *f.* soda-pulp manufacture.

**Natter-wurz, -wurzel,** *f.* bistort; cuckoopint.

**Natur,** *f.* nature.

**Natur-.** natural. **-erscheinung,** *f.* natural phenomenon. **-erzeugnis,** *f.* natural product. **-farbe,** *f.* natural color.

**natur-farbig, -farben,** *a.* of natural color, (of leather) fair.

**Natur-farbstoff,** *m.* natural dyestuff. **-fehler,** *m.* natural defect. **-fett,** *n.* natural fat, specif. suint.

**naturforschend,** *a.* for the investigation of nature, natural-science.

**Natur-forscher,** *m.* investigator of nature, scientific investigator, (formerly) natural philosopher; naturalist. **-forschung,** *f.* investigation of nature, scientific research; (formerly) natural philosophy. **-gas,** *n.* natural gas.

**naturgemäss,** *a.* according to nature, natural. —*adv.* naturally.

**Natur-gerbstoff,** *m.* natural tan. **-geschichte,** *f.* natural history. **-gesetz,** *n.* law of nature, natural law. **-härte,** *f.* natural hardness. **-heilung,** *f.* spontaneous cure. **-holz,** *n.* natural wood. **-körper,** *m.* natural substance, natural body. **-kraft,** *f.* natural force or power. **-lehre,** *f.* natural science, natural philosophy.

**natürlich,** *a.* natural; native.—*adv.* naturally.

**Natur-papier,** *n.* stuff-colored paper. **-produkt,** *n.* natural product, native substance. **-reich,** *n.* domain or kingdom of nature.

**-seide,** *f.* natural silk. **-stoff,** *m.* natural substance. **-trieb,** *m.* instinct. **-wasser,** *n.* natural water.

**naturwidrig,** *a.* unnatural, abnormal.

**Naturwissenschaft,** *f.* natural science.

**naturwissenschaftlich,** *a.* of or pertaining to natural science.

**Natur-zement,** *m.* natural cement. **-zustand,** *m.* natural state.

**Nd.,** *abbrev.* (Niederschlag) precipitate.

**N.D.,** *abbrev.* (Niederdruck) low pressure.

**Ndd.,** *abbrev.* (Niederschläge) precipitates.

**Ndl.,** *abbrev.* (Nadel) needle; (Niederlage) warehouse.

**N.E.,** *abbrev.* (Nicht-Eisen) nonferrous.

**Neapel-gelb,** *n.* Naples yellow. **-rot,** *n.* Naples red.

**Nebel,** *m.* mist, fog. **-apparat,** *m.* atomizer, sprayer.

**nebelartig,** *a.* mistlike, foglike, misty, foggy.

**Nebel-fleck,** *m.* nebula. **-geschoss,** *n.* smoke projectile or shell.

**nebelig,** *a.* misty, foggy.

**Nebel-kammer,** *f.* cloud chamber. **-kasten,** *m.* smoke box. **-topf,** *m.* smoke pot. **-trommel,** *f.* smoke drum.

**neben,** *prep.* beside, by, near.

**Neben-.** by-, side-, secondary, accessory, subsidiary, subordinate, supplementary, adjoining; collateral; (*Elec.*) shunt. **-achse,** *f.* secondary axis. **-apparat,** *m.* accessory apparatus, accessory. **-bestandteil,** *m.* secondary ingredient or constituent. **-betrieb,** *m.* by-operation, secondary process, "side line." **-beweis,** *m.* accessory proof, additional proof. **-bindung,** *f.* secondary union or bond, linkage of the second order. **-buhler,** *m.* rival. **-drüse,** *f.* accessory gland. **-eigenschaft,** *f.* secondary property.

**nebeneinander,** *adv.* side by side; (*Elec.*) in parallel. **-schalten,** *v.t.* (*Elec.*) connect in parallel.

**Neben-einanderstellung,** *f.* juxtaposition; comparison. **-einteilung,** *f.* subdivision. **-erzeugnis,** *f.* by-product. **-erzeugnisgewinnung,** *f.* by-product recovery. **-farbe,** *f.* secondary or tertiary color. **-fläche,** *f.* (*Cryst.*) secondary face. **-fluss,** *m.* tributary. **-gang,** *m.* by-way; (*Mining*) lateral vein. **-geschmack,** *m.* after-taste, tang. **-gestein,** *n.* (*Mining*) country rock. **-gewebe,** *n.* accessory tissue.

**nebenher,** *adv.* besides, by the way.

**Neben-hoden,** *m.* (*Anat.*) epididymis. **-kette,** *f.* side chain, subordinate chain. **-linie,** *f.* secondary line; branch line. **-luft,** *f.* admixed air. **-niere,** *f.* suprarenal capsule. ~~Cadre~~

**Nebennieren-.** suprarenal. (adrenal)

**Neben-produkt,** *n.* by-product. **-quantenzahl,**

*f.* secondary (or subsidiary) quantum number. **-rohr,** *n.* side tube (or pipe), branch tube (or pipe). **-rolle,** *f.* subordinate rôle. **-sache,** *f.* secondary matter.

**nebensächlich,** *a.* incidental, subsidiary, by-.

**Nebenschilddrüse,** *f.* parathyroid gland.

**nebenschliessen,** *v.t.* (*Elec.*) shunt.

**Neben-schliessung,** *f.,* **-schluss,** *m.* (*Elec.*) shunt, shunting. **-serie,** *f.* subsidiary series, secondary series, subordinate series. **-spirale,** *f.* secondary coil.

**nebenstehend,** *a.* standing beside, annexed.

**Neben-teil,** *m.* accessory part. **-titel,** *m.* subtitle. **-typus,** *m.* secondary type. **-valenz,** *f.* subsidiary valence, secondary valence. **-winkel,** *n.* adjacent angle. **-wirkung,** *f.* secondary action or effect. **-wort,** *n.* adverb. **-zelle,** *f.* accessory cell. **-zweig,** *m.* lateral branch.

**nebst,** *prep.* besides, including.

**negativ-elektrisch,** *a.* negatively electric, electronegative.

**Negativität,** *f.* negativity.

**Neger,** *m.* negro. **-kopf,** *m.* niggerhead.

**nehmen,** *v.t.* take; receive, get.

**neigbar,** *a.* inclinable.

**Neige,** *f.* inclination, slope, gradient; dregs, sediment; decline, wane.

**neigen,** *v.t.* incline, bend.—*v.r.* incline, bend, lean, slope, dip, decline, bow; tend.—**geneigt,** *p.a.* inclined, etc.; slanting; disposed, favorable.

**Neigung,** *f.* inclination; slope, pitch, dip; tendency.

**Neigungs-ebene,** *f.* inclined plane. **-winkel,** *m.* angle of inclination.

**nein,** *interj.* no.

**Nekrolog,** *m.* obituary.

**Nekrose,** *f.* necrosis.

**Nelke,** *f.* pink (the flower); clove.

**Nelken-öl,** *n.* clove oil (oil of cloves). **-pfeffer,** *m.* allspice, pimento. **-pfefferwasser,** *n.* (*Pharm.*) pimento water. **-säure,** *f.* eugenol; caryophyllic acid. **-stein,** *m.* iolite. **-wurzel,** *f.* avens root. **-zim(m)t,** *m.* clove cinnamon, clove cassia.

**Nenn-.** nominal.

**nennen,** *v.t.* name, call, term.

**nennenswert,** *a.* worth mentioning, noteworthy.

**Nenner,** *m.* denominator.

**Nenn-wert,** *m.* nominal value. **-wort,** *n.* noun, substantive.

**Neodym,** *n.* neodymium.

**Neroliöl,** *n.* neroli (oil of orange flowers).

**Nerv,** *m.* nerve; sinew; fiber; vein (of a leaf).

**Nerven-.** nerve, neuro-. **-entzündung,** *f.* neuritis **-gewebe,** *n.* nerve tissue. **-kitt,** *m.* (*Anat.*) neuroglia. **-kunde, -lehre,** *f.*

neurology. **-masse,** *f.,* **-stoff,** *m.* nerve substance, neural substance. **-system, -werk,** *n.* nervous system.

**nervig,** *a.* nervous; nerved; sinewy; vigorous, strong.

**nervös,** *a.* nervous; forcible.

**Nessel,** *f.* nettle.

**Nest,** *n.* nest; (of ore) pocket.

**nett,** *a.* neat; pleasant, kind; (*Sugar*) pure white.

**netto,** *adv.* net.

**Netto-ertrag,** *m.* net yield;· net proceeds. **-gewicht,** *n.* net weight.

**Netz,** *n.* net, netting; gauze; network, plexus; system (of piping, wiring, etc.); omentum; (of a telescope) reticle.

**Netz-.** steeping, wetting; net, netting, reticular, omental.

**netz-ähnlich, -artig,** *a.* netlike, reticular, plexiform.

**Netz-bad,** *n.* (*Dyeing*) wetting-out bath. **-beize,** *f.* (in Turkey-red dyeing) oil mordant.

**netzen,** *v.t.* wet, moisten, steep, soak.

**Netz-fass,** *n.* steeping cask or tub. **-flotte,** *f.* (*Dyeing*) wetting-out liquor.

**netzförmig,** *a.* net-shaped, reticular.

**Netzhaut,** *f.* retina.

**Netzhaut-.** retinal.

**Netz-kessel,** *m.* steeping copper or vat. **-magen,** *m.* second stomach (of ruminants). **-schutz,** *m.* protecting gauze or grid. **-spannung,** *f.* (*Elec.*) line voltage. **-ständer,** *m.* (*Paper*) steeping tub. **-strom,** *m.* (*Elec.*) current from a distributing system. **-werk,** *n.* network.

**neu,** *a.* new.—*adv.* newly, lately.—**aufs neue, von neuem,** anew, again.

**Neu-bildung,** *f.* new formation; (*Med.*) neoplasm. **-blau,** *n.* new blue.

**neuer,** *a.* newer; recent, modern, later. **-dings,** *adv.* newly, recently, lately; again.

**Neuerung,** *f.* innovation.

**Neu-erzeugung,** *f.* new production; reproduction. **-fundland,** *n.* Newfoundland.

**neugebildet,** *p.a.* newly formed.

**Neu-gelb,** *n.* new yellow. **-gestaltung,** *f.* reorganization; modification. **-gewürz,** *n.* allspice, pimento. **-gier, -gierde,** *f.* curiosity. **-gold,** *n.* Mannheim gold. **-heit,** *f.* novelty, newness. **-igkeit,** *f.* news; novelty. **-jahr,** *n.* New Year.

**neulich,** *adv.* lately, of late.—*a.* late, recent.

**Neu-ling,** *m.* novice. **-messing,** *n.* a kind of brass.

**neun,** *a.* nine. **-flächig,** *a.* nine-sided (or -faced).

**neunte,** *a.* ninth.

**neunwertig,** *a.* nonavalent.

neunzehn, *a.* nineteen.

neunzig, *a.* ninety.

Neu-prüfung, *f.* new test, reëxamination. -rot, *n.* new red. -seeland, *n.* New Zealand. -silber, *n.* German silver.

Neutralfett, *n.* neutral fat.

Neutralisationswärme, *f.* heat of neutralization.

neutralisieren, *v.t.* neutralize.

Neutral-isierung, *f.* neutralization. -ität, *f.* neutrality. -körper, *m.* neutral substance or body. -punkt, *m.* neutral point. -rot, *n.* neutral red. -salz, *n.* neutral salt. -salzwirkung, *f.* neutral salt effect.

Neuweiss, *n.* permanent white ($BaSO_4$).

Neuwieder Grün. Neuwied green (Paris green).

neuzeitlich, *a.* modern.

N.F., n.F., *abbrev.* (neue Folge) new series.

Nichin, *n.* niquine.

nicht, *adv.* not.—mit nichten, not at all.

Nicht-. non-, not, in-, un-. -auflösung, *f.* nonsolution. -chemiker, *m.* nonchemist, layman.

nichtdissoziiert, *p.a.* undissociated.

Nichte, *f.* niece.

Nichteignung, *f.* unsuitableness, unfitness.

nichteisenhaltig, *a.* nonferrous.

Nicht-eisenmetall, *n.* nonferrous metal. -elektrolyt, *n.* nonelectrolyte. -entartung, *f.* nondegeneration.

nicht-existenzfähig, *a.* incapable of existence. -flüchtig, *a.* nonvolatile. -gasförmig, *a.* nongaseous.

Nichtgerbstoff, *m.* nontannin, nontan.

nichthäufig, *a.* infrequent.

nichtig, *a.* null, void, invalid; futile, idle.

Nicht-igkeit, *f.* nullity; invalidation, annulment. -ion, *n.* non-ion.

Nichtionen-. non-ionic.

Nichtkarbonathärte, *f.* (*Water*) hardness not due to carbonates, permanent hardness.

nicht-kohärent, *a.* noncoherent. -leitend, *p.a.* nonconducting.

Nicht-leiter, *m.* nonconductor. -metall, *n.* nonmetal.

nichtmetallisch, *a.* nonmetallic.

Nichtmischbarkeit, *f.* immiscibility.

nicht-oxydierbar, *a.* unoxidizable. -reduzierbar, *a.* not reducible, irreducible. -rostend, *a.* nonrusting, rustproof. -russend, *a.* sootless.

nichts, *pron.*, Nichts, *n.* nothing, none.— weisses Nichts, nihil album (sublimed zinc oxide).

Nichtsättigung, *f.* nonsaturation, unsaturation.

nichtschmelzbar, *a.* nonfusible, infusible.

nichts-destoweniger, *adv.* nevertheless.

-sagend, *p.a.* meaningless. -würdig, *a.* worthless; base.

nicht-trocknend, *a.* nondrying. -umkehrbar, *a.* nonreversible, irreversible; uninvertible. -umwandelbar, *a.* inconvertible.

Nichtumwandelbarkeit, *f.* inconvertibility.

nichtvergasbar, *a.* nongasifiable, nonvolatile.

Nicht-vergrünen, *n.* ungreenable black. -wärmeleiter, *m.* nonconductor of heat.

nichtwässerig, *a.* nonaqueous.

Nichtzucker, *m.* nonsugar.

Nickel-antimonglanz, *m.* ullmannite. -arsenik, *n.* nickel arsenide. -arsen(ik)glanz, *m.* -arsen(ik)kies, *m.* gersdorffite.

nickelartig, *a.* nickel-like.

Nickel-bad, *n.* nickel bath. -blech, *n.* nickel sheet or plate. -blüte, *f.* nickel bloom (annabergite). -bromür, *n.* nickel(ous) bromide. -chlorür, *n.* nickel(ous) chloride. -chromstahl, *m.* chrome-nickel steel. -cyanür, *n.* nickelous cyanide. -draht, *m.* nickel wire. -drahtnetz, *n.* nickel gauze. -eisen, *n.* nickel iron, ferronickel. -erz, *n.* nickel ore. -fahlerz, *n.* (*Min.*) malinowskite. -flusseisen, *n.* nickel steel. -gefäss, *n.* nickel vessel. -gehalt, *m.* nickel content. -glanz, *m.* nickel glance (gersdorffite).

nickelhaltig, *a.* containing nickel, nickeliferous.

Nickelhydroxydul, *n.* nickelous hydroxide.

Nickeli-. nickelic, nickeli-. -cyanwasserstoffsäure, *f.* nickelicyanic acid. -oxyd, *n.* nickelic oxide. -verbindung, *f.* nickelic compound.

Nickel-kies, *m.* millerite. -kohlenoxyd, *n.* nickel carbonyl. -kühler, *m.* nickel condenser or cooler. -legierung, *f.* nickel alloy. -münze, *f.* nickel coin.

Nickelo-. nickelous, nickelo-.

Nickelocker, *m.* nickel ocher (annabergite).

Nickelo-cyanwasserstoffsäure, *f.* nickelocyanic acid. -verbindung, *f.* nickelous compound.

Nickeloxyd, *n.* nickel oxide, specif. nickelic oxide (as contrasted with Nickeloxydul). -salz, *n.* nickelic salt.

Nickeloxydul, *n.* nickelous oxide. -hydrat, *n.* nickelous hydroxide. -salz, *n.* nickelous salt. -verbindung, *f.* nickelous compound.

Nickel-salz, *n.* nickel salt. -schwamm, *m.* nickel sponge. -smaragd, *m.* emerald nickel (zaratite). -speise, *f.* nickel speiss. -spiessglanz, *m.* -spiessglanzerz, *n.* ullmannite. -stahl, *m.* nickel steel. -stein, *m.* (*Metal.*) nickel matte. -sulfür, *n.* nickelous sulfide. -tiegel, *m.* nickel crucible. -überzug, *m.* nickel plating. -vitriol, *m.* nickel sulfate. -zusatz, *m.* addition of nickel.

nie, *adv.* never.

**nieder,** *a.* low, lower, inferior, secondary, minor.—*adv.* low, down. **-blasen,** *v.t.* blow out (a furnace).

**Niederdruck,** *m.* low pressure. **-dampf,** *m.* low-pressure steam.

**nieder-drücken,** *v.t.* press down; depress. **-fallen,** *v.i.* fall down, precipitate, settle.

**Niedergang,** *m.* going down, descent.

**nieder-gerissen,** *p.p.* of niederreissen. **-geschlagen,** *p.p.* of niederschlagen.

**Nieder-lage,** *f.* warehouse; depot; defeat. **-lande,** *n.pl.* Netherlands.

**nieder-ländisch,** *a.* Dutch. **-legen,** *v.t.* lay down, put down; deposit. **-reissen,** *v.t.* carry down, drag down; tear down, destroy.

**Niederschlag,** *m.* precipitate, precipitation; deposit, sediment.

**niederschlag-arm,** *a.* poor in precipitate. **-bar,** *a.* precipitable.

**Niederschlagbarkeit,** *f.* precipitability.

**niederschlagen,** *v.t.* precipitate; beat down, quell, refute, depress.—*v.r.* precipitate.— **niederschlagend,** *.p.a.* precipitant; sedative; depressing.

**Niederschlag-gefäss,** *n.* precipitating vessel. **-menge,** *f.* amount of precipitate. **-messung,** *f.* measurement of precipitation or precipitate. **-mittel,** *n.* precipitant. **-raum,** *m.* precipitation space or chamber.

**Niederschlags-arbeit,** *f.* precipitation process; specif., (*Metal.*) iron reduction process (liberation of metals by means of iron). **-kessel,** *m.* precipitation pan. **-mittel,** *n.* precipitant.

**Niederschlagung,** *f.* precipitation, etc. (see niederschlagen).

**Niederschlag-verfahren,** *n.* precipitation process or method. **-vorrichtung,** *f.* precipitation apparatus, precipitator. **-wasser,** *n.* precipitated water; condensed water. **-zeit,** *f.* time of precipitation.

**niederschmelzen,** *v.t.* melt down.

**Niederspannung,** *f.* low tension; (of gases) low pressure; (*Elec.*) low voltage.

**Niederung,** *f.* low ground, flats.

**nieder-voltig,** *a.* low-voltage. **-wärts,** *adv.* downward.

**niedr.,** *abbrev.* niedrig.

**niedrig,** *a.* low.

**niedriger,** *a.* lower.

**niedrig-prozentig,** *a.* low-percentage. **-siedend,** *a.* low-boiling.

**niemals,** *adv.* never.

**niemand,** *pron.* nobody, no one.

**Niere,** *f.* kidney; nodule, concretion.

**Nieren-.** renal, nephro-. **-drüse,** *f.* renal gland. **-entzündung,** *f.* nephritis. **-erz,** *n.* kidney ore.

**nierenförmig,** *a.* kidney-shaped, reniform.

**Nieren-gries(s),** *m.* renal gravel. **-haut,** *f.* renal capsule. **-mittel,** *n.* kidney remedy, nephritic. **-stein,** *m.* kidney stone (either spherulite, nephrite, or renal calculus).

**nierig,** *a.* (*Mining*) nodular.

**Niese-fieber,** *n.* hay fever. **-mittel,** *n.* sternutative, sneeze-provoking agent.

**niesen,** *v.i.* sneeze.

**Nies-kraut,** *n.* sneezewort (*Achillea ptarmica*). **-wurz, -wurzel,** *f.* hellebore.

**Niet,** *n.,* **Niete,** *f.* rivet, pin.

**nieten,** *v.t.* rivet.

**Nietnagel,** *m.* rivet; hangnail.

**Nikotin,** *n.* nicotine.

**nikotinfrei,** *a.* nicotine-free.

**Nikotin-gehalt,** *m.* nicotine content. **-säure,** *f.* nicotinic (or nicotic) acid. **-vergiftung,** *f.* nicotine poisoning.

**Nilblau,** *n.* Nile blue.

**nimmer,** *adv.* never. **-satt,** *a.* insatiable.

**nimmt,** *pr. 3 sing.* of nehmen.

**Niob, Niobium,** *n.* niobium (columbium).

**Niobat,** *n.* niobate (columbate).

**Niob-säure,** *f.* niobic (columbic) acid. **-wasserstoff,** *m.* niobium (columbium) hydride.

**nippen,** *v.i.* sip.

**nirgend, nirgends,** *adv.* nowhere.

**-nis.** a noun suffix denoting quality, act, place or concrete effect; -ness, -tion, etc.; as, Kenntnis, knowledge, Ergebnis, result, Gefängnis, prison.

**Nitrat,** *n.* nitrate.

**Nitration,** *f.* nitration.—*n.* nitrate ion.

**Nitrid,** *n.* nitride (esp. an -ic nitride, as contrasted with Nitrür).

**Nitrierapparat,** *m.* nitrating apparatus.

**nitrierbar,** *a.* nitratable; nitrifiable; nitridable.

**Nitrierbaumwolle,** *f.* nitrating cotton.

**nitrieren,** *v.t.* nitrate; nitrify; (*Iron*) nitride.

**Nitrier-gemisch,** *n.* nitrating mixture. **-härtung,** *f.* (*Iron*) hardening by nitridation, nitride hardening. **-ofen,** *m.* nitriding furnace or oven. **-säure,** *f.* nitrating acid. **-sonderstahl,** *m.* special steel for nitriding. **-topf,** *m.* nitrating vessel.

**Nitrierung,** *f.* nitration; nitrification; (*Iron*) nitridation.

**Nitrierungsgrad,** *m.* degree of nitration or nitrification or nitridation.

**nitrifizieren,** *v.t.* nitrify.

**Nitrit,** *n.* nitrite.

**nitritfrei,** *a.* free from nitrites, nitrite-free.

**Nitro-benzol, -benzin,** *n.* nitrobenzene. **-chinon,** *n.* nitroquinone. **-cocussäure,** *f.* nitrococcic acid. **-derivat,** *n.* nitro derivative. **-farbstoff,** *m.* nitro dye. **-fettkörper,** *m.* aliphatic nitro compound. **-fettsäure,** *f.* nitro fatty acid. **-gruppe,** *f.* nitro group. **-halogenbenzole,** *n.pl.* halonitrobenzenes.

**-kohlenstoff,** *m.* tetranitromethane. **-körper,** *m.* nitro substance, nitro compound. **-kupfer,** *n.* nitrocopper.

**Nitrolsäure,** *f.* nitrolic acid.

**Nitro-prussidnatrium,** *n.* sodium nitroprusside. **-prussidwasserstoffsäure,** *f.* nitroprussic acid. **-pulver,** *n.* nitro powder.

**nitros,** *a.* nitrous.—**nitrose Säure,** = Nitrose.

**Nitroschwefelsäure,** *f.* nitrosulfuric acid.

**Nitrose,** *f.* (*Sulfuric Acid*) a solution of nitrosylsulfuric acid in sulfuric acid, formed in the lead-chamber process.

**Nitroseide,** *f.* nitrosilk.

**nitrosieren,** *v.t.* treat with nitrous acid, introduce the nitroso group into.

**Nitrosisulfosäure,** *f.* nitrosisulfonic acid.

**Nitroso-benzol,** *n.* nitrosobenzene. **-blau,** *n.* nitroso blue. **-gruppe,** *f.* nitroso group. **-kobaltwasserstoffsäure,** *f.* cobaltinitrous acid. **-sulfosäure,** *f.* nitrososulfonic acid. **-verbindung,** *f.* nitroso compound.

**Nitro-sprengstoff,** *m.* nitro explosive. **-stärke,** *f.* nitrostarch. **-sulfonsäure,** *f.* nitrosulfonic acid (nitrosylsulfuric acid).

**Nitrosyl-säure,** *f.* nitrosylic acid (hyponitrous acid). **-schwefelsäure,** *f.* nitrosylsulfuric acid.

**Nitro-toluol,** *n.* nitrotoluene. **-verbindung,** *f.* nitro compound. **-weinsäure,** *f.* nitrotartaric acid (tartaric acid dinitrate, also the mononitrate).

**Nitroxyd,** *n.* nitrogen oxide.

**Nitroxylgruppe,** *f.* nitroxyl group (nitro group).

**Nitroxylol,** *n.* nitroxylene.

**Nitrür,** *n.* (-ous) nitride. Cf. Chlorür.

**Niveau,** *n.* level. **-fläche,** *f.* level surface. **-flasche,** *f.* leveling bottle, leveling vessel (as for a gas burette). **-rohr,** *n.*, **-röhre,** *f.* level tube, leveling tube.

**nivellieren,** *v.t.* level.

**Nk., NK.** *abbrev.* (Normalkerze) standard candle.

**nl.,** *abbrev.* (nicht löslich) not soluble.

**Nm.,** *abbrev.* (Nachmittags) afternoon, P.M.

**n.M.,** *abbrev.* (nächsten Monats) of next month.

**noch,** *adv.* still, yet, more, else, however; nor. — — **immer,** still.— — **nicht,** not yet.

**noch-malig,** *a.* repeated. **-mals,** *adv.* once more, once again, again.

**Nocken,** *m.* cam, lifter, tappet, stud, etc. **-welle,** *f.* (*Mach.*) cam shaft.

**Nodus,** *m.* node.

**Nomenklatur,** *f.* nomenclature.

**Nonius,** *m.* (*pl.* Nonien) vernier. **-einteilung,** *f.* vernier scale.

**nonocarbozyklisch,** *a.* nonacarbocyclic.

**Noppe,** *f.* nap; burl.

**Noppenbeize,** *f.* burl dye.

**Nord, Norden,** *m.* north.

**nord-amerikanisch,** *a.* North American. **-deutsch,** *a.* North German.

**Nordhäuser Vitriolöl.** Nordhausen acid (fuming sulfuric acid).

**nördlich,** *a.* northerly, northern, arctic.

**Nord-ost,** *m.* northeast; northeaster. **-pol,** *m.* north pole.

**Norgeraniumsäure,** *f.* norgeranic acid.

**Norgesalpeter,** *m.* Norway saltpeter (calcium nitrate).

**Nor-guajakharzsäure,** *f.* norguaiaretic acid. **-homokamphersäure,** *f.* norhomocamphoric acid. **-kampher,** *m.* norcamphor. **-kamphersäure,** *f.* norcamphoric acid.

**normal,** *a.* normal; standard.

**Normal,** *f.* norm, standard. **-bedingungen,** *f.pl.* normal conditions; standard specifications. **-druck,** *m.* normal pressure; standard pressure. **-Eichungs-Kommission,** *f.* a government bureau corresponding to the Bureau of Standards. **-element,** *n.* (*Elec.*) standard cell. **-essig,** *m.* standard vinegar, proof vinegar. **-flüssigkeit,** *f.* = Normallösung. **-gewicht,** *n.* standard weight. **-grösse,** *f.* normal size; standard size.

**normalisieren,** *v.t.* standardize, normalize.

**Normalisierung,** *f.* standardization.

**Normalität,** *f.* normality.

**Normal-kerze,** *f.* standard candle **-kupfer,** *n.* (*Elec.*) standard copper. **-lösung,** *f.* normal solution; standard solution. **-säure,** *f.* normal acid; standard acid. **-schliff,** *m.* standard (interchangeable) ground joint. **-spannung,** *f.* (*Elec.*) normal voltage. **-stärke,** *f.* normal strength; standard strength. **-weingeist,** *m.* proof spirit. **-wert,** *m.* normal value; standard value. **-zustand,** *m.* normal or standard state or condition.

**normen,** *v.t.* standardize.

**Normensand,** *m.* (*Cement*) standard sand.

**normieren,** *v.t.* standardize, gage; regulate.

**Normierung,** *f.* normalization, standardization; gaging.

**Normung,** *f.* standardization.

**Norpinsäure,** *f.* norpinic acid.

**Norwegen,** *n.* Norway.

**Not,** *f.* need; necessity; want; emergency; distress; effort. **-behelf,** *m.* makeshift; last resort.

**notdürftig,** *a.* scanty, needy.

**Notfall,** *m.* emergency, exigency.

**not-gar,** *a.* (*Leather*) undertanned. **-gedrungen,** *p.a.* compulsory.—*adv.* necessarily.

**notieren,** *v.t.* note.

**nötig,** *a.* necessary, needful.— — **haben,** want, need.

**nötigen,** *v.t.* necessitate, force, urge. **-falls,** *adv.* if need be, if necessary.

**Notiz,** *f.* notice, note. **-blatt,** *n.* (literally) notice journal, notice sheet (a name used by periodicals). **-buch,** *n.* note book.

**Not-mittel,** *n.* expedient, shift. **-stand,** *m.* urgent state, urgency, need. **-wehr,** *f.* self-defense.

**notwendig,** *a.* necessary.

**Notwendigkeit,** *f.* necessity.

**Novojodin,** *n.* novoiodin.

**Nr.,** *abbrev.* (Nummer) number.

**Nro.,** *abbrev.* (Numero) number.

**N-Substanz,** *f.* nitrogenous substance.

**N.T.,** *abbrev.* (normale Temperatur) normal temperature.

**Ntf.,** *abbrev.* (Naturforscher) scientific investigator.

**Nu,** *m.* moment, trice.

**Nuance, Nüance,** *f.* shade, tint.

**nuancieren,** *v.t.* shade, shade off; modulate.

**nüchtern,** *a.* empty, fasting; sober, temperate, cool; flat, insipid.

**Nucleinsäure,** *f.* nucleic acid.

**Nudeln,** *f.pl.* noodles; vermicelli; macaroni.

**Nukleinsäure,** *f.* nucleic acid.

**Nukleoproteid,** *n.* nucleoprotein.

**Null,** *f.* zero, nought, cipher. **-ablesung,** *f.* zero reading. **-grad,** *m.* zero. **-lage,** *f.* zero position. **-linie,** *f.* zero line, null line. **-methode,** *f.* zero method. **-niveau,** *n.* zero level. **-punkt,** *m.* zero point, zero. **-setzen,** *n.* setting equal to zero. **-stellung,** *f.* zero position. **-strich,** *m.* zero mark.

**nullt,** *a.* zero.—**nullte Spalte,** zero column.

**Nullverfahren,** *n.* zero method.

**nullwertig,** *a.* nonvalent, avalent.

**Nullzweig,** *m.* zero branch.

**numerieren,** *vt.* number.

**Numerierung,** *f.* numbering, numeration.

**numerisch,** *a.* numerical.

**Nummer,** *f.* number.

**nummern,** *v.t.* number.

**nun,** *adv.* now; well, why; so.

**nunmehr,** *adv.* at present, now, by this time; henceforth; since then; then.

**nunmehrig,** *a.* present.

**nur,** *adv.* only, but, scarcely.

**Nürnberg,** *n.* Nuremberg.

**Nuss,** *f.* nut; specif., walnut. **-baum,** *m.* nut tree, specif. walnut.

**nussbraun,** *a.* nut-brown.

**Nuss-kernmehl,** *n.* nut meal. **-kohle,** *f.* nut coal. **-öl,** *n.* nut oil; specif., walnut oil.

**Nüster,** *f.* nostrils.

**Nut, Nute,** *f.* groove, rabbet, slot.

**Nut-.** grooving.

**Nutschapparat,** *m.* suction apparatus.

**Nutsche,** *f.,* **-filter,** *n.* suction filter, esp. a Büchner funnel.

**nutschen,** *v.t.* filter by suction (esp. thru a Büchner funnel).

**Nutschen-becher,** *m.* suction filter cup. **-sieb,** *n.* suction filter sieve. **-trichter,** *m.* suction funnel.

**Nuttharz,** *n.* acaroid resin, acaroid gum.

**Nutz-.** useful, practical, effective, economic, commercial. **-anwendung,** *f.* practical application. **-arbeit,** *f.* useful work.

**nutzbar,** *a.* useful; available; effective.

**Nutzbarmachung,** *f.* utilization.

**nutzbringend,** *a.* profitable.

**nutze, nütze,** *a.* useful, of use.

**Nutzeffekt,** *m.* useful effect, efficiency, effect.

**nutzen,** *v.t.* use.—*v.i.* be of use.

**Nutzen,** *m.* use, utility, advantage, profit.

**Nutz-holz,** *n.* commercial timber, lumber. **-kapazität,** *f.* useful capacity. **-leistung,** *f.* useful work, useful effect.

**nützlich,** *a.* useful, profitable, advantageous, expedient.

**nutzlos,** *a.* useless; unprofitable.

**Nutztier,** *n.* useful animal.

**Nutzung,** *f.* revenue; produce, yield.

**Nutz-wert,** *m.* economic value. **-wirkung,** *f.* useful effect, efficiency.

# O

o., *abbrev.* (oder) or; (oben) above; (ohne) without; (ordinär) ordinary.

O., *abbrev.* (Ost) east.

Oase, *f.* oasis.

ob, *conj.* whether, if; altho.—*prep.* on account of.

Obacht, *f.* heed, attention.

Obdach, *n.* shelter.

oben, *adv.* above; overhead, on top; before. -drein, *adv.* over and above. -erwähnt, *a.* above-mentioned. -hin, *adv.* superficially, slightly.

Ober-. upper, chief, high, supreme, head, top, epi-, super-, supra-, superior. -bau, *m.* superstructure.

Oberbauch-. epigastric.

Oberboden, *m.* top soil.

obere, *a.* upper; high, higher, superior, chief.

Oberfläche, *f.* surface; area.

oberflächenaktiv, *a.* =kapillaraktiv.

Oberflächen-bau, *m.* surface structure. -behandlung, *f.* surface treatment. -druck, *m.* surface pressure. -einheit, *f.* unit of area. -energie, *f.* surface energy. -farbe, *f.* surface color. -härtung, *f.* (*Metal.*) case-hardening.

oberflächeninaktiv, *a.* =kapillarinaktiv.

Oberflächen-kondensator, *m.* surface condenser. -kühlung, *f.* surface cooling. -ladung, *f.* (*Elec.*) surface charge. -leimung, *f.* (*Paper*) surface sizing. -lösung, *f.* surface solution. -schicht, *f.* surface layer. -spannung, *f.* surface tension. -wasser, *n.* surface water. -wirkung, *f.* surface action or effect.

oberflächlich, *a.* superficial.

obergärig, *a.* top-fermenting, top-fermented. —obergärige Hefe, top yeast.

Ober-gärung, *f.* top fermentation. -grund, *m.* surface soil.

oberhalb, *prep.* above.

Oberhaut, *f.* epidermis.

Oberhaut-. epidermic, epidermal.

Ober-häutchen, *n.* cuticle. -hefe, *f.* top yeast. -keim, *m.* (*Zoöl.*) ectoderm. -licht, *n.* light from above; skylight. -rinde, *f.* outer bark. -schalseife, *f.* top-layer soap (or one made to resemble it). -schicht, *f.* upper layer, upper stratum.

oberschlesisch, *a.* Upper Silesian.

Ober-schwingung, *f.* overtone, harmonic. -spannung, *f.* (*Elec.*) high tension.

oberst, *a.* uppermost, highest.

Ober-tasse, *f.* cup. -teig, *m.* (*Brewing*) upper-dough. -teil, *m.* upper part, top part. -ton, *m.* overtone, upper partial. -welle, *f.* (*Physics*) harmonic.

obgleich, *conj.* altho.

Obhut, *f.* protection, care.

obig, *a.* above, foregoing.

Objektglas, *n.* (*Micros.*) slide, mount.

Objektivwechsler, *m.* (*Micros.*) revolving nosepiece.

Objekt-sucher, *m.* (*Optics*) object finder. -tisch, *m.* (*Micros.*) stage, stand. -träger, *m.* (*Micros.*) slide, mount, also stage, stand.

Oblate, *f.* wafer.

obliegen, *v.i.* be incumbent (on); attend (to).

Obliegenheit, *f.* obligation, duty.

obligatorisch, *a.* obligatory.

Obmann, *m.* head man (chairman, superintendent, etc.).

obschon, *conj.* altho.

Observatorium, *n.* observatory.

Obst, *n.* fruit. -baum, *m.* fruit tree. -branntwein, *m.* fruit brandy, fruit spirit. -essig, *m.* fruit vinegar. -garten, *m.* orchard. -kern, *m.* fruit kernel, fruit stone. -konserve, *f.* fruit preserve, preserved fruit. -mark, *n.* fruit pulp. -most, *m.* fruit juice. -mus, *n.* fruit sauce, fruit butter, jam, marmalade. -saft, *m.* fruit juice. -wein, *m.* fruit wine, cider, perry, etc. -weinbereitung, *f.* fruit wine manufacture. -zucker, *m.* fruit sugar (levulose).

obwalten, *v.i.* exist; prevail, predominate.

obwohl, obzwar, *conj.* altho, tho.

Ocher-, ocher-. see Ocker-, ocker-.

ocherig, *a.* ocherous, ochery.

Ochras, *m.* black salt (crude potash or soda from ashes).

Ochs, Ochse, *m.* ox.

Ochsen-fleisch, *n.* beef. -galle, *f.* ox gall. -klauenfett, -klauenöl, *n.* neat's-foot oil. -leder, *n.* neat's leather. -zunge, *f.* bugloss (*Anchusa*); borage; (farbende) alkanet.

Ocker, *m.* ocher.

ocker-artig, -ähnlich, *a.* like ocher, ocherous.

Ockerfarbe, *f.* ocher (as a pigment).

ocker-farbig, *a.* ocher-colored, ocherous. -gelb, *a.* ocher-yellow. -haltig, *a.* containing ocher, ocherous.

ockerig, *a.* ocherous, ochery.

Oct-. see Okt-.

**od.,** *abbrev.* (oder) or.

**O.D.,** *abbrev.* (optisches Drehungsvermögen) optical rotatory power.

**öde,** *a.* waste, deserted.

**Ödem,** *n.* edema.

**oder,** *conj.* or.

**Odermennig,** *m.* (*Bot.*) agrimony.

**o. dgl., o. drgl.,** *abbrev.* (oder dergleichen) or the like.

**Oel, Oel-.** see Öl, Öl-.

**Öfchen,** *n.* little furnace, oven or stove.

**Ofen,** *m.* furnace; oven; kiln; stove. **-bruch,** *m.* (*Zinc*) tutty. **-futter,** *n.* furnace lining. **-galmei,** *m.* furnace cadmia, tutty. **-gang,** *m.* working or working order of a furnace, oven or kiln. **-kachel,** *f.* stove tile. **-lack,** *m.* stove varnish. **-putzmittel,** *n.* stove polish. **-russ,** *m.* furnace soot; oven soot. **-sau,** *f.* (*Metal.*) furnace sow. **-schlacke,** *f.* furnace slag. **-schwamm,** *m.* (*Zinc*) tutty.

**ofentrocken,** *a.* kiln-dried; oven-dried.

**Ofen-tür, -türe,** *f.* door (esp. the fire door) of a furnace, oven, kiln or stove; (*Ceram.*) wicket. **-verkokung,** *f.* coking in ovens. **-ziegel,** *m.* fire brick; stove tile.

**offen,** *a.* open; clear, clever, frank. **-bar,** *a.* manifest, obvious, plain. **-baren,** *v.t.* disclose, reveal. **-kundig,** *a.* well known, notorious; evident.

**öffentlich,** *a.* public; open.

**Öffentlichkeit,** *f.* publicity.

**Offerte,** *f.* offer, proffer.

**offiziell, officiell,** *a.* official.

**Offizier,** *m.* officer.

**Offizin,** *f.* (*Pharm.*) laboratory, dispensary, apothecary's shop; workshop, specif. printing shop.

**offizinell,** *a.* officinal.

**öffnen,** *v.t.* open.—**öffnend,** *p.a.* (*Med.*) aperient.

**Öffnung,** *f.* opening; aperture, orifice, mouth; dissection; evacuation.

**Öffnungsmittel,** *n.* (*Med.*) aperient.

**oft,** *adv.* often. **-malig,** *a.* frequent, repeated.

**ohne,** *prep.* without.—*conj.* but that.— **— weiteres,** without further ado, forthwith.

**ohne-dem, -dies,** *adv.* apart from that, besides. **-hin,** *adv.* besides.

**ohngefähr,** *adv.* approximately.—*a.* approximate.

**Ohnmacht,** *f.* weakness; fainting, syncope.

**ohnmächtig,** *a.* weak, faint, unconscious.

**Ohr,** *n.* ear.

**Ohr-.** aural, auricular.

**Öhr,** *n.* (*Tech.*) ear, handle, eye, loop, catch; bog iron ore.

**Ohren-schmalz,** *n.* ear wax, cerumen. **-stein,** *m.,* **-steinchen,** *n.* otolith.

**Ohrfinger,** *m.* little finger.

**ohrförmig,** *a.* auriform.

**Ohr-speicheldrüse,** *f.* parotid gland. **-trompete,** *f.* (*Anat.*) Eustachian tube. **-wachs,** *n.* ear wax, cerumen. **-wasser,** *n.* endolymph.

**Oker,** *m.* ocher. See ocker-, Ocker-.

**okkludieren,** *v.t.* occlude.

**ökonomisch,** *a.* economic, economical; agricultural.

**Oktaeder,** *n.* octahedron.

**oktaedrisch,** *a.* octahedral.

**Oktettregel,** *f.* octet rule.

**Okto-.** octa- (preferably), octo-.

**oktocarbocyclisch,** *a.* octacarbocyclic.

**Oktonaphten,** *n.* octanaphthene.

**-ol.** (1) in names of alcohols or phenols (*i.e.,* when the ending signifies hydroxyl), -ol. (2) in names of a few hydrocarbons, -ene; as, Benz*ol*, benzene (but the commercial product is called benzol or benzole). (3) in the case of other compounds, -ole; as, Pyrr*ol*, pyrrole.

**Öl,** *n.* oil. **-ablass,** *m.* oil draining; oil drain. **-abscheider,** *m.* oil separator; (*Brewing*) oil trap. **-abscheidung,** *f.* oil separation. **-anstrich,** *m.* painting in oil; coat of oil.

**ölartig,** *a.* =ölig.

**Öl-ausscheider,** *m.* oil separator. **-bad,** *n.* oil bath; (in Turkey-red dyeing) green liquor.

**Ölbaum,** *m.* olive tree.—**falscher —,** oleaster.

**Öl-baumgummi, -baumharz,** *n.* elemi. **-beere,** *f.* olive. **-behälter,** *m.* oil container, oil tank. **-beize,** *f.* oil mordant; (in Turkey-red dyeing) oiling.

**ölbildend,** *p.a.* oil-forming, olefiant.—**ölbildendes Gas,** olefiant gas (ethylene).

**Öl-blau,** *n.* smalt. **-bodensatz,** *m.* oil sediment, oil foot. **-bohrung,** *f.* oil well. **-brenner,** *m.* oil burner. **-dampf,** *m.* oil vapor, oil smoke. **-dämpfung,** *f.* oil damping.

**öldicht,** *a.* oil-tight, impermeable to oil.

**Öl-drass,** *m.* oil dregs, oil foots. **-druck,** *m.* oil pressure; oleography; oleograph. **-dunst,** *m.* oil vapor, oil fume.

**Olefin,** *n.* olefin, olefine. **-alkohol,** *m.* olefinic alcohol, olefin alcohol. **-haloid,** *n.* olefin halide.

**olefinisch,** *a.* olefinic.

**Olefinketon,** *n.* olefinic ketone, olefin ketone.

**Olein-säure,** *f.* oleic acid. **-säureseife, -seife,** *f.* olein soap, red-oil soap.

**ölen,** *v.t.* oil.

**Oleokreosot,** *n.* (*Pharm.*) creosote oleate.

**Ölerglas,** *n.* glass oil cup.

**Ölersatz,** *m.* oil substitute.

**Oleum,** *n.* oleum, fuming sulfuric acid; (in Latin *Pharm.* names) oil.

**Öl-fabrik,** *f.* oil factory. **-farbe,** *f.* oil color. **-farbenanstrich,** *m.* painting in oil colors; coat of oil paint. **-farbendruck,** *m.* oleography; oleograph. **-feuerung,** f. oil burning or heating; oil furnace. **-firnis,** m. oil varnish. **-fleck,** m. oil spot, oil stain.

**ölfrei,** a. free from oil, oil-free.

**Ölfüllung,** f. oil filling.

**ölgar,** a. oiled (leather); chamois.

**Öl-gas,** n. oil gas. **-gasteer,** m. oil-gas tar. **-gefäss,** m. oil vessel, oil tank. **-gehalt,** n. oil content. **-geläger,** n. oil dregs, oil foots. **-geschmack,** m. oily taste. **-gewinnung,** f. oil extraction, oil production.

**ölglanzend,** a. shining with, or as with, oil, having an oily luster.

**Ölgrün,** n. oil green.

**ölhaltig,** a. containing oil, oleiferous.

**Öl-handel,** m. oil trade. **-härtung,** f. oil hardening. **-harz,** n. oleoresin. **-hefen,** f.pl. oil dregs, oil lees.

**Oliban,** n. olibanum, frankincense.

**ölig, ölicht,** a. oily, oleaginous.

**Öligkeit,** f. oiliness.

**Oligoklas,** m. oligoclase.

**Öl-industrie,** f. oil industry. **-isolation,** f. oil insulation.

**Olive,** f. olive; enlargement on a tube for rubber connection.

**olivenartig,** a. (Anat.) olivary.

**Olivenbaum,** m. olive tree.

**olivenbraun,** a. olive-brown.

**Olivenfarbe,** f. olive color.

**oliven-farben, -farbig,** a. olive-colored. **-förmig,** a. (Anat.) olivary.

**Oliven-gelb,** n. olive yellow. **-grün,** n. olive green. **-kernasche,** f. olive-kernel ashes, pepperette. **-kernöl,** n. olive kernel oil. **-nachöl,** n. an inferior olive oil. **-öl,** n. olive oil. **-ölseife,** f. olive-oil soap, (genuine) Castile soap.

**Öl-kammer,** f. oil chamber. **-kautschuk,** m. factice. **-kitt,** m. putty. **-kohle,** f. oil carbon (formed from oil on heating). **-körper,** n. (Biol.) oil body. **-kuchen,** m. oil cake. **-kugel,** m. oil globule, oil drop. **-lack,** m. oil varnish. **-leder,** n. chamois. **-leinen,** n. oiled linen. **-malerei,** f. oil painting. **-menge,** f. amount of oil. **-messer,** m. eleometer, oleometer. **-milch,** f. oil emulsion. **-mühle,** f. oil mill. **-nuss,** f. oil nut, oleiferous nut. **-nussbaum,** m. butternut tree; horse-radish tree (Moringa). **-papier,** n. oil paper, oiled paper. **-probe,** f. sample of oil; test of oil. **-prüfer,** m. oil tester. **-pumpe,** f. oil pump. **-rauch, -qualm,** m. oil smoke, oil vapor.

**ölreich, -haltig,** a. rich in oil.

**Öl-reinigung,** f. purification of oil. **-rückstand,** m. oil residue. **-russ,** m. lampblack. **-saat,** oil seed, oleiferous seed. **-same(n),** m. oil seed, esp. rapeseed or linseed. **-satz,** m. oil sediment, oil foots.

**ölsauer,** a. of or combined with oleic acid, oleate of.

**Ölsäure,** f. oleic acid. **-reihe,** f. oleic-acid series.

**Öl-schiefer,** m. oil shale. **-schlagen,** n. oil pressing. **-schlamm,** m. oil sludge, oil sediment. **-schmierung,** f. oil lubrication. **-schwarz,** n. = Mineralschwarz. **-seide,** f. oiled silk. **-seife,** f. oil soap, soap made from oil; specif., olive-oil soap, Castile soap, Venetian soap. **-siederei,** f. oil refinery. **-sodaseife,** f. soda soap made from oil, specif. Castile soap. **-sorte,** f. kind, quality or brand of oil. **-spur,** f. trace of oil. **-staub,** m. oil spray. **-stein,** m. oilstone; stinkstone. **-stoff,** m. olein. **-süss,** n. glycerol, glycerin. **-sylvinsäure,** f. oleosylvic acid. **-trester,** m.pl. oil marc (residue left after expressing oil from olives, etc.). **-tuch,** n. oilcloth. **-umlauf,** m. oil circulation.

**Ölung,** f. oiling.

**Öl-verbrauch,** m. oil consumption. **-wa(a)ge,** f. oil hydrometer, eleometer. **-wasser,** n. oily water. **-werk,** n. oil works, oil mill, oil factory. **-zucker,** m. (Pharm.) elaeosaccharum, oleosaccharum; (formerly) glycerin. **-zufluss,** m. oil inflow, oil feed. **-zusatz,** m. addition of oil.

**-on.** (as a chemical ending denoting the ketonic group) **-one.**

**Önanth-.** enanth-, oenanth-. **-äther,** m. enanthic (or oenanthic) ether. **-säure,** f. enanthic (or oenanthic) acid. **-ylsäure,** f. enanthylic (or oenanthylic) acid.

**Önidin,** n. enidin, oenidin.

**Önin,** n. enin, oenin.

**Oolith,** m. oölite.

**oolithisch, oolitisch,** a. oölitic.

**O.P.,** abbrev. (Österreichisches Patent) Austrian patent.

**opak,** a. opaque.

**opalartig,** a. opal-like, opaline.

**Opalblau,** n. opal blue.

**opalescieren, opaleszieren,** v.i. opalesce.

**Opal-farbe,** f. opal color. **-firnis,** m. opal varnish. **-glanz,** m. opaline luster, opalescence.

**opalglänzend,** a. opalescent.

**opalisieren,** v.i. opalesce.—v.t. render opalescent, opalize.—**opalisierend,** p.a. opalescent.

**Opalmutter,** f. opal matrix.

**opalschillernd,** a. opalescent.

**Opazität,** f. opacity.

**Oper,** f. opera.

**Operment,** n. orpiment.

**Opfer,** n. offering, sacrifice, victim.

opfern, *v.t.* sacrifice.

Opheliasäure, *f.* ophelic acid.

Opiansäure, *f.* opianic acid.

Opiumsäure, *f.* meconic acid.

opt.-akt., *abbrev.* (optisch-aktiv) optically active.

Optik, *f.* optics.

optisch, *a.* optic, optical.

Orangefarbe, *f.* orange color or dye.

orange-farben, -farbig, *a.* orange-colored.

Orange-gelb, *n.* orange yellow. -lack, *m.* orange lac; orange lake. -mennig, *m.* orange minium, orange lead.

Orangen-blüte, *f.* orange blossom. -essenz, *f.* orange (peel) oil. -essig, *m.* orange vinegar. -öl, *n.* orange (peel) oil. -samenöl, *n.* orange seed oil. -schale, *f.* orange peel. -schalenöl, *n.* orange peel oil.

orangerot, *a.* orange-red.

Orangesamenöl, *n.* orange seed oil.

Orden, *m.* order.

ordentlich, *a.* ordinary; regular; orderly; exact; steady; downright.

ordinär, *a.* ordinary, regular; common, inferior.

Ordinierung, *f.* (*Med.*) prescription.

ordnen, *v.t.* order, arrange, regulate, settle.

Ordnung, *f.* order; arrangement, classification; class; succession, series.

ordnungs-mässig, *a.* orderly, methodical.— *adv.* duly, well. -widrig, *a.* irregular, disorderly.

Ordnungszahl, *f.* number in a series, specif. atomic number; ordinal number.

org., *abbrev.* (organisch) organic.

Organeiweiss, *n.* organ protein.

Organiker, *m.* organic chemist.

organisch, *a.* organic. -chemisch, *a.* pertaining to organic chemistry, organic chemical.

organisieren, *v.t.* organize.

Organismus, *m.* organism.

Organometall, *n.* organometallic compound.

organometallisch, *a.* organometallic.

Orgel, *f.* organ. -metall, *n.* organ-pipe metal.

orientalisch, *a.* Oriental.

orientieren, *v.t.* orient.

Orientierung, *f.* orientation.

Orseille, *f.* archil (the dyestuff). -flechte, *f.* archil (*Roccella tinctoria*).

Orsell-insäure, *f.* orsellinic acid. -säure, *f.* orsellic (diorsellinic, lecanoric) acid.

Ort, *m.* place; locus; region, locality, spot.

Ortho-ameisensäure, *f.* orthoformic acid. -antimonigsäure, *f.* orthoantimonious acid. -antimonsäure, *f.* orthoantimonic acid. -arsenigsäure, *f.* orthoarsenious acid. -arsensäure, *f.* orthoarsenic acid. -borsäure, *f.* orthoboric acid. -chinon, *n.* orthoquinone, *o*-quinone. -cymol, *n.* orthocymene,

*o*-cymene. -essigsäure, *f.* orthoacetic acid. -kieselsäure, *f.* orthosilicic acid. -klas, *m.* orthoclase. -kohlensäure, *f.* orthocarbonic acid. -phosphorsäure, *f.* orthophosphoric acid. -phtalsäure, *f.* orthophthalic acid.

orthorhombisch, *a.* orthorhombic.

Orthosalpetersäure, *f.* orthonitric acid.

orthosalpetrig, *a.* orthonitrous.

Orthosäure, *f.* ortho acid.

orthoständig, *a.* in the ortho position.

Ortho-stellung, *f.* ortho position. -verbindung, *f.* ortho compound. -xylol, *n.* orthoxylene, *o*-xylene. -zimtsäure, *f.* orthocinnamic acid.

-ortig. -place. (Proposed as a substitute for -wertig for coördination numbers; as, drei*ortig*, three-place, 3-place.)

Ortisomerie, *f.* position isomerism.

örtlich, *a.* local; topical; endemic.

Orts-. local.

Ortschaft, *f.* place, village.

ortsfest, *a.* stationary.

Orts-funktion, *f.* position function. -isomerie, *f.* place isomerism, position isomerism. -wechsel, *m.* change of position.

-ös. -ous.

Oschakkpflanze, *f.* oshac, ammoniac plant.

Öse, *f.* loop, ring, eye, lug, ear; specif., platinum-wire loop.

Ösenblatt, *n.* (*Tech.*) tongue, lip, flange.

osmig, *a.* osmious.

Osmiumchlorwasserstoffsäure, *f.* an acid containing osmium, chlorine and hydrogen (either $H_3OsCl_6$ or $H_2OsCl_6$).

osmiumhaltig, *a.* containing osmium.

Osmium-legierung, *f.* osmium alloy. -oxyd, *n.* osmium oxide, specif. osmic oxide ($OsO_2$). -oxydul, *n.* osmious oxide. -salmiak, *m.* ammonium chloroösmate. -säure, *f.* osmic acid. -verbindung, *f.* osmium compound.

Osmose, *f.* osmosis, osmose.

osmosieren, *v.t.* osmose.

osmotisch, *a.* osmotic.

Ost, Osten, *m.* east.

Osterluzei, *n.* birthwort (*Aristolochia*, esp. *A. clematitis* or *A. longa*).

Ostern, *n.* Easter.

Österreich, *n.* Austria.

österreichisch, *a.* Austrian. -ungarisch, *a.* Austro-Hungarian.

Österreich-Ungarn, *n.* Austria-Hungary.

Ostindien, *n.* (East) India.

ostindisch, *a.* East Indian.

östlich, *a.* eastern, oriental, easterly.

Östreich, *n.* Austria.

Ostritzwurzel, *f.* masterwort (*Imperatoria ostruthium*), or its rhizome.

Ostsee, *f.* Baltic (Sea).

oszillieren, *v.i.* oscillate.

Ö.U.P., O.U.P., *abbrev.* (Österreich-ungar-isches Patent) Austro-Hungarian patent.

Oxal-äther, *m.* oxalic ether (ethyl oxalate). -essigester, *m.* oxalacetic ester. -essigsäure, *f.* oxalacetic acid. -ester, *m.* oxalic ester (specif. ethyl oxalate).

Oxalkyl-. hydroxyalkyl-.

Oxalsalz, *n.* oxalate.

oxalsauer, *a.* of or combined with oxalic acid, oxalate of.

Oxalsäure, *f.* oxalic acid. -lösung, *f.* oxalic acid solution. -salz, *n.* oxalate.

Oxalursäure, *f.* oxaluric acid.

Oxamidsäure, Oxaminsäure, *f.* oxamic acid.

Oxäthyl-. hydroxyethyl-.

Oxhoft, *n.* hogshead.

Oxim, *n.* oxime.

Oxo-. (*Org. Chem.*) oxo- (denoting replace-ment of $H_2$ by O and often equivalent to keto-).

Oxy-. oxy-, hydroxy-. (In organic names this indicates, in the great majority of cases, the hydroxyl group and should then be trans-lated hydroxy- to conform to the best usage in English; *e.g.*, *Oxyäpfelsäure*, hydroxy-malic acid. If the group is known to be ketonic, the translation keto- or oxo- is preferable; if Oxy- denotes ring oxygen, the preferable translation is oxa-.)

Oxy-aldehyd, *n.* hydroxy aldehyde. -am-moniak, *n.* oxyammonia (hydroxylamine). -azoverbindung, *f.* hydroxyazo compound. -biazol, *n.* oxadiazole, oxdiazole. -carbon-säure, *f.* hydroxycarboxylic acid. -chinolin, *n.* hydroxyquinoline. -chinon, *n.* hydroxy-quinone. -chlorkupfer, *n.* copper oxy-chloride. -cyan, *n.* oxycyanogen.

Oxyd, *n.* oxide (specif. a higher or -ic oxide, as contrasted with Oxydul).

oxyd-abel, *a.* oxidizable. -artig, *a.* of the nature of, or like, an oxide.

Oxydase, *f.* oxidase.

Oxydationsartikel, *m.* (*Calico*) oxidation style.

oxydationsfähig, *a.* capable of oxidation.

Oxydations-flamme, *f.* oxidizing flame. -grad, *m.* degree of oxidation. -mittel, *n.* oxidizing agent. -ofen, *m.* oxidizing furnace or oven. -stufe, *f.* stage or degree of oxidation. -vorgang, *m.* oxidation process. -wirkung, *f.* oxidizing action or effect.

Oxydbeschlag, *m.* coating of oxide.

oxydbildend, *a.* oxide-forming.

Oxydchlorid, *n.* oxychloride.

oxydhaltig, *a.* containing oxide or oxides, oxidic.

Oxyd-haut, *f.*, -häutchen, *n.* film of oxide. -hydrat, *n.* hydrated oxide (hydroxide), esp. one from a higher oxide (-ic hydroxide), as contrasted with Oxydulhydrat.

oxydierbar, *a.* oxidizable.

Oxydierbarkeit, *f.* oxidizability.

oxydieren, *v.t. & i.* oxidize.

Oxydiermittel, *n.* oxidizing agent.

Oxydierung, *f.* oxidation.

oxydisch, *a.* oxidic, oxygenic; of higher valence, -ic.

Oxyd-oxydul, *n.* = Oxyduloxyd. -rot, *n.* a kind of iron red. -schicht, *f.* layer or film of oxide.

Oxydul, *n.* (lower or -ous) oxide, (formerly) protoxide. -eisen, *n.* ferrous iron. -hydrat, *n.* hydrated -ous oxide (-ous hydroxide).

oxydulisch, *a.* of lower valence, -ous.

Oxydul-oxyd, *n.* an oxide in which the metal has a lower and a higher valence, oso-ic oxide, mixed oxide. -salz, *n.* lower or -ous salt.

Oxyessigsäure, *f.* hydroxyacetic acid.

oxygenieren, *v.t.* oxygenate, oxygenize.

Oxygenierung, *f.* oxygenation.

Oxyketon, *n.* hydroxy ketone, ketol. -car-bonsäure, *f.* hydroxyketocarboxylic acid.

Oxymethyl-. hydroxymethyl-; (incorrectly) methoxy-. -gruppe, *f.* hydroxymethyl group.

Oxy-salz, *n.* oxysalt. -säure, *f.* oxyacid (either oxacid—an acid containing oxygen—or hydroxy acid). -schwefelsäure, *f.* oxy-sulfuric acid. -toluol, *n.* hydroxytoluene. -verbindung, *f.* oxy compound; hydroxy compound. -zellulose, *f.* oxycellulose.

Ozean, *m.* ocean.

o.Zers., *abbrev.* (ohne Zersetzung) without decomposition.

Ozobenzol, *n.* ozobenzene.

Ozokerit, *m.* ozocerite.

Ozon, *n.* ozone.

ozon-erzeugend, *p.a.* producing ozone, ozonif-erous. -haltig, *a.* containing ozone, ozonif-erous.

Ozonisator, *m.* ozonizer.

ozonisieren, *v.t.* ozonize.

Ozon-messer, *m.* ozonometer. -messung, *f.* ozonometry. -papier, -reagenspapier, *n.* ozone paper, ozone test paper.

ozonsauer, *a.* ozonate of.

Ozonsauerstoff, *m.* ozonized oxygen, oxygen in the form of ozone.

# P

paar, *a.* even; (a) pair (of).

Paar, *n.* pair, couple; few; (*Mech.*) couple.

paaren, *v.t.* conjugate; pair, couple, mate.— gepaart, *p.a.* conjugated, etc., conjugate.— gepaarte **Verbindung,** conjugated compound; (*Old Chem.*) copulated compound.

Paarling, *n.* conjugated substance; (*Old Chem.*) copula.

Paarung, *f.* pairing, coupling, conjugation.

paarweise, *adv.* in pairs, in couples.

Pacht, *f.* lease, tenure.

Pachter, Pächter, *m.* tenant.

Pack, *m.* pack, bale, packet, bundle.

packen, *v.t.* pack; seize.

Pack-haus, *n.* -hof, *m.* warehouse; custom house. -leinen, *n.,* -leinwand, *f.* packing cloth, pack cloth. -papier, *n.* wrapping paper, packing paper. -pappe, *f.* packing board, pasteboard for packing. -stoff, *m.* packing material, packing. -tuch, *n.* packing cloth.

Packung, *f.* packing; seizing.

Packzeug, *n.* packing material, packing; packing tools.

PAe., *abbrev.* (Petroleumäther) petroleum ether.

Paket, *n.* packet, parcel, bundle.

Palisanderholz, *n.* rosewood.

Palladgold, *n.* palladium-gold (alloy).

Palladi-. palladic. -chlorwasserstoffsäure, *f.* chloropalladic acid.

Palladium-bromür, *n.* palladous bromide. -chlorid, *n.* palladium chloride, specif. palladic chloride. -chlorür, *n.* palladous chloride. -chlorwasserstoff, *m.* chloropalladic acid. -erz, *n.* palladium ore, -gehalt, *m.* palladium content. -jodür, *n.* palladous iodide. -legierung, *f.* palladium alloy. -mohr, *m.* palladium black. -oxyd, *n.* palladium oxide, specif. palladic oxide.

Palladiumoxydul, *n.* palladous oxide. -nitrat, *n.* palladous nitrate. -salz, *n.* palladous salt.

Palladium-reihe, *f.* palladium series. -salz, *n.* palladium salt. -schwamm, *m.* palladium sponge. -schwarz, *n.* palladium black. -wasserstoff, *m.* palladium hydride.

Pallado-. palladous. -chlorwasserstoffsäure, *f.* chloropalladous acid. -hydroxyd, *n.* palladous hydroxide.

Palme, *f.* palm.

Palmen-öl, *n.* palm oil. -stärke, *f.* palm starch, sago.

Palm-fett, *n.* palm oil. -honig, *m.* palm honey.

Palmitin-säure, *f.* palmitic acid. -seife, *f.* palmitin soap.

Palm-kernöl, *n.* palm-kernel oil. -lilie, *f.* yucca. -nuss, *f.* palm nut, palm kernel; coconut. -nussöl, *n.* palm-kernel oil; coconut oil. -öl, *n.* palm oil. -ölseife, *f.* palm oil soap. -sekt, *m.* palm wine, palm toddy. -stärke, *f.* palm starch, sago. -wachs, *n.* palm wax. -zucker, *m.* palm sugar, jaggery.

Panaschierung, *f.* variegation.

Pankreas, *n.,* -drüse, *f.* pancreas. -saft, *m.* pancreatic juice.

pankreatisch, *a.* pancreatic.

Panzer, *m.* armor; (coat of) mail; cuirass. -blech, *n.,* -platte, *f.* armor plate.

panzern, *v.t.* armor, armor-plate.

Panzerstahl, *m.* armor plate.

Päon-. peon-, paeon-.

Päonie, *f.* peony.

Papagei, *m.* parrot.

Papel, *f.* papule, pimple.

Papier, *n.* paper. -abfall, -abgang, *m.* paper waste. -blatt, *n.* sheet (or leaf) of paper. -bogen, *m.* sheet of paper. -brei, *m.* paper pulp.

papieren, *a.* paper; papery.

Papier-fabrik, *f.* paper factory, paper mill. -fabrikant, *m.* paper maker. -fabrikation, *f.* paper making. -filter, *n.* paper filter. -fläche, *f.* paper surface, surface of the paper. -garn, *n.* paper yarn, paper twine. -handel, *m.* paper trade; stationery. -handlung, *f.* stationer's shop. -jod, *n.* a solution of iodine and potassium iodide for test paper. -kohle, *f.* paper coal (variety of lignite). -leim, *m.* paper size. -macher, *m.* paper maker. -masse, *f.* paper pulp; papier-mâché. -mühle, *f.* paper mill. -pergament, *n.* parchment paper. -prüfung, *f.* paper testing. -scheibe, *f.* paper disk. -sorte, *f.* sort or quality of paper. -stoff, *m.* paper pulp. -stoffbrei, *m.* paper pulp (in water). -streifen, *m.* paper strip; paper web. -teig, *m.* papier-mâché. -zeichen, *n.* watermark. -zeug, *n.* paper pulp, " stuff."

Papille, *f.* papilla; nipple.

Papillen-. papillary.

**papinianischer Topf, Papin'scher Topf.** Papin's digester (autoclave).

**Papp,** *m.* paste; pap.

**Papp-.** paperboard, pasteboard, cardboard. **-band,** *m.* board binding; volume bound in boards. **-bogen,** *m.* sheet of pasteboard (or cardboard). **-deckel,** *m.* pasteboard, paperboard.

**Pappe,** *f.* (paper)board, pasteboard, cardboard; pap; paste.—**geformte —,** millboard.

**Pappel,** *f.* poplar; mallow. **-art,** *f.* (variety of) poplar; (variety of) mallow. **-kraut,** *n.* mallow.

**pappen,** *v.t. & i.* paste; work in paperboard.

**Pappen-art,** *f.* (paper)board. **-deckel,** *m.* = Pappdeckel. **-fabrik,** *f.* (paper)board mill. **-leim,** *m.* pasteboard glue. **-stiel,** *m.* trifle.

**Papphülse,** *f.* paperboard case.

**pappig,** *a.* pasty, doughy; sticky.

**Papp-karton,** *m.* paperboard box, carton. **-masse,** *f.* papier-mâché. **-schachtel,** *f.* paperboard box. **-schirm,** *m.* paperboard screen.

**Parabansäure,** *f.* parabanic acid.

**Parabel,** *f.* parabola; parable.

**parabolisch,** *a.* parabolic.

**Para-chinon,** *n.* paraquinone, *p*-quinone. **-consäure,** *f.* paraconic acid. **-cyan,** *n.* paracyanogen. **-cymol,** *n.* paracymene, *p*-cymene.

**Paradies,** *n.* paradise. **-apfel,** *m.* tomato. **-feige,** *f.* banana. **-holz,** *n.* agalloch, aloes wood. **-körner,** *n.pl.* grains of paradise.

**Paraffinbad,** *n.* paraffin bath.

**paraffinieren,** *v.t.* paraffin.

**Paraffin-kerze,** *f.* paraffin candle. **-kohlenwasserstoff,** *m.* paraffin hydrocarbon, paraffin, alkane. **-lack,** *m.* paraffin varnish. **-öl,** *n.* paraffin oil. **-salbe,** *f.* petrolatum; paraffin ointment. **-säure,** *f.* paraffinic acid (any saturated aliphatic acid). **-tränkung,** *f.* impregnation with paraffin.

**Para-gummi,** *n.* Pará rubber. **-kamphersäure,** *f.* paracamphoric acid. **-kautschuk,** *m.* Pará rubber.

**Parallel-ität,** *f.* parallelism. **-schaltung,** *f.* (*Elec.*) connection in parallel. **-versuch,** *m.* parallel experiment, duplicate determination.

**Paralysator,** *m.* anticatalyst.

**Paralyse,** *f.* paralysis.

**paralysieren,** *v.t.* paralyze.

**paramagnetisch,** *a.* paramagnetic.

**Para-milchsäure,** *f.* paralactic acid (*d*-lactic acid). **-nuss,** *f.* Brazil nut. **-nussöl,** *n.* Brazil-nut oil. **-phtalsäure,** *f.* paraphthalic acid. **-rot,** *n.* para red.

**parasitär,** *a.* parasitic.

**Parasitenkunde,** *f.* parasitology.

**parasitentötend,** *a.* parasiticidal, -cide.

**parasitisch,** *a.* parasitic.

**parastündig,** *a.* in the para position.

**Para-stellung,** *f.* para position. **-verbindung,** *f.* para compound. **-weinsäure,** *f.* paratartaric acid (racemic acid). **-xylol,** *n.* paraxylene, *p*-xylene.

**Parellinsäure,** *f.* parellinic acid.

**Parellsäure,** *f.* parellic acid.

**Parenthese,** *f.* parentheses; brackets.

**Parfüm,** *n.* perfume.

**Parfümerie,** *f.* perfumery. **-seife,** *f.* perfumed soap.

**Parfümeur,** *m.* perfumer.

**parfümieren,** *v.t.* perfume, scent.

**Parfümör,** *m.* perfumer.

**Pari,** *n.* par.—**auf pari,** at par.

**Parininsäure,** *f.* parininic acid.

**Parinsäure,** *f.* parinic acid.

**Pariser,** *a.* Paris.— **— Blau,** Paris blue; **— Grün,** Paris green.

**Pariser-rot,** *n.* colcothar, Paris red. **-weiss,** *n.* Paris white (a good grade of whiting).

**Pariwert,** *m.* par value.

**parkesieren,** *v.t.* (*Metal.*) subject to the Parkes process.

**Parkesieren,** *n.* Parkes process.

**Parkettwachs,** *n.* floor wax.

**Partei,** *f.* part; party.

**parteiisch,** *a.* partial, prejudiced.

**Partialdruck,** *m.* partial pressure.

**partiär,** *a.* partial.

**Partie,** *f.* parcel, lot; batch; company; party, picnic; game; match.

**partiell,** *a.* partial.

**Partikel,** *f.* particle. **-chen,** *n.* small particle.

**Passagier,** *m.* passenger.

**passen,** *v.i.* fit, be fit, be suited; wait.—**passend,** *p.a.* fit, suitable, appropriate.

**Passglas,** *n.* graduated glass.

**passieren,** *v.t.* pass; (*Dyeing*) liquor.—*v.i.* pass, happen.

**Passivität,** *f.* passivity.

**Pastellfarbe,** *f.* pastel color.

**Pastete,** *f.* pie, pastry.

**pasteurisieren,** *v.t.* pasteurize.

**pastieren,** *v.t.* paste.

**pastig,** *a.* pasty.

**Pastinake,** *f.* parsnip.

**pastös,** *a.* pasty.

**Patent,** *n.* patent (in the proper sense; cf. Gebrauchsmuster). **-amt,** *n.* patent office. **-anmeldung,** *f.* application for a patent. **-anspruch,** *m.* patent claim or specification. **-anwalt,** *m.* patent attorney. **-beschreibung,** *f.* patent description or specification. **-frage,** *f.* patent question or problem. **-gelb,** *n.* patent yellow.

**patentierbar,** *a.* patentable.

**Patent-inhaber,** *m.* patentee. **-kohle,** *f.* briquette. **-recht,** *n.* patent right; patent law. **-salz,** *n.* ammonium antimony fluoride. **-schrift,** *f.* patent (the document), patent specification. **-schutz,** *m.* protection by patent. **-träger,** *m.* patentee. **-verletzung,** *f.* patent infringement. **-zement,** *m.* Roman cement.

**pathologisch,** *a.* pathological.

**patinieren,** *v.t.* patinate.

**Patrone,** *f.* thimble, shell (for extractions); cartridge; pattern; stencil; mandrel.

**Patronen-hülse,** *f.,* **-zylinder,** *m.* cartridge case.

**Patsche,** *f.* fix, mess; slush, mud.

**patschen,** *v.i.* splash; clap, slap.

**Patschulen,** *n.* patchoulene.

**Patschuli,** *n.* patchouli.

**pattinsonieren,** *v.t.* pattinsonize.

**Pauke,** *f.* (kettle) drum; (*Anat.*) tympanum; harangue.

**Paukenfell,** *n.* (kettle) drumhead; (*Anat.*) membrana tympani.

**Pauschal-.** total, lump (sum, etc.).

**pauschen,** *v.t.* swell; (*Metal.*) refine.

**Pauscht,** *m.& n.* (*Paper*) post.

**Pause,** *f.* tracing; pause.

**pausen,** *v.t.* trace, calk.

**Paus-leinwand,** *f.,* **-leinen,** *n.* tracing cloth. **-papier,** *n.* tracing paper. **-zeichnung,** *f.* tracing.

**-pctig.,** *abbrev.* (procentig) per cent.

**Pech,** *n.* pitch. **-art,** *f.* kind or variety of pitch.

**pechartig,** *a.* pitchy, bituminous.

**Pech-blende,** *f.* pitchblende. **-draht,** *m.* pitched thread, shoemaker's thread. **-eisenerz,** *n.* pitchy iron ore (applied to pitticite, triplite, and a compact variety of limonite).

**pecheln,** *v.i.* smell pitchy; extract pitch.—*v.t.* extract pitch from; pitch, coat with pitch.

**pechen,** *v.t.* pitch, coat with pitch.

**Pech-erde,** *f.* bituminous earth. **-erz,** *n.* = Pechblende; = Pecheisenerz.

**pechfinster,** *a.* pitch-dark.

**Pech-geschmack,** *n.* pitchy taste. **-glanz,** *m.* pitchy luster. **-granat,** *m.* colophonite (a variety of andradite of pitchy appearance).

**pechig,** *a.* pitchy.

**Pech-kiefer,** *f.* pitch pine. **-kohle,** *f.* pitch coal. **-koks,** *m.* coke from pitch or tar. **-öl,** *n.* tar oil, oil of tar.

**pechschwarz,** *a.* pitch-black.

**Pech-stein,** *m.* pitchstone. **-steinkohle,** *f.* pitch coal. **-tanne,** *f.* pitch pine. **-torf,** *m.* pitch peat. **-uran,** *n.* pitchblende.

**Pegel,** *m.* water gage.

**Pein,** *f.* pain, trouble, torture.

**peinigen,** *v.t.* torment, trouble.

**peinlich,** *a.* painful; precise, painstaking, careful; penal.

**Peitsche,** *f.* whip.

**peitschen,** *v.t.* whip, beat, lash. **-förmig,** *a.* whip-shaped, flagelliform.

**pektinartig,** *a.* pectin-like.

**pektinig,** *a.* pectinous.

**Pektin-säure,** *f.* pectic acid. **-stoff,** *m.* pectic substance. **-zucker,** *m.* arabinose.

**Pelargonsäure,** *f.* pelargonic acid.

**Péligot-rohr,** *n.,* **-röhre,** *f.* Péligot tube.

**Pelle,** *f.* peel, skin, husk.

**Pelz,** *m.* pelt, skin; fur.

**pelzig,** *a.* furry; cottony.

**Pendel,** *n.* pendulum.

**pendeln,** *v.i.* oscillate, vibrate, undulate.

**penetrieren,** *v.t.* penetrate.

**Pensee,** *n.* pansy.

**Pension,** *f.* pension; board; boarding house; boarding school.

**Pentabromphosphor,** *n.* phosphorus pentabromide.

**pentacarbocyclisch,** *a.* pentacarbocyclic

**Pentathionsäure,** *f.* pentathionic acid.

**pentazyklisch,** *a.* pentacyclic.

**Pentinsäure,** *f.* pentinoic (pentynoic) acid.

**Pentosurie,** *f.* pentosuria.

**Pentoxyd,** *n.* pentoxide.

**Pepsindrüse,** *f.* peptic gland.

**pepsinhaltig,** *a.* containing pepsin.

**Peptisator,** *m.* peptizer, peptizing agent.

**peptisch,** *a.* peptic.

**peptisieren,** *v.t.* peptize.

**Peptisierung,** *f.* peptization.

**pepton-erzeugend,** *a.* peptogenous, **-genic. -isieren,** *v.t.* peptonize.

**Per-acidität,** *f.* superacidity. **-ameisensäure,** *f.* performic acid. **-benzoesäure,** *f.* perbenzoic acid. **-borsäure,** *f.* perboric acid. **-bromsäure,** *f.* perbromic acid. **-buttersäure,** *f.* perbutyric acid.

**Percha,** *f.,* **-gummi,** *m.& n.* gutta-percha.

**Per-chlorsäure,** *f.* perchloric acid. **-chromsäure,** *f.* perchromic acid.

**perennierend,** *p.a.* perennial.

**Per-essigsäure,** *f.* peracetic acid. **-ferricyanwasserstoffsäure,** *f.* perferricyanic acid.

**perforieren,** *v.t.* perforate.

**Pergament,** *n.* parchment.

**pergament-ähnlich,** *a.* parchmentlike. **-ieren,** *v.t.* parchmentize.

**Pergamentpapier,** *n.* parchment paper.

**perhydrieren,** *v.t.* perhydrogenize.

**Perihel,** *n.* perihelion.

**Periklas,** *m.* periclase, periclasite.

**Perilla-aldehyd,** *n.* perillaldehyde. **-alkohol,** *m.* perillic alcohol. **-säure,** *f.* perillic acid.

**periodisch,** *a.* periodic, periodical.

**Periodizität,** *f.* periodicity.

peripher, a. peripheral.

Per-jodat, n. periodate. -jodsäure, f. periodic acid. -kohlensäure, f. percarbonic acid.

Perkussions-zünder, m. percussion fuse. -zündhütchen, n. percussion cap. -zündung, f. percussion priming.

perlartig, a. pearly, nacreous; beadlike.

Perlasche, f. pearlash.

Perle, f. pearl; bead.

perlen, v.t. form bubbles, sparkle; form drops; glisten like pearls. -artig, a. = perlartig.

Perlenglanz, Perlglanz, m. pearly (or nacreous) luster.

perlfarben, a. pearl-colored.

Perlglimmer, m. (Min.) margarite.

perlgrau, a. pearl-gray.

Perlgraupen, f.pl. pearl barley.

perlig, a. pearly.

Perl-kohle, f. pea coal. -koks, m. coke breeze. -moos, n. pearl moss, carrageen. -mutter, f. mother-of-pearl, nacre.

perlmutterartig, a. like mother-of-pearl, nacreous.

Perlmutter-blech, n. crystallized tinplate, moiré métallique. -glanz, m. mother-of-pearl luster, nacreous luster.

perlmutterglänzend, p.a. having a mother-of-pearl luster, pearly.

Perl-mutterpapier, n. nacreous paper. -rohr, n., -röhre, f. bead tube (tube filled with glass beads). -salz, n. microcosmic salt. -samen, m. seed pearl. -seide, f. ardassine. -spat, m. pearl spar (pearly dolomite). -stein, m. perlite; adularia. -weiss, n. pearl white.

Permanentweiss, n. permanent white.

Permanenzsatz, m. permanence principle.

Permanganatlösung, f. permanganate solution.

Permangansäure, f. permanganic acid.

permeabel, a. permeable.

Permeabilität, f. permeability.

permutieren, v.t. (Math.) permute.

Permutitverfahren, n. permutite process.

Perowskit, n. perovskite.

Peroxyd, n. peroxide.

Perpendikel, n. perpendicular; pendulum.

Persalz, n. per salt.

Persanerstahl, m. Brescian steel.

Per-säure, f. peracid. -schwefelsäure, f. persulfuric acid.

Perseit, n. perseitol, perseite.

Persien, n. Persia.

persisch, a. Persian.—persische Erde, persisches Rot, Persian red.

Personal, n. personnel, staff.

Personen-. of or for persons, passenger.

persönlich, a. personal.

Perstoff, m. (Mil.) diphosgene, superpalite ($ClCO_2CCl_3$).

Persulfo-cyansäure, f. perthiocyanic acid, persulfocyanic acid. -molybdänsäure, f. perthiomolybdic acid, thiopermolybdic acid. -zyansäure, f. perthiocyanic acid.

Perthiokohlensäure, f. perthiocarbonic acid.

peruanisch, a. Peru, Peruvian.

Peru-rinde, f. Peruvian bark. -salpeter, m. Peruvian saltpeter ($NaNO_3$). -silber, n. a kind of German silver.

Perylenchinon, n. perylenequinone.

Pest, f. plague, pest; pestilence.

Pestilenzkraut, n. = Geissraute.

Petersilie, f. parsley.

petersilienähnlich, a. parsleylike.

Petersilien-öl, n. parsley oil. -samen, m. parsley seed.

Peterskraut, n. (Bot.) wall pellitory.

petiotisieren, v.t. (Wines) petiotize.

Petri'sches Schälchen, Petri-Schale, f. Petri dish.

Petrol, n. petroleum.

Petroläther, m. petroleum ether.

Petroleum-äther, m. petroleum ether. -behälter, m. petroleum container, petroleum tank. -benzin, n. petroleum benzine, petroleum spirit. -dampf, m. petroleum vapor. -destillationsgefäss, n. petroleum still. -essenz, f. petroleum spirit. -geruch, m. petroleum odor.

petroleumhaltig, a. containing petroleum.

Petroleum-handel, m. petroleum trade. -heizung, f. heating with petroleum. -prober, m. petroleum tester. -prüfer, m. petroleum tester. -seifenbrühe, f. (Agric.) kerosene emulsion.

Petrol-koks, m. petroleum coke, oil coke. -pech, n. petroleum pitch. -säure, f. petrolic acid.

Petschaft, n. seal, signet; impression die.

Petsche, f. drying room; drying frame.

Pf., abbrev. (Pfund) pound; pfennig; (Pferd, Pferde) horse, horsepower, H.P.

Pfad, m. path.

Pfaff, m. rivet stamp; nut driver; (Brewing) underlet.

Pfaffe, m. priest.

Pfaffenhütchen, n. wahoo (Evonymus atropurpureus).

Pfahl, m. stake, pile, stick, pole, post, prop.

pfählen, v.t. pale; prop; empale.

Pfahlwurzel, f. taproot.

Pfalz, f. Palatinate.

Pfand, n. pledge, security, forfeit.

Pfännchen, n. little pan.

Pfanne, f. pan; copper, boiler; pantile; (Mach.) bearing, bush; (Anat.) socket, acetabulum.

Pfannen-stein, *m.* pan scale; boiler scale.
-werk, *n.* salt works. -ziegel, *m.* pantile.

Pfänner, *m.* salt manufacturer.

Pfau, *m.* peacock.

pfaublau, *a.* peacock-blue.

Pfeffer, *m.* pepper.

pfefferartig, *a.* like pepper, peppery.

Pfeffer-kraut, *n.* savory (*Satureia hortensis*);
peppergrass (*Lepidium*); stonecrop (*Sedum*).
-kuchen, *m.* gingerbread. -minze, *f.* peppermint.

Pfefferminz-geruch, *m.* peppermint odor.
-kampher, *m.* menthol. -öl, *n.* peppermint
oil.

Pfeffer-münze, *f.* = Pfefferminze. -öl, *n.* pepper oil. -stein, *m.* peperino.

Pfeife, *f.* pipe; whistle; fife.

pfeifen, *v.t. & i.* pipe, whistle.

Pfeifen-erde, *f.* pipe clay. -rohr, *n.* pipe-
stem. -stein, *m.* pipestone. -ton, *m.* pipe
clay.

Pfeil, *m.* arrow; dart.

Pfeiler, *m.* pillar; pier.

pfeilförmig, *a.* arrow-shaped, sagittate.

Pfeil-gift, *n.* arrow poison. -höhe, *f.* height
(of a meniscus, arch, etc.). -wurz, -wurzel,
*f.* arrowroot. -wurzelmehl, *n.* arrowroot
(starch). -zeichen, *n.* arrow.

Pfennig, *m.* penny, pfennig ($\frac{1}{100}$ mark).

Pferd, *n.* horse.

Pferde-bohne, *f.* horse bean. -dünger, *m.*
horse manure. -harnsäure, *f.* hippuric acid.
-kraft, *f.* horsepower. -milch, *f.* mare's
milk. -minze, *f.* horsemint. -mist, *m.* horse
manure. -stärke, *f.* horsepower.

-pferdig, (so many) horsepower.

Pfg., *abbrev.* pfennig, pfennigs.

Pfiff, *pret.* of pfeifen.

Pfiff, *m.* whistle; trick, knack.

Pfingstrose, *f.* peony.

Pfirsich, *m.*, Pfirsche, *f.* peach.

Pfirsich-blüte, *f.* peach blossom. -brannt-
wein, *m.* peach brandy.

Pfirsiche, *f.* peach.

Pfirsich-holz, *n.* peachwood. -kern, *m.* peach
kernel. -kernöl, *n.* peach-kernel oil.
-kernschwarz, *n.* peach black.

pflag, *pret.* of pflegen.

Pflanze, *f.* plant.

pflanzen, *v.t.* plant.

Pflanzen-. plant, vegetable. -alkali, *n.* vegetable alkali (old name for potash, also for
plant alkaloids). -alkaloid, *n.* plant alkaloid, vegetable alkaloid.

pflanzenartig, *a.* plantlike; vegetable.

Pflanzen-asche, *f.* plant ashes. -auszug, *m.*
plant (or vegetable) extract. -base, *f.*
vegetable base, (plant) alkaloid. -beschrei-
bung, *f.* description of plants, phytography.

-butter, *f.* vegetable butter. -chemie, *f.*
plant chemistry, phytochemistry.

pflanzenchemisch, *a.* phytochemical.

Pflanzen-eiweiss, *n.* vegetable albumin (or
albumen); vegetable protein. -erde, *f.*
vegetable mold, humus. -erzeugnis, *n.*
plant product, vegetable product. -farbe,
*f.* vegetable color. -farbstoff, *m.* plant pigment; vegetable dye. -faser, *f.* vegetable
fiber, plant fiber. -faserstoff, *m.*, -fibrin, *n.*
vegetable fibrin (gluten; cellulose). -fett, *n.*
vegetable fat. -fettseife, *f.* soap made from
vegetable oils. -forscher, *m.* botanist.

pflanzenfressend, *p.a.* herbivorous.

Pflanzen-gallert, *n.* vegetable gelatin, pectin.
-gift, *n.* plant poison. -grün, *n.* chlorophyll.
-haar, *n.* vegetable horsehair (palm fiber).
-harz, *n.* vegetable resin. -kasein, *n.*,
-käsestoff, *m.* vegetable casein, legumin.
-kleber, *m.* gluten. -kohle, *f.* vegetable
charcoal. -kunde, *f.* botany. -laugensalz,
*n.* (*Old Chem.*) potash. -lehre, *f.* botany.
-leim, *m.* vegetable glue, gliadin, gluten.
-nucleinsäure, *f.* vegetable nucleic acid.
-öl, *n.* vegetable oil. -pech, *n.* vegetable
pitch. -reich, *n.* vegetable kingdom. -rot,
*n.* carthamin. -saft, *m.* vegetable juice,
plant juice, sap. -salz, *n.* vegetable salt.
-säure, *f.* vegetable acid. -schleim, *m.*
mucilage. -schutzmittel, *n.* plant protective (agent). -schwarz, *n.* vegetable black.
-seide, *f.* vegetable silk. -stoff, *m.* vegetable
matter, plant substance. -talg, *m.* vegetable
tallow. -wachs, *n.* vegetable wax. -wachs-
tum, *m.& n.* plant growth, vegetation.
-zelle, *f.* plant cell, vegetable cell. -zellen-
stoff, *m.* cellulose.

pflanzlich, *a.* plant, vegetable.

Pflaster, *n.* plaster; pavement, paving.

pflastern, *v.t.* plaster; pave.

Pflaster-stein, *m.* paving stone. -werkstoff,
*m.* paving material. -ziegel, *m.* paving
brick, paving tile.

pflatschen, *v.t.* (*Calico*) pad.

Pflatschfarbe, *f.* (*Calico*) padding liquor.

Pflaume, *f.* plum; prune.

Pflaumen-baum, *m.* plum tree. -branntwein,
*m.* plum brandy.

pflaumen-farben, -farbig, *a.* plum-colored.

Pflaumensieder, *m.* plum distiller.

Pflege, *f.* care; nursing, rearing, education,
superintendence.

pflegen, *v.i.* be accustomed, be wont; indulge.
—*v.t.* attend to, care for, tend, cultivate,
nurse.

Pflicht, *f.* duty; obligation.

pflichtschuldig, *a.* in duty bound; obligatory.

Pflock, *m.* peg, pin; stake; plug, tampon;
(*Med.*) embolus.

**pflog,** *pret.* of pflegen.

**pflücken,** *v.t.* pluck, pick, gather.

**Pflug,** *m.* plow.

**pflügen,** *v.t.* plow.

**Pflugschar,** *f.* plowshare; (*Anat.*) vomer.

**Pfortader,** *f.* portal vein.

**Pforte,** *f.* gate, door, entrance; orifice.

**Pförtner,** *m.* porter, doorkeeper; (*Anat.*) pylorus.

**Pfoste,** *f.* plank; post.

**Pfosten,** *m.* post.

**Pfriem, Pfriemen,** *m.*, **Pfrieme,** *f.* punch, awl.

**Pfriemen-gras,** *n.* esparto; matgrass, matweed (*Nardus stricta*). **-kraut,** *n.* = Besenginster.

**Pfropf, Pfropfen,** *m.* stopper, plug, wad, cork; graft; (*Med.*) thrombus, embolus.

**pfropfen,** *v.t.* stopper, cork; cram; graft.

**Pfropfenzieher,** *m.* corkscrew.

**Pfropfwachs,** *n.* grafting wax.

**Pfuhl,** *m.* pool, slough.

**Pfühl,** *m. & n.* pillow, bolster.

**Pfund,** *n.* pound. **-leder,** *n.* sole leather.

**pfuschen,** *v.i.* bungle; meddle.

**Pfütze,** *f.* puddle, wallow.

**pH,** *abbrev.* pH, pₕ (symbol for hydrogen-ion concentration); (pro Hundert) per cent.

**phagedänisches Wasser.** (*Pharm.*) yellow mercurial lotion.

**Phänomen,** *n.* phenomenon.

**Phantasie,** *f.* imagination, fancy.

**phantasieren,** *v.i.* imagine, muse; be delirious, wander.

**Phantast,** *m.* dreamer, visionary.

**Phäo-.** pheo-, phaeo-.

**Pharaoschlange,** *f.* Pharaoh's serpent.

**Pharmako-log,** *m.* pharmacologist. **-logie,** *f.* pharmacology.

**pharmakologisch,** *a.* pharmacological.

**Pharmakopöe,** *f.* pharmacopeia.

**Pharmazeut,** *m.* pharmaceutist, pharmacist.

**Pharmazeutik,** *f.* pharmaceutics.

**pharmazeutisch,** *a.* pharmaceutical.

**Pharmazie,** *f.* pharmacy.

**Phasen-änderung,** *f.* phase change. **-gesetz,** *n.* phase law.

**phasengleich,** *a.* of like phase.—*adv.* in the same phase.

**Phasen-gleichgewicht,** *n.* equilibrium between (or among) phases, phase-rule equilibrium. **-grenze,** *f.* phase boundary. **-lehre,** *f.* doctrine of phases. **-regel,** *f.* phase rule. **-zahl,** *f.* number of phases.

**Phaseomannit,** *n.* phaseomannitol, -mannite.

**phasisch,** *a.* phasic, phase.

**Phasotropie,** *f.* phasotropy, phasotropism.

**Phenochinon,** *n.* phenoquinone.

**Phenol-.** phenol, phenol-, phenolic; (in combination with the name of a metal) phenolate (or phenoxide) of, as *Phenolaluminium,*

aluminum phenolate, aluminum phenoxide. **-äther,** *m.* phenol ether. **-carbonsäure,** *f.* phenolcarboxylic acid. **-gruppe,** *f.* phenol group. **-kalium,** *n.* potassium phenolate (or phenoxide). **-kalzium,** *n.* calcium phenolate (or phenoxide). **-lösung,** *f.* phenol solution. **-natrium,** *n.* sodium phenolate (or phenoxide). **-quecksilber,** *n.* mercury phenolate (or phenoxide). **-rot,** *n.* phenol red. **-säure,** *f.* phenol acid. **-schwefelsäure,** *f.* phenolsulfuric acid (general term, $ROSO_3H$, where R is an aromatic radical); specif. phenylsulfuric acid. **-sulfo(n)säure,** *f.* phenolsulfonic acid. **-wismut,** *m. & n.* bismuth phenolate (or phenoxide).

**Phensäure,** *f.* phenic acid (phenol, $C_6H_5OH$).

**Phenyl-arsenchlorür,** *n.* phenylarsenious chloride. **-äther,** *m.* phenyl ether. **-borchlorid,** *n.* phenylboron chloride. **-braun,** *n.* phenyl brown.

**Phenylenblau,** *n.* phenylene blue.

**Phenyl-essigsäure,** *f.* phenylacetic acid. **-fettsäure,** *f.* phenylated fatty acid.

**phenylieren,** *v.t.* phenylate.

**Phenyl-jodidchlorid,** *n.* phenyl iodochloride. **-milchsäure,** *f.* phenyllactic acid. **-säure,** *f.* phenylic acid (phenol, $C_6H_5OH$). **-schwefelsäure,** *f.* phenylsulfuric acid. **-senföl,** *n.* phenyl mustard oil. **-siliciumchlorid,** *n.* phenylsilicon chloride. **-wasserstoff,** *m.* phenyl hydride, benzene.

**Ph.g., Ph.G.,** *abbrev.* (Pharmakopoeia germanica) German pharmacopeia.

**philan-ieren, -isieren,** *v.t.* philanize (mercerize by a special process).

**Philosoph,** *m.* philosopher.

**Philosophenwolle,** *f.* philosopher's wool (sublimed zinc oxide).

**philosophisch,** *a.* philosophical.

**Phiole,** *f.* vial, phial.

**Phlegma,** *n.* phlegm.

**phlogistisch,** *a.* phlogistic.

**Phlorchinyl,** *n.* phloroquinyl.

**Phloro-glucid, -gluzid,** *n.* phloroglucidol, phloroglucide.

**Phokänsäure,** *f.* phocenic acid (valeric acid).

**Phön-.** phen-, phoen-.

**Phönicin, Phönizin,** *n.* phenicin, phoenicin.

**Phosgen,** *n.* phosgene, carbonyl chloride.

**Phosphat,** *n.* phosphate. **-dünger,** *m.* phosphate fertilizer.

**phosphatführend,** *a.* phosphate-bearing.

**phosphatisch,** *a.* phosphatic.

**phosphenylig,** *a.* phosphenylous.

**Phosphenylsäure,** *f.* phosphenylic acid.

**phosphinig,** *a.* phosphinous.

**Phosphinigsäure,** *f.* phosphinous acid.

**Phosphinsäure,** *f.* phosphinic acid.

**Phosphor,** *m.* phosphorus; phosphor, phosphorescent substance.

**Phosphor-.** phosphorus, phospho-, phosphide of.

**phosphorartig,** *a.* like phosphorus, phosphorous.

**Phosphor-äther,** *m.* phosphoric ether (ester of phosphoric acid, specif. ethyl phosphate). **-basis,** phosphorus base. **-bestimmung,** *f.* determination of phosphorus. **-blei,** *n.* lead phosphide; *(Min.)* pyromorphite. **-bromid,** *n.* phosphorus bromide, specif. phosphorus pentabromide. **-bromür,** *n.* phosphorus tribromide. **-calcium,** *n.* calcium phosphide. **-chlorid,** *n.* phosphorus chloride, specif. phosphoric chloride (phosphorus pentachloride). **-chlorür,** *n.* phosphorous chloride (phosphorus trichloride). **-dampf,** *m.* phosphorus vapor or fume. **-eisen,** *n.* ferrophosphorus; iron phosphide. **-eisensinter,** *m.* diadochite.

**phosphoreszieren,** *v.i.* phosphoresce.—**phosphoreszierend,** *p.a.* phosphorescent.

**Phosphor-eszierung,** *f.* phosphorescence. **-fleischsäure,** *f.* phosphocarnic acid.

**phosphorfrei,** *a.* free from phosphorus.

**Phosphor-gehalt,** *m.* phosphorus content. **-geruch,** *m.* phosphorus odor. **-gruppe,** *f.* phosphorus group. **-guano,** *m.* phosphatic guano.

**phosphorhaltig,** *a.* containing phosphorus, phosphatic, phosphorated.

**phosphorig,** *a.* phosphorous. **-sauer,** *a.* of or combined with phosphorous acid, phosphite of.

**Phosphorigsäureanhydrid,** *n.* phosphorous anhydride (phosphorus trioxide).

**phosphorisch,** *a.* phosphoric.

**phosphorisieren,** *v.t.* phosphorize, phosphorate.

**Phosphor-jodid,** *n.* phosphorus iodide, specif. a higher iodide ($PI_3$, sometimes $PI_5$). **-jodür,** *n.* phosphorus diiodide ($P_2I_4$); sometimes, phosphorus triiodide ($PI_3$). **-kalzium,** *n.* calcium phosphide. **-kerzchen,** *n.* wax match. **-kupfer,** *n.* copper phosphide; *(Min.)* libethenite. **-kupfererz,** *n.* libethenite. **-löffel,** *m.* phosphorus spoon (deflagrating spoon). **-mangan,** *n.* phosphormanganese. **-masse,** *f.* phosphorus paste or composition. **-metall,** *n.* phosphide (of a metal). **-molybdänsäure,** *f.* phosphomolybdic acid. **-natrium,** *n.* sodium phosphide. **-öl,** *n.* *(Pharm.)* phosphorated oil. **-oxyd,** *n.* (any) phosphorus oxide, specif. the pentoxide. **-oxydul,** *n.* phosphorus trioxide. **-proteid,** *n.* phosphoprotein. **-roheisen,** *n.* phosphoric pig iron. **-salz,** *n.* microcosmic salt ($HNaNH_4PO_4 \cdot 4H_2O$).

**phosphorsauer,** *a.* of or combined with phosphoric acid, phosphate of.

**Phosphorsäure,** *f.* phosphoric acid. **-anhydrid,** *n.* phosphoric anhydride (phosphorus pentoxide). **-lösung,** *f.* phosphoric acid solution. **-salz,** *n.* phosphate.

**Phosphor-stahl,** *m.* phosphorus steel. **-sulfid,** *n.* (any) phosphorus sulfide. **-verbindung,** *f.* phosphorus compound. **-vergiftung,** *f.* phosphorus poisoning. **-wasserstoff,** *m.* hydrogen phosphide, phosphorus hydride (gasförmiger, $PH_3$; flüssiger, $P_2H_4$; fester, $P_4H_2$). **-wasserstoffgas,** *n.* phosphoretted hydrogen gas (phosphine, $PH_3$). **-weinsäure,** *f.* phosphovinic acid *(Obs.).* **-wolframsäure,** *f.* phosphotungstic acid. **-zink,** *n.* zinc phosphide. **-zinn,** *n.* tin phosphide. **-zündhölzchen,** *n.* phosphorus match.

**Phosphosäure,** *f.* phosphonic acid ($RPO_3H_2$).

**Photochemie,** *f.* photochemistry.

**photo-chemisch,** *a.* photochemical. **-elektrisch,** *a.* photo-electric.

**Photoelektrizität,** *f.* photo-electricity.

**photogen,** *a.* photogenic.

**Photo-gramm,** *n.* photograph. **-graph,** *m.* photographer. **-graphie,** *f.* photography; photograph.

**photo-graphieren,** *v.t.* photograph. **-graphisch,** *a.* photographic.

**Photo-kopie,** *f.* photographic copy, photoprint. **-lyse,** *f.* photolysis. **-metrierung,** *f.* photometric evaluation or recording.

**photometrisch,** *a.* photometric.

**Photo-physik,** *f.* photophysics. **-sphäre,** *f.* photosphere. **-tropie,** *f.* phototropism, phototropy.

**phototropisch,** *a.* phototropic.

**Phtal-.** phthal-, phthalo-, phthalic. **-amidsäure, -aminsäure,** *f.* phthalamic acid. **-azin,** *n.* phthalazine. **-ein,** *n.* phthalein. **-id,** *n.* phthalide. **-monopersäure,** *f.* monoperphthalic acid. **-onsäure,** *f.* phthalonic acid. **-säure,** *f.* phthalic acid. **-säureanhydrid,** *n.* phthalic anhydride.

**Phthal-.** see Phtal-.

**Phyko-cyan, -zyan,** *n.* phycocyanin. **-phäin,** *n.* phycophein, phycophaein.

**Phyllohämin,** *n.* phyllohemin, phyllohaemin.

**Physciasäure,** *f.* physcic acid (physcione).

**Physik,** *f.* physics; *(Dyeing)* tin composition (solution of tin in aqua regia).

**physikalisch,** *a.* physical. **-chemisch,** *a.* physical-chemical, physicochemical.

**Physikbad,** *n.* *(Dyeing)* tin composition.

**Physiker,** *m.* physicist.

**physiko-chemisch,** *a.* physicochemical.

**Physiksalz,** *n.* *(Dyeing)* red spirit.

**Physiolog,** *m.* physiologist.

**physiologisch,** *a.* physiological.

**physisch,** *a.* physical.

**Phytochemie,** *f.* phytochemistry.

**phytochemisch,** *a.* phytochemical.

**Phytosterin,** *n.* phytosterol.

**Picenchinon,** *n.* picenequinone.

**Pichapparat,** *m.* (*Brewing*) pitching machine.

**pichen,** *v.t.* pitch.

**Pich-pech,** *n.* common pitch. **-wachs,** *n.* propolis.

**Picke,** *f.* pickax, pick.

**Pickel,** *m.* pimple; pickax, pick.

**picken,** *v.i.* peck, pick.

**Picolinsäure,** *f.* picolinic acid.

**Piezochemie,** *f.* piezochemistry.

**piezoelektrisch,** *a.* piezoelectric.

**Piezoelektrizität,** *f.* piezoelectricity.

**pigmentarisch,** *a.* pigmentary.

**Pigment-bildung,** *f.* (*Biol.*) pigment formation, chromogenesis. **-farbe,** *f.* pigment color.

**pigment-frei,** *a.* free from pigment, nonpigmented. **-haltig,** *a.* containing pigment, pigmented.

**pigmentieren,** *v.t.* pigment.—*v.i.* become pigmented.

**pigmentlos,** *a.* without pigment, nonpigmented.

**Pigmentpapier,** *n.* carbon paper.

**Pik,** *m.* peak; pique; (at cards) spades.

**pikant,** *a.* piquant, pungent.

**Piknometer,** *n.* pycnometer.

**Pikraminsäure,** *f.* picramic acid.

**Pikrin-pulver,** *n.* picric powder. **-säure,** *f.* picric acid.

**Pikro-.** picro-. **-toxininsäure,** *f.* picrotoxininic acid. **-toxinsäure,** *f.* picrotoxinic acid.

**Pikryl,** *n.* picryl.

**Pilee,** *f.*, **-zucker,** *m.* crushed sugar.

**pilieren,** *v.t.* grind, mill (as soap).

**Pille,** *f.* pill.

**Pillen-glas,** *n.* pill bottle, pill vial. **-schachtel,** *f.* pill box.

**Pilz,** *m.* fungus; mushroom.

**pilz-ähnlich, -artig,** *a.* like a mushroom or fungus, fungoid.

**Pilzenentwickelung,** *f.* fungus development.

**pilzförmig,** *a.* fungiform.

**pilzig, pilzicht,** *a.* fungous, fungoid, spongy.

**Pilz-kunde,** *f.* mycology. **-maischverfahren,** *n.* = Amyloverfahren. **-samen,** *m.* spawn (of fungi), mycelium. **-stoff,** *m.* fungin.

**pilztötend,** *p.a.* fungicidal.

**Pimarsäure,** *f.* pimaric acid.

**Pimelin-keton,** *n.* pimelic ketone (cyclohexanone). **-säure,** *f.* pimelic acid.

**Piment,** *n.* pimento, allspice. **-öl,** *n.* pimento oil, allspice oil. **-pfeffer,** *m.* pimento, allspice. **-rum,** *m.* bay rum.

**Pimpelstein,** *m.* (*Copper*) pimple metal.

**Pimpernuss,** *f.* bladder nut.

**Pimpinelle,** *f.* burnet saxifrage (*Pimpinella saxifraga*).

**Pimstein,** *m.* pumice stone.

**Pinakon,** *n.* pinacol, (less correctly) pinacone. **-bildung,** *f.* pinacol formation.

**Pinaldrüse,** *f.* pineal gland.

**Pincette,** *f.* = Pinzette.

**Pinealdrüse,** *f.* pineal gland.

**Pineytalg,** *m.* piney tallow.

**Pinie,** *f.* pine (esp. *Pinus pinea*); pine kernel, piñon.

**Pinien-kern,** *m.* pine kernel, piñon. **-talg,** *m.* piney tallow.

**Pininsäure,** *f.* pininic acid.

**Pinit,** *n.* pinitol, (less correctly) pinite.

**pinken,** *v.t.* treat with pink salt.

**Pinksalz,** *n.* pink salt (ammonium stannic chloride; less commonly, potassium sodium tartrate). **-bad,** *n.* pink-salt bath.

**Pinne,** *f.* (*Tech.*) pin, peg, (of a hammer) peen; quill feather.

**Pinokamphersäure,** *f.* pinocamphoric acid.

**Pinsäure,** *f.* pinic acid.

**Pinsel,** *m.* (painter's) brush, pencil.

**pinseln,** *v.t.* pencil, paint.

**Pinselschimmel,** *m.* any species of *Penicillium*.

**Pinusharz,** *n.* pine resin.

**Pinzette,** *f.* forceps, tweezers, nippers, pincers.

**Pionier,** *m.* pioneer (esp. in the *Mil.* sense).

**Piperinsäure,** *f.* piperic acid.

**Pipetten-etagere,** *f.* pipette rack, pipette stand. **-flasche,** *f.*, **-fläschchen,** *n.* pipette bottle (dropping bottle with pipette). **-gestell,** *n.* pipette stand. **-ständer,** *m.* pipette stand.

**pipettieren,** *v.t.* transfer or measure with a pipette, pipette.

**Pistazie,** *f.* pistachio (nut).

**Pistazien-grün,** *n.* pistachio green. **-öl,** *n.* pistachio oil.

**Pistill,** *n.* pestle; (*Bot.*) pistil.

**Pitehanf, Pitahanf,** *m.* pita hemp, pita.

**P.K.,** *abbrev.* (Pferdekraft) horsepower, H.P.

**placentar,** *a.* placental.

**placken,** *v.t.* flatten; ram; pester.

**Plackerei,** *f.* drudgery.

**Plage,** *f.* trouble, bother, plague, drudgery.

**plagen,** *v.t.* plague, trouble, bother, worry.

**Plagioklas,** *m.* plagioclase.

**Plakat,** *n.* placard, poster. **-farbe,** *f.* lithographic color.

**Plan,** *m.* plane, plain; plan; (*Painting*) ground.

**planieren,** *v.t.* plane, planish, smooth, level; size (paper).

**Planier-löffel,** *m.* skimmer. **-masse,** *f.* (*Paper*) size. **-wasser,** *n* glue water, size.

**plan-konkav,** *a.* plano-concave. **-konvex,** *a.*

plano-convex. -mässig, a. systematic, methodical.

planschen, v.i. splash.

Planspiegel, m. plane mirror.

plansymmetrisch, a. planisymmetric(al).

Plantage, f. plantation.

Plasmolyse, f. plasmolysis.

plasmolytisch, a. plasmolytic.

plastisch, a. plastic.

Plastizität, f. plasticity.

Platane, f. plane, plane tree.

Platin, n. platinum. -abfall, m. platinum waste.

platinartig, a. like platinum, platinoid.

Platin-asbest, m. platinized asbestos. -bad, n. platinum bath. -blase, f. platinum still. -blech, n. platinum foil. -chlorid, n. platinum chloride, specif. platinic chloride. -chlorür, n. platinous chloride. -chlorwasserstoff, m., -chlorwasserstoffsäure, f. chloroplatinic acid. -cyanür, n. platinous cyanide; cyanoplatinite, platinocyanide. -cyanürwasserstoff, m., -cyanürwasserstoffsäure, f. cyanoplatinous acid, platinocyanic acid. -draht, m. platinum wire. -drahtöse, f. platinum-wire loop. -dreieck, n. platinum triangle. -erz, n. platinum ore. -folie, f. platinum foil. -gefäss, n. platinum vessel. -gehalt, m. platinum content. -gerät, n. platinum apparatus.

platinhaltig, a. containing platinum, platiniferous.

Platini-. platinic, platini-. -chlorid, n. platinic chloride. -chlorwasserstoff, m., -chlorwasserstoffsäure, f. chloroplatinic acid. -cyanwasserstoffsäure, f. cyanoplatinic acid, platinicyanic acid.

platinieren, v.t. platinize.

Platinierung, f. platinization.

Platini-rhodanwasserstoffsäure, f. thiocyanoplatinic acid. -salz, n. platinic salt. -selencyanwasserstoffsäure, f. selenocyanoplatinic acid. -verbindung, f. platinic compound.

Platin-kegel, m. platinum cone. -kohle, f. platinized charcoal. -konus, m. platinum cone. -löffel, m. platinum spoon. -metall, n. platinum metal, metal of the platinum group. -mohr, m. platinum black.

Platino-. platinous, platino-. -chlorid, n. platinous chloride. -chlorwasserstoff, m., -chlorwasserstoffsäure, f. chloroplatinous acid. -cyanwasserstoff, m., -cyanwasserstoffsäure, f. cyanoplatinous acid, platinocyanic acid. -rhodanwasserstoffsäure, f. thiocyanoplatinous acid.

Platinöse, f. platinum-wire loop.

Platinoverbindung, f. platinous compound.

Platin-oxyd, n. platinum oxide, specif. platinic oxide. -oxydul, n. platinous oxide. -oxydulverbindung, f. platinous compound. -oxydverbindung, f. platinic compound.

Platinozyan-. see Platinocyan-.

Platin-plattierung, f. platinum plating. -reihe, f. platinum series. -rückstand, m. platinum residue. -salmiak, m. ammonium chloroplatinate. -salz, n. platinum salt. -sand, m. sand for cleaning platinum. -säure, f. platinic acid. -schale, f. platinum dish. -schiffchen, n. platinum boat. -schwamm, m. platinum sponge. -schwarz, n. platinum black. -spatel, m. platinum spatula. -spitze, f. platinum point. -stern, m. platinum star. -tiegel, m. platinum crucible. -verbindung, f. platinum compound.

Platinzyan-. see Platinocyan-.

plätschern, v.i. splash, plash, ripple.

platt, a. flat; plain; level; low.

Plättchen, n. platelet, lamella.

Platte, f. plate; slab; lamina; planchet; leaf (of a table); flagstone; (Bact.) plate culture.

Plätte, f. flatiron.

plätten, v.t. flatten; iron; flag.

Platten-druck, m. printing from plates. -flasche, f., -fläschchen, n. (Bact.) flat culture flask.

plattenförmig, a. platelike, lamellar, lamelliform.

Platten-glimmer, m. sheet mica. -gummi, n. sheet rubber. -kautschuk, n. sheet rubber. -kultur, f. plate culture. -kupfer, n. sheet copper. -schale, f. flat dish, specif. Petri dish. -turm, m. plate column, plate tower.

plattgedrückt, a. flat-pressed, flattened.

plattieren, v.t. plate.

Plattierung, f. plating, plate.

Plattine, f. (Tech.) plate; (Metal.) mill bar.

Platz, m. place; room, spot, seat, square, etc.

Plätzchen, n. little cake, lozenge, troche, tablet.

platzen, v.i. burst; explode; crack.

Platz-quecksilber, n. = Knallquecksilber. -wechsel, m. exchange of places (of electrons or atoms); migration.

plausibel, a. plausible.

Plejade, f. pleiad.

Pleochroismus, m. pleochroism.

pleochroitisch, a. pleochroic, pleochroitic.

Pleuelstange, f. connecting rod.

Plombe, f. filling, plug (for teeth); lead seal.

Plotz, m. explosion.

plotzen, v.i. explode.

plötzlich, a. sudden.

Plumbi-. plumbic, plumbi-. -oxyd, n. plumbic oxide (lead dioxide). -salz, n. plumbic salt. -verbindung, f. plumbic compound.

Plumbo-. plumbous, plumbo-. -salz, n.

plumbous salt. **-verbindung,** *f.* plumbous compound.

**plump,** *a.* bulky, clumsy, gross.

**Plunscher,** *m.* plunger.

**Plüsch,** *m.* plush.

**Plus-zeichen,** *n.* plus sign. **-zucker,** *m.* plus sugar, dextrorotatory sugar.

**pneumatisch,** *a.* pneumatic.

**pochen,** *v.t.* pound, stamp.—*v.i.* beat, knock, pound, stamp; brag.

**Poch-erz,** *n.* (*Mining*) poor ore, halvans. **-gestein,** *n.* (*Mining*) stamp rock. **-mehl,** *n.* pulverized ore. **-mühle,** *f.* stamp mill. **-satz, -schlamm, -schlich,** *m.* ore slime. **-stempelreihe,** *f.* stamp battery. **-werk,** *n.* stamp mill.

**Pocke,** *f.* pock; (*pl.*) smallpox.

**Pocken-lymphe,** *f.* vaccine lymph. **-wurzel,** *f.* chinaroot.

**Pockholz, Pockenholz,** *n.* lignum vitae, guaiacum wood, pockwood.

**Pokal,** *m.* goblet, cup.

**Pökel,** *m.* pickle (the liquid).

**Pökelei,** *f.* salting house (for meat).

**Pökel-fass,** *n.* pickling tub or vat. **-fleisch,** *n.* pickled meat, salt meat. **-kufe,** *f.* pickling vat or tub.

**pökeln,** *v.t.* pickle.

**Pökeltrog,** *m.* pickling trough.

**Pol,** *m.* pole. **-anziehung,** *f.* polar attraction.

**Polarisations-apparat,** *m.* polarizing apparatus. **-ebene,** *f.* plane of polarization. **-erscheinung,** *f.* polarization phenomenon. **-prisma,** *n.* polarizer. **-strom,** *m.* polarization current. **-winkel,** *m.* angle of polarization.

**Polarisator,** *m.* polarizer.

**polarisierbar,** *a.* polarizable.

**polarisieren,** *v.t.* polarize.

**Polarisierung,** *f.* polarization.

**Polarität,** *f.* polarity.

**Pol-bildung,** *f.* pole formation, polarization. **-eck,** *n.,* **-ecke,** *f.* (*Cryst.*) summit.

**Polei,** *m.* pennyroyal. **-öl,** *n.* pennyroyal oil.

**Polemik,** *f.* polemic, controversy; polemics.

**polen,** *v.t.* (*Metal.*) pole.

**Polen,** *n.* (*Metal.*) poling; Poland.

**Police,** *f.* (insurance) policy.

**Polier-.** polishing, burnishing.

**polierbar,** *a.* capable of being polished.

**polieren,** *v.t.* polish, burnish.

**polierfähig,** *a.* capable of being polished.

**Polier-flüssigkeit,** *f.* polishing liquid, liquid polish. **-kalk,** *m.* polishing chalk. **-masse,** *f.* polishing paste or composition. **-mittel,** *n.* polishing agent. **-papier,** *n.* polishing paper, sandpaper. **-pulver,** *n.* polishing powder. **-rot,** *n.* polishing red, colcothar,

crocus, rouge. **-staub,** *m.* polishing dust. **-wachs,** *n.* polishing wax.

**Politur,** *f.* polish; polishing; shellac varnish, French polish.

**politurfähig,** *a.* polishable.

**Politur-lack,** *m.* shellac varnish containing turpentine. **-masse,** *f.* polishing paste. **-öl,** *n.* polishing oil.

**Polizei,** *f.* police; police station.

**Pol-körper,** *m.,* **-körperchen,** *n.* (*Biol.*) polar body, polar cell.

**pollos,** *a.* poleless, without poles.

**Pol-papier, -reagenzpapier,** *n.* (*Elec.*) pole paper.

**Polster,** *n.* cushion; padding; pad; compress.

**Pol-suchpapier,** *n.* (*Elec.*) pole paper. **-wechsel,** *m.* change or reversal of poles.

**polychromatisch,** *a.* polychromatic, polychrome.

**Polychromsäure,** *f.* polychromic acid.

**polycyclisch,** *a.* polycyclic.

**Polyeder,** *n.* polyhedron.

**poly-edrisch,** *a.* polyhedral. **-gonisch,** *a.* polygonal. **-heteroatomig,** *a.* polyheteratomic.

**Poly-hyperjodat,** *n.* polyperiodate. **-kieselsäure,** *f.* polysilicic acid.

**polymer,** *a.* polymeric.

**Polymerie,** *f.* polymerism.

**poly-merisch,** *a.* polymeric. **-merisieren,** *v.t. & i.* polymerize.

**Polymolybdansäure,** *f.* polymolybdic acid.

**polymorph,** *a.* polymorphous, polymorphic.

**Poly-morphie,** *f.* polymorphism, polymorphy. **-nom,** *n.* polynomial. **-säure,** *f.* poly acid. **-schwefelwasserstoff,** *m.* hydrogen persulfide (either $H_2S_2$ or $H_2S_3$). **-siliciumsäure,** *f.* polysilicic acid. **-thionsäure,** *f.* polythionic acid. **-zimtsäure,** *f.* polycinnamic acid.

**polyzyklisch,** *a.* polycyclic.

**Pomeranze,** *f.* orange, esp. bitter orange.

**pomeranzenartig,** *a.* orangelike.

**Pomeranzen-bitter,** *n.* hesperidin. **-blütenöl,** *n.* orange-flower oil, neroli. **-branntwein,** *m.* orange brandy.

**pomeranzengelb,** *a.* orange-yellow, orange.

**Pomeranzen-liqueur, -likör,** *m.* curaçao. **-öl,** *n.* orange (peel) oil. **-schalenöl,** *n.* orange-peel oil, orange oil.

**pompejanisch,** *a.* Pompeian.

**Pompelmuse,** *f.* (*Bot.*) shaddock.

**ponderabel,** *a.* ponderable, weighable.

**Popanz,** *m.* bugbear.

**Porcellan,** *n.* = Porzellan.

**Porengrösse,** *f.* size of pore(s).

**porös, porig,** *a.* porous.

**Porosität,** *f.* porosity.

**Porphyr,** *m.* porphyry.

**porphyr-artig, -ähnlich,** *a.* porphyritic.

**Porphyr-felsen,** *m.,* **-gestein,** *n.* porphyritic rock.

**Porrissäure,** *f.* purreic acid (euxanthic acid).

**Porsch, Porst,** *m.* marsh tea (*Ledum palustre*).

**Porterwürze,** *f.* (*Brewing*) porter wort.

**Portier,** *m.* porter, doorkeeper.

**portionsweise,** *adv.* in portions.

**Portlandkalk,** *m.* Portland (lime)stone.

**Porto,** *n.* postage.

**portofrei,** *a.* post-free, postpaid.

**Portugalöl, Portugallööl,** *n.* Portugal (or portugallo) oil, orange-peel oil.

**Portugalwasser,** *n.* laurel water.

**Porzellan,** *n.* porcelain, china.

**porzellanartig,** *a.* porcelaneous.

**Porzellan-becher,** *m.* porcelain beaker. **-brei,** *m.* porcelain slip. **-brennofen,** *m.* porcelain kiln. **-dampfschale,** *f.* porcelain evaporating dish or basin. **-erde,** *f.* porcelain clay, china clay, kaolin. **-fabrikation,** *f.* porcelain manufacture. **-griff,** *m.* porcelain handle. **-isolator,** *m.* porcelain insulator. **-jaspis,** *m.* porcelain jasper (variety of porcelanite). **-kitt,** *m.* porcelain cement. **-löffel,** *m.* porcelain spoon. **-malerei,** *f.* china painting. **-masse,** *f.* porcelain body or paste. **-mörser,** *m.* porcelain mortar. **-mörtel,** *m.* pozzuolana mortar. **-platte,** *f.* porcelain plate. **-rohr,** *n.,* **-röhre,** *f.* porcelain tube. **-schale,** *f.* porcelain dish. **-schiffchen,** *n.* porcelain boat. **-spat,** *m.* scapolite. **-spatel,** *m.* porcelain spatula. **-tiegel,** *m.* porcelain crucible. **-ton,** *m.* porcelain clay, kaolin. **-tonumschlag,** *m.* (*Pharm.*) cataplasm of kaolin. **-trichter,** *m.* porcelain funnel. **-wanne,** *f.* porcelain trough.

**Pose,** *f.* quill; pose.

**positiv-elektrisch,** *a.* positively electric, electropositive.

**Post,** *f.* post, mail; news.—*m.* = Porsch.

**Postament,** *n.* stand, base, pedestal.

**Post-amt,** *n.,* **-anstalt,** *f.,* postoffice.

**Posten,** *m.* post, place; item; sum; lot, parcel; (*Metal.*) batch; (*Glass*) piece, lump.

**postfrei,** *a.* post-free, postpaid.

**Postkarte,** *f.* postcard, postal card; post map.

**postlagernd,** *p.a.* general delivery.

**Post-verein,** *m.* postal union. **-zeichen,** *n.* postmark.

**Potasche,** *f.* = Pottasche.

**Potential-abfall,** *m.* fall of potential. **-sprung,** *m.* (*Elec.*) difference of potential.

**potentiell,** *a.* potential.

**potentiieren,** *v.t.* render potent, potentize.

**Potenz,** *f.* power.

**potenzieren,** *v.t.* (*Math.*) raise to a higher power.

**Potenzreihe,** *f.* (*Math.*) exponential series; power series.

**Pottasche,** *f.* potash (potassium carbonate). **-lauge,** *f.* potash lye. **-lösung,** *f.* potash solution. **-(n)fluss,** *m.* crude potash (from ashes). **-(n)siederei,** *f.* potash factory.

**pottecht,** *a.* (*Dyeing*) fast to potting.

**Pottfisch,** *m.* sperm whale. **-öl,** *n.,* **-tran,** *m.* sperm oil.

**Pottlot,** *n.* graphite, black lead.

**poussieren,** *v.t.* push, promote; court.

**Pozzolanerde,** *f.* pozzuolana.

**Pracht,** *f.* pomp, splendor, magnificence, display. **-ausgabe,** *f.* edition de luxe.

**prächtig, prachtvoll,** *a.* splendid, magnificent, sumptuous.

**Präci-.** see Präzi-.

**pract-.** see prakt-.

**prädisponieren,** *v.t.* predispose.

**Präexistenz,** *f.* preëxistence.

**Prägeanstalt,** *f.* mint.

**prägen,** *v.t.* stamp, coin, imprint.

**Präglobulin,** *n.* preglobulin.

**Prägung,** *f.* coining, stamping; coinage.

**prahlen,** *v.i.* boast; (of colors) be loud.

**präjudizieren,** *v.i.* prejudge.

**prakt.,** *abbrev.* (praktisch) practical.

**Praktikant,** *m.* laboratory worker, laboratory student; practitioner.

**Praktiker,** *m.* practician, experienced person, expert.

**Praktikum,** *n.* practice; practical course, laboratory course.

**praktisch,** *a.* practical.

**praktizieren,** *v.t.* practice.

**prall,** *a.* tight, stretched, tense; plump.

**Prall,** *m.* shock; rebound; reflection.

**prallen,** *v.i.* bounce, bound; be reflected.

**Prall-kraft,** *f.* resiliency; elasticity. **-heit,** *f.* tightness, tension; plumpness. **-winkel,** *m.* angle of reflection.

**Prämie,** *f.* premium, prize.

**prangen,** *v.i.* make a show, be resplendent, shine.

**Pranke,** *f.* clutch.

**Präparat,** *n.* preparation.

**Präparaten-glas,** *n.* preparation glass. **-kunde,** *f.* knowledge relating to preparations. **-röhrchen,** *n.* preparation tube, specimen tube. **-schachtel,** *f.* (*Micros.*) slide box.

**präparativ,** *a.* relating to preparation(s), preparative.

**Präparier-.** preparing; dissecting.

**präparieren,** *v.t.* prepare; dissect.—**präpariertes Papier,** (*Photog.*) sensitized paper.

**Präparier-lupe,** *f.* (*Biol.*) dissecting lens. **-nadel,** *f.* (*Biol.*) dissecting needle. **-salz,** *n.* preparing salt (sodium stannate).

Prasenstein, Prasem, *m.* prase (green variety of quartz).

präsentieren, *v.t.* present.

Praseodym, *n.* praseodymium.

Praseokobaltsalz, *n.* praseocobaltic salt.

Präservativ, *n.* preservative.

Präserven, *n.pl.* preserves.

präservieren, *v.t.* preserve.

Präservierung, *f.* preservation, preserving.

Präservierungsmittel, *n.* preservative.

prasseln, *v.i.* crackle, rustle.

praxi, in. in practice.

Praxis, *f.* practice.

präzessieren, präzedieren, *v.i.* precess.

Präzession, *f.* precession.

Präzipitat, *n.& m.* precipitate.

Präzipitation, *f.* precipitation.

Präzipitationswärme, *f.* heat of precipitation.

Präzipitierbottich, *m.* precipitating vat.

präzipitieren, *v.t.* precipitate.

Präzipitier-fass, *n.* precipitating cask or vat. -gefäss, *n.* precipitating vessel. -mittel, *n.* precipitant. -zylinder, *m.* precipitating jar.

Präzipitin, *n.* precipitin.

präzis, *a.* precise.

präzisieren, *v.t.* render precise, define.

Präzision, *f.* precision.

Präzisions-gewicht, *n.* precision weight. -wa(a)ge, *f.* balance of precision, precision balance.

Preis, *m.* price; value; rate; prize; praise.

Preiselbeere, *f.* mountain cranberry.

preisen, *v.t.* praise, commend.

preisgeben, *v.t.* give over, give up, expose.

Preisselbeere, *f.* mountain cranberry.

preiswert, *a.* praiseworthy; worth the price.

prellen, *v.t.* toss; make to rebound; cheat.

Prellstein, *m.* curbstone.

Press-. pressed, compressed, expressed, pressing, press; glazed. -beutel, *n.* pressing bag, press bag, filter bag (for presses). -blei, *n.* (*Metal.*) inferior lead obtained in the Carinthian process after the addition of charcoal.

Presse, *f.* press; gloss.

pressen, *v.t.* press, compress; squeeze, pinch, cram.

Press-erzeugnis, *n.* pressings. -filter, *n.* pressure filter, press filter. -gas, *n.* compressed gas. -glanz, *m.* gloss from pressing. -glas, *n.* pressed glass. -glimmer, *m.* pressed mica. -hefe, *f.* pressed yeast, compressed yeast. -kohle, *f.* pressed charcoal; pressed coal. -ling, *m.* something pressed, pressed article; (*pl., Sugar*) expressed beet pulp. -luft, *f.* compressed air. -most, *m.* expressed fruit juice, must. -mühle, *f.* pressing mill. -öl, *n.* fixed oil. -rückstand, *m.* expressed residue. -sack, *m.* =Press-

beutel. -saft, *m.* expressed juice, press juice. -span, *m.* pressboard. -stoff, *m.* pressed material. -talg, *m.* pressed tallow. -torf, *m.* pressed peat. -tuch, *n.* filter cloth (for presses).

Pressung, *f.* pressure, pressing, compression.

Press-verfahren, *n.* pressing process. -walze, *f.* press roll. -ziegel, *m.* pressed brick. -zucker, *m.* compressed sugar.

Preussen, *n.* Prussia.

preussisch, *a.* Prussian.

Preussisch-blau, *n.* Prussian blue. -braun, *n.* Prussian brown.

prickeln, *v.t.* prickle, prick, sting.—prickelnd, *p.a.* sharp, pungent.

Priemtabak, *m.* chewing tobacco.

pries, *pret.* of preisen.

prim., *abbrev.* (primär) primary.

Prima-. of first, prime, or best quality.

primär, *a.* primary.

Primär-akt, *m.* primary act. -element, *n.* (*Elec.*) primary cell. -kreis, *m.* primary circuit. -linie, *f.* primary line. -strahlung, *f.* primary radiation. -strom, *m.* primary current.

Prima-soda, *f.* refined soda. -ware, *f.* prime or superior article or goods.

Primel, *f.* primrose. -kratzstoff, *m.* an unpleasant-tasting substance in primrose root.

Primzahl, *f.* prime number.

Princip, *n.* principle.

Prinz, *m.* prince.

Prinzip, *n.* principle.

Prinzmetall, *n.* Prince's metal, Prince Rupert's metal.

Priorität, *f.* priority.

Prise, *f.* prize; pinch.

Prisma, *n.* prism.

prisma-ähnlich, -artig, *a.* prism-like, prismoidal. -förmig, *a.* prism-shaped, prismatic.

prismatisch, *a.* prismatic.

Prismenfläche, *f.* prismatic face.

prismenförmig, *a.* prism-shaped, prismatic.

Prismen-glas, *n.* prism glass. -kante, *f.* prismatic edge. -spektrum, *n.* prismatic spectrum.

Pritsche, *f.* bat; (*Alum*) washing floor; (*Dyeing*) stillage (to support goods while drying).

Privatdozent, *m.* a licensed university lecturer receiving fees but no salary.

pro, *prep.* pro, per.

pro anal., *abbrev.* (pro analyse) for analysis.

probat, *a.* proved, tried.

Probe, *f.* test; assay; sample, specimen; proof; trial, probation; rehearsal. -abdruck, *m.* proof, proof print. -bogen, *m.* proof sheet, proof. -brühe, *f.* (*Dyeing*) test bath,

dye test. -druck, *m.* (printer's) proof.
-entnahme, *f.* sample taking, sampling.
-essig, *m.* proof vinegar. -färbung, *f.* test
dyeing. -flasche, *f.* sample bottle, specimen bottle. -fläschchen, *n.* sampling bottle.
-flüssigkeit, *f.* test liquid, test liquor.
-gewicht, *n.* test weight, standard weight.
-glas, *n.* sample glass, sample tube, specimen tube; test glass. -gold, *n.* standard
gold. -gut, *n.* sample material, sample.

probehaltig, *a.* proof, standard.

Probe-korn, *n.* assay button. -körper, *m.*
test body; sample. -löffel, *m.* assay spoon.
-machen, *n.* testing, assaying. -mass, *n.*
standard measure.

probemässig, *a.* according to sample.

Probe-münze, *f.* proof coin. -muster, *n.* sample for testing. -nadel, *f.* touch needle.
-nahme, *f.* sampling; sample. -nehmen, *n.*
sampling.

Proben-glas, *n.* specimen glass, specimen tube.
-stecher, *m.* = Probestecher.

Probepapier, *n.* test paper.

Prober, *m.* tester, specif. assayer.

Probe-rohr, -röhrchen, *n.*, -röhre, *f.* test
tube; (*Mach.*) trial pipe. -säure, *f.* test
acid, standard acid. -schachtel, *f.* sample
box. -scherbe, *f.*, -scherben, *m.* cupel;
(*Ceram.*) trial piece. -silber, *n.* standard
silver. -spiritus, *m.* proof spirit. -stab, *m.*
test rod or bar, trial rod. -stange, *f.* test
rod, test stick, test bar. -stecher, *m.*
sampler (inserted into the material to be
sampled); (for liquids) thief tube; (*Sugar*)
proof stick. -stein, *m.* touchstone; sample
stone. -stoff, *m.* sample material. -stück,
*n.* specimen, sample; test piece. -tiegel, *m.*
assay crucible (see Tüte); cupel. -wa(a)ge,
*f.* assay balance. -weingeist, *m.* proof spirit.

probeweise, *adv.* by way of testing, on trial, on
approval.

Probe-ziehen, *n.* sampling. -zieher, *m.*
sampler. -zinn, *n.* standard tin. -zylinder,
*m.* trial jar; test tube.

Probhahn, *m.* try cock, gage cock.

Probier-. testing, test; assaying, assay. -blei,
*n.* test lead, assay lead.

probieren, *v.t.* test; assay; try; prove.

Probierer, *m.* tester, assayer, analyst.

Probier-gefäss, *n.* testing (or assaying) vessel.
-geräte, *n.pl.*, -gerätschaften, *f.pl.* assaying
apparatus. -gewicht, *n.* assay weight.
-glas, *n.* test tube. -glätte, *f.* test litharge.
-gold, *n.* standard gold. -hahn, *m.* try cock,
gage cock. -kluft, *f.* assayer's tongs. -korn,
*n.* assay button. -kunst, *f.* assaying. -labo-
ratorium, *n.* assay laboratory. -löffel, *m.*
assay spoon. -metall, *n.* test metal. -nadel,
*f.* touch needle. -ofen, *m.* assay furnace.

-papier, *n.* test paper. -röhre, *f.* test tube.
-röhrengestell, *n.* test-tube rack. -scherben,
*m.* = Probescherben. -stein, *m.* touchstone.
-tiegel, *m.* = Probetiegel. -tüte, -tute, -tutte,
*f.* assay crucible. See Tüte. -wa(a)ge, *f.*
assay balance. -zange, *f.* assayer's tongs.

proc., *abbrev.* (procentig) per cent.

Proc., *abbrev.* (Procent) per cent.

Procent, *n.* per cent. See Prozent-.

procentig, *a.* per cent, percentage.

Prod., *abbrev.* (Produkt) product.

Produzent, *m.* producer, grower.

produzieren, *v.t.* produce.

Professorat, *n.* professorship.

professor-haft, -isch, *a.* professorial.

Professorschaft, Professur, *f.* professorship.

projektieren, *v.t.* project; design; purpose.

projizieren, *v.t.* project.

promillig, *a.* per mille, by the thousand (often
expressed ‰).

promovieren, *v.t.& i.* graduate (as a doctor).

prononcieren, *v.t.* pronounce.

Propansäure, *f.* propanoic (propionic) acid.

Propiolsäure, *f.* propiolic acid.

propionsauer, *a.* of propionic acid, propionate
of.

Propionsäure, *f.* propionic acid.

Propiopersäure, *f.* perpropionic acid.

Proportionalität, *f.* proportionality.

Propylwasserstoff, *m.* propyl hydride, pro-
pane.

prosthetisch, *a.* prosthetic.

proteinhaltig, *a.* containing protein.

Protein-körper, *m.* protein substance, protein.
-säure, *f.* proteic acid. -silber, *n.* silver
proteinate. -stoff, *m.* protein substance,
protein. -urie, *f.* albuminuria. -verbindung,
*f.* protein compound.

Proteolyse, *f.* proteolysis.

proteolytisch, *a.* proteolytic.

Proto-cocasäure, *f.* protococaic acid. -kate-
chusäure, *f.* protocatechuic acid.

Protokoll, *n.* minutes, record; protocol.

Protoxyd, *n.* protoxide.

Protozoen, *n.pl.* (*Zoöl.*) Protozoa.

Proviant, *m.* provisions, victuals.

Provision, *f.* provision; commission.

Provisor, *m.* pharmacist's assistant, dispenser.

provisorisch, *a.* provisional.

proz., *abbrev.* (prozentig) per cent.

Proz., *abbrev.* (Prozent) per cent.

Prozent, *n.* per cent. -gehalt, *m.* per cent
content, percentage.

prozentig, prozentisch, *a.* per cent, percentage.

Prozent-satz, *m.* percentage. -teilung, *f.* percentage scale.

prozentual, *a.* per cent, percentage.

Prozess, *m.* process.

prozessieren, *v.i.* litigate.

Prüfapparat, m. testing apparatus, tester.
prüfbar, a. capable of being tested, assayed, tried or examined.
prüfen, v.t. test; assay; try; prove; taste (wine, etc.); examine.
Prüfer, m. tester, assayer, examiner.
Prüf-gerät, n. testing apparatus or instrument, tester. -glas, n. test glass; test tube. -kelch, m. test glass, reaction glass. -mittel, n. testing agent. -stein, m. touchstone.
Prüfung, f. test, testing, assay, trial, examination, proof.
Prüfungs-methode, f. method of testing. -mittel, n. testing agent, means for testing or examining. -schein, m. certificate (that a thing has been tested). -schrift, f. (university) thesis. -stein, m. touchstone.
Prüfverfahren, n. testing method or process.
Prügel, m. cudgel, club; blow; drubbing.
Prunellensalz, Prunellsalz, n. sal prunelle (fused potassium nitrate).
Prunk, m. pomp, state, show.
PS, P.S., abbrev. (Pferdestärke) horsepower, H.P.
Pseudo-harnsäure, f. pseudouric acid. -harnstoff, m. pseudourea. -katalysator, m. pseudocatalyst. -katalyse, f. pseudocatalysis.
pseudokatalytisch, a. pseudocatalytic.
Pseudo-lösung, f. pseudo solution. -merie, f. pseudomerism.
pseudomorph, a. pseudomorphous.
Pseudo-morphose, f. pseudomorphosis; pseudomorph. -säure, f. pseudo acid. -schwefelzyan, n. pseudothiocyanogen.
Pst., abbrev. (Pferdestärke) horsepower.
Psylla-alkohol, m. psyllic alcohol. -säure, f. psyllic acid.
publizieren, v.t. publish.
Puddel-arbeiter, m. puddler. -bett, n. = Puddelsohle. -eisen, n. puddled iron. -luppe, f. puddle-ball.
puddeln, v.t. puddle.
Puddel-ofen, m. puddling furnace. -prozess, m. puddling process. -roheisen, n. forge pig (iron). -schlacke, f. puddling slag. -sohle, f. puddling-furnace bed. -spiegel, m. specular forge pig (iron). -spitze, f. puddler's paddle. -stab, m. puddle-bar. -stahl, m. puddled steel. -verfahren, n. puddling process, puddling. -walze, f. puddle roll. -werk, n. puddling works.
Pudel, m. poodle; blunder, miss.
Puder, m. powder.
puderig, a. powdery.
pudern, v.t. powder.
Puderzucker, m. powdered sugar.
pudrig, a. powdery.
Puff, m. blow, thump; puff.
puffen, v.i. puff (up), swell (up); pop.

Puffer, m. buffer. -lösung, f. buffer solution. -salz, n. buffer salt. -wert, m. buffer value. -wirkung, f. buffer action or effect.
Pulpe, f. pulp.
Puls, m. pulse. -ader, f. artery. -glas, n., -hammer, m. cryophorus.
pulsieren, pulsen, v.i. pulsate.
Pulsschlag, m. pulse beat, pulsation.
Pult, n. desk. -feuerung, f. firing on stepped grate bars. -ofen, m. (Metal.) back-flame hearth.
Pulver, n. powder.
pulverartig, a. powdery.
Pulver-dampf, m. powder smoke. -fabrik, f. powder factory. -fabrikation, f. powder manufacture. -fass, n. powder cask, powder keg. -flasche, f. powder bottle (widemouthed bottle).
pulverförmig, a. in the form of powder, powdery, pulverulent.
Pulver-förmigkeit, f. powderiness, pulverulence. -glas, n. = Pulverflasche. -holz, n. wood for gunpowder.
pulverig, a. powdery, pulverulent.
pulverisierbar, a. pulverable.
pulverisieren, v.t. powder, pulverize.
Pulver-isierung, f. pulverization. -kapsel, f. powder capsule; small powder scoop. -korn, n. grain of powder. -kuchen, m. (Gunpowder) press cake. -ladung, f. powder charge. -masse, f. powder composition. -mehl, n. mealed powder. -mörser, m. powder mortar, mortar for powdering. -mühle, f. powder mill.
pulvern, v.t. powder, pulverize.
Pulver-presskuchen,     m. = Pulverkuchen. -probe, f. powder test; powder sample. -probiermörser, m. small powder mortar. -rauch, m. powder smoke. -satz, m. powder composition. -schlag, m. (Pyro.) cracker, petard. -staub, m. powder dust. -tonne, f. powder cask, powder keg. -trichter, m. powder funnel.
pulvertrocken, a. dry as powder.
Pulverung, f. powdering, pulverization.
Pulverzucker, m. powdered sugar.
Pumpe, f. pump.
Punkt, m. point; dot; period.
punkten, v.t. dot.
punktförmig, a. in the form of points or dots, punctiform.
punktieren, v.t. point; dot; punctuate.
pünktlich, a. punctual; exact.
Punkt-schweissung, f. spot welding.
punktsymmetrisch, a. of or pertaining to point symmetry, point-symmetrical.
Punktum, n. period.
Punsch, m. punch (the drink).
Punzen, m. punch (the tool).

Pupille, *f.* pupil.

Puppe, *f.* pupa; cocoon; doll; puppet.

Purganz, *f.* purgative.

purgieren, *v.t.& i.* purge; boil off (silk) with soap.

Purgier-harz, *n.* scammony. -kassie, -kassia, *f.* purging cassia. -korn, *n.* purging grain or seed; (grosses) castor bean; (kleines) croton seed. -kraut, *n.* purgative herb, specif. hedge hyssop. -lein, *n.* purging flax. -mittel, *n.* purgative. -nuss, *f.* purging nut, physic nut. -paradiesapfel, *m.* colocynth. -salz, *n.* purgative salt.

purifizieren, *v.t.* purify.

Purin-basen, *f.pl.* purine bases. -gruppe, *f.* purine group.

Purpur, *m.* purple.

purpurblau, *a.* purple-blue.

Purpureo-kobaltverbindung, *f.* purpureocobaltic compound. -verbindung, *f.* purpureo compound.

Purpur-erz, *n.* purple ore, blue billy. -farbe, *f.* purple color, purple.

purpur-farben, -farbig, *a.* purple-colored.

Purpur-färbung, *f.* purple coloring. -holz, *n.* violet wood. -karmin, *m.* purple carmine, murexide. -muschel, *f.* purple shell.

purpurn, *a.* purple.

purpurrot, *a.* purple-red, crimson.

Purpur-säure, *f.* purpuric acid. -schwefelsäure, *f.* sulfopurpuric acid.

purzeln, *v.i.* tumble.

Pustel, *f.* pustule, pimple.

pusten, *v.i.* blow; pant.—*v.t.* blow.

Pust-probe, *f.* blow test, bubble test. -rohr, *n.* blowpipe. -span, *m.* skimmer.

Puter, *m.* turkey.

Putz, *m.* plaster, plastering; dress, ornament. -baumwolle, *f.* cotton waste (for cleaning).

putzen, *v.t.* clean, cleanse, scour, polish, trim, dress; plaster.

Putzerei, *f.* dressing.

Putz-kalk, *m.* plastering lime; stucco; polishing chalk. -lage, *f.* coat of plaster. -leder, *n.* chamois (leather). -macherei, *f.* millinery. -maschine, *f.* cleaning machine. -mittel, *n.* cleaning or polishing agent or material. -öl, *n.* polishing oil, cleaning oil.

-präparat, *n.* polishing preparation, polish. -pulver, *n.* cleaning powder, polishing powder. -schicht, *f.* = Putzlage. -stein, *m.* cleaning or polishing stone or brick. -tisch, *m.* dressing table; (*Ceram.*) cleaning table. -tuch, *n.* cloth for cleaning or polishing, sponge cloth. -wasser, *n.* dilute acid ¦or scouring. -wolle, *f.* (*Mach.*) waste.

Puzzolane, Puzzolanerde, *f.* pozzuolana.

Puzzolanzement, *m.* pozzuolana cement.

Puzzuolanerde, *f.* pozzuolana.

Pyämie, *f.* pyemia.

pyämisch, *a.* pyemic.

pyramidenförmig, *a.* pyramidal.

Pyramidenwürfel, *m.* tetrahexahedron.

Pyrenchinon, *n.* pyrenequinone.

Pyritabbrände, *m.pl.* pyrites cinders.

pyrithaltig, *a.* pyritiferous.

pyritisch, *a.* pyritic.

Pyritofen, *m.* pyrites oven, pyrites burner.

Pyro-antimonsäure, *f.* pyroantimonic acid. -arsensäure, *f.* pyroarsenic acid. -chinin, *n.* pyroquinine.

pyroelektrisch, *a.* pyroelectric.

Pyro-elektrizität, *f.* pyroelectricity. -gallussäure, *f.* pyrogallic acid (pyrogallol).

pyrogen, *a.* pyrogenic.

Pyrokatechin, *n.* pyrocatechol.

pyrometrisch, *a.* pyrometric.

Pyroperjodsäure, *f.* pyroperiodic acid, dimesoperiodic acid ($H_4I_2O_9$).

Pyrophor, *n.* pyrophorus.

pyro-phor, -phorisch, *a.* pyrophoric. -phosphorig, *a.* pyrophosphorous. -phosphorsauer, *a.* of or combined with pyrophosphoric acid, pyrophosphate of.

Pyro-phosphorsäure, *f.* pyrophosphoric acid. -säure, *f.* pyro acid. -schleimsäure, *f.* pyromucic acid. -schwefelsäure, *f.* pyrosulfuric acid, disulfuric acid ($H_2S_2O_7$).

pyroschweflig, *a.* pyrosulfurous.

Pyrotechnik, *f.* pyrotechnics, pyrotechny.

pyrotechnisch, *a.* pyrotechnic.—pyrotechnische Waren, fireworks.

Pyro-traubensäure, *f.* pyroracemic acid, pyruvic acid. -weinsäure, *f.* pyrotartaric acid.

Pyrrol, *n.* pyrrole. -blau, *n.* pyrrole blue

# Q

q., *abbrev.* (quadrat) square (esp. in qcm., etc.).
qcm., *abbrev.* square centimeter(s), sq. cm.
qdm., *abbrev.* square decimeter(s), sq. dm.
qkm., *abbrev.* square kilometer(s), sq. km.
qm., *abbrev.* square meter(s), sq. m.
qmm., *abbrev.* square millimeter(s), sq. mm.
Q.S., Q.-S., *abbrev.* (Quecksilbersäule) mercury column; (Quecksilberstand) mercury level.
quabbeln, *v.i.* shake, quiver; be flabby.
Quacksalber, *m.* quack, charlatan.
Quader, *m.* parallelepiped; ashlar; freestone. -stein, *m.* ashlar; freestone.
Quadrat, *n.* square.
quadratisch, *a.* square; quadratic; (*Cryst.*) tetragonal.
Quadrat-meter, *m.* square meter. -pyramide, *f.* square pyramid. -wurzel, *f.* square root. -zahl, *f.* square number, square. -zentimeter, *m.* square centimeter.
quadrieren, *v.t.* square.
Quadroxyd, *n.* quadroxide (tetroxide).
quälen, *v.t.* torment, worry, afflict, distress.
Qualität, *f.* quality.
Qualle, *f.* jellyfish.
Qualm, *m.* dense smoke, vapor.
qualmen, *v.i.* emit dense smoke or vapor.
Quant, *n.* quantum.
quanteln, *v.t.* quantize.
Quantelung, *f.* quantizing, quantization.
Quanten, *n.pl.* quanta, quantums. -bahn, *f.* quantum orbit. -empfindlichkeit, *f.* quantum sensitivity.
quantenhaft, *a.* of or pertaining to quanta, in the form of quanta.
Quantenhypothese, *f.* quantum hypothesis.
quanten-mässig, *a.* pertaining to quanta, in relation to quanta. -mechanisch, *a.* quantum-mechanical.
Quantensprung, *m.* quantum transition, quantum leap or jump.
quantentheoretisch, *a.* of or according to the quantum theory.
Quanten-theorie, *f.* quantum theory. -zahl, *f.* quantum number.
-quantig. -quantum.
Quantität, *f.* quantity.
Quantitätsbestimmung, *f.* quantitative determination.
Quantum, *n.* quantum; quantity, portion, quota.
Quark, *m.* curd, curds; trash.
quarkartig, quarkig, *a.* curdlike, curdy.
Quart, *n.* quarto; quart.

quartär, *a.* quaternary.
Quarte, *f.* quarter, fourth.
Quartier, *n.* quarter, quarters.
Quartierung, *f.* quartation.
quartmässig, *a.* by quartation.
Quartscheidung, *f.* separation by quartation.
Quarz, *m.* quartz.
quarz-ähnlich, -artig, *a.* quartzose, quartzous.
Quarz-faden, *m.* quartz thread. -fels, *m.* quartz rock, quartzite. -gefäss, *n.* quartz vessel. -gerät, *n.* quartz apparatus, quartz ware. -glas, *n.* quartz glass. -gut, *n.* quartz ware.
quarzhaltig, *a.* quartziferous.
quarzig, *a.* quartzy, quartzose.
Quarzit, *m.* quartzite.
Quarz-keil, *m.* (*Optics*) quartz wedge. -linse, *f.* quartz lens. -mehl, -pulver, *n.* quartz powder. -sinter, *m.* siliceous sinter. -ziegel, *m.* quartz brick, Dinas brick.
quasielastisch, *a.* quasi-elastic.
Quassiaholz, Quassienholz, *n.* quassia wood, quassia.
Quast, *m.*, Quaste, *f.* tassel, tuft; brush.
quaternär, *a.* quaternary.
Quebrachit, *n.* quebrachitol, quebrachite.
Quebrachorinde, *f.* quebracho bark.
Quecke, *f.* couch grass; (rote) (*Pharm.*) carex root.
Quecksilber, *n.* mercury, quicksilver.
quecksilberähnlich, *a.* mercury-like, mercurial.
Quecksilber-bad, *n.* mercury bath. -beizmittel, *n.* (*Med.*) mercurial disinfectant. -bogen, *m.* mercury arc. -branderz, *n.* idrialite. -bromid, *n.* mercury bromide. specif. mercuric bromide. -chlorid, *n.* mercury chloride, specif. mercuric chloride. -chlorür, *n.* mercurous chloride. -cyanid, *n.* mercury cyanide, specif. mercuric cyanide. -cyanür, *n.* mercurous cyanide. -cyanwasserstoffsäure, *f.* mercuricyanic acid. -dampf, *m.* mercury vapor. -druck, *m.* mercury pressure. -erz, *n.* mercury ore. -faden, *m.* mercury thread. -fahlerz, *n.* tetrahedrite containing mercury. -füllung, *f.* mercury filling. -gefäss, *n.* mercury vessel. -gehalt, *m.* mercury content. -halogen, *n.* mercury halide.
quecksilberhaltig, *a.* containing mercury, mercurial.
Quecksilber-hornerz, *n.* horn quicksilver (native calomel). -jodid, *n.* mercury iodide, specif. mercuric iodide. -jodür, *n.* mer-

curous iodide. -kuppe, f. mercury meniscus. -lebererz, n. hepatic cinnabar. -legierung, f. mercury alloy, amalgam. -licht, n. mercury light. -luftpumpe, f. mercury (air) pump. -mittel, n. (Pharm.) mercurial. -mohr, m. ethiops mineral (black mercuric sulfide).

quecksilbern, a. mercury, mercurial.

Quecksilber-ofen, m. mercury furnace. -oxyd, n. mercury oxide, specif. mercuric oxide. -oxydsalbe, f. mercury oxide ointment. -oxydsalz, n. mercuric salt. -oxydul, n. mercurous oxide. -oxydulsalz, n. mercurous salt. -pflaster, n. (Pharm.) mercurial plaster. -pille, f. blue pill. -präparat, n. mercurial preparation. -präzipitat, n. (Pharm.) (mercury) precipitate (rotes, red precipitate; gelbes, yellow precipitate). -rhodanid, n. mercury thiocyanate, specif. mercuric thiocyanate. -rhodanür, n. mercurous thiocyanate. -russ, m. mercurial soot, stupp. -salbe, f. mercurial ointment. -salz, n. mercury salt. -säule, f. column of mercury. -schliff, m. mercury ground-glass joint. -spat, n. horn quicksilver. -spiegel, m. mercury mirror. -stand, m. mercury level. -sublimat, n. corrosive sublimate. -sulfid, n. mercury sulfide, specif. mercuric sulfide. -sulfür, n. mercurous sulfide. -verbindung, f. mercury compound. -verfahren, n. mercury process. -vitriol, m. mercuric sulfate. -wa(a)ge, f. mercury level. -wanne, f. mercury trough. -zyanid, n. mercury (specif. mercuric) cyanide. -zyanür, n. mercurous cyanide.

Quell, m. = Quelle.

quellbar, a. capable of swelling.

Quell-barkeit, f. capability of swelling. -bottich, m. steeping vat, steeping tub.

Quelle, f. source; spring, well.

quellen, v.i. swell, expand; spring, well.— v.t. soak, steep.

Quell-gas, n. gas from springs. -grad, m. degree of swelling.

quellreif, a. sufficiently steeped.

Quell-reife, f. sufficient steeping. -salz, n. spring salt, well salt. -satzsäure, f. apocrenic acid. -säure, f. crenic acid. -sole, f. spring brine, well brine. -stock, m. steep tank, steeping cistern. -substanz, f. substance that swells.

Quellung, f. swelling, tumefaction; welling; soaking.

Quellungswärme, f. heat of swelling, heat of tumefaction.

Quellwasser, n. spring water, well water.

Quendel, m. wild thyme.

quer, a. cross, transverse, diagonal, oblique.

Quer-achse, f. transverse axis. -arm, m. cross arm, cross bar. -bewegung, f. transverse motion.

Quercit, n. quercitol, quercite.

Quercitronrinde, f. quercitron bark.

Quer-durchmesser, m. transverse diameter. -durchschnitt, m. = Querschnitt.

Quere, f. cross direction, transverse direction; breadth.

Quereffekt, m. transverse effect.

querlaufend, p.a. transversal, transverse.

Quer-profil, n. cross section. -riss, m. transverse crack, cross crack; cross section; (Min.) fracture.

querschleifen, v.t. grind (wood) across the grain.

Quer-schnitt, m. cross section, transverse section, crosscut; cross-sectional area. -schnittszeichnung, f. sectional drawing. -schwingung, f. transverse vibration. -spiessglanz, m. jamesonite. -stück, n. crosspiece. -wand, f. diaphragm; partition.

Querzit, n. quercitol, quercite.

Querzitronrinde, f. quercitron bark.

Querzusammenziehung, f. lateral contraction.

Quetsche, f. squeezer, wringer, presser, crusher.

quetschen, v.t. pinch, squeeze; crush, mash; bruise, contuse.

Quetscher, m. pincher, etc. (see quetschen); (Dyeing) squeezer.

Quetsch-hahn, m. pinchcock. -mühle, f. bruising mill, crushing mill.

Quetschung, f. pinching, etc. (see quetschen).

Quetschwerk, n. crushing mill, crusher.

Quick-. amalgamating. -arbeit, f. amalgamation. -beutel, m. amalgamating skin. -brei, m. amalgam.

quicken, v.t. amalgamate.

Quick-erz, n. mercury ore. -gold, n. gold amalgam. -metall, n. amalgamated metal. -mühle, f. amalgamating mill. -wasser, n. (Plating) quickening liquid (solution of a mercuric salt).

quicken, v.i. squeak, squeal.

Quillaja-rinde, f. quillai bark, quillaia bark. -säure, f. quillaic acid.

quillt, pr. 3 sing. of quellen.

Quirl, m. twirling device, twirl, whirl; (Bot.) whorl; restless person.

quirlen, v.t. twirl; stir with a whirling motion. —v.i. twirl, turn.

quitt, a. even, quits, rid.

Quitte, f. quince.

Quitten-äther, m., -essenz, f. quince essence. -kern, -samen, m. quince seed. -schleim, m. quince mucilage.

quittieren, v.t. quit, leave; receipt.

Quittung, f. receipt.

quoll, pret. of quellen.

# R

r., *abbrev.* (rechtsdrehend) dextrorotatory.

R., *abbrev.* (Referat) abstract, review; Réaumur; ring (cyclic); (Radikal) radical.

Rabatt, *m.* deduction, discount; rebate.

Rabe, *m.* raven.

rabenschwarz, *a.* jet black.

Rabenstein, *m.* gallows.

rac., *abbrev.* racemisch.

Racemie, *f.* racemism.

racemisch, *a.* racemic.

racemisieren, *v.t.* racemize.

Racemisierung, *f.* racemization.

Racem-körper, *m.* racemic substance (or compound). -verbindung, *f.* racemic compound.

Rache, *f.* revenge, vengeance.

Rachen, *m.* throat; mouth; jaws; (*Med.*) pharynx, fauces.

Rachen-. pharyngeal.

rächen, *v.t.* revenge, avenge.

Rachenlehre, *f.* calipers.

Rad, *n.* wheel. -achse, *f.* axle or shaft of a wheel. -bewegung, *f.* rotary motion, rotation. -drehung, *f.* rotation; torsion.

Rädelerz, *n.* wheel ore (bournonite).

Rädelsführer, *m.* ringleader.

rädern, *v.t.* sift, screen; furnish with wheels.

Räder-tierchen, -tier, *n.* rotifer. -werk, *n.* wheelwork, gearing; sifting apparatus.

radförmig, *a.* wheel-shaped, rotate.

Radien, *m.pl.* radii.

radieren, *v.t.* etch; erase.

Radier-firnis, *m.* etching varnish. -grund, *n.* etching ground. -gummi, *m.* (rubber) eraser. -kunst, *f.* (art of) etching. -messer, *n.* erasing knife.

Radierung, *f.* etching; erasure.

Radieschen, *n.* radish.

radiieren, *v.i.* radiate.

Radikalessig, *m.* radical vinegar (old name for acetic acid, esp. glacial acetic acid).

Radio-aktivität, *f.* radioactivity. -blei, *n.* radiolead. -chemie, *f.* radiochemistry. -tellur, *n.* radiotellurium (polonium). -thor, *n.* radiothorium.

Radium-jodid, *n.* radium iodide. -salz, *n.* radium salt. -strahlen, *m.pl.* radium rays.

radizieren, *v.t.* (*Math.*) extract the root of.

Rad-kranz, *m.* (wheel) rim, tire. -linie, *f.* cycloid. -reif, -reifen, *m.* tire; rim. -schuh, *m.* brake. -speiche, *f.* spoke. -welle, *f.* axle; wheel and axle. -zahn, *m.* tooth, cog (of a wheel).

raff., *abbrev.* (raffiniert) refined.

raffen, *v.t.* snatch up, snatch away.

Raffinade, *f.*, -zucker, *m.* refined sugar.

Raffination, *f.* refining.

Raffinations-ertrag, -wert, *m.* (*Sugar*) rendement. -verfahren, *n.*, -vorgang, *m.* refining process.

Raffinat-kupfer, *n.* refined copper. -silber, *n.* refined silver.

Raffinerie, *f.* refinery; finesse.

Raffineur, *m.* refiner.

Raffinieranlage, *f.* refining plant, refinery.

raffinieren, *v.t.* refine.

Raffinier-feuer, *n.*, -herd, *n.*, -ofen, *m.* refining furnace, refinery.

Raffinierung, *f.* refining; refinery.

ragen, *v.i.* project, tower.

Rahm, *m.* cream; crust (forming on the top of something); frame; soot.

rahm-ähnlich, -artig, *a.* creamlike, creamy.

Rahmeis, *n.* ice cream.

rahmen, *v.t.* skim, take the cream from; frame. — *v.i.* form a cream.

Rahmen, *m.* frame, framing; compass, bounds.

Rahm-erz, *n.* a foamy variety of wad. -farbe, *f.* cream color.

rahm-farbig, -farben, *a.* cream-colored.

rahmig, *a.* sooty; creamy.

Rahm-käse, *m.* cream cheese. -messer, *m.* creamometer.

Rain, *m.* ridge, headland.

Rainfarn, *m.*, -kraut, *n.* tansy. -öl, *n.* tansy oil.

Rainweide, *f.* privet.

Rakel, *m.& f.* (*Calico*) doctor.

Rakete, *f.* rocket; (less often) firecracker.

Raketen-satz, *m.* rocket composition. -zeichen, *n.* rocket signal.

Ramiefaser, *f.* ramie fiber.

ramifizieren, *v.t.& r.* ramify.

Ramifizierung, *f.* ramification.

Rammbär, *m.* rammer, monkey.

Ramme, *f.* ram, rammer.

rammen, *v.t.* ram, beat down.

Rammvorrichtung, *f.* ramming apparatus.

Rampe, *f.* ramp; platform; footlights.

ramponieren, *v.t.* damage, injure.

Ramsch, *m.* lot, bulk; cheap stuff.

Rand, *m.* edge; border, rim, margin, brim; boundary; flange.

Rand-. marginal, boundary. -bedingung, *f.* boundary condition.

**rändeln, rändern,** *v.t.* edge, border, rim; mill.

**Ränderscheibe,** *f.* edge cutter.

**Rand-fassung,** *f.* rim. **-fläche,** *f.* (*Cryst.*) lateral face. **-gärung,** *f.* (*Brewing*) rim fermentation. **-kante,** *f.* (*Cryst.*) lateral edge.

**randständig,** *a.* marginal, peripheral.

**Rand-wert,** *m.* boundary value. **-winkel,** *m.* angle of contact.

**rang,** *pret.* of ringen.

**Rang,** *m.* rank; quality; row, tier.

**Ranke,** *f.* tendril, runner.

**ranken,** *v.i.* (of plants) creep, climb.

**rann,** *pret.* of rinnen.

**rannte,** *pret.* of rennen.

**Ränzel,** *n.,* **Ranzen,** *m.* wallet, knapsack, satchel.

**Ranzidität,** *f.* rancidity.

**ranzig,** *a.* rancid.

**ranzigen,** *v.i.* become rancid.

**Ranzig-keit,** *f.* rancidity, rancidness. **-werden,** *n.* becoming rancid; tendency to rancidity.

**Raphia,** *f.* raffia.

**Rapp,** *m.,* **Rappe,** *f.* rape, grape pomace.

**Rappel,** *m.* rage, madness; staggers.

**Rapputz,** *m.* rough coat (of plaster).

**Raps,** *m.* rape; (*rotblühender*) garden rocket. **-öl,** *n.* rape oil, rapeseed oil. **-saat,** *f.,* **-same(n),** *m.* rapeseed, colza.

**rasch,** *a.* quick, brisk, swift, rapid, prompt. **—rascher Satz,** (*Pyro.*) meal-powder composition.

**rascheln,** *v.i.* rustle.

**Rasen,** *m.* turf, sod, lawn; furry coating, fur. **-bleiche,** *f.* grass bleaching, sun bleaching. **-eisenerz,** *n.,* **-eisenstein,** *m.,* **-erz,** *n.* bog iron ore.

**rasieren,** *v.t.* shave; raze.

**Rasier-klinge,** *f.* razor blade. **-messer,** *n.* razor. **-pulver,** *n.* shaving powder. **-seife,** *f.* shaving soap.

**Raspel, Raspe,** *f.* rasp.

**raspeln,** *v.t.* rasp, grate, scrape.

**Rasse,** *f.* race, breed, strain, type.

**rasseln,** *v.i.* rattle, clatter.

**Rast,** *f.* rest; (of a furnace) boshes.

**rasten,** *v.i.* rest; halt.

**Raster,** *m.* screen.

**Rastgärung,** *f.* (*Brewing*) arrested fermentation.

**rastlos,** *a.* restless.

**Rasur,** *f.* erasure.

**rät,** *pr. 3 sing.* of raten.

**Rat,** *m.* counsel, advice; means; council, board; councillor.

**Rata,** *f.* rate; installment.

**Ratanhia,** *f.* rhatany. **-wurzel,** *f.* rhatany root, rhatany.

**Rate,** *f.* rate; instalment.

**raten,** *v.t.& i.* advise, counsel; guess, solve.—**geraten,** *p.a.* advisable.

**Rathaus,** *n.* town hall.

**rationell,** *a.* rational, reasonable.

**rätlich,** *a.* advisable, expedient, wholesome.

**ratlos,** *a.* helpless, perplexed.

**ratsam,** *a.* advisable, expedient, fit.

**Ratschlag,** *m.* advice, counsel.

**ratschlagen,** *v.i.* consult, deliberate.

**Ratschluss,** *m.* resolution, decree.

**Rätsel,** *n.* riddle, puzzle.

**rätselhaft,** *a.* enigmatical, mysterious.

**Ratte,** *f.* rat.

**rätten,** *v.t.* screen, sieve, riddle.

**Ratten-gift,** *n.* rat poison, specif. white arsenic. **-schwanz,** *m.* rat-tail file.

**rauben,** *v.t.* rob.

**rauch.,** *abbrev.* (rauchend) fuming.

**Rauch,** *m.* smoke; fume; vapor. **-achat,** *m.* smoky agate.

**rauchartig,** *a.* smoky.

**Rauch-belästigung,** *f.* smoke nuisance. **-bildung,** *f.* formation of smoke. **-bombe,** *f.* smoke bomb.

**rauchdicht,** *a.* smoke-tight, smoke-proof.

**Rauch-dichte, -dichtigkeit,** *f.* density of smoke.

**rauchen,** *v.i.* fume; smoke; reek.—*v.t.* smoke.—**rauchend,** *p.a.* fuming; smoking.

**Räucher-.** fumigating; smoking (as of meat); perfuming; aromatic.

**Räucherer,** *m.* fumigator.

**Räucher-essenz,** *f.* aromatic essence. **-essig,** *m.* aromatic vinegar.

**räucherig,** *a.* smoky; dingy.

**Räucher-igkeit,** *f.* smokiness; dinginess. **-kerze,** *f.,* **-kerzchen,** *n.* fumigating candle. **-mittel,** *n.* fumigant.

**räuchern,** *v.t.* fumigate; smoke; perfume.

**Räucher-papier,** *n.* fumigating paper. **-pulver,** *n.* fumigating powder.

**Räucherung,** *f.* fumigation; smoking (of meat); incense burning.

**Räucherwerk,** *n.* perfume, perfumes; incense.

**Rauchfang,** *m.* chimney, flue.

**rauch-farben, -farbig,** *a.* smoke-colored.

**Rauch-färbung,** *f.* smoke coloring. **-fleisch,** *n.* smoked meat.

**rauchfrei,** *a.* free from smoke, smokeless.

**Rauchgas,** *n.* smoke gas, flue gas, chimney gas. **-analyse,** *f.* flue-gas analysis.

**rauchgeschwärzt,** *a.* blackened by smoke, smoke-stained.

**Rauchglas,** *n.* tinted glass.

**rauchgrau,** *a.* smoke-gray.

**Rauchhelm,** *m.* smoke helmet.

**rauchig,** *a.* smoky; fumy.

**Rauch-kalk,** *m.* magnesian limestone. **-kanal,** *m.* (smoke) flue.

**rauchlos**, *a.* smokeless.

**Rauch-losigkeit**, *f.* smokelessness. **-pulver**, *n.* fumigating powder. **-quarz**, *m.* smoky quartz. **-rohr**, *n.* smoke flue; fire tube. **-rohrkessel**, *m.* fire-tube boiler. **-schleier**, *m.* smoke screen.

**rauch-schwach**, *a.* giving little smoke, "smokeless." **-schwarz**, *a.* smoky black, sooty.

**Rauch-stärke**, *f.* density of smoke. **-tabak**, *m.* smoking tobacco. **-topas**, *m.* smoky topaz, smoky quartz. **-verbrennung**, *f.* smoke combustion; smoke consumption. **-verbrennungseinrichtung**, *f.* smoke consumer. **-verdünnung**, *f.* smoke dilution. **-verhütung**, *f.* smoke prevention. **-verminderung**, *f.* smoke reduction. **-verzehrung**, *f.* smoke consumption. **-vorhang**, *m.* smoke screen. **-waren**, *f.pl.* furs, peltry. **-wolke**, *f.* smoke cloud.

**Raude, Räude**, *f.* scab, scurf; mange.

**Raufe**, *f.* hackle; rack.

**raufen**, *v.t.* pull, pluck.—*v.r.& i.* scuffle.

**rauh**, *a.* rough (specif., unglazed); raw; coarse, rude; hoarse.

**Rauhartikel**, *m.* (*Calico*) raised style.

**Rauheit**, *f.* roughness, etc. (see rauh).

**Raum**, *m.* space; volume; room, scope; chamber; hold (of a ship); opportunity, occasion. **-analyse**, *f.* volumetric analysis (of gases).

**raumbeständig**, *a.* constant-volume.

**Raum-bestimmung**, *f.* determination of volume. **-bild**, *n.* space diagram; stereoscopic image. **-chemie**, *f.* stereochemistry.

**raumchemisch**, *a.* stereochemical.

**Raum-dichte**, *f.* density by volume. **-einheit**, *f.* unit of space or volume.

**räumen**, *v.t.* clear away, remove; clear; evacuate, leave.

**raumfest**, *a.* fixed in space, stationary.

**Raum-formel**, *f.* spatial formula. **-gebild(e)**, *n.* space diagram. **-gehalt**, *m.* content by volume, spatial content. **-geometrie**, *f.* solid geometry. **-gewicht**, *n.* weight per unit volume, bulk density. **-gitter**, *n.* (*Cryst.*) space lattice, "raumgitter."

**Räumigkeit**, *f.* specific volume; roominess.

**Rauminhalt**, *m.* volume, content, capacity.

**raumisomer**, *a.* stereoisomeric.

**Raumisomerie**, *f.* spatial isomerism, stereoisomerism.

**räumlich**, *a.* relating to or occupying space, spatial, steric; relating to volume.—**räumliche Behinderung, raümliche Hinderung**, steric hindrance.

**Räumlichkeit**, *f.* quality of occupying space, extension; specific volume; spatiality, space; room, part (of a house).

**Raum-mass**, *n.* measure of capacity. **-menge**,

*f.* amount of space, volume. **-meter**, *m.* cubic meter. **-quantelung**, *f.* spatial quantization. **-richtung**, *f.* direction in space. **-teil**, *m.* part by volume, volume. **-veränderung**, *f.* change in volume. **-verhältnis**, *f.* volume relation, proportion by volume **-verminderung**, *f.* decrease in volume.

**raumzentriert**, *a.* (*Cryst.*) body-centered

**raunen**, *v.t.& i.* whisper.

**Raupe**, *f.* caterpillar; worm; whim, fancy.

**Raupenleim**, *m.* raupenleim (trade name for a petroleum product used for protecting trees against caterpillars, etc.).

**Rausch**, *m.* drunkenness, intoxication; rushing, rush, roar; (*Mining*) pounded ore.

**rauschen**, *v.i.* rush, gurgle, murmur, rustle, whistle, roar.

**Rausch-gelb**, *n.* orpiment. **-gold**, *n.* Dutch gold, tinsel. **-mittel**, *n.* intoxicant. **-rot**, *n.* realgar. **-silber**, *n.* imitation silver foil.

**Raute**, *f.* rue; rhombus, diamond.

**rautenähnlich**, *a.* like rue; rhomboid.

**Rauten-flach**, *n.*, **-flächner**, *m.* rhombohedron. **-fläche**, *f.* rhombus.

**rautenförmig**, *a.* rhombic, diamond-shaped.

**Rauten-gewächse**, *n.pl.* (*Bot.*) Rutaceae. **-öl**, *n.* oil of rue. **-spat**, *m.* rhomb spar (dolomite).

**razem-**. see racem-.

**rd.**, *abbrev.* (rund) round, approximately.

**Reagens**, *n.* reagent. **-farbe**, *f.* test color. **-glas**, *n.* test tube. **-glashalter**, *m.* test-tube holder. **-kelch**, *m.* test glass, test cup. **-lösung**, *f.* test solution. **-mittel**, *n.* reagent. **-papier**, *n.* test paper. **-röhre**, *f.*, **-röhrchen**, *n.* test tube.

**Reagenzien, Reagentien**, *n.pl.* reagents. **-flasche**, *f.* reagent bottle. **-kasten**, *m.* reagent box or case.

**reagieren**, *v.i.* react.—**reagierend**, *p.a.* reactive.

**Reagierglas**, *n.* test tube. **-bürste**, *f.* test-tube brush. **-gestell**, *n.* test-tube stand. **-halter**, *m.* test-tube holder.

**Reagier-kelch**, *m.* test glass, test cup. **-zylinder**, *m.* test tube.

**Reaktanz**, *f.* reactance.

**Reaktions-bahn**, *f.* path of a reaction. **-bereitschaft**, *f.* readiness to react, reactivity.

**reaktionsfähig**, *a.* capable of reacting, reactive.

**Reaktions-fähigkeit**, *f.* capability of reacting, reactivity. **-flüssigkeit**, *f.* reaction liquid. **-gemisch**, *n.* reaction mixture. **-geschwindigkeit**, *f.* reaction velocity. **-gleichung**, *f.* equation (of a reaction). **-kern**, *m.* nucleus of reaction.

**reaktionslos**, *a.* reactionless.

**Reaktions-losigkeit**, *f.* absence of reaction, nonreaction. **-masse**, *f.* reaction mass, mass resulting from a reaction. **-mischung,** *f.* reaction mixture. **-mittel,** *n.* reagent. **-papier,** *n.* test paper. **-stufe,** *f.* step or stage of a reaction.

**reaktionsträge,** *a.* slow to react.

**Reaktions-turm,** *m.* reaction tower. **-verlauf,** *m.* course of a reaction. **-wärme,** *f.* heat of reaction.

**Reaktivität,** *f.* reactivity.

**realisieren,** *v.t.* realize.

**Realschule,** *f.* industrial school, scientific school (for teaching science, modern languages, etc.).

**Rebe,** *f.* vine.

**Reben-russ,** *m.* vine black, Frankfort black. **-saft,** *m.* juice of the grape, wine. **-schwarz,** *n.* = Rebenruss.

**Reb-huhn,** *n.* partridge. **-laus,** *f.* vine louse, phylloxera.

**Recept,** etc. = Rezept, etc.

**Rechen,** *m.* rake; rack.

**Rechen-.** calculating, counting, reckoning; rake, raking. **-beispiel,** *n.* example (in calculation). **-fehler,** *m.* error in calculation. **-kunst,** *f.* arithmetic.

**Rechenschaft,** *f.* account.— **— geben,** give account, answer.

**Rechen-schieber, -stab,** *m.* slide rule. **-stift,** *m.* slate pencil. **-tafel,** *f.* reckoning table; multiplication table; slate; blackboard; counting board.

**rechnen,** *v.t.& i.* calculate, reckon, count, compute, estimate.

**rechnerisch,** *adv.* mathematically.

**Rechnung,** *f.* calculation, etc. (see rechnen); arithmetic; calculus; account; bill.

**Rechnungs-betrag,** *m.* amount or total of an account. **-führer,** *m.* bookkeeper, accountant. **-jahr,** *n.* fiscal year, financial year.

**rechnungsmässig,** *a.* in accordance with calculation.

**Rechnungstafel,** *f.* reckoning table.

**recht,** *a.* right; true, genuine, legitimate, own; fitting, agreeable.—*adv.* right, rightly, very.

**Recht,** *n.* right; justice; law.—**mit —,** rightly, with reason.

**Recht-.** right, ortho-, rect-, legal.

**Rechte,** *f.* right (side, hand, party)

**Rechteck,** *n.* rectangle.

**rechteckig,** *a.* rectangular.

**rechten,** *v.i.* litigate; dispute; remonstrate

**rechterhand,** *adv.* on the right-hand side.

**Rechtfertigung,** *f.* justification.

**recht-gläubig,** *a.* orthodox. **-haberisch,** *a.* dogmatical. **-läufig,** *a.* running to the right; clockwise. **-lich,** *a.* just, honest, legal, judicial. **-los,** *a.* illegal; lawless. **-mässig,** *a.* legal, rightful.

**rechts,** *adv.* to the right, on the right, dextro-.

**Rechts-.** to the right, dextro-; of the law, legal. **-anwalt,** *m.* attorney, solicitor. **-beistand,** *m.* (legal) counsel.

**rechtsbeständig,** *a.* valid, legal.

**rechtschaffen,** *a.* just, honest, upright.

**Rechtschreibung,** *f.* orthography, spelling.

**rechtsdrehend,** *p.a.* dextrorotatory.

**Rechts-drehung,** *f.* dextrorotation, right-handed polarization. **-gelehrte,** *m.* lawyer; jurist. **-handel,** *m.* law case, lawsuit.

**rechtskräftig,** *a.* valid, legal.

**Rechtslauf,** *m.* motion to the right, clockwise motion.

**rechtsläufig,** *a.* to the right, clockwise.

**Rechts-milchsäure,** *f.* dextrolactic acid. **-mittel,** *n.* legal remedy. **-pflege,** *f.* administration of justice. **-polarisation,** *f.* = Rechtsdrehung. **-säure,** *f.* dextro acid. **-schraube,** *f.* right-handed screw. **-weinsäure,** *f.* dextrotartaric acid.

**recht-winklig,** *a.* right-angled, rectangular. **-zeitig,** *a.* opportune, seasonable, prompt.

**Recipient,** *m.* = Rezipient.

**reciprok,** *a.* reciprocal.

**Reck,** *n.,* **Recke,** *f.* rack, stretcher, horizontal pole or bar.

**recken,** *v.t.* stretch, extend, rack; (*Metal.*) shingle, tilt.

**Reck-walzen,** *f.pl.,* **-werk,** *n.* (*Metal.*) finishing rolls.

**Redakteur,** *m.* editor.

**Redaktion,** *f.* editing, editorship, editorial staff, editorial office.

**Rede,** *f.* speech, language, talk, discourse; rumor; account.

**reden,** *v.t.& i.* speak, talk, discourse.

**Redensart,** *f.* phrase, expression, term.

**Redeweise,** *f.* way of speaking, style, language.

**redigieren,** *v.t.* edit.

**redlich,** *a.* upright, honest, fair.

**Redner,** *m.* orator, speaker. **-bühne,** *f.* (public) platform.

**redselig,** *a.* talkative.

**reducier-.** see reduzier-.

**reduktionsfähig,** *a.* capable of reduction.

**Reduktions-flamme,** *f.* reducing flame. **-hütte,** *f.* (*Metal.*) reduction works. **-kraft,** *f.* reducing power. **-mittel,** *n.* reducing agent. **-ofen,** *m.* reduction furnace. **-ort,** *m.* reduction region. **-röhre,** *f.* reduction tube. **-tiegel,** *m.* reduction crucible. **-vermögen,** *n.* reducing power.

**reduktiv,** *a.* reductive, by reduction.

**reduzierbar,** *a.* reducible.

**Reduzierbarkeit,** *f.* reducibility.

**reduzieren,** *v.t.* reduce.

**reduzierfähig,** *a.* capable of reduction.

**Reduzier-salz,** *n.* reducing salt. **-stück,** *n.* reducing piece.

Reduzierung, f. reduction.

Reduzierventil, n. reducing valve.

reell, a. real, sound, honest.

Reep, n. rope.

Referat, n. abstract; review; report.

Referent, m. abstractor; reporter.

Referierdienst, m. abstracting service; reporting service.

referieren, v.t.& i. report; abstract.

reflektieren, v.t. reflect.—v.i. reflect, consider.

Reflexions-ebene, f. plane of reflection. -goniometer, n. reflecting goniometer. -winkel, m. angle of reflection.

Refr., abbrev. (Refraktion) refraction.

refraktär, a. refractory.

Refraktionswinkel, m. angle of refraction.

refrigerieren, v.t. refrigerate.—v.i. freeze.

Regal, n. shelves, case with shelves.

rege, a. moving, movable, quick, active, lively.

Regel, f. rule; principle, standard; (Med.) menstruation.

regelbar, a. regulable, adjustable.

Regelhahn, m. regulating cock.

regel-los, a. anomalous, irregular. -mässig, a. regular; ordinary.—adv. regularly.

regeln, v.t. regulate, order, arrange, govern.

regelrecht, a. regular, normal.

Regelung, f. regulation, control.

regelwidrig, a. irregular, abnormal.

regen, v.t. move, rouse.—v.r. stir, be active.

Regen, m. rain. -bogen, m. rainbow.

regenbogenfarbig, a. rainbow-colored, iridescent.

Regenbogenhaut, f. iris.

Regenerat, n., -gummi, m. reclaimed rubber.

regenerieren, v.t. regenerate.

Regenerierung, f. regeneration.

Regenfang, m. cistern.

regenlos, a. rainless, dry.

Regen-mass, n., -messer, m. rain gage. -menge, f. amount of rain. -schirm, m. umbrella. -wasser, n. rain water. -wurm, m. earthworm. -zeit, f. rainy season.

regieren, v.i. rule, reign.—v.t. rule, govern, regulate, manage.

Regierung, f. government, administration; rule; steerage.

Regieverschluss, m. bond.—unter —, in bond, bonded.

Register, n. index; (table of) contents; register; record. -band, n. index volume.

Registratur, f. registry; registry book.

Registrier-. recording; indexing.

registrieren, v.t. register, record; file; index.

Regler, m. regulator.

Reglisse, f. licorice (juice or drops); marshmallow paste.

regnen, v.i. rain.

regnerisch, a. rainy.

regsam, a. active, quick, agile.

regulieren, v.t. regulate.

Regulierhahn, m. regulating cock.

regulinisch, a. reguline.

Regung, f. motion, moving; emotion.

Reh, n. roe (deer), doe, buck. -braun, n.= Sammetbraun; fawn color.

reh-farben, -farbig, a. fawn-colored.

Reh-leder, n. doeskin. -posten, m.pl. buckshot.

Reibe, f. grater, rasp.

reibecht, a. fast to rubbing.

Reibeisen, n. rasp; grater.

Reibemühle, f. grinding mill, grinder.

reiben, v.t. rub; grind, triturate (colors, etc.); rasp, grate; scour; chafe.

Reibepulver, n. abrasive powder.

Reiber, m. rubber, brayer, pestle; grater.

Reib-kasten, m. grinding mill, grinder. -keule, f. pestle. -schale, f. mortar. -stein, m. grinding stone.

Reibung, f. friction; rubbing, etc. (see reiben); rub, difficulty.

Reibungselektrizität, f. frictional electricity.

reibungsfrei, a. frictionless.

Reibung-koeffizient, m. coefficient of friction. -probe, f. friction test. -wärme, f. frictional heat. -widerstand, m. frictional resistance. -zahl, -ziffer, f. coefficient of friction.

Reibzündhölzchen, n. friction match.

reich, a. rich; abundant.

Reich, n. state, body politic; empire, kingdom, etc.

-reich. rich (in), abounding (in).

Reichblei, n. rich lead (argentiferous).

reichen, v.t. reach, pass, give.—v.i. reach, extend, suffice, last.

Reichfrischen, n. (Copper) enriching.

reich-haltig, a. plentiful, abundant. -lich, a. abundant, copious, rich, full.

Reichs-. State, Government; (formerly, under the Kaiser) Imperial. -anstalt, f. Government Institute.

Reich-schaum, m. (Metal.) the zinc crust, rich in silver, etc., formed in the Parkes process. -schlacke, f. rich slag. -schmelzen, n. smelting of precious metals.

Reichs-gesundheitsamt, n. Government Board of Health. -kraftstoff, m. a motor fuel containing benzol, alcohol and tetralin. -mark, f. reichsmark (the German monetary unit). -patent, n. German patent.

Reich-tum, m. wealth, richness, abundance. -weite, f. range.

reif, a. ripe.

Reif, m, ring, hoop; tire; collar; hoarfrost.

Reife, f. ripeness; maturity; (of beer, etc.) age; puberty. -grad, m. degree of ripeness.

reifen, *v.t.& i.* ripen, mature.

Reifen, *m.* ring, hoop; tire; collar.

Reifezustand, *m.* ripe state, ripeness.

Reihe, *f.* series; row, succession; range; suite, train; rank, file; turn; column; line.—der — nach, in succession.

reihen, *v.t.* arrange in a series or row; string (beads); baste.

Reihen-folge, *f.* sequence, order, succession. -schaltung, *f.* (*Elec.*) connection in series.

Reiher, *m.* heron.

rein, *a.* pure; undiluted; clean, clear, tidy; sheer.—*adv.* purely, clean, absolutely.

Rein-benzol, *n.* (pure) benzene. -darstellung, *f.* preparation in a pure condition, purification. -element, *n.* pure element (consisting of but one isotope). -ertrag, *m.* net yield; net profit.

reingelb, *a.* pure yellow.

Reingewicht, *n.* net weight.

Reinheit, *f.* purity, pureness, etc. (see rein).

Reinheits-grad, *m.* degree of purity. -probe, *f.* test for purity.

reinigen, *v.t.* purify; refine (metals, etc.); rectify (spirits); clarify (liquids); clean, cleanse, scour (silk), purge; disinfect.

Reiniger, *m.* purifier, etc. (see reinigen). -masse, *f.* purifier mass. -wasser, *n.* cleansing water.

Reinigung, *f.* purification, etc. (see reinigen); menstruation.

Reinigungs-anlage, *f.* purifying plant. -apparat, *m.* purifying apparatus, purifier, etc. (see reinigen). -bassin, *n.* purifying tank or basin. -behälter, *m.* filtering basin or tank. -feuer, *n.* refining fire. -flasche, *f.* (for gases) washing bottle, wash bottle. -masse, *f.* purifying mass. -mittel, *n.* purifying agent, purifier; cleansing agent, detergent; purgative. -vermögen, *n.* detergent power, cleansing power, etc. (see reinigen).

Rein-kultur, -kultivierung, *f.* (*Bact.*) pure culture, pure cultivation.

reinst, *a.* purest, etc. (see rein).

Rein-xylol, *n.* (*Com.*) a mixture of the three xylenes (*m*-xylene predominating). -zellulose, *f.* pure cellulose. -zucht, *f.* (*Bact.*) = Reinkultur.

Reis, *m.* rice.—*n.* twig, sprig; shoot, scion. -branntwein, *m.* rice spirit.

Reise, *f.* journey, trip, travel, voyage.

reisen, *v.i.* travel, go, set out, leave.

Reisig, Reisicht, *n.* brushwood, twigs, prunings.

Reis-körper, *m.* (*Med.*) rice body. -mehl, *n.* rice flour. -papier, *n.* rice paper. -puder, *m.* rice powder.

Reissblei, *n.* graphite. -tiegel, *m.* graphite crucible.

Reisschleim, *m.* rice water.

reissen, *v.t.* tear, pull, drag, split; trace, draw; bruise, crush (malt); rough-grind (glass). —*v.i.* burst, split, crack, break; tear along. —*v.r.* scratch oneself, tear one's clothes; scramble (for).—reissend, *p.a.* tearing, etc. (see reissen); rapacious; rapid.

Reiss-festigkeit, *f.* resistance to tearing or breaking, tenacity, tensile strength. -gelb, *n.* orpiment. -kohle, *f.* charcoal crayon. -korn, *n.* (*Leather*) artificial grain.

Reisstärke, *f.* rice starch.

Reit-. riding.

reiten, *v.t.& i.* ride (horseback).

Reiter, *m.* rider; horseman. -gewicht, *n.* rider (the weight).

Reiz, *m.* irritation; excitement; irritant; stimulus; charm, attraction, grace.

reizbar, *a.* irritable, sensitive.

reizen, *v.t.* irritate, stimulate, excite; charm, attract, allure.

Reizgift, *n.* irritant poison.

reizlos, *a.* nonirritant, nonstimulating; unattractive, insipid.

Reiz-losigkeit, *f.* nonirritance, etc. (see reizlos). -mittel, *n.* irritant, stimulant, incitement, inducement. -stoff, *m.* (*Med.*) adjuvant.

Reizung, *f.* irritation, etc. (see reizen).

Reizwirkung, *f.* irritating effect; stimulating effect.

rekapitulieren, *v.t.* recapitulate.

Reklamation, *f.* complaint; claim.

Reklame, *f.* advertisement; puffery.

reklamieren, *v.t.* claim, reclaim.—*v.t.* object.

Rekteseite, *f.* right-hand page, odd page.

Rektifikations-apparat, *m.* rectifying apparatus, rectifier. -becken, *n.* rectifying vessel. -kolonne, *f.* rectifying column.

Rektifizierapparat, *m.* rectifying apparatus.

rektifizieren, *v.t.* rectify.

Rektifizierung, *f.* rectification.

relationieren, *v.t.* relate, correlate.

relativistisch, *a.* relativistic.

Relativität, *f.* relativity.

relaxieren, *v.t.& i.* relax.

Relevanz, *f.* relevance, relevancy.

remittieren, *v.t.& i.* remit.

Rendement, *m.* yield, rendement.

Rendita, *f.* extent of weighting (fabrics).

renken, *v.t.* bend, turn; wrench.

Renn-arbeit, *f.* (*Iron*) direct process. -eisen, *n.* malleable iron extracted by the direct process.

rennen, *v.i.* run; race.—*v.t.* run; (*Metal.*) extract (malleable iron) directly from the ore.

Renn-feuer, *n.* bloomery hearth (where malleable iron is extracted by the direct process). -feuereisen, n. = Renneisen. -feuerschlacke, f. (Iron) direct-process slag. -herd, m. = Rennfeuer. -schlacke, f. = Rennfeuerschlacke. -stahl, m. steel made directly from the ore, natural steel. -tier, n. reindeer.

Renommee, n. renown.

renommieren, v.i. boast, brag.—renommiert, p.a. renowned, well known.

rentabel, a. profitable.

Rentabilität, f. profitableness.

Rente, f. rent, revenue, income.

Rentenmark, f. a monetary unit based on securities and normally equivalent in value to the reichsmark.

rentieren, v.i.& r. be profitable, pay.

Reparatur, f. repair.

reparieren, v.t. repair.

repassieren, v.t. boil off (silk) a second time.

Repertorium, n. index, compendium (as in titles of periodicals); repertoire.

repetieren, v.t.& i. repeat.

Repetition, f. repetition; recapitulation.

Repetitorium, n. (as book title) compendium, summary; (in schools) review course.

Repräsentant, m. representative.

Reprise, f. normal or allowable moisture.

reproduzierbar, a. reproducible.

reproduzieren, v.t. reproduce.

Reps, m. rape. -öl, n. rape oil, rapeseed oil.

requirieren, v.t. request; requisition.

Reseda f. mignonette.—gelbe —, dyer's rocket.

Resedagrün, n. a kind of chrome green.

Reservage, f. (Calico) resist, reserve.

Reservage-artikel, m. (Calico) resist style. -druck, m. resist printing, resist style. -papp, m. resist paste.

Reserve, f. = Reservage.

Reserve-mittel, n. reserve, resist. -muster, n. reference pattern. -stoff, m. reserve material.

reservieren, v.t. reserve; (Calico) subject to the action of a reserve or resist.

Reservierungsmittel, n. (Calico) resist, reserve.

Residuum, n. residuum, residue.

resorbieren, v.t. resorb, reabsorb.

Resorbierung, f. resorption, reabsorption.

Resorcin, n. resorcinol, resorcin. -blau, n. resorcin blue. -gelb, n. resorcin yellow.

Resorzin, n. resorcinol, resorcin.

resp., abbrev. respektive.

respektive, adv. respectively, or rather, or.

Respirationsnahrungsmittel, n. respiratory food.

Rest, m. residue; remainder, rest, remains, remnant.

Rest-. residual. -flüssigkeit, f. residual liquid. -glied, n. residual term or member;

(Math.) remainder in an infinite series. -härte, f. residual hardness, (of water) permanent hardness.

restieren, v.i. remain, be left.

Restlauge, f. residual liquor or liquid.

restlos, a. without residue, without remainder.

Rest-stickstoff, m. residual nitrogen. -strahl, m. residual ray. -strom, m. residual current. -valenz, f. residual valence.

Resultat, n. result.

resultieren, v.i. result.—resultierend, p.a. resulting, resultant.

Retenchinon, n. retenequinone.

Retorte, f. retort.

Retorten-bauch, m. belly or bulb of a retort. -gestell, n. retort stand. -hals, m. neck of a retort. -halter, m. retort holder, retort stand. -haus, n. retort house. -helm, m. retort head, retort helm. -kitt, n. retort cement, retort lute. -kohle, f. retort carbon. -mündung, f. mouth of a retort. -ofen, m. retort furnace. -rückstand, m. retort residue. -vergasung, f. gasification in retorts. -verkokung, f. retort coking. -vorstoss, m. adapter; (Zinc) condenser (of clay or iron).

retouchieren, v.t. retouch.

Retour-. return, returning.

Retournöl, n. recovered oil.

retten, v.t. save, rescue, recover.

Rettich, Rettig, m. black radish.

Rettung, f. rescue, recovery, saving, salvage.

Rettungsmittel, n. remedy, resource.

reuen, v.t. repent of, regret.

Reugeld, n. forfeit.

Reusse, m. Russian.

reverberieren, v.t. reverberate.

Reverberier-ofen, m., -feuer, n. reverberatory furnace, reverberatory.

reversibel, reversierbar, a. reversible.

revidieren, v.t. revise; check.

Revier, n. district, region; (Mining) country.

rez., abbrev. reziprok (which see).

Rezension, f. review, criticism.

rezent, a. recent.

Rezept, n. recipe, prescription. -buch, n. receipt book.

Rezeptor, m. receptor.

Rezeptur, f. dispensing (of medicines); receivership.

Rezipient, m. receiver; (of persons) recipient.

reziprok, a. reciprocal.—adv. reciprocally, conversely.

RGT-Regel, abbrev. (Reaktionsgeschwindigkeit-Temperatur-Regel). reaction-velocity-temperature rule.

Rhabarber, m. rhubarb. — falscher —, (Pharm.) the root of European rhubarb.

Rhabarber-gelb, n. chrysophanic acid. -gerb-

säure, *f.* rheotannic acid. -säure, *f.* chryso-
phanic acid.
rheinisch, rheinländisch, *a.* Rhenish.
Rheinsäure, *f.* rheic acid (chrysophanic
acid).
Rheinwein, *m.* Rhine wine, Rhenish wine.
Rhizocarpinsäure, *f.* rhizocarpinic acid.
Rhizocarpsäure, *f.* rhizocarpic acid.
Rhizoninsäure, *f.* rhizoninic acid.
Rhizonsäure, *f.* rhizonic acid.
Rhld., *abbrev.* (Rheinland) Rhineland.
Rhöadin, *n.* rheadine, rhoeadine.
Rhodan, *n.* thiocyanogen, sulfocyanogen.
Rhodan-. thiocyanogen (or sulfocyanogen),
thiocyanate of, thiocyano-. -aluminium, *n.*
aluminum thiocyanate. -ammonium, *n.*
ammonium thiocyanate. -ammonlösung,
*f.* ammonium thiocyanate solution.
Rhodanat, *n.* thiocyanate, sulfocyanate. -lö-
sung, *f.* thiocyanate solution.
Rhodan-baryum, *n.* barium thiocyanate.
-eisen, *n.* iron thiocyanate, esp. ferric thiocyanate. -eisenrot, *n.* ferric thiocyanate.
Rhodanid, *n.* thiocyanate, sulfocyanate (esp.
an -ic salt; cf. Rhodanür).
Rhodanierung, *f.* introduction of thiocyanogen, thiocyanation.
Rhodan-ion, *n.* thiocyanogen ion, CNS⁻.
-kalium, *n.* potassium thiocyanate. -kalzi-
um, *n.* calcium thiocyanate. -kupfer, *n.*
cupric thiocyanate. -lösung, *f.* thiocyanate
solution. -metall, *n.* (metallic) thiocyanate.
-methyl, *n.* methyl thiocyanate. -nickel,
*m.* nickel thiocyanate. -quecksilber, *n.*
mercury thiocyanate. -salz, *n.* thiocyanate.
-säure, *f.* (*Org. Chem.*) thiocyano acid.
-tonerde, *f.* aluminum thiocyanate.
Rhodanür, *n.* (-ous) thiocyanate, (-ous) sulfocyanate.
Rhodan-verbindung, *f.* thiocyanogen compound. -wasserstoff, *m.* hydrogen thiocyanate, thiocyanic acid. -wasserstoff-
säure, *f.* thiocyanic acid, sulfocyanic acid.
-zinn, -zinnoxyd, *n.* stannic thiocyanate.
-zinnoxydul, *n.* stannous thiocyanate.
Rhodinasäure, *f.* rhodinic acid.
Rhodium-chlorwasserstoffsäure, *f.* acid containing rhodium, chlorine and hydrogen
(H₄RhCl₇ and H₃RhCl₆). -metall, *n.* rhodium metal, metallic rhodium. -salz, *n.*
rhodium salt. -verbindung, *f.* rhodium
compound.
Rhombendodekaeder, *n.* rhombic dodecahedron.
rhombenförmig, *a.* rhomb-shaped, rhombic.
rhombisch, *a.* rhombic.
Rhomboeder, *n.* rhombohedron.
rhomboedrisch, *a.* rhombohedral.
rhomboidisch, *a.* rhomboid, rhomboidal.

Rhuslack, *m.* rhus varnish (from the Japanese
varnish tree, *Rhus vernicifera*).
Richtblei, *n.* plumb line, plummet.
richten, *v.t.* direct, turn; arrange, adjust, set,
straighten; dress; raise, erect; judge.—*v.r.*
turn, rise, conform.
Richter, *m.* judge; justice.
richtig, *a.* right, correct, accurate, just, fair,
true.
Richtig-keit, *f.* rightness, etc. (see richtig).
-stellung, *f.* rectification, correction.
Richt-linie, *f.* guide line, guiding line. -mass,
*n.* standard, gage. -platte, *f.* adjusting
plate, adjusting table. -scheit, *n.* rule,
straight-edge. -schnur, *f.* chalk line; plumb
line.
Richtung, *f.* direction, bearing.
Richtungs-änderung, *f.* change of direction.
-quantelung, *f.* directional quantization.
Ricinölsäure, *f.* ricinoleic acid.
Ricinus, *m.* castor-oil plant. -öl, *n.* castor oil.
-ölsäure, *f.* ricinoleic acid. -samen, *m.*
castor bean. -seife, *f.* castor-oil soap.
rieb, *pret.* of reiben.
Riech-. smelling, scented, odoriferous; olfactory. -bein, *n.* ethmoid.
riechen, *v.i.& t.* smell.— nach, smell of.—
riechend, *p.a.* smelling, redolent, strong.
Riech-essig, *m.* aromatic vinegar. -fläsch-
chen, *n.* smelling bottle. -mittel, *n.* scent,
perfume. -nerv, *m.* olfactory nerve. -rohr,
*n.* volatilizing tube. -salz, *n.* smelling salts.
-stoff, *m.* odoriferous substance, perfume.
-wasser, *n.* scented water.
Ried, *n.* reed; moor; fagot.
rief, *pret.* of rufen.
Riefe, *f.* groove, channel.
riefeln, *v.t.* channel, groove; rifle.
Riegel, *m.* rail, bar, bolt.
Riemen, *m.* strap, thong, band, belt; oar.
-fett, *n.* belt dressing. -schmiere, *f.* belt
lubricant.
Ries, *n.* ream.
Riese, *m.* giant.
Riesel-feld, *n.* field irrigated with sewage.
-jauche, *f.* sewage (as a fertilizer).
rieseln, *v.i.* ripple, gush, trickle.
Rieselwasser, *n.* trickling water.
Riesen-. gigantic, colossal. -schlange, *f.*
python, boa constrictor, anaconda. -zelle,
*f.* giant cell.
riesig, *a.* gigantic.
riet, *pret.* of raten.
Riff, *n.* reef, ridge, shelf, ledge.
Riffel-. grooved, channeled, fluted; ribbed;
corrugated.
riffeln, *v.t.* ripple (flax); channel, groove, corrugate, rib.
Riffeltrichter, *m.* ribbed funnel.

Rille, *f.* furrow, groove.

Rind, *n.* bovine animal, neat, (*pl.*) cattle.

Rinde, *f.* rind; bark, cortex; crust.

Rinden-. cortical, bark. -farbstoff, *m.* phlobaphene. -gewebe, *n.* cortical tissue. -schicht, *f.* cortical layer.

Rinder-. beef, cattle, bovine. -braten, *m.* roast beef. -fett, *n.* beef suet, beef fat. -galle, *f.* ox gall. -klauenöl, *n.* neat's-foot oil. -markfett, *n.* beef marrow fat. -talg, *m.* beef tallow.

Rind-fleisch, *n.* beef. -fleischbrühe, *f.* beef broth, beef tea. -leder, *n.* neat's leather, cowhide.

Rinds-galle, *f.* ox gall. -klauenfett, *n.* neat's-foot oil. -leder, *n.* neat's leather, cowhide.

Rindspalte, *f.* split cowhide.

Rindstalg, *m.* beef tallow, beef fat.

Rindvieh, *n.* cattle.

Ring, *m.* ring; link; coil; collar, band, hoop, loop.

Ring-. (*Org. Chem.*) cyclic, ring.

ring-ähnlich, -artig, *a.* ringlike, circular, cyclic, annular, areolar.

Ring-alkohol, *m.* cyclic alcohol. -amin, *n.* cyclic amine. -aufspaltung, *f.* ring cleavage. -bildung, *f.* ring formation. -brenner, *m.* ring burner.

Ringelblume, *f.* marigold (*Calendula*).

ringelig, *a.* ringlike, annular.

ringeln, *v.t.* ring; curl; girdle (trees).—*v.r.* curl.

ringen, *v.i.* struggle, wrestle.—*v.t.* wring; ring; curl.

Ringerweiterung, *f.* ring extension.

ringförmig, *a.* cyclic; ring-shaped, annular.

Ring-keton, *n.* cyclic ketone. -ofen, *m.* (*Ceram.*) annular kiln, Hofmann kiln. -öffnung, *f.* ring opening.

rings, *adv.* around.

Ringschicht, *f.* annular layer.

ringschliessen, *v.r.* form a ring.

Ring-schliessung, *f.*, -schluss, *m.* ring closure, cyclization. -spaltung, *f.* ring cleavage. -spannung, *f.* ring tension. -sprengung, *f.* ring cleavage.

ringsum, *adv.* around, all around.

ringungesättigt, *p.a.* cyclically unsaturated, containing an unsaturated ring.

Ring-verbindung, *f.* cyclic compound, ring compound. -verkleinerung, *f.* reduction of a ring to smaller size.

Rinne, *f.* channel, groove, furrow, gutter.

rinnen, *v.i.* run, flow; leak.

Rinnstein, *m.* sink; gutter; gutter stone.

Rippe, *f.* rib.

rippen, *v.t.* rib.—gerippt, *p.a.* ribbed, fluted, corded, laid (paper).

Rippen-. ribbed; costal. -fell, *n.*, -haut, *f.* (costal) pleura. -glas, *n.* ribbed glass.

-rohr, *n.* ribbed pipe or tube. -trichter, *m.* ribbed funnel.

Risigallum, *n.* realgar.

Risiko, *n.* risk.

riskieren, *v.t.* risk.

Rispe, *f.* panicle.

riss, *pret.* of reissen.

Riss, *m.* fissure, crack, flaw; rent, tear, gap; draft, sketch, design, plan.

Rissebildung, *f.* formation of cracks, fissuring.

rissig, *a.* fissured, cracked, flawy, torn.

ritt, *pret.* of reiten.

Ritter, *m.* knight. -sporn, *m.* larkspur.

Ritz, *m.*, Ritze, *f.* rift, cleft, fissure, crack, chink; slit; scratch.

ritzen, *v.t.* crack; slit; scratch.

Ritz-härte, *f.* hardness to scratching. -versuch, *m.* scratch test.

Rizin, *n.* ricin.

Rizin-. see Ricin-.

Rk., *abbrev.* (Reaktion) reaction.

Rkk , *abbrev.* (Reaktionen) reactions.

rm., *abbrev.* (Raummeter) cubic meter, cu.m.

Rm., RM., *abbrev.* Reichsmark.

Robbe, *f.* (*Zoöl.*) seal.

Robbentran, *m.* seal oil.

roch, *pret.* of riechen.

Rochellesalz, *n.* Rochelle salt, sodium potassium tartrate.

röcheln, *v.i.* rattle.

Rock, *m.* coat; gown, robe; skirt; frock.

roden, *v.t.* root out, grub, clear.

Rogen, *m.* roe, spawn. -stein, *m.* oölite.

rogensteinartig, *a.* oölitic.

Roggen, *m.* rye. -brot, *n.* rye bread. -kleber, *m.* rye gluten. -mehl, *n.* rye flour. -mutter, *f.* ergot. -stärke, *f.* rye starch.

roh, *a.* raw, crude; rough, coarse; gross.

Roh-arbeit, *f.* (*Metal.*) ore smelting. -asbest, *m.* crude asbestos. -benzol, *n.* crude benzene, benzol (or benzole). -blei, *n.* crude lead. -brom, *n.* crude bromine.

Roheisen, *n.* crude iron, pig iron. -gans, *f.* (iron) pig. -guss, *m.* pig-iron casting.

Roh-ertrag, *m.* gross yield; gross returns. -erz, *n.* raw ore. -erzeugnis, *f.* raw product. -faser, *f.* crude fiber. -faserbestimmung, *f.* determination of crude fiber. -formel, *f.* empirical formula. -frischen, *n.* (*Metal.*) first refining. -frischperiode, *f.* (*Iron*) boiling stage, boil. -frucht, *f.* (*Brewing*) unmalted grain. -gang, *m.* (*Metal.*) irregular working.

rohgar, *a.* (*Metal.*) partly refined.

Roh-geschmack, *m.* raw taste. -gewicht, *n.* gross weight. -gift, *n.* crude poison; crude toxin. -gummi, *n.* crude rubber; crude gum. -haut, *f.* rawhide. -kautschuk, *m.* crude rubber, raw rubber. **-kohle,** *f.* rough coal, run of mine. **-kresol,** *n.* crude cresol. **-kultur,** *f.* (*Bact.*) impure culture; (*Agric.*) culture of new land. **-kupfer,** *n.* crude copper. **-material,** *n.* raw material. **-messing,** *n.* crude brass. **-metall,** *n.* crude metal. **-naphta,** *f.* crude naphtha; crude petroleum. **-ofen,** *m.* ore furnace. **-öl,** *n.* crude oil. **-paraffin,** *n.* crude paraffin. **-petroleum,** *n.* crude petroleum. **-phosphat,** *m.* (*Agric.*) rock phosphate. **-probe,** *f.* crude sample. **-produkt,** *n.* raw product.

**Rohr,** *n.* tube; pipe; reed, cane; flue; barrel (of a gun). **-bürste,** *f.* tube brush.

**Röhrchen,** *n.* little tube or pipe; tubule; cane; reed (in an organ).

**Röhre,** *f.* tube; pipe; nozzle; spout; channel, duct; conduit; shaft, tunnel.

röhrenartig, *a.* tubular; fistular.

**Röhrenbürste,** *f.* tube brush.

röhrenförmig, *a.* = röhrenartig.

**Röhren-halter,** *m.* tube (or pipe) holder, tube (or pipe) clamp. **-kassie,** *f.* purging cassia. **-klemme,** *f.* tube clamp. **-lot,** *n.* pipe solder. **-manna,** *f.* flake manna. **-nudeln,** *f.pl.* macaroni. **-ofen,** *m.* tube furnace (for heating tubes liable to explosion). **-substanz,** *f.* (*Anat.*) medullary substance. **-träger,** *m.* tube (or pipe) support. **-werk,** *n.* tubing; piping. **-wischer,** *m.* tube brush.

rohrförmig, *a.* tubular.

röhrig, *a.* tubular; fistular.

**Rohr-leitung,** *f.* tubing, piping, pipe line. **-mühle,** *f.* tube mill. **-pulver,** *n.* tubular powder. **-schlange,** *f.* coil (of pipe), worm, spiral tube. **-stutzen,** *m.* = Stutzen. **-weite,** *f.* bore of a tube or pipe. **-werk,** *n.* tubing. **-zange,** *f.* pipe wrench.

**Rohrzucker,** *m.* cane sugar. **-saft,** *m.* cane juice. **-verbindung,** *f.* cane-sugar compound, sucrate.

**Roh-salpeter,** *m.* crude saltpeter. **-schlacke,** *f.* raw slag, ore slag. **-schmelzen,** *n.* raw smelting, ore smelting. **-schwefel,** *m.* crude sulfur. **-seide,** *f.* raw silk. **-silber,** *n.* crude silver. **-soda,** *f.* crude soda, (in the Leblanc process) black ash. **-sole,** *f.* raw brine, crude brine. **-spiritus,** *m.* raw spirit, crude spirit. **-stahl,** *m.* raw steel; natural steel. **-stahleisen,** *n.* pig iron for steel making, steel pig. **-stein,** *m.* (*Copper*) coarse metal. **-steinschlacke,** *f.* coarse-metal slag. **-stoff,** *m.* raw material, crude substance. **-sulfat,** *n.* crude sulfate, raw sulfate. **-wasser,** *n.* raw water, untreated water. **-wolle,** *f.* raw wool. **-zucker,** *m.* raw sugar, unrefined sugar.

**Roll-.** rolling, roller; rolled, coiled.

**Rolle,** *f.* roll; roller; caster; pulley; calender; rôle.

rollen, *v.t.& i.* roll; rotate; calender. **-artig, -förmig,** *a.* cylindrical.

**Rollen-lager,** *n.* roller bearing. **-zug,** *m.* block and tackle.

**Roll-flasche,** *f.* a bottle of narrow-necked cylindrical form. **-mass,** *n.* (coiled) tape measure. **-schicht,** *f.* upright course (bricks set on end). **-stein,** *m.* boulder. **-wagen,** *m.* truck, lorry.

**Roman,** *m.* novel, romance.

**Römerkerze,** *f.* (*Pyrotechny*) Roman candle.

römisch, *a.* Roman.—römische Bertramwurzel = Bertramwurzel.— römische Kamille, Roman camomile (*Anthemis nobilis*).— römischer Kümmel, cumin.—römische Minze, spearmint.

**Römisch-kamillenöl,** *n.* Roman-camomile oil. **-kümmelöl,** *n.* cumin oil.

rönne, *pret. subj.* of rinnen.

**Röntgen-bremsstrahlung,** *f.* X-radiation due to checking or impact. **-röhre,** *f.* Röntgen (X-ray) tube. **-strahlen,** *m.pl.* Röntgen rays, X-rays.

**Rosa,** *n.* pink, rose (color).

rosa, **-farben, -farbig,** *a.* rose-colored, rose, pink, rosy.

**Rosa-färbung,** *f.* rose coloration, pink color. **-rot,** *n.* pink.

rösch, *a.* brittle; coarse; hard baked or roasted.

röschen, *v.t.* age or cure; dig (a trench or tunnel).

**Rösch-erz, -gewächs,** *n.* brittle silver ore, stephanite.

**Rose,** *f.* rose; rosette; erysipelas.

**Rosen-essenz,** *f.* attar of roses. **-farbe,** *f.* rose color.

rosen-farben, **-farbig,** *a.* rose-colored, rosy.

**Rosen-geruch,** *m.* rose odor. **-holz,** *n.* rosewood. **-honig,** *m.* (*Pharm.*) honey of rose. **-kohl,** *m.* Brussels sprouts. **-konserve,** *f.* (*Pharm.*) confection of rose. **-kranz,** *m.* rosary; rose garland. **-kupfer,** *n.* rose copper. **-lack,** *m.* rose lake. **-lorbeer,** *m.* oleander; mountain rose (*Rosa*). **-öl,** *n.* rose oil, attar of roses. **-quarz,** *m.* rose quartz.

rosenrot, *a.* rose-red.

**Rosen-schwamm,** *m.* bedeguar, bedegar. **-spat,** *m.* rhodochrosite. **-stahl,** *m.* rose steel. **-stock,** *m.* rosebush. **-wasser,** *n.* rose water.

**Roseokobaltsalz,** *n.* roseocobaltic salt.

rosettenartig, *a.* like a rosette.

**Rosetten-bahn,** *f.* rosette orbit or path. **-herd,** *m.* (*Copper*) refining hearth. **-kupfer,** *n.* rosette copper.

rosettieren, *v.i.* make rosette copper.

rosieren, *v.t.* dye pink or rose.

**Rosiersalz,** *n.* (*Dyeing*) rose salt, tin composition (solution of tin in aqua regia).

**rosig,** *a.* rosy; rosacic (uric; *Obs.*).

**Rosigsäure,** *f.* rosacic (uric) acid. *Obs.*

**Rosine,** *f.* raisin.

**Rosmarin,** *m.* rosemary. **-öl,** *n.* rosemary oil.

**Rosolsäure,** *f.* rosolic acid.

**Ross,** *n.* horse, steed. **-fenchel,** *m.* (*Pharm.*) water fennel, horsebane (*Oenanthe phellandrium*). **-huf,** *m.* coltsfoot (*Tussilago farfara*). **-kastanie,** *f.* horse-chestnut. **-schwefel,** *m.* horse brimstone (impure grayish sulfur). **-wurzel,** *f.* carline thistle; carline root.

**Rost,** *m.* rust; mildew; roasting charge; grate, gridiron.

**Röst-abgang,** *m.* loss of weight on roasting. **-anlage,** *f.* roasting plant. **-arbeit,** *f.* roasting process, roasting. **-betriebsdauer,** *f.* roasting time, duration of roasting. **-bett,** *n.* roasting bed.

**Rostbildung,** *f.* rust formation.

**Röstbitter,** *n.* assamar.

**Rostbrand,** *m.* rust, mildew, smut.

**rostbraun,** *a.* rust-brown, rusty brown.

**Röste,** *f.* roasting; roasting place; roasting charge; retting, steeping; rettery.

**rosten,** *v.i.* rust.

**rösten,** *v.t.* roast; calcine; torrefy; ret, steep (flax or hemp); broil, grill; toast.

**Rostentfernung,** *f.* rust removal.

**Röster,** *m.* roaster, calciner.

**Rösterzeugnis,** *n.* product of roasting, of calcining, etc. (see rösten).

**Rostfarbe,** *f.* rust color.

**rost-farben, -farbig,** *a.* rust-colored.

**Rost-fläche,** *f.* grate surface. **-fleck,** *m.* rust spot, iron spot.

**rost-fleckig,** *a.* rust-spotted, rust-stained. **-frei,** *a.* rust-free, stainless.

**Röstgas,** *n.* gas from roasting.

**rostgelb,** *a.* rust-yellow, rusty yellow.

**Rostgelb,** *n.* a buff pigment (hydrous iron oxide).

**Röst-gummi,** *n.* dextrin. **-gut,** *n.* material to be roasted; roasted material.

**rostig,** *a.* rusty; (of water) chalybeate.

**Rostig-keit,** *f.,* **-sein,** *n.* rustiness.

**Rostkitt,** *m.* iron-rust cement.

**Röst-kufe,** *f.* retting vat. **-malz,** *n.* roasted malt, black malt.

**Rostmittel,** *n.* rust preventive, anti-rust agent.

**Röst-ofen,** *m.* roasting furnace, roasting kiln, calciner, roaster. **-posten,** *m.* roasting charge. **-probe,** *f.* calcination assay or test. **-produkt,** *n.* = Rösterzeugnis. **-prozess,** *m.* roasting process, calcination process.

**rost-rein,** *a.* rust-free. **-rot,** *a.* rust-red, brown-red.

**Röst-rückstand,** *m.* residue from roasting. **-scherben,** *m.* roasting dish, scorifier.

**Rostschicht,** *f.* layer of rust; layer of material to be roasted.

**Röst-schlacke,** *f.* slag from roasting. **-schmelzen,** *n.* (*Metal.*) roasting and smelting.

**Rostschutz,** *m.* protection against rust, rust prevention.

**rostschützend,** *a.* rust-preventing.

**Rostschutzmittel,** *n.* antirust agent, rust preventive.

**rostsicher,** *a.* rust-proof.

**Röststaub,** *m.* dust of roasted ore.

**Röstung,** *f.* roasting, etc. (see rösten).

**Röstverfahren,** *n.* roasting process.

**rostverhütend,** *a.* rust-preventing, anti-rust, anti-corrosive.

**Röst-verlust,** *m.* loss from roasting. **-vorrichtung,** *f.* roasting apparatus or contrivance. **-wasser,** *n.* steeping water. **-zuschlag,** *m.* flux for roasting.

**rot,** *a.* red.—**roter Präzipitat,** red precipitate (red mercuric oxide).

**Rot,** *n.* red; rouge.

**Rotations-achse,** *f.* axis of rotation. **-bewegung,** *f.* rotational motion, rotary motion.

**Rotbeize,** *f.* (*Dyeing*) red mordant, red liquor.

**rotblau,** *a.* reddish-blue.

**Rotblei-erz,** *n.,* **-spat,** *m.* red lead ore (crocoite).

**rotbraun,** *a.* red-brown.

**Rot-braunstein,** *m.* **-braunsteinerz,** *n.* rhodonite. **-bruch,** *m.* red-shortness.

**rotbrüchig,** *a.* red-short; (of wood) rotten.

**Rotbuche,** *f.* red beech.

**Röte,** *f.* redness, red; madder; blush.

**Roteisen-erz,** *n.* red iron ore (hematite). **-ocker,** *m.* red iron ocher (earthy hematite). **-stein,** *m.* = Roteisenerz.

**Rötel,** *m.* ruddle, red ocher.

**Röteln,** *f.pl.* German measles.

**röten,** *v.t.* redden.—**rötend,** *p.a.* rubefacient.

**Roterde,** *f.* red earth.

**rot-färben,** *v.t.* color red. **-farbig,** *a.* red-colored.

**Rot-färbung,** *f.* red coloration, red color. **-fäule,** *f.* red rot, heart rot. **-feuer,** *n.* red fire.

**rot-gar,** *a.* tanned (to a russet color). **-gebrannt,** *a.* roasted red, red-burned. **-gelb,** *a.* reddish-yellow, orange. **-gerben,** *v.t.* tan.

**Rot-gerber,** *m.* tanner. **-giesser,** *m.* brazier. **-giesserei,** *f.* braziery. **-gilderz, -giltigerz,** *n.* = Rotgültigerz.

**rot-glühen,** *v.t.* heat to redness. **-glühend,** *p.a.* glowing red, red-hot.

**Rot-glühhitze, -glut,** *f.* red heat. **-gültig, -gültigerz, -gulden,** *n.* red silver ore

(dunkles, pyrargyrite; lichtes, proustite).
-guss, m. red brass or bronze; braziery.
roth, Röthe, etc. See rot, Röte, etc.
Rot-heizen, n. heating to redness. -hitze, f.
red heat. -holz, n. redwood.
rotieren, v.i. rotate.—rotierend, p.a. rotating,
rotary.
Rotierofen, m. rotating furnace or kiln.
Rot-kali, n. red prussiate of potash (potassium ferricyanide). -klee, m. red clover.
-kohl, m. red cabbage. -kohle, f. red charcoal. -kupfer, -kupfererz, n. red copper, red
copper ore (cuprite). -lauf, m. erysipelas.
rötlich, a. reddish. -braun, a. reddish-brown.
-gelb, a. reddish-yellow.
Rotliegendes, n. (Geol.) a system of sand-
stones, shales and conglomerates of the
lower Permian of Germany.
rotmachend, p.a. rubefacient.
Rot-nickelkies, m. niccolite, kupfernickel.
-ocker, m. red ocher. -öl, n. red oil.
-rauschgelb, n. realgar. -salz, n. crude
sodium acetate (from pyroligneous acid).
-säure, f. erythric acid (erythrin). -silber,
-silbererz, n.= Rotgültig. -spat, m. rhodonite. -spiessglanz, m., -spiessglanzerz,
n. kermesite. -stein, m. red ocher, ruddle;
rhodonite. -tanne, f. red fir.
Rotte, f. retting (of flax); troop, band, set,
gang.
rotten, v.t. ret (flax, etc.).
Rötung, f. reddening; red tint.
Rotverschiebung, f. displacement toward the
red.
rot-verschoben, p.p. displaced toward the red.
-warm, a. red-hot.
Rot-wein, m. red wine. -weinfarbe, f. color of
red wine, claret. -zinkerz, n. red zinc ore
(zincite).
R.-P., abbrev. (Reichs-Patent) Government
patent.
R-Säure, f. R-acid (2-naphthol-3,6-disulfonic
acid).
R.-T., abbrev. (Raumteil) part by volume.
Rübe, f. (rote) beet, beetroot; (gelbe) carrot;
(weisse) turnip; rape.
Rubeanwasserstoff, m. old name for dithio-
oxamide, $H_2NCSCSNH_2$.
Rüben-asche, f. beet ashes (usually; see
Rübe). -brei, m. beet(root) pulp. -breiap-
parat, m. (Sugar) root pulper. -brennerei,
f. beet (molasses) distillery. -essig, m. beet
vinegar, beetroot vinegar.
rübenförmig, a. turnip-shaped, napiform.
Rüben-harzsäure, f. resin acid of beets.
-melasse, f. beet molasses, beetroot molasses. -pottasche, f. potash from beet
molasses. -pulpe, f. beet pulp. -rohzucker,
m. raw beet sugar. -saft, m. beet(root)

juice. -samen, m. turnip, rape, beet or
carrot seed. -schlempe, f. beet vinasse.
-schnitzel, m. beet chip, beet slice. -sirup,
m. beet sirup, beetroot sirup. -spiritus, m.
beet spirit (from beet molasses). -stecher,
m. beet sampler.
Rübenzucker, m. beet sugar, beetroot sugar.
-fabrik, f. beet-sugar factory. -industrie, f.
beet-sugar industry.
Rubidium-alaun, m. rubidium alum. -chlorid,
n. rubidium chloride. -jodid, n. rubidium
iodide. -platinchlorid, n. rubidium chloroplatinate.
Rubin, m. ruby. -balas, m. balas ruby (ruby
spinel). -blende, f. pyrargyrite. -farbe, f.
ruby color, ruby.
rubin-farben, -farbig, a. ruby-colored, ruby.
Rubin-glas, n., -fluss, m., ruby glass. -glim-
mer, m. a variety of göthite. -granat, m.
rock ruby (variety of garnet).
rubinrot, a. ruby-red, ruby.
Rubin-schwefel, m. ruby sulfur (realgar).
-spinell, m. ruby spinel.
Rüböl, n. rape oil, rapeseed oil. -kuchen, m.
rapeseed cake.
Rubrik, f. heading; column.
Rübsamen, m.= Rübensamen.
Rübsen, m. rape seed. -öl, n. rape oil, rapeseed oil.
ruchlos, a. scentless; vicious, wicked.
Ruck, m. jerk, jolt, tug.
rück, adv. back, backward, behind.
Rück-. back, retro-, re- counter-.
rückbilden, v.t. form again, re-form.
Rückblick, m. retrospect.
rücken, v.t. move suddenly, push, pull.—v.i.
move, stir, proceed.
Rücken, m. back; ridge; rear.
Rücken-. back, dorsal. -lehne, f. back (of a
chair). -mark, n. spinal cord. -weh, n.
lumbago. -wirbel, m. dorsal vertebra.
Rück-erinnerung, f. reminiscence. -fahrt, f.
return. -fall, m. relapse; reversion.
rückfliessend, a. flowing back, reflux.
Rückfluss, m. reflux. -kühler, m. reflux condenser, return condenser. -luftkühler, m.
reflux air condenser.
Rückgang, m. return, retrogression; decline;
(Mach.) back stroke.
rückgängig, a. retrograde, retrogressive; of
no effect, null.
Rück-gewinnung, f. recovery. -grat, m. vertebral column, spine.
Rückgrats-. vertebral, spinal.
Rückhalt, m. support, stay; reserve.
rückhaltlos, a. unreserved.
Rück-kehr, -kunft, f. return. -kohlung, f.
recarbonization, recarburization; rechar-
ring. -kühlanlage, f. recooling plant.

**rück-laufend, -läufig,** *a.* recurrent; retrograde.

**Rück-leiter,** *m.* (*Elec.*) return conductor, return wire. **-leitung,** *f.* return line.

**rücklings,** *adv.* backward; from behind.

**Rück-prall,** *m.* rebound, recoil. **-saugung,** *f.* sucking back.

**Rückschlag,** *m.* striking back; back stroke, rebound, recoil, return; reaction; reverberation. **-hemmung,** *f.* prevention of, or device to prevent, "striking back." **-ventil,** *n.* check valve.

**Rückschluss,** *m.* inference, conclusion.

**rückschreitend,** *a.* retrogressive, retrograde.

**Rück-schritt,** *m.* backward motion, recession, retrogression; relapse. **-seite,** *f.* back side, back.

**Rücksicht,** *f.* regard, respect, attention, consideration; motive.—**mit — auf,** with regard to, with respect to, in consideration of.

**Rücksichtnahme,** *f.* allowance, consideration.

**Rücksprache,** *f.* consultation, conference.

**Rückstand,** *m.* residue, residuum; (often *pl.*) refuse, leavings, remains; (*pl.*) arrears. **-brenner,** *m.* burner for residues.

**rückständig,** *a.* residual, residuary; in arrears, overdue, outstanding.

**Rück-standsgewicht,** *n.* weight of residue. **-stein,** *m.* (*Metal.*) back stone; crucible bottom. **-stoss,** *m.* back stroke, recoil. **-stosselektron,** *n.* recoil electron. **-strahler,** *m.* reflector. **-strahlung,** *f.* reflection. **-streuung,** *f.* scattering (of rays). **-strom,** *m.* (*Elec.*) reverse current, return current. **-titrieren,** *n.* back titration.

**rücktreiben,** *v.t.* drive back.

**Rück-umwandlung, -verwandlung,** *f.* reconversion, retransformation. **-wand,** *f.* back wall, rear wall.

**rückwärts,** *adv.* backward, back.

**ruckweise,** *adv.* by jerks; intermittently.

**rückwirken,** *v.i.* react.

**Rück-wirkung,** *f.* reaction; retroaction. **-zug,** *m.* retreat; return.

**Rudel,** *n.* flock, herd; stirring pole.

**Ruder,** *n.* oar; rudder, helm.

**rudern,** *v.t. & i.* row, paddle.

**Ruf,** *m.* call; calling; report; reputation.

**rufen,** *v.t. & i.* call.

**Rufigallussäure,** *f.* rufigallic acid.

**Ruhbütte,** *f.* (*Brewing*) storage vat, stock tub.

**Ruhe,** *f.* rest; repose, quiet, peace. **-lage,** *f.* position of rest.

**ruhen,** *v.i.* rest, repose, sleep.—**ruhend,** *p.a.* resting, etc.; latent; stagnant; (*Elec.*) static.

**Ruhe-pulver,** *n.* sedative powder. **-punkt,** *m.* point of rest; fulcrum; pause. **-stoffwechsel,** *m.* resting metabolism. **-system,** *n.* static system. **-umsatz,** *m.* (*Physiol.*) resting metabolism. **-winkel,** *m.* angle of repose. **-zustand,** *m.* state of rest.

**ruhig,** *a.* at rest, quiet, still, calm.

**Ruhm,** *m.* fame, reputation, glory, praise.

**Ruhmasse,** *f.* rest mass, static mass.

**rühmen,** *v.t.* commend, praise, extol.—*v.r.* boast, pride oneself.

**Ruhr,** *f.* dysentery; diarrhea.

**Rühr-apparat,** *m.* stirring apparatus, stirrer, agitator, (*Ceram.*) blunger. **-aufsatz,** *m.* stirring attachment. **-blei,** *n.* (*Metal.*) the first lead removed in the Carinthian process. **-eisen,** *n.* poker, iron stirrer.

**rühren,** *v.t.* stir; agitate, beat; play (an instrument); strike; move, touch (one's feelings).

**Rührer,** *m.* stirrer, etc. (see rühren).

**Rühr-fass,** *n.* churn; (*Metal.*) dolly tub. **-form,** *f.* form or shape of stirrer. **-häkchen,** *n.* small stirring hook. **-haken,** *m.* stirring implement, rake, rabble. **-holz,** *n.* wooden stirrer, stirring stick, paddle.

**rührig,** *a.* stirring, busy, active, nimble.

**Rühr-krücke,** *f.* stirring crutch, rake. **-kühler,** *m.* condenser with stirrer. **-maschine,** *f.* stirring machine, agitator.

**Ruhr-mittel,** *n.* remedy for dysentery. **-rinde,** *f.* Simarouba bark.

**Rühr-scheit,** *n.* paddle, rake, stirrer; spatula. **-spatel,** *m.* stirring spatula. **-stab,** *m.* stirring rod, stirring pole, paddle, rabble. **-stativ,** *n.* stirring stand.

**Rührung,** *f.* stirring, etc. (see rühren); emotion, feeling.

**Rührwerk,** *n.* = Rührapparat.

**Ruhrwurzel,** *f.* tormentil root; ipecac; calumba.

**Rührzeit,** *f.* time of stirring or agitation.

**Ruinenmarmor,** *m.* ruin marble.

**Rujaholz,** *n.* Venetian sumac wood, young fustic.

**Rüllöl,** *n.* cameline oil.

**Rumänien,** *n.* Rumania, Roumania.

**Rum-äther,** *m.* rum ether (ethyl butyrate or formate). **-brennerei,** *f.* rum distillery. **-essenz,** *f.* rum essence (ethyl butyrate or formate). **-fabrik,** *f.* rum distillery.

**rumpeln,** *v.i.* rumble, rattle.

**Rumpf,** *m.* body (of an engine, etc.); trunk, torso; hull (of a ship). See also Atomrumpf. **-elektron,** *n.* inner electron (as distinguished from an optical or valence electron).

**Rumsprit,** *m.* double rum.

**rund,** *a.* round.

**Rund-brenner,** *m.* ring burner. **-eisen,** *n.* round iron, rod iron.

**runderhaben,** *a.* convex.

**Rund-feile,** *f.* round file. **-filter,** *m.* round or

circular filter. **-flasche,** *f.* round flask, Florence flask. **-funk,** *m.* (radio) broadcasting.

**rundhohl,** *a.* concave.

**Rund-kolben,** *m.* round-bottomed flask. **-reise,** *f.* round trip; circuit. **-schreiben,** *n.* circular.

**rundweg,** *adv.* plainly.

**Runkel,** *f.,* **-rübe,** *f.* beet, beetroot. **-rüben-melasse,** *f.* beet(root) molasses. **-rüben-zucker,** *m.* beet sugar, beetroot sugar.

**Runzel,** *f.* wrinkle; fold, rumple.

**runzelig, runzlig,** *a.* wrinkled, puckered, shriveled, rugose.

**Rupertsmetall,** *n.* Prince Rupert's metal.

**rupfen,** *v.t.* pluck, pick.

**Ruprechtskraut,** *n.* herb Robert (*Geranium robertianum*).

**Rusaöl,** *n.* ginger-grass oil.

**Russ,** *m.* soot; lampblack; (*Agric.*) rust. **-an-satz,** *m.* deposit of soot.

**russartig,** *a.* sootlike, fuliginous.

**Russ-bildung,** *f.* soot formation. **-braun,** *n.* bister. **-brennerei,** *f.* manufacture of lampblack. **-dampf,** *m.* sooty vapor.

**Rüssel,** *m.* nose, snout, nozzle; proboscis.

**russend,** *a.* sooty, smoky.

**Russ-farbe,** *f.* bister. **-flocke,** *f.* flake of soot. **-hütte,** *f.* lampblack works.

**russig,** *a.* sooty, fuliginous.

**russisch,** *a.* Russian.—**russisches Glas,** Muscovy glass, mica.

**Russ-kobalt,** *m.* asbolite. **-kohle,** *f.* sooty coal.

**Russland,** *n.* Russia.

**russschwarz,** *a.* soot-black.

**Russ-schwarz,** *n.* lampblack. **-vorlage,** *f.* soot collector.

**rüsten,** *v.t.* prepare, equip, furnish.

**Rüster,** *f.* elm. **-rinde,** *f.* elm bark.

**rüstig,** *a.* vigorous, robust, active.

**Rüstung,** *f.* preparation, equipment, armament; scaffolding; (*Elec.*) armature.

**Rüstzeug,** *n.* set of tools; crane; scaffolding.

**Rute,** *f.* rod, wand; yard, rod (measures); (*Med.*) penis.

**Ruthenium-oxyd,** *n.* (any) ruthenium oxide, esp. the sesquioxide. **-oxydul,** *n.* ruthenium monoxide. **-verbindung,** *f.* ruthenium compound.

**Rutsche,** *f.* shoot, chute, slide.

**rutschen,** *v.i.* slide, slip, glide.

**Rutschpulver,** *n.* talc powder.

**Rüttelbewegung,** *f.* shaking motion.

**rütteln,** *v.t.* shake, jolt.

# S

s., *abbrev.* (siehe) see; (symmetrisch) symmetric(al); (schwer) difficultly; (sehr) very.

S., *abbrev.* (Seite) page; (Säure) acid; (Sankt) Saint, St.

s.a., *abbrev.* (siehe auch) see also.

S.-A., *abbrev.* (Sonder-Abdruck) separate, reprint.

Sa., *abbrev.* (Summa) sum.

Saal, *m.* hall, assembly room.

Saat, *f.* seed; sowing; young crops. -beizmittel, *n.* seed disinfectant. -gut, *n.* seed grain, seed. -gutbeize, *f.* seed disinfection; seed steep.

Sabadillsamen, *m.pl.* sabadilla seeds.

Säbel, *m.* saber, sword. -kolben, *m.* = Schwertkolben.

Sabinerbaum, *m.* savin.

Saccharinsäure, *f.* saccharinic acid.

saccharoidisch, *a.* saccharoid, saccharoidal.

Sache, *f.* affair, matter, subject, thing, cause, case.

sachgemäss, *a.* appropriate, pertinent.

Sach-index, *m.* subject index. -kenner, *m.* expert. -kenntnis, *f.* expert knowledge; experience.

sachkundig, *a.* experienced, expert.

Sachlage, *f.* state of affairs.

sachlich, *a.* real, objective, material.—*adv.* objectively; positively; by subjects.

Sachregister, *n.* subject index.

Sachsen, *n.* Saxony.

sächsisch, *a.* Saxon.—sächsisches Blau, Saxony blue, Saxon blue.

Sächsischblau, *n.* Bremen blue.

sacht, sachte, *a.* soft, gentle, light, easy; (of silk) scoured.

Sach-verhalt, *m.,* -verhältnis, *n.* state of affairs.

sachverständig, *a.* = sachkundig.

Sach-verständiger, *m.* expert, authority. -verzeichnis, *n.* subject index. -walter, *m.* lawyer, attorney. -wörterbuch, *n.* encyclopedia.

Sack, *m.* bag, sack; pocket, pouch; sac, cyst. -band, *n.* bag string, sack tie.

Säckel, *m.* purse; little bag.

Sack-filter, *n.* bag filter, sack filter. -leinwand, *f.,* -leinen, *n.* sackcloth, sacking, bagging.

Sadebaum, *m.* savin. -öl, *n.* savin oil.

säen, *v.t.* sow.

Saffian, *m.* morocco (leather).

Safflor, *m.* safflower. -blüte, *f.* safflower blos-

som. -gelb, *n.* safflower (the dye). -öl, *n.* safflower oil. -rot, *n.* safflower red, carthamin.

Safran, *m.* saffron.

safranähnlich, *a.* saffronlike, saffrony.

Safranfarbe, *f.* saffron color.

safran-farben, -farbig, *a.* saffron-colored. -gelb, *a.* saffron-yellow, saffron. -haltig, *a.* containing saffron.

Safranöl, *n.* saffron oil.

Saft, *m.* juice; sap; lymph; fluid, liquor, sirup, gravy. -blau, *n.* sap blue. -grün, *n.* sap green.

saftig, *a.* juicy, succulent; sappy; (*Metal.*) wet.

Saftigkeit, *f.* juiciness; sappiness.

saftreich, *a.* rich in juice or sap.

Saftzelle, *f.* lymph cell.

Sagapengummi, *n.* sagapenum.

Sage, *f.* saying; rumor; tradition, legend.

Säge, *f.* saw.

sägeartig, *a.* saw-like, serrated.

Sägemehl, *n.* sawdust.

sägemehlartig, *a.* like sawdust.

sagen, *v.t.* say, tell, speak.

sägen, *v.t.* saw.

sagenhaft, *a.* legendary, traditionary.

Säge-späne, *m.pl.* sawdust. -zahn, *m.* saw tooth; (*pl.*) indentations.

Sagradarinde, *f.* cascara sagrada.

sah, *pret.* of sehen.

Sahlband, *n.* selvage; wall (of a lode).

Sahne, *f.* cream.

sahnen, *v.t.* skim (milk).

Sahnenkäse, *m.* cream cheese.

Saiger-. see Seiger-.

saigern, *v.t.* = seigern.

Saite, *f.* catgut; string (of an instrument); cord.

Saiten-draht, *m.* music wire. -galvanometer, *n.* string galvanometer.

säkulär, *a.* secular, of long duration.

Salat, *m.* salad; lettuce. -machen, *n.* (*Brewing*) doughing in and keeping the mash very cold. -öl, *n.* salad oil, specif. olive oil.

Salbe, *f.* salve, ointment.

Salbei, *f.* sage. -öl, *n.* sage oil, oil of sage.

salben, *v.t.* salve; anoint. -artig, *a.* salvelike, salvy, unctuous.

Salben-grundlage, *f.* ointment base. -spatel, *m.* salve spatula, slice.

salbig, *a.* salvy, unctuous.

Saldo, *m.* balance (of an account).

Salep, *m.*, -wurzel, *f.* salep. -schleim, *m.* salep mucilage.

Salicoylsäure, *f.* salicylic acid.

Salicyl-. salicyl; salicylic.

salicyliert, *p.a.* salicylated.

salicylig, *a.* salicylous.

salicylsauer, *a.* of or combined with salicylic acid, salicylate of.

Salicyl-säure, *f.* salicylic acid. -streupulver, *n.* salicylated talc. -talg, *m.* salicylated mutton fat. -ursäure, *f.* salicyluric acid.

Saline, *f.* salt works, saltern.

Salinenwasser, *n.* saline water.

salinisch, *a.* saline.

salivieren, *v.t.* salivate.

Salizyl-, etc. = Salicyl-, etc.

Salm, *m.* salmon; psalm.

Salmiak, *m.* sal ammoniac (ammonium chloride). -element, *n.* (*Elec.*) sal ammoniac cell, Leclanché cell. -geist, *m.* aqueous ammonia. -lösung, *f.* ammonium chloride solution. -salz, *n.* sal volatile (ammonium carbonate); sal ammoniac. -spiritus, *m.* aqueous ammonia.

Salmrot, *n.* salmon red.

Salomonssiegel, *n.* Solomon's seal.

Salpeter, *m.* saltpeter, niter.

salpeterartig, *a.* like saltpeter or niter.

Salpeter-äther, *m.* nitric ether (ethyl nitrate). -bildung, *f.* nitrification. -blumen, *f.pl.* niter efflorescence. -dampf, -dunst, *m.* nitrous fumes. -erde, *f.* nitrous earth. -erzeugung, *f.* niter production; nitrification.

salpeteressigsauer, *a.* nitrate and acetate of.

Salpeter-frass, *m.* corrosion by niter. -gas, *n.* nitrous oxide; nitric oxide.

Salpetergeist, *m.* spirit of niter (old name for nitric acid).—versüsster —, see versüssen.

Salpeter-grube, *f.* saltpeter mine. -gütemesser, *m.* nitrometer. -hafen, *m.* niter pot.

salpeterhaltig, *a.* containing saltpeter, nitrous. —salpeterhaltiger Höllenstein, (*Pharm.*) mitigated silver nitrate.

Salpeterhütte, *f.* niter works.

salpeterig, *a.* = salpetrig.

Salpeter-luft, *f.* nitrogen (old name). -messer, *m.* nitrometer. -milchsäure, *f.* lactic acid nitrate. -plantage, *f.* saltpeter plantation.

salpetersalzsauer, *a.* nitromuriate of.

Salpetersalzsäure, *f.* nitrohydrochloric acid, nitromuriatic acid, aqua regia.

salpetersauer, *a.* of or combined with nitric acid, nitrate of.

Salpetersäure, *f.* nitric acid. -anhydrid, *n.* nitric anhydride, nitrogen pentoxide. -äther, *m.* nitric ether (ethyl nitrate). -bad, *n.* nitric-acid bath.

salpetersäurehaltig, *a.* containing nitric acid.

Salpeter-säuresalz, *n.* salt of nitric acid, nitrate. -schaum, *m.* wall saltpeter (calcium nitrate efflorescence). -schwefelsäure, *f.* nitrosylsulfuric acid. -siederei, *f.* saltpeter works. -stärkemehl, *n.* nitrated starch. -stoff, *m.* nitrogen. -strauch, *m.* niter bush (*Nitraria*). -verbindung, *f.* nitrate. -wa(a)ge, *f.* nitrometer.

salpetrig, *a.* nitrous.—salpetrige Säure, nitrous acid.—salpetrige Schwefelsäure, nitrosylsulfuric acid.

Salpetrigäther, *m.* ethyl nitrite.

salpetrigsauer, *a.* of or combined with nitrous acid, nitrite of.

Salpetrigsäure, *f.* nitrous acid. -anhydrid, *n.* nitrous anhydride. -äther, *m.* nitrous ether (ethyl nitrite).

salpetrisch, *a.* nitrous.

Salve, *f.* volley; salute.

Salvei, *f.* sage.

Salz, *n.* salt.—schwefelsaures —, sulfate; palmitinsaures —, palmitate; etc.

Salz-ablagerung, *f.* salt deposit. -ader, *f.* salt vein.

salzartig, *a.* salt-like, saline.

Salz-äther, *m.* muriatic ether (old name for ethyl chloride). -bad, *n.* salt bath. -base, *f.* salifiable base (old term). -bedarf, *m.* salt requirement. -bergwerk, *n.* salt mine.

salzbildend, *p.a.* salt-forming.

Salz-bilder, -bildner, *m.* salt former, halogen. -bildung, *f.* salt formation, salification.

salzbildungs-fähig, *a.* salifiable. -unfähig, *a.* nonsalifiable.

Salz-blumen, *f.pl.* efflorescence of salt. -brühe, *f.* brine, pickle. -chemie, *f.* chemistry of salts, halochemistry. -decke, *f.* a quilted cover impregnated with salts to absorb toxic gases.

salzen, *v.t.* salt.

salzerzeugend, *a.* salt-producing.

Salzerzeugung, *f.* salt production; salification.

salzfähig, *a.* salifiable.

Salz-fehler, *m.* salt error. -fleisch, *n.* salt meat. -fluss, *m.* saline flux; salt rheum, eczema.

salz-förmig, *a.* saliniform. -frei, *a.* free from salt, salt-free.

Salz-garten, *m.* salt garden. -gehalt, *m.* salt content.

Salzgeist, *m.* (*Old Chem.*) spirit of salt (hydrochloric acid).—leichter —, light spirit of salt (ethyl chloride).—schwerer —, versüsster —, heavy spirit of salt, sweet spirit of salt.—Libavius' rauchender —, fuming liquor of Libavius (stannic chloride).

Salz-gemisch, *n.* salt mixture, mixture of salts. -geschmack, *m.* salty taste.

salzgetränkt, *a.* impregnated with salt.

Salz-glasur, f. salt glaze. -grube, f. salt pit,
salt mine.
salzhaltig, a. containing salt, salt-bearing,
saliferous.
Salzhaut, f. salted hide; film of salt.
salzig, a. salty, saline, briny.
Salz-igkeit, f. saltiness, salineness, salinity.
-ion, n. salt ion. -korn, n. grain of salt.
-kraut, n. saltwort. -kuchen, m. salt cake.
-kupfererz, n. atacamite. -lake, f. brine,
pickle. -lauge, f. =Salzbrühe. -löser, m.
salt dissolver, brine mixer. -lösung, f. salt
solution; brine. -messer, m. salimeter.
-messung, f. salimetry. -mutterlauge, f.
(Salt) bittern. -niederschlag, m. deposit of
salt, saline deposit. -paar, n. pair of salts,
salt pair. -pfanne, f. salt pan, brine pan.
-pfannenstein, m. (Salt) pan scale. -probe,
f. salt test; salt sample. -quelle, f. salt
spring, saline spring.
salzreich, a. rich in salt.
Salzsalpetersäure, f. nitrohydrochloric acid,
aqua regia.
salzsauer, a. of or combined with hydrochloric
acid, chloride of (metals, etc.), hydrochloride of (aniline and similar bases).
Salzsäure, f. hydrochloric acid, muriatic acid.
salzsäurebindend, a. fixing hydrochloric acid.
Salzsäure-gas, n. hydrochloric acid gas. -lö-
sung, f. hydrochloric acid solution.
Salz-schicht, f. layer of salt. -siedepfanne,
f. salt pan. -siederei, f. salt making; salt
works. -sole, -soole, f. brine, salt water;
salt spring. -stein, m. boiler scale; rock salt.
-ton, m. salt clay, saliferous clay. -wa(a)ge,
f. brine gage, salimeter.
Salz-wasser, n. salt water, brine. -kühlung, f.
brine cooling. -wa(a)ge, f. brine gage, salimeter.
Salz-werk, n. salt works, saltern. -wirkung,
f. effect (or action) of salt.
-sam. an adjective suffix attached to nouns,
adjectives and verb roots; -some, -ble, -ive,
etc.; as, heilsam, wholesome; biegsam,
flexible.
Same, Samen, m. seed; semen, sperm.
Samen-. seed; seminal, spermatic. -blättchen,
n. cotyledon. -drüse, f. testicle. -faden, m.
spermatozoön. -flüssigkeit, f. seminal fluid.
samenführend, p.a. seminiferous.
Samen-hefe, f. seed yeast. -keim, m. germ,
embryo. -kern, m. seed kernel; (Bot.) endosperm; (Physiol.) spermatic nucleus. -lap-
pen, m. seed lobe, cotyledon. -öl, n. seed
oil. -saft, m. seminal fluid. -staub, m.
pollen. -tierchen, n. spermatozoön. -zelle,
f. seminal cell, spermatozoön. -zucker, m.
quercitol, quercite.
samisch, a. Samian.

sämisch, a. -gar, oil-tanned, chamois
Sämisch-gerben, n. chamoising. -leder, n.
chamois leather, chamois.
Sammel-. collecting, collective. -bottich, m.
(Brewing) collecting vat, starting tub.
-gefäss, n. collecting vessel, receiver, reservoir. -glas, n. preparation tube, specimen
tube; converging lens. -linse, f. converging
lens.
sammeln, v.t. collect, gather, assemble, accumulate.
Sammel-raum, m. receiver, receptacle. -ref-
erat, n. collective review. -rohr, n. collecting tube or pipe. -schiene, f. (Elec.) bus
bar. -sirup, m. sirup from spilt sugar.
-stelle, f. collecting point, converging point.
-trichter, m. collecting funnel.
Sammet, m. velvet. -blende, f. göthite.
-braun, n. velvet brown (an iron pigment).
-eisenerz, n. göthite.
sammeten, a. velvet, velvety.
Sammet-erz, n. cyanotrichite. -schwarz, n.
ivory black.
Sammler, m. accumulator, storage battery;
gatherer, collector. -säure, f. accumulator
acid.
Sammlung, f. collection, gathering, assembly.
Sammlungsglas, n. specimen glass, display
glass.
samt, prep. together with.
Samt, m. velvet.
Samt-. see Sammet-.
samt-artig, a. velvet-like, velvety. -glänzerd,
a. velvety.
sämtlich, a. all together, all.—adv. jointly,
collectively.
Sandarak, Sandarach, m. realgar; sandarac.
Sandarak-gummi, -harz, n. sandarac resin,
sandarac.
sandartig, a. sandlike, sandy.
Sand-bad, n. sand bath. -badschale, f. sand-
bath dish. -beere, f. = Bärentraube; arbu-
tus. -büchsenbaum, m. sand-box tree
(Hura crepitans).
Sandel, m., -holz, n. sandalwood. -holzöl,
-öl, n. sandalwood oil, santal oil. -rot, n.
santalin.
sandfarben, a. sand-colored.
Sand-form, f. (Founding) sand mold. -gies-
serei, f. sand casting. -gries, m. coarse
sand, fine gravel. -gummi, n. sandarac
resin, sandarac. -guss, m. sand casting.
sandig, a. sandy, arenaceous.
Sand-kohle, f. coal forming a powdery coke,
sand coal. -korn, n. sand grain. -mergel,
m. sandy marl. -papier, n. sandpaper.
sandreich, a. rich in sand, sandy.
Sand-riedgras, n. sea sedge, carex. -schicht,
f. layer of sand. -schiefer, m. schistous

sandstone. **-segge,** f. sea sedge, carex. **-stein,** m. sandstone. **-strahl,** m. sand blast.

**sandte,** pret. of senden.

**Sand-traube,** f. = Bärentraube. **-uhr,** f. sand-glass. **-zucker,** m. raw ground sugar.

**sanft,** a. soft, mild, gentle, smooth.

**sang,** pret. of singen.

**Sang,** m. song.

**sanieren,** v.t. cure, restore; reorganize

**Sanikel,** m. sanicle.

**sanitär, sanitärisch,** a. sanitary.

**Sanität,** f. health, hygiene, sanity.

**Sanitäts-.** sanitary, hygienic, health. **-kollegium,** n. board of health. **-pflege,** f. sanitation. **-polizei,** f. sanitary police.

**sanitätspolizeilich,** a. of or pertaining to the sanitary police.

**Sanitätswesen,** n. sanitary affairs.

**sank,** pret. of sinken.

**sann,** pret. of sinnen.

**Santel, Santel-.** = Sandel, Sandel-.

**santonig,** a. santonous.

**Santoninsäure,** f. santoninic acid.

**Santonsäure,** f. santonic acid.

**Sapanholz,** n. sapanwood.

**Saphir,** m. sapphire. **-blau,** n. sapphire blue.

**saphiren,** a. sapphire, sapphirine.

**Saphirspat,** m. cyanite.

**Sardelle,** f. anchovy; sardine

**Sardinenöl,** n. sardine oil.

**Sarg,** m. coffin.

**Sark-.** sarc-.

**Sarkin,** n. sarcine (hypoxanthine).

**Sarkom,** n. sarcoma.

**Sarsa,** f. sarsaparilla.

**sass,** pret. of sitzen.

**Sassaparille,** f. sarsaparilla.

**Satinage,** f. glazing, finish.

**satinieren,** v.t. satin, glaze; calender or super-calender (paper).

**Satin-papier,** n. glazed paper. **-weiss,** n. satin white.

**satt,** a. satisfied; satiated; (of colors) saturated, deep, full. **-blau,** a. deep blue.

**Sattdampf,** m. saturated steam.

**Satte,** f. bowl, dish.

**Sattel,** m. saddle; bridge. **-fass,** n. (Brewing) rider cask.

**sattelförmig,** a. saddle-shaped.

**Sattelschlange,** f. saddle(shaped) coil.

**sättigen,** v.t. saturate; impregnate; satisfy; satiate, sate.

**Sättiger,** m. saturator.

**Sättigung,** f. saturation; satisfaction; satiety.

**Sättigungs-apparat,** m. saturating apparatus, saturator. **-druck,** m. saturation pressure.

**sättigungsfähig,** a. capable of saturation.

**Sättigungs-fähigkeit,** f. capability of saturation. **-grad,** m. degree of saturation.

**-kapazität,** f. saturation capacity. **-punkt,** m. saturation point. **-wert,** m. valence, valency.

**sattsam,** a. sufficient.—adv. sufficiently.

**Saturateur,** m. saturator.

**Saturations-gefäss,** n. saturation vessel, saturator. **-scheidung,** f. (Sugar) purification by carbonation (separation of impurities with the lime when the juice is saturated with carbon dioxide). **-schlamm,** m. (Sugar) sediment from carbonation.

**Saturei,** f., **-kraut,** n. savory. **-öl,** n. savory oil.

**saturieren,** v.t. saturate; (Sugar) carbonate.

**Saturnrot,** n. Saturn red, minium.

**Satz,** m. deposit, sediment, settlings; composition; set (of weights, beakers, etc.); charge, batch; principle, proposition; leap, jump; young (of fish), fry; price, rate; pool, stake; sentence; (Brewing) yeast, sediment. **-brauen,** n. brewing with cold malt extract. **-krücke,** f. (Brewing) yeast rouser. **-mehl,** n. fecula, starch flour. **-schale,** f. settling dish.

**satzweise,** adv. intermittently.

**Sau,** f. sow (also Metal.); drying kiln; blot.

**sauber,** a. clean; neat; pretty.

**Sauberkeit,** f. cleanness, cleanliness, neatness.

**säubern,** v.t. clean, cleanse.

**Saubohne,** f. fodder bean, specif. (1) vetch, (2) soy bean.

**Saubohnen-fett, -öl,** n. soy-bean oil.

**sauer,** a. acid; sour, tart; troublesome, hard. **— — machen,** acidify.

**Sauer-ampfer,** m. sorrel, sour dock (Rumex). **-bad,** n. (Bleaching) sour bath, sour.

**sauer-bar,** a. acidifiable. **-beständig,** a. = säurebeständig.

**Sauer-bleiche,** f. sour bleaching. **-brühe,** f. (Tech.) sour liquor, acid liquor. **-brunnen,** m. acidulous spring water.

**sauerchromsauer,** a. dichromate of.

**Sauer-dorn,** m. barberry. **-dornbitter,** n. berberine (old name). **-eisen,** n. (Metal.) iron oxide. **-futter,** n. ensilage.

**sauerhaltig,** a. acidiferous.

**Sauer-honig,** m. oxymel. **-keit,** f. acidity, sourness.

**Sauerklee,** m. clover sorrel, wood sorrel. **-salz,** n. salt of sorrel (acid potassium oxalate). **-säure,** f. oxalic acid.

**säuerlich,** a. sourish, acidulous, subacid.

**Säuerlichkeit,** f. (slight) acidity, subacidity.

**säuerlichsüss,** a. sourish-sweet.

**Säuerling,** m. acidulous mineral water, sparkling mineral water; sparkling mineral spring; sour wine; cheese from sour milk; = Sauerklee.

**Sauermachen,** n. acidification.

sauermachend, *p.a.* acidifying.

säuern, *v.t.* acidify; acidulate; sour; leaven (bread).—*v.i.* sour.

sauerreagierend, *a.* of acid reaction.

Sauer-salz, *n.* acid salt. -stoff, *m.* oxygen.

sauerstoffarm, *a.* poor in oxygen.

Sauerstoff-äther, *m.* acetaldehyde. -aufnahme, *f.* oxygen absorption. -brücke, *f.* oxygen bridge. -entwickelung, *f.* evolution of oxygen.

sauerstoffentziehend, *a.* removing oxygen, deoxidizing.

Sauerstoff-erzeuger, *m.* oxygen producer or generator. -fänger, *m.* a substance that absorbs oxygen, as barium oxide. -flasche, *f.* oxygen cylinder.

sauerstofffrei, *a.* free from oxygen.

Sauerstoff-gas, *n.* oxygen gas. -gehalt, *m.* oxygen content.

sauerstoffhaltig, *a.* containing oxygen.

Sauerstoff-ion, *n.* anion. -mangel, *m.* lack of oxygen, oxygen deficiency. -menge, *f.* amount of oxygen. -messer, *m.* eudiometer. -ort, *m.* oxidation region. -pol, *m.* oxygen pole, anode.

sauerstoffreich, *a.* rich in oxygen.

Sauerstoff-salz, *n.* oxysalt, salt of an oxyacid. -säure, *f.* oxygen acid, oxyacid. -strom, *m.* current of oxygen. -träger, -überträger, *m.* oxygen carrier. -überschuss, *m.* excess of oxygen. -verbindung, *f.* oxygen compound.

sauersüss, *a.* sour-sweet.

Sauerteig, *m.* leaven.

Säuerung, *f.* acidification; souring; leavening.

Säuerungsgrad, *m.* degree of acidity.

säuerungsfähig, *a.* acidifiable; capable of souring.

Säuerungsmittel, *n.* acidifying agent.

Sauer-wasser, *n.* sour water, sour (any of various dilute acid solutions used in the arts); acidulous (sparkling) water. -wein, *m.* sour wine; verjuice.

sauerweinsauer, *a.* bitartrate of.

Sauerwerden, *n.* souring; (of liquors) acetification.

sauerwerdend, *a.* souring, acescent.

Saug-. suction, sucking, absorbing, absorbent, aspirating. -ader, *f.* (*Anat.*) absorbing vessel, lymphatic vessel. -aderdrüse, *f.* lymphatic gland. -apparat, *m.* suction apparatus.

Sauge-. =Saug-.

saugen, *v.t. & i.* suck; suck up, absorb.

Saugen, *n.* sucking, suction

säugen, *v.t.* suckle; nurse.

Sauger, *m.* sucker; suction apparatus; aspirator; exhauster.

Säugetier, *n.* mammal.

Saug-fähigkeit, *f.* absorptive capacity, absorptivity. -festigkeit, *f.* resistance to suction, suction strength. -filter, *n.* suction filter. -flasche, *f.* suction bottle. -gas, *n.* generator gas, power gas. -glas, *n.* suction bottle; breast pump. -hahn, *m.* suction cock. -heber, *m.* siphon. -höhe, *f.* suction head, suction height, absorption height. -kolben, *m.* suction flask. -leitung, *f.* suction pipe (or piping).

Säugling, *m.* suckling, infant.

Saug-lüfter, *m.* exhauster. -messer, *m.* vacuometer. -pipette, *f.* suction pipette. -pumpe, *f.* suction pump. -raum, *m.* suction chamber. -rohr, *n.,* -röhre, *f.* suction tube or pipe, sucking pipe. -schiefer, *m.* absorbent shale. -schlauch, *m.* suction tubing or hose. -stäbchen, *m.* micro immersion filter, filterstick. -strahlpumpe, *f.* jet suction pump. -trockner, *m.* suction drier.

Saugung, *f.* suction, sucking.

Saug-ventil, *n.* suction valve. -widerstand, *m.* resistance to suction. -wirkung, *f.* suction effect, sucking action. -zug, *m.* suction draft, induced draft.

Säulchen, *n.* little column, etc. (see Säule).

Säule, *f.* column, pillar; (*Cryst.*) prism; (*Elec.*) pile.

Säulen-. columnar; (*Cryst.*) prismatic. -achse, *f.* prismatic axis.

säulen-artig, -förmig, *a.* columnar; prismatic.

Saum, *m.* seam, hem, edge, fringe, selvage; border, margin; (*Tin Plate*) list.

säumen, *v.t.* hem, edge, border; square (planks).—*v.i.* tarry, stay.

Saum-pfanne, *f.,* -topf, *m.* (*Tin Plate*) list pot. -spiegel, *m.* gray spiegeleisen.

Säure, *f.* acid; sourness, acidity. -amid, *n.* acid amide. -angriff, *m.* attack by acid, acid corrosion. -anhydrid, *n.* acid anhydride. -anzug, *m.* acid-proof clothing.

säureartig, *a.* acid-like, of acid nature.

Säure-äther, *m.* ester. -bad, *n.* acid bath. -ballon, *m.* acid carboy. -behälter, *m.* acid container. -beize, *f.* (*Leather*) sour.

säure-beständig, *a.* stable toward acids, acidproof, acid-resisting, (of colors) fast to acid. -bildend, *p.a.* acid-forming.

Säure-bildner, *m.* acid former, acidifier. -bildung, *f.* acid formation, acidification. -bindungsvermögen, *n.* power to combine with acids, acid capacity. -braun, *n.* acid brown. -bromid, *n.* acid bromide. -chlorid, *n.* acid chloride. -dampf, *m.* acid vapor, acid fume.

säure-echt, *a.* fast to acid. -empfindlich, *a.* sensitive to acids.

Säure-empfindlichkeit, *f.* sensitiveness to acids. -ester, *m.* ester of an acid, ester.

säurefähig, a. acidifiable.

Säurefarbstoff, m. acid dye.

säurefest, a. acid-proof, acid-fast.

Säure-flasche, f. acid bottle. -fluorid, n. acid fluoride.

säurefrei, a. free from acid, nonacid.

Säure-gehalt, m. acid content, acidity. -gelb, n. acid yellow. -grad, m. (degree of) acidity. -grün, n. acid green. -grundlage, f. acidifiable base. -haloid, n. acid halide.

säurehaltig, a. containing acid, acidiferous.

Säure-heber, m. acid siphon. -hydrat, n. acid hydrate. -imid, n. acid imide.

säurelöslich, a. acid-soluble.

Säure-lösung, f. solution of an acid. -maschine, f. souring machine. -menge, f. amount of acid. -messer, m. acidimeter. -messkunst, f. acidimetry. -messung, f. acidimetry. -probe, f. acid test; acid sample. -radikal, n. acid radical.

säurereich, a. rich in acid.

Säure-rest, m. acid residue. -schlauch, m. acid hose. -schwarz, n. acid black. -spaltung, f. acid cleavage. -ständer, m. acid cistern. -titer, m. acid titer. -trog, m. acid trough. -turm, m. acid tower. -überschuss, m. excess of acid. -ventil, n. acid valve. -wechsel, m. change in acidity.

säure-widerstehend, p.a. resistant (or fast) to acid. -widrig, a. antacid.

Säure-wirkung, f. action of acids. -zahl, f. acid number. -zufuhr, f. addition of acid.

Säurung, f. = Säuerung.

säuseln, v.i. rustle; murmur; lisp; hum.

sausen, v.i. rush, whiz, whistle, hum.

Sca-. see Ska-.

Schabe, f. scraper; grater; scab, itch; cockroach; moth.

Schäbe, f. awn, chaff (of flax or hemp); scab, itch.

Schabeisen, n. scraper; shaver.

schaben, v.t. scrape; shave, pare; grate, rub.

Schabenpulver, n. white-arsenic powder.

Schaber, m. scraper, etc. (see schaben).

schäbig, a. shabby; mean.

Schabin, n., Schabine, f. parings (of gold, etc.).

Schablone, f. model, pattern, template; mold, form; stencil.

schablonen-artig, -mässig, a. according to pattern, mechanical, automatic.

Schablonenblech, n. sheet metal for stencils.

Schabsel, n. scrapings, parings, shavings.

Schach, n. chess; check. -brett, n. chessboard, checkerboard.

Schacht, m. shaft; tunnel; pit; gorge.

Schachtel, f. box, case. -halm, m., -kraut, n. horsetail (Equisetum). -halmsäure, f. equisetic acid.

schachteln, v.t. put in a box, box, pack.

Schacht-ofen, m. shaft furnace; shaft kiln. -trockner, m. tunnel drier.

schade, a. unfortunate, a pity.

Schade, m. damage, injury, loss

Schädel, m. skull, cranium.

Schädel-. cranial.

schaden, v.i. do injury, damage, hurt.

Schaden, m. = Schade. -ersatz, m. compensation, damages.

schadhaft, a. damaged, defective, spoiled.

schädigen, v.t. harm, injure, damage.

Schädigung, f. injury, damage, harm.

schädlich, a. noxious, injurious, harmful, deleterious, detrimental; (Mach., of space) dead.

Schädlich-keit, f. injuriousness, harmfulness. -keitsgrad, m. degree of injuriousness. -machung, f. rendering noxious, vitiation, contamination.

Schädling, m. pest.

schadlos, a. harmless; compensated.— — halten, compensate, indemnify.

Schaf, n. sheep; ewe. -bein, n. bone ash; sheep bone; sheep's leg. -bock, m. ram. -darmsaite, f. catgut. -fell, n. sheepskin.

schaffen, v.t. make, produce, create, do; get; provide; take, bring.—v.i. work, be busy.

Schaffleisch, n. mutton.

Schaffner, m. manager, conductor, guard.

Schaffnerin, f. housekeeper, stewardess, manageress.

Schaf-garbe, f. yarrow, milfoil. -haut, f. sheepskin; amnion. -häutchen, n. amnion. -käse, m. cheese from ewe's milk. -leder, n. sheepskin (leather), sheep. -milch, f. ewe's milk.

Schafott, n. scaffold.

Schaf-schmiere, f. sheep dip. -schweiss, m. suint, yolk.

Schaft, m. shaft, shank, stock, handle, stalk, trunk.

-schaft. a noun suffix used to form abstract and collective nouns, cognate with the English -ship; as, Freundschaft, friendship.

Schaf-waschmittel, n. sheep dip. -wasser, n. amniotic fluid. -wolle, f. sheep's wool.

Schagrin, n. shagreen.

schal, a. stale, flat, insipid.

Schälchen, n. little dish or cup, capsule; cupel.

Schale, f. dish, basin, bowl; pan, scale (of a balance); shell; husk, skin, peel, rind, bark; cover (of a book); (Founding) chill.

schälen, v.t. shell, husk, peel, pare, bark.—v.r. peel off, scale off.

Schalen-bau, m. shell structure. -blende, f. fibrous sphalerite. -guss, m. chill casting. -gussform, f. chill.

schalenhart, a. chilled.

Schalen-lack, *m.* shellac. -lederhaut, *f.* chorion. -träger, *m.* dish support, tripod.

schalig, *a.* scaly, foliated; crusted; shelled.

Schall, *m.* sound; ring, peal; resonance.

Schall-. sound, acoustic.

schallen, *v.i.* sound, resound, ring.

Schall-geschwindigkeit, *f.* velocity of sound. -lehre, *f.* acoustics. -platte, *f.* (flat) phonograph record. -schwingung, *f.* sound vibration. -welle, *f.* sound wave.

Schalt-. inserted, interposed, intercalary; (*Elec.*) switch. -brett, *n.* switchboard.

schalten, *v.t.* insert; (*Elec.*) connect.—*v.i.* rule, have one's way.

Schalter, *m.* wicket, window; ruler, manager; (*Elec.*) switch. -öl, *n.* circuit-breaker oil.

Schaltier, *n.* crustacean.

Schalt-jahr, *n.* leap year. -tafel, *f.* switchboard; instrument board.

Schaltung, *f.* disposal; (*Elec.*) connection.

Schälung, *f.* shelling, etc. (see schälen); excoriation, desquamation.

Scham, *f.* shame; modesty, chastity; pudenda.

Scham-. pudic. -bein, *n.* pubis.

schämen, *v.r.* be ashamed.

Schamgang, *m.* vagina.

Schamotte, *f.* (*Ceram.*) chamotte (deadburned fireclay grog with plastic fire clay as binder). -retorte, *f.* fireclay retort. -stein, *m.* firebrick. -tiegel, *m.* chamotte crucible. -ziegel, *m.* chamotte brick.

Schande, *f.* shame, dishonor, disgrace.

Schankbier, Schänkbier, *n.* schenk beer, draft beer.

Schanze, *f.* trench, intrenchment; chance.

Schar, *f.* troop, band, host, crowd, herd, flock; (fig.) group, family; (plow) share.

Scharbock, *m.* scurvy.

scharbockheilend, *p.a.* antiscorbutic.

Scharbockmittel, *n.* antiscorbutic.

scharen, *v.r.* flock together, assemble.

scharf, *a.* sharp; acrid, pungent, corrosive; acute; severe, rigorous.

Schärfe, *f.* sharpness, etc. (see scharf); edge.

schäfen, *v.t.* sharpen; strengthen (a solution).

Scharffeuer, *n.* (*Ceram.*) hard fire, sharp fire. -farbe, *f.* hard-fire color.

scharfkantig, *a.* acute-angled; sharp-edged.

Scharfmanganerz, *n.* hausmannite.

scharf-salzig, *a.* very salty. -sauer, *a.* strongly acid, very sour. -schmeckend, *p.a.* of a sharp taste, acrid, pungent, tart. -schweflig, *a.* strongly sulfurous.

Scharfsinn, *m.* acuteness, acumen.

scharf-sinnig, *a.* clever, sagacious, shrewd. -winklig, *a.* acute-angled.

Scharlach, *m.* scarlet; scarlet fever; scarlet

runner. -beeren, *f.pl.* kermes berries, kermes.

scharlachen, scharlachfarben, *a.* scarlet.

Scharlachfarbe, *f.* scarlet color or dye.

scharlachrot, *a.* scarlet, bright red.

Scharlach-rot, *n.* scarlet; cochineal. -wurm, *m.* cochineal insect.

Scharnier, *n.* hinge, joint. -ventil, *n.* clack valve, flap valve.

Schärpe, *f.* scarf, sash; (*Med.*) sling.

Scharpie, *f.* charpie, lint.

Scharre, *f.* rake, raker, scraper.

scharren, *v.t.* scrape, scratch.

Scharrwerk, *n.* scraping mechanism, scraper.

Scharte, *f.* notch, nick, fissure; sawwort.

schartig, *a.* notchy, nicked, jagged.

Schatten, *m.* shade, shadow.

schattieren, *v.t.* shade.

Schattierung, *f.* shading; shade, tint.

Schatz, *m.* treasure; stock; wealth. -amt, *n.* (public) treasury.

schätzbar, *a.* capable of valuation or estimation; valuable, esteemed.

schatzen, *v.t.* assess, tax.

schätzen, *v.t.* value; estimate; appraise, appreciate, esteem.

Schatzkammer, *f.* treasury; storehouse.

Schätzung, *f.* valuation, etc. (see schätzen); estimate.

Schau, *f.* view, review; show. -bild, *n.* diagram; (picture for) exhibit.

schaubildlich, *a.* diagrammatic, graphic.

schaudern, *v.t.* cause to shudder.—*v.i.* shudder.

schauen, *v.t.* look at, behold, examine.—*v.i.* look, gaze.

Schauer, *m.* shudder, thrill, fit; shower; spectator; inspector; shed.

Schaufel, *f.* shovel, scoop; paddle; blade.

Schau-fenster, *n.* show window. -glas, *n.* display glass, specimen glass, sample glass.

schaukeln, *v.t.& i.* swing, rock.

Schau-linie, *f.* line, curve (in a graph). -loch, *n.* peephole.

schaulustig, *a.* curious.

Schaum, *m.* foam, froth; scum; lather; (*Brewing*) head.

schaum-ähnlich, *a.* foamlike, foamy. -artig, *a.* foamy, frothy.

Schaum-beständigkeit, *f.* foam-holding capacity. -bier, *n.* foaming beer. -bildner, *m.* frothing agent, foamer. -bildung, *f.* formation of foam or froth. -blase, *f.* bubble. -brecher, *m.* foam breaker, froth killer.

schäumen, *v.i.* froth, foam; (of wine, etc.) sparkle, fizz; (of soap) lather.—*v.t.* skim, scum.

Schaum-erde, *f.* aphrite (variety of calcite). -erz, *n.* (soft or foamy) wad. -gips, *m.*

foliated gypsum. **-gold,** n. Dutch metal, imitation gold. **-gummi,** n. crêpe rubber.

**schaumhaft,** a. foamy, frothy.

**Schaum-hahn,** m. scum cock. **-haken,** m. skimmer. **-haube,** f. (Brewing) head.

**schaumig, schäumig,** a. foamy, frothy; porous.

**Schäumigkeit,** f. foaminess, frothiness.

**Schaum-kalk,** n. sparry aphrite (form of aragonite). **-kelle,** f. skimming ladle, skimmer. **-korb,** m. (Sugar) scum basket. **-löffel,** m. skimming spoon, skimmer.

**schaumlos,** a. foamless, frothless.

**Schaum-rohr,** n., **-röhre,** f. foam tube; scum pipe. **-schwärze,** f. finely powdered animal charcoal. **-seife,** f. lathering soap. **-spat,** m. a hard, foliated variety of calcite. **-stand,** m. (Brewing) head. **-ton,** m. fuller's earth. **-wein,** m. sparkling wine.

**Schau-platz,** m. scene, stage, theater. **-spiel,** n. spectacle, sight; play, drama. **-stellung,** f. exhibition.

**Scheabutter,** f. shea butter.

**Scheck,** m. check; ticket.

**schecken,** v.t. dapple, spot.

**scheckig,** a. dappled, spotted, mottled.

**Scheel-bleierz,** n., **-bleispat,** m. scheeletite. **-erz,** m. scheelite.

**Scheele'sches Grün.** Scheele's green.

**Scheele'sches Süss.** glycerol, glycerin.

**scheelisieren,** v.t. (Wine) scheelize (treat with glycerin).

**Scheelsäure,** f. tungstic acid.

**Scheere,** f. = Schere.

**Scheffel,** m. bushel.

**Scheibchen,** n. little disk, little slice.

**Scheibe,** f. disk; slice; cake (of wax, etc.); pane (of glass); (honey)comb; washer; pulley, wheel, target, dial, etc.

**scheiben-ähnlich, -artig,** a. disklike, discoid, discoidal.

**Scheiben-blei,** n. window lead. **-eisen,** n. pig iron in disks.

**scheibenförmig,** a. disk-shaped, discoid.

**Scheiben-glas,** n. window glass. **-kupfer,** n. rose copper, rosette copper. **-lack,** m. shellac. **-reissen,** n. (Metal.) conversion into disks or rosettes. **-wachs,** n. cake wax.

**scheidbar,** a. separable; analyzable.

**Scheidbarkeit,** f. separability; analyzability.

**Scheide,** f. sheath; vagina; boundary, border.

**Scheide-.** separating, parting; separated. **-bock,** m. retort stand. **-bürette,** f. separating burette. **-erz,** n. picked ore; screened ore.

**scheidefähig,** a. separable, etc. (see scheiden).

**Scheide-flüssigkeit,** f. separating (or parting) liquid. **-gang,** m. poor ore (separated from good). **-gefäss,** n. separating or parting vessel. **-gold,** n. gold purified by parting.

**-gut,** n. material to be separated. **-kapelle,** f. cupel. **-kolben,** m. separating flask; (Old Chem.) alembic. **-kuchen,** m. (Metal.) liquation disk. **-kunst,** f. (analytical) chemistry. **-künstler,** m. (analytical) chemist.

**scheidekünstlerisch,** a. chemical.

**Scheide-linie,** f. boundary line. **-mehl,** n. dust of picked ore. **-mittel,** n. separating agent, parting agent. **-münze,** f. billon; small coin.

**scheiden,** v.t. separate; part; analyze, decompose; pick, sort (ore); clear, clarify (a liquid); divide, sever, divorce.—v.r. separate; (of milk) turn; divide.—v.i. separate, part, depart.

**Scheiden-.** (Physiol.) vaginal. **-schleim,** m. vaginal mucus.

**Scheide-ofen,** m. parting furnace, almond furnace. **-pfanne,** f. (Sugar) defecating pan, clarifier. **-punkt,** m. separation point.

**Scheider,** m. separator, etc. (see scheiden).

**Scheiderz,** n. separated ore.

**Scheide-schlamm,** m. (Sugar) defecation slime. **-sieb,** n. separating sieve. **-silber,** n. parting silver. **-trichter,** m. separating funnel, separatory funnel. **-vorrichtung,** f. separating (or parting) apparatus; screening or sorting device. **-wand,** f. partition wall, partition, midfeather, septum, diaphragm. **-wasser,** n. nitric acid (for parting); aqua regia. **-weg,** m. forked way, crossroads.

**Scheidung,** f. separation, etc. (see scheiden).

**Scheidungsmittel,** n. = Scheidemittel.

**Schein,** m. appearance; luster, light, shine; (of oils, etc.) bloom; document, paper, bill, certificate.

**Schein-.** apparent, mock, false, pseudo-.

**scheinbar,** a. apparent, seeming, plausible.

**scheinen,** v.i. shine; appear, seem.

**Schein-farbe,** f. accidental color. **-fuss,** m. pseudopodium. **-gold,** n. imitation gold. **-grund,** m. apparent reason, fallacy. **-werfer,** m. projector; reflector; headlight; searchlight; flashlight.

**Scheit,** n. log, billet, block.

**Scheitel,** m. vertex, apex, summit, crown, top.

**Scheitel-.** vertical; peak, maximum; (Anat.) parietal. **-linie,** f. vertical line. **-punkt,** m. vertex; zenith.

**scheitelrecht,** a. vertical.

**Scheitelwert,** m. peak value, maximum value.

**scheitern,** v.i. suffer wreck, be wrecked.

**Schelfe,** f. husk, shell, pod.

**Schellackfirnis,** m. shellac varnish.

**schellackieren,** v.t. shellac.

**Schellan,** n. shellan ($C_{13}H_{22}$); schellan (a synthetic resin).

**schellen,** v.t. ring.

**Schell-fisch,** *m.* cod; haddock. **-harz,** *n.* white rosin. **-ölsäure,** *f.* shellolic acid.

**Schema,** *n.* model, pattern; blank, form; schedule; scheme; diagram.

**schematisch,** *a.* schematic, diagrammatic.

**schematisieren,** *v.t.& i.* sketch; schematize.

**Schemen,** *m.* shadow, phantom.

**Schenkbier,** *n.* draft beer, schenk beer (contrasted with Lagerbier).

**Schenke,** *f.* public house, tavern.

**Schenkel,** *m.* leg; shank; thigh; side, side piece.

**Schenkel-.** femoral, crural. **-bein,** *n.* thigh bone, femur. **-rohr,** *n.,* **-röhre,** *f.* bent tube, V-tube, elbow tube, elbow pipe.

**schenken,** *v.t.* pour out; give, present; retail (liquors); suckle.

**Scherbe,** *f.,* **Scherben,** *m.* potsherd, shard; fragment, piece; crock, pot (esp. flowerpot); cupel; scorifier; (*Ceram.*) body.

**Scherbel,** *m.* = Scherbe; = Schirbel. **-krautwurzel,** *f.* asarum, asarabacca.

**Scherben-kobalt, -stein,** *m.* native arsenic.

**Schere,** *f.* scissors, shears; notch, nick; groove; shafts; claw.

**scheren,** *v.t.* shear, clip, cut; plague, vex.— *v.r.* go, be off; care.

**Scherel-bindung,** *f.* chelation. **-stahl,** *m.* shear steel. **-zange,** *f.* cutting forceps; wire cutter; (*Metal.*) shingling tongs.

**Scherfestigkeit,** *f.* shearing strength.

**Scherflein,** *n.* mite.

**Scher-spannung,** *f* shearing stress. **-versuch,** *m.* shearing test.

**Scherz,** *m.* joke, jest, fun, sport.

**scherzen,** *v.i.* joke, jest.

**scheuen,** *v.t.* shun, avoid, dread, grudge.— *v.i.* shy.

**Scheuer,** *f.* barn, granary.

**Scheuermittel,** *n.* scouring agent.

**scheuern,** *v.t.* scour, wash, clean; rub, chafe.

**Scheuerpulver,** *n.* scouring powder.

**Scheune,** *f.* = Scheuer.

**Schicht,** *f.* layer; stratum, bed, course; (when thin) film, coat; charge (of a furnace); batch; shift, turn (of work). **-boden,** *m.* (*Metal.*) mixing place.

**schichten,** *v.t.* arrange in layers or beds, stratify; pile, stack; charge.

**Schichten-bau,** *m.* layered or stratified structure. **-gitter,** *n.* layer lattice. **-gruppe,** *f.* (*Geol.*) group of strata, formation. **-kohle,** *f.* foliated coal.

**schichtenweise,** *a.& adv.* in layers or strata, stratified.

**Schichtgestein,** *n.* stratified rock.

**Schichtung,** *f.* stratification; arranging in layers; piling; charging.

**Schichtwasser,** *n.* ground water.

**Schick,** *m* skill; tact; order; fitness; style.

**schicken,** *v.t.* send; cause to happen.—*v.r.* happen; suit, fit; conform, accommodate oneself; prepare.—**geschickt,** *p.a.* sent, etc.; skilled, qualified, clever; suitable, fit.

**schicklich,** *a.* becoming, proper, fit, suitable.

**Schicksal,** *n.* fate, destiny.

**Schickung,** *f.* dispensation.

**Schieb-.** sliding, slide.

**Schiebehülse,** *f.* sliding sleeve.

**schieben,** *v.t.* shove, push, slide, slip.

**Schieber,** *m.* slide, slider, slide bar, slide valve, carriage; shovel; pusher, shover; damper. **-kasten,** *m.* (*Mach.*) slide box, valve chest.

**Schieberohr,** *n.* sliding tube or sleeve.

**Schieberventil,** *n.* slide valve.

**Schiebung,** *f.* shoving, etc. (see schieben); glide (of metals); maneuver.

**schied,** *pret.* of scheiden.

**Schieds-analyse,** *f.* umpire analysis. **-mann, -richter,** *m.* umpire, arbiter, referee. **-spruch,** *m.* award.

**schief,** *a.* inclined, oblique; skew, crooked.— *adv.* obliquely; askew, awry, amiss.

**Schiefagarkultur,** *f.* sloped-agar culture.

**Schiefe,** *f.* inclination, slope; obliqueness; crookedness.

**Schiefer,** *m.* slate; schist; shale; flaw (in iron).

**schiefer-ähnlich, -artig,** *a.* slatelike, slaty, schistous. **-blau,** *a.* slate-blue.

**Schieferfarbe,** *f.* slate color.

**schiefer-farben, -farbig,** *a.* slate-colored.

**Schiefergips,** *m.* foliated gypsum.

**schiefer-grau,** *a.* slate-gray. **-haltig,** *a.* containing slate, slaty.

**schieferig,** *a.* slaty, slate-like; schistous, schistose; scaly, flaky, foliated, foliaceous.

**Schiefer-kohle,** *f.* slaty coal; splint coal. **-mehl,** *n.* ground shale. **-mergel,** *m.* slaty marl.

**schiefern,** *v.i.& r.* scale off, exfoliate.

**Schiefer-öl,** *n.* shale oil. **-platte,** *f.* slab or plate of slate. **-spat,** *m.* slate spar (lamellar variety of calcite). **-stein,** *n.* slate. **-talk,** *m.* talc slate, indurated talc. **-teer,** *m.* shale tar. **-teeröl,** *n.* shale tar oil. **-ton,** *m.* slate clay, shale.

**Schieferung,** *f.* scaling off, exfoliation; schistosity, foliated structure.

**Schieferweiss,** *n.* flake white.

**Schiefheit,** *f.* = Schiefe.

**schiefliegend,** *p.a.* inclined, sloping, oblique.

**schiefrig,** *a.* = schieferig.

**schiefwinklig,** *a.* oblique-angled.

**schien,** *pret.* of scheinen.

**Schienbein,** *n.* shin bone, tibia.

**Schiene,** *f.* rail; slat, strip, bar; tube support; rim, tire (of a wheel); (*Med.*) splint.

Schienen-weg, *m.* railway; tramway. -weite, *f.* railway gage.

schier, *a.* sheer, pure.—*adv.* simply; nearly.

Schierling, *m.* hemlock (the herb). -saft, *m.* hemlock juice, juice of conium.

Schierlings-kraut, *n.* hemlock (the herb). -tanne, *f.* hemlock spruce, hemlock.

schiert, *pr. 3 sing.* of scheren.

Schiessbaumwolle, *f.* guncotton.

schiessen, *v.t.& i.* shoot; fire; dart, emit, dash; (of dyes) flush on.

Schiess-ofen, *m.* bomb oven, tube furnace, Carius oven. -pulver, *n.* gunpowder. -rohr, *n.*, -röhre, *f.* a sealed tube in which substances are heated under pressure, bomb tube. -stoff, *m.* powder (for shooting). -stoffwesen, *n.* powder business. -wolle, *f.* guncotton. -wollpulver, *n.* guncotton powder.

Schiff, *n.* ship, vessel; shuttle; nave.

schiffbar, *a.* navigable.

Schiff-bruch, *m.* shipwreck. -chen, *n.* boat; little ship; shuttle; (*Bot.*) keel

schiffen, *v.t.& i.* navigate, sail.

Schifffahrt, *f.* navigation.

Schiffsbedürfnisse, *n.pl.* naval stores.

Schiff'sche Base. Schiff base.

Schiffs-leim, *m.* marine glue. -pech, *n.* common black pitch.

Schild, *n.* label; sign, signboard; badge; (turtle) shell.—*m.* shield; escutcheon. -chen, *n.* little label, little shield, etc. (see Schild). -drüse, *f.* thyroid gland.

Schilddrüsen-. thyroid. -essenz, *f.*, -extrakt, *n.* (*Pharm.*) thyroid solution.

Schilderblau, *n.* (*Dyeing*) pencil blue.

schildern, *v.t.* depict, portray, draw.

schildförmig, *a.* shield-shaped, scutiform; (*Anat.*) thyroid.

Schild-knorpel, *m.* thyroid cartilage. -kraut, *n.* skullcap (*Scutellaria*). -kröte, *f.* turtle, tortoise. -laus, *f.* cochineal insect. -patt, *n.* tortoise shell.

schildpatten, *a.* tortoise-shell.

Schildwache, *f.* sentinel.

Schilf, *n.* reed.

schilferig, *a.* scaly.

schilfern, *v.i.* scale off, exfoliate.

Schilfglaserz, *n.* freieslebenite.

Schiller, *m.* play of colors, iridescence; surface color, metallic color, schiller. -farbe, *f.* changeable color; schiller color, surface color, metallic color.

schillerfarbig, *a.* showing a play of colors, iridescent; exhibiting schiller or metallic color.

Schillerglanz, *m.* iridescent luster; colored metallic luster, schiller.

schillerig, *a.* iridescent, chatoyant.

schillern, *v.i.* exhibit a play of colors, iridesce, opalesce; exhibit surface color or schiller.— schillernd, *p.a.* iridescent, opalescent, chatoyant; possessing schiller.

Schiller-quarz, *m.* (*Min.*) cat's-eye. -seide, *f.* shot silk, changeable silk. -spat, *m.* schiller spar (altered enstatite); diallage. -stein, *n.* schiller spar. -stoff, *m.* iridescent substance. -wein, *m.* wine from red and white grapes mixed.

schilt, *pr. 3 sing.* of schelten.

Schimmel, *m.* mold; mildew; gray or white horse.

schimmelartig, *a.* moldlike, moldy.

Schimmelfarbe, *f.* mold color.

schimmelfleckig, *a.* spotted with mold.

Schimmelgeruch, *m.* moldy smell.

schimmelgrau, *a.* moldy gray.

schimmelig, schimmelicht, *a.* moldy, musty.

schimmeln, *v.i.* mold.

Schimmelpilz, *m.* mold fungus, mold.

Schimmer, *m.* glimmer, shimmer, glitter.

schimmern, *v.i.* glisten, glitter, gleam, shine.

Schindel, *f.* shingle; (*Med.*) splint.

schinden, *v.t.* skin, flay.

Schinken, *m.*, -fleisch, *n.* ham.

Schippe, *f.* shovel, scoop.

schipperig, *a.* (*Dyeing*) mixtury, not solid.

Schiras, *m.* (*Wines*) Shiraz.

Schirbel, *m.* (*Metal.*) bloom; piece of a bloom, stamp.

Schirm, *m.* screen; shelter; shade; umbrella; visor (of a cap); (*Bot.*) umbel.

schirmen, *v.t.* screen; shelter.

Schirm-pflanze, *f.* umbelliferous plant. -wirkung, *f.* screening effect.

schlabbern, *v.i.* slobber; overflow; gossip.

Schlabber-rohr, *n.* overflow pipe or tube. -ventil, *n.* check valve.

Schlacht, *f.* battle.

schlachten, *v.t.* kill, slaughter.

Schlachthaus, *n.* slaughterhouse, abbatoir.

Schlack, *m.* niter deposit.

Schlacke, *f.* slag; cinder, scoria, dross; (in coal) clinker.

schlacken, *v.i.* slag, form slag, clinker. -artig, *a.* slaggy, scoriaceous, drossy.

Schlacken-auge, *n.*= Schlackenloch. -beton, *m.* slag concrete.

schlackenbildend, *a.* slag-forming.

Schlacken-bildner, *m.* slag former. -bildung, *f.* formation of slag, scorification. -blei, *n.* slaggy lead. -eisen, *n.* cinder iron. -form, *f.* cinder block; cinder notch.

schlackenfrei, *a.* slag-free, clinkerless.

Schlacken-frischen, *n.* = Schlackenpuddeln. -gang, *m.* slag duct, cinder fall. -grube, *f.* slag pit. -halde, *f.* slag dump, cinder tip.

schlackenhaltig, *a.* containing slag or clinker.

**Schlacken-herd,** m. slag hearth, slag furnace. **-klumpen,** m. lump of slag, clinker. **-kobalt,** m. safflorite. **-kuchen,** m. cake of slag or clinker. **-lava,** f. scoriaceous lava. **-loch,** n. cinder notch, slag hole, cinder tap. **-mehl,** n. ground slag, Thomas meal. **-ofen,** m. slag furnace. **-puddeln,** n. pig boiling.

**schlacken-reich,** a. rich in slag or clinker, slaggy. **-rein,** a. free from slag or clinker.

**Schlacken-rösten,** n. roasting of slag; scorification roasting. **-scherbe,** f., **-scherben,** m. scorifier. **-spiess,** m. cinder iron, slag iron. **-spur,** f. = Schlackenloch. **-staub,** m. coal dust. **-stein,** m. slag block, slag brick. **-stich,** m., **-stichloch,** n. cinder notch, slag hole. **-wolle,** f. slag wool, mineral wool. **-zacken,** m. cinder plate, front plate. **-ziegel, -ziegelstein,** m. slag brick. **-zinn,** n. tin extracted from slag, prillion.

**schlackig,** a. slaggy, drossy, scoriaceous; (of coal) clinkering.

**Schlaf,** m. sleep; temple (of the head). **-arznei,** f. soporific, hypnotic, narcotic.

**schlafbefördernd,** p.a. soporific.

**Schläfe,** f. temple (of the head).

**schlafen,** v.i. sleep; lie dormant.

**Schläfen-.** (Anat.) temporal.

**schlaff,** a. slack, loose, flabby, flaccid, soft.

**Schlaf-mittel,** n. soporofic, narcotic. **-mohn,** m. opium poppy.

**schläft,** pr. 3 sing. of schlafen.

**Schlaf-trank,** m. sleeping draft. **-zimmer,** n. bedroom.

**Schlag,** m. stroke, blow, percussion, knock, shock, kick, beat; apoplexy; coinage, stamp, sort; cutting (of wood or in the woods); field; song (of birds). **-ader,** f. artery. **-arbeit,** f. work resulting from a blow or percussion.

**Schlägel,** m. = Schlegel.

**Schlagelot,** n. hard solder.

**Schlagempfindlichkeit,** f. sensitiveness to percussion.

**schlagen,** v t. strike, beat, hit, knock; cut (wood); churn (butter); press (oil); drive (nails, etc.); put (into barrels); etc., etc.— v.i. strike, beat, knock, kick; warble; belong, concern.—**schlagend,** p.a. striking, impressive.—**schlagende Wetter,** fire damp.

**Schläger,** m. beater, etc. (see schlagen); fighter; batter; rapier.

**Schlag-festigkeit,** f. resistance to shock. **-figur,** f. percussion figure. **-fläche,** f. striking surface, surface of impact. **-gold,** n. leaf gold. **-härte,** f. impact hardness. **-kreuzmühle,** f. cross-beater mill. **-lot,** n. hard solder. **-probe,** f. percussion test, impact test. **-pulver,** n. fulminating powder; (Pharm.) antapoplectic powder. **-saat,** f.

hempseed. **-sahne,** f. whipped cream. **-siebprobe,** f. shatter test.

**schlägt,** pr. 3 sing. of schlagen.

**Schlag-versuch,** m. impact test. **-wasser,** n. bilge water. **-weite,** f. striking distance (of an electric spark), spark distance. **-werk,** n. striking apparatus, specif. rammer. **-wetter,** n.pl. fire damp.

**schlagwetter-sicher,** a. proof against fire damp. **-zündfähig,** a. ignitable by fire damp.

**Schlag-widerstand,** m. impact resistance. **-zünder,** m. percussion fuse.

**Schlamm,** m. mud, sludge, slime; slurry; silt; ooze; (Ceram.) slip.

**Schlämm-.** elutriating, washing, elutriated, washed. **-analyse,** f. analysis by elutriation. **-apparat,** m. elutriating apparatus. **-arbeit,** f. elutriation, washing.

**schlammartig,** a. in the form of mud or slime.

**schlämmen,** v.t. elutriate, wash (powdered substances); levigate; (Mining) buddle.

**Schlämm-fass,** n. washing tub or tank (for precipitates, etc.); (Mining) dolly tub. **-flasche,** f. elutriating flask. **-gefäss,** n. elutriating vessel or reservoir. **-glas,** n. elutriating glass.

**schlammhaltig,** a. containing mud or sludge, muddy.

**Schlämmherd,** m. (Metal.) slime pit, also slime table.

**schlammig,** a. muddy, sludgy, slimy, oozy.

**Schlammkohle,** f. coal slime, mud coal.

**Schlämm-kohle,** f. washed coal. **-kreide,** f. prepared chalk; whiting.

**Schlamm-pfännchen,** n. (Salt) scum pan. **-scheider,** m. slime separator.

**Schlammschlich, Schlämmschlich,** m. washed ore slime.

**Schlämmtrichter,** m. elutriating funnel.

**Schlammtrübe,** f. (Metal.) slime pulp.

**Schlämmung,** f. elutriating, etc. (see schlämmen).

**Schlämm-verfahren,** n. elutriating or washing process. **-vorrichtung,** f. elutriating apparatus, washing apparatus.

**Schlammwasser,** n. water charged with sludge or slime.

**Schlämmzylinder,** m. elutriating cylinder.

**schlang,** pret. of schlingen.

**Schlange,** f. snake, serpent; (Tech.) worm, coil; hose (flexible tube).

**schlängeln,** v.r. wind, meander.—**schlängelnd,** p.a. sinuous, winding, serpentine.

**schlangenartig,** a. snakelike, serpentine.

**Schlangen-gift,** n. snake venom. **-holz,** n. snakewood. **-kühler,** m. spiral (or coil) condenser. **-rohr,** n., **-röhre,** f. worm, spiral pipe (or tube), coil. **-stein,** m. ophite; serpentine. **-wurzel,** f. snakeroot.

schlank, a. slender, slim.

Schlappermilch, f. curdled milk.

Schlauch, m. tube, tubing, pipe (of flexible material), hose; skin (for holding something); drunkard; glutton.

schlauchen, v.t. (Brewing) hose, transfer (beer) or fill (casks) by means of hose or pipes.

Schlauch-klemme, f. tube clamp. -leitung, f. hose line. -pilze, m. ascomycete. -sicherung, f. hose protection (as spiral wire rings). -stück, n. tubing attachment (part to which tubing may be attached). -verbindung, f. rubber-tube connection; hose connection.

schlecht, a. bad, ill, poor.—adv. badly, ill. -erdings, adv. utterly, absolutely. -hin, -weg, adv. merely, plainly.

schlecken, schleckern, v.t. lick, lap.—v.i. be dainty.

Schlegel, m. mallet, beater, (wooden) hammer; drumstick.

Schlehdorn, m. blackthorn, sloe tree.

Schlehe, f. sloe.

schleichen, v.i. slink, sneak; creep.—schleichend, p.a. slow.

Schleich-gut, n. smuggled goods, contraband. -handel, m. smuggling, illicit trade.

Schleier, m. veil; haze; screen, curtain (as of smoke); lawn (the fabric).

schleiern, v.t. veil; (Photog.) fog.

Schleife, f. loop; noose, knot; slide; sled.

schleifen, v.t. grind, sharpen, polish; cut (gems); abrade; drag, trail.—v.i. slip, slide.

Schleiferei, f. grindery; grinder's trade.

Schleif-material, -mittel, n. abrasive. -pulver, n. grinding powder, polishing powder. -rad, n. grinding wheel, polishing wheel. -sel, n., -staub, m. grindings. -stein, m. grinding stone, grindstone, whetstone. -stoff, m. (Paper) ground pulp.

Schleifung, f. grinding, etc. (see schleifen).

Schleim, m. slime; mucilage; mucus.

schleim-artig, a. slimy, glutinous; mucoid. -bildend, p.a. slime-forming; (Physiol.) muciparous.

Schleim-drüse, f. mucous gland. -gärung, f. viscous fermentation. -harz, n. gum resin. -haut, f. mucous membrane.

schleimig, a. slimy, mucilaginous; mucous. —schleimige Gärung, mucous, or viscous, fermentation.

Schleimpilz, m. slime fungus, slime mold (Myxomycetes).

schleimsauer, a. of or combined with mucic acid, mucate of.

Schleim-säure, f. mucic acid. -stoff, m. mucin.

schleimstoffartig, a. mucinlike, mucoid.

Schleim-tier, n. mollusk. -zellulose, f. mucocellulose. -zucker, m. levulose.

Schleisse, f. splint, splinter.

schleissen, v.t. slit; split; strip; wear, wear out.

Schleisswirkung, f. abrasive action.

Schlemm-. = Schlämm-.

schlemmen, v.i. eat greedily; carouse.

Schlempe, f. residual liquid from distillation of alcoholic liquors, vinasse, slops, spent wash. -kohle, -asche, f. crude potash from beet vinasse, saline.

schlenkern, v.t. swing, sling, fling.

Schleppe, f. train, trail; (Paper) felt board; (Founding) truck.

schleppen, v.t. & i. drag, trail; tow.

Schlepper, m. tractor; hauler; tug.

Schleppmühle, f. drag mill, drag-stone mill.

Schlesien, n. Silesia.

schlesisch, a. Silesian.

Schleuder, f. centrifuge; sling. -guss, m. centrifugal casting. -korb, m. centrifuge basket. -maschine, f. centrifugal machine, centrifugal (specif. hydro-extractor); catapult.

schleudern, v.t. centrifuge, hydro-extract; sling, fling, hurl.—v.i. swing, roll; cut prices.

schleunig, a. speedy, hasty, quick, immediate. —adv. speedily, etc.

Schleuse, f. sluice; sewer.

Schleusengas, n. sewer gas.

Schlich, m. byway; trick; (Metal.) slimes, schlich. -arbeit, f. smelting of slimes.

schlicht, a. smooth, even, sleek; (of files) fine; (of fabrics) plain; simple, homely.

Schlichte, f. dressing; size (for fabrics); (Founding) black wash; (Plastering) skim coat, white coat.

schlichtecht, a. fast to sizing.

schlichten, v.t. smooth, plane, dress; sleek (leather, etc.); planish (metals); size (fabrics); blackwash (molds); adjust, settle.

Schlicht-leim, m. sizing, size. -öl, n. sizing oil. -walze, f. finishing roll.

Schlick, m. slime, mud; (Metal.) schlich (ore slimes).

Schlicker, m. (Ceramics) slip, slop; (Metal.) dross.

Schliech, m. (Metal.) slimes, schlich.

schlief, pret. of schlafen.

schliefen, v.i. slip, creep.

Schlieren, f.pl. schlieren (regions of varying refraction, as in liquids); streaks, striae, schlieren (as in glass and igneous rocks).

Schliesse, f. pin, peg, catch, anchor.

schliessen, v.t. close; shut, lock; seal (tubes); bind; embrace; contract; conclude.—v.r. close; be related, be apropos.—v.i. close.

—geschlossene Kette, closed chain; (*Mech.*) endless chain.

schliesslich, *a.* final, ultimate.—*adv.* finally.

Schliess-rohr, *n.*, -röhre, *f.* sealed tube.

schliff, *pret.* of schleifen.

Schliff, *m.* grinding, sharpening; smoothness, polish; grindings; powder; cut (of a gem); ground section or specimen (as of metals for etching); ground joint. -kolben, *m.* flask with ground top. -stelle, *f.* ground place, grinding. -stopfen, *m.* ground-in stopper. -stück, *n.* ground piece.

schlimm, *a.* bad; sad, severe, sore, ill.—*adv.* badly, ill.

Schling-. winding, twisting, (of plants) climbing; pertaining to swallowing or deglutition.

Schlinge, *f.* loop, noose, sling; trap, snare.

schlingen, *v.t.* wind, twine, twist; swallow, gulp.

Schlippe'sches Salz. Schlippe's salt.

schliss, *pret.* of schleissen.

Schlitten, *m.* sledge, sled, sleigh; truck; sliding carriage.

Schlittschuh, *m.* skate.

Schlitz, *m.* slit, slot, fissure, cleft, slash. -brenner, *m.* batswing burner.

schlitzen, *v.t.* slit, slot, slash, split, cleave, rip.

schloff, *pret.* of schliefen.

schloss, *pret.* of schliessen.

Schloss, *n.* lock; snap, clasp; castle, palace.

Schlosse, *f.* hailstone.

Schlot, *m.*, Schlotte, *f.* flue, smokestack, stack; soil pipe.

Schlotter, *m.* (*Salt*) sediment from boiling.

schlottern, *v.i.* dangle, flap, hang loose, shake, wabble.

Schlucht, *f.* ravine, gorge.

schluchzen, *v.i.* sob; hiccup.

schlucken, *v.t.& i.* swallow, gulp.

schlug, *pret.* of schlagen.

Schlummer, *m.* slumber.

Schlund, *m.* throat, pharynx; gulf, chasm.

Schlund-. pharyngeal. -kopf, *m.* upper pharynx.

schlupfen, schlüpfen, *v.i.* slip, slide.

Schlupfloch, *n.* loophole.

schlüpfrig, *a.* slippery; lascivious.— — machen, lubricate.

Schlüpfrigkeit, *f.* slipperiness, lubricity, (of lubricants) oiliness.

Schlupfwinkel, *m.* lurking place, haunt.

schlürfen, *v.t.* sip, lap; (of pumps) suck air.

Schluss, *m.* closing; close; conclusion; end; (*Elec.*) connection.

Schlüssel, *m.* key; screw driver or wrench; (*Elec.*) key, switch. -bein, *n.* collar bone, clavicle. -blume, *f.* primrose. -formel, *f.* key formula. -nummer, *f.* key number.

Schluss-folge, -folgerung, *f.* conclusion, in-

ference. -stein, *m.* keystone. -weise, *f.* manner of reasoning.

Schlutte, *f.* alkekengi.

schm., *abbrev.* (schmelzend) melting; (schmilzt) melts.

Schmack, *m.* sumac.

schmacken, *v.t.* treat with sumac, sumac.

schmack-gar, *a.* dressed with sumac. -haft, *a.* palatable, savory. -ieren, *v.t.* treat with sumac, sumac.

schmal, *a.* narrow; slender; scanty.

schmälern, *v.t.* narrow, reduce, abridge.

Schmal-leder, *n.* small tanned hides, tanned skins. -seite, *f.* narrow side, edge.

Schmaltblau, *n.* smalt.

Schmalte, *f.* smalt.

Schmalz, *n.* lard; melted fat.

schmalzartig, *a.* lardaceous, lardy.

Schmalzbutter, *f.* melted butter.

Schmälze, *f.* (*Textiles*) oil, softener.

schmalzen, schmälzen, *v.t.* grease, lard; (*Textiles*) oil.

schmalzig, *a.* lardy, lardaceous.

Schmalzmasse, *f.* (*Textiles*) softening material, softener.

Schmalzöl, *n.* lard oil; oleo oil; wool oil.

Schmälzvorgang, *m.* (*Textiles*) oiling process.

Schmand, Schmant, *m.* slime, sludge; cream.

Schmarotzer, *m.* parasite.

schmarotzerisch, *a.* parasitic.

Schmauch, *m.* smoke.

schmauchen, *v.t.& i.* smoke.

schmecken, *v.t.& i.* taste; relish, like.

Schmeer, *m.* = Schmer.

schmeichelhaft, *a.* flattering, complimentary.

schmeicheln, *v.i.* flatter; coax.

schmeissen, *v.t.* throw, fling, dash; deposit (insect eggs).

Schmelz, *m.* enamel, glaze; fusion, melting, melt.

Schmelz-. melting; smelting; fusible. -anlage, *f.* smeltery; melting plant; foundry. -arbeit, *f.* smelting, smelting process; enameling, enameled work. -arbeiter, *m.* smelter; founder; enameler.

schmelz-artig, *a.* enamel-like. -bar, *a.* fusible, meltable.

Schmelz-barkeit, *f.* fusibility. -blau, *n.* smalt. -butter, *f.* melted butter. -draht, *m.* (*Elec.*) fuse wire.

Schmelze, *f.* melting, fusion; smelting; smeltery; fused mass, melt; (*Glass*) batch; (*Soda*) ball; (*Spinning*) mill oil.

Schmelzeinsatz, *m.* (*Elec.*) fuse.

schmelzen, *v.t.* melt, fuse; smelt; (*teilweise*) frit.—*v.i.* melt, fuse; smelt; deliquesce.— geschmolzen, *p.a.* melted, fused, molten; smelted.

Schmelzen, n. melting, fusion; smelting.
Schmelzer, m. melter; founder; smelter.
Schmelzerde, f. fusible earth.
Schmelzerei, f. smeltery; foundry.
Schmelz-erz, n. smelting ore. -farbe, f. enamel color, vitrifiable pigment, majolica color. -feuer, n. (Iron) refinery. -fluss, m. fused mass, melt; fusion. -glas, n. fusible glass; enamel. -glasur, f. enamel. -grad, m. melting point. -gut, n. material suitable for smelting (or melting), material to be smelted (or melted). -hafen, m. melting pot. -herd, m. smelting hearth; smelting furnace; (Soda) front hearth of a black-ash furnace. -hitze, f. melting heat. -hütte, f. smelting house or works, smeltery; foundry.
schmelzig, a. fusible.
Schmelz-kegel, m. (Ceram.) fusible cone. -kessel, m. melting kettle or vessel; smelting crucible; (Soda) caustic pan. -koks, m. smelting coke. -küche, f. laboratory. -kunst, f. (art of) enameling; smelting. -kurve, f. melting-point curve, fusion curve. -lampe, f. glass-blower's lamp; enameler's lamp. -legierung, f. fusible alloy. -linie, f. line of fusion, fusion curve. -löffel, m. melting ladle. -malerei, f. enamel painting. -mittel, n. flux. -ofen, m. melting furnace; smelting furnace.
Schmelzp., abbrev. (Schmelzpunkt) melting point.
Schmelz-perle, f. blowpipe bead; enamel bead, bugle. -pfanne, f. melting pan. -pfropfen, m. fusible plug. -post, f. smelting charge, post. -prozess, m. melting or smelting process. -pulver, n. (powdered) flux.
Schmelzpunkt, m. melting point, fusing point. -bestimmung, f. melting-point determination. -bestimmungsrohr, n. (or -röhre, f.), melting-point tube.
Schmelz-raum, m. (Metal.) hearth. -röhrchen, n. melting tube. -soda, f. a crude recovered sodium carbonate. -stahl, m. German steel, natural steel. -stein, m. (Min.) mizzonite. -temperatur, f. fusing temperature.
Schmelztiegel, m. crucible, melting pot. -deckel, m. crucible cover; (Metal.) tile. -halter, m. crucible holder, crucible support. -zange, f. crucible tongs.
Schmelztröpfchen, n. blowpipe bead.
Schmelzung, f. = Schmelzen.
Schmelzungspunkt, m. melting point.
Schmelz-verfahren, n. melting process, fusion process; smelting process. -wärme, f. heat of fusion. -wasser, n. water from melting ice or snow. -werk, n. smeltery; foundry; enameled work.
schmelzwürdig, a. suitable for smelting, workable.

Schmelz-zeit, f. time of melting or fusion; (Glass) journey. -zement, m. alumina cement. -zeug, n. smelting tools. -zone, f. zone of fusion; smelting zone.
Schmer, m.& n. fat, grease; suet.
Schmergel, m. emery. See Schmirgel-.
Schmerz, m. pain; grief, sorrow.
schmerzen, v.t. pain; grieve.—v.i.& r. hurt, ache.
schmerz-haft, a. painful; distressing. -los, a. painless.
Schmerzlosigkeit, f. painlessness.
Schmetterling, m. butterfly; lint.
Schmetterlings-blütler, m. papilionaceous plant, fabaceous plant (such as the bean, pea, etc.; not so wide a term as "leguminous plant"). -brenner, m. wing burner.
schmettern, v.t. dash, smash.—v.i. clang, ring, crash, blare.
Schmied, m. smith; blacksmith.
schmiedbar, a. malleable, forgeable.
Schmiedbarkeit, f. malleability.
Schmiede, f. forge, smithy. -arbeit, f. forging, smithing.
schmiedebar, a. capable of being wrought, forgeable.
Schmiedeeisen, n. wrought iron; malleable iron.
schmiedeeisern, a. wrought-iron.
Schmiede-feuer, n. smith's hearth, forge. -herd, m. forge; forge hearth.
Schmiedeisen, n. = Schmiedeeisen.
schmiedeisern, a. wrought-iron.
schmieden, v.t. forge, smith; devise, concoct.—geschmiedetes Eisen, wrought iron.
Schmiedeschlacke, f. forge cinder.
schmiegen, v.t. bend; bevel.
schmiegsam, a. flexible, pliant.
Schmiegsamkeit, f. flexibility, pliancy.
Schmierbüchse, f. grease cup, oil cup, lubricator.
Schmiere, f. grease (for smearing or lubricating), smear; ointment; (for animals) dip.
schmieren, v.t. lubricate, oil; grease, smear, anoint; spread (butter); butter (bread); scrawl; thrash.
schmierfähig, a. capable of acting as a lubricant.
Schmier-fähigkeit, f. lubricating property. -fett, n. = Schmiere. -fleck, m. grease spot. -flüssigkeit, f. lubricating fluid. -hahn, m. lubricating cock, grease cock.
schmierig, a. greasy, smeary, oily; glutinous, viscous; dirty.
Schmier-kanne, f. oil can. -käse, m. cottage cheese, smearcase. -leder, n. leather dressed with oil. -masse, f. (Mach.) lubricating paste. -mittel, -material, n. lubricant; ointment, salve, liniment. -mittelindustrie, f.

lubricant industry. -öl, *n.* lubricating oil.
-seife, *f.* soft soap.

Schmierung, *f.* lubrication, etc. (see schmieren).

Schmier-vorrichtung, *f.* lubricating device, lubricator. -wert, *m.* lubricating value. -wirkung, *f.* lubricating effect. -wolle, *f.* greasy wool.

schmilzt, *pr. 2 & 3 sing.* of schmelzen.

Schminke, *f.* (face) paint.

Schmink-mittel, *n.* cosmetic. -rot, *n.* rouge (the cosmetic). -weiss, *n.* flake white, pearl white (basic nitrate or oxychloride of bismuth).

Schmirgel, *m.* emery. -leinen, *n.,* -leinwand, *f.* emery cloth.

schmirgeln, *v.t.* rub with emery, emery.

Schmirgel-papier, *n.* emery paper. -pulver, *n.* emery powder. -scheibe, *f.* emery wheel.

schmiss, *pret.* of schmeissen.

schmitzen, *v.t.* splash; blur; dye (leather); dress (cloth); lash.

schmolz, *pret.* of schmelzen.

schmoren, *v.t. & i.* stew.

Schmpt., *abbrev.* (Schmelzpunkt) melting point.

schmuck, *a.* neat, trim, pretty.

Schmuck, *m.* ornament; jewelry; finery.

schmücken, *v.t.* adorn, decorate, dress.

Schmuck-stein, *m.* gem, gem stone. -waren, *f.pl.* jewelry, jewels.

Schmutz, *m.* dirt, filth, smut. -decke, *f.* a thin upper layer of sand in a filter bed.

schmutzig, *a.* dirty, soiled, filthy, smutty.

Schmutz-wasser, *n.* dirty water; sewage. -wolle, *f.* wool in the yolk.

Schnabel, *m.* beak, bill; nozzle, nose.

schnabelförmig, *a.* beak-shaped.

Schnalle, *f.* buckle, clasp.

schnallen, *v.t.* buckle.

schnalzen, *v.i.* smack, cluck, snap.

Schnappdecke, *f.* extension (to the drum of a German mask).

schnappen, *v.i.* snap; gasp.

Schnaps, *m.* spirits; dram. -brenner, *m.* distiller (of spirits).

schnarchen, *v.i.* snore.

schnattern, *v.i.* cackle; chatter.

Schnatterrohr, *n.* direct steam pipe.

Schnauze, *f.* snout, mouth; (*Tech.*) nose, nozzle, spout.

Schnecke, *f.* snail; slug; worm (of a still); (*Mach.*) worm, endless screw; volute; spiral stairway; (*Anat.*) cochlea.

schneckenförmig, *a.* spiral, helical.

Schnecken-gang, *m.* auger; spiral walk; snail's pace. -getriebe, *n.* worm gear. -gewinde, *n.* helix. -klee, *m.* snail clover (*Medicago* species).

Schnee, *m.* snow.

schneeartig, *a.* snowlike.

Schnee-flocke, *f.* snowflake. -gips, *m.* snowy (foliated) gypsum. -glöckchen, *n.* snowdrop. -grenze, *f.* snow line. -wehe, *f.* snowdrift.

schneeweiss, *a.* snow-white.

Schneeweiss, *n.* snow white (zinc white).

Schneidbrenner, *m.* cutting torch.

Schneide, *f.* knife edge; edge; keenness. -maschine, *f.* cutting machine.

schneiden, *v.t.* cut; saw; prune; adulterate; gripe.—*v.i.* cut, carve.

Schneider, *m.* cutter; tailor.

Schneidflamme, *f.* cutting flame.

schneidig, *a.* sharp, keen; (of rock) soft; plucky.

Schneid-kante, *f.* cutting edge. -legierung, *f.* alloy for cutting tools.

schneien, *v.i.* snow.

schnell, *a.* fast, rapid, quick, sudden.—*adv.* quickly, rapidly. -abbindend, *a.* quicksetting.

Schnell-analyse, *f.* rapid analysis. -auflöser, *m.* rapid dissolver. -binder, *m.* quicksetting cement. -bleiche, *f.* quick bleaching, chemical bleaching. -drehstahl, *m.* highspeed steel.

schnellen, *v.i.* spring, snap, jerk.—*v.t.* let fly, fling; jerk; cheat.

Schnell-essig, *m.* quick vinegar. -essigbereitung, *f.* quick vinegar process. -färbung, *f.* (*Micros.*) quick staining. -filter, *n.* rapid filter. -filtrieren, *n.* rapid filtration. -fluss, *m.* quick flux.

schnellflüssig, *a.* easily fusible.

Schnell-gärung, *f.* quick (or accelerated) fermentation. -gerben, *n.* rapid tanning.

Schnell-igkeit, *f.* rapidity, quickness, speed, velocity. -kochtopf, *m.* autoclave, pressure cooker. -kraft, *f.* elasticity.

schnell-kräftig, *a.* elastic. -laufend, *a.* highspeed, rapid.

Schnell-lot, *n.* soft solder; fusible metal. -methode, *f.* rapid method, quick method. -photographie, *f.* instantaneous photography or photograph. -probe, *f.* rapid test. -röste, *f.* quick retting, chemical retting. -säurer, *m.* acetifier (in the quick vinegar process). -schrift, *f.* shorthand, stenography. -stahl, *m.* high-speed steel. -trockenfarbe, *f.* quick-drying color or ink.

schnelltrocknend, *p.a.* quick-drying, siccative.

Schnell-verfahren, *n.* rapid or quick process. -wa(a)ge, *f.* steelyard. -zug, *m.* fast train, express train. -zünder, *m.* quick match.

Schneppe, *f.* spout, snout, nozzle, lip.

schnitt, *pret.* of schneiden.

Schnitt, *m.* cut; cutting, incision; section; intersection; slice; edge (of a book); (surgical) operation; crop. **-brenner,** *m.* slit burner, batswing burner.

**Schnitte,** *f.* cut, slice; sulfur match (for casks); chop; steak.

**Schnitt-fänger,** *m.* (*Micros.*) section lifter. **-färbung,** *f.* (*Micros.*) section staining. **-fläche,** *f.* surface of a cut or section, sectional plane, section. **-holz,** *n.* sawed timber. **-lauch,** *m.* chive. **-linie,** *f.* line of section or intersection. **-punkt,** *m.,* **-stelle,** *f.* point or place of intersection. **-waren,** *f.pl.* draper's goods, dry goods.

**Schnitz,** *m.* cut, slice, chip; cutlet.

**Schnitzel,** *n.* slice, chip, clipping, snipping, shred, scrap; cutlet. **-maschine,** *f.* slicing machine, slicer (as for sugar beets), shredding machine.

**schnitzeln, schnitzen,** *v.t.& i.* cut, carve, chip, whittle.

**Schnitzer,** *m.* cutter, carver; blunder.

**Schnupfen,** *m.* cold, catarrh.

**Schnupftabak,** *m.* snuff.

**Schnur,** *f.* string, cord, line, twine, tape, band.

**schnüren,** *v.t.* tie up, string, lace, strap, constrict.

**Schnürkolben,** *m.* a flask with neck constricted at the top.

**Schnurre,** *f.* rattle; joke, story.

**schnurren,** *v.i.* buzz, hum, whir, whiz, purr.

**schob,** *pret.* of schieben.

**schobern,** *v.t.* pile, stack.

**Schock,** *n.* sixty; mass, lot.

**Schofel,** *m.* trash, refuse.

**Schokolade,** *f.* chocolate.

**Schokoladentafel,** *f.* cake of chocolate.

**Scholle,** *f.* clod; soil; lump; flounder.

**Schöllkraut,** *n.* celandine.

**schon,** *adv.* already; yet, since, ever, now, duly; indeed, surely, no doubt, to be sure; merely, alone; even.

**schön,** *a.* beautiful, handsome, fine, lovely.

**Schöne,** *f.* fining, isinglass; fair one.

**schonen,** *v.t.& i.* spare, save, protect, care for. **—schonend,** *p.a.* careful; considerate; sparing.

**schönen,** *v.t.* fine, clarify, clear; gloss; brighten (colors); beautify.

**Schön-färber,** *m.* garment dyer, dyer in fine colors. **-färberei,** *f.* garment dyeing. **-grün,** *n.* Paris green. **-heit,** *f.* beauty; fineness.

**Schönheits-mittel,** *n.* cosmetic. **-wasser,** *n.* beauty wash, liquid cosmetic.

**Schönseite,** *f.* right side (of fabrics).

**schonungslos,** *a.* unsparing, pitiless.

**Schönungsmittel,** *n.* fining agent, fining; (for colors) brightening agent.

**Schopf,** *m.* tuft; (head of) hair; (tree) top.

**Schöpfbütte,** *f.* (*Paper*) pulp vat, stuff vat.

**schöpfen,** *v.t.* draw (liquids, air, containers); scoop, dip, bale, ladle.

**Schöpfer,** *m.* drawer (of water, etc.), dipper, scoop, ladle, bucket; creator, maker, author, originator.

**Schöpf-gefäss,** *n.* scoop, dipper, ladle, bucket. **-herd,** *m.* casting crucible (of a furnace). **-kelle,** *f.* **-löffel,** *m.* scoop, ladle. **-probe,** *f.* drawn (dipped, ladled) sample. **-rad,** *n.* bucket wheel. **-rahmen,** *m.* (*Paper*) deckle.

**Schöpfung,** *f.* creation.

**Schöps,** *m.* wether; mutton; simpleton.

**Schöpsen-fleisch,** *n.* mutton. **-talg,** *m.* mutton tallow, (*Pharm.*) prepared suet.

**schor,** *pret.* of scheren.

**Schorf,** *m.* scurf, scab, crust, eschar.

**Schörl,** *m.* schorl.

**Schörlit,** *m.* pycnite (variety of topaz).

**Schornstein,** *m.* chimney, stack, flue.

**schoss,** *pret.* of schiessen.

**Schoss,** *m.* lap; womb; (coat) tails; shoot, sprig. **-gerinne,** *n.* channel, trough.

**Schössling,** *m.* shoot, sprout, sucker.

**Schote,** *f.* pod, shell, husk.

**Schoten-dorn,** *m.* acacia; black locust. **-gewächse,** *n.* leguminous plants. **-pfeffer,** *m.* red pepper, capsicum. **-pflanze,** *f.* leguminous plant.

**Schotter,** *m.* broken stone, macadam.

**schottisch,** *a.* Scotch.

**Sch. P.,** *abbrev.* (Schmelzpunkt) melting point, m.p.

**schr.,** *abbrev.* (schriftlich) in writing.

**schraffieren,** *v.t.* (in drawings, etc.) shade, hatch, line.

**schräg,** *a.* oblique, sloping, slanting, inclined, bevel.

**Schräge,** *f.* slant, slope, bevel.

**schräg-stellbar,** *a.* inclinable. **-stellen,** *v.t.* incline, tilt.

**schrak,** *pret.* of schrecken.

**Schramme,** *f.* scratch, slash; scar, cicatrix.

**schrammen,** *v.t.* scratch, score, slash, scar.

**Schrank,** *m.* cabinet, case, press, cupboard, closet, safe.

**Schranke,** *f.* bar, barrier; bound, limit.— **in die Schranken treten,** enter the lists.

**schränken,** *v.t.* put across, cross.

**schränkweise,** *adv.* crosswise.

**Schraper,** *m.,* **Schrape,** *f.* scraper; tracer.

**Schraubdeckel,** *m.* screw cap, screw cover.

**Schraube,** *f.* screw; (screw) bolt.

**schrauben,** *v.t.* screw; banter, mock. **-artig,** *a.* =schraubenförmig.

**Schrauben-bakterie,** *f* spirillum. **-bohrer,** *m.* screw tap; screw auger; twist drill. **-dreher,** *m.* screw driver; wrench. **-feder,** *f.* helical spring.

**schraubenförmig**, *a.* screw-shaped, spiral, helical.

**Schrauben-gang**, *m.* pitch of a screw. **-gewinde**, *n.* screw thread. **-linie**, *f.* helical line, helix. **-mutter**, *f.* nut, female screw. **-presse**, *f.* screw press, fly press. **-quetsch-hahn**, *m.* screw pinchcock. **-rohr**, *n.*, **-röhre**, *f.* spiral (helical) tube. **-schlüssel**, *m.* screw wrench, nut wrench. **-stock**, *m.* vise. **-zieher**, *m.* screw driver.

**Schraub-glas**, *n.* screw-top glass bottle, tube or jar. **-stock**, *m.* vise. **-zwinge**, *f.* screw clamp.

**Schreck**, *m.* fright, terror.

**schrecken**, *v.t.* chill; frighten.—*v.i.* be afraid.

**schrecklich**, *a.* frightful, terrible, awful.

**Schrei**, *m.* cry, shriek, shout; bloom, cake (of metal).

**Schreibart**, *f.* mode of writing; style; spelling.

**schreiben**, *v.t.& i.* write; (of instruments) record.

**Schreib-feder**, *f.* (writing) pen. **-fehler**, *m.* error in writing, clerical error. **-kies**, *m.* marcasite. **-kreide**, *f.* writing chalk. **-maschine**, *f.* typewriter. **-maschinenband**, *n.* typewriter ribbon. **-materialien**, *f.* writing materials, stationery. **-papier**, *n.* writing paper. **-stift**, *m.* pencil; crayon. **-tinte**, *f.* writing ink. **-waren**, *f. pl.* writing materials, stationery. **-weise**, *f.* manner of writing.

**schreien**, *v.i.* cry, shout, scream, shriek, bray. —**schreiend**, *p.a.* (of colors) loud.

**Schreien**, *n.* crying, etc. (see schreien); (of tin) cry.

**Schrein**, *m.* case, cabinet, chest, casket, press.

**schreiten**, *v.i.* step, stride; proceed.

**schrie**, *pret.* of schreien.

**schrieb**, *pret.* of schreiben.

**Schrift**, *f.* writing; characters; type; paper, publication, work; pitch (of a screw). **-absatz**, *m.* paragraph. **-erz**, *n.* sylvanite. **-flasche**, *f.* bottle with permanent label, labeled reagent bottle. **-führer**, *m.* secretary. **-giesser**, *m.* type founder. **-giesser-metall**, *n.* type metal. **-gold**, *n.* sylvanite. **-granit**, *m.* graphic granite. **-guss**, *m.* type founding. **-jaspis**, *m.* jasper opal. **-leiter**, *m.* editor.

**schriftlich**, *a.* written, in writing.

**Schrift-malerei**, *f.* lettering. **-metall**, *n.* type metal. **-mutter**, *f.* type mold, matrix. **-setzer**, *m.* typesetter, compositor. **-stein**, *m.* graphic granite. **-steller**, *m.* writer, author. **-tellur**, *n.* graphic tellurium (sylvanite). **-zeichen**, *n.* character, letter. **-zeug**, *n.* type metal. **-zug**, *m.* (written) character; stroke; handwriting.

**schritt**, *pret.* of schreiten.

**Schritt**, *m.* step; stride; pace.

**schrittweise**, *adv.* step by step, gradually.

**Schrittweite**, *f.* interval (as between spectral lines).

**schrob**, *pret.* of schrauben.

**schroff**, *a.* rough, harsh; steep, abrupt; gruff.

**schröpfen**, *v.t.* cup; scarify.

**Schrot**, *n.& m.* cut, piece, block, clipping; small shot; groats; selvage; due weight (of a coin); plumb bob; (*Brewing*) grist.

**schroten**, *v.t.* cut in pieces, chip, clip; bruise, rough-grind; shoot (casks); gobble (food).

**Schröter**, *m.* handler of barrels; woodcutter; stag beetle.

**Schrot-fabrik**, *f.* shot factory. **-korn**, *n.* grain of shot, (single) shot.

**Schrötling**, *m.* piece, cutting; (*Minting*) blank, planchet.

**Schrot-mehl**, *n.* coarse meal. **-metall**, *n.* shot metal. **-mühle**, *f.* grist mill, bruising mill; malt mill.

**Schrott**, *m.* scrap (metal), esp. scrap iron.

**schrubben**, *v.t.* scrub, scour.

**Schrubber**, *m.* scrubber.

**schrüen**, *v.t.* give the biscuit baking to (porcelain).

**Schrulle**, *f.* whim, crotchet.

**schrumpfen**, *v.t.& i.* shrink, contract, shrivel. —**schrumpfend**, *p.a.* astringent.

**Schrumpfmass**, *n.* (amount of) shrinkage, contraction.

**Schrumpfung**, *f.* shrinking, contraction, shriveling.

**Schub**, *m.* shove, push; thrust; throw; batch, lot. **-fach**, *n.* drawer. **-fenster**, *n.* sash window, sash. **-festigkeit**, *f.* shearing strength. **-kraft**, *f.* shearing force or strain. **-kurbel**, *f.* (*Mach.*) crank. **-lade**, *f.* drawer. **-lehre**, **-leere**, *f.* sliding gage, slide gage. **-spannung**, *f.* shearing stress. **-vektor**, *m.* thrust vector.

**schubweise**, *adv.* by shoves, by thrusts; in batches; gradually.

**schuf**, *pret.* of schaffen.

**schuften**, *v.i.* drudge, toil.

**Schuh**, *m.* shoe. **-krem**, *f.* shoe cream, shoe polish. **-leder**, *n.* shoe leather. **-macher-wachs**, **-pech**, *n.* cobbler's wax. **-riemen**, *m.* shoestring, shoe lace. **-schmiere**, *f.* dubbing. **-schwärze**, *f.* shoe blacking. **-wachs**, *n.*, **-wichse**, *f.* shoe polish.

**Schuld**, *f.* debt; fault, blame; guilt; crime. **-buch**, *n.* ledger, account book.

**schulden**, *v.t.* owe.

**schuldig**, *a.* guilty, at fault; indebted, owing; due.

**Schuldigkeit**, *f.* duty, obligation, debt.

**Schuldner**, *m.* debtor.

**Schule**, *f.* school.

Schüler, *m.* scholar, pupil.

Schulter, *f.* shoulder.

schund, *pret.* of schinden.

Schund, *m.* refuse, offal, rubbish.

Schüppchen, *n.* little scale, flake.

Schuppe, *f.* scale; flake.

Schüppe, *f.* shovel, scoop.

schuppen, *v.t. & r.* scale, scale off, desquamate.

Schuppen, *m.* shed, garage, hangar.

schüppenartig, *a.* scaly, squamous.

Schuppen-glätte, *f.* flake litharge. -graphit, *m.* flaky graphite. -stein, *m.* lepidolite.

schuppig, *a.* scaly, flaky, squamous.

Schuppigkeit, *f.* scaliness.

Schur, *f.* shearing; fleece; annoyance.

Schürbel, *m.* = Schirbel.

Schüreisen, *n.* poker, fire hook, fire iron.

schüren, *v.t.* stir, poke, stoke (fire).

Schurf, *n.* scratch, abrasion; hole, pit.

schürfen, *v.t.* scratch, scrape; open (a mine).—*v.i.* prospect.

Schür-haken, *n.* = Schüreisen. -loch, *n.* stoke hole, fire hole.

Schurre, *f.* slide, chute.

Schurz, *m.*, Schürze, *f.* apron.

schürzen, *v.t.* tie; tuck up, gird up.

Schuss, *m.* shot; blast; charge; shoot, shooting; weft (of fabrics); ring, collar; (*Baking*) batch.

Schüssel, *f.* dish; bowl; pan. -zinn, *n.* pewter.

Schussweite, *f.* range.

Schuster, *m.* shoemaker; cobbler. -pech, *n.* shoemaker's wax.

Schutt, *m.* rubbish, refuse; ruins; batch.

Schüttbeton, *m.* poured concrete.

Schüttel-apparat, *m.* shaking apparatus. -bewegung, *f.* shaking motion. -glas, *n.* shaking glass, shaking bottle, shaking tube. -maschine, *f.* shaking machine.

schütteln, *v.t.* shake, agitate, churn.

Schüttel-trichter, *m.* separatory funnel. -werk, *n.* shaking mechanism or apparatus. -zylinder, *m.* shaking cylinder (stoppered cylinder).

schütten, *v.t.* pour, pour out; discharge; shed; yield.

Schütt-gelb, *n.* Dutch pink. -gut, *n.* bulk goods. -loch, *n.* feed hole. -röstofen, *m.* continuous roasting furnace.

Schüttung, *f.* pouring, etc. (see schütten); ballasting; (*Brewing*) extract-yielding materials.

Schutz, *m.* protection, defense, shelter, screen.

Schutz-. protecting, protective, guard, preserving. -anstrich, *m.* protective coating. -beize, *f.* (*Calico*) resist, reserve. -beizendruck, *m.* resist style. -brille, *f.* protecting spectacles, goggles. -decke, *f.* protective cover or coating.

schützen, *v.t.* protect, guard, defend, shelter.

Schützengrabenkrieg, *m.* trench warfare.

Schutz-firnis, *m.* protective varnish. -gas, *n.* protective gas, safety gas. -glas, *n.* protecting glass. -glocke, *f.* bell jar, bell glass (for covering). -handschuh, *m.* protective glove. -hülle, *f.* protective covering or casing. -impfung, *f.* protective inoculation, vaccination. -kappe, *f.* protecting cap. -kleidung, *f.* protective clothing. -kolloid, *n.* protective colloid. -kraft, *f.* protective power. -lack, *m.* protective varnish.

Schützling, *m.* protégé, charge.

schutzlos, *a.* unprotected.

Schutz-mann, *m.* policeman. -mantel, *m.* protecting jacket (or case). -marke, *f.* trademark. -maske, *f.* protecting mask, face guard. -masse, *f.* (*Calico*) resist. -mittel, *n.* preservative; preventive, prophylactic; (*Calico*) resist. -papp, *m.* = Schutzbeize. -pockengift, *n.* vaccine virus. -ring, *m.* guard ring. -salzlösung, *f.* protective salt solution (as for gas masks). -schicht, *f.* protective layer. -stoff, *m.* protective substance or material; specif., alexin. -trichter, *m.* protecting funnel (see Ablauftrichter). -vorrichtung, *f.* protecting device, protective contrivance. -wand, *f.* protecting screen. -wert, *m.* protective value. -widerstand, *m.* (*Elec.*) protective resistance. -wirkung, *f.* protective effect. -zoll, *m.* protective duty.

Schwabbel, Schwabber, *m.* swab; mop.

schwach, *a.* weak; feeble, faint, low, dim, thin, poor, slight, light.

Schwäche, *f.* weakness, etc. (see schwach).

schwächen, *v.t.* weaken; enfeeble, impair; tender (fibers); seduce.

Schwachgas, *n.* poor gas.

schwach-säuerlich, *a.* weakly acid. -siedend, *p.a.* gently boiling, simmering.

Schwächung, *f.* weakening, etc. (see schwächen).

Schwächungsmittel, *n.* depressant.

schwachwirksam, *a.* feebly active.

Schwaden, *m.* suffocating vapor or exhalation, damp; specif., choke damp; swath.—feuriger —, fire damp.

Schwadenfang, *m.* hood; ventilator.

Schwahl, Schwal, *m.* (*Iron*) rich finery cinder, slag. -arbeit, *f.* (*Iron*) single refining, slag washing. -boden, *m.* slag bed, slag bottom.

Schwalbe, *f.* swallow.

Schwalben-wurz, -wurzel, *f.* swallowwort; (*Pharm.*) vincetoxicum.

Schwall, *m.* swell, flood, throng; = Schwahl.

schwamm, *pret.* of schwimmen.

**Schwamm,** *m.* sponge; mushroom; fungus; tinder; spongy growth; (*Zinc*) tutty; mass, lot.

**schwammartig,** *a.* sponge-like, spongy; fungous.

**Schwamm-filter,** *n.* sponge filter. **-gewebe,** *n.* spongy tissue. **-gift,** *n.* mushroom poison, muscarine. **-gummi,** *n.* spongy rubber, rubber sponge. **-holz,** *n.* spongy wood, decayed wood.

**schwammig,** *a.* spongy, porous; (of paper) bibulous; fungous, fungoid.

**Schwamm-igkeit,** *f.* sponginess. **-kupfer,** *n.* spongy copper, copper sponge. **-säure,** *f.* boletic acid (fumaric acid); fungic acid (a mixture). **-stoff,** *m.* fungin. **-tod,** *m.* fungicide. **-zucker,** *m.* mannitol.

**Schwan,** *m.* swan.

**schwand,** *pret.* of schwinden.

**Schwand,** *m.* shrinkage, etc. (see schwinden).

**schwang,** *pret.* of schwingen.

**Schwang,** *m.* swing; vogue.

**schwanger,** *a.* pregnant.

**schwängern,** *v.t.* impregnate, saturate.

**Schwangerschaft,** *f.* pregnancy.

**Schwängerung,** *f.* impregnation, saturation.

**schwank,** *a.* flexible; slender; wavering.

**schwanken,** *v.i.* fluctuate, oscillate; vary; shake, rock, reel; hesitate, waver.— **schwankend,** *p.a.* unsettled, unsteady, uncertain.

**Schwankung,** *f.* fluctuation, etc. (see schwanken).

**Schwanz,** *m.* tail; train. **-hahn,** *m.* stopcock with an outlet thru the end of the key. **-pfeffer,** *m.* cubebs. **-stern,** *m.* comet.

**schwären,** *v.i.* fester, suppurate.

**Schwarm,** *m.* swarm, crowd, throng; (*Bact.*) colony.

**schwärmen,** *v.i.* swarm; wander, migrate; revel; daydream; rave.

**Schwärmer,** *m.* rover; reveler; visionary; enthusiast; (*Zoöl.*) sphinx; firecracker, serpent.

**Schwarte,** *f.* rind, skin, crust, covering; scalp.

**schwarz,** *a.* black; dark, swarthy.—— **liegen,** (of beer, etc.) be settled, be clear.— **schwarzes Wasser,** (*Pharm.*) black mercurial lotion.

**Schwarz,** *n.* black; blackness. **-beere,** *f.* bilberry; elder(berry); melastoma. **-beize,** *f.* (*Dyeing*) black liquor, iron liquor.

**schwarzblau,** *a.* very dark blue.

**Schwarz-blech,** *n.* black plate (untinned iron plate). **-blei,** *n.* black lead (graphite). **-bleierz,** *n.* black lead spar (carboniferous cerussite).

**schwarzbraun,** *a.* very dark brown.

**Schwarzbraunstein,** *m.* psilomelane.

**schwarzbrüchig,** *a.* (*Metal.*) black-short.

**Schwarzdruck,** *m.* printing in black.

**Schwärze,** *f.* black; blacking; printer's ink; (*Founding*) black wash; blackness; swarthiness.

**Schwarzeisen,** *n.* high-silicon pig iron.

**schwärzen,** *v.t.* blacken, black.

**Schwarz-erz,** *n.* tetrahedrite; stephanite. **-färber,** *m.* dyer in black.

**schwarz-farbig,** *a.* black-colored, black. **-gar,** *a.* black-tanned. **-gebrannt,** *p.a.* (*Metal.*) kishy. **-gelb,** *a.* very dark yellow, tawny. **-grau,** *a.* very dark gray. **-grün,** *a.* very dark green.

**Schwarz-gültigerz,** *n.* stephanite; polybasite. **-kohle,** *f.* black charcoal; black coal. **-kümmel,** *m.* nutmeg flower (*Nigella sativa*). **-kupfer,** *n.* black copper; coarse copper. **-kupfererz,** *m.* melaconite. **-lauge,** *f.* black liquor.

**schwärzlich,** *a.* blackish.

**Schwarz-manganerz,** *n.* hausmannite. **-mehl,** *n.* dark-colored flour, esp. rye flour. **-öl,** *n.* black oil, specif. a dark, pasty, boiled linseed oil. **-pech,** *n.* black pitch, common pitch. **-pulver,** *n.* black powder.

**schwarzrot,** *a.* very dark red.

**Schwarz-schmelz,** *m.* black enamel. **-seher,** *m.* pessimist. **-senföl,** *n.* black-mustard oil. **-silbererz,** *n.,* **-silberglanz,** *m.* black silver (stephanite). **-spiessglanzerz,** *n.* bournonite.

**Schwärzung,** *f.* blackening.

**Schwarz-vitriol,** *m.* black vitriol (impure ferrous sulfate). **-werden,** *n.* blackening. **-wurz, -wurzel,** *f.* (*Pharm.*) symphytum; (**amerikanische**) baneberry root. **-zinkerz,** *n.* franklinite.

**Schwebe,** *f.* suspension; suspense; sling; suspender. **-methode,** *f.* suspension method.

**schweben,** *v.i.* hang, hover, float, be suspended, be pending.—**schwebend,** *p.a.* suspended, in suspension, hanging, floating.

**Schwebe-stoff,** *m.* suspended substance (or matter). **-teilchen,** *n.* suspended particle.

**Schwebstoff,** *m.* = Schwebestoff.

**Schwebungstheorie,** *f.* beat theory.

**Schweden,** *n.* Sweden.

**schwedisch,** *a.* Swedish.—**schwedisches Grün,** Swedish green (Scheele's green).—**schwedisches Hölzchen,** *n.* safety match.

**Schwedisch, Schwedische,** *n.* Swedish (language).

**schweel-.** see schwel-.

**Schwefel,** *m.* sulfur.

**Schwefel-.** of sulfur, sulfur, sulfuric, sulfide of, thio-, sulfo-. **-alkali,** *n.* alkali sulfide. **-alkohol,** *m.* carbon disulfide (old name). **-ammonium, -ammon,** *n.* ammonium sulfide. -antimon, n. antimony sulfide. -antimonblei, n. antimony lead sulfide; (Min.) boulangerite.

schwefel-antimonig, a. thioantimonious. -antimonsauer, a. of or combined with thioantimonic acid, thioantimonate of.

Schwefel-antimonsäure, f. thioantimonic acid, sulfantimonic acid. -arsen, n. (any) sulfide of arsenic.

schwefelarsenig, a. thioarsenious, sulfarsenious.

Schwefelarsenik, n. = Schwefelarsen. -säure, f. = Schwefelarsensäure. -verbindung, f. arsenic sulfide; sulfarsenide.

Schwefel-arsensäure, f. thioarsenic acid, sulfarsenic acid. -art, f. kind or variety of sulfur.

schwefelartig, a. sulfurous, sulfureous.

Schwefel-äther, m. sulfuric ether (ethyl ether). -ausscheidung, f. separation of sulfur. -bad, n. sulfur bath.

schwefelbar, a. sulfurizable.

Schwefel-baryum, n. barium sulfide. -bestimmung, f. sulfur determination. -blau, n. sulfur blue. -blausäure, f. thiocyanic acid, sulfocyanic acid. -blei, n. lead sulfide. -blumen, -blüten, f.pl. flowers of sulfur. -brennofen, m. sulfur kiln. -bromid, n. sulfur bromide, specif. sulfur dibromide, SBr₂. -bromür, n. sulfur monobromide. -brot, n. loaf of sulfur. -cadmium, n. cadmium sulfide. -calcium, n. calcium sulfide. -chlorid, n. sulfur chloride, specif. sulfur dichloride, SCl₂. -chlorür, n. sulfur monochloride (S₂Cl₂). -chrom, n. chromium sulfide. -cyan, n. thiocyanogen, sulfocyanogen; cyanogen sulfide.

Schwefelcyan-. thiocyanate of. -ammonium, n. ammonium thiocyanate (or sulfocyanate). -kalium, n. potassium thiocyanate (or sulfocyanate). -metall, n. metallic thiocyanate (or sulfocyanate). -säure, f. thiocyanic acid, sulfocyanic acid.

schwefelcyanwasserstoffsauer, a. thiocyanate of.

Schwefel-cyanwasserstoffsäure, f. thiocyanic acid, sulfocyanic acid. -dampf, m. sulfur vapor. -dioxyd, n. sulfur dioxide. -dunst, m. sulfurous vapor.

schwefelecht, a. (Dyeing) fast to stoving, fast to sulfurous acid.

Schwefel-einschlag, m. sulfur match (for casks); sulfuring (of casks). -eisen, n. iron (usually ferrous) sulfide. -erz, n. sulfur ore. -faden, m. sulfured wick, sulfur match. -farbe, f. sulfur color.

schwefelfarben, a. sulfur-colored.

Schwefel-farbstoff, m. sulfur dye. -form, f. mold for sulfur, brimstone mold.

schwefelfrei, a. free from sulfur.

Schwefel-gallium, n. gallium sulfide. -gehalt, m. sulfur content.

schwefelgelb, a. sulfur-yellow.

Schwefel-gerbung, f. sulfur tannage. -germanium, n. germanium sulfide. -geruch, m. sulfur odor.

schwefelgesäuert, a. treated with sulfuric acid, sulfated.

Schwefel-gold, n. gold sulfide. -grube, f. sulfur pit, sulfur mine. -halogen, n. sulfur halide.

schwefelhaltig, a. containing sulfur, sulfurous.

Schwefel-harnstoff, m. thiourea. -hölzchen, -holz, n. sulfur match. -hütte, f. sulfur refinery.

schwefelig, a. = schweflig.

Schwefel-indium, n. indium sulfide. -jodür, n. sulfur monoiodide. -kadmium, n. cadmium sulfide. -kalium, n. potassium sulfide. -kalk, m. lime-sulfur. -kalzium, n. calcium sulfide. -kammer, f. sulfur chamber, sulfuring room, sulfur stove. -karbolsäure, f. sulfocarbolic acid.

Schwefelkies, m. iron pyrites.—gemeiner —, pyrite.—prismatischer —, marcasite.

Schwefel-kobalt, m. cobalt sulfide. -kohle, f. sulfurous coal. -kohlensäure, f. sulfocarbonic acid (trithiocarbonic acid, H₂CS₃). -kohlenstoff, m. carbon disulfide. -kolben, m. retort for distilling sulfur. -kuchen, m. cake of sulfur. -kupfer, n. copper sulfide. -latwerge, f. (Pharm.) confection of sulfur. -läuterofen, m. sulfur refining furnace. -leber, f. liver of sulfur, hepar. -leinöl, n. (Pharm.) balsam of sulfur. -magnesium, n. magnesium sulfide. -mangan, n. manganese sulfide. -metall, n. metallic sulfide. -milch, f. milk of sulfur. -molybdän, n. molybdenum sulfide.

schwefeln, v.t. sulfurize, sulfurate, sulfur; vulcanize.

Schwefel-natrium, -natron, n. sodium sulfide. -nickel, m. nickel sulfide. -niederschlag, m. precipitate of sulfur, precipitated sulfur. -ofen, m. sulfur burner. -oxyd, n. (any) sulfur oxide. -phosphor, m. (any) phosphorus sulfide. -pulver, n. powdered sulfur. -quecksilber, n. mercury sulfide. -quelle, f. sulfur spring. -räucherung, f. sulfur fumigation. -rubin, m. ruby sulfur, realgar. -salz, n. sulfur salt, thio salt, sulfo salt; sulfate.

schwefelsauer, a. of or combined with sulfuric acid, sulfate of.

Schwefelsäure, f. sulfuric acid. -anhydrid, n. sulfuric anhydride, sulfur trioxide. -ballon, m. sulfuric-acid carboy. -bestimmung, f. determination of sulfuric acid. -fabrik, f.

sulfuric-acid works. **-fabrikation,** *f.* manufacture of sulfuric acid. **-kammer,** *f.* sulfuric-acid chamber. **-salz,** *n.* salt of sulfuric acid, sulfate.

**Schwefel-schlacke,** *f.* sulfur dross. **-schwarz,** *n.* sulfur black. **-selen,** *n.* selenium sulfide; (*Min.*) selensulfur. **-silber,** *n.* silver sulfide. **-spiessglanz,** *m.*, **-spiessglanzerz,** *n.* stibnite. **-stange,** *f.* roll of sulfur. **-stickstoff,** *m.* nitrogen sulfide. **-stück,** *n.* piece of sulfur. **-thallium,** *n.* thallium sulfide. **-tonerde,** *f.* aluminum sulfide.

**Schwefelung,** *f.* sulfurization, sulfuring.

**Schwefelungsmittel,** *n.* sulfur(iz)ing agent.

**Schwefel-verbindung,** *f.* sulfur compound. **-wasser,** *n.* sulfur water.

**Schwefelwasserstoff,** *m.* hydrogen sulfide. **-rest,** *m.* mercapto group, sulfhydryl, SH. **-säure,** *f.* hydrosulfuric acid (H₂S). **-strom,** *m.* current of hydrogen sulfide. **-verbindung,** *f.* hydrosulfide.

**Schwefel-weinsäure,** *f.* sulphovinic acid (old name for ethylsulfuric acid). **-werk,** *n.* sulfur refinery. **-wismut,** *n.* bismuth sulfide. **-wurz,** *f.* brimstonewort. **-wurzel,** *f.* (*Pharm.*) peucedanum root, brimstonewort root. **-zink,** *m.& n.* zinc sulfide. **-zinkweiss,** *n.* a pigment containing chiefly zinc sulfide (lithopone, zincolith). **-zinn,** *n.* tin sulfide.

**Schwefelzyan-.** see Schwefelcyan-.

**schweflig,** *a.* sulfurous.—**schweflige Säure,** sulfurous acid.

**schwefligsauer,** *a.* of or combined with sulfurous acid, sulfite of.

**Schwefligsäure,** *f.* sulfurous acid. **-anhydrid,** *n.* sulfurous anhydride, sulfur dioxide. **-gas,** *n.* sulfur dioxide. **-wasser,** *n.* aqueous sulfurous acid.

**Schweif,** *m.* tail; train; warp (of fabrics).

**schweifen,** *v.t.* curve; chamfer; rinse; tail.—*v.i.* stray, ramble.

**Schweifung,** *f.* curve, rounding, swell.

**schweigen,** *v.i.* be silent, hush.

**Schweigen,** *n.* silence.

**schweigsam,** *a.* silent; taciturn, reserved.

**Schwein,** *n.* hog, pig, swine. **-brot,** *n.* = Erdbrot. **-chen,** *n.* weighing bottle with feet; little pig.

**Schweine-fett,** *n.* hog fat, lard. **-fleisch,** *n.* pork. **-schmalz, -schmer,** *n.* lard.

**Schweinfurtergrün,** *n.* Schweinfurt green, Paris green.

**Schweins-gummi,** *n.* hog gum. **-haut,** *f.* hogskin, pigskin. **-leder,** *n.* hogskin, pigskin (leather).

**Schweiss,** *m.* sweat; suint, yolk (of wool).

**Schweiss-.** welding, weld; sweat, sweaty, sudorific. **-arbeit,** *f.* welding. **-asche,** *f.* suint ash (a source of potash).

**schweissbar,** *a.* weldable, welding.

**Schweissbarkeit,** *f.* weldability.

**schweiss-befördernd,** *p.a.* sudorific, diaphoretic. **-echt,** *a.* fast to perspiration.

**Schweisseisen,** *n.* weld iron.

**schweissen,** *v.t.* weld.—*v.i.* begin to melt; (of liquids) leak.

**Schweissen,** *n.* welding.

**Schweisser,** *m.* welder.

**schweisserregend,** *p.a.* = schweissbefördernd.

**Schweiss-fehler,** *m.* defect in welding. **-flüssigkeit,** *f.* sweat. **-gehalt,** *m.* suint content.

**schweissgewaschen,** *p.a.* (of wool) washed in the grease.

**Schweiss-hitze,** *f.* welding heat. **-loch,** *n.* sweat pore. **-metall,** *m.* wrought iron. **-mittel,** *n.* sudorific, diaphoretic; welding agent, flux. **-naht,** *f.* weld seam. **-ofen,** *n.* welding furnace, reheating furnace. **-prozess,** *m.* welding process. **-pulver,** *n.* welding powder; diaphoretic powder. **-schmiedeeisen,** *n.* weld iron (as distinguished from weld steel). **-stahl,** *m.* weld steel. **-stelle,** *f.* place where metal is welded, shut.

**schweisstreibend,** *p.a.* = schweissbefördernd.

**Schweissung,** *f.* welding, weld.

**Schweiss-verfahren,** *n.* welding process. **-wachs,** *m.* wax from suint, yolk wax. **-walzen,** *f.pl.* roughing rolls.

**schweisswarm,** *a.* welding-hot.

**Schweiss-wärme,** *f.* welding heat. **-wolle,** *f.* wool containing suint, wool in the yolk.

**Schweiz,** *f.* Switzerland.

**Schweizer,** *m.* Swiss.

**schweizerisch,** *a.* Swiss.

**Schweizerkäse,** *m.* Swiss cheese, Gruyère cheese.

**Schwel-.** relating to low-temperature carbonization; smoldering. **-anlage,** *f.* low-temperature carbonizing plant.

**schwelchen,** *v.t.* (*Brewing*) wither, air-dry.

**Schwelchmalz,** *n.* withered (air-dried) malt.

**schwelen,** *v.t.& i.* burn slowly, smolder; distill (or carbonize) at low temperature.

**Schweler,** *m.* low-temperature carbonizer.

**Schwelerei,** *f.* low-temperature carbonization process or plant.

**Schwelgas,** *n.* gas from low-temperature carbonization; producer gas; partially burned gas.

**schwelken,** *v.t.* = schwelchen.

**Schwel-kohle,** *f.* a kind of lignite rich in volatile matter (and hence suitable for carbonization). **-koks,** *m.* low-temperature coke.

**Schwell-.** swelling; (*Anat.*) erectile.

**schwellbar,** *a.* capable of swelling; (*Anat.*) erectile.

Schwellbeize, f. (Leather) swelling liquor.

Schwelle, f. sill, threshold; beam, sleeper, (railroad) tie; cross bar.

schwellen, v.t.& i. swell, distend; (Leather) plump.

Schwellenwert, m. threshold value, threshold.

Schwell-gewebe, n. (Anat.) erectile tissue. -körper, m. (Anat.) corpus cavernosum. -kraft, f. (Leather) plumping power. -mittel, n. (Leather) plumping agent.

Schwellung, f. swelling, tumefaction.

Schwel-ofen, m. low-temperature carbonizing furnace. -raum, m. carbonizing space or chamber. -retorte, f. retort for low-temperature distillation. -teer, m. tar from low-temperature carbonization. -teeröl, n. carbonization tar oil, esp. from lignite.

Schwelung, f. low-temperature carbonization; slow burning, smoldering.

Schwel-vorgang, m. low-temperature process of carbonization. -wasser, n. an aqueous liquid from the low-temperature carbonizing process, containing ammonia, phenols, etc. -werk, n. = Schwelanlage.

Schwemme, f. watering; watering place.

schwemmen, v.t. water; wash; flush; float; deposit.

Schwemm-stein, m. a kind of porous brick made from clay and gravel; pumice stone. -wasser, n. wash water; flushing water.

schwenken, v.t. swing, wave; rinse.—v.i. turn about, swing, swivel.

schwer, a. heavy; difficult, hard, severe, serious.—adv. heavily, difficultly, etc. —schweres Weinöl, see Weinöl.

Schwer-benzin, n. heavy benzine (boiling over 100–120° C), heavy petrol. -benzol, n. heavy benzol (boiling at about 160–200° C.). -bleierz, n. plattnerite.

Schwere, f. heaviness, weight; gravity; difficulty, hardness. -messer, m. barometer.

Schwererde, f. heavy earth, baryta (BaO).

schwererlöslich, a. more difficultly soluble.

schwer-fällig, a. clumsy, heavy, dull, slack. -flüchtig, a. difficultly volatile.

Schwerflüchtigkeit, f. difficult volatility.

schwerflüssig, a. difficultly fusible, refractory; viscous.

Schwer-flüssigkeit, f. difficult fusibility, refractoriness. -frucht, f. heavy grain (as wheat, rye). -kraft, f. force of gravity.

schwerl., abbrev. (schwerlöslich) difficultly soluble.

Schwerleder, n. sole leather.

schwer-lich, adv. hardly, scarcely, difficultly. -löslich, a. difficultly soluble.

Schwer-löslichkeit, f. difficult solubility. -metall, n. heavy metal. -metallsalz, n. salt of a heavy metal. -mut, f. melan-

choly. -öl, n. heavy oil. -punkt, m. center of gravity.

schwer-schmelzbar, a. difficultly fusible. -schmelzend, a. fusing with difficulty.

Schwer-schwarz, n. (Dyeing) weighted black. -spat, m. heavy spar, barite. -stein, m. scheelite.

Schwert, n. sword.

Schwertantalerz, n. (Min.) tantalite.

Schwert-kolben, m. sausage flask (Anschütz distillation flask). -lilie, f. iris, fleur-de-lis.

Schweruranerz, n. (Min.) uraninite.

schwerwiegend, p.a. weighty, serious.

Schwester, f. sister.

schwieg, pret. of schweigen.

Schwiele, f. callosity; wale, welt.

schwielig, a. callous, horny; waled.

schwierig, a. hard, difficult; fastidious.

Schwierigkeit, f. difficulty, obstacle.

schwiert, pr. 3 sing. of schwären.

schwillt, pr. 3 sing. of schwellen.

Schwimm-aufbereitung, f. (Ores) flotation. -badeseife, f. floating bath soap. -blase, f. air bladder, sound.

schwimmen, v.i. swim; float.

Schwimmer, m. float; swimmer.

Schwimm-fähigkeit, f. buoyancy. -gerste, f. (Brewing) float barley, skimmings. -kiesel, m. floatstone. -körper, m. swimming or floating body, float. -kraft, f. buoyancy. -methode, f. flotation method. -sand, m. quicksand. -stein, m. floatstone. -ziegel, m. floating brick.

Schwindel, m. vertigo; sell, swindle; kit, lot.

schwindelhaft, a. fraudulent; dizzy.

Schwindelkorn, n. cubeb; coriander seed.

schwinden, v.i. shrink, contract; dwindle, waste; disappear, vanish.

Schwinden, n. shrinking, shrinkage, etc. (see schwinden).

Schwind-mass, n. amount of shrinkage, shrinkage. -sucht, f. consumption, phthisis.

Schwindung, f. = Schwinden.

Schwindungs-fähigkeit, f. tendency to shrink, property of shrinking. -loch, n. shrinkage cavity.

Schwinge, f. wing; swingle.

Schwingelgras, n. fescue grass, fescue.

schwingen, v.i. vibrate; swing, oscillate.— v.t. swing, wave; centrifuge; winnow; swingle. —schwingend, p.a. vibrating, vibratory, oscillating, oscillatory, swinging.

Schwingung, f. vibration; swinging, swing, oscillation.

Schwingungs-bewegung, f. vibratory (or oscillatory) motion. -ebene, f. plane of vibration. -gleichung, f. vibration equation. -weite, f. amplitude of vibration. -welle, f. undulation, vibrational wave. -zahl, f.

vibration number, vibration frequency. -zeit, *f.* time of vibration.

**schwirren,** *v.i.* whiz, whir, buzz, hum.—*v.t.* whiz, centrifuge.

**Schwitze,** *f.* sweat, sweating.

**schwitzen,** *v.i.& t.* sweat.

**Schwitz-mittel,** *n.* sudorific, diaphoretic. **-pulver,** *n.* diaphoretic powder. **-röste,** *f.* steam retting.

**Schwöde,** *f.* place where hides are limed; state of being limed. **-brei,** *m.* (*Leather*) lime cream. **-fass,** *n.* (*Leather*) lime vat, lime. **-grube,** *f.* (*Leather*) lime pit, lime. **-masse,** *f.* (*Leather*) lime cream.

**schwöden,** *v.t.* lime (hides).

**schwoll,** *pret.* of schwellen.

**schwomm,** *pret.* of schwimmen.

**schwor,** *pret.* of schwären and of schwören.

**schwören,** *v.t.& i.* swear.

**schwül,** *a.* sultry, close.

**Schwulst,** *m.* swelling, tumor.

**Schwund,** *m.* atrophy, withering, disappearance; shrinkage.

**Schwung,** *m.* vibration, oscillation, swing; soaring, flight, activity. **-bewegung,** *f.* vibratory motion. **-gewicht,** *n.* pendulum.

**schwunghaft,** *a.* swinging, soaring, lively.

**Schwung-kraft,** *f.* centrifugal force; vibrating power; liveliness. **-maschine,** *f.* centrifugal whirler. **-rad,** *n.* flywheel; balance wheel.

**schwur,** *pret.* of schwären and of schwören.

**Schwur,** *m.* oath.

**schwürig,** *a.* suppurating.

**sd.,** *abbrev.* (siedend) boiling; (siedet) boils.

**Sd.,** *abbrev.* (Siedepunkt) boiling point.

**s.d.,** *abbrev.* (siehe dies) see this, which see, q.v.; (siehe dort) see there; (siehe den, siehe die, siehe das) see the.

**Sdp.,** *abbrev.* (Siedepunkt) boiling point.

**SE,** *abbrev.* (Siemens-Einheit) Siemens unit.

**Sebacinsäure,** *f.* sebacic acid.

**secernieren,** *v.t.* secrete.

**sechs,** *a.* six.

**sechs-, Sechs-.** six-, hexa-, sex-, sexi-, sextuple.

**sechsatomig,** *a.* hexatomic.

**Sechseck,** *n.* hexagon.

**sechseckig,** *a.* hexagonal.

**Sechsergruppe,** *f.* group of six, 6-group.

**sechs-fach, -fältig,** *a.* sixfold, sextuple.

**Sechs-flach,** *n.,* **-flächner,** *m.* hexahedron.

**sechs-flächig,** *a.* hexahedral. **-gliedrig,** *a.* six-membered. **-monatlich,** *a.* half-yearly, semi-annual.

**Sechsring,** *m.* six-membered ring.

**sechs-säurig,** *a.* hexacid. **-seitig,** *a.* six-sided, hexagonal.

**sechste,** *a.* sixth.

**Sechstel,** *n.* sixth.

**sechswertig,** *a.* sexivalent, hexavalent.

**Sechswertigkeit,** *f.* sexivalence.

**sechs-winklig,** *a.* six-angled, hexangular, hexagonal. **-zählig,** *a.* sixfold.

**sechzehn,** *a.* sixteen.

**Sechzehntel,** *n.* sixteenth.

**sechzig,** *a.* sixty.

**Sedanschwarz,** *n.* Sedan black.

**Sedativsalz,** *n.* sedative salt (old name for boric acid).

**sedimentär,** *a.* sedimentary.

**Sedimentgestein,** *n.* sedimentary rock.

**sedimentieren,** *v.i.* deposit sediment.

**Sedimentieren,** *n.* **Sedimentierung,** *f.* sedimentation.

**See,** *f.* sea; lake. **-algen,** *f.pl.* marine algæ. **-erz,** *m.* lake (iron) ore. **-gewächs,** *n.* sea plant, marine plant, seaweed. **-höhe,** *f.* height above sea level. **-hund,** *m.* seal. **-hundstran,** *m.* seal oil. **-kabel,** *n.* submarine cable. **-kohl,** *m.* sea kale. **-krebs,** *m.* lobster.

**Seele,** *f.* soul; shaft (of a blast furnace); core (of a rope); bore (of a firearm).

**Seelenruhe,** *f.* tranquillity; mental rest.

**See-licht,** *n.* marine phosphorescence. **-moos,** *n.* sea moss, carrageen. **-pflanze,** *f.* marine plant, sea plant. **-rose,** *f.* water lily (esp. *Nymphaea*). **-salz,** *n.* sea salt. **-sand,** *m.* sea sand. **-schlick,** *m.* sea ooze. **-tang,** *m.* seaweed (esp. *Fucus*), sea tang. **-tier,** *n.* marine animal. **-wasser,** *n.* sea water.

**Segel,** *n.* sail; (*Anat.*) velum.

**Segen,** *m.* blessing, benediction; abundance, yield.

**Segerkegel,** *m.,* **Seger'scher Kegel.** Seger cone.

**segnen,** *v.t.* bless; cross.

**Seh-.** of sight, visual, optic, opto-.

**Sehe,** *f.* pupil (of the eye).

**sehen,** *v.t.* see.—*v.i.* see, look.

**Sehen,** *n.* seeing, sight, vision.

**Sehenswürdigkeit,** *f.* sight, spectacle, curiosity.

**Seher,** *m.* seer.

**Seh-feld,** *n.* field of vision. **-lehre,** *f.* optics. **-linse,** *f.* (*Anat.*) crystalline lens.

**Sehne,** *f.* sinew, tendon; (*Metal.*) fiber; (*Geom.*) chord.

**Sehneisen,** *n.* fibrous iron.

**sehnen,** *v.r.* long, yearn.

**Sehnen-.** of a tendon, tendinous. **-schmiere,** *f.* (*Physiol.*) synovial fluid.

**Sehnepuddeln,** *n.* puddling of fibrous iron.

**Sehnerv,** *m.* optic nerve.

**sehnig,** *a.* tendinous, sinewy; (*Metal.,* etc.) fibrous.

**Sehnsucht,** *f.* longing, yearning, desire.

**Sehpurpur,** *m.* visual purple.

**sehr,** *adv.* very, very much, very well.

Seh-rohr, n. periscope. -schärfe, f. sharpness of vision. -weite, f. visual range or distance.

sei, pr. subj. of sein.

seicht, a. shallow; low, flat.

Seide, f. silk.

Seidel, n. pint, half-liter; tankard (for beer). -bast, m. mezereon (Daphne mezereum).

seiden, a. silk, silken.

Seidenabfall, m. silk waste, waste silk.

seidenartig, a. silky.

Seiden-asbest, m. silky asbestos. -bast, m. tussah silk; sericin. -bau, m. silk culture, sericulture. -fabrik, f. silk mill. -faden, m. silk thread. -faserstoff, m. fibroin. -fibrin, n. fibroin. -flor, m. silk gauze. -florsieb, n. sieve of silk gauze. -garn, n. silk yarn, spun silk. -glanz, m. silky luster.

seidenglänzend, a. of silky luster, silky.

Seiden-holz, n. satinwood. -leim, m. silk glue, sericin. -papier, n. tissue paper. -raupe, f. silkworm. -schrei, m. scroop of silk.

Seidlitz-pulver, n. Seidlitz powder. -salz, n. Epsom salt.

seiend, p.pr. of sein.

Seife, f. soap; alluvial ore, placer.

selfecht, a. fast to soaping.

seifen, v.t. soap, lather; wash, scour; (Mining) wash.

Seifenabfälle, m.pl. soap scraps.

seifenartig, a. soapy, saponaceous.

Seifen-asche, f. soap ashes. -bad, n. soap bath. -balsam, m. soap liniment, opodeldoc. -baum, m. soapbark tree, quillai. -baumrinde, f. soapbark, quillai bark. -bereitung, f. soap making. -bildung, f. formation of soap, saponification. -blase, f. soap bubble. -brühe, f. soap suds. -erde, f. fuller's earth. -ersatz, m., -ersatzmittel, n. soap substitute. -erz, n. alluvial ore. -fabrik, f. soap factory, soap works. -fabrikant, m. soap maker. -fabrikation, f. soap making or manufacture. -flocken, f.pl. soap flakes. -form, f. soap frame. -gold, n. placer gold.

seifenhaltig, a. containing soap.

Seifen-industrie, f. soap industry. -kessel, m. soap boiler. -kocher, m. soap boiler. -kraut, n. soap plant, soap weed. -krem, m. soap cream. -lauge, f. soap solution, soap suds. -leim, m. soap glue, soap paste; (Paper) soap size. -lösung, f. soap solution. -pflaster, n. soap plaster. -probe, f. soap test; sample of soap. -pulver, n. soap powder. -riegel, m. bar of soap, soap bar. -rinde, f. soapbark. -schabsel, n. soap scraps. -schaum, m. lather. -schmiere, f. (Leather) soap stuff. -sieder, m. soap boiler. -siederasche, f. soap ashes. -siederei, f. soap works. -siederlauge, f.

soap boiler's lye. -spiritus, m. spirit of soap (alcoholic soap solution). -stein, m. soapstone, steatite; caustic soda. -stoff, m. saponin. -tafel, f. slab of soap. -täfelchen, n. cake or tablet of soap. -teig, m. soap paste. -ton, m. fuller's earth. -wasser, n. soap suds, soap water. -wurzel, f. soapwort; soaproot. -zinn, n. stream tin.

seifig, a. soapy, saponaceous.

seiger, a. perpendicular.

Seiger-arbeit, f. (Metal.) liquation, liquation process. -blei, n. liquation lead. -dörner, m.pl. liquation dross.

seigergerade, a. perpendicular.

Seiger-herd, m. liquation hearth. -hütte, f. liquation works.

seigern, v.t. (Metal.) liquate.—v.i. segregate.

Seiger-ofen, m. liquation furnace. -pfanne, f. liquation pan. -schlacke, f. liquation slag. -stück, n. liquation cake.

Seigerung, f. liquation; segregation.

Seigerwerk, n. liquation works.

Seignettesalz, n. Seignette salt (Rochelle salt, sodium potassium tartrate).

Seihe, f. strainer, filter; (Brewing) spent malt. -beutel, m. filtering bag. -boden, m. strainer bottom, perforated bottom. -fass, n. filtering cask or tub. -gefäss, n. straining vessel, filtering vessel. -löffel, m. straining ladle, strainer.

seihen, v.t. strain, filter.

Seihepapier, n. filter paper.

Seiher, m. strainer, filter.

Seihe-rahmen, m. filtering frame. -sack, m. filtering bag. -stein, m. filtering stone. -trichter, m. straining funnel, strainer. -tuch, n. straining cloth, filtering cloth. -vermögen, n. straining power, filtering power.

Seihgefäss, etc. = Seihegefäss, etc.

Seil, n. rope, cable, cord, line.

Seiler, m. rope maker. -waren, f.pl. cordage.

Seim, m. glutinous liquid; strained honey.

seimen, v.i. yield a glutinous liquid.—v.t. strain (as barley water).

seimig, a. glutinous, mucilaginous.

sein, v.i. be.—pron. his, its.

Sein, n. being, existence.

seiner, pron. of him, of it, his, its. -seits, adv. for his part.

seinige, pron. his, his own.

seit, prep.& conj. since.— — kurzem, recently, lately.— — langem, this long time, for a long time.

seitdem, adv. since then, ever since.—conj. since.

Seite, f. side; face (of a solid); page (of a book).

Seiten-. side, lateral. -achse, f. lateral axis.

-anmerkung, f. marginal note. -druck, m.
lateral pressure. -eck, n., -ecke, f. lateral
summit. -fläche, f. lateral face; flat side,
facet. -isomerie, f. chain isomerism.
-kante, f. lateral edge. -kette, f. side chain.
-länge, f. length of a side, lateral length.
-rohr, n., -röhre, f. side tube, branch tube,
branch pipe.

seitens, adv. on behalf (of), on the part (of).

seitenständig, a. lateral.

Seiten-stück, n. sidepiece; counterpart. -wand,
f. side wall; side plate.

seither, adv. since then; till now.

-seitig. -sided. -lateral.

seit-lich, a. side, lateral; collateral.—adv. at
the side, laterally. -wärts, adv. sideways;
laterally; aside.

Sekante, f. secant.

Sekret, n. secretion; privy.

sekretorisch, a. secretory.

Sekt, m. champagne; dry wine.

Sektion, f. section; (Med.) dissection.

Sektwein, m. dry wine.

sekundär, a. secondary.

Sekundär-kreis, m. (Elec.) secondary circuit.
-strahlung, f. secondary radiation.

Sekunde, f. second.

Sekundenuhr, f. watch (or clock) with a
seconds hand.

selbe, a. same.

selber, pron. self.

selbst, pron. self, myself, himself, etc.—
adv. even.

Selbst-. self-, automatic, spontaneous, auto-.
-achtung, f. self-respect, self-esteem.

selbständig, a. independent, self-dependent.

Selbstbeherrschung, f. self-control.

selbstbewusst, p.a. self-conscious; conceited.

Selbstbiographie, f. autobiography.

selbstentzündlich, a. spontaneously inflammable.

Selbst-entzündlichkeit, f. spontaneous inflammability. -entzündung, f. spontaneous
ignition. -erhitzung, f. self-heating.

selbsterregend, p.a. self-exciting.

Selbst-erzeugung, f. spontaneous generation,
autogenesis. -farbe, f. self color, solid color.
-gärung, f. spontaneous fermentation.
-gefühl, n. self-consciousness; self-con-
fidence.

selbstgemacht, p.a. self-made; home-made.

Selbstgift, n. autotoxin.

selbsthemmend, a. irreversible; self-locking.

Selbst-kante, f. selvage, list. -laut, -lauter,
m. vowel.

selbstlos, a. unselfish.

Selbst-löschung, f. (of lime) spontaneous
slaking. -lötung, f. autogenic soldering.
-oxydation, f. autoxidation, self-oxidation.

selbstredend, p.a. self-evident.

Selbstreinigung, f. self-purification, auto-
purification.

selbst-schmierend, a. self-lubricating. -schrei-
bend, a. self-registering, recording.

Selbstschrift, f. autograph.

selbst-ständig, a. = selbständig. -tätig, a. self-
acting, automatic; (of flour) self-raising.

Selbst-umkehr, f. self-reversal (as of a spectral
line). -unterbrecher, m. (Elec.) automatic
interrupter. -verbrennung, f. spontaneous
combustion. -verdauung, f. autodigestion.

selbst-verständlich, a. self-evident.—adv. of
course. -wirkend, p.a. self-acting, automatic.

Selbst-zersetzung, f. spontaneous decomposition. -zeugung, f. spontaneous generation,
abiogenesis.

selbstzündend, a. self-igniting, pyrophoric.

Selbst-zünder, m. pyrophorus; self-igniter,
automatic lighter. -zündung, f. spontaneous
ignition.

Selen, n. selenium.

Selen-. selenium, selenic, selenide of, seleno-.
-ammonium, n. ammonium selenide. -äthyl,
n. ethyl selenide. -blei, n. lead selenide.
-bleisilber, n. (Min.) naumannite. -bleiwis-
mutglanz, m. galenobismuthite. -brücke, f.
selenium bridge. -chlorid, n. selenium
chloride, specif. selenium tetrachloride.
-chlorür, n. selenium monochloride ($Se_2Cl_2$).
-cyanid, n. selenocyanate. -cyankalium, n.
potassium selenocyanate. -cyansäure, f.
selenocyanic acid. -eisen, n. ferrous selenide
(FeSe). -erz, n. selenium ore. -halogen, n.
selenium halide.

selenhaltig, a. containing selenium, seleniferous.

Selen-harnstoff, m. selenourea. -hydrat, n.
hydroselenide.

Selenid, n. selenide, specif. -ic selenide
(cf. Selenür).

selenig, a. selenious.—selenige Säure, selenious acid.

selenigsauer, a. of or combined with selenious
acid, selenite of.

Selenigsäure, f. selenious acid. -anhydrid, n.
selenious anhydride ($SeO_2$).

Selen-kupfer, n. copper selenide. -kupfer-
silber, n. copper silver selenide; (Min.)
eucairite. -metall, n. metallic selenide.

Selenocyan, n. selenocyanogen.

Selen-oxyd, n. selenium oxide. -quecksilber,
n. mercury selenide. -quecksilberblei, n.
(Min.) lehrbachite. -salz, n. selenide.

selensauer, a. of or combined with selenic
acid, selenate of.

Selen-säure, f. selenic acid. -säureanhydrid,
n. selenic anhydride ($SeO_3$). -schlamm, m.

selenium mud, selenium slime (seleniferous deposit in sulfuric acid works). -schwefel, m. (Min.) selensulfur. -silber, n. silver selenide. -silberglanz, m. naumannite.

Selenür, n. (lower or -ous) selenide.

Selen-verbindung, f. selenium compound. -wasserstoff, m. hydrogen selenide. -wasserstoffsäure, f. hydroselenic acid. -wismutglanz, m. guanajuatite. -zelle, f. selenium cell.

selig, a. blessed; happy; late, deceased.

Sellerie, m.& f. celery.

selten, a. rare, scarce, unusual.—adv. seldom, rarely.—seltene Erde, rare earth.

Seltenheit, f. rareness, rarity, scarcity.

Selterswasser, n. Seltzer water, seltzer.

seltsam, a. singular, strange, curious.

Selzerbrunnen, m. Seltzer water.

semicyclisch, a. semicyclic.

Semidinumlagerung, f. semidine rearrangement.

semimer, a. semimeric.

Semmel, f. roll (the bread). -mehl, n. flour for rolls; ground rolls.

senden, v.t.& i. send.

Sendung, f. sending; shipment; parcel; mission.

Senegawurzel, f. senega root.

Senf, m. mustard. -gas, n. mustard gas. -geist, m. (volatile) oil of mustard. -korn, n. mustard seed. -mehl, n. ground mustard. -öl, n. mustard oil. -ölessigsäure, f. (literally, mustard-oil-acetic-acid) 2,4-thiazoledione. -pulver, n. ground mustard. -same, m. mustard seed.

sengen, v.t. singe; flame; scorch, parch.

Senkboden, m. (Brewing) false bottom, strainer.

Senkel, m. plummet; lace.

senken, v.t. sink, lower.—v.r. sink, subside.

Senk-grube, f. cesspool; sump; catch basin. -körper, m. sinker, bob.

senkrecht, a. perpendicular, vertical.

Senkspindel, f. specific-gravity spindle, hydrometer.

Senkung, f. sinking, lowering, subsiding; inclination; hollow, depression.

Senk-wa(a)ge, f. = Senkspindel; plumb rule. -zylinder, m. separating cylinder.

Sennes-blätter, n.pl. senna leaves, senna. -strauch, m. senna (the herb).

Sense, f. scythe.

sensibel, a. sensitive, sensible; sensory.

Sensibil-isator, m. sensitizer. -isierung, f. sensitization. -ität, f. sensibility, sensitiveness.

separat, a. separate, detached.

Separatabdruck, m. separate impression, reprint.

separieren, v.t.& r. separate.

sepiabraun, a. sepia-brown.

Septikämie, f. septicemia.

septisch, a. septic.

Serie, f. series.

serienfremd, a. of another series, of different series.

Seriengrenze, f. series limit.

serienmässig, a.& adv. in a series, in series.

Serien-schnitt, m. serial section. -spektrum, n. series spectrum.

serös, a. serous.

Serviette, f. napkin.

Sesam, m. sesame. -öl, n. sesame oil.

Sessel, m. easy-chair, stool, seat.

sesshaft, a. resident, settled; stationary; sedentary.

Setzbottich, m. settling vat or tank.

setzen, v.t. set, put, place; apply; plant; jig, sieve (ore); wager.—v.r. settle, precipitate, be deposited; sink, subside; sit down.— v.i. run, leap, cross.—gesetzt, p.a. set, etc.; settled, steady, serious; supposing, assuming.

Setzer, m. compositor; setter; tamper. -fehler, m. compositor's error.

Setz-kasten, m. settling tank; type case. -phiole, f. (flat-bottomed) vial. -zapfen, m. suppository

Seuche, f. contagious or infectious disease, pestilence.

seuchen-artig, a. contagious, infectious, epidemic. -fest, a. immune. -haft, a. = seuchenartig.

Seven-baum, m., -kraut, n. savin.

sexuell, a. sexual.

sezernieren, v.t. secrete.

sezieren, v.t. dissect.

s.g., abbrev. (sogenannt) so-called.

Sg., abbrev. (Streckung) stretching, spread.

s.G., abbrev. (spezifisches Gewicht) specific gravity, sp. gr.

Shikimisäure, f. shikimic acid.

siamesisch, a. Siamese, Siam.

sibirisch, a. Siberian.

sich, pron. oneself, himself, herself, itself, themselves; each other, one another.

Sichel, f. sickle; crescent.

sichelförmig, a. crescent-shaped.

sicher, a. safe, secure, certain, sure, true.

Sicherheit, f. safety, security, certainty.

Sicherheits-flasche, f. safety bottle or flask. -grad, m. degree of safety; safety factor. -koeffizient, m. factor of safety. -lampe, f. safety lamp. -rohr, n., -röhre, f. safety tube. -sprengstoff, m. safety explosive. -trichterrohr, n. safety tube. -ventil, n. safety valve. -waschflasche, f. safety wash bottle. -wasserbad, n. safety water bath. -zündhölz-chen, n. safety match.

sichern, v.t. secure, ensure, guarantee; check. —gesichert, p.a. secured; guaranteed; safe, certain.

Sicherung, f. securing, security; security (or securing) device, safety device, as an electric fuse or cut-out.

Sicherungs-. safety, security; (Elec.) fuse.

Sicht, f. sight; visibility.

sichtbar, a. visible; evident.

Sichtbarkeit, f. visibility; obviousness.

sichten, v.t. sift; sort, classify; bolt (flour).

sichtlich, a. visible; evident.

sicilianisch, a. Sicilian.

sickern, v.i. trickle, ooze.

Sickerwasser, n. ground water.

sie, pron. she, her, it, they, them.

Sie, pron. you.

Sieb, n. sieve; screen, riddle, bolter, strainer. -boden, m. bottom of a sieve; perforated bottom.

sieben, a. seven.—v.t. sift, sieve; riddle, screen, bolt. -atomig, a. heptatomic. -flächig, a. heptahedral. -gliedrig, a. seven-membered.

Siebenring, m. seven-membered ring.

siebente, a. seventh.

siebenwertig, a. septivalent, heptavalent.

Siebenwertigkeit, f. septivalence.

siebförmig, a. sieve-shaped, sievelike.

Sieb-maschine, f. sifting machine, screening machine. -mehl, n. coarse flour; siftings. -platte, f. sieve plate; filter plate. -satz, m. set of sieves. -schale, f. dish with per-forated bottom. -sel, n. siftings. -staub, m. siftings. -trichter, m. strainer funnel. -trommel, f. revolving screen. -tuch, n. bolting cloth. -wasser, n. (Paper) back water.

siebzehn, a. seventeen.

siebzig, a. seventy.

siech, a. sick, sickly, infirm.

sied., abbrev. (siedend) boiling.

Siede-. boiling; distilling, distillation. -abfälle, m.pl. scum or sediment from boil-ing. -analyse, f. analysis by fractional dis-tillation. -apparat, m. boiling (or boiling-point) apparatus. -blech, n. boiling liquid; (Metal.) -flüssigkeit, f. boiling liquid; (Metal.) blanching liquid. -gefäss, n. boiling vessel, boiler; distillation flask. -grad, m. boiling point. -haus, n. boiling house, boilery. -hitze, f. boiling heat. -kessel, m. boiling vessel, boiling pan, boiler. -kolben, m. boiling flask; distillation flask. -kurve, f. boiling-point curve. -lauge, f. boiling lye, boiling liquor.

sieden, v.t.& i. boil; brew (beer); distill.

Sieden, n. boiling, ebullition. -lassen, n. allowing to boil.

Siedep., abbrev. (Siedepunkt) boiling point.

Siedepfanne, f. boiling pan, evaporating pan.

Siedepunkt, m. boiling point. -bestimmung, f. boiling-point determination. -(s)erhöh-ung, f. boiling-point elevation.

Siederei, f. boilery, boiling room or house; (Sugar) refinery.

Siede-rohr, n., -röhre, f. boiling tube, dis-tilling tube; boiler tube. -röhrchen, n. small boiling (or distilling) tube. -salz, n. common salt. -sole, f. brine. -stein, m. boiling stone (or other object to facilitate boiling). -temperatur, f. boiling tempera-ture. -verzug, m. delay in boiling. -zeit, f. boiling period or time.

Sied-kessel, m.= Siedekessel. -kolben, m. boiling flask.

Sieg, m. victory.

Siegel, n. seal. -erde, f. terra sigillata (Lemnian earth). -lack, m.& n. sealing wax. -wachs, n. soft sealing wax.

siegen, v.i. be victorious, triumph, conquer.

sieht, pr. 3 sing. of sehen.

sieken, v.t. crease, seam.

Siel, m. & n. sluice; sewer, drain. -wasser, n. effluent; sewage.

Sienaerde, f. sienna.

Sigel, -zeichen, n. sign, symbol.

Signatur, f. signature; mark, stamp.

signieren, v.t. sign; mark, brand.

Sikkativ, n. siccative.

Silbe, f. syllable.

Silber, n. silver.

silberartig, a. silvery, argentine.

Silber-ätzstein, m. lunar caustic (silver nitrate). -bad, n. silver bath. -baum, m. silver tree, arbor Dianæ. -belegung, f. silver coating. -blatt, n. silver leaf, silver foil. -blech, n. silver foil, (thin) silver plate. -blende, f. pyrargyrite; proustite. -blick, m. brightening or fulguration of silver, silver "blick." -brennen, n. silver refining. -brennherd, m. silver-refining hearth. -bromid, n. silver bromide. -bromür, n. silver subbromide. -chlorid, n. silver chloride. -chlorür, n. silver subchloride. -draht, m. silver wire, silver thread. -erz, n. silver ore. -essigsalz, n. silver acetate. -fahlerz, n. argentiferous tetrahedrite. -farbe, f. silver color, silver.

silberfarben, a. silver-colored, silvery.

Silber-fluorür, n. silver subfluoride. -folie, f. silver foil.

silberführend, a. silver-bearing, argentif-erous.

Silber-gare, f. silver refining. -gehalt, m. silver content. -gewinnung, f. extraction of silver.

-glanz, m. silvery luster; silver glance, argentite.

silberglänzend, p.a. silvery.

Silber-glas, -glaserz, n. argentite. -glätte, f. litharge. -glimmer, m. common mica, muscovite. -gold, n. argentiferous gold, electrum.

silbergrau, a. silver-gray.

Silbergrube, f. silver mine.

silberhaltig, a. containing silver, argentiferous.

Silber-hornerz, n. horn silver, cerargyrite. -hütte, f. silver foundry, silver works.

silberig, a. silvery.

Silber-jodid, n. silver iodide. -jodür, n. silver subiodide. -kies, m. sternbergite. -kupferglanz, m. stromeyerite. -legierung, f. silver alloy. -lösung, f. silver solution. -lot, n. silver solder. -münze, f. silver coin.

silbern, a. silver.

Silber-niederschlag, m. silver precipitate. -nitrat, n. silver nitrate.

Silberoxyd, n. silver oxide. -ammoniak, n. fulminating silver. -salz, n. silver oxysalt.

Silber-oxydul, n. silver suboxide. -oxydverbindung, f. compound of silver oxide; specif., argentate. -papier, n. silver paper, silvered paper.

silberplattiert, p.a. silver-plated.

Silber-plattierung, f. silver plating. -probe, f. test for silver, silver assay.

silberreich, a. rich in silver.

Silber-salbe, f. (Pharm.) colloid silver ointment. -salpeter, m. silver nitrate. -salz, n. silver salt. -sau, f. silver ingot. -schaum, m. silver in thin leaves, or an imitation of it. -scheidung, f. separation of silver; silver refining. -schein, m. silvery luster. -schicht, f. layer of silver; silver film or coating. -schlaglot, n. silver solder. -schwärze, f. earthy argentite.

silberschweflig, a. argentosulfurous.

Silber-spat, m. cerargyrite. -spiessglanz, m. antimonial silver, dyscrasite. -stahl, m. silver steel. -tanne, f. silver fir. -tiegel, m. silver crucible. -vitriol, m. silver sulfate. -waren, f.pl. silverware. -wasser, n. nitric acid (for dissolving silver).

silberweiss, a. silver-white.

Silber-weiss, n. silver white. -wismutglanz, m. matildite.

Silicierung, f. silication; silicification.

Silicium, n. silicon.

Silicium-. silicon, silico-, silicide of. -ameisensäure, f. silicoformic acid. -äthan, n. silicoethane. -bromid, n. silicon bromide. -chlorid, n. silicon chloride. -chloroform, n. silicochloroform. -eisen, n. iron silicide; (Metal.) ferrosilicon. -fluorid, n. silico-

fluoride (fluosilicate). -fluorverbindung, f. fluosilicate.

Siliciumfluorwasserstoff, m., -säure, f. fluosilicic acid. -salz, n. fluosilicate.

Siliciumgehalt, m. silicon content.

siliciumhaltig, a. containing silicon, siliceous.

Silicium-jodid, n. silicon iodide. -karbid, n., -kohlenstoff, m. silicon carbide. -kupfer, n. copper silicide; (Metal.) cuprosilicon. -legierung, f. silicon alloy. -magnesium n. magnesium silicide. -metall, n. metallic silicide. -methan, n. silicomethane; silicon tetrahydride. -oxalsäure, f. silicoöxalic acid. -oxyd, n. silicon dioxide. -oxydhydrat, n. hydrated oxide of silicon (silicic acid). -spiegel, m. siliceous ferromanganese. -stahl, m. silicon steel. -tetrahydrür, n. silicon tetrahydride. -verbindung, f. silicon compound. -wasserstoff, m. hydrogen silicide, silicon hydride.

Silicon, n. silicone (the silicon analog of ketone, RR'SiO).

Silikastein, m. silica brick.

Silikat, n. silicate. -gestein, m. silicate rock.

Siliko-ameisensäure, f. silicoformic acid. -äthan, n. silicoethane. -essigsäure, f. silicoacetic acid.

Silikon, n. = Silicon.

Silizid, n. silicide.

Silizium, n. = Silicium.

Silo, m. silo; (Brewing) bin.

simpel, a. simple.

Sims, m. molding; shelf; cornice.

simultan, a. simultaneous.

Sinapinsäure, f. sinapic acid.

sind, pr. 1 & 3 pl. of sein.

singen, v.t.& i. sing.

Singrün, n. = Sinngrün.

Singulett, n. singlet.

Singulosilikat, n. monosilicate.

sinken, v.i. sink, fall, subside, drop.

Sinkstoff, m. deposited substance or matter, sediment, settlings.

Sinn, m. sense; mind; inclination, feeling; taste. -bild, n. symbol, emblem.

sinnen, v.i. meditate, speculate, think.— gesinnt, p.a. minded, disposed.—gesonnen sein, be inclined, intend.

Sinnen-. of the senses, sensory, sensual. -welt, f. external world.

Sinnes-. of sense, sensory; of mind, mental. -werkzeug, n. organ of sense.

Sinngedicht, n. epigram.

sinn-gemäss, adv. accordingly. -getreu, a. faithful (translation).

Sinngrün, n. periwinkle, myrtle (Vinca).

sinnig, a. sensible; thoughtful; ingenious; pretty.

**sinn-lich,** *a.* sentient, sensitive, sensuous, sensual. **-los,** *a.* senseless.

**Sinnpflanze,** *f.* sensitive plant.

**sinnreich,** *a.* ingenious; witty.

**Sinnspruch,** *m.* maxim, motto, sentiment.

**sinn-verwandt,** *p.a.* synonymous. **-widrig,** *a.* unmeaning, absurd.

**sinopische Erde.** (*Min.*) sinopite.

**Sinter,** *m.* iron dross, cinder; sinter. **-kohle,** *f.* sintering coal, sinter coal.

**sintern,** *v.i.* sinter; trickle, drop; form sinter; form clinker or slag; (*Ceram.*) vitrify.

**Sinter-prozess,** *m.* (*Metal.*) slag process. **-quarz,** *m.* siliceous sinter. **-schlacke,** *f.* clinker. **-stein,** *m.* sinter brick.

**Sinterung,** *f.* sintering, etc. (see sintern).

**Sinterungshitze,** *f.* sintering heat.

**Sinter-vorgang,** *m.* (*Metal.*) slag process. **-wasser,** *n.* (*Min.*) water impregnated with mineral matter so as to be capable of forming sinter.

**Sinus,** *m.* (*Math.*) sine; (*Anat.*) sinus.

**siphonieren,** *v.t.* siphon.

**Sippe, Sippschaft,** *f.* kin, kindred, set; (*Biol.*) tribe.

**sirupartig,** *a.* sirupy.

**Sirup-dichte, -dicke,** *f.* sirupy consistency.

**sirup-dick,** *a.* thick like sirup, sirupy. **-haltig,** *a.* containing sirup, sirupy.

**sirupös,** *a.* sirupy.

**Siruppfanne,** *f.* sirup pan.

**Sitte,** *f.* habit, custom, usage, practice; (*pl.*) manners, morals.

**Sittenlehre,** *f.* ethics.

**sittlich,** *a.* moral.

**Sitz,** *m.* seat; (of clothes) fit.

**sitzen,** *v.i.* sit; stay; dwell; (of clothes) fit. **—sitzend,** *p.a.* sitting; fixed; sedentary; (*Bot.*) sessile.

**Sitzung,** *f.* sitting, session, meeting.

**Sitzungsberichte,** *m.pl.* reports of sessions, proceedings (of a society).

**sizilianisch,** *a.* Sicilian.

**S. K.,** *abbrev.* (Seger-Kegel) Seger cone.

**Skala,** *f.* scale.

**Skalen-ablesung,** *f.* scale reading. **-aräometer,** *n.* graduated hydrometer. **-intervall,** *n.* scale interval, scale division.

**Skalenoeder,** *n.* scalenohedron.

**skalenoedrisch,** *a.* scalenohedral.

**Skalen-rohr,** *n.* scale tube (of a spectroscope). **-reilung,** *f.* scale division.

**Skammoniaharz, Skammonienharz, Skammonium,** *n.* scammony resin, scammony.

**skandinavisch,** *a.* Scandinavian.

**Skapolith,** *m.* scapolite.

**Skelett,** *n.* skeleton.

**Skizze,** *f.* sketch.

**skizzieren,** *v.t.* sketch.

**Sklave,** *m.* slave.

**sklerosieren,** *v.i.* become indurated, harden.

**Skleroskophärte,** *f.* scleroscope hardness.

**Skonto,** *m.* discount.

**Skorbut,** *m.* scurvy.

**Skorie,** *f.* scoria, dross, slag, cinder.

**Skrofel,** *f.* scrofula.

**Sliwowitz, Slibowitz,** *m.* a kind of spirit made from plums.

**sll.,** *abbrev.* (sehr leicht löslich) very readily soluble.

**Sm.,** *abbrev.* (Schmelzpunkt) melting point.

**S.M.,** *abbrev.* (Seine Majestät) His Majesty.

**Smalte,** *f.* smalt.

**Smaragd,** *m.* emerald.

**smaragd-farben,** *a.* emerald. **-grün,** *a.* emerald-green, emerald.

**Smaragd-grün,** *n.* Guignet's green. **-malachit,** *m.* euchroite. **-spat,** *m.* green feldspar, amazonite.

**Smekalsprung,** *m.* Smekal transition.

**Smirgel,** *m.* emery. See Schmirgel-.

**so,** *adv.* so, thus.—*conj.* so, then.— — **ein guter,** such a good; **—** etwas, such a thing; **—** ... wie, as ... as; **—** viel, so far as; **—** ... auch, however.

**s.o.,** *abbrev.* (siehe oben) see above, vide supra.

**sobald,** *conj.* as soon as.

**Sociëtät,** *f.* society, company, partnership.

**Sockel,** *m.* base; pedestal; socket.

**socken,** *v.i.* crystallize out; (of metals) contract.

**Soda,** *f.* soda (usually, neutral sodium carbonate; cf. Natron).—**kaustische —,** caustic soda.

**sodaalkalisch,** *a.* alkaline with soda.

**Soda-asche,** *f.* soda ash. **-auszug,** *m.* soda extract. **-bad,** *n.* soda bath. **-blau,** *n.* ultramarine (made with soda). **-fabrik,** *f.* soda factory, alkali works. **-fabrikation,** *f.* manufacture of soda.

**sodahaltig,** *a.* containing soda.

**Soda-kristalle,** *m.pl.* soda crystals, sal soda. **-küpe,** *f.* soda vat. **-lauge,** *f.* soda lye.

**sodalkalisch,** *a.* alkaline with soda.

**Soda-lösung,** *f.* soda solution. **-mehl,** *n.* (*Soda*) sodium carbonate monohydrate in the form of powder. **-menge,** *f.* amount of soda.

**sodann,** *adv.* then.

**Soda-ofen,** *m.* soda furnace, black-ash furnace. **-rückstände,** *m.pl.* soda residues, tank waste (in the Leblanc process). **-salz,** *n.* soda salt (sodium salt), specif. sodium carbonate. **-schmelze,** *f.* black ash. **-see,** *m.* soda lake. **-seife,** *f.* soda soap. **-stein,** *m.* caustic soda. **-wasser,** *n.* soda water. **-zahl,** *f.* soda number.

**Sodbrennen,** *n.* heartburn.

Sode, *f.* salt works; salt making; sod.

Sodenbrot, *n.* carob bean, St.-John's-bread.

sodieren, *v.t.* treat or wash with soda.

soeben, *adv.* just, just now.

sof., *abbrev.* (sofort) immediately; (sofortig) immediate; (sofern) so far as.

sofern, *conj.* so far as, inasmuch as.

soff, *pret.* of saufen.

sofort, *adv.* immediately, at once.

sofortig, *a.* immediate, instantaneous.

sog, *pret.* of saugen.

sog., *abbrev.* (sogenannt) so-called.

sogar, *adv.* even.

sogen., *abbrev.* sogenannt.

sogenannt, *p.a.* so-called.

soggen, *v.i.* crystallize out.—*v.t.* precipitate in the form of crystals, salt down.

Sogge-pfanne, *f.* crystallizing pan. -salz, *n.* common salt.

sogleich, *adv.* at once.

Sohlband, *n.* (*Mining*) matrix, gangue.

Sohle, *f.* sole, bottom, bottom part, floor.

Sohlenleder, Sohlleder, *n.* sole leather.

Sohn, *m.* son.

Soja, *f.* soy (the sauce); soy bean. -bohne, *f.* soy bean, soja bean.

Sol-. brine, salt-water. -behälter, *m.* brine cistern. -bohrloch, *n.* salt well.

solch, solcher, *pron.* such, such a.—solche die, such as.

Sold, *m.* pay.

Soldat, *m.* soldier.

Sole, *f.* brine, salt water; salt spring. -bereiter, *m.* brine mixer. -eindampfer, *m.* brine concentrator. -erzeuger, *m.* brine mixer.

Solenhofener, *a.* of Solenhofen, hence, lithographic.—— Platte (Schiefer, Stein), lithographic stone.

Solfass, *n.* brine tub.

Soll, *n.* debit.

sollen, *v.i.* shall; be, be destined, be supposed; should.

Sollwert, *m.* theoretical value.

Solorinsäure, *f.* solorinic acid.

Solorsäure, *f.* soloric acid.

Sol-pfanne, *f.* brine pan. -quelle, *f.* brine spring, salt well. -salz, *n.* spring salt, well salt.

Solvens, *n.* solvent.

Solvenzien, *n.pl.* solvents.

solvieren, *v.t.* dissolve.—solvierend, *p.a.* solvent, dissolving.

Sol-wa(a)ge, *f.* brine gage, salimeter. -wasser, *n.* brine, salt water.

somit, *adv.* therefore, consequently, so.

Sommer, *m.* summer. -flecken, *m.*, -sprosse, *f.* freckle. -weizen, *m.* spring wheat.

sonach, *adv.* accordingly, so.

Sonde, *f.* sound, probe; plummet; riser (vertical pipe).

Sonder-. separate, special, peculiar, exclusive. -abdruck, *m.* separate impression, reprint, separate. -ausgabe, *f.* separate edition.

sonder-bar, *a.* strange, singular. -gleichen, *a.* unequaled.

Sondergusseisen, *n.* special cast iron.

sonderlich, *a.* special, particular.

Sondermethode, *f.* special method.

sondern, *v.t.* separate; sever; segregate; sort (ore, etc.).—*conj.* but.

sonders, *adv.* separately.

Sonder-schrift, *f.* separate or special work or treatise. -stahl, *m.* special steel. -stellung, *f.* separate or special position.

Sonderung, *f.* separation, etc. (see sondern).

Sonder-werk, *n.* special work, special treatise. -zweck, *m.* special purpose, special object.

Sonne, *f.* sun.

Sonnen-. of the sun, sun, solar, helio-. -auge, *n.* adularia. -bahn, *f.* ecliptic. -blume, *f.* sunflower; heliotrope. -distel, *f.* carline thistle (*Carlina*). -finsternis, *f.* solar eclipse. -fleck, *m.* sun spot. -geflecht, *n.* solar plexus. -gelb, *n.* sun yellow.

sonnenhaft, *a.* sunny, radiant.

Sonnen-hitze, *f.* solar heat. -licht, *n.* sunlight. -schein, *m.* sunshine. -schirm, *m.* sunshade, parasol. -spektrum, *n.* solar spectrum. -stein, *m.* sunstone (aventurine feldspar). -strahl, *m.* solar ray, sunbeam. -strahlung, *f.* solar radiation. -tau, *m.* sundew (*Drosera*). -uhr, *f.* sundial. -wärme, *f.* sun's heat, solar heat. -wende, *f.* solstice; heliotrope.

Sonntag, *m.* Sunday.

sonst, *adv.* else; otherwise, besides, in other respects, usually, formerly.

sonstig, *a.* other, remaining; former.

Soole, *f.* =Sole.

Sorbett, *n.* sherbet.

Sorbinsäure, *f.* sorbic acid.

Sorge, *f.* care; concern, sorrow.

sorgen, *v.i.* care, provide; be anxious, worry.

Sorgfalt, *f.* carefulness, care.

sorg-fältig, *a.* careful.—*adv.* carefully. -lich, *a.* anxious, solicitous. -los, *a.* careless, unconcerned, reckless.

Sorte, *f.* sort, quality, brand, grade.

sortieren, *v.t.* sort, assort, size, grade.

sott, *pret.* of sieden.

Soupleseide, *f.* souple silk.

souplieren, *v.t.* souple (silk).

soviel, *a.& adv.* so much.—*conj.* as much as, so far as.

soweit, *adv.* so far.—*conj.* as far as.

**sowie,** *adv.* as, as well as, as also.

**sowohl,** *conj.* as well.— — . . .**als,** both . . . and.

**Soya, -bohne,** *f.* soy bean. **-bohnenöl,** *n.* soy bean oil.

**So.Z.,** *abbrev.* (Sodazahl) soda number or value.

**Sozolsäure,** *f.* sozolic acid (*o*-phenolsulfonic acid).

**sozusagen,** *adv.* so to speak, as it were.

**Spachtel,** *f.* spatula.

**spachteln,** *v.t.* smooth (by filling up depressions, as with a spatula); putty.

**spagirisch,** *a.* spagyric, spagyrical

**Spalt,** *m.* split, rent, fissure, slit, crack, cleft, gap.

**spaltbar,** *a.* cleavable, scissile, fissile.

**Spalt-barkeit,** *f.* cleavability, cleavage. **-breite,** *f.* width of slit (of a spectroscope or the like).

**Spalte,** *f.* split, etc. (see Spalt); column (of printed matter).

**spalten,** *v.t.* cleave, split, slit, rend, fissure.— *v.i.* cleave, split, chink.

**Spaltfläche,** *f.* cleavage surface.

**spaltig,** *a.* split, fissured, cracked; (*Printing*) -columned.

**Spalt-körper,** *m.* cleavage substance, cleavage product. **-mündung, -öffnung,** *f.* (*Bot.*) stoma. **-pflanze,** *f.* schizophytum. **-pilz,** *m.* fission fungus, schizomycete; splitting mold. **-produkt,** *n.* =Spaltungsprodukt. **-riss,** *m.* cleavage crack (or fissure). **-rohr,** *n.* slit tube, collimator (of a spectroscope). **-stück,** *n.* detached portion, segment, fragment; cleavage product.

**Spaltung,** *f.* cleaving, etc. (see spalten), cleavage, scission, fission, division.

**Spaltungs-fläche,** *f.* cleavage plane, cleavage face. **-gärung,** *f.* cleavage fermentation. **-kristall,** *m.*, cleavage crystal. **-produkt,** *n.* cleavage product, fission product. **-prozess,** *m.* cleavage (fission, scission) process. **-richtung,** *f.* direction of cleavage, cleavage. **-stück,** *n.* =Spaltstück. **-vorgang,** *m.* = Spaltungsprozess.

**Span,** *m.* chip, splinter, shaving, boring, turning, filing, shred.

**Spänfass,** *n.* (*Brewing*) chip cask.

**Spange,** *f.* clasp, buckle; stay bolt; bracelet; spangle.

**Spangeleisen,** *n.* crystalline pig iron.

**spangelig, spanglig, spanglich,** *a.* spangled, glistening, (hence) crystalline.

**Spangrün,** *n.* verdigris.

**Spanien,** *n.* Spain.

**spanisch,** *a.* Spanish.—**spanische Fliegen,** Spanish flies, cantharides.—**spanischer Pfeffer,** red pepper, capsicum.—**spanisches**

**Rohr,** Spanish (or Italian) reed (*Arundo donax*); rattan.

**Spanischbraun,** *n.* Spanish brown.

**Spanischfliegen-.** cantharides.

**spann,** *pret.* of spinnen.

**Spann,** *m.* instep.

**Spann-.** tension, stretching; coupling.

**spannbar,** *a.* tensile, extensible, ductile.

**Spannbarkeit,** *f.* tensibility, extensibility, ductility.

**Spanne,** *f.* span.

**spannen,** *v.t.* stretch, strain; tighten; (of steam) increase the tension of, superheat; span; cock (a gun).—*v.i.* pinch; be exciting. —**gespannt,** *p.a.* stretched, superheated, etc.; tight; intense.

**Spann-knorpel,** *m.* thyroid cartilage. **-kraft,** *f.* tension; extensibility, expansibility, elasticity.

**spannkräftig,** *a.* elastic.

**Spannung,** *f.* tension; (gaseous) pressure; stretching, etc. (see spannen); (*Elec.*) potential, voltage; stress; tenseness, strain.

**spannungsfrei,** *a.* free from tension.

**Spannungsgrad,** *m.* degree of tension.

**spannungslos,** *a.* without tension; (*Elec.*) dead.

**Spannungs-messer,** *m.* (*Elec.*) voltmeter. **-reihe,** *f.* electromotive series. **-theorie,** *f.* (*Org. Chem.*) strain theory, tension theory. **-unterschied,** *m.* difference in tension; (*Elec.*) potential difference. **-verlust,** *m.* loss of tension, specif. (*Elec.*) loss of voltage. **-zeiger,** *m.* tension indicator; (*Elec.*) voltmeter.

**Spannweite,** *f.* span, width, distance.

**Sparbrenner,** *m.* economical burner; pilot burner.

**sparen,** *v.t.* spare, save.

**Sparflämmchen,** *n.* pilot flame.

**Spargel,** *m.* asparagus. **-stein,** *m.* asparagus stone (variety of apatite). **-stoff,** *m.* asparagine.

**Spar-kalk,** *m.* = Estrichgips. **-kapsel,** *f.* (*Ceram.*) space-saving sagger, economy sagger.

**spärlich,** *a.* sparse, scarce, scanty.

**Sparmittel,** *n.* (*Biol. Chem.*) sparing substance, protein sparer (substance which economizes protein metabolism).

**Sparren,** *m.* rafter; spar.

**sparsam,** *a.* sparing, economical, close.

**Spartgras,** *n.* esparto grass, esparto.

**Spat,** *m.* spar; spavin.

**spät,** *a. & adv.* late.

**spatartig,** *a.* sparry, spathic.

**Spateisenstein,** *m.* spathic iron ore, sparry iron, siderite.

**Spatel,** *m.* spatula.

spatelförmig, *a.* spatula-shaped, spatulate.

Spatelmesser, *n.* steel spatula (shaped like a knife).

spateln, *v.t.* smooth (as with a spatula).

Spaten, *m.* spade.

später, *a.& adv.* later. -hin, *adv.* later on.

spätestens, *adv.* at the latest.

Spatfluss, *m.* fluor spar, fluorite.

spatig, *a.* sparry, spathic; spavined.

Spat-säure, *f.* hydrofluoric acid. -stein, *m.* selenite (the mineral).

Spätwirkung, *f.* tardy action; after-effect.

spazieren, *v.i.* walk, stroll, ride, drive.

spec., *abbrev.* (specifisch) specific.

speci-, Speci-. see spezi-, Spezi-.

Speck, *m.* lard; fat; bacon; blubber.

Speck-. fatty, lardaceous, amyloid.

speck-ähnlich, -artig, *a.* fatty, lardaceous.

Speckhaut, *f.* (*Physiol.*) buffy coat.

speckig, *a.* lardy, lardaceous, very fat; heavy (bread); flinty (barley).

Speck-öl, *n.* lard oil. -stein, *m.* soapstone, steatite, talc.

specksteinartig, *a.* steatitic.

Speck-stoff, *m.*, -substanz, *f.* lardaceous substance, amyloid substance. -torf, *m.* pitch peat. -tran, *m.* train oil.

spedieren, *v.t.* forward, dispatch.

Speer, *m.* spear. -kies, *m.* spear pyrites (variety of marcasite).

Speiche, *f.* spoke; (*Anat.*) radius.

Speichel, *m.* saliva, spittle.

Speichel-. salivary.

speichelbefördernd, *p.a.* promoting the flow of saliva, sialagog.

Speichel-drüse, *f.* salivary gland. -fluss, *m.* flow of saliva; salivation. -flüssigkeit, *f.* saliva. -kasten, *m.* saliva chamber (as in a blowpipe). -mittel, *n.* sialagog. -stoff, *m.* ptyalin.

Speicher, *m.* loft, granary, warehouse, storehouse, elevator; (*Mech.*) accumulator.

speichern, *v.t.* store, store up, accumulate.

Speicherung, *f.* storage; accumulation.

speien, *v.i.& t.* spit; vomit.

Speiköl, *n.* oil of Celtic nard.

Speise, *f.* food, nourishment; material (for a process); (*Metal.*) speiss; bell metal; gun metal; mortar.

Speise-. feed, feeding, food, nutrient. -apparat, *m.* (*Mech.*) feed apparatus. -bestandteil, *m.* constituent of food. -brei, *m.* chyme. -eis, *n.* ice cream. -fett, *n.* edible fat; nutrient fat. -gang, *m.* alimentary canal.

speisegelb, *a.* pale bronze-yellow like speiss.

Speise-hahn, *m.* feed cock. -kanal, *m.=* Speisegang. -karte, *f.* bill of fare. -kobalt, *m.* smaltite. -masse, *f.* ration.

speisen, *v.t.* feed; charge (as a battery); eat. —*v.i.* eat, take food, board.

Speise-öl, *n.* edible oil; specif., olive oil. -ordnung, *f.* diet, regimen. -pumpe, *f.* feed pump.

Speiser, *m.* feeder.

Speise-rohr, *n.* feed pipe or tube, supply pipe or tube. -röhre, *f.=* Speiserohr; (*Anat.*) esophagus. -saft, *m.* chyle. -salz, *n.* common salt. -walze, *f.* feed roll. -wasser, *n.* feed water. -zucker, *m.* table sugar.

speisig, *a.* cobaltiferous.

Speiskobalt, *m.* smaltite.

Speisung, *f.* feeding, etc. (see speisen); feed, supply.

Spektralanalyse, *f.* spectrum analysis.

spektralanalytisch, *a.* spectroscopic, spectrometric.

Spektral-apparat, *m.* spectroscopic apparatus. -beobachtung, *f.* spectroscopic observation. -bereich, *m.* spectral region. -farbe, *f.* spectral color, spectrum color. -gegend, *f.* spectral region. -linie, *f.* spectrum line, spectral line. -probe, *f.* spectrum test. -rohr, *n.*, -röhre, *f.* spectrum tube, spectral tube. -tafel, *f.* spectrum chart, spectral chart.

Spektren, *n.pl.* spectrums, spectra.

spektrometrisch, *a.* spectrometric.

Spektroskop, *n.* spectroscope.

Spektroskopiker, *m.* spectroscopist.

spektroskopisch, *a.* spectroscopic.

Spelz, *m.* spelt.

Spelze, *f.* chaff, husk, glume (of grains); awn, beard.

Spelzmehl, *n.* spelt flour.

spenden, *v.t.* spend, distribute.

Sperbeere, *f.* service berry.

Sperma, *n.* sperm, semen.

Spermazet, Spermazeti, *n.* spermaceti.

Spermöl, *n.* sperm oil.

Sperrdruck, *m.* spaced type.

sperren, *v.t.* shut, shut up, confine close, seal, stop, bar, block, obstruct; spread out, space.—*v.r.* resist, struggle, refuse.

Sperr-flüssigkeit, *f.* sealing liquid (to prevent escape of a gas). -hahn, *m.* stopcock. -haken, *m.* (*Mach.*) catch, pawl. -holz, *n.* plywood.

sperrig, *a.* bulky, unwieldy; wide open.

Sperr-rad, *n.* ratchet wheel, cog wheel. -ventil, *n.* stop valve. -wasser, *n.* sealing water.

Spesen, *f.pl.* charges, expenses, costs.

spez., *abbrev.* (spezifisch) specific; (speziell) special(ly).

Spezerei, *f.* spices; spicery, grocery.

spez.Gew., *abbrev.* (spezifisches Gewicht) specific gravity.

spezial, *a.* special.

Spezial-fall, *m.* special case. -gusseisen, *n.* special cast iron.

spezialistisch, *a.* specialistic.

Spezialität, *f.* specialty.

Spezial-öl, *n.* special oil. -reagens, *n.* special reagent. -stahl, *m.* special steel.

speziell, *a.* special, specific.

Spezies, *f.* species; specie; (*Pharm.*) simples, herbs, drugs.

spezifisch, *a.* specific.

Spezifität, *f.* specificity.

sp.G., *abbrev.* (spezifisches Gewicht) specific gravity, sp. gr.

Sphäre, *f.* sphere; province, range, domain.

sphärisch, *a.* spherical.

Sphäro-kristall, *m.* spherical crystal, spherocrystal. -siderit, *n.* spherosiderite.

Sphen, *m.* sphene, titanite.

sphenoidisch, *a.* sphenoid, sphenoidal.

spicken, *v.t.* lard; smoke.

Spicköl, *n.* wool oil.

spie, *pret.* of speien.

Spiegel, *m.* mirror, speculum; polished surface; surface (of liquids, fabrics, etc.); level (as in *Biochem.*); specular cast iron, spiegeleisen; stern (of a ship).

Spiegel-. mirror, specular, reflected, reflecting. -bild, *n.* reflected image, mirror image.

spiegel-bildisomer, *a.* showing isomerism characterized by enantiomorphism. -blank, *a.* highly polished.

Spiegel-eisen, *n.* specular cast iron, spiegeleisen; specular iron (hematite of metallic appearance). -erz, *n.* specular iron ore. -faser, *f.* medullary ray. -floss, *n.* spiegeleisen. -folie, *f.* tin foil; silvering (of a mirror). -giesserei, *f.* plate-glass factory. -glanz, *m.* wehrlite. -glas, *n.* plate glass.

spiegelglatt, *a.* extremely smooth.

Spiegelgleichheit, *f.* mirror symmetry.

spiegelig, *a.* specular, mirror-like.

Spiegelmetall, *n.* speculum metal.

spiegeln, *v.t.* reflect.—*v.i.* shine, glitter.—*v.r.* be reflected.—spiegelnd, *p.a.* reflecting, specular, shining.

Spiegelskala, *f.* mirror scale.

Spiegelung, *f.* reflection; mirage.

Spiegler, *m.* reflector.

Spieke, *f.* spike, spike lavender.

Spieköl, *n.* oil of spike.

Spiel, *n.* play, playing; game, sport; pack (of cards); (*Mech.*) working, action. -art, *f.* variety; (*Biol.*) sport.

spielen, *v.i.* play; (of a gem) sparkle; (*Mach.*) work, have play.—*v.t.* play.—— in, incline toward, be tinged with (a color).

Spiel-raum, *m.* play, latitude, margin, elbow-room; (*Mach.*) play; backlash. -waren, *f.pl.* toys. -zeug, *n.* plaything, toy.

Spiess, *m.* spear, lance; spit; (*Cryst.*) long needle.

spiessen, *v.t.* spear, spit, pierce.

Spiessglanz, *m.* antimony; stibnite.

spiessglanzartig, *a.* antimonial.

Spiessglanz-asche, *f.* antimony ash. -bleierz, *n.* bournonite. -blende, *f.* antimony blende, kermesite. -blumen, *f.pl.* flowers of antimony. -butter, *f.* butter of antimony (old name for antimony trichloride). -erz, *n.* antimony ore (graues, stibnite; schwarzes, bournonite; weisses, valentinite). -glas, *n.* glass of antimony.

spiessglanzhaltig, *a.* containing antimony, antimonial.

Spiessglanz-kermes, *m.* kermesite; kermes mineral. -könig, *m.* regulus of antimony. -leber, *f.* liver of antimony, hepar antimonii. -metall, *n.* antimony. -mittel, *n.* antimonial remedy. -mohr, *m.* aethiops antimonialis (old pharmaceutical preparation of mercury and antimony sulfides). -ocker, *m.* antimony ocher. -oxyd, *n.* antimony trioxide. -safran, *m.* crocus of antimony. -säure, *f.* antimonic acid. -schwefel, *m.* antimony sulfide. -silber, *n.* dyscrasite. -wein, *m.* antimonial wine. -weinstein, *m.* (*Pharm.*) tartrated antimony. -weiss, *n.* antimony white (trioxide). -zinnober, *m.* kermesite.

Spiessglas, *n.* antimony. See also Spiessglanz-. -erz, *n.* stibnite. -weiss, *n.* antimony white (trioxide).

spiessig, *a.* (*Cryst.*) spearlike, lancelike, in long needles; (*Leather*) badly tanned; (*Metal.*) brittle.

Spiesskobalt, *m.* smaltite.

Spik-blüten, *f.pl.* spike-lavender flowers. -öl, *n.* oil of spike, oil of spike lavender.

Spinat, *m.* spinach.

Spindel, *f.* spindle, pivot, axle, arbor. -baum, *m.* spindle tree; (*Pharm.*) euonymus.

spindelförmig, *a.* spindle-shaped, fusiform.

spindeln, *v.t.* test with a hydrometer.

Spindel-öl, *n.* spindle oil. -presse, *f.* screw press.

spinnen, *v.t.* spin; twist (tobacco).—*v.i.* spin; purr.

Spinnengewebe, *n.* spider web, cobweb.

Spinnerei, *f.* spinning; spinning mill.

Spinn-faser, *f.* fiber for spinning, textile fiber. -gewebe, *n.* cobweb, spider web. -lösung, *f.* spinning solution. -stoff, *m.* spinning material. -webe, *f.* cobweb, spider web.

spinnwebenartig, *a.* cobweblike, arachnoid.

Spinnwolle, *f.* wool for spinning, spinning wool.

Spiräa, Spiräe, *f.* spiraea, spirea.

Spiralbohrer, *m.* (*Mach.*) twist drill.

Spirale, *f.* spiral; spiral condenser.

Spiralfeder, *f.* spiral spring.

spiralförmig, *a.* spiral, helical.

spiralig, *a.* spiral.—*adv.* spirally.

Spiral-linie, *f.* spiral line, spiral. -rohr, *n.*, -röhre, *f.* spiral tube or pipe, worm.

Spirituosa, Spirituosen, *n.pl.* spirituous liquors, alcoholic liquors.

Spiritus, *m.* spirit, spirits, specif. alcohol.

spiritusartig, *a.* spirituous, alcoholic.

Spiritus-beize, *f.* spirit mordant. -blau, *n.* spirit blue. -brenner, *m.* (spirit) distiller. -brennerei, *f.* distillery. -dampf, *m.* alcohol vapor. -fabrik, *f.* spirit manufactory, distillery. -geruch, *m.* odor of spirits. -industrie, *f.* spirit industry. -lampe, *f.* spirit lamp. -mischung, *f.* alcoholic mixture. -pumpe, *f.* alcohol pump. -wa(a)ge, *f.* alcoholometer; spirit level.

spiroylig, *a.* spiroylous.—spiroylige Säure, spiroylous acid (former name for salicylaldehyde).

Spiroylsäure, Spirsäure, *f.* salicyclic acid (old names).

Spital, *n.* hospital.

spitz, *a.* pointed, acute, sharp, acicular.

Spitz, *m.* (*Metal.*) paddle. -becherglas, *n.* sedimenting glass.

Spitze, *f.* point; tip, top, apex, vertex, summit, cusp; lace.

spitzen, *v.t.* point, sharpen (to a point).—*v.i.* (of grain), sprout, spire, chit.

Spitzen-entladung, *f.* (*Elec.*) point discharge. -glas, *n.* reticulated glass. -leistung, *f.* peak output. -papier, *n.* lace paper. -strom, *m.* (*Elec.*) peak current.

Spitz-glas, *n.* a glass of tall, conical form; specif., sedimentation glass. -hacke, *f.* pickax, pick. -haufen, *m.* (*Brewing*) couch.

spitzig, *a.* pointed, acute, sharp, tapering; (of colors) mixtury, not uniform.

Spitz-kolben, *m.* a flask with long, tapering neck. -malz, *n.* chit malt. -röhrchen, *n.* small pointed tube (as for centrifuges). -trichter, *m.* tapering separatory funnel, Squibb funnel.

spitzwinklig, *a.* acute-angled.

Spleisse, *f.* splint, splinter, shard.

spleissen, *v.t.& i.* split, cleave; splice.

Splint, *m.* sap, sapwood; pin, peg, key; splint. -holz, *n.* sapwood, sap.

spliss, *pret.* of spleissen.

Splitter, *m.* splinter, splint, chip, scale, fragment. -kohle, *f.* splint coal.

splittern, *v.i.& t.* shiver, shatter, splinter, split (up).

spönne, *pret. subj.* of spinnen.

spontan, *a.* spontaneous.

sporenbildend, *p.a.* spore-forming.

Sporen-bildung, *f.* formation of spores, sporulation. -färbung, *f.* spore staining; spore stain.

sporenhaltig, *a.* containing spores.

Sporn, *m.* spur; spine.

Sportel, *f.* fee, perquisite.

spotten, *v.i.* mock, scoff, ridicule.

sprach, *pret.* of sprechen.

Sprache, *f.* speech; language; discussion.

Sprach-eigenheit, *f.* idiom. -forschung, *f.* philology. -lehre, *f.* grammar.

sprach-lich, *a.* lingual; grammatical. -los, *a.* speechless, dumb.

Sprachschatz, *m.* vocabulary; thesaurus.

sprachwidrig, *a.* ungrammatical.

sprang, *pret.* of springen.

spratzen, spratzeln, *v.i.* spit, spurt, sputter, splutter.

Spratzkupfer, *n.* = Streukupfer.

sprechen, *v.i.& t.* speak, talk, say.

Sprech-maschine, *f.* talking machine, phonograph. -saal, *m.* hall for speaking, forum.

spreiten, *v.t.* spread, spread out.

spreizen, *v.t.* spread; prop up.—*v.r.* strive.

Spreng-. explosive, blasting; sprinkling. -apparat, *m.* sprinkling apparatus, sprinkler, sparger. -arbeit, *f.* blasting. -eisen, *n.* (*Glass*) cracking ring.

sprengen, *v t.* explode, blow up, blast, burst; rupture; sprinkle.—*v.i.* gallop, dash; sprinkle, drizzle.

sprengfähig, *a.* explosive.

Spreng-flüssigkeit, *f.* explosive liquid. -gelatine, *f.* explosive gelatin. -granate, *f.* high-explosive grenade or shell, H. E. shell. -kapsel, *f.* detonating cap, detonator. -kohle, *f.* cracking coal (for cracking glass). -kraft, *f.* explosive force, explosive power.

sprengkräftig, *a.* powerfully explosive.

Spreng-ladung, *f.* bursting charge; charge of explosive. -loch, *n.* blast hole. -luft, *f.* liquid-air explosive. -mittel, *n.* explosive. -öl, *n.* nitroglycerin. -patrone, *f.* explosive cartridge. -pulver, *n.* blasting powder. -salpeter, *m.* saltpeter blasting powder. -schlag, *m.* explosion. -schnur, *f.* fuse. -schuss, *m.* shot.

Sprengstoff, *m.* explosive. -wesen, *n.* all that concerns explosives, subject of explosives.

Sprengtechnik, *f.* technics or manufacture of explosives.

Sprengung, *f.* exploding, explosion, etc. (see sprengen).

Spreng-wirkung, *f.* explosive effect, explosive action. -zünder, *m.* fuse.

Sprenkel, *m.* speckle, spot.

sprenkeln, v.t. sprinkle; speckle, mottle, spot.

Sprenkler, m. sprinkler, sparger.

sprenklig, a. speckled, spotted.

Spreu, f. chaff.

spricht, pr. 3 sing. of sprechen.

Sprichwort, n. saying, proverb.

spriessen, v.i. sprout, germinate.

Springbrunnen, m. fountain.

springen, v.i. burst, break, crack; spring, leap, jump, spout.

Spring-feder, f. (elastic) spring. -federwa(a)ge, f. spring balance. -gurke, f. squirting cucumber. -gurkenextrakt, m. elaterium. -kolben, m. Bologna flask. -kraft, f. springiness, power of recoil, elastic force, elasticity.

springkräftig, a. springy, elastic.

Sprit, m. spirit, spirits. -blau, n. spirit blue. -drucken, n. (Calico) spirit printing. -essig, m. spirit vinegar. -farbe, f. (Calico) spirit color. -gelb, n. spirit yellow.

sprithaltig, a. containing spirit, spirituous, (of wine) fortified.

Spritlack, m. spirit varnish.

spritlöslich, a. spirit-soluble.

Spritz-apparat, m. sprayer, sprinkler. -beton, m. concrete for first coat, rendering concrete. -bewurf, m. rough plastering.

Spritze, f. syringe, squirt, sprayer.

spritzen, v.i.& t. squirt; spurt, spout, spatter, sputter; spit; spray; throw (with a hose); inject (with a syringe).

Spritz-flasche, f. washing bottle, wash bottle (for washing precipitates). -gurke, f. squirting cucumber. -guss, m. die casting -kopf, m. spraying nozzle. -kork, m. sprinkler stopper. -kranz, m. (Brewing) sparger. -mittel, n. remedy administered by injection. -nudeln, f.pl. vermicelli. -rohr, n., -röhre, f. syringe; wash-bottle tube.

spröde, a. brittle, short; friable; shy, prim.

Spröd-glanzerz, -glaserz, n. brittle silver ore, stephanite (sometimes, polybasite). -igkeit, f. brittleness, shortness; friability; reserve, primness.

spross, pret. of spriessen.

Spross, m., Sprosse, f. shoot, sprout, germ; scion, offspring.

sprossen, v.i. shoot, sprout, germinate; spring, descend.

Sprossen-bier, n. spruce beer. -extrakt, m. essence of spruce. -fichte, f. spruce fir, (true) spruce. -kohl, m. broccoli; (Brüsseler) Brussels sprouts. -tanne, f. hemlock spruce.

Sprosspilz, m. gemmiparous fungus, budding fungus (specif. yeast fungus, Saccharomyces).

Spruch, m. sentence, verdict; saying, motto, text.

Sprudel, m. hot spring.

sprudeln, v.i. bubble, spout.

Sprudel-salz, n. Karlsbad salt. -stein, m. deposit from hot springs.

sprühen, v.i. spray, spit, scintillate, drizzle.— v.t. scatter, sprinkle, emit.

Sprüh-kupfer, n.= S teukupfer. -regen, m. spray.

Sprung, m. crack, chink, fissure; (of strata) fault; jump, spring, bounce, leap; (in a curve) break, discontinuity; (in spectra) transition. -feder, f. (elastic) spring.

sprunghaft, a. pertaining to or of the nature of a leap or jump.—adv. by leaps or jumps.

Sprung-variation, f. (Biol.) mutation. -weite, f. range (as of a water jet). -zeit, f. time of transition (of an electron).

spucken, v.t.& i. spit.

Spül-. rinsing, washing, flushing, irrigating. -bad, n. rinsing bath.

Spule, f. spool; (Elec.) coil; bobbin; quill.

Spüleimer, m. rinsing pail.

spulen, v.t. wind, reel.

spülen, v.t. rinse, wash, flush.

Spüler, m. rinser, washer.

Spülerei, f. rinsing; rinsing plant.

Spül-flüssigkeit, f. rinsing liquid. -gas, n. rinsing gas (for sweeping out a tube or the like). -gefäss, n. rinsing vessel. -icht, n. dishwater, slop; (Distilling) spent wash. -maschine, f. rinsing machine. -topf, m. rinsing pot, rinsing jar.

Spülung, f. rinsing, washing, flushing.

Spülwasser, n. rinsing water; dishwater; water for flushing.

Spund, m. stopper, plug, bung; tongue (of a board).

spunden, v.t. bung (casks); cask (wine, etc.); tongue and groove.

Spund-gärung, f. bunghole fermentation. -loch, n. bunghole.

spundvoll, a. brim-full.

Spur, f. trace; track; trail, scent; mark; gage; gutter, channel, groove. -arbeit, f. (Metal.) concentration.

spuren, v.t. (Metal.) concentrate.

spüren, v.t. track, trace, notice.

spurenhaft, a.& adv. in traces.

Spurensuche, f. search for traces.

spurenweise, adv. in traces.

Spur-schlacke, f. concentration slag. -stein, m. concentration metal, concentrated matte.

Sr., abbrev. (Seiner) His (in titles).

S-Rohr, n., S-Röhre, f. S-tube, S-pipe.

s.S., abbrev. (siehe Seite) see page . . . .

S.S., abbrev. (Schwefelwasserstoffsäure) hydrosulfuric acid (H₂S).

SS., abbrev. (Säuren) acids.

s. str., abbrev. (sensu stricto) in a strict sense.

**St.,** *abbrev.* (Stunde) hour; (Sankt) Saint; (Stärke) thickness; (Stück) piece, each.

**St. A.,** *abbrev.* (Stammaktien) shares of common stock.

**Staat,** *m.* state.

**staatlich,** *a.* state, civil, public.

**Staats-.** state, government, public, political. **-amt,** *n.* public office. **-bürger,** *m.* subject, citizen. **-lehre,** *f.* political science. **-rat,** *m.* council of state, state council; state councilor. **-zeitung,** *f.* (official) gazette.

**Stab,** *m.* rod; stick; bar; staff. **-bakterie,** *f.* bacillus.

**Stäbchen,** *n.* little rod or stick; pin; bacillus.

**stäbchenförmig,** *a.* rod-shaped.

**Stabeisen,** *n.* bar iron.

**stabförmig,** *a.* rod-shaped, bar-shaped.

**stabil,** *a.* stable.

**stabilisieren,** *v.t.* stabilize.

**Stabilität,** *f.* stability.

**Stabilitätsprüfer,** *m.* stability tester.

**Stab-kranz,** *m.* (*Biol.*) corona radiata. **-kraut,** *n.* = Eberraute. **-magnet,** *m.* bar magnet. **-thermometer,** *n.& m.* a thermometer graduated directly on the stem (instead of having a separate scale).

**stach,** *pret.* of stechen.

**Stachel,** *m.* sting, thorn, spine, prickle, prong, point. **-beere,** *f.* gooseberry. **-draht,** *m.* barbed wire.

**stachelig,** *a.* prickly, thorny; pungent, biting.

**Stachelmohn,** *m.* prickly poppy (*Argemone*).

**stacheln,** *v.t.* sting, prick, prod; spur.

**Stachel-schwein,** *n.* porcupine. **-walzwerk,** *n.* (*Mach.*) toothed rolls.

**Stadel,** *m.* shed; (*Metal.*, etc.) open kiln, stall. **-röstung,** *f.* stall roasting.

**Stadium,** *n.* stage, phase.

**Stadt,** *f.* town; city. **-haus,** *n.* town house, town hall.

**städtisch,** *a.* town, city, municipal.

**Staffel,** *f.* step.

**staffieren,** *v.t.* trim, equip; prepare (a dye bath).

**stagnieren,** *v.i.* stagnate.

**stahl,** *pret.* of stehlen.

**Stahl,** *m.* steel. **-abfall,** *m.* waste steel, steel scrap.

**stahlähnlich,** *a.* steel-like.

**Stahlarbeit,** *f.* steel process; steel work.

**stahlartig,** *a.* steel-like, steely; chalybeate.

**Stahl-arznei,** *f.* medicine containing iron, chalybeate. **-bereitung,** *f.* steel making. **-beton,** *m.* steel concrete.

**stahlblau,** *a.* steel-blue.

**Stahl-blech,** *n.* steel plate, sheet steel. **-block,** *m.* (*Metal.*) steel ingot. **-brunnen,** *m.* chalybeate spring. **-draht,** *m.* steel wire. **-eisen,** *n.* steely iron, steel pig.

**stählen,** *v.t.* steel, harden; convert into steel.

**stählern,** *a.* of steel, steel.

**Stahl-erz,** *n.* steel ore, specif. siderite. **-erzeugung,** *f.* steel production.

**stahlfarbig,** *a.* steel-colored.

**Stahl-feder,** *f.* steel spring; steel pen. **-flasche,** *f.* steel bottle, steel cylinder. **-formguss,** *m.* steel casting. **-frischfeuer,** *n.* steel finery. **-gattung,** *f.* grade of steel. **-gefäss,** *n.* steel vessel, steel receptacle. **-gewinnung,** *f.* steel making. **-giesserei,** *f.* steel founding; steel foundry.

**stahlgrau,** *a.* steel-gray.

**Stahlguss,** *m.* steel casting; cast steel; toughened cast iron.

**Stahlguss-.** cast-steel, steel-cast.

**Stahl-güte,** *f.* quality or grade of steel. **-hahn,** *m.* steel cock. **-hütte,** *f.* steel works. **-kobalt,** *m.* smaltite. **-kohlen,** *n.* conversion of wrought iron into steel by carbonization. **-kraut,** *n.* vervain. **-legierung,** *f.* steel alloy. **-mittel,** *n.* = Stahlarznei. **-mörser,** *m.* steel mortar. **-ofen,** *m.* steel furnace. **-perle,** *f.* steel bead. **-platte,** *f.* steel plate. **-präparat,** *n.* (*Pharm.*) iron preparation. **-probe,** *f.* steel sample; test of steel. **-puddeln,** *n.* steel puddling. **-quelle,** *f.* chalybeate spring. **-roheisen,** *n.* open-hearth pig iron. **-rohr,** *n.* steel pipe or tube. **-säuerling,** *m.* acidulous iron water. **-schmelzen,** *n.* steel melting, steel making. **-schrot,** *m.* steel scrap. **-späne,** *m.pl.* steel turnings, steel chips. **-stange,** *f.* steel bar. **-stechen,** *n.,* **-stecherei,** *f.* steel engraving. **-stein,** *m.* (*Min.*) siderite. **-stich,** *m.* steel engraving. **-trommel,** *f.* steel drum.

**Stählung,** *f.* steeling, hardening; conversion into steel, acieration.

**Stahl-waren,** *f.pl.* steel articles. **-wasser,** *n.* chalybeate water. **-wein,** *m.* iron wine. **-werk,** *n.* steel mill, steelworks.

**stak,** *pret.* of stecken.

**Staket,** *n.* stockade; railing.

**Stall,** *m.* stable, stall, sty, shed.

**Stamm,** *m.* stem; stalk, trunk, stock; staff; breed, race, strain; tribe.

**Stamm-.** parent, original, primary, main. **-aktie,** *f.* share of common stock. **-baum,** *m.* flow sheet; pedigree.

**stammeln,** *v.t.& i.* stammer.

**stammen,** *v.i.* spring, descend, come (of or from); date (from).

**Stammfarbe,** *f.* primary color.

**stämmig,** *a.* robust, strong; stumpy.

**Stamm-körper,** *m.* parent substance (or compound); parent body. **-linie,** *f.* trunk line, main line. **-lösung,** *f.* stock solution. **-substanz,** *f.* parent substance. **-tafel,** *f.* flow sheet.

**stammverwandt**, *p.a.* kindred, cognate.

**Stammwürze**, *f.* original wort.

**Stampf-asphalt**, *m.* compressed asphalt. **-beton**, *m.* tamped concrete.

**Stampfe**, *f.* stamp, stamper, pestle, punch, rammer, ram.

**stampfen**, *v.t.* stamp, beat, pound, ram, tamp, punch.—*v.i.* stamp, pitch.

**Stampfer**, *m.* = Stampfe.

**Stampf-futter**, *n.* tamped lining. **-haufen**, *m.* (*Paper*) batch. **-masse**, *f.* tamping mass, ramming mass. **-mörtel**, *m.* tamped mortar. **-werk**, *n.* stamp mill.

**stand**, *pret.* of stehen.

**Stand**, *m.* position; stand; state, condition; stage; height, level (of a liquid); rank, station.

**Standard-fehler**, *m.* standard error. **-lösung**, *f.* standard solution. **-wert**, *m.* standard value.

**Standbild**, *n.* statue.

**Ständer**, *m.* stand, standard, pillar, post, pedestal; cistern, tank, holder. **-klemme**, *f.* clamp for a stand.

**stand-fähig**, *a.* stable, firm. **-fest**, *a.* stable; rigid, firm.

**Stand-festigkeit**, *f.* stability; rigidity. **-flasche**, *f.* a bottle (or flask) to be stood in a fixed place, as a reagent bottle; flat-bottomed flask. **-gärung**, *f.* standing fermentation. **-gefäss**, *n.* a vessel made to stand in a fixed place, as a museum jar; stock tub. **-glas**, *n.* a glass vessel to be stood in a fixed place, as a reagent bottle; glass cylinder; glass gage.

**stand-haft**, *a.* steady, constant, firm. **-halten**, *v.i.* stand firm, hold out.

**ständig**, *a.* stationary, fixed; constant, permanent.

**-ständig.** in the (given) position.

**Stand-kugel**, *f.* stationary bulb. **-mörser**, *m.* a heavy mortar with a firm base. **-öl**, *n.* stand oil, lithographic oil (made by heating linseed oil). **-ort**, *m.& n.* station, stand; (*Bot.*) habitat. **-punkt**, *m.* standpoint; standard. **-sicherheit**, *f.* stability. **-tropfglas**, *n.* dropping bottle. **-zylinder**, *m.* a standing cylindrical vessel, cylinder.

**Stange**, *f.* stick; rod, bar; pole; (of sulfur) roll; (of gold) ingot; (of a valve) stem.

**Stängelchen**, *n.* little stick, small stick.

**Stangen-blei**, *n.* bar lead. **-eisen**, *n.* bar iron, rod iron. **-gold**, *n.* ingot gold. **-kali**, *n* potash in sticks, stick potash. **-kitt**, *m.* stick cement. **-kupfer**, *n.* bar copper, rod copper. **-lack**, *m.* stick-lac. **-schwefel**, *m.* roll sulfur, stick sulfur, cane brimstone. **-seife**, *f.* bar soap. **-silber**, *n.* ingot silver. **-spat**, *m.* columnar barite. **-stahl**, *m.* bar

steel; rod steel. **-stein**, *m.* pycnite (columnar topaz). **-tabak**, *m.* roll tobacco. **-zinn**, *n.* bar tin.

**stank**, *pret.* of stinken.

**stänkern**, *v.i.* stink.

**Stannatlauge**, *f.* stannate liquor.

**Stanni-**. stannic, stanni-. **-chlorid**, *n.* stannic chloride. **-chlorwasserstoffsäure**, *f.* chlorostannic acid. **-hydroxyd**, *n.* stannic hydroxide. **-jodid**, *n.* stannic iodide.

**Stanniol**, *f.* tin foil.

**Stanni-oxyd**, *n.* stannic oxide. **-reihe**, *f.* stannic series. **-salz**, *n.* stannic salt. **-verbindung**, *f.* stannic compound.

**Stanno-**. stannous, stanno-. **-chlorid**, *n.* stannous chloride. **-chlorwasserstoffsäure**, *f.* chlorostannous acid. **-hydroxyd**, *n.* stannous hydroxide. **-jodid**, *n.* stannous iodide. **-jodwasserstoffsäure**, *f.* iodostannous acid. **-oxyd**, *n.* stannous oxide. **-salz**, *n.* stannous salt. **-sulfid**, *n.* stannous sulfide. **-verbindung**, *f.* stannous compound.

**Stanzabfall**, *m.* stamping, punching (waste).

**Stanze**, *f.* puncher, punch; (usually *pl.*) stamping, punching.

**stanzen**, *v.t.* stamp; punch.

**Stanz-porzellan**, *n.* porcelain for punching. **-presse**, *f.* stamping press.

**Stapel**, *m.* staple; warehouse; pile, heap. **-faser**, *f.* a short-fibered rayon.

**Star**, *m.* (*Med.*) cataract; starling.

**starb**, *pret.* of sterben.

**stark**, *a.* strong; powerful, loud, heavy, fat, large, thick.—*adv.* strongly, hard.

**Starkbrenner**, *m.* a kind of burner with self-forced draft.

**Stärke**, *f.* starch; strength; thickness; diameter; corpulency. **-abbau**, *m.* degradation of starch. **-art**, *f.* variety of starch.

**stärkeartig**, *a.* starchy, amylaceous, amyloid.

**Stärke-bildner**, *m.* (*Bot.*) leucoplast. **-bildung**, *f.* formation of starch. **-blau**, *n.* starch blue. **-fabrik**, *f.* starch factory.

**stärkeführend**, *a.* amylaceous.

**Stärke-gehalt**, *m.* starch content. **-grad**, *m.* degree of strength, intensity. **-gummi**, *n.* starch gum, dextrin.

**stärkehaltig**, *a.* containing starch, starchy, amylaceous.

**Stärke-kleister**, *m.* starch paste. **-korn**, **-körnchen**, *n.* starch granule. **-lösung**, *f.* starch solution. **-mehl**, *n.* starch flour, starch powder, starch.

**stärkemehl-ähnlich**, *a.* amylaceous, amyloid. **-artig**, *a.* starchy, amylaceous.

**Stärke-messer**, *m.* amylometer. **-milch**, *f.* thin starch paste. **-mittel**, *n.* strengthening remedy, tonic, restorative.

stärken, *v.t.* starch; strengthen; refresh; confirm.

Stärke-papier, *n.* starch paper. -pulver, *n.* starch powder, powdered starch. -sirup, *m.* starch sirup, glucose. -wasser, *n.* starch water. -weizen, *m.* starch wheat, emmer. -zucker, *m.* starch sugar, (dextro)glucose.

stark-farbig, *a.* strongly colored. -faserig, *a.* strong-fibered. -klopfend, *a.* strongly knock-producing.

Starkstrom, *m.* (*Elec.*) heavy current.

Stärkung, *f.* starching; strengthening.

Stärkungsmittel, *n.* = Stärkemittel.

stark-wandig, *a.* stout-walled, thick-walled. -wirkend, *p.a.* powerful, efficacious, drastic. -wirksam, *a.* highly active, powerful. -zügig, *a.* (*Paints*) long-stroke.

starr, *a.* rigid, stiff; numb; stern, stubborn.

Starre, *f.* = Starrheit.

starren, *v.i.* stare; be numb, be stiff.

Starr-heit, *f.* rigidity, stiffness; rigor; obstinacy. -krampf, *m.* tetanus; tonic convulsion. -leinen, *n.*, -leinwand, *f.* buckram. -schmiere, *f.* solid lubricant. -sucht, *f.* catalepsy.

stät, stätig, *a.* fixed, stable, constant.

Statik, *f.* statics.

stationär, *a.* stationary.

statisch, *a.* static.

statistisch, *a.* statistical.

Stativ, *n.* stand, support. -chen, *n.* small stand or support.

statt, *prep.* instead of.

Statt, *f.* place, stead.

Stätte, *f.* place, room.

statten. In the phrases: von — gehen, take place, go off, pass off; zu — kommen, be of use or advantage.

stattfinden, statthaben, *v.i.* take place, occur. —stattgehabt, *p.a.* previous.

statt-haft, *a.* allowable, permissible; legal. -lich, *a.* fine, splendid, stately; portly.

Staub, *m.* dust; powder.

staubartig, *a.* dustlike, powdery, pulverulent.

Stäubchen, *n.* tiny particle, mote.

staubdicht, *a.* dust-tight, dustproof.

stäuben, *v.t.* dust, powder; spray.

Staub-fänger, *m.* dust catcher. -farbe, *f.* powdered color.

staubfein, *a.* fine as dust, very fine.

Staubfeuerung, *f.* firing with powdered fuel.

staub-förmig, *a.* in the form of dust, pulverulent. -frei, *a.* dust-free, dustless.

Staubgefäss, *n.* (*Bot.*) stamen.

staubhaltig, *a.* containing dust, dust-laden.

staubig, *a.* dusty; pulverulent, powdery.

Staub-kalk, *m.* air-slaked lime, powdered lime. -kohle, *f.* coal dust. -korn, *n.* dust particle.

staubsicher, *a.* dustproof.

Staub-sieb, *n.* dust sieve. -tee, *m.* tea dust. -teilchen, *n.* dust particle.

staubtrocken, *a.* dry as dust.

stauchen, *v.t.* compress (by a blow); knock, beat; bulge; (*Metals*) upset.—*v.r.* buckle.

Stauchprobe, *f.* compression test; bulging test; hammering test.

Staude, *f.* shrub, bush.

stauen, *v.t.* stow; dam up; congest.—*v.i.* choke.

Staufferfett, *n.* Stauffer grease, cup grease.

staunen, *v.i.* be astonished, be surprised.

Staunen, *n.* astonishment, surprise.

staunenswert, *a.* wonderful.

Stauung, *f.* obstruction, congestion; rise (of water); stowage.

Std., *abbrev.* (Stunde, Stunden) hour, hours.

Stde., *abbrev.* (Stunde) hour.

Stdn., *abbrev.* (Stunden) hours.

Stearinkerze, *f.* stearin candle.

stearinsauer, *a.* of or combined with stearic acid, stearate of.

Stearin-säure, *f.* stearic acid. -seife, *f.* stearin soap, common soap.

steatinisch, *a.* tallowy.

Stechapfel, *m.* thorn apple (*Datura*, esp. *D. stramonium*); (*Pharm.*) stramonium.

stechen, *v.t.* stick, prick, pierce, puncture, stab; sting; tap; turn (malt); cut; engrave. —*v.i.* sting; incline; spout, spire.—stechend, *p.a.* stinging, piercing, penetrating, pungent.

Stecher, *m.* something that pierces or is stuck in, as a proof stick (for sugar) or a sampler (of various kinds); engraver; pricker.

Stech-heber, *m.* plunging siphon, thief tube; pipette. -kolben, *n.* pipette. -kunst, *f.* engraving. -palme, *f.* holly; Christ's-thorn (*Paliurus*). -palmenbitter, *n.* ilicin. -pipette, *f.* (ordinary) pipette. -probe, *f.* touchstone test.

Steckdose, *f.* (*Elec.*) plug.

stecken, *v.i.* stick, stay, remain; hide.—*v.t.* stick, set, fix, put.— — bleiben, be stuck, break down.

Stecker, *m.* (*Elec.*) plug.

Stecknadel, *f.* pin.

Steg, *m.* path; (small) bridge; cross-piece, stay, strap, bar.

Steh-bolzen, *m.* stay bolt. -bütte, *f.* stock tub.

stehen, *v.i.* stand; be; become, fit; be responsible.—stehend, *p.a.* standing, stationary, staple, upright, vertical.

Steh-kölbchen, *n.* small flat-bottomed flask. -kolben, *m.* flat-bottomed flask.

stehlen, *v.t.* steal.

steierisch, *a.* Styrian.

Steiermark, *f.* Styria.

steif, *a.* stiff, rigid, firm; awkward; formal; precise.

**Steife,** *f.* stiffening (starch, glue, size); prop, stay; stiffness.

**steifen,** *v.t.* stiffen; stay, prop.

**Steif-heit,** *f.* stiffness, rigidity. **-leinen,** *n.,* **-leinwand,** *f.* buckram.

**Steifung,** *f.* stiffening, sizing.

**Steig,** *m.* path.

**Steige,** *f.* steps; ladder.

**steigen,** *v.i.* rise, ascend, mount, increase.

**steigern,** *v.t.* raise, increase.

**Steigerohr,** *n.* = Steigrohr.

**Steigerung,** *f.* raising, increase, heightening; comparison (of adjectives, etc.).

**Steig-höhe,** *f.* height of ascent, rise; pitch (of a screw). **-raum,** *m.* (Brewing) unfilled space above the wort. **-rohr,** *n.,* **-röhre,** *f.* ascending or rising tube or pipe.

**Steigung,** *f.* rising, rise, ascent, increase; incline, pitch, gradient.

**steil,** *a.* steep; precipitous.

**Steile,** *f.* steepness; declivity.

**Steilheit,** *f.* steepness, slope.

**Stein,** *m.* stone; rock; brick; (Metal.) matte; (Med.) calculus, concretion.— **— der Weisen,** philosopher's stone.

**Steinabfälle,** *m.pl.* stone chips, spalls.

**steinähnlich,** *a.* stonelike, stony.

**Stein-alaun,** *m.* rock alum. **-arbeit,** *f.* metal smelting; stone work.

**steinartig,** *a.* = steinähnlich.

**Stein-auflösungsmittel,** *n.* solvent for calculus. **-brech,** *m.* saxifrage. **-brecher,** *m.* stone breaker, stone crusher. **-brech-maschine,** *f.* stone crusher, rock crusher. **-bruch,** *m.* quarry. **-bühlergelb,** *n.* barium yellow (barium chromate). **-butter,** *f.* rock butter.

**Steindruck,** *m.* lithography; lithograph. **-farbe,** *f.* lithographic ink. **-kalkstein,** *m.* lithographic limestone.

**steinern,** *a.* stone, of stone.

**Stein-farbe,** *f.* stone color. **-flachs,** *m.* mountain flax, amianthus. **-flasche,** *f.* stoneware bottle. **-frucht,** *f.* stone fruit, drupe. **-grau,** *n.* a gray pigment made from clay slate. **-gries,** **-griess,** *m.* gravel. **-grün,** *n.* terre verte (pigment made from glauconite or celadonite). **-gut,** *n.* (Ceram.) white ware (having a white absorbent body and soft glaze). **-gutgeschirr,** *n.* white ware (articles).

**steinhart,** *a.* hard as stone.

**Steinholz,** *n.* xylolith (magnesia cement mixed with sawdust or the like).

**steinig,** *a.* stony, of stone, rocky.

**Stein-kitt,** *m.* cement for stone. **-klee,** *m.* melilot (Melilotus, esp. M. officinalis); white clover (Trifolium repens). **-kohle,** *f.* mineral coal, coal.

**Steinkohlen-asche,** *f.* coal ashes. **-benzin,** *n.* benzene (or benzol(e), the commercial mixture). **-bergwerk,** *n.* coal mine. **-gas,** *n.* coal gas. **-kampher,** *n.* naphthalene. **-klein,** *n.* slack, culm. **-öl,** *n.* coal-tar oil. **-pech,** *n.* coal-tar pitch. **-schicht,** *f.* coal seam, coal measure. **-schiefer,** *m.* coal-bearing shale. **-schlacke,** *f.* (coal) cinders. **-schwelteer,** *m.* low-temperature coal tar. **-schwelung,** *f.* (low-temperature) carbonization of coal. **-staub,** *m.* coal dust.

**Steinkohlenteer,** *m.* coal tar. **-benzin,** *n.* benzol, benzene. **-blase,** *f.* coal-tar still. **-essenz,** *f.* first light oil. **-farbe,** *f.* coal-tar color. **-kampher,** *m.* naphthalene. **-öl,** *n.* coal-tar oil (leichtes, light oil; schweres, heavy oil). **-pech,** *n.* coal-tar pitch. **-präparat,** *n.* coal-tar preparation, coal-tar product.

**Steinkohlen-verkohlung,** **-verkokung,** *f.* coking of coal, coking. **-zeit,** *f.* Coal Age, Carboniferous.

**Stein-kraut,** *n.* stonecrop (Sedum), also various other plants. **-malz,** *n.* glassy or vitreous malt. **-mark,** *n.* (Min.) lithomarge. **-mehl,** *n.* stone powder. **-meissel,** *m.* stone chisel. **-metz,** *m.* stone mason. **-mörtel,** *m.* hard mortar; concrete; (Portland) cement; badigeon. **-nuss,** *f.* ivory nut. **-obst,** *n.* stone fruit. **-öl,** *n.* petroleum.

**steinölhaltig,** *a.* petroliferous, oil-bearing.

**Stein-pappe,** *f.* roofing fabric, roofing paper or board; carton pierre. **-pech,** *n.* stone pitch (hard pitch); (hard) asphalt. **-pilz,** *m.* Boletus edulis. **-porzellan,** *n.* hard porcelain. **-reich,** *n.* mineral kingdom. **-rösten,** *n.* roasting of the regulus or matte. **-salz,** *n.* rock salt. **-salzlager,** *n.* rock salt bed. **-säure,** *f.* lithic acid (uric acid). **-schlag,** *m.* broken stone. **-schmelzen,** *n.* (Metal.) matte smelting. **-waren,** *f.pl.* stoneware. **-zeit,** *f.* Stone Age. **-zement,** *m.* concrete. **-zeug,** *n.* (Ceram.) stoneware (having a vitreous gray, yellow or brown body).

**steirisch,** *a.* Styrian.

**Stell-.** (Mach.) stay, set-, adjusting, regulating.

**stellbar,** *a.* adjustable; movable.

**Stellbottich,** *m.* (Brewing) fermenting vat; (Dyeing) settling vat.

**Stelle,** *f.* place, spot.

**stellen,** *v.t.* place, put, set; regulate, adjust; standardize; stop, check; supply, furnish; shade (colors).—*v.r.* place oneself, stand, appear; prove, be; pretend to be. **-weise,** *adv.* in spots, in places.

**Stellenzahl,** *f.* position number, specif. atomic number; (Math.) index.

**Stell-hahn,** *m.* regulating cock. **-hefe,** *f.*

pitching yeast. **-mutter,** *f.* adjusting nut.
**-schraube,** *f.* set screw; adjusting screw.

**Stellung,** *f.* placing, etc. (see stellen); position; arrangement; attitude; constellation.

**Stellungsisomerie,** *f.* position isomerism.

**Stell-vertreter,** *m.* deputy, substitute. **-vertretung,** *f.* substitution; proxy. **-vorrichtung,** *f.* adjusting device.

**Stemmeisen,** *n.* chisel.

**stemmen,** *v.t.* prop, support; calk; dam up (water); fell (wood).

**Stempel,** *m.* stamp; stamper, die, punch, pestle; piston; brand, mark; pistil. **-farbe,** *f.* stamping ink. **-marke,** *f.* stamp.

**stempeln,** *v.t.* stamp; mark; prop.

**Stempelzeichen,** *n.* stamp, mark.

**Stengel,** *m.* stalk, stem.

**stengelig,** *a.* stalked; (*Metal.*) spiky.

**Stengelkohle,** *f.* columnar coal.

**Stephanskörner,** *n.pl.* stavesacre seeds.

**Steppdecke,** *f.* quilt.

**steppen,** *v.t.* quilt; stitch.

**sterben,** *v.i.* die; die away.

**sterblich,** *a.* mortal.

**Sterblichkeit,** *f.* mortality.

**Stereochemie,** *f.* stereochemistry.

**stereo-chemisch,** *a.* stereochemical. **-isomer,** *a.* stereoisomeric.

**Stereoisomerie,** *f.* stereoisomerism.

**stereometrisch,** *a.* stereometric.

**Sterilisator,** *m.* sterilizer.

**sterilisieren,** *v.t.* sterilize.

**Sterilisierung,** *f.* sterilization.

**Sterilität,** *f.* sterility.

**sterisch,** *a.* steric, spatial.

**Stern,** *m.* star; asterisk; pupil (of the eye). **-anis,** *m.* star anise. **-bild,** *n.* constellation. **-chen,** *n.* little star; asterisk.

**sternförmig,** *a.* star-shaped, stellate.

**Stern-kunde,** *f.* astronomy. **-rohr,** *n.* telescope. **-saphir,** *m.* star sapphire. **-schnuppe,** *f.* shooting star, meteor. **-warte,** *f.* observatory. **-zeit,** *f.* sidereal time.

**Sterrometall,** *n.* sterro metal.

**stet, stetig,** *a.* continuous; constant; stable.

**Stetigkeit,** *f.* continuity; constancy, steadiness; stability.

**stets,** *adv.* continually, ever, always.

**Steuer,** *f.* tax, duty.—*n.* rudder, helm. **-amt,** *n.* revenue board or office; customhouse.

**steuerfrei,** *a.* duty-free; exempt from taxes.

**Steuermarke,** *f.* revenue stamp.

**steuern,** *v.t.* steer; regulate, control; pay (taxes), contribute.

**Steuerung,** *f.* steering, etc. (see steuern); (*Mach.*) distribution, distributor (also, steering gear).

**Stich,** *m.* prick, puncture, stab; sting; stitch; engraving; shooting pain; thrust, pass; (of

colors) cast, tinge; (*Metal.*) tapping, tapped metal, tap hole.—**im Stiche lassen,** leave in the lurch.

**Stich-auge,** *f.* tap hole. **-eisen,** *n.* (*Metal.*) tapping bar.

**Stichel,** *m.* graver, burin.

**sticheln,** *v.t.* prick, puncture.—*v.i.* stitch; jeer, sneer.

**Stichflamme,** *f.* fine pointed flame.

**stichhaltig,** *a.* proof, valid, sound.

**-stichig.** (with names of colors) **-tinged, -ish.**

**Stich-kultur,** *f.* stab culture. **-loch,** *n.* tap hole. **-pfropf,** *m.* tap-hole plug. **-probe,** *f.* sample at random; sample taken by tapping or piercing; random test; (*Metal.*) assay of tapped metal; (*Brewing*) pricking test.

**sticht,** *pr. 3 sing.* of stechen.

**Stich-wein,** *m.* sample wine. **-wort,** *n.* heading; catchword; password; cue.

**Stick-dampf, -dunst,** *m.* choke damp; suffocating vapor.

**sticken,** *v.i.& t.* choke, suffocate; embroider.

**Stickerei,** *f.* embroidery, fancywork.

**Stick-gas,** *n.* nitrogen gas, nitrogen; carbon dioxide. **-kohlenstoff,** *m.* nitrogen carbide, carbon nitride. **-luft,** *f.* close air; nitrogen. **-oxyd,** *n.* nitric oxide. **-oxydul,** *n.* nitrous oxide. **-stoff,** *m.* nitrogen.

**Stickstoff-.** nitrogen, nitrogenous, nitric, nitrous, nitride of. **-ammonium,** *n.* ammonium nitride.

**stickstoffarm,** *a.* poor in nitrogen.

**Stickstoff-ausscheidung,** *f.* nitrogen separation or elimination. **-benzoyl,** *n.* benzoyl nitride (or azide). **-bestimmung,** *f.* determination of nitrogen. **-bor,** *n.* boron nitride. **-cyantitan,** *n.* titanium cyanonitride. **-dioxyd,** *n.* nitrogen dioxide. **-dünger,** *m.* nitrogenous manure, nitrogenous fertilizer.

**stickstofffrei,** *a.* nitrogen-free, non-nitrogenous.

**Stickstoff-gas,** *n.* nitrogen gas. **-gehalt,** *m.* nitrogen content. **-halogen,** *n.* nitrogen halide.

**stickstoffhaltig,** *a.* containing nitrogen, nitrogenous.

**Stickstoff-kalk,** *m.* = Kalkstickstoff. **-kalomel,** *n.* mercurous azide. **-kalzium,** *n.* calcium nitride. **-kohlenoxyd,** *n.* carbonyl nitride (or azide), carbodiazide. **-lithium,** *n.* lithium nitride. **-magnesium,** *n.* magnesium nitride. **-metall,** *n.* metallic nitride. **-natrium,** *n.* sodium nitride. **-oxyd,** *n.* (any) oxide of nitrogen. **-oxydul,** *n.* nitrous oxide. **-oxydulgas,** *n.* nitrous oxide gas. **-quecksilber,** *n.* mercury nitride. **-quecksilberoxydul,** *n.* mercurous azide.

**stickstoffreich,** *a.* rich in nitrogen, highly nitrogenous.

**Stickstoff-sammler,** *m.* collector of nitrogen, specif. a nitrogen-storing plant (leguminous plant). **-säure,** *f.* nitrogenous acid; specif., hydrazoic acid, hydronitric acid. **-silber,** *n.* silver nitride; fulminating silver. **-silizid,** *n.* nitrogen silicide (silicon nitride). **-titan,** *n.* titanium nitride. **-vanadin,** *n.* vanadium nitride. **-verbindung,** *f.* nitrogen compound. **-wasserstoff,** *m.* hydrogen nitride, nitrogen hydride (specif. the trinitride, HN₃).

**stickstoffwasserstoffsauer,** *a.* of or combined with hydrazoic acid, azide (or hydrazoate) of.

**Stickstoffwasserstoffsäure,** *f.* hydrazoic acid, hydronitric acid. **-phenylester,** *m.* phenyl azide (or hydrazoate).

**Stickstoffzyantitan,** *n.* titanium cyanonitride.

**stickt,** *pr. 3 sing.* of stecken.

**Stickwetter,** *n.pl.* (*Mining*) foul air, choke damp, after-damp.

**stieben,** *v.i.* fly about (like dust), be scattered; drizzle.

**Stief-.** step-.

**Stiefel,** *m.* boot; case, barrel, tube. **-lack,** *m.* shoe polish. **-schwärze, -wichse,** *f.* shoe blacking.

**Stiefmütterchen,** *n.* pansy.

**stieg,** *pret.* of steigen.

**Stiege,** *f.* stairs; ladder; score.

**stiehlt,** *pr. 3 sing.* of stehlen.

**Stiel,** *m.* handle, shaft; stem, stalk. **-pfeffer,** *m.* cubeb(s).

**Stier,** *m.* bull; steer; ox.

**stieren,** *v.i.* stare.

**stiessen,** *pret.* of stossen.

**Stift,** *m.* pin, peg, tack, stud, nail; pencil, crayon; tag; snag, stump; apprentice.— *n.* (philanthropic) foundation; monastery; seminary.

**stiften,** *v.t.* tack; found, establish, make.

**Stift-farbe,** *f.* pencil color, colored crayon, pastel. **-schraube,** *f.* stud bolt, stud.

**Stiftung,** *f.* foundation, endowment.

**Stil,** *m.,* **Stilart,** *f.* style.

**Stilbenchinon,** *n.* stilbenequinone.

**still, stille,** *a.* still, silent, quiet; inanimate; stagnant, dull.—**stille Entladung,** (*Elec.*) silent discharge.—**das Stille Meer,** the Pacific Ocean.

**Stille,** *f.* stillness, etc. (see still).

**stillen,** *v.t.* still, allay, calm; gratify; stop, stay.—**stillend,** *p.a.* calming, allaying, sedative.

**stilllegen,** *v.t.* stop, close, shut down.

**Still-mittel,** *n.* sedative. **-schweigen,** *n.* silence.

**still-schweigend,** *a.* silent, tacit; implied. **-setzen,** *v.t.* stop, close, shut down.

**Stillstand,** *m.* standstill, stop; (*Med.*) stasis.

**stillstehen,** *v.i.* stand still, stop.—**stillstehend,** *p.a.* stationary; stagnant.

**Stillung,** *f.* stilling, etc. (see stillen); (*Med.*) lactation.

**Stillungsmittel,** *n.* sedative.

**Stimm-.** of the voice, vocal; tuning; of votes. **-band,** *n.* vocal chord.

**Stimme,** *f.* voice; vote; (musical) part.

**stimmen,** *v.i.* be in tune; accord, agree; vote. —*v.t.* tune; dispose.

**Stimm-gabel,** *f.* tuning fork. **-recht,** *n.* suffrage, franchise.

**Stimmung,** *f.* tuning, tune, key; mood.

**Stimulantia,** *n.pl.* stimulants.

**stimulieren,** *v.t.* stimulate.

**Stimulierung,** *f.* stimulation.

**Stink-.** stinking, fetid. **-asand, -asant,** *m.* asafetida.

**stinken,** *v.i.* stink, smell foul.—**stinkend,** *p.a.* stinking, fetid, ill-smelling.

**Stink-fluss, -flussspat,** *m.* fetid fluor spar (bituminous fluorite). **-harz,** *n.* asafetida. **-kalk,** *m.* anthraconite (bituminous limestone). **-kohle,** *f.* fetid coal. **-mergel,** *m.* fetid marl (bituminous marl). **-öl,** *n.* fetid oil, specif. animal oil. **-quarz,** *m.* fetid quartz (bituminous quartz). **-raum,** *m.* gas chamber. **-raumprobe,** *f.* gas-chamber test. **-schiefer,** *m.* fetid shale. **-spat,** *m.* = Stinkfluss. **-stein,** *m.* stinkstone (any fetid stone, specif. anthraconite).

**Stippe,** *f.* speck, spot; gravy, sauce.

**stirbt,** *pr. 3 sing.* of sterben.

**Stirn, Stirne,** *f.* forehead, brow.

**Stirn-.** frontal, front. **-fläche,** *f.* face, front. **-rad,** *n.* spur wheel. **-seite,** *f.* front side, front.

**Stirrholz,** *n.* (wooden) stirrer.

**stob,** *pret.* of stieben.

**stöbern,** *v.i.* hunt about, rummage; drift; drizzle.

**stochern,** *v.t.* stir, poke (fire).

**Stöchiometrie,** *f.* stoichiometry.

**stöchiometrisch,** *a.* stoichiometric(al).

**Stock,** *m.* stick, staff; stock; block; trunk, butt, stump; main part, body; story (of a building); mold; (*Brick*) clamp; (*Brewing,* etc.) vat, back.

**stock-.** utterly, entirely. **-blind,** *a.* stone-blind.

**stocken,** *v.i.* stop, slacken, stagnate; curdle; mold; decay; hesitate, falter.

**Stockerz,** *n.* ore in big lumps.

**stockfinster,** *a.* pitch-dark.

**Stock-fisch,** *m.* stockfish (esp. dried codfish). **-fischlebertran,** *m.* cod-liver oil. **-fleck,** *m.* moldy stain, mildew.

**stockfleckig,** *a.* spotted with mold, moldy.

stockig, stöckig, *a.* moldy, musty; stubborn.

Stock-lack, *m.* stick-lac. -lacksäure, *f.* laccaic acid. -punkt, *m.* (*Oils*) solidifying point. -schlacke, *f.* shingling slag.

Stockung, *f.* stopping, etc. (see stocken); stoppage; dry rot.

Stockwerk, *n.* story, floor (of a building); tier.

Stoff, *m.* substance; stuff; matter, material; cloth, fabric; (*Paper*) stuff, pulp. -ableitung, *f.* (*Biol.*) translocation. -ansatz, *m.* (*Biol.*) anabolism. -austausch, *m.* exchange of material. -bildung, *f.* formation of a substance. -brei, *m.* (*Paper*) pulp (mixed with water). -bütte, *f.* (*Paper*) stuff chest. -fänger, *m.* (*Paper*) save-all. -filter, *m.* cloth filter. -gattung, *f.* kind of material, class of substances. -kufe, *f.* (*Paper*) stuff vat. -lehre, *f.* chemistry.

stoff-lich, *a.* material. -los, *a.* immaterial, unsubstantial.

Stoff-menge, *f.* quantity of a substance; amount of material. -mühle, *f.* (*Paper*) stuff engine, hollander. -patent, *n.* patent on a substance. -rahmen, *m.* filter disk. -teilchen, *n.* particle of matter. -verbrauch, *m.* consumption of material. -verwandtschaft, *f.* chemical affinity.

Stoffwechsel, *m.* metabolism; change of substance. -analyse, *f.* metabolism analysis. -grösse, *f.* metabolic rate. -produkt, *n.* product of metabolism. -prozess, -vorgang, *m.* metabolic process.

Stoffzahl, *f.* number of substances.

stöhle, *pret. subj.* of stehlen.

Stollen, *m.* gallery, drift, tunnel; post, prop; cake of butter.

stolpern, *v.i.* stumble; blunder.

stolz, *a.* proud, lofty.

Stolz, *m.* pride, loftiness.

Stomachale, Stomachalmittel, *n.* stomachic.

Stopf-buchse, -büchse, *f.* (*Mach.*) stuffing box. Stöpfel, *m.* stopper, plug, cork.

stopfen, *v.t.* stuff, fill; stop; constipate; darn, mend.—*v.i.* be costive.—stopfend, *p.a.* stuffing, etc.; astringent, styptic.

Stopfen, *n.* stuffing, etc. (see stopfen); stopper, plug, cork.

Stopf-mittel, *n.* (*Med.*) astringent, styptic. -werg, *n.* oakum.

Stoppel, *f.* stubble.

Stöpsel, *m.* stopper, plug, cork. -flasche, *f.* stoppered bottle (or flask). -glas, *n.* stoppered glass. -hahn, *m.* stopper cock, cock stopper. -kasten, *m.* (*Elec.*) resistance box.

stöpseln, *v.t.* stopper, cork, plug.

Stör, *m.* sturgeon.

Storaxharz, *n.* storax resin, storax.

Storch-schnabel, *m.*, -schnabelkraut, *n.* crane's-bill, geranium. esp. herb Robert.

stören, *v.t.* disturb; trouble, derange, annoy; stir, poke.—*v.i.* stir.

störrig, störrisch, *a.* troublesome, refractory.

Störung, *f.* disturbance; perturbation; trouble, derangement, disorder.

störungsfrei, *a.* undisturbed, uninterrupted.

Störungsgleichung, *f.* perturbation equation.

Störzel, *m.* see Kandisstörzel.

Stoss, *m.* impulse, thrust, push, blow, stroke; impact, collision, percussion, shock, jolt, bump; recoil; pile, heap, (of papers) file; joint; blast (of a horn).

Stössel, *m.* pestle; stamper, rammer.

stossen, *v.t.* push, thrust, hit, knock, ram; pound, bray, pulverize; join; slot.—*v.i.* thrust, dash, hit (at, against, or upon); (of boiling liquids) bump, knock; recoil.

Stösser, *m.* pestle; rammer, pounder, knocker.

Stoss-fänger, *m.* pressure equalizer, shock absorber. -ionisation, *f.* ionization by collision. -kette, *f.* chain (or succession) of collisions. -punkt, *m.* point of impact. -querschnitt, *m.* collision area.

stösst, *pr. 3 sing.* of stossen.

stossweise, *adv.* by starts or jolts, jerkily; percussively.

Stoss-welle, *f.* percussion wave. -zahl, *f.* number of collisions. -zünder, *m.* percussion fuse.

stottern, *v.i.* stutter.

Str., *abbrev.* (Strasse) street, St.

stracks, *adv.* straightway.

Strafe, *f.* punishment; penalty, fine.

strafen, *v.t.* punish; fine; rebuke.

straff, *a.* stretched, tight, tense, taut.

straffen, *v.t.* tighten, stretch.

Straffheit, *f.* tightness, tenseness, tension.

Strafgeld, *n.* fine; forfeit.

sträflich, *a.* criminal, wrong.

straflos, *a.* unpunished; innocent.

Strahl, *m.* ray; jet (of liquid or gas); flash (of lightning); (*Geom.*) straight line, radius. -α-—, α-ray, alpha ray; β-—, β-ray, beta ray; etc.

Strahl-apparat, *m.* jet apparatus (as a steam-jet injector, pump, or blower). -asbest, *m.* plumose asbestos. -baryt, *m.* radiated barite, Bologna stone. -blende, *f.* a variety of sphalerite.

strahlen, *v.i.* emit rays, radiate.—strahlend, *p.a.* radiating, radiant.—β-strahlend, emitting beta rays.—gestrahlt, *p.a.* radiated, radiate.

Strahlen-. pertaining to rays or radiation; radiated, radiating; (*Anat.*) ciliary. -art, *f.* kind of ray or rays.

strahlen-artig, *a.* raylike, radiating. -brechend, *p.a.* refracting, refractive.

Strahlen-brechung, *f.* refraction. -brechungsmesser, *m.* refractometer. -bündel, *n.*, -büschel, *m.* pencil of rays. -figur, *f.* radiating figure. -filter, *n.* ray filter.

strahlenförmig, *a.* radiated, radiate.

Strahlen-glimmer, *m.* striated mica. -kegel, *m.* cone of rays. -kupfer, *n.* clinoclasite. -messer, *m.* radiometer; actinometer. -optik, *f.* geometrical optics.

strahlenoptisch, *a.* of or pertaining to geometrical optics.

Strahlen-pilz, *m.* actinomyces. -stein, *m.* = Strahlstein. -werfen, *n.* radiation.

Strahler, *m.* radiator.

Strahlerz, *n.* clinoclasite.

strahlförmig, *a.* raylike.

Strahlgips, *m.* fibrous gypsum.

strahlig, *a.* radiated, in rays; radiant.

Strahl-keil, *m.* belemnite. -kies, *m.* marcasite. -pumpe, *f.* jet pump. -punkt, *m.* radiating point, radiant point. -quarz, *m.* fibrous quartz. -schörl, *m.* radiated tourmaline. -stein, *m.* actinolite; amianthus.

Strahlung, *f.* radiation; radiance.

Strahlungs-druck, *m.* radiation pressure. -vermögen, *n.* radiating power. -wärme, *f.* heat of radiation; radiant heat.

Strahl-wäsche, *f.* washing with a jet. -zeolith, *m.* stilbite.

Strähne, *f.* skein, hank; strand.

stramm, *a.* tight, tense; robust; strict.

Strand, *m.* shore, strand. -nelke, *f.* sea lavender (*Limonium*). -pflanze, *f.* seaside plant, littoral plant.

Strang, *m.* rope, cord; halter; skein.

Strängchen, *n.* small rope; small skein.

strangfarbig, *a.* dyed in the yarn.

Strang-presse, *f.* (*Ceram.*) press for wire cutting; (*Metals*) extruding press. -pressen, *n.* (*Metals*) extrusion.

Strapaze, *f.* hardship, toil.

Strasse, *f.* street; way, road; train (of rolls); strait.

Strassen-bahn, *f.* street railway, tramway. -bau, *m.* road building. -belag, -beleg, *m.* road surface. -beleuchtung, *f.* street lighting. -decke, *f.* street (or road) surface.

stratifizieren, *v.t.* stratify.

sträuben, *v.t.* ruffle up.—*v.r.* bristle up; resist.

straubig, sträubig, *a.* (of wool) rough, coarse; rebellious.

Strauch, *m.* shrub, bush.

strauchartig, *a.* shrublike, shrubby, frutescent.

straucheln, *v.i.* stumble.

Strauss, *m.* bush; tuft, crest, bunch, bouquet; (*Bot.*) thyrsus; combat, strife; ostrich.

Strebe, *f.* stay, strut, brace, prop.

streben, *v.i.* strive, struggle, press; tend.

strebsam, *a.* industrious; aspiring; pushing.

streckbar, *a.* extensible; ductile; malleable.

Streckbarkeit, *f.* extensibility; ductility.

Strecke, *f.* distance, space, stretch, extent; (railway) line; (*Mining*) drift; (*Metal.*) drawing.

strecken, *v.t.* stretch; extend, flatten, spread, draw (metal or thread), roll (metal, glass, etc.); dilute; lay low, lay down.—*v.r.* stretch, spread, extend.—gestrecktes Eisen, wrought iron.—gestreckter Winkel, angle of 180 degrees.

Streckenteilchen, *n.* (*Math.*) linear element.

Strecker, *m.* stretcher; (*Med.*) extensor; (*Glass*) flattener.

Streck-festigkeit, *f.* resistance to stretching, elongation resistance. -grenze, *f.* yield point. -metall, *n.* expanded metal. -mittel, *n.* diluting agent, diluent. -ofen, *m.* (*Glass*) flattening furnace. -stahl, *m.* rolled steel.

Streckung, *f.* stretching, etc. (see strecken); spread.

Streckungsmittel, *n.* diluting agent, diluent.

Streckwerk, *n.* (*Metal.*) rolling mill; rolls.

Streich, *m.* stroke; blow, stripe; trick, prank.

streichbar, *a.* plastic (see also streichen and -bar).

Streichbürste, *f.* paint brush, varnish brush.

Streiche, *f.* spatula.

streichen, *v.t.* stroke, rub; paint, varnish; whet; strike (matches); erase, cancel, knock off; mold (brick or tile); stain or coat (paper); card (wool); scrape (skins); spread (butter).—*v.i.* move, rush, sweep, etc.; rove, roam; (*Mining*) strike, run (in a certain direction).

Streich-farbe, *f.* (*Paper*) staining color. -fläche, *f.* striking surface (for matches), rubber. -holz, -hölzchen, *n.* friction match. -instrument, *n.* stringed instrument. -kasten, *m.* (*Dyeing*) color tub. -kraut, *n.* dyer's rocket. -masse, *f.* friction composition (for matches). -muster, *m.* (*Paper*) stained-paper pattern. -ofen, *m.* reverberatory furnace. -stein, *m.* touchstone; hone. -torf, *m.* pressed peat. -zündhölzchen, *n.* friction match.

Streif, *m.* = Streifen.

streifen, *v.t.* stripe, streak, striate; graze; channel, flute; strip off; touch on.—*v.i.* graze, touch (on); wander, ramble.

Streifen, *m.* band, strip, stripe, stria; streak, vein (in marble, etc.); strap. -spektrum, *n.* band spectrum.

streifig, *a.* streaked, striated, striped, banded.

Streifung, *f.* striping, etc. (see streifen); striation.

Streit, *m.* contest, combat, strife; debate, dispute.

streiten, *v.i.* & *r.* struggle, contend, dispute.

Streitfall, m. matter in dispute, point at issue.

streitig, a. disputed, questionable.

Streitigkeit, f. contest, dispute.

streng, strenge, a. severe, rigorous, harsh, strict.

strengflüssig, a. difficultly fusible, refractory; viscous.

Strengflüssigkeit, f. difficult fusibility, refractoriness; viscosity.

strenggenommen, adv. in a strict sense, strictly speaking.

Strenglot, n. hard solder.

Streu, f. litter.

Streu-. scattering, scattered; strewing; dusting; stray. -blau, n. powder blue.

streuen, v.t. scatter; strew; dust.

Streu-glanz, m. brass powder. -gold, n. gold dust. -gut, n. material to be scattered. -körper, m. scattering body. -kupfer, n. copper rain (particles of copper thrown from the surface of the molten metal). -licht, n. scattered light. -linie, f. scattered line. -pulver, n. powder for strewing or dusting, as insect powder, lycopodium, or (for use against "mustard gas") bleaching powder. -spektrum, n. scattered spectrum. -strahlung, f. scattered radiation.

Streuung, f. scattering; strewing; dusting; (Elec.) leakage; deviation, variation.

Streuungswinkel, m. angle of scattering.

Streu-vermögen, n. scattering power. -welle, f. scattered wave. -wert, m. erratic value. -winkel, m. angle of scattering. -zucker, m. powdered sugar.

strich, pret. of streichen.

Strich, m. stroke; streak; stria; line; dash; graduation; mark; (of wood) grain; train (of powder); batch (of bricks); (of cloth) nap; tract, region; course, direction; flock, brood.

stricheln, v.t. streak; shade, hatch; (of lines) break (at short intervals).

Strich-formulierung, f. formula writing with lines or dashes (to represent bonds). -gitter, n. simple line grating. -kultur, f. streak culture.

strichliert, a. (of a line) broken (- - - -).

Strichpunkt, m. semicolon.

strichpunktiert, a. (of a line) dash-and-dot (— · — · —).

Strick, m. cord, string, line, rope; snare.

stricken, v.t. reticulate, net; knit.

strickförmig, a. cordlike, ropelike; (Anat.) restiform.

stritt, pret. of streiten.

strittig, a. contested, in dispute; questionable.

Stroh, n. straw. -blume, f. everlasting. -dach, n. thatched roof.

stroh-farbig, -farben, a. straw-colored.

Strohflachs, m. raw flax.

strohgelb, a. straw-yellow.

Stroh-halm, m. (a single) straw. -hülse, f. straw envelope or case. -kessel, -kocher, m. (Paper) straw boiler. -papier, n. straw paper. -pappe, f. straw board. -ring, m. straw ring. -stein, m. (Min.) carpholite. -stoff, m. (Paper) straw stuff, straw pulp. -wein, m. straw wine. -zellstoff, m. (Paper) straw pulp. -zeug, n. = Strohstoff.

Strom, m. stream, current, flow; (Elec.) current. -abnehmer, m. (Elec.) brush (also, consumer). -abweichung, f. variation of current. -anzeiger, m. current indicator. -art, f. (Elec.) kind of current. -dichte, -dichtigkeit, f. current density. -durchgang, m. passage of current.

stromdurchflossen, a. current-carrying.

Stromeinheit, f. unit of current.

strömen, v.i. stream, flow, pour.

Strom-entnahme, f. (Elec.) consumption of current. -erzeuger, m. current generator.

stromführend, a. (Elec.) current-carrying, live.

Strom-geschwindigkeʹt, f. velocity of current. -indikator, m. current indicator. -induktion, f. induction of currents, electromagnetic induction. -kreis, m. (Elec.) circuit. -lauf, m. flow of current. -leiter, m. (Elec.) conductor. -leitung, f. (Elec.) conduction.

stromlos, a. (Elec.) without current, dead.

Strom-losigkeit, f. (Elec.) absence of current. -menge, f. (Elec.) amount of current, current strength. -messer, m. current meter; specif., (Elec.) ammeter, amperemeter. -quelle, f. (Elec.) source of current. -regulator, m. current regulator. -richtung, f. direction of current. -schluss, m. (Elec.) circuit closing. -schlüssel, m. (Elec.) key, switch. -schwankung, f. fluctuation of current. -spannung, f. current potential, voltage of a current. -stärke, f. current intensity, current strength. -stoss, m. current pulsation, current impulse. -umkehrer, m. current reverser, commutator. -umkehrung, f. reversal of current.

Strömung, f. streaming, flowing, pouring; current, stream, flow, flood; transpiration (of gases); (magnetic) flux.

Strömungsmesser, m. current meter, flow meter.

Strom-unterbrecher, m. circuit breaker; interrupter. -verbrauch, m. consumption of current. -verlust, m. loss of current. -wandler, m. (Elec.) current transformer. -wechsel, m. (Elec.) alternation. -wechsler, m. (Elec.) commutator. -wender, m. (Elec.) current reverser; specif., commutator. -zeiger, m.

current indicator; specif., ammeter. -zinn, n. stream tin.

Strontian, m. strontia. -erde, f. strontia.

strontianhaltig, a. containing strontia, strontianiferous.

Strontian-salpeter, m. strontium nitrate. -salz, n. strontium salt. -wasser, n. strontia water. -zucker, m. strontium sucrate.

Strontium-gehalt, m. strontium content. -jodid, n. strontium iodide. -salpeter, m. strontium nitrate. -salz, n. strontium salt. -wasserstoff, m. strontium hydride.

Strophant(h)-insäure, f. strophanthinic acid. -säure, f. strophanthic acid.

strotzen, v.i. swell, swell up, be swollen.

Strudel, m. whirlpool, eddy, vortex.

Struktur, f. structure. -änderung, f. change in structure. -chemie, f. structural chemistry.

strukturell, a. structural.

Struktur-farbe, f. structural color. -formel, f. structural formula.

strukturidentisch, a. structurally identical.

Strukturisomerie, f. structural isomerism.

strukturlos, a. structureless, amorphous.

Strukturveränderung, f. change of structure.

Strumpf, m. stocking; hose; mantle (of a gas burner). -band, n. garter. -waren, f.pl. hosiery.

Strunk, m. stump, trunk, stalk, stock.

struppig, a. bristly, shaggy, rough.

Stubbfett, n. stubb fat.

Stube, f. room, apartment.

Stuccatur, f., Stuck, m. = Stukkatur.

Stück, n. piece; bit, lump, fragment; gun, cannon; (Metal.) bloom.

Stückchen, n. little piece, bit, particle.

Stückenzucker, m. crushed sugar; lump sugar.

Stück-erz, n. lump ore. -färber, m. piece dyer. -färberei, f. piece dyeing.

stückfarbig, a. dyed in the piece.

Stück-färbung, f. piece dyeing; (Micros.) staining in toto, tissue staining. -gewicht, n. (individual) weight.

Stuckgips, m. plaster of Paris (common grade).

Stück-grösse, f. size of piece or lump. -gut, n. gun metal; (pl.) piece goods; parcel, bale.

stückig, a. in pieces, in lumps; lumpy.

Stück-kohle, f. lump coal. -koks, m. lump coke. -lohn, m. piece wages. -metall, n. gun metal.

Stuckmörtel, m. stucco; badigeon.

Stück-ofen, m. high bloomery furnace. -preis, m. piece price, price by the piece. -schlacke, f. lump slag. -waren, f.pl. piece goods.

stückweise, adv. piece by piece, piecemeal; by retail.

Studie, f. study.

studieren, v.t.& i. study.

Studierende, m.& f.pl. students.

Studium, n. study.

Stufe, f. step; stage; degree, rank, grade.— Stufen, pl., (Mercury) poorest ore.

stufenartig, a. step-like, graduated, graded, gradual.

Stufenfolge, f. succession of steps or stages; gradation.

stufenförmig, a. = stufenartig.

Stufen-gesetz, n. law of stages. -gitter, n. echelon grating. -photometer, m. step photometer. -reaktion, f. reaction in stages. -regel, f. = Stufengesetz.

stufenweise, adv. in stages or steps, stepwise; by degrees; gradually.

Stuhl, m. chair, stool, seat; (Med.) stool.

Stuhl-. chair; fecal.

stuhlbefördernd, p.a. aperient, laxative.

Stuhl-gang, m. stool, discharge from the bowels. -zäpfchen, n. suppository.

Stukkatör, Stukkateur, m. stucco worker; plasterer.

Stukkatur, f. stucco work; plastering.

stülpen, v.t. turn upside down (or inside out); put (over or upon).

stumm, a. dumb; mute, speechless, silent.

Stummel, m. stump, stub, end.

stumpf, a. blunt; obtuse; dull.

Stumpf, m. stump.

stumpf-eckig, a. blunt-cornered. -kantig, a. blunt-edged; obtuse-angled.

Stumpf-kegel, m. truncated cone. -schweissung, f. butt welding; upset welding.

stumpfwinklig, a. obtuse-angled.

Stunde, f. hour; lesson.

stünde, pret. subj. of stehen.

stündig, a. of an hour's length, for an hour.

stündlich, a.& adv. hourly.

Stupp f. stupp, mercurial soot.

Stuppeasäure, f. stuppeic acid, stuppeaic acid.

Stuppfett, n. a greasy mixture of hydrocarbons (phenanthrene, pyrene, etc.) obtained in refining stupp.

stürbe, pret. subj. of sterben.

Sturm, m. storm; tumult, alarm, fury. -hut, m. monkshood, aconite.

stürmisch, a. stormy, turbulent; boiling (fermentation).

Sturz, m. plunge, fall, overthrow; failure (in business); waterfall; (Iron) slab, plate. -acker, m. new-plowed land. -blech, n. thin plate iron, (black) sheet iron.

Stürze, f. lid, cover.

stürzen, v.t. hurl, throw, plunge; overturn; dump; plow for the first time; overthrow.— v.r. rush, plunge, dash.—v.i. fall; rush; pour.

Sturzflamme, f. reverberatory flame.

Stürzgüter, *n.pl.* goods loaded in bulk.

Stute, *f.* mare.

Stutenmilch, *f.* mare's milk.

Stützapparat, *m.* supporting apparatus, support.

Stütze, *f.* support, stay, prop.

stutzen, *v.t.* clip, top, crop, trim, curtail.

Stutzen, *m.* (a short piece of tube or pipe serving as an) opening, connection, socket, nipple; a broad cylindrical vessel.

stützen, *v.t.* support, prop, stay.—*v.r.* lean, rest, be based.

Stütz-fläche, *f.* supporting surface. -gewebe, *n.* supporting tissue.

stutzig, *a.* startled, perplexed, nonplussed.

Stütz-mittel, *n.* supporting medium. -punkt, *m.* point of support; bearing surface; fulcrum. -substanz, *f.* supporting substance.

Stutzuhr, *f.* mantle clock.

Styphninsäure, *f.* styphnic acid.

Styrol, *n.* styrene.

s.u., *abbrev.* (siehe unten) see below.

subatomar, *a.* subatomic.

Subchlorür, *n.* subchloride.

Suberinsäure, *f.* suberic acid.

Subhaloid, *n.* subhalide.

subkutan, *a.* subcutaneous.

Sublimat, *n.* sublimate; specif., corrosive sublimate, mercuric chloride.

Sublimationswärme, *f.* heat of sublimation.

sublimierbar, *a.* sublimable.

Sublimierbarkeit, *f.* sublimability.

sublimieren, *v.t.* sublime, sublimate.

Sublimier-gefäss, *n.* sublimation vessel. -ofen, *m.* subliming furnace. -topf, *m.* subliming pot, aludel.

Sublimierung, *f.* sublimation.

Suboxyd, *n.* suboxide.

Subphosphorsäure, *f.* hypophosphoric acid.

Substanz, *f.* substance; matter. -menge, *f.* amount of substance.

Substituent, *m.* substituent; substitute.

substituierbar, *a.* replaceable.

substituieren, *v.t.* substitute.

Substituierung, *f.* substitution.

Substrat, *n.* foundation; substratum, substrate.

subtrahieren, *v.t.* subtract.

Suche, *f.* search.

suchen, *v.t.& i.* seek; look for, want, try.—gesucht, *p.a.* sought for, in demand.

Sucher, *m.* seeker, searcher; (*Optics*) finder; probe.

Such-licht, *n.* searchlight. -spindel, *f.* exploring spindle (to indicate which of a set of hydrometer spindles is to be used).

Sucht, *f.* disease, sickness; epidemic; mania.

Sud, *m.* boiling; brewing, brew, gyle; decoction; (*Dyeing*) mordant.

Süd, *m.* south. -afrika, *n.* South Africa.

südafrikanisch, *a.* South African.

Südamerika, *n.* South America.

Sudan-braun, *n.* Sudan brown. -rot, *n.* Sudan red.

Süden, *m.* south.

Südfrankreich, *n.* Southern France.

Sudhaus, *n.* boiling house (or room); brewing house, brew house.

südlich, *a.* south, southern.—*adv.* south.

Sud-salz, *n.* boiled salt (common salt from boiled-down brine). -seifenbad, *n.* (*Dyeing*) broken soap bath, broken suds.

südwärts, *adv.* southward.

Sud-werk, *n.* brew-house outfit, brewing plant. -wesen, *n.* brewing.

süffig, *a.* palatable; bibulous.

Sukzession, *f.* succession.

sukzessiv, *a.* successive.

Sulf-. sulf-, sulfo-, thio- (see note under Sulfo-). -amidsäure, *f.* sulfamic acid. -aminsäure, *f.* sulfamic acid. -anilsäure, *f.* sulfanilic acid.

sulfantimonig, *a.* thioantimonious, sulfantimonious.

Sulfantimonsäure, *f.* thioantimonic acid, sulfantimonic acid.

sulfarsenig, *a.* thioarsenious, sulfarsenious.

Sulfarsensäure, *f.* thioarsenic acid, sulfarsenic acid.

Sulfat, *n.* sulfate. -ablauge, *f.* sulfate waste liquor.

sulfat-haltig, *a.* containing sulfate, sulfatic. -ieren, *v.t.* sulfate.

Sulfat-ierung, *f.* sulfating. -ion, *n.* sulfate ion.

sulfatisieren, *v.t.* sulfatize.

Sulfat-isierung, *f.* sulfatization. -isierungs-mittel, *n.* sulfatizing agent. -schmelze, *f.* = Schmelzsoda. -schwefel, *m.* sulfur in the form of sulfate, sulfate sulfur. -stoff, *m.* (*Paper*) sulfate pulp. -zellstoff, *m.* sulfate cellulose, sulfate pulp.

Sulf-carbaminsäure, *f.* thiocarbamic acid, specif. β-thiocarbamic acid, HOCSNH₂. -carbanil, *n.* thiocarbanil (phenyl isothiocyanate) -hydrid, -hydrat, *n.* hydrosulfide.

Sulfid, *n.* sulfide; specif., -ic sulfide (cf. Sulfür). -erz, *n.* sulfide ore.

sulfidieren, *v.t.* sulfide, sulfidize.

sulfidisch, *a.* sulfidic, pertaining to or containing sulfide(s).

Sulfidschwefel, *m.* sulfide sulfur.

sulfieren, *v t.* sulfonate.

Sulfieren, *n.,* Sulfierung, *f.* sulfonation.

Sulfin, *n.* sulfonium, sulfine, —SH₃. -farbe, *f.* sulfur dye. -salz, *n.* sulfonium salt, sulfine salt. -säure, *f.* sulfinic acid.

Sulfit, *n.* sulfite. -ablauge, *f.* sulfite waste liquor. -cellulose, *f.* (*Paper*) sulfite pulp.

**-kochung,** f. (*Paper*) sulfite cooking or cook.
**-lauge,** f. sulfite liquor. **-sprit,** m. sulfite spirit, alcohol from sulfite liquor. **-turm,** m. sulfite tower. **-verfahren,** n. sulfite process.
**-zellstoff,** m. sulfite cellulose, sulfite pulp.
**-zellstofffabrikation,** f. manufacture of sulfite cellulose (or pulp).

**Sulfkohlensäure,** f. sulfocarbonic acid (trithiocarbonic acid); thionocarbonic acid (HOCSOH).

**Sulfo-.** sulfo-, thio-. (Preferably, sulfo- is used to designate the sulfonic group, and thio- to denote that sulfur replaces oxygen.) **-azetat,** n. sulfoacetate. **-base, -basis,** f. sulfur base.

**Sulfocyan,** n. thiocyanogen, sulfocyanogen. **-eisen,** n. iron (esp. ferric) thiocyanate. **-kalium,** n. potassium thiocyanate.

**sulfocyansauer,** a. of or combined with sulfocyanic (thiocyanic) acid, sulfocyanate (thiocyanate) of.

**Sulfocyan-säure,** f. sulfocyanic acid (thiocyanic acid). **-verbindung,** f. sulfocyanate (thiocyanate).

**Sulfo-gruppe,** f. sulfo group, sulfonic group. **-harnstoff,** m. sulfourea (thiourea). **-hydrat,** n. hydrosulfide. **-karbolsäure,** f. sulfocarbolic acid. **-kohlensäure, -karbonsäure,** f. sulfocarbonic acid (trithiocarbonic acid, $H_2CS_3$). **-lyse,** f. sulfolysis. **-monopersäure,** f. permonosulfuric acid.

**Sulfoncarbonsäure,** f. sulfonocarboxylic acid, sulfonecarboxylic acid.

**sulfonierbar,** a. capable of being sulfonated.

**sulfonieren,** v.t. sulfonate.

**Sulfon-ierung,** f. sulfonation. **-säure,** f. sulfonic acid. **-säurecarbonsäure,** f. sulfocarboxylic acid, $R''(SO_3H)CO_2H$.

**Sulfo-persäure,** f. persulfuric acid. **-salz,** n. thio salt, sulfo salt. **-säure,** f. sulfo acid (either a sulfonic acid or a sulfacid).

**Sulfozyan,** n. thiocyanogen, sulfocyanogen. See Sulfocyan-.

**Sulfozyanat,** n. sulfocyanate (thiocyanate).

**Sulfthiokohlensäure,** f. thiolthionocarbonic acid (HOCSSH).

**Sulfür,** n. (lower or -ous) sulfide, (formerly) protosulfide.

**sulfurieren,** v.t. sulfonate; sulfurize.

**Sulfuröl,** n. sulfocarbon oil (olive oil extracted from marc, esp. with $CS_2$).

**Sulfürschwefel,** m. sulfur in the form of sulfide.

**Sulph-.** see Sulf-.

**Sulze, Sülze,** f. jelly; gelatin; brine; pickled meat.

**Sulzfleisch,** f. pickled meat.

**sulzig, sülzig,** a. gelatinous.

**Sumbulwurzel,** f. sumbul root, musk root.

**Summa,** f. sum.

**Summand,** m. (*Math.*) term of a sum.

**summarisch,** a. summary.

**Summe,** f. sum, amount.

**summen,** v.i. hum, buzz.—v.t. sum up, add.

**Summen-gleichung,** f. summation equation. **-regel,** f. sum rule, rule of sums. **-satz,** m. principle or law of sums. **-wirkung,** f. combined action or effect.

**Summer,** m. buzzer, vibrator.

**summieren,** v.t. sum up, add.

**Sumpf,** m. swamp, marsh, bog; (*Tech.*) pit, sump. **-eisenstein,** m. bog iron ore. **-erz,** n. bog ore. **-gas,** n., **-luft,** f. marsh gas. **-nelke,** f. purple avens (*Geum rivale*). **-porsch, -porst,** m. = Porsch. **-silge,** f. marsh parsley (*Peucedanum palustre*).

**Sund,** m. sound, strait.

**Sünde,** f. sin.

**Superazidität,** f. hyperacidity.

**superficiell,** a. superficial.

**Super-oxyd,** n. superoxide (peroxide). **-oxydhydrat,** n. hydrated peroxide. **-phosphatschlempe,** f. a fertilizer made by incorporating superphosphate with molasses residue.

**super-ponieren,** v.t. superpose. **-saturieren,** v.t. supersaturate.

**Suppe,** f. soup.

**Supraleitfähigkeit,** f. supraconductivity.

**surren,** v.i. hum, whir, buzz.

**Surrogat,** n. substitute. **-stoff,** m. substitute material; (*Paper*) pulp substitute (for rags).

**suspendieren,** v.t. suspend.

**süss,** a. sweet; (of water) fresh.

**Süssbier,** n. sweet beer.

**Süsse,** f. sweetness.

**süssen,** v.t. sweeten.

**Süsserde,** f. beryllia, glucina (BeO).

**Süssholz,** n. licorice. **-saft,** m. extract of licorice. **-zucker,** m. glycyrrhizic acid.

**Süssigkeit,** f. sweetness; sweets; suavity.

**süsslich,** a. sweetish.

**Süssmandelöl,** n. oil of sweet almonds.

**süsssauerlich,** a. sourish-sweet.

**Süss-stoff,** m. sweet substance; sweetening agent, dulcifier. **-wasser,** n. fresh water. **-wein,** m. sweet wine.

**s.W.,** *abbrev.* (spezifische Wärme) specific heat.

**swl.,** *abbrev.* (sehr wenig löslich) very difficultly soluble.

**s.w.u.,** *abbrev.* (siehe weiter unten) see below.

**Sylvanerz,** n. sylvanite.

**Sylvesterabend,** m. New Year's eve.

**Sylvin,** m. (*Min.*) sylvite. **-säure,** f. sylvic acid (abietic acid).

**Symbiose,** f. symbiosis.

**Symmetrie-achse,** f. axis of symmetry. **-ebene,** f. plane of symmetry.

symmetrisch, *a.* symmetrical, symmetric.
Symmetrisierung, *f.* symmetrization.
sympathetisch, *a.* sympathetic.
Synäresis, *f.* syneresis.
synchron, *a.* synchronous.
Syndikat, *n.* syndicate.   Cf. Konsortium.
Synergismus, *m.* synergism (mutual action).
syntetisch, *a.* synthetic.
Synthese, *f.* synthesis.
synthesieren, *v.t.* synthesize.

synthetisch, *a.* synthetic.
synthetisieren, *v.t.* synthetize, synthesize.
Syringasäure, *f.* syringic acid.
syrup-. see sirup-.
systematisch, *a.* systematic.
s.Z., *abbrev.* (seiner Zeit) in his (or its) time, at that time.
SZ., S.Z., *abbrev.* (Säurezahl) acid number.
szientifisch, *a.* scientific.
szintillieren, *v.i.* scintillate.

# T

**T.,** *abbrev.* (Teil, Teile) part, parts; (Tausend) thousand, (Temperatur) temperature, esp. absolute.

**Tab.,** *abbrev.* (Tabelle) table.

**Tabak,** *m.* tobacco. **-asche,** *f.* tobacco ashes. **-auszug,** *m.* tobacco extract. **-beize,** *f.* sauce (for tobacco). **-blatt,** *n.* tobacco leaf.

**tabakbraun,** *a.* tobacco-brown.

**Tabak-brühe,** *f.* sauce (for tobacco). **-dampf,** *m.* tobacco smoke. **-fabrik,** *f.* tobacco factory. **-kampher,** *m.* nicotianin. **-rauch,** *m.* tobacco smoke. **-saft,** *m.* tobacco juice.

**Tabaks-asche, -auszug,** etc. See Tabakasche, Tabakauszug, etc.

**Tabaschir, Tabaxir,** *m.* tabasheer, tabashir.

**tabellarisch,** *a.* tabular.—*adv.* in tabular form.

**tabellarisieren,** *v.t.* tabulate, tabularize.

**Tabelle,** *f.* table; synopsis.

**Tablette,** *f.* tablet, lozenge.

**Tadel,** *m.* fault; blame; reproof.

**tadel-frei, -los,** *a.* faultless, perfect.

**tadeln,** *v.t.* blame, criticize, reprove.

**Tafel,** *f.* table; plate, slab, tablet; sheet (of metal); cake (of chocolate); pane (of glass); slate; blackboard; chart; index; list.

**tafelartig,** *a.* tabular.

**Tafel-bier,** *n.* table beer. **-blei,** *n.* sheet lead.

**Täfelchen,** *n.* little table, tablet, platelet.

**Tafelfarbe,** *f.* (*Calico*) local color, topical color.

**tafelförmig,** *a.* tabular.

**Tafel-geschirr,** *n.* table service, tableware. **-glas,** *n.* sheet glass.

**tafelig,** *a.* tabular.

**Tafel-lack,** *m.* shellac. **-leim,** *m.* glue in flat pieces. **-messing,** *n.* sheet brass.

**tafeln,** *v.i.* dine, sup, feast.

**täfeln,** *v.t.* floor; wainscot.

**Tafel-öl,** *n.* salad oil, esp. olive oil. **-paraffin,** *n.* cake paraffin. **-quarz,** *m.* tabular quartz. **-salz,** *n.* table salt. **-schiefer,** *m.* roofing slate. **-spat,** *m.* tabular spar, wollastonite. **-wa(a)ge,** *f.* counter scales; platform scales.

**Taffet, Taft,** *m.* taffeta.

**Taftpapier,** *n.* satin paper.

**Tag,** *m.* day.

**Tage-bau,** *m.* open working. **-blatt,** *n.* daily paper. **-buch,** *n.* diary, journal.

**tagelang,** *adv.* the day long, for days.

**Tage-lohn,** *m.* daily wages, day's wages. **-löhner,** *m.* day laborer.

**tagen,** *v.i.* dawn; (of assemblies) sit.

**Tages-frage,** *f.* question of the day. **-licht,** *n.* daylight. **-preis,** *m.* current price. **-zeit,** *f.* daytime; hour of the day.

**täglich,** *a.* daily, diurnal, quotidian.

**tagtäglich,** *a.* daily, everyday.

**Tagung,** *f.* session, sitting.

**Tagwasser,** *n.* surface water.

**Takt,** *m.* (musical) time, measure; tact; (*Mach.*) stroke.

**Tal,** *n.* valley.

**Taler,** *m.* thaler (now three marks).

**Talg,** *m.* tallow; (solid) fat, grease; suet; (*Anat.*) sebum.

**talgähnlich,** *a.* tallowlike; sebaceous.

**Talgart,** *f.* (variety of) tallow or solid fat.

**talgartig,** *a.* tallowy; (*Anat.*) sebaceous.

**Talg-baum,** *m.* tallow tree. **-brot,** *n.* tallow cake. **-drüse,** *f.* sebaceous gland.

**talgen,** *v.t.* tallow; grease.

**talggebend,** *a.* yielding tallow or fat, sebiferous.

**Talggrieben,** *f.pl.* tallow cracklings, greaves.

**talghaltig,** *a.* containing tallow or fat, sebaceous.

**talgig,** *a.* tallowy; sebaceous; adipose.

**Talg-licht,** *n.* tallow candle. **-öl,** *n.* tallow oil. **-säure,** *f.* stearic acid. **-schmelzen,** *n.* rendering of suet or tallow. **-seife,** *f.* tallow soap. **-stein,** *m.* soapstone. **-stoff,** *m.* stearin. **-zelle,** *f.* sebaceous cell.

**Talk,** *m.* talc, talcum.

**talkartig,** *a.* talcose, talcous.

**Talk-erde,** *f.* magnesia; magnesite. **-hydrat,** *n.* (*Min.*) brucite.

**talkig,** *a.* talcose, talcous.

**Talk-pulver,** *n.* talcum powder. **-schiefer,** *m.* talcose slate, slaty talc. **-spat,** *m.* magnesite. **-stein,** *m.* soapstone, steatite.

**Talkum,** *n.* talc, talcum.

**Tallöl,** *n.* tall oil, talloel (by-product from chemical wood pulp). **-säure,** *f.* talloleic acid.

**Taloschleimsäure,** *f.* talomucic acid.

**Tamarindenmus,** *n.* tamarind pulp.

**Tambour,** *m.* drum; drummer.

**Tang,** *m.* seaweed.

**tangieren,** *v.t.* touch, be tangent to.

**Tangsäure,** *f.* tangic acid, tang acid.

**Tankwagen,** *m.* tank car; tank wagon.

**Tanne,** *f.* fir, fir tree (*Abies* species); (loosely) pine.

**Tannen-baum,** *m.* fir tree; pine tree. **-baum-**

334

kristall, *m.* arborescent crystal. **-harz,** *n.* fir resin. **-zapfen,** *m.* fir cone.

**tannieren,** *v.t.* tan; (*Dyeing*) mordant with tannic acid.

**Tannin,** *n.* tannin, tannic acid, specif. gallotannin. **-bleisalbe,** *f.* tannate of lead ointment. **-lösung,** *f.* tannin solution. **-salbe,** *f.* tannin ointment. **-stoff,** *m.* tannic acid, tannin.

**Tantal,** *n.* tantalum. **-erz,** *n.* tantalum ore, specif. tantalite. **-lampe,** *f.* tantalum lamp. **-oxyd,** *n.* tantalum oxide, specif. tantalum pentoxide. **-säure,** *f.* tantalic acid. **-verbindung,** *f.* tantalum compound.

**Tanz,** *m.* dance; brawl, row.

**tanzen,** *v.i.* dance.

**Tapete,** *f.* tapestry, hanging; wallpaper; (*Anat.*) tapetum.

**Tapetenpapier,** *n.* wallpaper.

**tapezieren,** *v.t.* hang with tapestry; paper.

**Tapezierung,** *f.* papering.

**tappen,** *v.i.* grope.

**täppisch,** *a.* clumsy, awkward.

**Tara,** *f.* tare. **-fläschchen,** *n.* small tare bottle or flask.

**Tarierbecher,** *m.* tare cup.

**tarieren,** *v.t.* tare.

**Tarier-granat,** *m.* garnet for taring. **-schrot,** *n.& m.* tare shot. **-stück,** *n.* tare. **-wa(a)ge,** *f.* tare balance.

**tarnen,** *v.t.* camouflage.

**tartarisieren,** *v.t.* tartarize.

**Tartronsäure,** *f.* tartronic acid.

**Tasche,** *f.* pocket; pouch; bin; chamber; (*Med.*) bursa.

**Taschen-ausgabe,** *f.* pocket edition. **-buch,** *n.* pocket book. **-format,** *n.* pocket size. **-krebs,** *m.* common crab. **-lupe,** *f.* pocket lens. **-spiel,** *n.* jugglery. **-tuch,** *n.* pocket handkerchief. **-uhr,** *f.* watch.

**Tasmanien,** *n.* Tasmania.

**Tasse,** *f.* cup; cup and saucer.

**tastbar,** *a.* palpable, tangible.

**Taste,** *f.* (*Mech.*) key.

**tasten,** *v.t.* touch, feel; (*Med.*) palpate.—*v.i.* feel, grope.

**Taster,** *m.* calipers; key; feeler, antenna.

**Tastversuch,** *m.* tentative experiment, preliminary experiment.

**tat,** *pret.* of tun.

**Tat,** *f.* deed, doing, action, act; fact.—**in der —,** in fact, indeed.

**-tät.** a suffix used to form abstract nouns; -ty, -ness.

**Tatbestand,** *m.* matter of fact, facts.

**Täter,** *m.* doer, author, perpetrator.

**tätig,** *a.* active; busy.

**Tätigkeit,** *f.* activity; action; occupation; function.

**tatkräftig,** *a.* energetic.

**tätlich,** *a.* actual; violent.

**tätowieren,** *v.t.* tattoo.

**Tatsache,** *f.* fact.

**tatsächlich,** *a.* actual, real.

**Tatze,** *f.* paw; (*Tech.*) cam.

**Tau,** *m.* dew.—*n.* rope, cord, cable.

**taub,** *a.* deaf; numb; empty, barren.

**Taube,** *f.* pigeon, dove.

**Taubkohle,** *f.* anthracite.

**Tauch-anlage,** *f.* dipping plant; steeping plant. **-bahn,** *f.* penetrating orbit. **-batterie,** *f.* plunge battery. **-beize,** *f.* disinfection by immersion; disinfecting steep. **-element,** *n.* (*Elec.*) plunge cell.

**tauchen,** *v.t.* dip, plunge, immerse, steep.— *v.i.& r.* dive, dip, plunge.

**Taucherkolben,** *m.* (*Mach.*) plunger.

**Tauch-filter,** *n.* immersion filter. **-flüssigkeit,** *f.* dipping fluid. **-korn,** *n.* (*Brewing*) sinker. **-lack,** *m.* dipping varnish. **-zylinder,** *m.* plunge cylinder, plunger (of a colorimeter).

**tauen,** *v.t.* taw (hides).—*v.i.* thaw; dew.

**taugen,** *v.i.* be fit, be good, be of value.

**tauglich,** *a.* good, fit, able.

**tauig,** *a.* dewy.

**Taumel,** *m.* reeling; giddiness; intoxication; transport, frenzy. **-korn,** *n.* darnel (*Lolium temulentum*).

**taumeln,** *v.i.* reel; be giddy; be intoxicated.

**Taupunkt,** *m.* dew point; thaw point.

**Taurochol-salz,** *n.* taurocholate. **-säure,** *f.* taurocholic acid.

**Tauröste,** *f.* dew retting.

**Tausch,** *m.* exchange; barter.

**tauschen,** *v.t.& i.* exchange; barter.

**täuschen,** *v.t.* deceive, delude, cheat.

**Täuschung,** *f.* illusion; delusion, deception.

**Tauschzersetzung,** *f.* double decomposition.

**tausend,** *a.* thousand.

**Tausend-güldenkraut,** *n.* lesser centaury (*Erythraea centaurium*). **-schön,** *n.* daisy.

**tautomer,** *a.* tautomeric.

**Tautomerie,** *f.* tautomerism, tautomery.

**Taxe,** *f.* tax, duty; set price, rate.

**taxieren,** *v.t.* tax; assess; value, appraise.

**Technik,** *f.* technic, technique; technics, arts.

**Techniker,** *m.* technologist, technicist, technician.

**Technikum,** *n.* technical institution.

**technisch,** *a.* technical. **-chemisch,** *a.* technochemical.

**Technolog, Technologe,** *m.* technologist.

**technologisch,** *a.* technological.

**Tee,** *m.* tea. **-öl,** *n.* tea oil.

**Teer,** *m.* tar. **-abscheider,** *m.* tar separator.

**teerartig,** *a.* tarry.

**Teer-asphalt,** *m.* tar asphalt, coal-tar pitch. **-ausscheider,** *m.* tar separator. **-band,** *n.*

tarred tape. **-baum,** *m.* Scotch pine (*Pinus sylvestris*). **-benzin,** *n.* benzene, benzol. **-bestandteil,** *m.* constituent of tar. **-bildung,** *f.* formation of tar. **-bitter,** *n.* picamar. **-brennerei,** *f.* tar factory. **-dampf, -dunst,** *m.* tar vapor, tar fumes. **-destillat,** *n.* tar distillate.

**teeren,** *v.t.* tar.—*v.i.* tar, form tarry matter.

**Teer-fabrikation,** *f.* tar manufacture or production. **-farbe,** *f.,* **-farbstoff,** *m.* coal-tar color, coal-tar dye. **-fettöl,** *n.* fatty tar oil (higher-boiling part of anthracene oil). **-feuerung,** *f.* tar furnace.

**teerfrei,** *a.* tar-free.

**Teer-gas,** *n.* tar gas. **-gehalt,** *m.* tar content. **-hefe,** *f.* tar dregs.

**teerig,** *a.* tarry.

**Teer-kessel,** *m.* tar kettle. **-kocherei,** *f.* tar boiling; tar-boiling plant. **-nebel,** *m.* tar mist. **-öl,** *n.* tar oil, oil of tar, esp. coal-tar oil. **-papier,** *n.* tarred paper, tar paper. **-pappe,** *f.* tar board. **-pech,** *n.* tar pitch. **-prüfer,** *m.* tar tester.

**teerreich,** *a.* rich in tar.

**Teer-rückstand,** *m.* tarry residue; residue from tar. **-satz,** *m.* tar sediment. **-säure,** *f.* tar acid (any phenol from coal tar). **-scheider,** *m.* tar separator. **-schwelapparat,** *m.* apparatus for distilling tar. **-seife,** *f.* tar soap. **-wäsche,** *f.* (*Gas*) tar extraction. **-wäscher,** *m.* tar washer. **-wasser,** *n.* tar water, specif. (*Gas*) ammoniacal liquor. **-werg,** *n.* tarred oakum. **-zahl,** *f.* tar number.

**Teich,** *m.* pond, pool, tank.

**Teig,** *m.* dough; paste.

**teigartig,** *a.* doughy, pasty.

**Teig-farbe,** *f.* paste color. **-form,** *f.* doughy or pasty form, dough, paste.

**teigig,** *a.* doughy, pasty; mellow.

**Teigware,** *f.* an article (*e.g.*, a dye) in paste form; alimentary paste.

**Teil,** *m.* part; portion, division; party.— **zwei Teile,** two thirds; **drei Teile,** three fourths; etc.

**Teil-.** partial; divisional, dividing. **-bande,** *f.* component band.

**teilbar,** *n.* divisible.

**Teilbarkeit,** *f.* divisibility.

**Teilchen,** *n.* small part, particle; (*Math.*) element.—*α-* **—,** alpha particle, α-particle.

**Teildruck,** *m.* partial pressure.

**teilen,** *v.t.* divide; graduate; share, participate in.—*v.r.* divide; share.

**Teiler,** *m.* divider; (*Math.*) divisor.

**teilhaben,** *v.i.* share, take part, partake.

**Teilhaber,** *m.* sharer, participator, partner.

**teil-haft, -haftig,** *a.* sharing, participating. **-teilig.** of . . . parts, **-part, -partite.**

**Teil-kraft,** *f.* (*Mech.*) component force.

**-kurve,** *f.* partial curve. **-nahme,** *f.* participation; sympathy, interest.

**teilnehmen,** *v.i.* take part, participate.

**Teil-niveau,** *n.* partial level. **-reaktion,** *f.* partial reaction.

**teils,** *adv.* in part, partly.

**Teilstrich,** *m.* graduation mark, graduation.

**Teilung,** *f.* division; graduation, scale; partition; sharing.

**Teilungs-ebene,** *f.* plane of division. **-gesetz,** *n.* law of partition. **-koeffizient,** *m.* distribution coefficient. **-zahl,** *f.* dividend. **-zeichen,** *n.* mark of division. **-zustand,** *m.* state of division.

**Teil-verflüssigung,** *f.* partial liquefaction. **-vorgang,** *m.* partial process. **-wand,** *f.* division wall.

**teilweise,** *a.* partial.—*adv.* partially.

**Teilzahl,** *f.* quotient.

**Teïn,** *n.* theine (caffeine).

**Teint,** *m.* complexion.

**Tekholz,** *n.* teakwood.

**Teklubrenner,** *m.* Teclu burner.

**tektonisch,** *a.* tectonic, structural.

**Teller,** *m.* plate (dish); disk; palm (of the hand); seat (of a valve). **-fuss,** *m.* plate-shaped base. **-wäscher,** *m.* plate scrubber. **-zinn,** *n.* plate pewter.

**Tellur,** *n.* tellurium.

**Tellur-.** tellurium, telluric, telluride of. **-alkyl,** *n.* alkyl telluride. **-blei,** *n.* lead telluride, (*Min.*) altaite. **-cyansäure,** *f.* tellurocyanic acid. **-diäthyl,** *n.* diethyl telluride. **-erz,** *n.* tellurium ore.

**tellurführend,** *a.* telluriferous.

**Tellur-glanz,** *m.* tellurium glance (nagyagite). **-gold,** *n.* gold telluride. **-goldsilber,** *n.* gold silver telluride. **-halogen,** *n.* tellurium halide.

**tellurhaltig,** *a.* containing tellurium.

**tellurig,** *a.* tellurous.

**Tellurigsäureanhydrid,** *n.* tellurous anhydride ($TeO_2$).

**tellurisch,** *a.* telluric.

**Tellur-kohlenstoff,** *m.* carbon telluride. **-metall,** *n.* metal(lic) telluride. **-nickel,** *m.* nickel telluride. **-ocker, -ocher,** *m.* (*Min.*) tellurite. **-oxyd,** *n.* tellurium oxide. **-salz,** *n.* tellurium salt, specif. tellurate.

**tellursauer,** *a.* of or combined with telluric acid, tellurate of.

**Tellur-säure,** *f.* telluric acid. **-silber,** *n.* silver telluride. **-silberblei,** *n.* lead silver telluride, (*Min.*) sylvanite. **-silberblende,** *f.* sylvanite; stützite.

**Tellurür,** *n.* (lower or -ous) telluride.

**Tellur-verbindung,** *f.* tellurium compound. **-wasserstoff,** *m.* hydrogen telluride. **-wasserstoffsäure,** *f.* hydrotelluric acid (hydrogen telluride). **-wismut**, *n.* bismuth telluride.

**Temp.,** *abbrev.* of Temperatur.

**Tempel,** *m.* temple.

**Temperatur-änderung,** *f.* change of temperature. **-beobachtung,** *f.* temperature observation. **-einfluss,** *m.* influence of temperature. **-grad,** *m.* degree of temperature. **-grenze,** *f.* temperature limit. **-leitfähigkeit,** *f.* thermal conductivity. **-messer,** *m.* temperature measurer, thermometer, pyrometer. **-messung,** *f.* temperature measurement. **-mittel,** *n.* mean temperature. **-schwankung,** *f.* variation of temperature. **-steigerung,** *f.* rise in temperature. **-überführung,** *f.* heat transfer. **-veränderung,** *f.* change of temperature. **-wechsler,** *m.* heat exchanger. **-zahl,** *f.* temperature coefficient. **-zunahme,** *f.* increase of temperature.

**Temper-erz,** *n.* annealing ore, iron ore for malleable iron. **-guss,** *m.* malleable cast iron; (less often) malleable casting. **-guss- eisen,** *n.* malleable cast iron. **-ierbad,** *n.* tempering bath.

**temperieren,** *v.t.* temper; give (a certain) temperature to.**—temperiert,** *p.a.* tempered; having (a certain) temperature.

**Temper-kohle,** *f.,* temper carbon. **-kohlebildung,** *f.* formation of temper carbon, graphitization. **-mittel,** *n.* (*Metal.*) tempering material, packing.

**tempern,** *v.t.* temper.

**Temper-ofen,** *m.* annealing furnace. **-roheisen,** *n.* malleable pig (iron). **-rohguss,** *m.* unannealed malleable iron. **-stahlguss,** *m* = Temperguss.

**temporär,** *a.* temporary.

**Tenakel,** *n.* filtering frame; (*Printing*) copyholder.

**Tenazität,** *f.* tenacity.

**Tendenz,** *f.* tendency.

**Tenne,** *f.* floor.

**Teppich,** *m.* carpet; rug; tapestry; (table) cover; blanket.

**Terbinerde,** *f.* terbia, terbium oxide.

**Terebinsäure,** *f.* terebic acid.

**Terephtalsäure,** *f.* terephthalic acid.

**Termfolge,** *f.* sequence of terms.

**Termin,** *m.* term; time.

**Term-schema,** *n.* term diagram. **-wert,** *m.* term value.

**ternär,** *a.* ternary.

**Terneblech,** *n.* terneplate.

**Terpen,** *m.* terpene. **-chemie,** *f.* chemistry of the terpenes.

**terpenfrei,** *a.* terpene-free, terpeneless.

**Terpengruppe,** *f.* terpene group.

**Terpentin,** *m.* turpentine. **-alkohol,** *m.* spirits of turpentine. **-art,** *f.* kind or variety of turpentine.

**terpentinartig,** *a.* like turpentine, terebinthine.

**Terpentin-firnis,** *m.* turpentine varnish. **-geist,** *m.* spirits of turpentine (oil of turpentine).

**terpentinhaltig,** *a.* containing turpentine.

**Terpentin-harz,** *n.* turpentine resin. **-öl,** *n.* (oil of) turpentine. **-ölersatz,** *m.* turpentine substitute. **-ölfirnis,** *m.* turpentine varnish. **-pech,** *n.* turpentine pitch. **-salbe,** *f.* turpentine ointment. **-spiritus,** *m.* = Terpentingeist.

**Terpin,** *n.* terpinol, terpin.

**terrestrisch,** *a.* terrestrial.

**tertiär,** *a.* tertiary.

**Tesseral-kies,** *m.* skutterudite; smaltite. **-system,** *n.* (*Cryst.*) isometric system.

**Test,** *m.* test; cupel; test furnace; cupellation furnace; indicator; graphite; molybdenite. **-asche,** *f.* bone ash. **-körper,** *m.* test body, test piece.

**tetanisieren,** *v.t.* tetanize.

**Tetra-borsäure,** *f.* tetraboric acid. **-brom- kohlenstoff,** *m.* carbon tetrabromide. **-chlorkohlenstoff,** *m.* carbon tetrachloride. **-chlorzinn,** *n.* tin tetrachloride. **-eder,** *n.* tetrahedron.

**tetraedrisch,** *a.* tetrahedral.

**Tetra-edrit,** *m.* tetrahedrite. **-fluorkohlenstoff,** *m.* carbon tetrafluoride. **-hexaeder,** *m.* tetrahexahedron.

**Tetrajod-.** tetraiodo-; tetraiodide of. **-koh- lenstoff,** *m.* carbon tetraiodide.

**Tetra-kontan,** *n.* tetracontane. **-kosan,** *n.* tetracosane.

**Tetraoxy-.** (usually) tetrahydroxy-. See Oxy-.

**Tetra-thionsäure,** *f.* tetrathionic acid. **-vanadinsäure,** *f.* tetravanadic acid.

**Tetrinsäure,** *f.* tetrinic acid.

**teuer,** *a.* dear.

**Teuerung,** *f.* dearth, famine.

**Teufe,** *f.* depth.

**Teufel,** *m.* devil.

**Teufels-dreck,** *m.* asafetida. **-wurz,** *f.* aconite (*Aconitum napellus*).

**Textabbildung,** *f.* illustration in the text.

**Textil-seife,** *f.* textile soap. **-veredelung,** *f.* finishing or dressing of textiles. **-waren,** *f.pl.* textile goods.

**Tfl.,** *abbrev.* (Tafel) table.

**Th-.** see also T-.

**Thal,** *n.* valley.

**Thalleio-chin(in),** *n.* thalleioquin. **-chinolin,** *n.* thalleioquinoline.

**Thalli-.** thallic. **-chlorat,** *n.* thallic chlorate. **-chlorid,** *n.* thallic chloride. **-ion,** *n.* thallic ion. **-oxyd,** *n.* thallic oxide. **-salz,** *n.* thallic salt. **-sulfat,** *n.* thallic sulfate.

**Thallium-alaun,** *m.* thallium alum. **-bromür,** *n.* thallous bromide. **-chlorid,** *n.* thallium chloride, specif. thallic chloride. **-chlorür,** *n.* thallous chloride. **-fluorür,** *n.* thallous fluoride. **-hydroxyd,** *n.* thallic hydroxide. **-hydroxydul,** *n.* thallous hydroxide. **-jodür,** *n.* thallous iodide. **-oxyd,** *n.* thallium oxide, specif. thallic oxide. **-oxydul,** *n.* thallous oxide. **-sulfür,** *n.* thallous sulfide. **-verbindung,** *f.* thallium compound.

**Thalliverbindung,** *f.* thallic compound.

**Thallo-.** thallous. **-bromid,** *n.* thallous bromide. **-chlorat,** *n.* thallous chlorate. **-chlorid,** *n.* thallous chloride. **-ion,** *n.* thallous ion. **-jodat,** *n.* thallous iodate. **-salz,** *n.* thallous salt. **-sulfat,** *n.* thallous sulfate. **-verbindung,** *f.* thallous compound.

**Thapsiasäure,** *f.* thapsic acid.

**That, Thatsache,** etc. See Tat, Tatsache, etc.

**Thee,** *m.* tea.

**Theer,** *m.* tar. For compounds see Teer-.

**Theil,** *m.* = Teil.

**Thema,** *n.* theme, subject, topic.

**Theoretiker,** *m.* theorist.

**theoretisch,** *a.* theoretical.

**Theorie,** *f.* theory.

**therapeutisch,** *a.* therapeutic.

**Therapie,** *f.* therapeutics.

**Therme,** *f.* hot spring, thermal spring.

**Thermik,** *f.* heat (as a branch of knowledge).

**thermisch,** *a.* thermal.

**Thermitverfahren,** *n.* thermite process.

**Thermo-analyse,** *f.* thermal analysis. **-chemie,** *f.* thermochemistry. **-chemiker,** *m.* thermochemist.

**thermochemisch,** *a.* thermochemical.

**Thermodynamik,** *f.* thermodynamics.

**thermo-dynamisch,** *a.* thermodynamic. **-elektrisch,** *a.* thermoelectric.

**Thermo-elektrizität,** *f.* thermoelectricity. **-kette,** *f.* thermoelement. **-lyse,** *f.* thermolysis.

**Thermometer-kugel,** *f.* thermometer bulb. **-röhre,** *f.* thermometer tube.

**thermometrisch,** *a.* thermometric.

**Thermo-paar,** *n.* thermocouple. **-säule,** *f.* thermopile.

**These,** *f.* thesis.

**Thiacetsäure,** *f.* thioacetic acid.

**Thier, Thier-.** see Tier, Tier-.

**Thio-ameisensäure,** *f.* thioformic acid. **-antimonsäure,** *f.* thioantimonic acid. **-arsenigsäure,** *f.* thioarsenious acid. **-arsensäure,** *f.* thioarsenic acid. **-äther,** *m.* thio ether. **-carbaminsäure,** *f.* thiocarbamic acid, specif. thiolcarbamic acid, $HSCONH_2$.

**Thiochin-.** thioquin-.

**Thiocyan,** *n.* thiocyanogen. **-kalium,** *n.* potassium thiocyanate.

**thiocyansauer,** *a.* of or combined with thiocyanic acid, thiocyanate of.

**Thiocyan-säure,** *f.* thiocyanic acid, sulfocyanic acid. **-verbindung,** *f.* thiocyanate.

**Thioessigsäure,** *f.* thioacetic acid.

**Thiogenfarbe,** *f.* thiogene dye.

**Thio-germaniumsäure,** *f.* thiogermanic acid. **-harnstoff,** *m.* thiourea. **-kohlensäure,** *f.* thiocarbonic acid, specif. trithiocarbonic acid, $H_2CS_3$.

**Thiolsäure,** *f.* thiolic acid.

**Thiomilchsäure,** *f.* thiolactic acid.

**Thion-farbe,** *f.* thion dye. **-carbaminsäure,** *f.* thionocarbamic acid. **-kohlensäure,** *f.* thionocarbonic acid. **-kohlenthiolsäure,** *f.* thiolthionocarbonic acid (HOCSSH). **-säure,** *f.* thionic acid.

**Thio-phosphorsäure,** *f.* thiophosphoric acid. **-phtalid,** *n.* thiophthalide.

**Thiophten,** *n.* thiophthene.

**Thio-salz,** *n.* thio salt. **-säure,** *f.* thio acid. **-schwefelsäure,** *f.* thiosulfuric acid. **-sulfatlösung,** *f.* thiosulfate solution. **-sulfosäure,** *f.* thiosulfonic acid. **-verbindung,** *f.* thio compound. **-zinnsäure,** *f.* thiostannic acid.

**Thiozyan,** *n.* = Thiocyan.

**Thl.,** *abbrev.* (Theil) part.

**Thln.,** *abbrev.* (Theilen) parts.

**Thomas-eisen,** *n.* Thomas iron. **-flusseisen,** *n.* Thomas low-carbon steel. **-mehl,** *n.* Thomas meal (ground basic slag used as a fertilizer). **-roheisen,** *n.* Thomas pig (iron), basic pig (iron). **-schlacke,** *f.* Thomas slag, basic slag. **-stahl,** *m.* Thomas steel, basic steel. **-verfahren,** *n.* (*Iron*) Thomas process, basic process.

**Thon,** *m.* clay. For compounds see ton-, Ton-.

**Thor,** *n.* thorium; gate.—*m.* fool. **-erde,** *f.* thoria (thorium oxide).

**thorieren,** *v.t.* thoriate.

**Thorium-salz,** *n.* thorium salt. **-verbindung,** *f.* thorium compound.

**Thoroxyd,** *n.* thorium oxide.

**Thran,** *m.* = Tran.

**Thräne,** *f.* tear. For compounds see Tränen-.

**Thujaöl,** *n.* thuja oil.

**thun,** *v.t. & i.* = tun.

**Thür, Thüre,** *f.* door.

**thüringisch,** *a.* Thuringian.

**Thurm,** *m.* = Turm.

**thut,** *pr. 3 sing.* of thun. See tun.

**Thymian,** *m.* thyme. **-kampher,** *m.* thymol. **-öl,** *n.* oil of thyme.

**Thymo-chinhydron,** *n.* thymoquinhydrone. **-chinon,** *n.* thymoquinone. **-hydrochinon,** *n.* thymohydroquinone.

Th_ usnucleinsäure, *f.* thymonucleic acid, th_ us nucleic acid.

Thyrojodin, *n.* thyroiodin (iodothyrin).

tief, *a.* deep; low; (of colors) dark. -blau, *a.* deep blue, dark blue.

Tiefblick, *m.* insight.

t.fbraun, *a.* deep brown, dark brown.

Tief-brunnen, *m.* deep well. -druck, *m.* low pressure; intaglio printing.

Tiefe, *f.* depth, deepness; deep.

Tiefebene, *f.* low plain, lowland.

tiefen, *v.t.* deepen.

Tiefengestein, *n.* plutonic rock.

tief-gelb, *a.* deep yellow. -greifend, *a.* penetrating, thorogoing, radical, deep-seated. -grün, *a.* deep green, dark green.

Tiefkühlung, *f.* low cooling, intense cooling.

tiefliegend, *a.* deep-lying.

Tiefofen, *m.* (*Metal.*) soaking pit.

tief-rot, *a.* deep red. -rund, *a.* concave. -schmelzend, *a.* low-melting. -siedend, *a.* low-boiling. -sinnig, *a.* pensive; profound; melancholy. -stellen, *v.t.* lower.

Tiefstwert, *m.* lowest value.

Tieftemperaturteer, *m.* low-temperature tar.

Tiegel, *m.* crucible; pot, skillet, stewpan. -boden, *m.* bottom of a crucible. -brenner, *m.* crucible maker. -brennofen, *m.* crucible oven. -deckel, *m.* crucible cover (or lid). -einsatz, *m.* crucible charge. -flussstahl, *m.* crucible cast steel. -form, *f.* crucible mold. -formerei, *f.* crucible molding. -futter, *n.* crucible lining. -giesserei, *f.*, -guss, *m.* casting in crucibles.

Tiegelgussstahl, *m.* crucible cast steel, crucible steel. -giessen, *n.* casting of crucible steel.

Tiegel-hohlform, *f.* crucible mold, pot mold. -inhalt, *m.* contents of a (or the) crucible. -ofen, *m.* crucible furnace. -probe, *f.* crucible test. -rand, *m.* rim of a crucible. -stahl, *m.* crucible steel. -trockner, *m.* crucible drier. -untersatz, *m.* crucible stand (or support). -zange, *f.* crucible tongs.

Tier, *n.* animal; beast.

Tier-, animal; veterinary. -arzneimittel, *n.* veterinary remedy. -arzt, *m.* veterinary surgeon.

tierärztlich, *a.* veterinary.

Tier-blase, *f.* bladder of an animal. -bude, *f.* menagerie. -chemie, *f.* animal chemistry. -chen, *n.* animalcule; little animal. -faser, *f.* animal fiber. -fett, *n.* animal fat. -fibrin, *n.* animal fibrin, fibrin. -garten, *m.* zoölogical garden. -gattung, *f.* genus of animals. -gift, *n.* animal poison, venom.

tierisch, *a.* animal; brutish, bestial.

Tier-keim, *m.* animal germ, animal embryo. -kenner, *m.* zoölogist. -kohle, *f.* animal

charcoal. -körper, *m.* animal body. -kreis, *m.* zodiac. -kunde, -lehre, *f.* zoölogy. -leim, *m.* animal glue (or size). -milch, *f.* animal milk. -öl, *n.* animal oil, specif. bone oil. -pflanze, *f.* zoöphyte. -reich, *n.* animal kingdom. -säure, *f.* zoönic (acetic) acid. *Obs.* -schutzverein, *m.* society for the prevention of cruelty to animals. -stoff, *m.* animal substance. -versuch, *m.* experiment on an animal. -zelle, *f.* animal cell.

Tigerauge, *f.* tiger-eye.

Tiglin-aldehyd, *n.* tiglic (or tiglinic) aldehyde, tiglaldehyde. -säure, *f.* tiglic (or tiglinic) acid.

tilgen, *v.t.* destroy, eradicate; cancel, annul; erase, blot out, delete; extinguish (light); pay (debts).

Tilgung, *f.* destruction, etc. (see tilgen).

tingibel, *a.* (*Micros.*) stainable.

tingieren, *v.t.* dye, stain.

Tinktion, *f.* staining or dyeing, tinction.

tinktoriell, *a.* tinctorial.

Tinktur, *f.* tincture.

Tinte, *f.* (writing) ink; tint; pickle, mess.

tintenartig, *a.* like ink, inky.

Tinten-fabrikant, *m.* ink maker. -fass, *n.* inkstand. -fassfeder, *f.* fountain pen. -fisch, *m.* cuttlefish, sepia. -fischschwarz, *n.* sepia (the pigment). -flasche, *f.* ink bottle. -fleck, *m.* ink stain, ink spot. -gummi, *n.* (rubber) ink eraser. -löscher, *m.* blotter. -pulver, *n.* ink powder. -stein, *m.* inkstone. -wein, *m.* tent (a deep red wine).

tintig, *a.* inky.

tippen, *v.t.* strike gently, tap, tip.

Tisane, *f.* ptisan, tisane.

Tisch, *m.* table; (of a microscope) stage. -bier, *n.* table beer. -chen, *n.* little table; tablet. -decke, *f.* table cover, tablecloth. -gerät, -geschirr, *n.* tableware.

Tischler, *m.* joiner, cabinet maker, carpenter. -leim, *m.* joiner's glue, glue.

Tischwein, *m.* table wine.

Titan, *n.* titanium. -chlorid, *n.* titanium chloride, esp. the tetrachloride.

Titaneisen, *n.* titaniferous iron. -erz, *n.* titanic iron ore, ilmenite. -sand, *m.* titaniferous iron sand (a form of ilmenite). -stein, *m.* = Titaneisenerz.

Titan-erz, *n.* titanium ore. -fluorwasserstoffsäure, -flusssäure, *f.* fluotitanic acid.

titanführend, *a.* titaniferous.

Titan-gehalt, *m.* titanium content. -halogen, *n.* titanium halide.

titanhaltig, *a.* containing titanium, titaniferous.

titanig, *a.* titanous.

**titanisch,** *a.* titanic.

**Titan-metall,** *n.* titanium metal. **-nitrid,** *n.* titanium nitride.

**Titanofluorwasserstoffsäure,** *f.* fluotitanous acid.

**Titan-oxyd,** *n.* titanium oxide. **-salz,** *n.* titanium salt.

**titansauer,** *a.* of or combined with titanic acid, titanate of.

**Titan-säure,** *f.* titanic acid. **-säureanhydrid,** *n.* titanic anhydride (TiO₂). **-schwefelsäure,** *f.* titanosulfuric acid. **-stahl,** *m.* titanium steel. **-stickstoff,** *m.* titanium nitride. **-verbindung,** *f.* titanium compound. **-weiss,** *n.* titanium white.

**Titel,** *m.* title. **-blatt,** *n.* title page.

**Titer,** *n.* titer, titre. **-apparat,** *m.* = Titrierapparat. **-flüssigkeit,** *f.* standard solution.

**titern,** *v.t.* titrate.

**Titerstellung,** *f.* establishment of titer, standardization.

**Titrage,** *f.* titration.

**Titrations-verfahren,** *n.* titration method. **-wert,** *m.* titration value.

**Titrier-analyse,** *f.* analysis by titration, volumetric analysis. **-apparat,** *m.* titrating apparatus, volumetric apparatus. **-becher,** *m.,* titrating beaker.

**titrieren,** *v.t.* titrate.

**Titrier-flüssigkeit,** *f.* titrating solution, standard solution. **-geräte,** *n.pl.* titrating apparatus. **-methode,** *f.* titration method, volumetric method. **-säure,** *f.* titrating acid, standard acid.

**Titrierung,** *f.* titration.

**Titriervorrichtung,** *f.* titrating apparatus.

**titrimetrisch,** *a.* titrimetric.

**Tl.,** *abbrev.* (Teil) part.

**Tle.,** *abbrev.* (Teile) parts.

**Tln.,** *abbrev.* (Teilen) parts.

**Tobsucht,** *f.* delirium, raving.

**Tochter,** *f.* daughter.

**Tochter-.** daughter, filial, secondary.

**Tod,** *m.* death.

**todbringend,** *p.a.* deadly, fatal.

**Todes-gabe,** *f.* fatal dose, lethal dose. **-kampf,** *m.* death struggle, agony. **-stoss,** *m.* death blow. **-strafe,** *f.* death penalty; capital punishment.

**tödlich,** *a.* deadly, fatal, lethal.

**todt, todtbrennen,** etc. See tot, totbrennen, etc.

**Toilette(n)seife,** *f.* toilet soap.

**Toilette(n)seifenfabrikation,** *f.* toilet soap manufacture.

**Tokaier,** *m.* Tokay (wine).

**Tolerierung,** *f.* (*Tech.*) tolerance.

**toll,** *a.* mad; crazy, furious, nonsensical.

**Toll-beere, -kirsche,** *f.* belladonna. **-k..t,** *n.* belladonna; stramonium.

**tollkühn,** *a.* foolhardy.

**Tollwut,** *f.* rabies, hydrophobia.

**Tolubalsam,** *m.* balsam of Tolu, tolu.

**Toluchin-.** toluquin-.

**Toluchinon,** *n.* toluquinone.

**Toluol,** *m.* toluene. **-süss,** *n.* saccharin. **-trockenschrank,** *m.* toluene drying closet.

**Tolu-sirup,** *m.* sirup of tolu. **-tinktur,** *f.* tincture of tolu.

**Toluylenrot,** *n.* toluylene red.

**Toluylsäure,** *f.* toluic acid.

**Tomate,** *f.* tomato.

**Ton,** *m.* clay; tone; sound; key; tune; accent; fashion. **-art,** *f.* kind of clay; key; tune; (musical) pitch.

**tonartig,** *a.* clayey, argillaceous.

**Ton-bad,** *n.* toning bath. **-beize,** *f.* (*Dyeing*) red liquor. **-beschlag,** *m.* coat of clay. **-bildnerei,** *f.* ceramics. **-boden,** *m.* clay soil, clay ground. **-brei,** *m.* (*Ceram.*) clay slip. **-decke,** *f.* clay cover.

**toneisenhaltig,** *a.* argilloferruginous.

**Toneisenstein,** *m.* clay ironstone.

**tonen,** *v.t.* (*Photog.*) tone.

**tönen,** *v.i.* sound, ring.—*v.t.* tone, tint; sound.

**Tonerde,** *f.* alumina; argillaceous earth. **-beize,** *f.* (*Dyeing*) red liquor. **-gehalt,** *m.* alumina content.

**tonerdehaltig,** *a.* containing alumina, aluminiferous.

**Tonerde-hydrat,** *n.* hydrate of alumina (aluminum hydroxide). **-kali,** *n.* potassium aluminate. **-metall,** *n.* aluminum. **-natron,** *n.* sodium aluminate. **-präparat,** *n.* alumina preparation.

**tonerdereich,** *a.* rich in alumina, aluminous.

**Tonerde-salz,** *n.* aluminum salt. **-stein,** *m.* alumina brick. **-sulfat,** *n.* sulfate of alumina (aluminum sulfate).

**tönern,** *a.* of clay, clay, clayey, argillaceous.

**tonfarbig,** *a.* clay-colored.

**Ton-filter,** *n.* clay filter. **-gefäss,** *n.* clay vessel, earthenware vessel. **-geschirr,** *n.* pottery, earthenware. **-gips,** *m.* argillaceous gypsum.

**tonhaltig,** *a.* containing clay, argillaceous.

**Tonhöhe,** *f.* (musical) pitch.

**tonig, tonicht,** *a.* clayey, argillaceous.

**Ton-industrie,** *f.* clay industry. **-industrieller,** *m.* clayworker.

**tonisch,** *a.* tonic.

**Tonkabohne,** *f.* tonka bean.

**Ton-kalk,** *m.* argillaceous limestone, argillocalcite. **-kegel,** *m.* clay cone. **-kerze,** *f.* clay filter candle. **-kunst,** *f.* music; phonetics. **-lager,** *n.* clay bed, stratum of clay. **-masse,** *f.* (*Ceram.*) paste. **-mehl,** *n.* clay dust, ground clay. **-mergel,** *m.* clay marl. **-mörtel,** *m.* clay (esp. fireclay) mortar. **-mühle,** *f.* clay mill, pug mill.

**Tönnchen,** *n.* small cask, keg.

**Tonne,** *f.* ton (in Germany now 1000 kilograms); tun, cask, barrel, keg.

**tonnenförmig,** *a.* barrel-shaped.

**Ton-papier,** *n.* tinted paper. **-platte,** *f.* clay plate; earthenware slab. **-prüfung,** *f.* clay testing. **-reiniger,** *m.* (*Ceram.*) stone separator. **-retorte,** *f.* clay retort. **-rohr,** *n.*, **-röhre,** *f.* clay tube, clay pipe. **-rohrkrümmer,** *m.* bent clay pipe, clay elbow. **-sand,** *m.* argillaceous sand. **-sandstein,** *m.* argillaceous sandstone. **-schicht,** *f.* layer or stratum of clay. **-schiefer,** *m.* clay slate, argillite. **-schlamm,** *m.* clay slip. **-schneider,** *m.* pug mill. **-seife,** *f.* aluminous soap. **-speise,** *f.* tempered clay; clay slip; clay mortar. **-stein,** *m.* clay stone. **-steingut,** *n.* (*Ceram.*) high-clay white ware. **-substanz,** *f.* (*Min.*) clay substance, kaolinite; (*Ceram.*) clay body. **-teller,** *m.* clay plate, clay dish (unglazed). **-tiegel,** *m.* clay crucible. **-topf,** *m.* clay pot, earthenware jar. **-waren,** *f.pl.* pottery, earthenware. **-zelle,** *f.* clay cell (unglazed). **-zeugwaren,** *f.pl.* crockery. **-ziegel,** *m.* clay tile. **-zuschlag,** *m.* (*Metal.*) aluminous flux.

**Topas,** *m.* topaz. **-fluss,** *m.* artificial topaz. **-schörlit,** *m.* pycnite (columnar topaz).

**Topf,** *m.* pot; jar, crock; top.

**Töpfchen,** *n.* small pot.

**Topfdeckel,** *m.* pot lid.

**Töpfer,** *m.* potter.

**Töpferei,** *f.* ceramics, pottery.

**Töpfer-erde,** *f.* potter's earth, potter's clay. **-erz,** *n.* potter's ore, alquifou. **-farbe,** *f.* pottery color, ceramic color. **-geschirr,** **-gut,** *n.* pottery.

**töpfern,** *a.* earthen.

**Töpfer-ofen,** *m.* potter's kiln. **-scheibe,** *f.* potter's wheel. **-ton,** *m.* potter's clay. **-ware,** *f.* pottery.

**Topf-giesserei,** *f.* making of crucible steel; casting of pots. **-glasur,** *f.* earthenware glaze, specif. alquifou. **-glühverfahren,** *n.* pot annealing. **-mühle,** *f.* barrel mill. **-rösten,** *n.* pot roasting. **-scherbe,** *f.* potsherd. **-stein,** *m.* potstone, soapstone.

**topisch,** *a.* topical.

**Tor,** *n.* gate.—*m.* fool.

**Torf,** *m.* peat.

**torfartig,** *a.* like peat, peaty.

**Torf-asche,** *f.* peat ashes. **-boden,** *m.* peat soil. **-eisenerz,** *n.* bog iron ore. **-erde,** *f.* peat soil, peat mold. **-gas,** *n.* peat gas. **-geruch,** *m.* peaty odor. **-geschmack,** *m.* peaty taste, flavor of peat.

**torfhaltig,** *a.* containing peat, peaty.

**torfig,** *a.* peaty.

**Torf-kohle,** *f.* peat charcoal. **-koks,** *m.* peat coke. **-lager,** *n.* peat bog; peat yard. **-masse,** *f.* peat. **-mehl,** *n.* powdered peat. **-moos,** *n.* peat moss, specif. sphagnum moss. **-rauchgeschmack,** *m.* flavor of peat smoke. **-staub,** *m.* peat dust. **-teer,** *m.* peat tar.

**Torgummi,** *n.* Bassora gum.

**Torheit,** *f.* folly, foolishness.

**töricht,** *a.* foolish, silly, absurd.

**torquieren,** *v.t.* twist.

**Torsions-festigkeit,** *f.* torsional strength. **-wa(a)ge,** *f.* torsion balance.

**Tort,** *m.* wrong, injury.

**Torte,** *f.* tart; cake.

**tot,** *a.* dead.—**toter Gang,** lost motion.

**totbrennen,** *v.t.* overburn (gypsum, etc.), dead-burn.—**totgebrannt,** *p.a.* overburned, dead-burned, dead.

**töten,** *v.t.* kill; deaden, soften (colors).

**Toten-blume,** *f.* marigold. **-farbe,** *f.* livid color. **-geruch,** *m.* cadaveric odor. **-kopf,** *m.* caput mortuum, specif. colcothar; death's-head.

**Töter,** *m.* killer; murderer; extinguisher.

**tot-gar,** *a.* (*Metal.*) over-refined. **-geboren,** *p.a.* stillborn. **-gebrannt,** *p.a.* see totbrennen. **-gegerbt,** *p.a.* overtanned. **-gekocht,** *p.a.* dead-boiled, overboiled.

**tötlich,** *a.* deadly, mortal, lethal, fatal.

**Tot-mahlen,** *n.* overgrinding, overmilling, (*Paper*) overbeating, deadgrinding. **-punkt,** *m.* dead center.

**totrösten,** *v.t.* dead-roast, dead-burn.

**touchieren,** *v.t.* touch; corrode slightly.

**Tour,** *f.* turn; revolution; round; tour.

**Touren-zahl,** *f.* number of turns or revolutions. **-zähler,** *m.* revolution counter, speed counter.

**Tourill,** *m.* bombonne, tourie (Woulfe bottle used in distilling acids).—*pl.* **Tourills.**

**Tournantöl,** *n.* rank olive oil.

**Toxämie,** *f.* toxemia.

**toxikologisch,** *a.* toxicological. **-chemisch,** *a.* toxicological-chemical.

**toxisch,** *a.* toxic.

**Toxizität,** *f.* toxicity.

**Trabant,** *m.* attendant; (*Astron.*) satellite; (*Spect.*) attendant line, satellite.

**Tracht,** *f.* load; pregnancy; litter (of kittens, etc.); course; costume; fashion.

**trachten,** *v.i.* try, attempt, strive.

**trächtig,** *a.* pregnant.

**Trächtigkeit,** *f.* pregnancy, gestation.

**traf,** *pret.* of treffen.

**Tragant,** *m.* tragacanth. **-gummi,** *n.* gum tragacanth. **-stoff,** *m.* bassorin.

**Trag-bahre,** *f.* handbarrow; stretcher, litter.

-band, n. strap, sling, suspenders, suspensory.

tragbar, a. portable; bearing, productive; wearable; (*Dyeing*) fast to wearing.

träge, a. inert; inactive, sluggish, idle, lazy, slow, dull.

tragecht, a. fast to wearing.

tragen, v.t. bear, carry, support; yield, produce; endure; wear.—v.r. wear; dress.—v.i. carry; be pregnant.

Träger, m. carrier; bearer, supporter, support; girder; wearer.

Trag-fähigkeit, f. buoyancy; bearing strength; capacity; productiveness. -gas, n. buoyant gas, supporting gas.

Trägheit, f. inertia; inertness; laziness, idleness, slowness.

Trägheitsmoment, n. moment of inertia.

Trag-kraft, f. supporting power, carrying capacity. -lager, n. journal bearing.

Tragödie, f. tragedy.

trägt, pr. 3 sing. of tragen.

Trag-weite, f. range; significance. -zapfenreibung, f. journal-bearing friction.

Traktat, m. treatise; tract; treaty.

traktieren, v.t. treat.

Trambahn, f. tramway.

Tran, m. train oil (from any marine animal); (with a prefix) oil; blubber. -brennerei, f.= Transiederei.

Träne, -f. tear.

Tränen-. of tears, lachrymal. -drüse, f. lachrymal gland.

tränenerregend, a. tear-exciting, lachrymatory.

Tränen-flüssigkeit, f. lachrymal fluid. -gas, n. tear gas, lachrymator.

Trangeruch, m. odor of train oil.

tranhaltig, a. containing train oil, oily.

tranig, a. like train oil; greasy.

trank, pret. of trinken.

Trank, m. drink, beverage, potion.

Tränkchen, n. draft, physic.

Tränke, f. watering, water.

tränken, v.t. steep, soak, saturate, impregnate; water; suckle, give to drink.

Tränk-gefäss, n. drinking vessel. -kessel, m. steeping vessel, impregnating vessel. -masse, f. impregnating material.

Tränkung, f. steeping, etc. (see tränken).

Tränkungsmittel, n. steeping agent, steep, impregnating agent.

Tran-leder, n. leather dressed with train oil. -schmiere, f. (*Leather*) daubing. -seife, f. train-oil soap.

Transformator, m. (*Elec.*) transformer.

transformieren, v.t. transform.

Transiederei, f. train-oil boilery, blubber boilery.

Transkörper, m. trans substance.

translatorisch, a. translational.

Transpeck, m. blubber.

Trans-porteur, m. transporter, conveyor. -portflasche, f. carboy; cylinder. -stellung, f. trans position.

Trantrester, m.pl. blubber residue.

Trapez, n. trapezium; trapeze.

Trapezoeder, n. trapezohedron.

Trapp, m. trap (rock).

trappartig, a. of the nature of trap, trappean.

Trappe, f. footstep, footprint; trap; bustard.

trappeln, trappen, v.i. trample, stamp, patter.

Trassbeton, m. trass concrete.

trassieren, v.t. trace, mark out.

Trassmörtel, m. trass mortar.

trat, pret. of treten.

Tratte, f. draft, bill of exchange.

Traube, f. bunch of grapes; grape; cluster, (*Bot.*) raceme.

Traubenabfall, m. husks or marc of grapes.

trauben-ähnlich, -artig, a. like grapes or a bunch of grapes, botryoidal; in clusters, racemose.

Trauben-beere, f. grape. -blei, n. mimetite; pyromorphite. -essig, m. grape vinegar.

traubenförmig, a. of the form of a grape or bunch of grapes, grapelike, botryoidal; (*Bot.*) aciniform, racemose.

Trauben-kern, m. grape seed, grapestone. -kernöl, n. grapeseed oil. -kraut, n. sea wormwood; (mexikanisches) Mexican tea. -lese, f. vintage. -most, m. grape must, must. -saft, m. grape juice.

traubensauer, a. of or combined with racemic acid, racemate of.

Trauben-säure, f. racemic acid. -vitriol, m. copperas (FeSO$_4$·7H$_2$O). -zucker, m. grape sugar (dextrose).

trauen, v.i. trust, rely.—v.t. marry.

Trauer, f. mourning; sorrow. -birke, f. weeping birch.

trauern, v.i. mourn.

Trauerspiel, n. tragedy.

Traufe, f. drip; eaves; gutter, trough.

träufeln, v.i. drip, drop, trickle.—v.t. drop, add dropwise.

Traufwasser, n. rainwater.

traulich, a. intimate, cordial; cozy, snug.

Traum, m. dream.

träumen, v.t.& i. dream.

Träumerei, f. dreaming; reverie; fancy.

traurig, a. sad; melancholy; wretched.

Treber, f. spent residue, draff (as the marc of grapes or spent malt); (*Brewing*) grains. -branntwein, m. marc brandy.

treffen, v.t. hit, strike; find, meet with; take, provide.—v.r. happen.—treffend, p.a. striking, appropriate.

Treffen, n. engagement, battle.

Treffer, m. hit; prize.

trefflich, a. excellent, choice, admirable.

Treffpunkt, m. point of impact or of meeting.

Treib-arbeit, f. cupellation. -asche, f. cupel ashes, bone ash. -brühe, f. (Tech.) old liquor. -eisen, n. white pig iron.

treiben, v.t. drive, propel, impel; cupel; sublime; refine; raise (dough or hides); work, hammer, chase or emboss (metal); force (plants); put forth (leaves); (of occupations) practice, carry on, work at; stimulate, promote.—v.i. drive, drift; shoot, sprout; circulate; ferment; act as a diuretic; (Cement) blow.—getriebenes Eisen, wrought iron.

Treibeofen, m. = Treibofen.

Treiber, m. driver; propeller; (Metal.) refiner.

Treib-haus, n. hothouse. -herd, m. refining hearth or furnace, cupellation furnace. -holz, n. driftwood. -kraft, f. motive power; moving force. -ladung, f. propelling charge. -mittel, n. propellant; (Med.) purgative. -ofen, m. refining furnace; cupelling furnace. -öl, n. motor (fuel) oil. -prozess, m. cupellation. -riemen, m. driving belt. -riss, m. expansion crack. -satz, m. propelling composition. -scherben, m. cupel. -schwefel, m. native sulfur. -sprengstoff, m. propellant. -stoff, m. motor fuel.

trennbar, a. separable; divisible.

trennen, v.t. separate; sever, sunder, divide; resolve, decompose; (Elec.) disconnect. —getrennt, p.a. separated, etc., separate.

Trennung, f. separation, etc. (see trennen).

Trennungs-fläche, f. parting plane; cleavage plane; surface of separation. -gang, m. course or procedure of separation or analysis. -methode, f. method of separation. -mittel, n. means of separation. -strich, m. line of separation. -verfahren, n., -vorgang, m. separation process. -wärme, f. heat of separation or decomposition.

Treppe, f. staircase, stairs.

Treppenabsatz, m. landing.

treppenförmig, a. in the form of stairs, stepped.

Treppen-rost, m. step grate. -stufe, f. step, stair.

Tresor, m. treasury. -stahl, m. a kind of steel for safes.

Trespe, f. brome grass.

Trester, m.pl. residue (as the marc of grapes, the husks of olives, or the remains of blubber after the making of train oil). -branntwein, m. brandy made from the marc of grapes. -wein, m. wine made from the marc of grapes, piquette.

Tret-. treading, tread.

treten, v.i. tread, step, go, pass, enter.—v.t. tread; trample.

Tretgebläse, n. foot bellows, foot blower.

treu, a. true, faithful.

Treue, f. faithfulness, faith, sincerity; uniformity.

Triakisoktaeder, n. triakisoctahedron (trigonal trisoctahedron).

Triakontan, n. triacontane.

Triamido-. triamino-, triamido-. (See Amido-.)

Triazojodid, n. triazoiodide (iodine azide, $N_3I$).

Tribolumineszenz, f. triboluminescence.

Tribüne, f. platform, rostrum; gallery.

Tricarbonsäure, f. tricarboxylic acid.

Trichinoyl, n. triquinoyl.

Trichloressigsäure, f. trichloroacetic acid.

Trichromsäure, f. trichromic acid.

Trichter, m. funnel; hopper; (Biol.) infundibulum; (Founding) gate. -chen, n. small funnel; small hopper. -einlage, f. filter cone.

trichterförmig, a. funnel-shaped, infundibular, infundibuliform.

Trichter-gestell, n. funnel stand. -hals, m. neck of a funnel. -halter, m. funnel holder. -kolben, m. funnel flask.

trichtern, v.t. pour thru a funnel.

Trichter-rohr, n., -röhre, f. funnel tube, tube funnel; funnel pipe. -stativ, n. funnel stand. -stiel, m. funnel stem. -wandungen, f.pl. funnel walls.

Tricyan, n. tricyanogen. -chlorid, n. tricyanyl chloride (cyanuryl chloride). -säure, f. tricyanic acid (cyanuric acid).

trieb, pret. of treiben.

Trieb, m. driving force, impetus; drive; (of beer) life; impulse, inclination; instinct; shoot, sprout; driving, drifting; drove. -kraft, f. motive power, moving force. -malz, n. leavening malt. -mittel, n. leavening agent. -rad, n. driving wheel. -rinde, f. (Bot.) cambium. -salz, n. leavening salt. -schraube, f. (Micros.) coarse adjustment. -stahl, m. pinion steel. -werk, n. machine, machinery, mechanism; motor; gearing; gear; transmission.

triefen, v.i. drop, drip, trickle, water.

trifft, pr. 3 sing. of treffen.

Trift, f. drift; pasture; drove, herd.

triftig, a. weighty, sound, valid; adrift.

Trijod-. triiodo-; triiodide of.

Trikaliumphosphat, n. tripotassium phosphate.

triklin, triklinisch, a. triclinic.

Trikosan, n. tricosane.

Trilit, n. (Expl.) " trilit " (trinitrotoluene).

Trimellit(h)säure, f. trimellitic acid.

Trimesinsäure, *f.* trimesic acid.

trimetrisch, *a.* trimetric.

Trimolybdänsäure, *f.* trimolybdic acid.

trimorph, *a.* trimorphous, trimorphic.

Trimorphie, *f.* trimorphism.

Trinatriumphosphat, *n.* trisodium phosphate.

trinkbar, *a.* drinkable, potable.

Trink-becher, *m.* drinking cup (or glass). -branntwein, *m.* potable spirits.

trinken, *v.t. & i.* drink.

Trink-gefäss, *n.* drinking vessel. -glas, *n.* drinking glass. -wasser, *n.* drinking water, potable water.

Trioxy-. trihydroxy-, trioxy- (see Oxy-).

Tripel, *n.* triplet.—*m.* tripoli.

Tripel-. triple; tripoli.

tripelartig, *a.* like tripoli, tripoline.

Tripel-erde, *f.* tripoli. -phosphat, *n.* triple phosphate. -punkt, *m.* triple point. -salz, *n.* triple salt. -stein, *m.* tripoli stone.

Triphenylsiliziumchlorid, *n.* triphenylsilicon chloride.

triplieren, *v.t.* triple, treble.

Trippel, *m.* tripoli. See Tripel-.

Tripper, *m.* clap, gonorrhea. -gift, *n.* gonorrheal virus.

Trisulfaminsäure, *f.* trisulfamic acid.

Trithionsäure, *f.* trithionic acid.

tritt, *pr. 3 sing.* of treten.

Tritt, *m.* tread, step; footprint, track. -gebläse, *n.* foot bellows, foot blower.

trivial, *a.* trivial; trite.

Trivial-bezeichnung, *f.* common (or popular) designation. -name, *f.* common (or popular) name.

Trizyan-. see Tricyan-.

trocken, *a.* dry.—auf trockenem Wege, in the dry way.

Trocken-. dry; drying. -anlage, *f.* drying establishment or plant. -apparat, *m.* drying apparatus, drier, desiccator. -batterie, *f.* dry battery. -beerwein, *m.* straw wine. -beize, *f.* dry disinfection (as of seeds); dry disinfectant. -bestimmung, *f.* dry determination. -boden, *m.* drying loft. -brett, *n.* drying board. -brikett, *n.* dry-pressed briquet. -chlor, *n.* (*Bleaching*) dry-chemicking. -dampf, *m.* dry steam. -dauer, *f.* duration of drying, drying time. -destillation, *f.* dry distillation. -element, *n.* dry cell. -entgasung, *f.* dry distillation. -extrakt, *m.* dry extract. -farbe, *f.* dry color, pastel color.

Trockene, *f.* dryness.

Trockenfäule, *f.* dry rot.

trockenfest, *a.* resistant to dryness or drying.

Trocken-festigkeit, *f.* resistance to dryness. -filz, *m.* drying felt. -firnis, *m.* siccative varnish, japan. -flasche, *f.* drying bottle;

drying flask. -füllung, *f.* dry filling, specif. (*Elec.*) solid electrolyte. -gefäss, *n.* drying vessel. -gehalt, *m.* dry content, content of solid material. -gehaltsbestimmung, *f.* determination of dry content. -gerüst, *n.* drying frame or rack, hack. -gestell, *n.* drying frame, drying stand. -gewicht, *n.* dry weight. -glas, *n.* drying glass. -gut, *n.* material to be dried. -haus, *n.* drying house. -hefe, *f.* dry yeast. -heit, *f.* dryness; drought. -heitsgrad, *m.* degree of dryness. -kammer, *f.* drying chamber, drying room. -kasten, *m.* = Trockenschrank. -legen, *n.*, -legung, *f.* drainage. -malerei, *f.* pastel painting. -maschine, *f.* drying machine, drier. -mass, *n.* dry measure, -milch, *f.* dried milk, powdered milk. -mittel, *n.* drying agent, drier, siccative, desiccative. -nährboden, *m.* (*Bact.*) desiccated medium. -ofen, *m.* drying oven, drying kiln, dry kiln, drying stove. -öl, *n.* siccative oil, drier. -pistole, *f.* drying pistol. -platte, *f.* drying plate; (*Photog.*) dry plate. -präparat, *n.* dry preparation. -probe, *f.* dry test, dry assay. -puddeln, *n.* dry puddling. -pulver, *n.* drying powder. -raum, *m.* drying room, drying space, drier. -reinigung, *f.* dry cleaning. -riss, *m.* check, crack (due to drying). -rohr, *n.*, -röhre, *f.* drying tube. -rückstand, *m.* dry residue. -schälchen, *n.* drying capsule. -schale, *f.* drying dish. -scheibe, *f.* drying plate. -schleuder, *f.* centrifugal drier. -schrank, *m.* drying closet, drying oven, drying chamber, drier. -schwindung, *f.* shrinkage in drying. -stoff, *m.* drying substance, drier; dry substance. -stube, *f.* drying room, drying stove. -substanz, *f.* dry substance, solid matter; drying agent. -teller, *m.* drying plate, drying dish. -temperatur, *f.* temperature of drying. -treber, *f.* (*Brewing*) dried grains. -trommel, *f.* drying drum, rotary drier. -tunnel, *m.* tunnel drier. -turm, *m.* drying tower; (*Leather*) turret drier. -verfahren, *n.* drying process; dry process. -verlust, *m.* loss on drying. -vorgang, *m.* drying process. -vorrichtung, *f.* drying apparatus or contrivance. -walze, *f.* drying roll, drying roller. -zylinder, *m.* drying cylinder.

Trockne, *f.* dryness.

trocknen, *v.t. & i.* dry, desiccate.—trocknend, *p.a.* drying, siccative, desiccative.—trocknendes Öl, drying oil.

Trockner, *m.* drier.

Trocknis, *f.* dryness.

Trocknung, *f.* drying, desiccation.

Trocknungs-anlage, *f.* drying plant. -gut, *n.* material to be dried. -mittel, *n.* drying agent. -ofen, m.= Trockenofen. -vorlage, f. drying device (placed before or in front).

troff, pret. of triefen.

trog, pret. of trügen.

Trog, m. trough; vat; hod. -apparat, m. trough apparatus, specif. (Elec.) trough battery. -batterie, f. trough battery.

Trögelchen, n. little trough.

Trogstecher, m. (Sugar) stirrer.

T-Rohr, n. T-tube, T-pipe.

Trommel, f. drum; (Anat.) tympanum. -darre, f. drum kiln. -fell, n., -haut, f. drumhead; (Anat.) tympanic membrane. -mischer, m. drum mixer. -mühle, f. drum mill, (Ceram.) Alsing cylinder. -probe, f. (Ceram.) rattler test.

Trompete, f. trumpet; (Anat.) tube.

Trona, f., Tronasalz, n. trona.

Tropäolin, n. (Dyes) tropeolin, tropæolin.

Tropasäure, f. tropic acid.

Tropen, f.pl. tropics. -frucht, f. tropical fruit. -gewächs, n., -pflanze, f. tropical plant.

tropfbar, a. capable of forming drops, liquid. -flüssig, a. liquid.

Tropf-barkeit, f. capability of forming drops, liquidity. -behälter, m. dripping pan, cup, etc. -bernstein, m. liquidambar. -bier, n.= Trubbier. -brett, n. dripping board.

Tröpfchen, n. little drop, droplet. -kultur, f. hanging-drop culture.

Tröpfel, m. drippings, drips. -fett, n. drippings.

tröpfeln, v.i. drop, drip, trickle.

Tröpfel-pfanne, f. dripping pan, dripper. -werk, n. (Salt) graduation house, drying house.

tropfen, v.i. drop; drip, trickle.

Tropfen, m. drop. -bildung, f. drop formation. -flasche, f. dropping bottle.

tropfenförmig, a. drop-shaped, guttiform.

Tropfen-glas, n. dropping glass, dropping tube. -messer, m. drop counter, dropper; burette. -mixtur, f. (Med.) drops. -wasser, n. drip water.

tropfenweise, adv. dropwise, drop by drop.

Tropfenzähler, m. dropping bottle; drop counter, dropper.

Tropf-flasche, f. dropping bottle. -glas, n. dropping glass (a pipette or a dropping bottle). -gläschen, n. small dropping bottle or pipette. -hahn, m. dropping cock; drip cock. -harz, n. resin exuded in drops. -kante, f. (Tin Plate) list. -kasten, m. (Paper) save-all. -rohr, n. dropping tube. -schale, f. dripping dish or basin, drip tray. -schwefel, m. drop sulfur. -stein, m. dripstone.

tropfsteinartig, a. of or like dripstone, stalactitic, stalagmitic.

Tropf-trichter, m. dropping funnel. -wasser, n. drip water. -wässer, n.pl. (Med.) drops. -wein, m. wine leakings, droppings. -zink, n. drop zinc. -zinn, n. drop tin, granulated tin.

tropisch, a. tropical.

Tross, m. baggage, baggage train.

trösten, v.t. comfort, console.

Trotte, f. wine press; bruising mill.

Trottoir, n. sidewalk.

Trotyl, n. trotyl (trinitrotoluene).

trotz, prep. in spite of.

Trotz, m. defiance, scorn, spite.

trotzdem, adv. nevertheless.—conj. notwithstanding.—prep. equal to.

trotzen, v.i. bid defiance (to); be obstinate; be sulky; presume, boast (of).

Trub, m. sediment, dregs; (Wine) cloudiness.

Trubbier, Trübbier, n. beer from the sediment bag.

trübe, a. turbid; muddy, cloudy, dull, (of wine) thick; gloomy, sad.

Trübe, f. turbidity, etc. (see trübe); sludge, slime; (Metal.) pulp; dross.

trüben, v.t. render turbid, trouble; dull, dim, cloud; make gloomy.—getrübt, p.a. troubled, etc., turbid, cloudy, dull, dim, opaque.

Trubsack, m. (Brewing) sediment bag, filter bag.

Trübung, f. rendering turbid, etc. (see trüben); turbidity.

Trübungs-grad, m. degree of turbidity. -punkt, m. turbidity point. -stoff, m. substance causing turbidity.

Trüffel, f. truffle.

trug, pret. of tragen.

Trug, m. deception, fraud. -bild, n. phantom, illusion.

trügen, v.i. be deceitful or deceptive.—v.t. deceive, cheat.

Truhe, f. trunk, chest.

Trümmer, n.pl. fragments; remains; wreck, ruin. -achat, m. brecciated agate. -gestein, n. breccia; conglomerate.

Trunk, m. drink, potion; liquor; draft; drinking.

Trupp, m. troop, band, set, flock, etc.

Truppe, f. troop, body; company, troupe.

Truthahn, m. turkey cock, turkey.

Trutz, m. offensive, offense.

Truxinsäure, f. truxinic acid.

Trypan-blau, n. trypan blue. -rot, n. trypan red.

tryptisch, a. tryptic.

Tschecho-Slowakei, f. Czechoslovakia.

tschecho-slowakisch, a. Czechoslovakian.

T-Stück, n. T-piece, T, tee.

Tubasäure, f. tubaic acid.

Tube, Tübe, f. tube.

**Tuben-.** tubular, tube.
**Tuberkel,** *f.* tubercle.
**Tuberkel-.** tubercle, tubercular.
**Tubulator,** *m.* tubulure, tubulation.
**tubuliert,** *p.a.* tubulated.
**tubulös,** *a.* tubulous, tubular.
**Tubulus,** *m.* tubulure, tubulation; tubule.
**Tubus,** *m.* tube. **-aufsatz,** *m.* tube attachment. **-auszug,** *m.* drawtube. **-röhre,** *f.* (*Micros.*) drawtube. **-träger,** *m.* tube support.
**Tuch,** *n.* cloth; fabric; handkerchief; shawl.
**tuchartig,** *a.* of or like cloth.
**Tuch-fabrik,** *f.* cloth factory, cloth mill. **-färberei,** *f.* cloth dyeing. **-rot,** *n.* cloth red.
**tüchtig,** *a.* capable, skilful, effective, efficient; strong, sound, able.
**Tücke,** *f.* malice, spite.
**tückisch,** *a.* malignant; insidious.
**tuffartig,** *a.* tufaceous.
**Tuff-erde,** *f.* tufaceous earth. **-kalk,** *m.* tufaceous limestone. **-stein,** *m.* tufa, tuff.
**tuffsteinartig,** *a.* tufaceous.
**Tugend,** *f.* virtue.
**tugendhaft,** *a.* virtuous.
**Tülle,** *f.* nozzle, spout; socket.
**Tulpe,** *f.* tulip.
**Tulpenbaum,** *m.* tulip tree.
**tumeszieren,** *v.i.* tumefy, swell.
**tummeln,** *v.t.* exercise, keep moving.—*v.r.* bestir oneself.
**Tummler,** *m.* porpoise; dolphin; tumbler.
**Tümpel,** *m.* pool; (*Metal.*) tymp.
**tun,** *v.t.* do; make, perform; put.—**zu wissen —**, give notice.
**Tun,** *n.* doing, action, conduct.
**Tünche,** *f.* whitewash, parget, plaster.
**tünchen,** *v.t.* whitewash; rough-cast, plaster.
**Tünch-farbe,** *f.* plastering color. **-kalk,** *m.* lime for whitewashing. **-schicht,** *f.* finishing coat (in plastering). **-werk,** *n.* whitewashing, pargeting.
**Tungöl,** *n.* tung oil.
**Tungstein,** *m.* scheelite. **-säure,** *f.* tungstic acid.
**tunken,** *v.t.* dip, steep, soak.
**tunlich,** *a.* practicable, feasible; convenient.
**Tunlichkeit,** *f.* practicability, feasibility; convenience.

**Tupf,** *m.* spot.
**Tüpfel,** *m.* spot, dot, point; pit. **-analyse,** *f.* spot analysis, drop analysis.
**tüpfelig,** *a.* speckled, spotted, dotted, mottled.
**Tüpfelmethode,** *f.* spot method, drop method.
**tüpfeln,** *v.t.* spot, dot, speckle, stipple; test by the spot method.
**Tüpfelprobe,** *f.* spot test, drop test.
**tupfen,** *v.t.* touch, dab, tip, spot, dot.
**Tupfer,** *m.* pledget, tampon; swab.
**Tupfreaktion,** *f.* spot reaction.
**turbinieren,** *v.t.* centrifuge.
**Tür, Türe,** *f.* door.
**Turil(l),** *m.* = Tourill.
**Türkei,** *f.* Turkey.
**Türkis,** *m.* turquoise. **-blau,** *n.* turquoise blue.
**türkisch,** *a.* Turkish.—**türkische Bohne,** scarlet runner.—**türkischer Weizen,** maize.
**Türkischrot,** *n.* Turkey red. **-öl,** *n.* Turkey-red oil.
**Türkisgrün,** *n.* turquoise green.
**Turm,** *m.* tower.
**Turmalin,** *m.* tourmaline. **-zange,** *f.* tourmaline tongs.
**türmen,** *v.t.* pile up.—*v.r.* tower.
**Turmlauge,** *f.* (*Paper*) tower liquor.
**turnen,** *v.i.* practice gymnastics.
**Turnus,** *m.* turn, rotation; cycle.
**Tusch,** *m.*, **Tusche,** *f.* India ink.
**Tuschen,** *n.* painting with India ink; painting with water colors.
**Tuschfarbe,** *f.* water color.
**tut,** *pr. 3 sing.* of tun.
**Tute, Tüte,** *f.* assay crucible (usually a little lead or iron cup with foot); (*Glass*) glass cylinder; paper bag.
**tuten,** *v.i.* toot.
**Tutia,** *f.* (*Zinc*) tutty.
**Tutte,** *f.* = Tute.
**T.W.,** *abbrev.* (Teile(n) Wasser), parts of water.
**Tyndallkegel,** *m.* Tyndall cone.
**Typen-metall,** *n.* type metal. **-molekül,** *n.* type molecule. **-muster,** *n.* standard sample. **-theorie,** *f.* type theory.
**typisch,** *a.* typical.
**Typus,** *m.* type.

# U

u, *abbrev.* (Undichtigkeitsgrad) degree of porosity.

u., *abbrev.* (und) and; (unter) under, among, etc.; (unten) below.

U, *abbrev.* (Umdrehung) revolution.

u.a., *abbrev.* (unter anderen) among others; (und andere) and others.

u.ä., *abbrev.* (und ähnliche) and similar ones.

u.a.a.O., *abbrev.* (und an anderen Orten) and elsewhere.

u.a.m., *abbrev.* (und andere mehr) and others; (und anderes mehr) and so forth, and so on.

u.ä.m., *abbrev.* (und ähnliches mehr) and the like.

u.a.O., *abbrev.* (und andere Orte) and elsewhere; (unter andere Orten) among other places.

übel, *a.* evil, ill, bad.—*adv.* ill, badly.

Übel, *n.* evil, ill; disease; injury; misfortune. -keit, *f.* nausea. -klang, *m.* dissonance.

übelriechend, *p.a.* ill-smelling, foul, fetid.

Übelstand, *m.* disadvantage; nuisance.

üben, *v.t.* practice, exercise, exert.

über, *prep.* over, above, on, upon; across, beyond, by way of; about, concerning.—*adv.* over.

Über-. per-; over-, super-, hyper-, supra-.

überall, *adv.* everywhere, all over; universally.

über-anstrengen, *v.t.* overexert, strain. -antworten, *v.t.* deliver, consign. -äschern, *v.t.* (*Leather*) overlime.

überaus, *adv.* exceedingly, extremely.

über-basisch, *a.* superbasic. -bieten, *v.t.* outbid; outdo, surpass.

Über-bleibsel, *n.* residue, residuum, remainder, remnant. -bleiche, *f.* overbleaching. -blick, *m.* survey, general view, synopsis.

überborsauer, *a.* of or combined with perboric acid, perborate of.

Überborsäure, *f.* perboric acid.

über-brennen, *v.t.* overburn, etc. (see brennen). -bringen, *v.t.* deliver, transmit.

Überbromsäure, *f.* perbromic acid.

über-brücken, *v.t.* bridge over, bridge, span. -chlorsauer, *a.* of or combined with perchloric acid, perchlorate of.

Über-chlorsäure, *f.* perchloric acid. -chromsäure, *f.* perchromic acid.

über-dauern, *v.t.* outlast, survive. -decken, *v.t.* cover over, spread over; overlap.

überdem, *adv.* besides.

überdestillieren, *v.i.* distill over.

überdies, *adv.* besides.

Überdruck, *m.* excess pressure; overprint; (*Calico*) cover printing. -artikel, *m.* (*Calico*) cover-print style.

übereilt, *p.a.* precipitate, premature.

übereinander, *adv.* one upon another.

Übereinander-lagerung, *f.* superposition. -schweissung, *f.* lap weld.

übereinkommen, *v.i.* agree.

Übereinkommen, *n.* agreement.

übereinstimmen, *v.i.* agree; harmonize, correspond.—*v.t.* (*Dyeing*) dye to pattern.— übereinstimmend, *p.a.* agreeing, consistent, concordant, corresponding.

Übereinstimmung, *f.* agreement, conformity, correspondence, harmony.

überelastisch, *a.* hyperelastic.

Über-empfindlichkeit, *f.* hypersensitiveness. -entwicklung, *f.* overdevelopment; (*Biol.*) hypertrophy. -erzeugung, *f.* overproduction.

über-eutektisch, *a.* hypereutectic. -eutektoid, *a.* hypereutectoid. -exponiert, *a.* overexposed.

Überexposition, *f.* overexposure.

über-fahren, *v.i.* drive over, pass over.—*v.t.* convey over, take across; cover. -fallen, *v.t.* fall upon, surprise, overtake. -fangen, *v.t.* (*Glass*) flash, case, plate.

Überfärbeartikel, *m.* (*Calico*) cross-dyed style.

überfärben, *v t.* overcolor, overdye, overstain; cross-dye; top; fill up, pad (cotton warp); dye on a mordant.

Überfärbung, *f.* overdyeing, etc. (see überfärben).

über-faulen, *v.i.* overferment. -fein, *a.* overfine, over-refined. -fetten, *v.t.* (*Soap*) superfat; (*Leather*) overstuff. -feuern, *v.t.* overfire, overheat. -fliessen, *v.i.* overflow. -flügeln, *v.t.* outflank.

Überfluss, *m.* abundance, plenty; superfluity, surplus; overflow.

über-flüssig, *a.* overflowing, waste (water); in excess; superfluous; abundant, plentiful. -fluten, *v.t.* overflow, flood. -formen, *v.t.* (*Ceram.*) mold on an inside mold. -führbar, *a.* convertible, etc. (see überführen). -führen, *v.t.* convert; transport, transfer, convey; convince, convict.

Über-führung, *f.* conversion, etc. (see überführen); transport, transfer. -führungszahl,

f. transference number, transport number.
-fülle, f. excess, repletion, plethora. -füt-
terung, f. overfeeding, forced alimentation.
-gabe, f. surrender; delivery. -gang, m.
transition; passage, crossing; (of colors)
blending, shading off.

Übergangs-farbe, f. transition color. -punkt,
m. transition point. -rohr, n., -röhre, f.
reducing tube or pipe. -stelle, f. place of
transition, transition point. -stufe, f.
transition stage. -temperatur, f. transition
temperature. -zustand, m. transition state.

übergar, a. overdone; (Metal.) over-refined;
(of copper) dry; (of the state of a furnace)
too hot.

über-gären, v.i. overferment; ferment over,
run over in fermenting. -geben, v.t. deliver,
surrender, commit.—v.r. vomit; surrender.
-gehen, v.i. go over, pass over; change, turn;
(of colors) shade; overflow.—v.t. pass over,
overlook, omit.

Übergewicht, n. overweight, extra weight.

über-giessen, v.t. cover (by pouring); (Med.)
irrigate, douche; transfer (by pouring),
transfuse; spill. -gipsen, v.t. plaster, parget.
-glasen, v.t. overglaze, glaze over, glaze.

Über-glasung, f. overglazing, overglaze, glazing, glaze. -glasur, f. overglaze.

übergolden, v.t. gild.

Übergoldung, f. gilding.

übergreifen, v.i. overlap; encroach, infringe.

Überguss, m. covering, etc. (see übergiessen);
that which is poured over; (of sugar) crust,
icing.

übergut, a. above standard; too good.

Überhand-nahme, f., -nehmen, n. prevalence,
too great increase, becoming too powerful.

überhäufen, v.t. overload, overstock.

überhaupt, adv. in general, on the whole, at all.

über-heben, v.t. exempt, excuse.—v.r. overstrain; be conceited, boast. -heizen, v.t.
overheat; superheat.

Überhitze, f. excess heat; waste heat; superheat.

überhitzen, v.t. overheat, superheat.

Überhitzer, m. superheater.

überholen, v.t. overtake, outstrip, pass; overhaul.—überholt, p.a. antiquated.

über-impfen, v.t. inoculate, vaccinate (from
one to another). -irdisch, a. superterres-
trial, heavenly.

Über-jodid, n. periodide. -jodsäure, f. periodic
acid.

über-kalken, -kälken, v.t. overlime. -kalten,
v.t. supercool, undercool.

Über-kaltung, f. supercooling, undercooling.
-kieselung, f. silicification. -kiste, f. outside box or case.

über-klotzen, v.t. (Calico) slop-pad. -kochen,
v.i. boil over.

Über-kohlensäure, f. percarbonic acid. -koh-
lung, f. (Metal.) supercarbonization.

über-kommen, v.t. receive, get; attack, seize.
-kriechen, v.i. creep over. -krusten, v.t.
incrust. -kühlen, v.t. overcool, supercool.
-laden, v.t. overload, overcharge.

Überlagerung, f. superposition, superimposi-
tion.

überlappen, v.t. overlap.—überlappte Schweissung, lap welding.

über-lassen, v.t. leave, give up, abandon.
-lasten, v.t. overload, overburden, overtax.

Überlauf, m. overflow; net profit.

überlaufen, v.i. run over, overflow; desert.
—v.t. run over; annoy.

Überlaufrohr, n. overflow tube (or pipe).

über-leben, v.t. outlive, survive. -legen, v.t.
reflect, consider; lay over.—p.a. superior;
prevalent.

Über-legenheit, f. superiority. -legung, f.
consideration, reflection, deliberation.

über-leiten, v.t. lead over, conduct over, pass
over; transfuse (blood). -lichten, v.t. over-
expose (to light).

Über-lichtgeschwindigkeit, f. velocity greater
than that of light. -lieferung, f. delivery,
transmission; surrender; tradition.

überlöst, a. overgrown (malt).

Übermacht, f. superior force, predominance.

übermangansauer, a. of or combined with permanganic acid, permanganate of.

Über-mangansäure, f. permanganic acid.
-mass, n. excess.

über-mässig, a. excessive. -menschlich, a.
superhuman.

Übermut, m. arrogance; exuberance.

über-nähren, v.t. overfeed. -nehmen, v.t.
accept, receive; take charge of, enter upon;
overcharge.—v.r. overdo; overeat.

Über-osmiumsäure, f. perosmic acid. -oxyd,
n. peroxide. -oxydation, f.=Überoxydie-
rung.

überoxydieren, v.t. peroxidize; overoxidize.

Überoxydierung, f. peroxidation; overoxida-
tion.

über-pflatschen, v.t. (Calico) pad. -phosphor-
sauer, a. of or combined with perphosphoric acid, perphosphate of.

Überphosphorsäure, f. perphosphoric acid.

überpolen, v.t. overpole.

Über-probe, f., -probeweingeist, m. overproof
spirit. -produkt, n. residual product, by-
product. -produktion, f. surplus production; overproduction.

überragen, v.t. surpass, excel; overtop.—
überragend, p.a. surpassing, excelling,
transcendent; overtowering.

überraschen, *v.t.* surprise.—überraschend, *p.a.* astonishing, surprising.

über-reden, *v.t.* talk over, persuade. -reichen, *v.t.* hand over, present, deliver.

Überrest, *m.* residue, remainder; (*pl.*) remains, scraps, waste.

über-rieseln, *v.t.* irrigate. -rosten, *v.i.* become covered with rust. -rösten, *v.t.* overroast, burn.

Überrutheniumsäure, *f.* perruthenic acid.

übersäen, *v.t.* strew.

Übersalpetersäure, *f.* pernitric acid.

übersättigen, *v.t.* supersaturate; surfeit.

Übersättigung, *f.* supersaturation; satiety.

übersauer, *a.* too acid, too sour; (of salts) containing more than two equivalents of acid to one of base, as übersaures oxalsaures Kali, potassium tetroxalate.

übersäuern, *v.t.* overacidify; peroxidize.

Übersäuerung, *f.* overacidification; peroxidation.

über-schäumen, *v.i.* foam over, froth over. -schichten, *v.t.* cover with a layer (as of another liquid); arrange in layers, stratify.

Überschlag, *m.* estimate, calculation; covering, coating; (*Elec.*) flash-over; somersault.

über-schlagen, *v.t.* pass over, omit; estimate, compute.—*v.i.* become lukewarm.—*v.r.* turn a somersault. -schmelzen, *v.t.* superfuse; enamel.

Überschmelzung, *f.* superfusion; enameling.

überschmieren, *v.t.* smear, daub.

Überschneidung, *f.* overlapping (of lines).

über-schreiben, *v.t.* inscribe, head; address (a letter, parcel, etc.). -schreiten, *v.t.* go beyond, overstep; exceed; transgress.

Über-schreitung, *f.* overstepping, exceeding (of a limit or normal point); transgression. -schrift, *f.* inscription, heading; address (of a letter). -schuss, *m.* excess; surplus.

über-schüssig, *a.* excess, in excess, excess of; surplus, remaining. -schwänzen, *v.t.* (*Brewing*) sparge.

Überschwefelblei, *n.* lead persulfide.

überschwefelsauer, *a.* of or combined with persulfuric acid, persulfate of.

Überschwefelsäure, *f.* persulfuric acid.

über-schwellen, *v.t.* (*Leather*) overplump. -schwemmen, *v.t.* overflow, flood. -schwenglich, *a.* exuberant, excessive. -schwimmen, *a.* supernatant. -seeisch, *a.* oversea, transmarine. -sehen, *v.t.* oversee; overlook. -setzen, *v.t.* translate; transport; overcharge; (*Dyeing*) top.

Über-setzung, *f.* translation, etc. (see übersetzen); (*Mach.*) transmission. -sicht, *f.* survey, review; synopsis, summary, abstract; view; insight.

übersichtlich, *a.* easily visible, clear.

Übersichts-spektrum, *n.* general spectrum. -tabelle, *f.* tabular summary.

übersieden, *v.i.* boil over.

Übersieden, *n.* boiling over; (*Brewing*) extra brew.

über-silbern, *v.t.* silver, silver-plate. -sinnlich, *a.* metaphysical, abstract, supersensible. -spannen, *v.t.* overstrain, force; (over)-spread; cover; span. -spannt, *p.a.* overstrained; exaggerated; eccentric.

Überspannung, *f.* overstraining, etc. (see überspannen); (*Elec.*) overvoltage.

über-spinnen, *v.t.* spin over, cover. -sponnen, *p.a.* (of wire, etc.) covered. -springen, *v.i.* jump over, jump across; pass abruptly. —*v.t.* skip, omit; jump over. -spritzen, *v.i.* spurt over.—*v.t.* spray. -sprudeln, *v.i.* bubble over, gush over. -spülen, *v.t.* wash, drench; overflow. -stehen, *v.t.* endure, overcome.—*v.i.* stand over; project, stand out. -stehend, *p.a.* standing over, overlying, (of liquids) supernatant; projecting. -steigen, *v.t.* exceed; surmount.—*v.i.* overflow; mount or step over.

Über-steiger, *m.* overflow (device); siphon. -steiggefäss, *n.* overflow vessel.

überstrahlen, *v.t.* illuminate, irradiate; outshine.

Überstrahlung, *f.* overradiation, overexposure (to radiation).

über-streichen, *v.t.* paint over, coat; apply (color); overspread. -streuen, *v.t.* strew over. -strömen, *v.i.* flow over, overflow. -stürzen, *v.t.&i.* overturn.—*v.r.* hurry; act rashly. -stürzt, *p.a.* precipitate, hasty.

Übersulfid, *n.* persulfide.

über-täuben, *v.t.* deafen; drown (a sound). -teuern, *v.t.* overcharge. -tragbar, *a.* transferable, etc. (see übertragen); infectious (disease). -tragen, *v.t.* transfer; carry (oxygen, etc.); transmit; transport; translate; transcribe; assign (patents, etc.).

Über-trager, -träger, *m.* carrier; transferrer; transmitter; transporter; translator; transcriber. -tragung, *f.* transference, transfer, etc. (see übertragen).

über-treffen, *v.t.* surpass, exceed, excel. -treiben, *v.t.* drive over; distill; sublimate; overdo, exaggerate.

Übertreibkühler, *m.* = Abflusskühler.

über-treten, *v.t.* overstep, transgress.—*v.i.* step over, go over. -trieben, *p.a.* excessive; exaggerated.

Übertritt, *m.* going over, passage.

über-trocknen, *v.t.* overdry. -tünchen, *v.t.* whitewash; plaster; gloss over.

Übervergrösserung, *f.* supplementary magnification; overmagnification.

über-wachen, *v.t.* supervise, superintend; control. -wachsen, *v.t.& i.* overgrow.

Über-wachsung, *f.* overgrowth. -wachung, *f.* control; supervision.

über-wallen, *v.i.* boil over, overflow; heal over. -wältigen, *v.t.* overpower, overcome. -wiegen, *v.t.* outweigh, overbalance. -wiegend, *p.a.* preponderant; overpowering. —*adv.* preponderantly. -winden, *v.t.* overcome; surmount. -wintern, *v.t.* winter, keep thru the winter.

Über-wurf, *m.* overgarment; roughcast. -zahl, *f.* greater number; surplus; excess; odds.

über-zählig, *a.* supernumerary, surplus. -zeugen, *v.t.* persuade, convince.

Über-zeugung, *f.* persuasion, conviction. -zeugungskraft, *f.* persuasive power.

überziehen, *v.t.* cover, coat, line, plate, overlay, incrust; put on, put over.—*v.r.* become covered or coated.

Über-zug, *m.* coating, coat, covering, cover, crust, incrustation, plating, skin, lining. -zugslack, *m.* coating varnish; finishing varnish coat.

Übf., *abbrev.* (Überführung) conversion, etc.

üblich, *a.* customary, usual.

übrig, *a.* over, left, remaining, to spare; superfluous.—im übrigen, =übrigens.

übrigbleiben, *v.i.* remain (over); survive.— übriggeblieben, *p.a.* residual, remaining.

übrigens, *adv.* as for the rest; besides; however.

übriggeblieben, *p.a.* see übrigbleiben.

Übung, *f.* practice; exercise, use; dexterity; routine; discipline.

Übungsbeispiel, *n.* example (for practice).

Uchatiusstahl, *m.* Uchatius steel, direct steel.

u.dergl., *abbrev.* (und dergleichen) and the like.

u.d.f., *abbrev.* (und die folgende) and those following.

u.dgl., *abbrev.* (und dergleichen) and the like.

u.dgl.m., *abbrev.* (und dergleichen mehr) and the like, and so forth.

u.E., *abbrev.* (unseres Erachtens) in our opinion.

Ue-. see Ü-.

u.e.a., *abbrev.* (und einige andere) and some others.

Ueb-. see Üb-.

u.f., u.ff., uff., *abbrev.* (und folgende) and following, *et seq.*

Ufer, *n.* bank, shore, coast, beach.

U-förmig, *a.* U-shaped.

Uhr, *f.* watch; clock; meter; hour, o'clock.

Uhrenöl, *n.* watch oil, clock oil.

Uhr-feder, *f.* watch spring. -glas, *n.* watch glass, (of large sizes) clock glass. -macheröl,

*n.* watchmaker's oil. -werk, *n.* clockwork. -zeigersinn, *m.* clockwise direction.

Ulme, *f.* elm.

Ulmenrinde, *f.* elm bark.

Ulminsäure, *f.* ulmic acid.

Ultramarinfarbe, *f.* ultramarine color.

ultra-mikroskopisch, *a.* ultramicroscopic. -rot, *a.* ultra-red, infra-red.

Ultra-wage, -waage, *f.* ultrabalance. -wasser, *n.* optically empty water.

um, *prep.* round, about, at, for, by.—*adv.* about, over, up, in order to, to.—einen Tag — den andern, every other day.

um-. round, about, over, up, re-, inversely.

umändern, *v.t.* convert, change, alter.

Umänderung, *f.* conversion, change.

umarbeiten, *v.t.* work over, recast; rewrite; work up.

Umbau, *m.* rebuilding, reconstruction.

Umber, *m.*, Umbererde, *f.* umber.

umbiegen, *v.t.* bend round, double back.

umbilden, *v.t.* remodel; transform; reform.

umblasen, *v.t.* blow down.

umbördeln, umbörteln, *v.t.* turn, turn over (all around).

Umbra, Umbraerde, *f.* umber.

umbringen, *v.t.* kill, destroy.

Umdestillation, *f.* redistillation.

umdestillieren, *v.t.* redistill, rectify.

Umdeutung, *f.* reinterpretation.

umdrehen, *v.t.& r.* turn round, rotate, twirl, twist.—umdrehend, *p.a.* rotatory.

Umdrehung, *f.* rotation; revolution; turn.

Umdrehungs-achse, *f.* axis of rotation (or revolution). -bewegung, *f.* rotatory motion. -geschwindigkeit, *f.* speed of rotation (or revolution). -punkt, *m.* center of rotation (or revolution). -richtung, *f.* direction of rotation (or revolution). -zähler, *m.* revolution counter.

Umdruck, *m.* reprint; reprinting. -farbe, *f.* reprinting ink. -papier, *n.* transfer paper.

Umesterung, *f.* interchange of ester radicals.

umfällen, *v.t.* dissolve and reprecipitate.

Umfang, *m.* circumference; circuit, extent, range, compass, radius.

umfangen, *v.t.* embrace; surround.

umfangreich, *a.* extensive, ample, wide.

umfärben, *v.t.* redye.

umfassen, *v.t.* embrace; comprise; span.— umfassend, *p.a.* comprehensive, extensive.

umflechten, *v.t.* twist or weave about.

umformen, *v.t.* transform; remodel.

Umformer, *m.* (*Elec.*) converter, transformer.

Umformung, *f.* transformation, change.

Umfrage, *f.* inquiry.

umfüllen, *v.t.* transfer (liquids); decant; (*Brewing*) re-rack.

**Umgang,** *m.* round, circuit, turn, rotation; convolution; intercourse; society.

**umgänglich,** *a.* sociable.

**umgearbeitet,** *p.a.* worked over, etc. (see umarbeiten).

**umgeben,** *v.t.* surround; inclose.

**Umgebung,** *f.* surrounding(s), environment.

**Umgegend,** *f.* surroundings, vicinity.

**umgehen,** *v.i.* go round, go about; work, be in action; associate; manage, deal.—*v.t.* go round; avoid, evade.

**umgekehrt,** *p.a.* see umkehren.

**umgelegt,** *p.p.* of umlegen.—**umgelegter Hals,** ring neck.

**umgeschmolzen,** *p.a.* see umschmelzen.

**umgestalten,** *v.t.* change, transform; recast, remodel.

**umgestülpt,** *p.a.* overturned, inverted.

**umgewandelt,** *p.a.* see umwandeln.

**umgiessen,** *v.t.* transfer (by pouring); decant; recast.

**Umguss,** *m.* transfer (by pouring); decantation; recasting, recast.

**umher,** *adv.* around, about, here and there.

**umhin,** *adv.* otherwise, but.

**umhüllen,** *v.t.* wrap up, envelop, cover, case.

**Umhüllung,** *f.* covering, wrapping, casing, jacket, envelope.

**u.Mk.,** *abbrev.* (unter dem Mikroskop) under the microscope.

**Umkehr,** *f.* reversal; return; sudden change.

**umkehrbar,** *a.* reversible, invertible, capable of being turned about, over, or inside out.

**Umkehrbarkeit,** *f.* reversibility, invertibility.

**umkehren,** *v.t.* turn round, about, over, or inside out; invert; reverse.—*v.i.* turn round or back, return.—**umgekehrt,** *p.a.* inverted, inverse, reverse, converse; (*adv.*) inversely, conversely.—**umgekehrte Fällung,** reverse precipitation.

**Umkehrung,** *f.* inversion; turning about, etc. (see umkehren).

**umkippen,** *v.t.* overturn, upset.

**umkleiden,** *v.t.* coat; case, jacket; clothe.

**umkochen,** *v.t.* boil.

**umkommen,** *v.i.* perish; spoil.

**Umkreis,** *m.* = Umfang.

**umkreisen,** *v.t.* turn, circle, or revolve around.

**umkristallisieren,** *v.t.* (dissolve and) recrystallize.

**Umkristallisierung,** *f.* (dissolving and) recrystallization.

**umkrücken,** *v.t.* rake, rabble; (*Brewing*) mash.

**Umladung,** *f.* reloading; (*Elec.*) change in potential.

**umlagern,** *v.t.* rearrange; surround, besiege.

**Umlagerung,** *f.* rearrangement; surrounding, besieging.

**Umlauf,** *m.* revolution; rotation; circulation.

**umlaufen,** *v.i.* revolve; rotate; circulate.—*v.t.* run over.

**Umlauf-zahl,** *f.* rotation number. **-zeit,** *f.* time of rotation, revolution period.

**umlegbar,** *a.* reversible; inclinable; hinged.

**umlegen,** *v.t.* change, shift; turn (malt); put round, put on; turn down.

**umlernen,** *v.t.* learn anew, relearn.

**umlösen,** *v.t.* dissolve and allow to crystallize (wihout filtration).

**ummanteln,** *v.t.* jacket, sheathe, case, incase.

**umpacken,** *v.t.* repack; pack all around.

**Umrahmung,** *f.* framing, frame, (*Printing*) box.

**umrechnen,** *v.t.* convert (into), reduce (to).

**Umrechnung,** *f.* conversion, reduction.

**Umrechnungs-faktor,** *m.* conversion factor. **-tafel,** *f.* conversion table.

**umringen,** *v.t.* encircle, surround.

**Umriss,** *m.* outline; sketch.

**umrühren,** *v.t.* stir, stir up, work (with some implement).

**Umrühren,** *n.* stirring, stirring up, specif. (*Iron*) puddling, (*Copper*) poling.

**Umsatz,** *m.* exchange; sale, business. **-produkt,** *n.* product of exchange, specif. metabolism product.

**umschalten,** *v.t.* (also *Elec.*) reverse; (*Elec.*) commutate.

**Umschalter,** *m.* reverser; commutator; switch board.

**Umschaltfeuerung,** *f.* regenerative furnace.

**Umschau,** *f.* survey, review.

**umschaufeln,** *v.t.* turn (as with a shovel), stir.

**umschichtig,** *adv.* in layers; alternately.

**Umschlag,** *m.* cover, covering, wrapper, envelope; sudden change, turn, turning; cataplasm, poultice; sale; hem, facing, collar.

**umschlagen,** *v.t.* wrap about; apply (a poultice); turn over, up, or down; knock down.—*v.i.* turn, change; decompose; overturn, upset.

**Umschlagpapier,** *n.* wrapping paper.

**Umschlags-punkt,** *m.* transition point. **-zahl,** *f.* titration value.

**umschlingen,** *v.t.* wind around, clasp, cling to.

**umschmelzen,** *v.t.* remelt, recast, refound.

**Umschmelzofen,** *m.* remelting furnace.

**Umschmelzung,** *f.* remelting, recasting, refounding.

**umschreiben,** *v.t.* rewrite, transcribe; circumscribe; paraphrase; (*Math.*) describe.

**umschütteln,** *v.t.* shake, shake up, agitate.

**umschütten,** *v.t.* transfer (by pouring); decant.

**Umschweif,** *m.* roundabout way; digression.

**umschwenken,** *v.t.* turn round, rotate.

**Umschwung,** *m.* rotation, revolution.

**umsetzen,** *v.t.* transpose; change the position

of; change, convert; transform; cause to react; transplant; exchange, sell.

**Umsetzung,** *f.* transposition; double decomposition; conversion, change; transformation; reaction; transplantation; exchange, sale, business.

**Umsicht,** *f.* prospect; panorama; circumspection.

**umsomehr,** *adv.* so much the more, the more.

**umsonst,** *adv.* for nothing, gratis; in vain; aimlessly; causelessly.

**umspülen,** *v.t.* wash, wash round.

**Umstand,** *m.* circumstance; condition; (*pl.*) ceremonies.—**unter Umständen,** under certain circumstances, on occasion.

**umständlich,** *a.* circumstantial; ceremonious; bothersome, troublesome.

**Umstandswort,** *n.* adverb.

**umstechen,** *v.t.* turn, stir up; re-engrave.

**umstehend,** *p.a.* next, following; standing about; surrounding.

**umstellbar,** *a.* reversible, invertible, transposable.

**umstellen,** *v.t.* reverse, transpose, invert; surround.

**umsteuern,** *v.t.* (*Mach.*) reverse.

**Umstimmungsmittel,** *n.* alterative.

**umstossen,** *v.t.* throw down, overthrow; abolish, cancel.

**umstülpen,** *v.t.* overturn, invert.

**umstürzen,** *v.t.* overthrow, upset.—*v.i.* fall down.

**umtauschen,** *v.t.* exchange.

**umtun,** *v.t.* put on, put around.—*v.r.* seek, inquire.

**umwälzen,** *v.t.* roll or turn round; revolutionize.—*v.r.* revolve, rotate.

**umwandelbar,** *a.* convertible, transformable.

**Umwandelbarkeit,** *f.* convertibility, transformability.

**umwandeln,** *v.t.* convert, transform, change; (*Grammar*) inflect.—*v.r.* become converted or changed.

**Umwandler,** *m.* converter; (*Elec.*) transformer.

**Umwandlung,** *f.* conversion, transformation, change; metamorphosis; (*Grammar*) inflection.

**umwandlungsfähig,** *a.* capable of being converted, etc. (see umwandeln), convertible, transformable.

**Umwandlungs-produkt,** *n.* transformation product. **-punkt,** *m.* transformation point, transition point. **-spannung,** *f.* (*Elec.*) transformation potential. **-theorie,** *f.* transformation theory. **-wärme,** *f.* heat of transformation.

**Umweg,** *m.* roundabout way, detour.

**Umwelt,** *f.* world about us.

**umwenden,** *v.t.* turn over, about, or upside down, invert, reverse.

**umwickeln,** *v.t.* wrap round, cover.

**Umwick(e)lung,** *f.* wrapping, covering, casing.

**umziehen,** *v.t.* draw round, cover, wrap; pull down.—*v.i.* change, move.

**Umzug,** *m.* wandering; procession; removal, change.

**umzüngeln,** *v.t.* (of flames) play about, envelop.

**un-.** a prefix used like English un-, but even more widely, to give a reverse meaning; also to denote immensity. Equivalents: un-, non-, not, in-, il-, im-, ir-, an-, dis-, de-, mis-; prodigious, countless, etc.

**unabhängig,** *a.* independent.

**Unabhängigkeit,** *f.* independence.

**un-ablässig,** *a.* incessant, uninterrupted. **-absehbar,** *a.* unbounded, incalculable, immense. **-absichtlich,** *a.* unintentional. **-ächt,** *a.* not genuine, false. **-achtsam,** *a.* inadvertent, negligent. **-ähnlich,** *a.* unlike, dissimilar. **-angegriffen,** *a.* unattacked, unaffected. **-angelassen,** *a.* untempered, unannealed. **-angemessen,** *p.a.* unsuitable, inadequate. **-angenehm,** *a.* unpleasant, disagreeable. **-angeregt,** *a.* unexcited, in the normal state. **-angreifbar,** *a.* unattackable.

**Unannehmlichkeit,** *f.* inconvenience, annoyance.

**un-atembar,** *a.* irrespirable. **-aufhaltsam,** *a.* irresistible. **-aufhörlich,** *a.* incessant, continual, perpetual. **-auflösbar,** *a.* insoluble.

**Unauflösbarkeit,** *f.* insolubility.

**unauflöslich,** *a.* insoluble.

**Unauflöslichkeit,** *f.* insolubility.

**un-ausdehnbar,** *a.* inexpansible; nonductile. **-ausführbar,** *a.* impracticable, unfeasible. **-ausgefällt,** *a.* unprecipitated. **-ausgemacht,** *p.a.* undecided, uncertain. **-ausgesetzt,** *p.a.* uninterrupted. **-auslöschbar,** **-auslöschlich,** *a.* indelible (ink); inextinguishable. **-aussprechlich,** *a.* inexpressible, unspeakable. **-auswaschbar,** *a.* incapable of being washed out. **-bearbeitet,** *p.a.* unwrought, raw; unmachined; (of hides) undressed; (of land) untilled. **-bedeckt,** *p.a.* uncovered. **-bedenklich,** *a.* unobjectionable; unhesitating. **-bedeutend,** *p.a.* insignificant, unimportant. **-bedingt,** *a.* unconditional; unlimited.—*adv.* unconditionally, absolutely. **-befangen,** *p.a.* unprejudiced; unconcerned. **-befriedigend,** *a.* unsatisfactory. **-begrenzt,** *a.* unlimited.

**Unbehagen,** *n.* uneasiness, discomfort.

**un-behandelt,** *p.a.* untreated; unworked. **-bekannt,** *p.a.* unknown; unacquainted. **-belebt,** *p.a.* inanimate, lifeless. **-belichtet,** *a.* unexposed (to light). **-bemerkt,** *p.a.*

unnoticed, unobserved. **-benannt,** *p.a.* unnamed, anonymous; (*Math.*) indefinite; (*Anat.*) innominate.

**Unbequemlichkeit,** *f.* inconvenience.

**un-berechenbar,** *a.* incalculable. **-berechtigt,** *p.a.* unauthorized; unjustified. **-beschädigt,** *p.a.* undamaged, intact. **-beschränkt,** *p.a.* unlimited; uncontrolled. **-besetzt,** *p.a.* (of positions) unoccupied; unset, etc. (see besetzen). **-beständig,** *a.* unstable; fickle.

**Unbeständigkeit,** *f.* instability; fickleness.

**un-bestimmt,** *p.a.* undetermined; indeterminate, indefinite. **-beteiligt,** *p.a.* not concerned, non-participating. **-beugsam,** *a.* inflexible. **-bewaffnet,** *p.a.* unarmed; (of the eye) unaided, naked. **-beweglich,** *a.* immovable, fixed. **-bewusst,** *p.a.* unknown; ignorant (of); unaware; involuntary. **-biegsam,** *a.* inflexible. **-brauchbar,** *a.* useless, unserviceable. **-brennbar,** *a.* noncombustible.

**Unbrennbarmachung,** *f.* fireproofing.

**und,** *conj.* and.

**Undefiniertheit,** *f.* indefiniteness.

**un-dehnbar,** *a.* inextensible, nonductile. **-deutlich,** *a.* indistinct. **-dicht,** *a.* not tight, pervious.

**Undicht-heit, -igkeit,** *f.* leakiness, perviousness; porosity; leak. **-igkeitsgrad,** *m.* degree of perviousness or porosity.

**Unding,** *n.* absurdity; nonentity.

**un-durchdringlich,** *a.* impermeable, impervious; impenetrable. **-durchführbar,** *a.* impracticable, unfeasible. **-durchlässig,** *a.* impermeable, impervious. **-durchsichtig,** *a.* non-transparent, opaque.

**Undurchsichtigkeit,** *f.* opacity.

**uneben,** *a.* uneven.

**Unebenheit,** *f.* unevenness, inequality.

**un-echt,** *a.* not genuine, false, counterfeit, artificial; (of colors) not fast, fugitive, loose. **-edel,** *a.* not noble, base. **-egal,** *a.* unequal; uneven.

**Unegalität,** *f.* inequality; unevenness.

**un-eigentlich,** *a.* not true or real or proper, not in a strict sense; not literal, figurative. **-einheitlich,** *a.* nonuniform, inhomogeneous. **-elastisch,** *a.* inelastic, unelastic. **-empfänglich,** *a.* unreceptive, insusceptible. **-empfindlich,** *a.* insensitive.

**unendlich,** *a.* infinite; endless.—**ins Unendliche,** to infinity, ad infinitum.

**un-entbehrlich,** *a.* indispensable. **-entgeltlich,** *a.* gratuitous, free. **-entwickelt,** *a.* undeveloped. **-entwirrbar,** *a.* inextricable. **-entzündbar, -entzündlich,** *a.* uninflammable, noninflammable. **-erbittlich,** *a.* inexorable. **-erfahren,** *p.a.* inexperienced. **-erforschlich,** *a.* inscrutable. **-erforscht,** *a.* un-

explored. **-erheblich,** *a.* insignificant, unimportant. **-erhört,** *p.a.* unheard of; ungranted. **-erklärbar,** *a.* unexplainable, inexplicable. **-erlässlich,** *a.* indispensable. **-ermesslich,** *a.* immeasurable, immense. **-erregt,** *a.* unexcited. **-erreichbar,** *a.* unattainable. **-erschöpflich,** *a.* inexhaustible. **-ersetzbar,** *a.* irreparable. **-erträglich,** *a.* intolerable, insupportable. **-erwähnt,** *p.a.* unmentioned. **-erwartet,** *p.a.* unexpected. **-erwünscht,** *a.* undesired, undesirable. **-explodierbar,** *a.* inexplosive. **-fähig,** *a.* incapable.

**Unfall,** *m.* accident; misfortune.

**un-fehlbar,** *a.* infallible, unfailing. **-fern,** *a.& prep.* near. **-fertig,** *a.* unfinished; unready.

**Unfug,** *m.* disorder, mischief.

**unfühlbar,** *a.* impalpable; imperceptible.

**ung.,** *abbrev.* (ungefähr) about, approximately.

**-ung.** a suffix attached to verb roots to form nouns denoting the action or an effect of it; -ing, -tion, -sion, etc.; as, Verbrenn*ung*, combustion, Bind*ung*, binding, union, bond.

**ungar,** *a.* not done, etc. (see gar); underdone; (*Leather*) untanned.

**ungarisch,** *a.* Hungarian.

**Ungarn,** *n.* Hungary.

**un-geachtet,** *prep.* notwithstanding.—*conj.* altho. **-gebleicht,** *p.a.* unbleached. **-gebrannt,** *p.a.* unburnt. **-gebührlich,** *a.* indecent, improper, undue. **-gebunden,** unbound, (of elements) uncombined; dissolute; prose.

**Ungeduld,** *f.* impatience.

**ungeeignet,** *a.* unsuited, unfit.

**ungefähr,** *adv.* about.—*a.* approximate.

**Ungefähr,** *n.* chance.

**un-gefährlich,** *a.* harmless, inoffensive. **-gefällig,** *a.* disagreeable. **-gefärbt,** *p.a.* undyed; uncolored; unstained. **-gefrierbar,** *a.* nonfreezing. **-gegerbt,** *p.a.* untanned. **-gegoren,** *p.a.* unfermented. **-gehalten,** *p.a.* indignant. **-gehärtet,** *a.* unhardened, soft. **-geheissen,** *p.a.* unasked; spontaneous. **-geheizt,** *p.a.* unheated. **-geheuer,** *a.* enormous, huge; amazing. **-gehörig,** *a.* improper, undue. **-gekocht,** *p.a.* unboiled. **-gekränkt,** *p.a.* uninjured. **-gekünstelt,** *p.a.* unaffected, artless. **-geladen,** *p.a.* unloaded; uninvited. **-geläutert,** *p.a.* unpurified, unrefined. **-gelegen,** *p.a.* inconvenient, inopportune. **-gelehrt,** *p.a.* unlearned. **-geleimt,** *p.a.* unglued; (*Paper*) unsized. **-gelöscht,** *p.a.* unslaked. **-gelöst,** *p.a.* undissolved; unsolved. **-gemein,** *a.* uncommon. **-gemessen,** *p.a.* unmeasured; boundless. **-gemischt,** *p.a.* unmixed. **-gemünzt,** *p.a.* uncoined.

-gemütlich, *a.* uncomfortable, unpleasant.
-genannt, *p.a.* unnamed, anonymous;
(*Anat.*) innominate. -genau, *a.* inexact,
inaccurate.
Ungenauigkeit, *f.* inaccuracy; uncertainty;
lack of sharpness (of definition).
un-geneigt, *p.a.* disinclined; unfriendly.
-geniessbar, *a.* uneatable, unpalatable.
-genügend, *p.a.* insufficient. -genügsam, *a.*
insatiable. -genutzt, *p.a.* unused. -geprüft,
*p.a.* unexamined, untried. -gequantelt, *a.*
unquantized. -gerade, *a.* uneven, odd; not
straight.
ungerad-wertig, *a.* of odd valence. -zahlig, *a.*
(*Math.*) uneven, odd.
un-gerechnet, *p.a.* not counted. -gereinigt,
*p.a.* unpurified. -gerinnbar, *a.* incoagulable.
-gern, *adv.* unwillingly. -geröstet, *p.a.* un-
roasted, not calcined. -gerufen, *p.a.* un-
called.
unges., *abbrev.* (ungesättigt) unsaturated.
un-gesalzen, *p.a.* unsalted, fresh; insipid.
-gesättigt, *p.a.* unsaturated; not satiated.
-gesäuert, *p.a.* not acidified; (*Baking*) un-
leavened. -gesäumt, *p.a.* immediate; seamless. -geschält, *p.a.* unhusked, unpeeled.
-geschehen, *a.* undone. -geschichtet, *p.a.*
unstratified. -geschickt, *a.* awkward.
-geschliffen, *p.a.* unground; unpolished.
-geschlossen, *a.* unclosed, open. -gestalt,
*a.* misshapen. -gesucht, *p.a.* unsought; unaffected. -gesund, *a.* unhealthy; unhealth-
ful. -geteilt, *p.a.* undivided; ungraduated.
-gewaschen, *p.a.* unwashed. -gewiss, *a.*
uncertain.
Ungewitter, *n.* thunder storm.
un-gewöhnlich, *a.* unusual, extraordinary.
-gewohnt, *p.a.* unaccustomed; unusual.
Ungeziefer, *n.* vermin.
un-gezwungen, *p.a.* unconstrained. -giftig, *a.*
nonpoisonous. -glasiert, *a.* unglazed; un-
varnished.
Unglaube, *m.* incredulity; unbelief.
unglaublich, *a.* incredible.
ungleich, *a.* unequal; unlike, dissimilar;
uneven, (of numbers) odd; not uniform.—
*adv.* incomparably, far, by far. -artig, *a.*
dissimilar; heterogeneous.
Ungleichartigkeit, *f.* dissimilarity; heterogeneity.
ungleichförmig, *a.* not uniform, unsymmetrical, heterogeneous, irregular.
Ungleichheit, *f.* inequality; dissimilarity; unevenness.
ungleich-mässig, *a.* not uniform; disproportionate, unsymmetrical, irregular. -namig,
*a.* unlike, opposite. -seitig, *a.* scalene
(triangle).
Unglück, *n.* misfortune, bad luck.

unglücklich, *a.* unfortunate, unlucky, ill-
fated. -erweise, *adv.* unfortunately.
Unglücksfall, *m.* disaster, accident.
ungültig, *a.* not valid, void.
Ungunst, *f.* disfavor; unfavorableness.
un-günstig, *a.* unfavorable. -gut, *adv.* ill,
amiss. -haltbar, *a.* not durable; untenable.
-haltig, *a.* (*Mining*) containing no metal.
-hämmerbar, *a.* not malleable. -handlich,
*a.* unhandy, unwieldy. -heilbar, *a.* incur-
able. -heilsam, *a.* unwholesome, noxious.
-heizbar, *a.* that cannot be heated. -hörbar,
*a.* inaudible.
uniert, *p.a.* united.
Unifarbe, *f.* (*Dyeing*) self color, uniform color,
plain color.
unifärben, *v.t.* dye a self (uniform) shade, dye
solid.
Unistückware, *f.* plain-shade piece goods.
unitarisch, *a.* unitary.
Universal-arznei, *f.* universal remedy, cure-all.
-gelenk, *n.* universal joint. -mittel, *n.* =
Universalarznei.
Universität, *f.* university.
unk., *abbrev.* (unkorrigiert) uncorrected.
un-kennbar, -kenntlich, *a.* undiscernible, un-
recognizable.
Unkenntnis, *f.* ignorance.
un-klar, *a.* not clear; indistinct; turbid; confused. -kontrollierbar, *a.* uncontrollable.
-korrigiert, *p.a.* uncorrected.
Un-kosten, *f.pl.* expenses, charges. -kraut, *n.*
weed, weeds.
un-kristallinisch, *a.* noncrystalline, amorphous. -kristallisierbar, *a.* uncrystallizable.
unl., *abbrev.* (unlöslich) insoluble.
un-längst, *adv.* of late, recently. -lauter, *a.*
impure; unfair; sordid. -legiert, *a.* unalloyed. -leidlich, *a.* insufferable, intolerable.
-lesbar, -leserlich, *a.* illegible. -leugbar, *a.*
undeniable, indisputable. -lieb, -liebsam,
*a.* unpleasant, objectionable. -lösbar, *a.*
indissoluble; not solvable. -löschbar, *a.*
slakeless; unquenchable. -löslich, *a.* insoluble.
Un-löslichkeit, *f.* insolubility. -lust, *f.* dislike,
displeasure.
unmagnetisch, *a.* nonmagnetic.
Unmasse, *f.* great quantity.
un-massgeblich, *a.* unauthoritative. -mässig,
*a.* immoderate, intemperate. -menschlich,
*a.* inhuman; superhuman. -merklich, *a.*
imperceptible. -messbar, *a.* immeasurable;
(*Math.*) incommensurable. -mischbar, *a.*
immiscible.
Unmischbarkeit, *f.* immiscibility.
un-mittelbar, *a.* immediate, direct.—*adv.* immediately, directly. -möbliert, *p.a.* unfur-
nished. -modern, *a.* not in fashion, old-

fashioned. **-möglich**, *a.* impossible.—*adv.* impossibly.

**Unmöglichkeit**, *f.* impossibility.

**un-nachahmlich**, *a.* inimitable. **-nachgiebig**, *a.* unyielding, inflexible. **-nahbar**, *a.* inaccessible. **-nennbar**, *a.* unutterable, inexpressible. **-nötig**, *a.* unnecessary. **-nütz**, **-nützlich**, *a.* useless, unprofitable; naughty. —*adv.* uselessly, vainly.

**Unordnung**, *f.* disorder; litter.

**un-organisch**, *a.* inorganic. **-oxydierbar**, *a.* inoxidizable. **-paarwertig**, *a.* of odd valence. **-parteiisch**, *a.* impartial, unprejudiced. **-pass**, *a.* unwell. **-passend**, *p.a.* unfit, unsuitable. **-pässlich**, *a.* unwell, indisposed. **-plastisch**, *a.* nonplastic. **-polarisierbar**, *a.* unpolarizable. **-pressbar**, *a.* incompressible.

**Un-pressbarkeit**, *f.* incompressibility. **-rat**, *m.* dirt, trash, refuse, offal, garbage; (*Metal.*) dross.

**unrecht**, *a.* wrong; false, unfair, undue.

**Unrecht**, *n.* wrong, injustice; fault, error.— **— haben**, be wrong.

**un-rechtmässig**, *a.* unlawful, illegal. **-regelmässig**, *a.* irregular; abnormal. **-reif**, *a.* unripe; immature. **-rein**, *a.* impure; unclean.

**Un-reinheit**, **-reinigkeit**, *f.* impurity.

**un-reinlich**, *a.* uncleanly. **-reizbar**, *a.* nonirritable, not sensitive. **-rettbar**, *a.* irrecoverable, past help. **-richtig**, *a.* wrong, false, erroneous, unjust.

**Unruhe**, *f.* disquiet, uneasiness, trouble, commotion; balance (of a watch).

**unruhig**, *a.* unquiet, restless, troubled.

**uns**, *pron.* us, to us, ourselves, to ourselves.

**uns.**, *abbrev.* (unsymmetrisch) unsymmetrical.

**un-sagbar**, **-säglich**, *a.* unspeakable. **-sanft**, *a.* harsh, rough. **-schädlich**, *a.* harmless, innocuous. **-scharf**, *a.* not sharp; blurred.

**Unschärfe**, *f.* lack of sharpness.

**unschätzbar**, *a.* invaluable, inestimable.

**Unschlitt**, *n.* tallow, suet. **-seife**, *f.* tallow soap.

**un-schlüssig**, *a.* undecided, irresolute. **-schmackhaft**, *a.* insipid, unpalatable. **-schmelzbar**, *a.* infusible.

**Unschmelzbarkeit**, *f.* infusibility.

**un-schuldig**, *a.* innocent. **-schweissbar**, *a.* unweldable. **-schwer**, *a.* not difficult, easy.

**unser**, *pron.* our, ours; of us.

**unsicher**, *a.* unsafe, insecure, uncertain, unsteady; (*Mech.*) unstable.

**Unsicherheit**, *f.* insecurity, uncertainty.

**unsichtbar**, *a.* invisible.

**Unsinn**, *m.* nonsense.

**un-sinnig**, *a.* nonsensical; irrational; insane. **-spaltbar**, *a.* uncleavable. **-stät**, **-stätig**, *a.* unsteady, unstable, variable; discontinuous.

**Unstätigkeit**, *f.* unsteadiness, instability, variableness, variation; discontinuity.

**un-statthaft**, *a.* inadmissible; illicit. **-stet**, etc. = unstät, etc.

**Unstimmigkeit**, *f.* lack of agreement.

**un-sträflich**, *a.* blameless, irreproachable. **-streckbar**, *a.* not extensible, nonductile, nonmalleable. **-streitig**, *a.* indisputable, unquestionable. **-studiert**, *p.a.* unstudied; unlettered. **-sulfiert**, *p.a.* unsulfonated.

**Unsumme**, *f.* immense sum.

**unsymmetrisch**, *a.* unsymmetrical.

**unt.**, *abbrev.* unter.

**untätig**, *a.* inactive, inert; dormant; indolent.

**Untätigkeit**, *f.* inactivity, inertness; indolence.

**un-tauglich**, *a.* unfit, unsuitable, useless. **-teilbar**, *a.* indivisible.

**Unteilbarkeit**, *f.* indivisibility.

**unteilhaftig**, *a.* not sharing in.

**unten**, *adv.* below, beneath, underneath, at the bottom.

**unter**, *prep.* under, below, beneath; during; among, amidst, between, with.

**Unter-**. hypo-; under, inferior, lower, sub-, infra-. **-abschnitt**, *m.* subsection.

**unterabteilen**, *v.t.* subdivide.

**Unter-abteilung**, *f.* subdivision, **-arm**, *m.* forearm.

**Unteraugenhöhlen-**. infra-orbital.

**Unter-bau**, *m.* substructure, foundation. **-bauch**, *m.* hypogastrium. **-beamter**, *m.* inferior officer, subordinate official.

**unter-belichtet**, *a.* underexposed (to light). **-bewusst**, *a.* subconscious.

**Unterbilanz**, *f.* deficit.

**unterbinden**, *v.t.* stop; (*Med.*) tie up, ligature.

**Unterbindung**, *f.* ligature; ligation.

**unterbleiben**, *v.i.* not occur, be left undone; cease.

**unterbrechen**, *v.t.* interrupt; break, stop.— **unterbrochen**, *p.a.* interrupted, discontinuous.

**Unter-brecher**, *m.* interrupter. **-brechung**, *f.* interruption; break, stop. **-brechungsstrom**, *m.* interrupted current.

**unter-breiten**, *v.t.* submit. **-bringen**, *v.t.* provide for; dispose of, sell; invest; give lodging to. **-brochen**, *p.a.* see unterbrechen.

**unterbromig**, *a.* hypobromous.—**unterbromige Säure**, hypobromous acid.

**unterbromigsauer**, *a.* of or combined with hypobromous acid, hypobromite of.

**unterchlorig**, *a.* hypochlorous.—**unterchlorige Säure**, hypochlorous acid.

**unterchlorigsauer**, *a.* of or combined with hypochlorous acid, hypochlorite of.

**Unter-chlorigsäure**, *f.* hypochlorous acid. **-chlorsäure**, *f.* hypochloric acid (formerly applied to chlorine dioxide).

unterdes, unterdessen, *adv.* meanwhile.

Unterdruck, *m.* diminished pressure, vacuum.

unterdrücken, *v.t.* suppress; repress; oppress.

Unterdrückung, *f.* suppression; repression.

untere, *a.* low, lower, under, inferior.

untereinander, *adv.* among one another, together, confusedly.

Untereinteilung, *f.* subdivision.

unter-essigsauer, *a.* subacetate of. -eutektisch, *a.* hypoeutectic. -eutektoid, *a.* hypoeutectoid. -exponiert, *a.* underexposed. -fangen, *v.r.* dare, venture.

Unter-fläche, *f.* under surface, base. -form, *f.* subvariety, subspecies. -futter, *n.* lining. -gang, *m.* going down, (of the sun) setting; fall, ruin.

untergärig, *a.* fermented from below, bottom-fermenting.—untergärige Hefe, bottom yeast.

Unter-gärung, *f.* bottom fermentation. -gattung, *f.* subgenus.

unter-geben, *v.t.* place under; subject, submit.—*p.a.* inferior, subordinate. -gehen, *v.i.* go down; (of the sun, etc.) set; perish; become extinct. -geordnet, *p.a.* see unterordnen. -geschoben, *p.a.* see unterschieben.

Unter-geschoss, *n.* ground floor. -gestell, *n.* underframe, substructure. -glasur, *f.* underglaze. -glasurfarbe, *f.* under-glaze color.

unter-graben, *v.t.* undermine; dig (something) in. -grädig, *a.* underproof.

Untergräten-. (*Anat.*) infraspinous.

Untergrund, *m.* subsoil; underground; background; (*Dyeing*) bottom; (*Calico*) bottom print, first print. -farbe, *f.* (*Dyeing*) bottom color.

Untergruppe, *f.* subgroup.

unter-halb, *prep.* below, beyond, under. -halogenig, *a.* hypohal(ogen)ous. -halten, *v.t.* support; maintain, keep up, keep; entertain.—*v.r.* discourse; amuse oneself.

Unterhaltung, *f.* support, maintenance; entertainment; conversation.

unterhandeln, *v.i.* treat, negotiate.

Unterhaut, *f.* under skin, derma, hypodermis.

Unterhaut-. subcutaneous.

Unterhefe, *f.* bottom yeast.

unter-irdisch, *a.* subterranean, underground. -jochen, *v.t.* subjugate, subdue. -jodig, *a.* hypoiodous. -jodigsauer, *a.* of or combined with hypoiodous acid, hypoiodite of. -kommen, *v.i.* find shelter, find employment. -kriechen, *v.i.* crawl under. -kriegen, *v.t.* get the better of. -kühlen, *v.t.* supercool, undercool.

Unter-kühlung, *f.* supercooling, undercooling. -lage, *f.* support, base, stand; substratum; subsoil; lining; (supporting) document.

-lagsring, *m.* supporting ring. -lass, *m.* intermission, cessation.

unterlassen, *v.t.* leave off, discontinue; omit, fail.

Unterlauf, *m.* lower course, lower side.

unterlaufen, *p.a.* extravasated, bloodshot.

Unterlauge, *f.* (*Soap*) underlye, spent lye.

unterlegen, *v.t.* lay under, put under, underlay.

Unterleg-ring, *m.* supporting ring. -scheibe, *f.* supporting disk.

Unterleib, *m.* abdomen, belly.

Unterleibs-. abdominal. -entzündung, *f.* peritonitis.

unter-liegen, *v.i.* succumb; be liable, be subject. -löst, *a.* insufficiently grown (malt).

unternehmen, *v.t.* undertake.—unternehmend, *p.a.* enterprising.

Unternehmung, *f.* undertaking, enterprise, venture.

Unternehmverband, *m.* combination (of any kind in business), syndicate, trust, pool, etc.

unterordnen, *v.t.* subordinate.—untergeordnet, *p.a.* subordinate, secondary.

Unterpfand, *n.* pledge, security, mortgage.

unter-phosphorig, *a.* hypophosphorous. -phosphorigsauer, *a.* of or combined with hypophosphorous acid, hypophosphite of. -phosphorsauer, *a.* of or combined with hypophosphoric acid, hypophosphate of.

Unter-phosphorsäure, *f.* hypophosphoric acid. -probe, *f.*, -probeweingeist, *m.* underproof spirit. -redung, *f.* conference, conversation, interview. -richt, *m.* instruction, teaching.

unterrichten, *v.t.* teach, instruct; inform.

Unter-richtsanstalt, *f.* school, academy. -rinde, *f.* under bark; under crust.

Unters., *abbrev.* (Untersuchung) investigation, examination.

untersagen, *v.t.* forbid, prohibit.

Untersalpetersäure, *f.* hyponitric acid (old name for nitrogen peroxide).

unter-salpetrig, *a.* hyponitrous. -salpetrigsauer, *a.* of or combined with hyponitrous acid, hyponitrite of. -sättigen, *v.t.* undersaturate.

Untersatz, *m.* support, stand; stay; saucer; assumption. -schale, *f.* supporting dish.

unter-schätzen, *v.t.* undervalue, underrate. -scheidbar, *a.* distinguishable, discernible. -scheiden, *v.t.* distinguish; discern.

Unter-scheidungsmarkierung, *f.* distinctive marking. -schicht, *f.* under layer, under stratum.

unterschieben, *v.t.* push under; substitute; forge.—untergeschoben, *p.a.* substituted, spurious.

Unterschied, *m.* difference; distinction; partition.

unter-schiedlich, *a.* different, distinct; differential. -schreiben, *v.t.* sign. -schreiten, *v.t.* fall below, keep within.

Unterschrift, *f.* signature; subscription.

unterschwefelsauer, *a.* of or combined with hyposulfuric acid, hyposulfate of (dithionate of).

Unterschwefelsäure, *f.* hyposulfuric acid (dithionic acid).

unterschweflig, *a.* hyposulfurous. -sauer, *a.* of or combined with hyposulfurous acid, hyposulfite of.

Unterseeboot, *n.* undersea boat, submarine.

unterseeisch, *a.* submarine.

Untersetzscherbe, *f.* plate or saucer set under something, (for crucibles) crucible stand.

untersetzt, *p.a.* thick-set.

unterst, *a.* lowest, undermost.

unter-stehen, *v.i.* pertain.—*v.r.* dare, venture. -stellen, *v.t.* place under; impute.

Unterstock, *m.* (*Brewing*) underback.

unter-streichen, *v.t.* underline. -stützen, *v.t.* support; assist. -suchen, *v.t.* investigate; examine; probe.

Untersuchung, *f.* investigation, research; examination, inquiry.

Untersuchungs-chemiker, *m.* research chemist. -laboratorium, *n.* research laboratory. -material, *n.* material for investigation or under investigation. -methode, *f.* investigational method, research method. -mittel, *n.* means of research or examination; indicator.

unter-tan, *a.* subject, dependent (on). -tänig, *a.* subject; submissive, obedient.

Untertasse, *f.* saucer.

untertauchen, *v.t.* immerse, submerge.

Unter-tauchung, *f.* immersion, submersion. -teig, *m.* (*Brewing*) underdough. -teil, *m.* under part, lower part. -teilung, *f.* subdivision. -wald, *m.* underbrush. -walze, *f.* under roll, bottom roll.

unterwärts, *adv.* downward, underneath.

Unterwasseranstrich, *m.* underwater (antifouling) painting.

unter-wegs, *adv.* on the way, en route. -weisen, *v t.* instruct, teach. -werfen, *v.t.* subject. -wühlen, *v.t.* undermine. -zeichnen, *v.t.* sign; underwrite.

Unterzeug, *n.* underclothing.

unterziehen, *v.t.* draw or lay under; put on underneath.—*v.r.* undergo.

Unterzungen-. sublingual.

unthätig, *a.* =untätig.

Untier, *n.* monster.

un-tilgbar, *a.* indelible; irredeemable. -trennbar, *a.* inseparable.

Untrennbarkeit, *f.* inseparability.

un-trinkbar, *a.* undrinkable. -trüglich, *a.* infallible, unmistakable.

unt.Zers., *abbrev.* (unter Zersetzung) with decomposition.

un-übersteiglich, *a.* insurmountable. -übertrefflich, *a.* unsurpassable, unrivaled. -überwindlich, *a.* invincible. -umgänglich, *a.* indispensable, unavoidable. -umschränkt, *p.a.* unlimited. -umstösslich, *a.* irrefutable. -umwunden, *p.a.* frank, plain. -unterbrochen, *p.a.* uninterrupted, unbroken. -unterscheidbar, *a.* indistinguishable. -untersucht, *p.a.* uninvestigated.

unv., *abbrev.* (unveröffentlicht) unpublished.

un-veränderlich, *a.* invariable, unchangeable. -verändert, *p.a.* unchanged, unaltered. -verantwortlich, *a.* inexcusable; irresponsible. -verarbeitet, *p.a.* unwrought, not made up. -veräusserlich, *a.* inalienable. -verbesserlich, *a.* incorrigible. -verbindlich, *a.* not binding; disobliging. -verblümt, *p.a.* plain. -verbrannt, *p.a.* unburned. -verbrennbar, -verbrennlich, *a.* incombustible.

Unverbrennbarkeit, *f.* incombustibility.

un-verbrüchlich, *a.* inviolable. -verbunden, *p.a.* uncombined; unconnected. -verbürgt, *p.a.* unwarranted, unconfirmed. -verdaulich, *a.* indigestible.

Unverdauung, *f.* indigestion.

unverdichtbar, *a.* incondensable.

Unverdichtbarkeit, *f.* incondensability.

un-verdient, *p.a.* undeserved. -verdrossen, *a.* unwearied, patient. -vereinbar, *a.* incompatible, irreconcilable. -verestert, *a.* unesterified. -verfälscht, *p.a.* unadulterated. -verfaulbar, *a.* unputrefiable, imputrescible. -verflüchtigt, *a.* unvolatilized. -vergänglich, *a.* not perishable. -vergärbar, *a.* unfermentable. -vergasbar, *a.* ungasifiable. -vergesslich, *a.* unforgettable. -verglast, *p.a.* unvitrified. -vergleichbar, -vergleichlich, *a.* incomparable. -vergrünbar, -vergrünlich, *a.* ungreenable. -verhältnismässig, disproportionate. -verhohlen, *p.a.* unconcealed, open. -verholzt, *p.a.* unlignified. -verkäuflich, *a.* unsalable, unmarketable. -verkennbar, *a.* unmistakable. -verkittet, *a.* uncemented, unluted. -verkürzt, *p.a.* unabridged. -verletzt, *p.a.* unimpaired, intact. -vermeidlich, *a.* unavoidable, inevitable. -vermengt, *p.a.* unmixed. -vermerkt, *p.a.* unperceived, imperceptible. -vermindert, *p.a.* undiminished. -vermischbar, *a.* immiscible. -vermischt, *p.a.* unmixed, unalloyed, pure. -vermittelt, *a.* sudden; unassisted.—*adv.* suddenly.

Unvermögen, *n.* inability, impotence.

unvermutet, *p.a.* unexpected.

Unvernunft, *f.* unreasonableness, absurdity.

**un-veröffentlicht,** *p.a.* unpublished. **-verrichtet,** *p.a.* unperformed. **-verschuldet,** *p.a.* not in debt; unmerited. **-versehens,** *adv.* unexpectedly. **-versehrt,** *p.a.* uninjured, undamaged. **-verseifbar,** *a.* unsaponifiable. **-versiegbar,** *a.* inexhaustible. **-versorgt,** *p.a.* unprovided for. **-verständig,** *a.* unwise, imprudent. **-verständlich,** *a.* unintelligible. **-versteuert,** *p.a.* duty unpaid. **-versucht,** *p.a.* untried. **-vertilgbar,** *a.* ineradicable; indelible. **-verträglich,** *a.* incompatible; unsociable.

**Unverträglichkeit,** *f.* incompatibility; unsociability.

**un-verwandt,** *p.a.* unrelated; unmoved. **-verweilt,** *adv.* without delay. **-verweslich,** *a.* imputrescible, undecaying. **-verwüstlich,** *a.* indestructible. **-verzeihlich,** *a.* unpardonable. **-verzollt,** *p.a.* duty unpaid. **-verzüglich,** *a.* immediate, instant. **-verzweigt,** *p.a.* unbranched. **-vollendet,** *a.* unfinished, incomplete. **-vollkommen,** *a.* imperfect, incomplete. **-vollständig,** *a.* incomplete, imperfect.

**Unvollständigkeit,** *f.* incompleteness, imperfection.

**un-vorbereitet,** *p.a.* unprepared. **-vorhergesehen,** *p.a.* unforeseen. **-vorsätzlich,** *a.* unpremeditated. **-vorsichtig,** *a.* incautious, careless. **-vorteilhaft,** *a.* disadvantageous, unprofitable. **-wägbar,** *a.* unweighable; imponderable.

**Unwägbarkeit,** *f.* unweighability; imponderability.

**un-wahr,** *a.* untrue, false. **-wahrscheinlich,** *a.* improbable. **-wandelbar,** *a.* unchangeable, invariable. **-wegsam,** *a.* impassable; impervious; pathless. **-weit,** *adv.* not far.— *prep.* not far from.

**Unwesen,** *n.* disorder; nuisance; monster.

**unwesentlich,** *a.* unessential, immaterial, accidental.

**Unwetter,** *n.* bad weather, storm.

**un-wichtig,** *a.* unimportant. **-widerlegbar,** **-widerleglich,** *a.* irrefutable. **-widerstehlich,** *a.* irresistible. **-willkürlich,** *a.* involuntary. **-wirksam,** *a.* inactive; ineffective, inefficient; void.

**Un-wirksamkeit,** *f.* inactivity; ineffectiveness. **-zahl,** *f.* immense number.

**unzählig,** *a.* innumerable.

**Unze,** *f.* ounce.

**Unzeit,** *f.* wrong time.

**un-zeitig,** *a.* untimely; immature. **-zerbrechlich,** *a.* unbreakable. **-zerlegbar,** *a.* indecomposable; indivisible. **-zerlegt,** *a.* undecomposed, etc. (see zerlegen). **-zerreissbar,** *a.* untearable, indestructible. **-zersetzbar,** *a.* indecomposable. **-zersetzt,** *p.a.* unde-composed.—*adv.* without decomposition. **-zerstörbar,** *a.* indestructible.

**Unzerstörbarkeit,** *f.* indestructibility.

**un-zerstört,** *p.a.* undestroyed. **-zertrennbar,** *a.* inseparable. **-ziehbar,** *a.* not ductile. **-zufrieden,** *p.a.* discontented, dissatisfied. **-zugänglich,** *a.* inaccessible. **-zulänglich,** *a.* insufficient, inadequate. **-zulässig,** *a.* inadmissible. **-zusammendrückbar,** *a.* incompressible.

**Unzusammendrückbarkeit,** *f.* incompressibility.

**un-zuträglich,** *a.* disadvantageous; unhealthy. **-zuverlässig,** *a.* unreliable, uncertain. **-zweckmässig,** *a.* unsuitable, inexpedient. **-zweideutig,** *a.* unequivocal, unambiguous. **-zweifelhaft,** *a.* indubitable, undoubted.—*adv.* undoubtedly.

**U. P.,** *abbrev.* (Ungarisches Patent) Hungarian patent.

**Upas-baum,** *m.* upas tree, upas. **-gift,** *n.* upas poison, upas.

**U.p.M.,** *abbrev.* (Umlaufungen pro Minute) revolutions per minute, r.p.m.

**üppig,** *a.* luxuriant, rich, rank.

**-ür. -ide** (for "ous" compounds. See Chlorür).

**Ur-.** primitive, original, primordial, primary. **-ahn,** *m.* original ancestor; great grandfather.

**uralt,** *a.* very old, ancient.

**Urämie,** *f.* uremia.

**Uran,** *n.* uranium. **-blei,** *n.* uranium lead. **-carbid,** *n.* uranium carbide. **-erz,** *n.* uranium ore.

**Uranfang,** *m.* origin, very beginning.

**Uran-gehalt,** *m.* uranium content. **-gelb,** *n.* uranium yellow. **-glas,** *n.* uranium glass. **-glimmer,** *m.* (*Min.*) torbernite. **-grün,** *n.* (*Min.*) uranochalcite. **-gummi,** *n.* (*Min.*) gummite.

**uranhaltig,** *a.* containing uranium, uraniferous.

**Urani-.** uranic (uranyl).

**uranig,** *a.* uranous.

**Urani-nitrat,** *n.* uranic nitrate (uranyl nitrate). **-oxyd,** *n.* uranic oxide. **-verbindung,** *f.* uranic compound (uranyl compound).

**Uran-metall,** *n.* uranium metal. **-nitrat,** *n.* uranium nitrate.

**Urano-.** uranous, uranoso-.

**Uranocker,** *m.* uranium ocher, uraconite (variety of uranopilite).

**Urano-hydroxyd,** *n.* uranous hydroxide. **-reihe,** *f.* uranous series. **-salz,** *n.* uranous salt. **-uranat,** *n.* uranous uranate. **-verbindung,** *f.* uranous compound.

**Uran-oxyd,** *n.* uranium oxide, specif. uranic oxide. **-oxydoxydul,** *n.* = Uranoxyduloxyd.

-oxydul, *n.* uranous oxide, uranium dioxide.
-oxyduloxyd, *n.* uranoso-uranic oxide (uranous uranate). -oxydulsalz, *n.* uranous salt.
-pecherz, *n.* pitchblende. -phosphat, *n.* uranium phosphate. -salz, *n.* uranium salt.

uransauer, *a.* of or combined with uranic acid, uranate of.

Uran-säure, *f.* uranic acid. -strahlen, *m.pl.* uranium rays.

uranuranig, *a.* uranoso-uranic.

Uran-verbindung, *f.* uranium compound. -vitriol, *n.* (*Min.*) johannite.

Uratom, *n.* primordial atom.

urbar, *a.* arable, tillable.

Ur-bestandteil, *m.* ultimate constituent. -bewohner, *m.* original inhabitant. -bild, *n.* prototype, original. -destillation, *f.* low-temperature distillation. -farbe, *f.* primary color. -fels, *m.* primitive rock. -form, *f.* original form, prototype. -gebirg, *n.* (*Geol.*) primitive rock.

urgeschichtlich, *a.* prehistoric.

Ur-gestein, *n.* primitive rock; (*Ceram.*) native kaolinic rock (from which kaolin is obtained by elutriation). -gewicht, *n.* standard weight. -granit, *m.* primitive granite. -heber, *m.* author; originator, founder.

Urin-absatz, *m.* urinary sediment. -stein, *m.* urinary calculus.

Ur-kalk, *m.* primitive limestone. -koks, *m.* low-temperature coke..

urkräftig, *a.* very powerful, hearty.

Ur-kunde, *f.* document, record, voucher, diploma. -laub, *m.* leave of absence. -läuter, *m.* (*Leather*) sod oil. -mass, *n.* standard measure.

Urne, *f.* urn.

U-Rohr, *n.*, U-Röhre, *f.* U-tube.

urplötzlich, *a.* very sudden.—*adv.* very suddenly.

Ur-preis, *m.* original price, manufacturer's price. -quell, *m.* fountain head, origin. -sache, *f.* cause, reason.

ursächlich, *a.* causal, causative.

Ursäure, *f.* a ureide of acid character, as barbituric or oxaluric acid, a "-uric" acid.

Ur-schleim, *m.* protoplasm. -sprung, *m.* origin, source.

ursprünglich, *a.* original, primitive, first.

Urstoff, *m.* primary matter; (formerly) element; initial material. -lehre, *f.* the theory of a primary matter of which the elements are composed; atomism, atomic theory.

urstofflich, *a.* elementary.

Ur-stoffteilchen, *n.* primordial particle. -substanz, *f.* original substance; primary matter. -teer, *m.* low-temperature tar; original tar, crude tar.

Urteil, *n.* judgment, decision, opinion, verdict; (*Logic*) proposition.

urteilen, *v.i.* judge, form an opinion; decide, pass sentence.

Ur-tier, *n.* protozoön. -tinktur, *f.* mother tincture. -titer, *m.* original titer, titrimetric standard. -titersubstanz, *f.* standard titrimetric substance. -verkokung, *f.* low-temperature coking (or carbonization). -verschwelung, *f.* low-temperature distillation (or carbonization). -wasser, *n.* primordial water.

urwellen, *v.t.* (*Metal.*) double.

Urwelt, *f.* primeval world.

urwüchsig, *a.* original, native; rough, blunt.

Ur-zelle, *f.* primitive cell, ovum. -zeugung, *f.* abiogenesis.

u.s.f., *abbrev.* (und so fort) and so on.

Usnet-insäure, *f.* usnetinic acid. -säure, *f.* usnetic acid.

Usninsäure, *f.* usnic acid.

u.s.w., usw., *abbrev.* (und so weiter) and so forth, and so on, etc.

Utensilien, *n.pl.* utensils, implements.

u.U., *abbrev.* (unter Umständen) under certain circumstances.

u.ü.V., *abbrev.* (unter üblichen Vorbehalt) with the usual reservations.

Uvinsäure, *f.* uvic acid, pyrotritaric acid.

Uvitinsäure, *f.* uvitic acid.

Uwarowit, *m.* uvarovite.

Uwp., *abbrev.* (Umwandlungspunkt) transformation point, transition point.

u.Z., u.Zers., *abbrev.* (unter Zersetzung) with decomposition.

u.zw., *abbrev.* (und zwar) namely, that is, i.e.

# V

**v.,** *abbrev.* vicinal; (von) of, from, etc., (in titles) von.

**V.,** *abbrev.* (Vormittags) in the forenoon, A.M.; (Vorkommen) occurrence, presence.

**vaccinieren,** *v.t.* vaccinate.

**Vacheleder,** *n.* neat's leather.

**vagabundieren,** *v.i.* rove, wander.—**vagabundierend,** *p.a.* vagrant, roving, stray.

**Vakanz,** *f.* vacancy; (*pl.*) vacation, holidays.

**Vakuomesser,** *m.* vacuum gage.

**Vakuum-birne,** *f.* vacuum bulb. **-gärung,** *f.* vacuum fermentation. **-glocke,** *f.* vacuum bell jar. **-glühlampe,** *f.* vacuum incandescent lamp. **-meter,** *n.* vacuum gage. **-pfanne,** *f.* vacuum pan. **-pumpe,** *f.* vacuum pump. **-rohr,** *n.* vacuum tube. **-schlauch,** *m.* vacuum hose, vacuum tubing. **-teer,** *m.* vacuum tar. **-trockner,** *m.* vacuum drier. **-verdampfung,** *f.* vacuum evaporation.

**vakzinieren,** *v.t.* vaccinate.

**Valenz,** *f.* valence, valency. **-einheit,** *f.* valence unit, valence. **-kraft,** *f.* valence (or valency) force. **-lehre,** *f.* doctrine of valence. **-richtung,** *f.* valence direction. **-strich,** *m.* valence line or dash. **-stufe,** *f.* valence stage.

**Valerian-öl,** *n.* valerian oil. **-säure,** *f.* valeric acid, valerianic acid. **-säureamyläther,** *m.* amyl valerate. **-säuresalz,** *n.* salt of valeric acid, valerate.

**Valet,** *n.* farewell.

**Valone,** *f.* valonia.

**Valuta,** *f.* value; standard; rate, equivalent. **-aufschlag,** *m.* increase or advance in value or price due to exchange.

**Vanadin, Vanad,** *n.* vanadium.

**Vanadin-bleierz,** *n.*, **-bleispat,** *m.* vanadinite. **-eisen,** *n.* ferrovanadium.

**vanadinenthaltend,** *a.* containing vanadium, vanadiferous.

**vanadinig,** *a.* vanadous.

**Vanadinsalz,** *n.* vanadium salt.

**vanadinsauer,** *a.* of or combined with vanadic acid, vanadate of.

**Vanadin-säure,** *f.* vanadic acid. **-säureanhydrid,** *n.* vanadic anhydride, vanadium pentoxide. **-stahl,** *m.* vanadium steel. **-stickstoff,** *m.* vanadium nitride. **-verbindung,** *f.* vanadium compound.

**Vanadium-chlorür,** *n.* vanadous chloride. **-eisen,** *n.* ferrovanadium.

**vanadiumenthaltend,** *a.* = vanadinenthaltend.

**Vanadiumstahl,** *m.* vanadium steel.

**Vanadosulfat,** *n.* vanadous sulfate.

**Vanille,** *f.* vanilla.

**Vanillen-kampfer,** *m.* vanillin. **-pflanze,** *f.* vanilla plant.

**variabel,** *a.* variable.

**Variabilität,** *f.* variability.

**Varietät,** *f.* variety.

**variieren,** *v.t. & i.* vary.

**Variierung,** *f.* variation.

**Vater,** *m.* father. **-land,** *n.* native land; Germany.

**vaterländisch,** *a.* native, national.

**väterlich,** *a.* fatherly, paternal.

**Vb.,** *abbrev.* (Verbindung) compound.

**Vbb.,** *abbrev.* (Verbindungen) compounds.

**v.Chr.,** *abbrev.* (vor Christus) before Christ, B.C.

**V.d.E.,** *abbrev.* (Verein deutscher Eisenhüttenleute) Association of German Metallurgists.

**V.d.I., VDI,** *abbrev.* (Verein deutscher Ingenieure) Association of German Engineers.

**v.d.L.,** *abbrev.* (vor dem Lötrohr) before the blowpipe, B.B.

**Vegetabilien,** *pl.* vegetables; botanical drugs.

**vegetabilisch,** *a.* vegetable.

**Veilchen,** *n.* violet; (dreifarbiges) pansy.

**veilchen-blau,** *a.* violet. **-farben,** *a.* violet-colored.

**Veilchen-holz,** *n.* violet wood. **-keton,** *n.* ionone. **-öl,** *n.* violet oil. **-stein,** *m.* iolite. **-wurzel,** **-wurz,** *f.* orris root.

**Veitstanz,** *m.* St. Vitus's dance, chorea.

**Vektorgerüst,** *n.* vector diagram.

**vektoriell,** *a.* vectorial.

**Velin,** *n.* vellum. **-form,** *f.* (*Paper*) wove mold. **-papier,** *n.* wove paper, vellum paper.

**veloutieren,** *v.t.* flock (paper).

**Vene,** *f.* vein.

**Venedig,** *n.* Venice.

**Venen-blut,** *n.* venous blood. **-häutchen,** *n.* choroid membrane. **-stein,** *m.* vein stone, phlebolite.

**Venerie,** *f.* syphilis.

**venerisch,** *a.* syphilitic.

**Venet-.** see Venez-.

**Venezianer-seife,** *f.* Venetian soap. **-weiss,** *n.* Venetian white.

**venezianisch,** *a.* Venetian.

**Venezianischrot,** *n.* Venetian red.

**venös,** *a.* venous.

**Ventil,** *n.* valve.

**Ventilator,** *m.* ventilator, fan, blower.

**Ventil-deckel,** *m.* valve lid. **-gehäuse,** *n.* valve chamber.

**ventilieren,** *v.t.* ventilate.

**Ventil-sitz,** *m.* valve seat. **-stopfen,** *n.* stopper with a valve, valve stopper.

**ver.,** *abbrev.* (vereinigt) united.

**ver-.** a verbal prefix meaning: (1) forth, away, out, either in the sense of removal, as *ver*treiben, drive away, dispel; or of the perfecting of an action, as *ver*schliessen, close up, *ver*blühen, cease blooming, fade. (2) a reversal of meaning, as *ver*bieten, forbid (from *bieten*, offer). (3) wrongly, too much, mis-, as *ver*salzen, oversalt. (4) " make, convert into, or become " as *ver*grössern, make larger, magnify, *ver*kalken, calcine, calcify, *ver*käsen, become cheesy.

**verab-folgen,** *v.t.* deliver, hand over, surrender. **-reden,** *v.t.* agree upon, appoint. **-reichen,** *v.t.* deliver, dispense. **-schieden,** *v.t.* dismiss, discharge.—*v.r.* take leave.

**verachten,** *v.t.* despise, scorn.

**verallgemeinern,** *v.t.* generalize.

**Verallgemeinerung,** *f.* generalization.

**veralten,** *v.i.* grow old or obsolete.—**veraltet,** *p.a.* obsolete, antiquated.

**veränderlich,** *a.* variable; changeable, fluctuating, unstable, unsteady.

**Veränderliche,** *f.* variable.

**Veränderlichkeit,** *f.* variability, etc. (see *veränderlich*).

**verändern,** *v.t.* alter, change, vary; concentrate (ore).—*v.r.* vary; change.

**Veränderung,** *f.* variation; change, alteration.

**veranlassen,** *v.t.* occasion, cause, give rise to; induce.

**Veranlassung,** *f.* occasion, cause; motive, inducement.

**veran-schaulichen,** *v.t.* illustrate, make clear. **-schlagen,** *v.t.* estimate, value. **-stalten,** *v.t.* arrange, manage.

**verantworten,** *v.t.* answer for, justify.

**verantwortlich,** *a.* answerable, responsible.

**verarbeiten,** *v.t.* work, work up, treat, manufacture.

**Verarbeitung,** *f.* working, working up, treatment, manufacture.

**verarmen,** *v.i.* become poor.—*v.t.* reduce in strength; impoverish.

**veraschen,** *v.t.* ash, incinerate.

**Veraschung,** *f.* ashing, incineration.

**Veraschungsschale,** *f.* incinerating dish.

**Verästelung, Verästung,** *f.* ramification.

**veräthern,** *v.t.* etherify.

**Veratrinsäure,** *f.* veratric acid.

**Veratrum-aldehyd,** *n.* veratraldehyde. **-alko-**

hol, *m.* veratric alcohol. **-säure,** *f.* veratric acid.

**verausgeben,** *v.t.* spend, expend, pay.

**verb.,** *abbrev.* (of books, verbessert) revised.

**Verb.,** *abbrev.* (Verbindung) compound; (Verband) association, union.

**Verband,** *m.* binding, fastening; bandaging, bandage; association, union; (*Masonry*) bond.

**verbannen,** *v.t.* banish.

**Verbb.,** *abbrev.* (Verbindungen) compounds.

**verbeissen,** *v.t.* suppress, stifle.

**verbeizen,** *v.t.* (*Leather*) overbate.

**Verbene,** *f.* vervain.

**verbergen,** *v.t.& r.* hide.—**verborgen,** *p.a.* latent; hidden, secret.

**verbessern,** *v.t.* better, improve; correct, revise (books).

**Verbesserungsmittel,** *n.* corrective.

**verbeugen,** *v.r.* bow.

**verbiegen,** *v.t.* bend wrong, strain.—*v.r.* warp.

**verbieten,** *v.t.* forbid, prohibit.

**verbilligen,** *v.t.* cheapen, reduce in price.

**verbinden,** *v.t.* combine; bind, bind up, join, link, connect; oblige.—*v.r.* combine, unite.

**verbindlich,** *a.* obliging; binding, obligatory; obliged.—**verbindlichen Dank!** best thanks!

**Verbindlichkeit,** *f.* civility, kindness; obligation; obligatoriness.

**Verbindung,** *f.* compound; combining, combination, union; connection; blending (of colors); joining, fastening, binding; joint, bond; communication; union, alliance, society.

**Verbindungs-fähigkeit,** *f.* combining ability. **-form,** *f.* form of combination. **-gang,** *m.* connecting passage. **-gewicht,** *n.* combining weight. **-gleichung,** *f.* equation of combination. **-glied,** *n.* connecting link. **-hahn,** *m.* connecting cock. **-kitt,** *m.* cement or lute for joints. **-klammer,** *f.* brace. **-kraft,** *f.* combining power. **-molekül,** *n.* molecule of a compound. **-punkt,** *m.* juncture, junction. **-rohr,** *n.,* **-röhre,** *f.* connecting tube or pipe. **-schlauch,** *m.* connecting tube or tubing. **-schliff,** *m.* ground joint. **-stelle,** *f.* juncture, junction. **-streben,** *n.* (chemical) affinity. **-strich,** *m.* hyphen. **-stück,** *n.* connecting piece. **-stufe,** *f.* stage of combination. **-verhältnis,** *n.* combining proportion. **-volumen,** *n.* combining volume. **-wärme,** *f.* heat of combination. **-wert,** *m.* combining value. **-zeichen,** *n.* hyphen.

**verbitten,** *v.t.* object to, decline.

**verblasen,** *v.t.* blow (glass or metal); dilute (colors).

**verblassen,** *v.i.* fade; pale.

**verbleiben,** *v.i.* remain, continue.

**verbleichen,** *v.i.* fade; grow pale; expire.

**verbleien,** *v.t.* lead (treat with lead).

**Verbleiung,** *f.* leading; lead lining.

**verblenden,** *v.t.* blind, dazzle; face (with some material); delude.

**Verblender,** *m.* (*Ceram.*) face brick.

**verblühen,** *v.i.* fade, wither.

**verblümen,** *v.t.* disguise.—**verblümt,** *p.a.* figurative.

**verbluten,** *v.i.& r.* bleed to death; cease bleeding.

**verborgen,** *v.t.* lend, sell on credit.—*p.a.* see verbergen.

**Verbot,** *n.* prohibition.

**verboten,** *p.p.* of verbieten.

**verbr.,** *abbrev.* (verbraucht) consumed, used.

**verbrämen,** *v.t.* trim, border, adorn.

**verbrannt,** *p.p.* of verbrennen; burnt, etc.

**Verbrauch,** *m.* consumption, use.

**verbrauchen,** *v.t.* consume, use up.—**verbraucht,** *p.a.* spent, used up, worn out, stale (air).

**Verbrauchs-gegenstand,** *m.* article of consumption, commodity. **-stelle,** *f.* place of consumption, place of use. **-stoff,** *m.* article of consumption.

**verbrausen,** *v.i.* cease fermenting; subside.

**Verbrechen,** *n.* crime, offense, guilt.

**verbreiten,** *v.t.* spread, disseminate, diffuse.—*v.r.* spread.—**verbreitet,** *p.a.* widespread, widely distributed.

**verbreitern,** *v.t.* widen, broaden.

**Verbreiterung,** *f.* widening, broadening.

**verbreitet,** *p.a.* see verbreiten.

**Verbreitung,** *f.* spreading, dissemination, distribution; circulation (of journals); range.

**verbrennbar,** *a.* combustible.

**Verbrennbarkeit,** *f.* combustibility.

**verbrennen,** *v.t.* burn; scorch, tan, scald; bake.

**verbrennlich,** *a.* combustible; inflammable.— **verbrennliche Luft,** inflammable air (old name for hydrogen).

**Verbrennlichkeit,** *f.* combustibility; inflammability.

**Verbrennung,** *f.* combustion; burning; cremation.

**Verbrennungs-analyse,** *f.* combustion analysis, analysis by combustion. **-ergebnis,** *n.* product of combustion. **-gase,** *n.pl.* gases of combustion. **-glas,** *n.* combustion glass. **-intensität,** *f.* intensity of combustion. **-kammer,** *f.* combustion chamber. **-kapillare,** *f.* capillary combustion tube. **-kraftmaschine,** *f.* (internal) combustion engine. **-löffel,** *m.* combustion spoon. **-luft,** *f.* air for combustion. **-ofen,** *m.* combustion furnace. **-produkt,** *n.* product of combustion, combustion product. **-raum,** *m.* combustion chamber, fire chamber; combustion space.

**-rohr,** *n.,* **-röhre,** *f.* combustion tube. **-rückstand,** *m.* residue on ignition (or combustion). **-schiffchen,** *n.* combustion boat. **-versuch,** *m.* combustion experiment. **-vorgang,** *m.* process of combustion. **-wärme,** *f.* heat of combustion. **-wert,** *m.* combustion value, specif. calorific power. **-zone,** *f.* zone of combustion.

**verbriefen,** *v.t.* confirm or secure by writing.

**verbringen,** *v.t.* spend, pass, waste.

**verbrühen,** *v.t.* scald.

**Verbund-.** (*Mach.*) compound.

**verbunden,** *p.p.* of verbinden; combined, etc.

**Verbund-glas,** *n.* compound glass (consisting of two layers). **-maschine,** *f.* compound engine. **-stahl,** *m.* compound steel. **-stück,** *n.* fitting.

**verbürgen,** *v.t.* warrant, guarantee.

**verchloren,** *v.t.* chlorinate.

**Verchlorung,** *f.* chlorination.

**verchromen,** *v.t.* chrome; plate with chromium.

**Verchromung,** *f.* chroming; chromium plating.

**vercoken,** *v.t.* coke.

**verd.,** *abbrev.* (verdünnt) diluted, dilute.

**Verdacht,** *m.* suspicion, distrust.

**verdächtig,** *a.* suspicious, suspected.

**verdämmen,** *v.t.* tamp, dam.

**Verdampfapparat,** *m.* evaporating apparatus, evaporator; carburetor.

**verdampfbar,** *a.* vaporizable; volatile.

**Verdampfbarkeit,** *f.* vaporizability, volatility.

**verdampfen,** *v.t.* evaporate (either vaporize or concentrate by evaporation).—*v.i.* evaporate, vaporize.

**Verdampfer,** *m.* evaporator; carburetor.

**Verdampf-pfanne,** *f.* evaporating pan. **-schale,** *f.* evaporating dish.

**Verdampfung,** *f.* evaporation, evaporating; vaporization.

**verdampfungsfähig,** *a.* capable of evaporation.

**Verdampfungs-fähigkeit,** *f.* evaporative capacity; volatility. **-pfanne,** *f.* evaporating pan, boiling-down pan. **-punkt,** *m.* vaporization point. **-rückstand,** *m.* residue on evaporation. **-vermögen,** *n.* evaporating power. **-wärme,** *f.* heat of vaporization or evaporation. **-wert,** *m.* evaporating value. **-zahl,** **-ziffer,** *f.* coefficient of evaporation.

**verdanken,** *v.t.* owe, have to thank.

**verdarb,** *pret.* of verderben.

**verdauen,** *v.t.* digest.—*v.r.* be digested, be digestible.

**Verdauung,** *f.* digestion.

**Verdauungs-dauer,** *f.* duration of digestion. **-eingeweide,** *n.* digestive tract.

**verdauungsfähig,** *a.* digestible.

**Verdauungs-fähigkeit,** *f.* digestibility. **-flüssigkeit,** *f.* digestive fluid, specif. gastric juice. **-geschäft,** *n.* digestive process

-kanal, *m.* alimentary canal. -mittel, *n.* digestive remedy. -ofen, *m.* digesting oven. -rohr, *n.* alimentary canal. -saft, *m.* = Verdauungsflüssigkeit. -tractus, *m.* digestive tract. -vorgang, *m.* digestive process.

verdecken, *v.t.* cover, conceal, mask.

verdenken, *v.t.* find fault with.

verderben, *v.t.* spoil, damage; ruin, corrupt.— *v.i.* be spoiled, spoil, decay.—verdorben, *p.a.* spoiled, damaged, foul, rotten.

verderblich, *a.* perishable; destructive, injurious.

verdeutlichen, *v.t.* elucidate.

verdeutschen, *v.t.* Germanize.

verdichtbar, *a.* condensable.

Verdichtbarkeit, *f.* condensability.

verdichten, *v.t.* condense; compress; pack; consolidate; concentrate.

Verdichter, *m.* condenser; compressor.

Verdichtung, *f.* condensation, etc. (see verdichten).

Verdichtungs-apparat, *m.* condensing apparatus, condenser. -grad, *m.* degree of condensation or compression (or concentration). -hub, *m.* compression stroke. -wärme, *f.* heat of condensation or compression.

verdicken, *v.t.* thicken, concentrate, inspissate; coagulate, curdle.—*v.r.* thicken; jell; become viscous; coagulate, curd.

Verdicker, *m.* thickener, etc. (see verdicken).

Verdickung, *f.* thickening, etc. (see verdicken); (*Calico*) paste.

Verdickungsmittel, *n.* thickening agent, thickener.

verdienen, *v.t.* deserve; gain, earn, make.

Verdienst, *n.* merit, deserts; earnings, profit.

verdoppeln, *v.t.* double; duplicate.

Verdopp(e)lung, *f.* doubling; duplication.

verdorben, *p.p.& p.a.* see verderben.

verdorren, *v.i.* dry up, dry; wither.

verdrahten, *v.t.* wire.

verdrängbar, *a.* displaceable.

verdrängen, *v.t.* displace; drive out, remove.

Verdrängung, *f.* displacement; removal, dispossession.

verdrehen, *v.t.* twist; distort, wrench.

Verdrehung, *f.* twisting, torsion; distortion.

Verdrehungswinkel, *m.* angle of torsion.

verdreifachen, *v.t.* triple, treble.

Verdreifachung, *f.* tripling, trebling.

verdriessen, *v.t.* grieve, vex, annoy.—verdrossen, *p.a.* grieved, etc.; loath, indolent.

verdrucken, *v.t.* misprint; use up in printing.

verdrücken, *v.t.* mash, crush, crumple, overpress.

Verdruss, *m.* ill will; trouble, annoyance.

verduften, *v.i.* evaporate.

verdunkeln, *v.t.* darken, obscure.

verdünnbar, *a.* capable of dilution; rarefiable.

verdünnen, *v.t.* dilute (liquids); rarefy (gases); attenuate (wort); thin.—verdünnt, *p.a.* diluted, etc., dilute, rare, thin.

Verdünnung, *f.* dilution; rarefaction; thinning; (*Brewing*, etc.) attenuation.

Verdünnungs-gesetz, *n.* dilution law. -grad, *m.* degree of dilution. -mittel, *n.* diluent; (*Med.*) attenuant. -wärme, *f.* heat of dilution.

verdunstbar, *a.* capable of evaporation, vaporizable.

verdunsten, *v.i.& t.* evaporate.

Verdunsten, *n.* evaporation.

verdünsten, *v.t.* evaporate.

Verdunster, *m.* evaporator.

Verdunstung, Verdünstung, *f.* evaporation.

Verdunstungs-kälte, *f.* cold due to evaporation. -kühlung, *f.* cooling by evaporation. -wärme, *f.* heat of vaporization.

verdutzen, *v.t.* nonplus.

veredeln, *v.t.* improve; purify, refine; enrich; cultivate (plants); finish, dress (textiles); ennoble.

Vered(e)lung, *f.* improvement, etc. (see veredeln).

verehren, *v.t.* revere, adore, admire.

Verein, *m.* union, association, society, club, company.

verein-bar, *a.* combinable; compatible. -baren, *v.t.* reconcile, agree upon.

Vereinbarung, *f.* agreement, reconcilement.

vereinen, *v.t. & r.* = vereinigen.

vereinfachen, *v.t.* simplify; (*Math.*) reduce.

Vereinfachung, *f.* simplification; (*Math.*) reduction.

vereinheitlichen, *v.t.* standardize, render uniform.

vereinigen, *v.t.& r.* unite, combine; collect; make agree, agree; (of colors) blend.— vereinigt, *p.a.* united, etc.—die Vereinigten Staaten, the United States.

Vereinigung, *f.* union, combination; association, club; agreement.

Vereinigungsstelle, *f.* place of union; junction.

vereinzeln, *v.t.* isolate, detach, separate.— vereinzelt, *a.* isolated, solitary; *adv.* sporadically.

vereisen, *v.t.& i.* turn to ice, freeze.

vereiteln, *v.t.* balk, thwart, defeat.

vereitern, *v.i.* suppurate.

verengen, verengern, *v.t.& r.* narrow, contract.

vererben, *v.t.* transmit, hand down.—vererbt, *p.a.* hereditary.

Vererbung, *f.* inheritance; transmission.

Vererbungs-forschung, *f.* genetics. -substanz, *f.* (*Biol.*) idioplasm.

vererden, *v.t.& i.* turn to earth, specif. oxidize.

vererzbar, *a.* mineralizable.

vererzen, *v.t.* mineralize.

Vererzung, *f.* mineralization.

Vererzungsmittel, *n.* mineralizer.

veresterbar, *a.* esterifiable.

verestern, *v.t.* esterify.

Veresterung, *f.* esterification.

verewigen, *v.t.* perpetuate; immortalize.—verewigt, *p.a.* late, deceased.

Verf., *abbrev.* (Verfasser) author; (Verfahren) process, method.

verfahren, *v.i.* proceed; act, manage, deal.—*v.t.* transport; work; muddle.—*v.r.* blunder.

Verfahren, *n.* process, method, procedure, proceeding, mode; conduct; management.

Verfahrungs-art, -weise, *f.* mode of proceeding, process.

Verfall, *m.* decay, decline, deterioration; expiration, lapse.

verfallen, *v.i.* decay, decline; fall; chance, hit; (of time) expire.

verfälschen, *v.t.* adulterate; debase (coins); falsify, counterfeit.

Verfälscher, *m.* adulterator; falsifier, forger.

Verfälschung, *f.* adulteration; falsification, forgery.

Verfälschungsmittel, *n.* adulterant.

verfangen, *v.i.* operate, have effect, be of avail.—*v.r.* be caught.

verfänglich, *a.* insidious, deceitful.

verfärben, *v.r.* change color; fade.—*v.t.* use up (in dyeing); dye poorly.

Verfärbung, *f.* discoloration; fading.

verfassen, *v.t.* compose, write.

Verfasser, *m.*, Verfasserin, *f.* author, writer.

Verfassung, *f.* composition, writing; constitution; condition.

verfaulbar, *a.* putrescible.

verfaulen, *v.i.* putrefy, rot, decompose.

verfechten, *v.t.* defend, advocate.

verfehlen, *v.t.* miss.—*v.i.* fail.—verfehlt, *p.a.* unsuccessful, misplaced.

verfeinern, *v.t.* refine; improve.

Verfeinerung, *f.* refinement; improvement.

verfertigen, *v.t.* make, prepare, manufacture; compose.

Verfertigung, *f.* making, etc. (see verfertigen); make, manufacture.

verfestigen, *v.t.* fasten; make firm, strengthen, solidify.

Verfettung, *f.* fatty degeneration.

verfeuern, *v.t.* burn up, burn.

verfilzen, *v.t.& i.* felt, mat.

Verfilzung, *f.* felting, matting.

Verfilzungsfähigkeit, *f.* felting or matting property.

verfinstern, *v.t.* darken, obscure.

verflachen, *v.t.* flatten, level.—*v.r.& i.* become flat or level.

verflechten, *v.t.* interlace, involve.

Verflechtung, *f.* interweaving; complexity.

verfliegen, *v.i.* volatilize; fly away, vanish.—verfliegend, *p.a.* volatile; evanescent.

verfliessen, *v.i.* blend; flow away; (of time) pass, elapse.

verflüchtigbar, *a.* volatilizable.

verflüchtigen, *v.t.& r.* volatilize, evaporate.

Verflüchtigung, *f.* volatilization.

Verflüchtigungs-fähigkeit, *f.* volatility. -verlust, *m.* loss by volatilization.

verflüssigen, *v.t.& r.* liquefy; (*Metal.*) thin, dilute.—verflüssigt, *p.a.* liquefied, liquid.

Verflüssiger, *m.* liquefier, condenser.

Verflüssigung, *f.* liquefaction; (*Metal.*) thinning.

Verflüssigungsmittel, *n.* liquefacient; (*Metal.*) thinning agent.

verfolgen, *v.t.* pursue; prosecute, carry on; follow (up); persecute.

Verfolgung, *f.* pursuit; prosecution, persecution.

verformen, *v.t.* deform; form, work.

Verformung, *f.* deformation; working.

verfrischen, *v.t.* (*Metal.*) refine.

verfrüht, *p.a.* premature.

verfügbar, *a.* at disposal, available.

verfügen, *v.i.* (with über) have at one's disposal, dispose (of).—*v.t.* order, arrange.

verführen, *v.t.* transport; mislead; corrupt, seduce.

verfüllen, *v.t.* fill.

verfuttern, verfüttern, *v.t.* feed (something); overfeed.

Verfutterung, Verfütterung, *f.* feeding; overfeeding.

Verfütterungsversuch, *m.* feeding experiment.

vergällen, *v.t.* denature.

Vergällung, *f.* denaturing.

Vergällungsmittel, *n.* denaturant.

vergangen, *p.a.* gone, past.

Vergangenheit, *f.* the past.

vergänglich, *a.* transient, perishable.

vergärbar, *a.* fermentable, attenuable.

Vergärbarkeit, *f.* fermentability.

vergären, *v.t.* ferment; attenuate (wort).—vergoren, *p.a.* fermented, (*Brewing*) finished.

Vergärung, *f.* fermentation; attenuation (of wort).

Vergärungs-fähigkeit, *f.* fermentability. -grad, *m.* degree of fermentation or attenuation. -messer, *m.* zymometer.

vergasbar, *a.* gasifiable; vaporizable.

vergasen, *v.t.* gasify; vaporize.

Vergaser, *m.* gasifier; vaporizer; carburetor. -graphit, *m.* retort graphite.

vergass, *pret.* of vergessen.

Vergasung, *f.* gasification; vaporization; carburetion.

vergeben, *v.t.* give, bestow; forgive.

vergebens, *adv.* in vain.

vergeblich, *a.* vain, futile.

vergegenwärtigen, *v.t.* represent, figure.—*v.r.* imagine, realize.

vergehen, *v.i.* vanish, perish, cease, (of time) pass, elapse.—*v.r.* transgress; exercise.

Vergeilen, *n.* (*Bot.*) etiolation.

vergelben, *v.i.* turn yellow.

vergelten, *v.t.* reward, repay, return.

Vergeltung, *f.* reward, remuneration, retaliation.

vergessen, *v.t.* forget.

Vergessenheit, *f.* forgetfulness, oblivion.

vergesslich, *a.* forgetful, oblivious.

vergeuden, *v.t.* squander, waste.

vergewissern, *v.t.* convince, assure, confirm.

vergiessbar, *a.* castable, ready to cast.

vergiessen, *v.t.* cast in, run in; fill in, fill up; cast badly; spill, shed.

vergiften, *v.t.* poison.

Vergiftung, *f.* poisoning, intoxication.

Vergiftungserscheinung, *f.* symptom of poisoning.

vergilben, *v.t.& i.* turn yellow.—vergilbt, *p.a.* yellowed.

vergipsen, *v.t.* plaster.

vergisst, *pr. 2 & 3 sing.* of vergessen.

vergittern, *v.t.* grate, lattice.

vergl., *abbrev.* (vergleiche) compare, cf.

verglasbar, *a.* vitrifiable.

verglasen, *v.t.* vitrify; glaze.—*v.i.& r.* vitrify.

Verglasung, *f.* vitrification; glaze; glazing.

Vergleich, *m.* comparison; agreement, arrangement, contract.

vergleichbar, *a.* comparable.

vergleichen, *v.t.* compare.—*v.r.* agree, come to terms.—vergleichend, *p.a.* comparative.

Vergleichprisma, *n.* comparison prism.

Vergleichs-fähigkeit, *f.* comparability. -flüssigkeit, *f.* comparison liquid. -lösung, *f.* comparison solution, standard solution. -massstab, *m.* standard of comparison. -präparat, *n.* comparison preparation. -verfahren, *n.* comparison method. -versuch, *m.* comparative experiment.

vergleichsweise, *adv.* by way of comparison, comparably.

Vergleichswert, *m.* comparative value.

Vergleichung, *f.* comparison.

verglimmen, *v.i.& r.* cease glowing, die out.

Verglühbrand, *m.* (*Ceram.*) biscuit baking.

verglühen, *v.t.* bake, give the biscuit fire to (porcelain).—*v.i.* cease glowing, cool down; burn out.

Verglühen, *n.* (*Ceram.*) biscuit baking.

Verglühofen, *m.* (*Ceram.*) biscuit kiln.

vergnügen, *v.t.* please, gratify.—*v.r.* enjoy

oneself, be delighted.—vergnügt, *p.a.* pleased, delighted; cheerful, gay.

Vergnügung, *f.* pleasure, amusement, sport.

vergolden, *v.t.* gild; plate with gold.—vergoldet, *p.a.* gilded, gilt; gold-plated.

Vergolderwachs, *n* gilder's wax.

Vergoldung, *f.* gilding; gold plating.

Vergoldungs-wachs, *n.* gilder's wax. -wasser, *n.* quickening liquid.

vergönnen, *v.t.* permit, grant.

vergoren, *p.a.* see vergären.

vergossen, *p.p.* of vergiessen.

Vergr., *abbrev.* (Vergrösserung) magnification.

vergraben, *v.t.* bury; intrench.

vergreifen, *v.r.* mistake; attack, violate; steal, embezzle.—*v.t.* buy up, buy out.—vergriffen, *p.a.* sold out; exhausted; out of print.

vergröbern, *v.t.* make coarser, coarsen.

vergrössern, *v.t.* increase, enlarge; magnify; exaggerate.—*v.r.* grow larger.

Vergrösserung, *f.* increase, enlargement; magnification; exaggeration.

Vergrösserungs-glas, *n.* magnifying glass. -kraft, *f.* magnifying power. -linse, *f.* magnifying lens.

vergrünen, *v.i.* turn green; lose green color, fade.

vergrünlich, *a.* (*Dyeing*) greenable.

vergüten, *v.t.* make good; improve; (*Metal.*) temper; compensate, allow.

Verh., *abbrev.* (Verhalten) behavior; (Verhältnis) proportion, ratio.

verhaften, *v.t.* arrest, apprehend.

verhagern, *v.i.* become lean or thin.

Verhalt, *m.* state, condition.

verhalten, *v.r.* behave, act, be.—*v.t.* hold (back), retain.

Verhalten, *n.* behavior; conduct; retention, suppression.

Verhältnis, *n.* proportion; ratio, rate; relation; situation, connection, circumstance. -anzeiger, *m.* (*Math.*) exponent. -gleichheit, *f.* proportion.

verhältnis-mässig, *a.* proportional, proportionate; relative; commensurable, commensurate.—*adv.* proportionately, relatively. -widrig, *a.* disproportionate.

Verhältniszahl, *f.* proportional number.

Verhaltung, *f.* = Verhalten.

verhandeln, *v.t.* transact; try; sell.—*v.i.* treat, negotiate.

Verhandlung, *f.* transaction; proceeding; debate.

verhängen, *v.t.* hang; decree, proclaim.

Verhängnis, *n.* destiny, fate.

verharren, *v.i.* remain, persist.

verhärten, *v.t.& i.* harden, indurate.

Verhärtung, *f.* hardening, induration.

verharzen, *v.i.& r.* become resinous, resinify.
—*v.t.* resin; convert into resin.

Verharzen, *n.*, Verharzung, *f.* resinification; resining.

verhauen, *v.t.* cut up, hack, prune.

verhehlen, *v.t.* hide, conceal; (*Warfare*) camouflage.

verheimlichen, *v.t.* keep secret, disguise.

verheiraten, *v.t.* give in marriage, marry.

verheissen, *v.t.* promise.

verhelfen, *v.t.* help, raise (to).

verhindern, *v.t.* hinder, prevent.

Verhinderung, *f.* hindrance, obstacle.

verholzen, *v.i.* lignify, become wood.

Verholzung, *f.* lignification.

Verhör, *n.* trial, hearing.

verhornen, *v.i.* become horny.

Verhornung, *f.* cornification.

verhüllen, *v.t.* wrap up, cover; veil, conceal.

verhungern, *v.i.* starve.

Verhungerung, *f.* starvation.

verhunzen, *v.t.* botch, bungle.

verhüten, *v.t.* avert, prevent.—verhütend, *p.a.* preventive.

verhütten, *v.t.* work, smelt (ores).

Verhüttung, *f.* (*Metal.*) working (off), smelting.

Verhütung, *f.* prevention, (*Med.*) prophylaxis.

Verhütungsmittel, *n.* preventive, prophylactic.

verimpfen, *v.t.* transmit (by inoculation or contagion).

verirren, *v.r.* err, go astray.

verjagen, *v.t.* drive out, drive off, expel.

verjähren, *v.i.* grow old; (*Law*) pass the time limit.

verjauchen, *v.i.* putrefy.

Verjauchung, *f.* putrefaction.

verjüngen, *v.t.* reduce, diminish, constrict, narrow; taper; rejuvenate, renew.

Verjüngung, *f.* diminution, reduction, (of a tube) constriction; rejuvenation.

verkadmiumieren, *v.t.* plate with cadmium.

verkalkbar, *a.* calcinable.

verkalken, *v.t.& i.* calcine; calcify.

Verkalkung, *f.* calcination; calcification.

verkannt, *p.p.* of verkennen.

verkappen, *v.t.* mask, disguise.

verkäsen, *v.i.* (*Med.*) become caseous, or cheesy.

Verkäsung, *f.* caseation.

verkauen, verkäuen, *v.t.* chew, chew up.—*v.r.* be chewed up.

Verkauf, *m.* sale.

verkaufen, *v.t.& r.* sell.

verkäuflich, *a.* salable, marketable.

Verkehr, *m.* traffic, commerce, trade; communication, intercourse.

verkehren, *v.t.* invert, reverse; pervert.—*v.i.* visit, associate.—verkehrt, *p.a.* inverted, reversed; wrong; absurd; perverted, perverse.

verkehrssicher, *a.* safe for commerce.— — Sprengstoff, safety explosive.

verkennen, *v.t.* mistake; misunderstand.

verketten, *v.t.* link (together), form into a chain.

Verkettung, *f.* linking, linkage.

Verkettungsfähigkeit, *f.* linking capacity, ability to form chains.

verkieseln, *v.t.* silicify.

Verkieselung, *f.* silicification.

verkiesen, *v.t.* gravel, ballast; pyritize.

verkitten, *v.t.* cement, lute; seal.

Verkittung, *f.* cementing, luting.

verklammern, *v.t.* clamp; (*Printing*) brace.

verkleben, *v.t.* cement, lute, cover or close by the use of an adhesive; agglutinate.

verkleiden, *v.t.* face, case, line; disguise, mask.

Verkleidung, *f.* facing, casing, lining; disguise.

verkleinern, *v.t.* diminish, reduce; disparage.

Verkleinerung, *f.* diminution, reduction; detraction.

verkleistern, *v.t.* paste up; make into paste; clog.—verkleistert, *p.a.* pasty.

Verkleisterung, *f.* conversion into paste; pasting; clogging.

verknallen, *v.t.& r.* detonate.

verknistern, *v.i.* decrepitate.

Verknisterung, *f.* decrepitation.

verknöchern, *v.i.* ossify.

Verknöcherung, *f.* ossification.

verknorpeln, *v.i.* become cartilaginous.— verknorpelt, *p.a.* cartilaginous.

Verknorpelung, *f.* chondrification.

verknüpfen, *v.t.* tie, bind, connect, join, link.

Verknüpfung, *f.* connection; linkage; union.

verkobalten, *v.t.* plate with cobalt.

Verkobaltung, *f.* cobalt plating.

verkochen, *v.t.* boil down, concentrate; injure by boiling, overheat.

verkohlen, *v.t.& i.* char, carbonize.

Verkohlung, *f.* charring, carbonization.

verkoken, *v.t.* coke.

Verkokung, *f.* coking.

verkokungsfähig, *a.* capable of coking.

Verkokungs-ofen, *m.* coke oven. -vorgang, *m.* coking process. -zeit, *f.* coking time.

verkommen, *v.i.* decay, degenerate; die.

verkoppeln, *v.t.* couple, link.

verkorken, *v.t.* cork.

verkörpern, *v.t.* embody.

verkreiden, *v.t.* calcify.

Verkreidung, *f.* calcification.

verkrümmen, *v.t.* crook, curve.

verkrusten, *v.i.* become incrusted.

verkühlen, *v.t.& r.* cool down.

verkümmern, *v.t.* stunt; interfere with, spoil. —*v.i.* be stunted; languish.

**verkünden, verkündigen,** *v.t.* announce, publish.

**verküpbar,** *a.* capable of use as a vat dye.

**verküpen,** *v.t.* reduce (a vat dye) preparatory to dyeing.

**verkupfern,** *v.t.* copper.

**Verkupferung,** *f.* coppering, copper plating.

**verkuppeln,** *v.t.* couple.

**verkürzen,** *v.t.* shorten, abridge, curtail, contract.

**Verl.,** *abbrev.* (Verlag) publishing house.

**verladen,** *v.t.* load; ship.

**Verlag,** *m.* publication; publishing house.

**Verlagerung,** *f.* displacement.

**Verlags-buchhändler,** *m.* publisher. **-buchhandlung,** *f.* publishing house. **-recht,** *n.* copyright.

**verlangen,** *v.t.* ask, demand, require; long for, want.—*v.i.* long, wish (for).

**verlängern,** *v.t.* lengthen, prolong, extend; replenish (dye liquor); (*Math.*) produce.— **verlängertes Mark,** medulla oblongata.

**Verlängerung,** *f.* prolongation, elongation, extension; (*Math.*) production.

**Verlängerungsstück,** *n.* extension piece.

**verlangsamen,** *v.t.* retard, slow down.

**Verlangsamung,** *f.* retardation.

**Verlass,** *m.* trust, reliance.

**verlassen,** *v.t.* leave, give up, abandon.— *v.r.* depend, rely.—*p.a.* abandoned, forsaken.

**verlässig, verlässlich,** *a.* reliable.

**Verlaub,** *m.* permission.

**Verlauf,** *m.* course; progress; lapse (of time).

**verlaufen,** *v.i.& r.* follow a course, proceed; (of time) pass; be scattered; run off; (of colors) blend.

**verlauten,** *v.i.* be heard, be reported.

**verleben,** *v.t.* live, pass (time).—**verlebt,** *p.a.* used up, decrepit.

**verlegen,** *v.t.* lay; mislay; transport, transfer; delay; obstruct; publish (books); misplace. —*p.a.* spoiled, stale; embarrassed, confused.

**Verlegenheit,** *f.* perplexity, difficulty.

**Verleger,** *m.* publisher.

**verleihen,** *v.t.* lend; bestow, confer, grant.

**verlernen,** *v.t.* unlearn, forget.

**verlesen,** *v.t.* pick; sort; read aloud.—*v.r.* read wrong.

**verletzen,** *v.t.* injure, damage, offend, infringe.

**verleugnen,** *v.t.* deny, disavow.

**verlieren,** *v.t.& i.* lose.—*v.r.* get lost; disappear.—**verlorener Kopf,** (*Metal.*) feedhead, dead head, top end.

**verlohnen,** *v.r.* be worth.

**verlor, verloren,** *pret. & p.p.* of verlieren.

**verlöschen,** *v.i.* go out, be extinguished.—

*v.t.* overburn (lime).—**verloschen,** *p.a.* gone out, dead.

**verlöten,** *v.t.* solder, solder up; (*Med.*) close by adhesion.

**Verlust,** *m.* loss; waste, escape; damage, detriment.

**verlustlos,** *a.& adv.* without loss, without waste.

**Verlustquelle,** *f.* source of loss.

**verm.,** *abbrev.* (vermehrt) enlarged; (vermindert) diminished, reduced.

**vermag,** *pr. 1 & 3 sing.* of vermögen.

**vermahlen,** *v.t.* grind; spoil in grinding.

**vermehren,** *v.t.* increase; enlarge; multiply; propagate.

**Vermehrung,** *f.* increase; enlargement; propagation.

**vermeidbar,** *a.* avoidable.

**vermeiden,** *v.t.* avoid; evade, elude, shirk.

**vermeinen,** *v.t.* think, suppose; mean.

**vermeintlich,** *a.* supposed; pretended; supposititious.

**vermengen,** *v.t.* mix, mingle, blend; confuse.

**Vermengung,** *f.* mixing, mixture, blending.

**Vermerk,** *m.* remark, note.

**vermessen,** *v.t.* measure; survey (land).— *v.r.* mismeasure; venture.—*p.a.* bold, presumptuous.

**vermessingen,** *v.t.* (*Metal.*) brass.

**Vermessingung,** *f.* brassing, brass plating.

**Vermessung,** *f.* measuring, measurement; surveying.

**vermieten,** *v.t.* let, hire out.

**Vermillon,** *m.* vermilion.

**vermindern,** *v.t.* diminish, lessen, reduce.— *v.r.* decline, diminish.

**Verminderung,** *f.* decrease, reduction, diminution.

**vermischen,** *v.t.* mix; adulterate; mingle, blend, alloy.—**vermischt,** *p.a.* mixed, miscellaneous; adulterated.

**Vermischung,** *f.* mixing, mixture; adulteration; alloy; medley.

**vermissen,** *v.t.* miss.

**vermitteln,** *v.t.* facilitate; mediate; adjust, arrange, bring about.—*v.i.* mediate.

**vermittelst,** *prep.* by means of, by help of.

**Vermittelung,** *f.* agency, means; mediation, interposition; adjustment; conveyance.

**vermodern,** *v.i.* molder, decay.—**vermodert,** *p.a.* moldy, decayed.

**vermöge,** *prep.* by virtue of, according to.

**vermögen,** *v.t.* be able, have power, have influence; induce.—**vermögend,** *p.a.* propertied, wealthy.

**Vermögen,** *n.* ability, power; property.

**vermuten,** *v.t.* suppose, think, conjecture, suspect.

**vermutlich,** *a.* probable.—*adv.* probably.

**Vermutung,** *f.* supposition, conjecture, surmise.

**vernachlässigbar,** *a.* negligible.

**vernachlässigen,** *v.t.* neglect, disregard.

**vernarben,** *v.i.* scar, be cicatrized.

**vernebeln,** *v.t.* convert into mist or fog, atomize.

**vernehmen,** *v.t.* perceive, distinguish; hear, learn.

**Vernehmen,** *n.* hearing, report; understanding.

**vernehmlich,** *a.* perceptible; audible; distinct.

**verneinen,** *v.t.* deny, disavow, contradict.— **verneinend,** *p.a.* negative.

**vernichten,** *v.t.* destroy, annihilate, annul.

**Vernichtung,** *f.* destruction, annihilation.

**vernickeln,** *v.t.* nickel, nickel-plate.

**Vernickelung,** *f.* nickeling, nickel plating.

**vernieten,** *v.t.* rivet.

**Vernunft,** *f.* reason, intellect, intelligence, judgment.

**vernünftig,** *a.* rational, reasonable, sensible.

**veröden,** *v.i.* become waste.—*v.t.* lay waste.

**veröffentlichen,** *v.t.* publish; advertise.

**Veröffentlichung,** *f.* publication; announcement; advertisement.

**Veroneser-erde,** *f.* Verona earth. **-gelb,** *n.* Verona yellow. **-grün,** *n.* Verona green (Verona earth).

**verordnen,** *v.t.* order, prescribe, decree; appoint.

**Verordnung,** *f.* order, decree, regulation; appointment; (*Med.*) prescription.

**verpacken,** *v.t.* pack, pack up.

**Verpackflasche,** *f.* packing bottle (ordinary round bottle, with or without glass stopper).

**Verpackung,** *f.* packing; bagging, casking, etc.; casing, lining.

**verpassen,** *v.t.* lose, miss.

**verpechen,** *v.t.* pitch, treat with pitch.

**verpesten,** *v.t.* infect, poison, taint.

**verpflanzen,** *v.t.* transplant; transmit.

**verpflegen,** *v.t.* take care of, nurse, tend.

**verpflichten,** *v.t.* oblige; bind.

**Verpflichtung,** *f.* obligation, duty.

**verpfuschen,** *v.t.* bungle, botch.

**verpichen,** *v.t.* pitch, treat with pitch.

**Verpichung,** *f.* pitching; pitch formation.

**verplatinieren,** *v.t.* platinize.

**Verplatinierung,** *f.* platinization.

**verpönen,** *v.t.* forbid.

**verpuffen,** *v.i.* puff off, deflagrate; explode, detonate.

**Verpuffung,** *f.* deflagration; explosion, detonation.

**Verpuffungs-apparat,** *m.* explosion apparatus. **-probe,** *f.* deflagration test. **-röhre,** *f.* explosion tube.

**Verputz,** *m.* plastering, plaster.

**verputzen,** *v.t.* plaster; dress, clean.

**verquellen,** *v.i.* swell, swell up; warp; flow away.

**verquicken,** *v.t.* quicken, amalgamate.

**verraten,** *v.t.* betray.

**verrauchen,** *v.i.* evaporate.

**verrechnen,** *v.t.* reckon.—*v.r.* be mistaken, miscalculate.

**verreiben,** *v.t.* grind fine, triturate; spread by rubbing.

**verrenken,** *v.t.* sprain, dislocate.

**verrichten,** *v.t.* do, perform, execute.

**Verrichtung,** *f.* performance, execution, action; business, affair, function.

**verringern,** *v.t.* diminish, lessen, decrease, reduce, attenuate.

**verrinnen,** *v.i.* run off; (of time) pass.

**verrosten,** *v.i.* rust.—**verrostet,** *p.a.* rusted, rusty.

**Verrostung,** *f.* rusting.

**verrotten,** *v.i.* rot.—**verrottet,** *p.a.* rotten.

**verrucht,** *p.a.* infamous, nefarious.

**verrücken,** *v.t.* displace, disturb, derange.— **verrückt,** *p.a.* deranged, insane, crazy.

**Verrückung,** *f.* displacement.

**verrühren,** *v.t.* stir up, mix up (by stirring).

**verrussen,** *v.t.* foul with soot, smoke; Russianize.—*v.i.* become sooty or smoked.

**Vers.,** *abbrev.* (Versuch) experiment, test, effort; (Versammlung) meeting.

**versagen,** *v.t.* deny, refuse; promise.—*v.i.* fail to work, miss.

**versalzen,** *v.t.* oversalt; mar.

**versammeln,** *v.t.& r.* assemble.

**Versammlung,** *f.* assembly, meeting, convention, congress.

**Versand,** *m.* shipping, dispatch; exportation. **-bier,** *n.* export beer.

**versandfähig,** *a.* fit for shipment.

**Versand-fass,** *n.* shipping cask (barrel, keg). **-schachtel,** *f.* shipping case.

**Versatz,** *m.* mixing, etc. (see versetzen); packing; (*Ceram.*) batch; (*Leather*) layer (also, lay-away); (*Mining*) gobbing.

**versauern,** *v.i.* turn sour.

**versäuern,** *v.t.* acidify, make sour.

**Versäuerung,** *f.* acidification; souring.

**versäumen,** *v.t.* miss, fail, neglect.

**verschaffen,** *v.t.* procure, supply, secure, get.

**verschärfen,** *v.t.* sharpen, intensify.

**verschäumen,** *v.i.* cease foaming; foam away.

**verscheiden,** *v.i.* expire, die.

**verschenken,** *v.t.* give away; retail.

**verschiebbar,** *a.* displaceable; movable, sliding.

**verschieben,** *v.t.* displace; shift, remove; postpone.

**Verschiebung,** *f.* displacement, etc. (see verschieben); (*Geol.*) dislocation, slip; (*Elec.*) lag.

**Verschiebungs-gesetz,** *n.* displacement law. **-satz,** *m.* displacement principle.

**verschieden,** *a.* different, differing, various; deceased. **-artig,** *a.* different, unlike, various, heterogeneous. **-farbig,** *a.* of different colors, varicolored.

**Verschiedenheit,** *f.* difference, variety, diversity.

**verschiedentlich,** *a.* different.—*adv.* differently, variously, at different times.

**verschiessen,** *v.i.* fade, discolor; shoot away. —*v.t.* shoot off, discharge; shade off (colors).

**verschimmeln,** *v.i.* mold, grow moldy.— **verschimmelt,** *p.a.* moldy.

**verschlacken,** *v.t.* scorify.—*v.i.* be reduced to scoria, slag.

**Verschlackung,** *f.* scorification; slagging.

**Verschlackungsprobe,** *f.* scorification assay.

**verschlafen,** *v.t.* sleep away, sleep off, oversleep.—*p.a.* sleepy.

**Verschlag,** *m.* partition; compartment.

**verschlagen,** *v.i.* warm a little, grow lukewarm; matter, make a difference.—*v.t.* take the chill off; board up, close up; partition; lose or spoil by striking; recoin; drive away. —*p.a.* slightly warmed, tepid; cunning, wily.

**verschlechtern,** *v.r.* deteriorate, spoil.—*v.t.* make worse, impair, debase.

**verschleiern,** *v.t.* veil.—**verschleiert,** *p.a.* (of beer, etc.) hazy, slightly cloudy.

**verschleimen,** *v.t.* choke up with mucus or slime, foul.—**verschleimt,** *p.a.* slimy.

**Verschleiss,** *m.* wear (and tear); retail, sale.

**verschleissen,** *v.t.* wear out; retail.

**verschleppen,** *v.t.* misplace, carry off; protract.

**verschleudern,** *v.t.* squander, sell very cheap.

**verschliessbar,** *a.* capable of being closed (or locked).

**verschliessen,** *v.t.* close, stop; stopper; shut; lock; reserve; protect.

**verschlimmern,** *v.t.* make worse.

**verschlingen,** *v.t.* twist, entangle; intertwine, interweave; devour, swallow.

**verschlossen,** *p.p.* of verschliessen.

**verschlucken,** *v.t.* absorb; swallow.

**verschlungen,** *p.p.* of verschlingen.

**Verschluss,** *m.* closing, closure, stopping; fastening; shutting; locking; fastener, stopper, seal, lock, clasp, snap; trap (for water, etc.); (*Photog.*) shutter; (of dutiable goods) bond. **-hahn,** *m.* stopcock. **-kölbchen,** *n.* a small flask with a special fastening, pressure flask. **-stück,** *n.* plug, stopper; lid.

**verschmälern,** *v.t.* narrow, diminish.

**verschmelzen,** *v.t.* melt, smelt, fuse; melt together; solder; blend (colors).—*v.i.* melt, melt away; blend, merge, coalesce.

**Verschmelzung,** *f.* melting, smelting, fusion; alloy; blending, coalescence.

**Verschmelzungskörper,** *m.* alloy constituent.

**verschmieren,** *v.t.* smear, daub, lute.

**verschmitzt,** *p.a.* artful, subtle.

**verschmutzen,** *v.t.* soil, pollute.

**verschneiden,** *v.t.* clip, cut, prune; castrate; blend; adulterate.

**Verschnitt,** *m.* cuttings, chips. **-wein,** *m.* adulterated wine.

**verschoben,** *p.p.* of verschieben.

**verschollen,** *p.a.* missing, lost.

**verschonen,** *v.t.* spare, excuse.

**verschönern,** *v.t.* beautify.

**verschossen,** *p.p.* of verschiessen.

**verschränken,** *v.t.* cross, interlace.

**verschrauben,** *v.t.* screw up; screw wrong.— **verschroben,** *p.a.* distorted, tangled; eccentric, queer.

**Verschraubung,** *f.* screwing; screw cap; screw joint.

**verschreiben,** *v.t.* prescribe; order; transfer in writing; miswrite; use up (paper) in writing.

**Verschreibung,** *f.* prescription; order; assignment, note, bond.

**verschroben,** *p.a.* see verschrauben.

**verschrumpfen,** *v.i.* shrink, contract.

**verschuldet,** *p.a.* indebted, in debt; merited.

**verschütten,** *v.t.* spill, shed; fill up, choke, bury.

**verschweigen,** *v.t.* keep secret, suppress.

**verschwelen,** *v.t. & i.* = schwelen.

**verschwellen,** *v.i.* swell, swell up, swell shut.

**Verschwelung,** *f.* = Schwelung.

**verschwenden,** *v.t.* waste, squander.

**verschwimmen,** *v.i.* (of colors) blend; blur; dissolve, vanish.—**verschwommen,** *p.a.* indistinct, indefinite, blurred.

**verschwinden,** *v.i.* disappear, vanish.

**verschwommen,** *p.a.* see verschwimmen.

**versehen,** *v.t.* provide, supply, furnish; perform, conduct, attend to; be mistaken in. —*v.r.* be aware, expect; provide oneself; make a mistake, be in error.—*p.a.* provided, furnished, supplied.

**Versehen,** *n.* oversight, error.

**verseifbar,** *a.* saponifiable.

**Verseifbarkeit,** *f.* saponifiability.

**verseifen,** *v.t.* saponify.

**Verseifung,** *f.* saponification.

**Verseifungs-fass,** *n.* saponifying tun. **-mittel,** *n.* saponifying agent. **-zahl,** *f.* saponification number or value.

**versenden,** *v.t.* send, transmit, forward, export.

**Versender,** *m.* sender, shipper, consigner, exporter.

**versengen,** *v.t.* singe, scorch.

**versenken,** *v.t.* sink, lower, submerge.

**versetzbar,** *a.* capable of being mixed, treated, etc. (see versetzen); portable.

**versetzen,** *v.t.* mix, treat, compound (— A mit B, add B to A); alloy (metals); handle (hides); stop, tamp, obstruct; transfer, transpose, transplant; stagger; misplace; pledge, mortgage.—*v.r.* change course; be stopped up.

**Versetzung,** *f.* mixing, etc. (see versetzen); (*Med.*) retention; (*Math.*) permutation; alligation.

**verseuchen,** *v.t.* infect.

**versichern,** *v.t.* insure; assure, assert.—*v.r.* make sure (of).

**Versicherung,** *f.* insurance; assurance, affirmation.

**Versicherungsschein,** *m.* insurance policy; bond.

**versickern,** *v.i.* ooze away, seep away.

**Versickerung,** *f.* seepage.

**versiegen,** *v.i.* dry up, be exhausted.

**versilbern,** *v.t.* silver, silver-plate.

**Versilberung,** *f.* silvering, silver plating.

**Versilberungsbad,** *n.* silver bath.

**versinken,** *v.i.* sink.

**versinn-bilden, -bildlichen,** *v.t.* symbolize, represent.

**versintern,** *v.i.* sinter.

**versorgen,** *v.t.* provide for, provide, supply.

**Versorgung,** *f.* provision, maintenance, supply; situation.

**verspäten,** *v.t.* retard, delay.—*v.r.* be late.

**versperren,** *v.t.* obstruct, block.

**versprechen,** *v.t.* promise.—*v.r.* make a slip; be engaged.

**verspritzen,** *v.t.* spurt, squirt, spill, spatter.

**versprühen,** *v.i.* fly away in spray or sparks.

**verspüren,** *v.t.* perceive, feel.

**Verss.,** *abbrev.* (Versuche) experiments, trials.

**verstaatlichen,** *v.t.* take over by the government, nationalize.

**Verstaatlichung,** *f.* nationalization.

**verstählen,** *v.t.* convert into steel; coat or edge with steel, steel.

**Verstand,** *m.* understanding, intelligence, sense.

**verständig,** *a.* intelligent, reasonable, sensible.

**verständigen,** *v.t.* inform.—*v.r.* agree, arrange.

**verständlich,** *a.* intelligible.

**Verständnis,** *n.* comprehension, intelligence.

**verstärken,** *v.t.* strengthen, increase, reinforce, fortify, concentrate, intensify, amplify.

**Verstärker,** *m.* intensifier; (*Elec.*) amplifier.

**Verstärkung,** *f.* strengthening, etc. (see verstärken).

**verstatten,** *v.t.* permit, allow.

**verstauben,** *v.i.* become dusty.

**verstäuben,** *v.t.* convert into dust; scatter as dust, atomize.

**verstauchen,** *v.t.* sprain, strain.

**verstechen,** *v.t.* blend; adulterate.

**verstecken,** *v.t.* hide, conceal.—*v.r.* hide, lurk.—**versteckt,** *p.a.* hidden; insincere.

**verstehen,** *v.t.* understand; mean.—*v.r.* agree, consent; be good or skilled (at); have an understanding; be understood.

**versteifen,** *v.i. & r.* stiffen.

**versteigern,** *v.t.* sell at auction.

**versteinern,** *v.t.* petrify.

**Versteinerung,** *f.* petrifaction.

**Versteinerungsmittel,** *n.* (*Min.*) mineralizing agent.

**Versteinung,** *f.* (*Metal.*) devitrification.

**verstellbar,** *a.* movable, adjustable.

**verstellen,** *v.t.* shift, move; transpose; misplace; obstruct; disguise.—*v.r.* dissemble. **verstellt,** *p.a.* feigned, fictitious.

**Verstellvorrichtung,** *f.* adjusting device.

**versteuern,** *v.t.* pay duty on.—**versteuert,** *p.a.* duty-paid.

**verstocken,** *v.t.* harden.—*v.i.* mold, rot; grow stubborn.

**verstopfen,** *v.t.* stop, stop up, choke, clog, obstruct; (*Med.*) constipate.

**Verstopfung,** *f.* stopping up, clogging, obstruction; (*Med.*) constipation.

**verstöpseln,** *v.t.* stopper.

**verstorben,** *p.a.* deceased, late.

**verstören,** *v.t.* disturb, confuse, trouble.

**verstossen,** *v.t.* cast off, repel, reject.—*v.i.* blunder, offend.

**verstreichen,** *v.t.* fill up, stop up, spread over.—*v.i.* elapse, expire.

**verstreuen,** *v.t.* disperse, scatter.

**verstricken,** *v.t.* entangle.

**verstümmeln,** *v.t.* mutilate, maim; curtail.

**verstummen,** *v.i.* become dumb.

**Versuch,** *m.* experiment; assay, trial, test; attempt, effort.

**versuchen,** *v.t.* try, test; taste, sample (liquors, etc.); attempt.—*v.i.* experiment.

**Versuchs-anlage,** *f.* testing plant; experimental plant. **-anordnung,** *f.* mode of (experimental) procedure. **-anstalt,** *f.* research institute or institution; experimental plant. **-bedingung,** *f.* experimental condition(s). **-dauer,** *f.* duration of experiment, time of experimentation. **-fehler,** *m.* experimental error. **-feld,** *n.* field for experiment. **-gefäss,** *n.* experimental vessel (in which an experiment is conducted). **-laboratorium,** *n.* experimental laboratory. **-material,** *n.* experimental material. **-methode,** *f.* experimental method; tentative method. **-muster,**

*n.* = Gebrauchsmuster. **-raum,** *m.* laboratory; research space. **-reihe,** *f.* series of experiments or tests. **-rohr,** *n.,* **-röhre,** *f.* experimental tube. **-serie,** *f.* = Versuchsreihe. **-stab,** *m.* test rod or bar. **-station, -stelle,** *f.* experiment station. **-tier,** *n.* experimental animal. **-vorschrift,** *f.* experimental directions.

**versuchsweise,** *adv.* by way of experiment, tentatively; on approval.

**Versuchswesen,** *n.* research.

**Versuchtier,** *n.* experimental animal.

**Versuchung,** *f.* experimenting, experiment; temptation.

**versüssen,** *v.t.* sweeten; purify by washing, edulcorate; oversweeten.—**versüsster Salpetergeist,** (*Pharm.*) sweet spirit of niter, spirit of nitrous ether.—**versüsster Salzgeist,** sweet spirit of salt.

**Versüssung,** *f.* sweetening, etc. (see versüssen).

**Versüssungsmittel,** *n.* sweetening agent, sweetener.

**vertagen,** *v.t.* adjourn.

**vertauschen,** *v.t.* exchange, change.

**Vertauschung,** *f.* exchange, interchange.

**verte,** *v.* turn over, turn the leaf.

**verteeren,** *v.t.* tar.

**verteidigen,** *v.t.* defend, maintain.

**Verteidigung,** *f.* protection; defense, advocacy.

**verteilen,** *v.t.* distribute; divide; disperse; disseminate, diffuse, spread; dispense, apportion, assign.

**Verteiler,** *m.* distributor.

**Verteilung,** *f.* distribution, etc. (see verteilen); division.

**Verteilungs-gesetz,** *n.* law of distribution. **-mittel,** *n.* distributing agent. **-rohr,** *n.,* **-röhre,** *f.* distributing tube or pipe; (of a blast furnace) blast main. **-satz,** *m.* principle of distribution, distribution law.

**verteuern,** *v.t.* raise in price.

**Vertheil-.** see Verteil-.

**vertiefen,** *v.t.* deepen.—*v.r.* be deeply engaged.

**Vertiefung,** *f.* deepening; depression, cavity, recess, indentation.

**Vertikalachse,** *f.* vertical axis.

**vertilgen,** *v.t.* extirpate, eradicate, destroy.

**Vertilgungsmittel,** *n.* eradicator, destroyer.

**Vertrag,** *m.* contract, agreement, bargain, treaty.

**vertragen,** *v.t.* bear, endure, tolerate.—*v.r.* be compatible, be consistent, agree, harmonize.

**verträglich,** *a.* compatible, consistent, amicable.

**Verträglichkeit,** *f.* compatibility, peaceableness.

**vertrauen,** *v.t.& i.* trust, confide.—**vertraut,** *p.a.* intimate, conversant.

**vertrauenswürdig,** *a.* trustworthy.

**vertraulich,** *a.* confidential, intimate.

**vertreiben,** *v.t.* drive away, dispel, expel, disperse; sell; soften (colors).

**vertretbar,** *a.* replaceable; capable of being attended to, or represented, by deputy.

**Vertretbarkeit,** *f.* replaceability, etc. (see vertretbar).

**vertreten,** *v.t.* replace, take the place of; represent; stretch, strain; obstruct.

**Vertreter,** *m.* substituent; representative; substitute, deputy; intercessor.

**Vertrieb,** *m.* sale, market.

**vertrocknen,** *v.i.* dry up, wither.

**Vertrocknung,** *f.* drying up, desiccation.

**vertun,** *v.t.* waste, lavish.

**verunglücken,** *v.i.* come to grief.

**verunreinigen,** *v.t.* render impure, contaminate, soil, vitiate, pollute.

**Verunreinigung,** *f.* impurity; contamination, pollution.

**verunstalten,** *v.t.* deform, disfigure.

**verunzieren,** *v.t.* deface, disfigure.

**verursachen,** *v.t.* cause, produce.

**verurteilen,** *v.t.* condemn, sentence.

**verviel-fachen, -fältigen,** *v.t.* multiply.

**vervierfachen,** *v.t.* quadruple.

**vervollkommnen,** *v.t.* perfect, improve.

**vervollständigen,** *v.t.* complete.

**Vervollständigung,** *f.* completion.

**verw.,** *abbrev.* (verwandt) related.

**verwachsen,** *v.i.* grow together, coalesce; grow crooked; be overgrown.—*v.t.* outgrow.—*p.a.* grown together, intergrown; deformed.

**verwahren,** *v.t.* keep, guard, preserve.

**verwahrlosen,** *v.t.* neglect, slight.

**Verwahrung,** *f.* keeping, preservation; protest.

**verwalten,** *v.t.* manage, administer.

**Verwaltung,** *f.* administration; management.

**verwandelbar,** *a.* transformable, convertible.

**Verwandelbarkeit,** *f.* transformability, convertibility.

**verwandeln,** *v.t.* transform, convert, turn, change; metamorphose.

**Verwandlung,** *f.* transformation, etc. (see verwandeln).

**verwandt,** *p.a.* related; allied, cognate; analogous.

**Verwandte,** *m.& f.* relative, relation.

**Verwandtschaft,** *f.* affinity; relationship; kindred; congeniality.

**Verwandtschafts-einheit,** *f.* unit of affinity, valence. **-lehre,** *f.* doctrine of affinity.

**verwaschen,** *v.t.* wash, wash out.—*p.a.* washed out, faded.

**Verwaschenheit,** *f.* washed-out or faded state, indistinctness.

**verwässern,** *v.t.* water, dilute, weaken.

**verweben,** *v.t.* weave.—*v.r.* interlace, intermingle.

**verwechseln,** *v.t.* exchange; mix up, confound.

**verwehen,** *v.t.* blow away.—*v.i.* blow over.

**verwehren,** *v.t.* prevent, forbid, refuse.

**verweigern,** *v.t.* refuse, decline.

**verweilen,** *v.i.* stay, tarry.

**Verweilzeit,** *f.* duration, time of stay.

**verweisen,** *v.t.* refer; expel, banish; rebuke.

**Verweisung,** *f.* reference; banishment; reproof.

**verwelken,** *v.i.* fade, wither.

**verwendbar,** *a.* available, applicable.

**verwenden,** *v.t.* employ, apply, use; invest; turn away.—*v.r.* intercede.

**Verwendung,** *f.* application, use; appropriation; intercession.

**Verwendungs-stoffwechsel,** *m.* catabolism. **-zweck,** *m.* intended use.

**verwerfen,** *v.t.* reject, repudiate, abandon; misplace, (*Mining*) dislocate.—*v.r.* warp; misthrow.

**Verwerfung,** *f.* rejection; (*Mining*) dislocation, throw, slip, fault.

**verwertbar,** *a.* utilizable.

**verwerten,** *v.t.* utilize, turn to account.

**Verwertung,** *f.* utilization.

**verwesen,** *v.i.* rot, decay, decompose.—*v.t.* administer, manage.

**verweslich,** *a.* liable to decay.

**Verwesung,** *f.* decay, (slow) decomposition; administration.

**Verwesungsprozess,** *m.* process of decay or decomposition.

**verwichen,** *p.a.* past, former.

**verwickeln,** *v.t.* complicate, involve, entangle. —**verwickelt,** *p.a.* complicated, involved.

**Verwickelung,** *f.* complication; complexity; plot.

**verwiegen,** *v.t.* weigh, weigh out.—*v.r.* weigh wrong.

**verwinden,** *v.t.* get over, recover from.

**verwirklichen,** *v.t.* realize.

**verwirren,** *v.t.* tangle; perplex, embarrass.— **verworren, verwirrt,** *p.a.* complicated, complex; confused; puzzled, distracted.

**verwischen,** *v.t.* blot out, efface.

**verwittern,** *v.i.* effloresce; disintegrate; (of rocks, etc.) weather; (of lime) air-slake.

**Verwitterung,** *f.* efflorescence; weathering.

**verworfen,** *p.p.* of verwerfen.

**verworren,** *p.a.* see verwirren.

**verwunden,** *v.t.* wound.

**verwundern,** *v.t.* astonish, surprise.—*v.r.* wonder.

**verzählen,** *v.t.* miscount.

**verzahnen,** *v.t.* tooth, cog, indent.

**verzapfen,** *v.t.* join, mortise; retail (liquors).

**verzehren,** *v.t.* consume; spend.

**verzeichnen,** *v.t.* note down, record, catalog, specify; misdraw; (*Optics*) distort.

**Verzeichnis,** *n.* list, register, index, catalog, inventory, invoice.

**Verzeichnung,** *f.* listing, etc. (see verzeichnen).

**verzeihen,** *v.t.* pardon, excuse.

**verzerren,** *v.t.* distort, deform.

**Verzicht,** *m.* renunciation.—**auf ... — leisten,** relinquish, give up, waive.

**verzichten,** *v.i.* (with auf) relinquish, give up.

**verziehen,** *v.t.* distort; pardon.—*v.r.* warp; buckle; withdraw, disappear.—*v.i.* stay; move.

**verzieren,** *v.t.* decorate, ornament, illustrate (books).

**Verzierung,** *f.* decoration, ornamentation.

**verzinken,** *v.t.* coat with zinc, galvanize, zinc.

**Verzinken,** *n.,* **Verzinkung,** *f.* zincking, galvanizing.

**verzinnen,** *v.t.* tin.—**verzinntes Eisenblech,** tin plate.

**Verzinnen,** *n.,* **Verzinnung,** *f.* tinning.

**verzinsen,** *v.t.* pay interest on.—*v.r.* yield interest, pay.

**verzogen,** *p.p.* of verziehen.

**Verzögerer,** *m.* retarder, retarding agent; (*Photog.*) restrainer.

**verzögern,** *v.t.* retard; delay, postpone.

**Verzögerung,** *f.* retardation; delay, postponement; lag.

**verzollen,** *v.t.* pay duty on.—**verzollt,** *p.a.* duty paid.

**verzuckern,** *v.t.* saccharify; sugar, candy.

**Verzuckerung,** *f.* saccharification; sugaring, candying.

**Verzuckung,** *f.* convulsion.

**Verzug,** *m.* delay; distortion, deformation.

**verzweifeln,** *v.i.* despair.

**verzweigen,** *v.t.* branch, ramify.

**Verzweigung,** *f.* branching, ramification.

**verzwillingt,** *p.a.* twinned.

**vexieren,** *v.t.* vex, puzzle.

**Vf.,** *abbrev.* (Verfasser) author.

**Vff.,** *abbrev.* (Verfasser) authors.

**V-förmig,** *a.* V-shaped.

**vgl.,** *abbrev.* (vergleiche) compare, see, cf.

**v.H.,** *abbrev.* (vom Hundert) per cent.

**vibrieren,** *v.i.* vibrate.

**Vidalschwarz,** *n.* Vidal black.

**Vieh,** *n.* cattle; beast, brute. **-dünger,** *m.* stable manure. **-futter,** *n.* fodder, forage. **-salz,** *n.* cattle salt, salt for animals. **-waschmittel,** *n.* dip (for animals).

**viel,** *a.* much; (*pl.*) many.—*adv.* much.

**viel-.** much, many, multi-, poly-. **-atomig,** *a.* polyatomic. **-deutig,** *a.* ambiguous.

**Vieleck,** *n.* polygon.

**viel-eckig,** *a.* polygonal, multangular. **-erlei,**

*a.* various, multifarious. **-fach,** *a.* manifold, various; frequent.

**Vielfach, Vielfache,** *n.* multiple.

**vielfältig,** *a.* manifold, various; frequent.

**Vielfältigkeit,** *f.* multiplicity, variety.

**vielfarbig,** *a.* many-colored, variegated, polychromatic.

**Vielflach,** *n.* polyhedron.

**vielflächig,** *a.* polyhedral.

**Vielflächner,** *m.* polyhedron.

**viel-förmig,** *a.* multiform, polymorphous. **-gliederig,** *a.* (*Math.*) polynomial. **-kernig,** *a.* polycyclic; multinuclear, polynuclear.

**vielleicht,** *adv.* perhaps, possibly.

**Viellinienspektrum,** *n.* many-line spectrum.

**viellinig,** *a.* many-line, multilinear.

**vielmehr,** *adv.* much more, more.—*conj.* rather.

**viel-polig,** *a.* multipolar. **-sagend,** *p.a.* expressive, significant. **-säurig,** *a.* polyacid.

**Vielseit,** *n.* polyhedron.

**viel-seitig,** *a.* many-sided; (*Geom.*) polyhedral. **-teilig,** *a.* of many parts; (*Math.*) polynomial. **-versprechend,** *a.* very promising. **-wertig,** *a.* multivalent, polyvalent.

**Vielwertigkeit,** *f.* multivalence, polyvalence.

**vielzellig,** *a.* multicellular.

**vier,** *a.* four.

**vier-, Vier-.** four-, tetra-, quadri-, quadruple.

**vier-atomig,** *a.* tetratomic. **-basisch,** *a.* tetrabasic.

**vierdrittel,** *a.* designating a salt which contains four units of base to three of acid; as, — **kohlensaures Natrium,** $Na_2CO_3 \cdot 2NaHCO_3 \cdot 3H_2O$ (trona).

**Viereck,** *n.* quadrangle.

**viereckig,** *a.* four-cornered, quadrangular (specif. square).

**Vierervektor,** *m.* four-component vector, four-vector.

**vierfach, vierfältig,** *a.* fourfold, quadruple, quadruplex; quaternary.

**vierfach-.** (in old names) tetra-, quadri-. **— -Chlorkohlenstoff,** carbon tetrachloride.

**Vier-flach,** *n.,* **-flächner,** *m.* tetrahedron.

**vierflächig,** *a.* four-faced, tetrahedral.

**Vierfuss,** *m.* four-footed stand.

**vier-gliedrig,** *a.* four-membered; (*Cryst.*) tetragonal; (*Math.*) quadrinomial. **-jährig,** *a.* quadrennial.

**Vierkant-.** square.

**vier-kantig,** *a.* = viereckig. **-komponentig,** *a.* four-component. **-phasig,** *a.* four-phase. **-quantig,** *a.* of four quanta, 4-quantum. **-reihig,** *a.* of four series, four-series.

**Vierring,** *m.* four-membered ring.

**viersäurig,** *a.* tetracid.

**Vierseit,** *n.* quadrilateral.

**vierseitig,** *a.* four-sided, quadrilateral (specif. square).

**Viertakt,** *m.* (*Mach.*) four-stroke cycle.

**vierte,** *a.* fourth.

**vierteilen,** *v.t.* quarter.

**Viertel,** *n.* fourth, quarter. **-jahr,** *n.* quarter (of a year), three months. **-jahresschrift,** *f.* quarterly. **-stunde,** *f.* quarter of an hour.

**Vierundzwanzigflächner,** *m.* icositetrahedron.

**vierwandig,** *a.* four-walled.

**Vierweg(e)hahn,** *m.* four-way cock.

**vierwertig,** *a.* quadrivalent, tetravalent.

**Vierwertigkeit,** *f.* quadrivalence, tetravalence.

**vierzählig,** *a.* fourfold.

**vierzehn,** *a.* fourteen.

**vierzig,** *a.* forty.

**Vinylcyanür,** *n.* vinyl cyanide.

**Viole,** *f.* violet; viol.

**Violenwurzel,** *f.* orris root.

**Violettschwarz,** *n.* violet black.

**violettstichig,** *a.* violet-tinged.

**virginisch,** *a.* Virginian.

**Virialsatz,** *m.* virial principle.

**virtuell,** *a.* virtual.

**visc-, Visc-.** see visk-, Visk-.

**Visetholz,** *n.* fustet, young fustic.

**visieren,** *v.t.* gage; aim; visé.

**Visitenkarte,** *f.* visiting card.

**visitieren,** *v.t.* visit; search.

**viskos, viskös,** *a.* viscous.

**Viskosität,** *f.* viscosity.

**visuell,** *a.* visual.

**Vitalfärbung,** *f.* vital staining, *intra-vitam* staining.

**vitrifizieren,** *v.t.* vitrify.

**vitriolartig,** *a.* vitriolic, like vitriol.

**Vitriol-bildung,** *f.* vitriolation. **-blei,** *n.* lead vitriol ($PbSO_4$). **-bleierz,** *n.,* **-bleispat,** *m.* anglesite. **-erz,** *n.* vitriol(ic) ore. **-fabrik,** *f.* vitriol (sulfuric-acid) works. **-flasche,** *f.* carboy. **-gelb,** *n.* (*Min.*) jarosite.

**vitriolhaltig,** *a.* containing vitriol, vitriolic.

**Vitriolhütte,** *f.* = Vitriolfabrik.

**vitriolisch, vitriolig,** *a.* vitriolic.

**vitriolisieren,** *v.t.* vitriolate.

**Vitriol-kies,** *m.* marcasite. **-küpe,** *f.* blue vat, copperas vat. **-öl,** *n.* oil of vitriol (sulfuric acid). **-säure,** *f.* vitriolic acid (sulfuric acid). **-schiefer,** *m.* pyritic shale or schist. **-siederei,** *f.* = Vitriolfabrik.

**Vitsbohne,** *f.* kidney bean.

**vizinal,** *a.* vicinal, neighboring.

**v.J., v.Jr.,** *abbrev.* (vorigen Jahres) of last year; (vom Jahre) of the year.

**Vlies, Vliess,** *n.* fleece.

**v.M.,** *abbrev.* (vorigen Monats) last month.

**v.o.,** *abbrev.* (von oben) from above, from the top.

**Vogel,** *m.* bird. **-amber,** *m.* spermaceti.

-beerbaum, *m.* mountain ash, service tree.
-beere, *f.* berry of the mountain ash, service berry. -beersäure, *f.* sorbic acid. -dunst, *m.* fine bird shot, dust shot. -ei, *n.* bird's egg. -kirsche, *f.* bird cherry. -kunde, *f.* ornithology. -leim, *m.* birdlime, bird glue. -mist, *m.* bird dung. -perspektive, *f.* bird's-eye (view).

Vogt, *m.* magistrate (of various kinds, as bailiff, judge, governor, etc.); steward.

Vokal, *m.* vowel.

Vol-.Gew., *abbrev.* (Volumgewicht) volume weight.

Volk, *n.* people; nation; forces, men; flock, herd.

Völkerbund, *m.* league of nations.

Volks-. popular, people's, public, national.

volkstümlich, *a.* popular, national.

Volkswirtschaft, *f.* political economy.

voll, *a.* full; (of leather) compact, plump; whole, entire, complete; gross (price). -auf, *adv.* in abundance, plentifully. -blütig, *a.* plethoric. -bringen, *v.t.* accomplish, execute, achieve.

Volldruck, *m.* full pressure.

vollenden, *v.t.* finish, terminate, complete, perfect.—vollendet, *p.a.* accomplished, perfect.

vollends, *adv.* wholly, altogether; besides.

Vollfeuer, *n.* full fire, full heat.

vollflächig, *a.* (*Cryst.*) holohedral.

Vollflächner, *m.* (*Cryst.*) holohedron.

vollfüllen, *v.t.* fill.

Voll-gehalt, *m.* full value. -gummi, *n.* solid rubber.

vollhaltig, *a.* of full value, standard.

Vollheit, *f.* fullness.

völlig, *a.* full, entire, complete, total.—*adv.* fully, completely.

voll-jährig, *a.* of age. -kommen, *a.* complete, entire, perfect.

Voll-kraft, *f.* vigor, energy. -macht, *f.* full power, power of attorney. -milch, *f.* whole milk.

vollmundig, *a.* (of beer, etc.) full, having good body.

Voll-mundigkeit, *f.* (of liquors) body, palate fullness. -pipette, *f.* a pipette delivering a single definite amount, without a graduated scale; transfer pipette. Cf. Messpipette.

voll-ständig, *a.* complete; entire, total.—*adv.* completely, fully. -strecken, *v.t.* execute, carry out. -wertig, *a.* perfect; up to standard. -wichtig, *a.* of full weight; weighty. -zählig, *a.* complete.

Vollziegel, *m.* solid brick or tile.

vollziehen, *v.t.* execute, consummate, put into effect, carry out.

Vollziehung, *f.* execution, consummation.

Vol.T., *abbrev.* (Volumenteil) part by volume.

voltaisch, *a.* voltaic.

Voltspannung, *f.* (*Elec.*) voltage.

Volum, *n.* volume. -abnahme, *f.* decrease in volume. -änderung, *f.* change of volume, alteration in volume. -dichte, *f.* density by volume. -einheit, *f.* unit of volume.

Volumen, *n.* volume. For compounds see Volum-.

volumetrisch, *a.* volumetric.

Volum-gesetz, *n.* law of volumes. -gewicht, *n.* volume weight, weight of unit volume.

Volumina, *n.pl.* volumes.

voluminös, *a.* voluminous.

Volum-messer, *m.* volumeter. -prozent, *n.* per cent by volume.

volumprozentig, *a.* per cent by volume.

Volum-teil, *m.* part by volume. -vergrösserung, *f.* increase in volume. -verhältnis, *n.* volume relation; proportion by volume. -verlust, *m.* loss in volume. -vermehrung, *f.* increase in volume. -verminderung, *f.* decrease in volume. -zunahme, *f.*, -zuwachs, *m.* increase in volume.

vom, *abbrev.* (von dem) of the, from the.

Vomhundertgehalt, *m.* percentage content.

vomieren, *v.i.* vomit.

von, *prep.* from, of, about, by, on.

vonnöten, *adv.* in need, necessary.

vor, *prep.* before; for, from, of.—*adv.* forward, on; before, formerly.— allem, above all. — einem Jahre, a year ago.

vor-, *abbrev.* (vorig) former, preceding.

Vor-. fore-, pre-, pro-, preliminary, previous, prior, first. -abend, *m.* eve. -ahnung, *f.* presentiment.

voran, *adv.* before, on. -schicken, *v.t.* premise, observe beforehand; send before.

Vor-anschlag, *m.* estimate. -anzeige, *f.* preliminary notice; previous announcement. -arbeit, *f.* preliminary work, preparation.

vorauf, *adv.* before, on.

voraus, *adv.* beforehand, in advance. -bezahlen, *v.t.* pay in advance, prepay. -gegangen, *p.a.* previous, preliminary. -gehen, *v.i.* go before, go ahead. -haben, *v.t.* have the better of. -nehmen, *v.t.* anticipate. -sagen, *v.t.* predict, foretell. -schicken, *v.t.* = voranschicken. -sehen, *v.t.* foresee, anticipate. -setzen, *v.t.* suppose, presuppose, assume.

Voraus-setzung, *f.* hypothesis, assumption, supposition, provision. -sicht, *f.* foresight, forethought.

voraussichtlich, *a.* probable, prospective.—*adv.* presumably, most probably.

vorbauen, *v.i.* guard against, prevent.

Vor-bauung, *f.* = Vorbeugung. -bauungsmittel, *n.* (*Med.*) prophylactic. -bearbeitung, *f.* preliminary working or treatment. **-bedacht,** *m.* forethought. **-bedingung,** *f.* preliminary condition. **-behalt,** *m.* reservation, proviso.

**vorbehalten,** *v.t.* reserve, stipulate for.

**Vorbehandlung,** *f.* preliminary (or previous) treatment.

**vorbei,** *adv.* by, past, over, gone, done. **-fliegen,** *v.i.* fly by, fly past. **-führen,** *v.t.* lead past; (of gas, etc.) furnish, pass.

**vorbeizen,** *v.t.* (*Dyeing*) mordant previously.

**Vor-belichtung,** *f.* preliminary illumination, preliminary exposure. **-bemerkung,** *f.* preliminary remark. **-berechnung,** *f.* preliminary calculation.

**vorbereiten,** *v.t. & r.* prepare.—**vorbereitend,** *p.a.* preparatory.

**Vor-bereitung,** *f.* preparation. **-bericht,** *m.* preface, introduction. **-besprechung,** *f.* previous discussion, preliminary discussion.

**vor-beugen,** *v.t.* guard against, prevent; bend forward. **-beugend,** *p.a.* preventive, precautionary, prophylactic.

**Vor-beugung,** *f.* prevention; (*Med.*) prophylaxis. **-beugungsmittel,** *n.* preservative; preventive; (*Med.*) prophylactic. **-bild,** *n.* pattern, model; prototype, type.

**vorbilden,** *v.t.* represent, typify; prepare, school.

**Vorbildung,** *f.* preparation.

**vor-binden,** *v.t.* tie on, put on. **-bringen,** *v.t.* bring forward, produce, utter, adduce.

**vordem,** *adv.* formerly.

**vordere,** *a.* fore, front, anterior.

**Vorder-finger,** *m.* forefinger. **-glied,** *n.* antecedent; front rank. **-grund,** *m.* foreground.

**vorderhand,** *adv.* for the present, provisionally.

**Vorder-herd,** *m.* forehearth. **-satz,** *m.* antecedent, premise. **-seite,** *f.* front side, front, obverse, face.

**vorderste,** *a.* foremost.

**Vorder-wand,** *f.* front wall, front, (of a blast furnace) breast. **-würze,** *f.* first wort.

**vor-drängen,** *v.t. & r.* press forward, push forward. **-dringen,** *v.i.* push on, advance.

**Vordruck,** *m.* first impression, proof; form, blank; (*Calico*) first or bottom printing.

**vor-drucken,** *v.t.* prefix. **-eilen,** *v.i.* hasten, anticipate; lead.

**Vor-eilen,** *n.,* **-eilung,** *f.* advance; (*Mach.*) lead. **-eilungswinkel,** *m.* angle of lead.

**voreingenommen,** *p.a.* prepossessed, prejudiced.

**Voreltern,** *pl.* ancestors.

**vorenthalten,** *v.t.* withhold.

**vorerst,** *adv.* first of all; for the present.

**vorerwähnt,** *p.a.* aforementioned.

**Vor-fahr,** *m.* predecessor, ancestor. **-fall,** *m.* occurrence, event; (*Med.*) prolapse.

**vorfallen,** *v.i.* happen, occur; prolapse.

**Vor-färbung,** *f.* preliminary dyeing or staining; specif., (*Dyeing*) grounding, bottoming. **-fechter,** *m.* champion. **-filter,** *m.* first filter. **-filtern,** *n.* preliminary filtering.

**vorfinden,** *v.t.* come upon, find.—*v.r.* be found, be forthcoming.

**Vorfrischen,** *n.* preliminary refining.

**vorführen,** *v.t.* bring out, produce, present.

**Vorgang,** *m.* process; (chemical) reaction; proceeding, procedure; occurrence, event; transaction; priority, precedence; precedent, example; (*Distilling*) first runnings.

**Vorgänger,** *m.* predecessor.

**vorgängig,** *a.* foregoing, previous; preliminary.

**vorgeben,** *v.t.* pretend; suggest; give (odds).

**Vorgebirge,** *n.* headland, promontory; foothill.

**vor-geblich,** *a.* pretended, would-be, so-called. **-gefasst,** *p.a.* preconceived. **-gehen,** *v.i.* go before, precede; proceed; go on, happen; (of a watch) be fast.

**Vorgelege,** *n.* connecting gearing.

**vorgeschichtlich,** *a.* prehistoric.

**Vorgesetzte,** *m.* superior, head.

**vorgestern,** *adv.* day before yesterday.

**Vor-glühen,** *n.* preliminary heating; (*Metal.*) annealing. **-glühofen,** *m.* annealing oven or furnace; (*Ceram.*) biscuit kiln.

**vor-greifen,** *v.t.* anticipate. **-haben,** *v.t.* intend, purpose; be engaged in; have on, wear; reprimand. **-halten,** *v.t.* hold before; reproach.—*v.i.* hold out, last. **-handen,** *adv. & a.* at hand, on hand, ready, present, existing.

**Vor-handensein,** *n.* presence, existence. **-hang,** *m.* curtain, drop. **-haupt,** *n.* forehead.

**vorher,** *adv.* previously, before. **-bedenken,** *v.t.* premeditate. **-bestimmen,** *v.t.* predetermine, predestine.

**Vorherd,** *m.* forehearth.

**vorhergehen,** *v.i.* go before, precede.

**vorherig,** *a.* previous, preceding.

**vorherrschen,** *v.i.* predominate, prevail.

**vorhersagen,** *v.t.* predict, prophesy.

**vorhin,** *adv.* before, heretofore, lately.

**Vorhut,** *f.* vanguard, van.

**vorig,** *a.* former, preceding, last.

**Vor-jahr,** *n.* preceding year. **-kehr, -kehrung,** *f.* precaution, provision. **-kenntnis,** *n.* preliminary knowledge; (*pl.*) rudiments, elements.

**vorkommen,** *v.i.* occur, be found; happen; appear, seem; be admitted, be presented, come up; come sooner.

**Vorkommen,** *n.* occurrence, etc. (see vorkommen); presence, existence.

**Vor-kondensator,** *m.* preliminary condenser. **-kost,** *f.* provisions.

**Vorkriegs-.** pre-war.

**vorkühlen,** *v.t.* forecool, precool.

**Vor-kühler,** *m.* forecooler. **-kühlung,** *f.* forecooling, precooling. **-kultur,** *f.* preliminary culture.

**vor-küpen,** *v.t.* bottom with a vat dye. **-laden,** *v.t.* summon.

**Vorlage,** *f.* something put before or in front; specif.: receiver; absorption bulb; (*Zinc*) condenser; (*Gas*) collector main; matter, proposal, bill; text, copy; pattern.

**vorlagern,** *v.r.& i.* extend in front of or before; protrude.

**Vorlass,** *m.* = Vorlauf.

**vorlassen,** *v.t.* admit, give access to; give precedence to.

**Vor-lauf,** *m.* first runnings; specif.: (*Whisky*) foreshot, (*Coal Tar*) first light oil. **-läufer,** *m.* forerunner, precursor, sign, indication; (mountain) spur.

**vorläufig,** *a.* preliminary, previous, provisional.—*adv.* previously, meantime, for the present.

**Vorlaugung,** *f.* preliminary leaching.

**vorlegen,** *v.t.* put on, apply; lay before, place before, submit, propose; display, exhibit.

**Vorlegierung,** *f.* key alloy.

**vorlesen,** *v.t.* read aloud, recite.

**Vorlesung,** *f.* lecture, discourse; reading.

**Vorlesungstisch,** *m.* lecture table.

**vorletzt,** *a.* next to last, penultimate.

**Vorliebe,** *f.* preference, fondness.

**vorliegen,** *v.i.* lie before, be in hand or at hand, be present, exist.

**Vorliegen,** *n.* presence, existence.

**vorm.,** *abbrev.* (vormals) formerly; (vormittags) a.m.

**Vor-mahlen,** *n.* preliminary grinding. **-maisch-apparat,** *m.* fore-mashing a p p a r a t u s. **-maischen,** *n.* (*Brewing*) foremashing (soaking of the grist before mashing). **-maischer,** *m.* foremasher, external mash machine.

**vormals,** *adv.* formerly.

**Vormann,** *m.* foreman.

**vormerken,** *v.t.* note, note down.

**Vor-milch,** *f.* colostrum, foremilk. **-mischung,** *f.* premixing. **-mittag,** *m.* forenoon, morning. **-mund,** *m.* guardian, trustee.

**vorn, vorne,** *adv.* in front, before.—**von —,** from before; from the beginning.—**von — herein,** at first, to begin with.

**Vorname,** *m.* first name, given name.

**vornehm,** *a.* noble, aristocratic; distinguished.

**vor-nehmen,** *v.t.* take, take up, undertake; intend. **-nehmlich,** *adv.* chiefly, especially. **-nehmste,** *a.* chief, foremost.

**vornherein,** *adv.*—**von —, im —,** from the outset, from the first, to begin with.

**Vorniere,** *f.* head kidney, pronephros.

**Vornierengang,** *m.* Wolffian duct.

**Vor-posten,** *m.* outpost. **-probe,** *f.* preliminary test. **-prüfung,** *f.* previous or preliminary examination. **-pumpe,** *f.* (*Brewing*) circulator, wort pump.

**vor-raffinieren,** *v.t.* (*Lead*) soften, improve. **-ragen,** *v.i.* stand out, be prominent.— **-ragend,** *p.a.* prominent, outstanding.

**Vorrang,** *m.* precedence, superiority.

**Vorrat,** *m.* stock, store, supply. **-flasche,** *f.* stock bottle. **-gefäss,** *n.* stock vessel, reservoir.

**vorrätig,** *a.* in stock, on hand.

**Vorratlösung,** *f.* stock solution.

**Vorrats-eiweiss,** *n.* supply protein, circulating protein. **-flasche,** *f.* stock bottle. **-gefäss,** *n.* supply vessel, reservoir. **-lösung,** *f.* stock solution.

**Vor-recht,** *n.* privilege. **-rede,** *f.* preface; preamble.

**vor-reduzieren,** *v.t.* prereduce. **-reiben,** *v.t.* grind beforehand. **-reinigen,** *v.t.* purify in a preliminary way.

**Vorreinigung,** *f.* preliminary purification.

**vorrichten,** *v.t.* prepare.

**Vorrichtung,** *f.* contrivance, device, appliance, apparatus, arrangement; preparation, dressing.

**Vorrösten,** *n.* preliminary roasting.

**vorrücken,** *v.i.* advance, progress.—*v.t.* advance; reproach.

**Vorsatz,** *m.* something put before, or in front (*e.g.*, screen); design, intention.

**vorsätzlich,** *a.* intentional.

**Vorsatzlinse,** *f.* lens placed in front.

**vorschalten,** *v.t.* (*Elec.*) introduce (into a circuit), cut in, connect.

**Vorschaltwiderstand,** *m.* (*Elec.*) (rheostatic) resistance.

**Vorschein,** *m.* appearance.

**vor-schieben,** *v.t.* push forward, advance. **-schiessen,** *v.i.* shoot forward.—*v.t.* circulate (wort, etc.); advance (money).

**Vorschlag,** *m.* proposal, proposition; (*Metal.*) fusion, flux; blank space on the first page of a book.

**vorschlagen,** *v.t.* propose, suggest, move; overcharge; put on before, prefix.

**Vorschmack,** *m.* foretaste.

**vor-schmecken,** *v.i.* (of a flavor) predominate. **-schnell,** *a.* hasty, rash. **-schreiben,** *v.t.* prescribe, dictate, direct.

**Vorschrift,** *f.* prescription; recipe; directions, instructions; order, command; rule, precept; copy; decree.

**vorschriftsmässig,** *adv.* as prescribed, as directed.

**Vor-schub,** *m.* assistance, furtherance; (*Mech.*) feed; advance, lead. **-schuh,** *m.* upper leather, vamp. **-schule,** *f.* preparatory school; primer. **-schuss,** *m.* advance (of money).

**vor-schützen,** *v.t.* pretend, allege. **-schweben,** *v.i.* float; be in one's mind. **-sehen,** *v.t.* foresee; provide for.—*v.r.* take care; provide.

**Vor-sehung,** *f.* providence. **-setzblatt,** *n.* fly-leaf.

**vorsetzen,** *v.t.* set before, put before, prefix; propose (to oneself).

**Vorsetzer,** *m.* something put in front, specif. fire screen.

**Vorsicht,** *f.* foresight, caution, prudence; precaution; providence; take care!

**vorsichtig,** *a.* cautious, careful, prudent, provident.—*adv.* cautiously, carefully.

**Vorsichtsmassregel,** *f.* precaution, precautionary measure.

**Vor-sieden,** *n.* preliminary boiling. **-silbe,** *f.* prefixed syllable, prefix. **-sitz,** *m.* presidency, chair. **-sitzend, -sitzender,** *m.* chairman, president. **-sorge,** *f.* precaution, care, forethought. **-spektrum,** *n.* preliminary spectrum (applied by Goldstein to certain low-temperature spectra).

**vorspiegeln,** *v.t.* exhibit in a false light, pretend, simulate.

**Vorspiel,** *n.* prelude.

**vorspringen,** *v.i.* project; leap out.—**vorspringend,** *p.a.* projecting, prominent, (of colors) glaring.

**Vor-sprung,** *m.* projection, prominence; advantage. **-stadt,** *f.* suburb. **-stand,** *m.* directory, executive committee; director, head.

**vor-stecken,** *v.t.* put, stick or fasten before; prefix; mark out, propose. **-stehen,** *v.i.* stand before, precede; stand out, be prominent; direct, preside (over).

**Vorsteher,** *m.* director, manager, superintendent, etc. **-drüse,** *f.* prostate gland, prostate.

**vorstellen,** *v.t.* represent; imagine; demonstrate; personate, play; introduce; put before, put ahead, advance. |

**Vorstellung,** *f.* conception, idea, notion; representation, performance; introduction; review (of troops); remonstrance.

**Vor-stoss,** *m.* adapter; lap (of a tile); edging; attack, advance. **-stufe,** *f.* first step; first stage; primer. **-sud,** *m.* first boiling.

**vortäuschen,** *v.t.* simulate.

**Vorteil,** *m.* advantage, profit, benefit; knack.

**vorteilhaft,** *a.* advantageous, profitable, favorable.

**Vor-tiegel,** *m.* (*Lead*) outer basin, lead pot;

(*Tin*) forehearth. **-trag,** *m.* discourse, lecture, address, recital; report; exposition; delivery, enunciation; (*Com.*) balance.

**vor-tragen,** *v.t.* carry before; report on; deliver; lecture on. **-trefflich,** *a.* excellent, superior, prime. **-treten,** *v.i.* step forward, stand out.

**Vortritt,** *m.* precedence.

**vortrocknen,** *v.t.* dry beforehand, pre-dry.

**vorüber,** *adv.* past, gone, over, done. **-gehen,** *v.i.* pass, pass by, pass away. **-gehend,** *p.a.* temporary, transient.

**Vor-untersuchung,** *f.* preliminary investigation. **-urteil,** *n.* prejudice, bias. **-verdauung,** *f.* predigestion. **-versuch,** *m.* preliminary experiment or test. **-wachs,** *n.* bee glue, propolis.

**vor-walken,** *v.t.* scour (cloth). **-walten,** *v.i.* prevail, predominate. **-walzen,** *v.t.* (*Metal.*) rough down (blooms).

**Vor-walzwerk,** *n.* (*Metal.*) roughing rolls. **-wand,** *m.* pretext, pretense. **-wärmapparat,** *m.* preheating apparatus, forewarming apparatus.

**vorwärmen,** *v.t.* heat (beforehand), preheat, (fore)warm, anneal.

**Vor-wärmer,** *m.* (pre)heater, (fore)warmer. **-wärmofen,** *m.* preheating oven, annealing oven (or furnace). **-wärmung,** *f.* forewarming, preheating. **-wärmzone,** *f.* zone of preparatory heating.

**vorwärts,** *adv.* forward, onward, on, ahead.

**Vorwäsche,** *f.* preliminary washing.

**vorweg,** *adv.* before, beforehand. **-nehmen,** *v.t.* take beforehand, anticipate.

**Vor-wein,** *m.* (*Wine*) first runnings. **-welt,** *f.* prehistoric world; antiquity.

**vor-werfen,** *v.t.* throw before; cast in one's teeth. **-wiegen,** *v.i.* outweigh, preponderate. **-wiegend,** *adv.* preponderantly, predominantly, especially, chiefly.

**Vor-wissen,** *n.* foreknowledge. **-wort,** *n.* foreword, preface; preposition. **-wurf,** *m.* subject, object; reproach, blame. **-zeichen,** *n.* indication, symptom, omen; (*Math.*) sign. **-zeichenwechsel,** *m.* (*Math.*) change of sign.

**vorzeigen,** *v.t.* show, exhibit; present.

**Vor-zeiger,** *m.* pointer, indicator; bearer. **-zeit,** *f.* ancient times, past ages, antiquity.

**vor-zeitig,** *a.* premature, untimely. **-ziehbar,** *a.* preferable. **-ziehen,** *v.t.* prefer; draw forth.

**Vorzug,** *m.* advantage, merit, virtue; preference; precedence, priority, superiority, privilege.

**vorzüglich,** *a.* preferable; excellent, superior, choice; distinguished.—*adv.* preferably; chiefly, especially.

**Vorzugs-.** preferred, preferential. **-aktien,** *f.pl.*

(shares of) preferred stock. **-richtung,** *f.* preferred direction.

**vorzugsweise,** *adv.* preferably, especially, pre-eminently.

**Vorzündung,** *f.* early ignition.

**V.St.,** *abbrev.* (Vereinigte Staaten) United States.

**v.T.,** *abbrev.* (von Tausend) per thousand, per mille.

**V.T.,** *abbrev.* (Volumenteil) part by volume.

**v.u.,** *abbrev.* (von unten) from below, from beneath, from the bottom.

**Vulkan,** *m.* volcano; Vulcan. **-fiber,** *f.* vulcanized fiber. **-gas,** *n.* volcanic gas. **-glas,** *n.* volcanic glass; tempered glass.

**Vulkanisator,** *m.* vulcanizer.

**vulkanisch,** *a.* volcanic.

**vulkanisieren,** *v.t.* vulcanize.

**Vulkanisierpresser,** *m.* vulcanizer.

**Vulkanisierung,** *f.* vulcanization.

**Vulkanöl,** *n.* mineral lubricating oil.

**Vuzin,** *n.* vuzine, vuzin.

**VZ.,** *abbrev.* (Verseifungszahl) saponification number.

# W

w., *abbrev.* warm.

W., *abbrev.* (Wasser) water; (no period) symbol for Wolfram (tungsten).

Waag-, Waage, *f.* = Wag-, Wage.

Waare, *f.* = Ware.

Wabe, *f.* honeycomb.

wabenartig, *a.* honeycombed.

wach, *a.* awake, waking.

Wache, *f.* watch, watching; guard house.

wachen, *v.i.* be awake, wake; watch.

Wachmittel, *n.* antisoporific.

Wacholder, *m.* juniper. -beere, *f.* juniper berry. -branntwein, -geist, *m.* (Holland) gin. -harz, *n.* juniper resin; gum juniper (sandarac). -öl, *n.* juniper oil; (brenzliches) oil of cade. -spiritus, *m.* (*Pharm.*) spirit of juniper.

Wachs, *n.* wax.

Wachs-. wax, waxen; growing, sprouting. -abdruck, *m.* impression in wax.

wachsähnlich, *a.* like wax, waxy.

Wachsalaun, *m.* crystallized alum.

wachsam, *a.* watchful, vigilant.

Wachsart, *f.* (variety of) wax.

wachsartig, *a.* waxy, wax-like.

Wachs-baum, *m.* wax myrtle, bayberry tree. -bildnerei, *f.* modeling in wax. -bleichen, *n.* wax bleaching. -boden, *m.* wax cake. -bottich, *m.* (*Alum*) roching cask. -drüse, *f.* ceruminous gland.

wachsen, *v.i.* grow; increase; (*Malting*) sprout; (of lime) swell.—*v.t.* wax.—gewachsen, *p.a.* grown, etc.; native; equal (to).

wächsen, *v.t.* wax.

wächsern, *a.* waxen, wax.

Wachsfarbe, *f.* wax color.

wachsfarben, *a.* wax-colored.

Wachs-firnis, *m.* wax varnish. -gagel, *m.& f.* wax myrtle. -gehalt, *m.* wax content.

wachsgelb, *a.* wax-yellow.

Wachs-glanz, *m.* waxy luster. -handel, *m.* wax trade. -kerzchen, *n.* wax match. -kerze, *f.* wax candle. -kitt, *m.* wax cement. -kohle, *f.* paraffin coal. -kuchen, *m.* cake of wax. -leinen, *n.*, -leinwand, *f.* = Wachstuch. -machen, *n.* roching (crystallization) of alum. -myrte, *f.* wax myrtle. -öl, *n.* wax oil. -opal, *m.* wax opal. -palme, *f.* wax palm. -papier, *n.* wax paper. -pflaster, *n.* cerate. -präparat, *n.* preparation in wax. -salbe, *f.* cerate; ointment. -schmelze, *f.* wax-melt-

ing house. -seife, *f.* wax soap. -stock, *m.* wax candle.

wächst, *pr. 3 sing.* of wachsen.

Wachs-tafel, *f.* tablet of wax. -taffet, *m.* oiled silk; waxed silk. -tuch, *n.* oilcloth; (formerly) cerecloth.

Wachstum, *n.* growth; increase.

wachsweich, *a.* soft like wax.

Wachszündholz, *n.* wax match, vesta.

Wacht, *f.* guard, watch.

wackelig, *a.* shaky, rickety, wabbly.

wackeln, *v.i.* shake, totter, wabble, rock.

wacker, *a.* stout, brave, good.

Wade, *f.* calf (of the leg).

Wadenbein, *n.* fibula.

Waderz, *n.* wad (the mineral).

Waffe, *f.* weapon, (*pl.*) arms.

Waffen-dienst, *m.* military service. -fabrik, *f.* arms factory. -haus, *n.* arsenal, armory. -rüstung, *f.* armor; arming; armament.

waffen, *v.t.* arm.

wägbar, *a.* weighable, ponderable.

Wägbarkeit, *f.* weighableness, ponderability.

Wage, *f.* balance, scales; hydrometer; weighhouse; level (the instrument). -arm, *m.* arm of a balance. -balken, *m.* beam of a balance, scale beam.

Wäge-fläschchen, *n.* weighing bottle. -garnitur, *f.* weighing set.

Wagegehäuse, *n.* balance case.

Wäge-glas, -gläschen, *n.* weighing glass.

Wagekasten, *m.* balance case.

wagen, *v.t.* venture, risk.

Wagen, *m.* vehicle, conveyance (carriage, wagon, cart, truck, car, etc.).

wägen, *v.t.* weigh; poise, balance; ponder.

Wagen-fett, *n.* wagon grease, axle grease. -lack, *m.* carriage varnish, coach varnish. -schmiere, *f.* wagon grease.

Wägepipette, *f.* weighing pipette.

Wäger, *m.* weigher.

wagerecht, *a.* horizontal, level.

Wäge-röhrchen, *n.*, -röhre, *f.* weighing tube.

Wageschale, *f.* balance pan, scale pan.

Wäge-schale, *f.* weighing dish. -schiffchen, *n.* weighing boat. -vorrichtung, *f.* weighing device. -zimmer, *n.* weighing room, balance room.

Waggon, *m.* car, (railway) carriage.

Wagnis, *n.* hazard, hazardous affair.

wagrecht, *a.* = wagerecht.

**Wagschale,** *f.* balance pan, scale pan.

**Wägung,** *f.* weighing.

**Wagzimmer,** *n.* weighing room, balance room.

**Wahl,** *f.* choice, selection; option; election.

**wählbar,** *a.* eligible.

**Wählbarkeit,** *f.* eligibility.

**wählen,** *v.t.* choose, select; elect.

**Wähler,** *m.* chooser; elector, voter.

**wählerisch,** *a.* particular, fastidious.

**Wahl-recht,** *n.* suffrage, franchise. -spruch, *m.* motto, device. -verwandtschaft, *f.* elective affinity; congeniality.

**wahlweise,** *adv.* as one chooses, at will.

**Wahn,** *m.* illusion, delusion; fancy; folly. -bild, *n.* phantom, illusion, delusion.

**wähnen,** *v.i.* fancy, imagine, suppose.

**Wahnsinn,** *m.* insanity; delirium; frenzy.

**wahnsinnig,** *a.* insane, mad; frantic.

**wahr,** *a.* true, real, genuine.—*adv.* truly.

**wahren,** *v.t.* keep, preserve; guard, look after.

**währen,** *v.i.* last, continue.

**während,** *prep.* during, for.—*conj.* while; whereas.

**wahrhaft,** *a.* true, genuine; truthful, sincere; sure; regular.

**wahrhaftig,** *a.* true; truthful.—*adv.* truly, verily, really.

**Wahrheit,** *f.* truth; truthfulness; reality, fact.

**wahr-lich,** *adv.* surely, really, truly, verily. -nehmbar, *a.* perceptible. -nehmen, *v.t.* perceive, notice, observe; attend to, profit by.

**Wahrnehmung,** *f.* perception; observation; attention.

**wahr-sagen,** *v.t.& i.* prophesy, divine, predict. -scheinlich, *a.* probable, likely; plausible.

**Wahrscheinlichkeit,** *f.* probability; plausibility.

**Wahrscheinlichkeits-rechnung,** *f.* calculus of probabilities. -wert, *m.* probable value.

**Wahrspruch,** *m.* verdict.

**Wahrung,** *f.* support, vindication.

**Währung,** *f.* standard, value, currency; duration.

**Wahrzeichen,** *n.* distinctive mark, sign.

**Waid,** *m.* woad.

**Wal,** *m.* whale.

**Wald,** *m.* wood, forest.

**Wald-.** wood, forest, wild. -ahorn, *m.* sycamore.

**Walden'sche Umkehrung.** Walden inversion.

**Wald-gewächs,** *n.* forest plant. -kirsche, *f.* wild cherry. -malve, *f.* mallow (*Malva sylvestris*). -meister, *m.* woodruff (*Asperula odorata*). -rebe, *f.* clematis.

**Waldung,** *f.* woods, forest.

**Wald-wolle,** *f.* pine wool. -wollöl, *n.* pine-needle oil.

**Walfisch,** *m.* whale. -speck, *m.* whale blubber. -tran, *m.* whale oil, train oil.

**Walk-.** fuller's, fulling; felting, felted.

**Walke,** *f.* fulling; fulling machine; fulling mill.

**walken,** *v.t.* full (cloth); felt.

**Walker,** *m.* fuller.

**Walkerde, Walkererde,** *f.* fuller's earth.

**Walker-distel,** *f.* fuller's teasel. -seife, *f.* fuller's soap. -ton, *m.* fuller's earth.

**Walk-fett,** *n.* fulling fat. -seife, *f.* fuller's soap. -ton, *n.* fuller's earth.

**Wall,** *m.* rampart; dam, bank; coast.

**Wallach,** *m.* gelding; Wallachian.

**wallen,** *v.i.* bubble, boil up, simmer; wave, heave, undulate.

**wällen,** *v.t.* boil, simmer.

**wallisisch,** *a.* Welsh; Valaisan.

**Wallnuss,** *f.* = Walnuss.

**Wallonen-arbeit,** *f.*, -frischen, *n.*, -schmiede, *f.* Walloon process.

**Wallrat, Wallross.** = Walrat, Walross.

**Wallstein,** *m.* dam (of a blast furnace). -platte, *f.* (*Metal.*) dam plate.

**Wallung,** *f.* boiling, ebullition, simmering; undulation; excitement.

**Walnuss,** *f.* walnut. -baum, *m.* walnut tree (*Juglans* species, esp. *J. regia*); (grauer) butternut tree (*J. cinerea*); (weisser) hickory (*Hicoria* sp.).

**walnussgross,** *a.* walnut-sized, nut-sized.

**Walnuss-grösse,** *f.* size of walnuts, nut size. -öl, *n.* walnut oil.

**Walrat,** *m.* spermaceti. -öl, *n.* sperm oil.

**Walross,** *n.* walrus.

**walten,** *v.i.* dispose, manage, govern, rule.

**Wal-tier,** *n.* cetacean. -tran, *m.* whale oil.

**walzbar,** *a.* capable of being rolled.

**Walz-blech,** *n.* rolled plate. -blei, *n.* sheet lead.

**Walze,** *f.* roller, roll; cylinder, drum.

**Walzeisen,** *n.* rolled iron, drawn iron; pin, axle.

**walzen,** *v.t.* roll, mill.—*v.i.* waltz.

**wälzen,** *v.t.* roll, turn (over).—*v.r.* roll, revolve. —wälzende Reibung, rolling friction.

**Walzen-apparat,** *m.* (*Dyeing*) rolling frame. -druck, *m.* cylinder printing.

**walzenförmig,** *a.* cylindrical.

**Walzen-glas,** *n.* cylinder glass. -kessel, *m.* cylinder boiler, cylindrical boiler. -mühle, *f.* roller mill. -sinter, *m.* mill scale. -strecke, *f.* roll train.

**Walzer,** *m.* waltz.

**Walzsinter,** *m.* mill scale.

**Wälzverfahren,** *n.* rotary process.

**Walzung,** *f.* rolling, milling.

**Walz-werk,** *n.* rolls, roll train, rolling mill, blooming mill, crushing mill, etc. -zinn, *n.* rolled tin, sheet tin.

**wand,** *pret.* of winden.

**Wand,** *f.* wall; partition, septum; (*Tech.*) side, cheek. **-bewurf,** *m.* plastering. **-dicke,** *f.* thickness of wall (as of a tube).

**Wandel,** *m.* change, variation; conduct, life; trade, traffic.

**wandelbar,** *a.* changeable, convertible, variable; perishable.

**Wandelbarkeit,** *f.* changeableness, etc. (see wandelbar).

**wandellos,** *a.* unalterable.

**wandeln,** *v.i.* walk, travel, wander; trade. —*v.t.* change, convert.—*v.r.* change.

**Wandelstern,** *m.* planet.

**Wandelung,** *f.* transformation, change.

**Wander-.** migratory, wandering, movable. **-block,** *m.* (*Geol.*) erratic block.

**wandern,** *v.i.* migrate; wander; creep; travel, walk, go.

**Wander-rost,** *m.* traveling grate. **-schaft,** *f.* traveling, travels, tour. **-stärke,** *f.* translocatory starch.

**Wanderung,** *f.* migration; creeping; traveling, travels, walking, walking trip.

**Wanderungs-geschwindigkeit,** *f.* migration velocity. **-sinn,** *m.* direction of migration (of ions). **-zahl,** *f.* transport number.

**Wandlung,** *f.* transformation, change.

**Wand-malerei,** *f.* house painting; mural painting. **-putz,** *m.* plastering.

**wandständig,** *a.* parietal, marginal.

**Wand-stärke,** *f.* thickness of wall. **-tafel,** *f.* wall chart; blackboard.

**wandte,** *pret.* of wenden.

**Wandung,** *f.* wall; partition.

**Wange,** *f.* cheek.

**wankelhaft,** *a.* unsteady, inconstant.

**wanken,** *v.i.* totter, stagger, waver.

**wann,** *adv.* when, then.—*conj.* when.

**Wanne,** *f.* trough; tub; vat; tank.

**Wannenofen,** *m.* (*Glass*) tank furnace.

**Wanze,** *f.* bug (specif. bedbug).

**Wanzenkraut,** *n.* marsh tea; cimicifuga.

**war,** *pret.* of sein.

**warb,** *pret.* of werben.

**ward,** *pret.* of werden.

**Wardein,** *m.* mint warden, assay master.

**Ware,** *f.* ware, article, manufacture; specif., textile fabric; (*pl.*) goods, merchandise.

**Waren-haus, -lager,** *n.* warehouse. **-stempel,** *m.,* **-zeichen,** *n.* trademark.

**warf,** *pret.* of werfen.

**warm,** *a.* warm; hot.— **— laufen,** (of moving parts) heat up.

**Warmbehandlung,** *f.* heat treatment.

**Warmblase-.** hot-blast.

**Warmblüter,** *m.pl.* warm-blooded animals.

**warmbrüchig,** *a.* (*Metal.*) hot-short, brittle when hot.

**Warmbrunnen,** *m.* hot spring, thermal spring.

**warmdehnbar,** *a.* (*Metal.*) hot-ductile.

**Wärme,** *f.* heat; warmth, warmness. **-abgabe,** *f.* loss of heat. **-änderung,** *f.* change of temperature. **-aufnahme,** *f.* absorption of heat. **-ausdehnung,** *f.* thermal expansion. **-ausnutzung,** *f.* heat efficiency. **-ausstrahlung,** *f.* radiation of heat. **-austausch,** *m.* heat exchange. **-behandlung,** *f.* heat treatment.

**wärmebeständig,** *a.* resistant to heat, heat-proof, stable on heating; of constant temperature.

**Wärme-bewegung,** *f.* heat motion. **-bilanz,** *f.* heat balance. **-bildner,** *m.* heat producer. **-bildung,** *f.* production of heat. **-bindung,** *f.* absorption of heat.

**wärmedurchlässig,** *a.* diathermic.

**Wärme-effekt,** *m.* heat effect. **-einfluss,** *m.* influence of heat; heat influx. **-einheit,** *f.* heat unit.

**wärmeelektrisch,** *a.* thermo-electric.

**Wärmeelektrizität,** *f.* thermo-electricity.

**wärmeempfindlich,** *a.* sensitive to heat.

**Wärme-entbindung,** *f.* disengagement of heat. **-entwickelung,** *f.* evolution of heat.

**wärmeerzeugend,** *p.a.* heat-producing.

**Wärmeerzeuger,** *m.* heat producer, heat-producing substance.

**wärmegebend,** *a,* heat-yielding, specif. exothermic.

**Wärme-gleiche,** *f.* isothermal line, isotherm. **-grad,** *m.* degree of heat; temperature. **-gradmesser,** *m.* thermometer. **-grösse,** *f.* specific heat. **-inhalt,** *m.* heat content. **-kraftlehre,** *f.* thermodynamics. **-kraftmaschine,** *f.* heat engine. **-lehre,** *f.* (science of) heat, theory of heat.

**wärmeleitend,** *p.a.* heat-conducting.

**Wärme-leiter,** *m.* conductor of heat. **-leitfähigkeit,** *f.* thermal conductivity. **-leitung,** *f.* conduction of heat. **-mechanik,** *f.* thermodynamics.

**wärmemechanisch,** *a.* thermodynamic.

**Wärme-menge,** *f.* amount or quantity of heat. **-mengenmessung,** *f.* calorimetry. **-messer,** *m.* calorimeter; thermometer. **-messung,** *f.* measurement of heat, calorimetry.

**wärmen,** *v.t.* warm; heat.—*v.r.* warm oneself, become warm.

**Wärme-platte,** *f.* warming plate. **-quantum,** *n.* quantity of heat; heat quantum. **-quelle,** *f.* source of heat.

**Wärmer,** *m.* heater.

**Wärme-regler,** *m.* thermoregulator. **-sammler,** *m.* heat accumulator. **-schrank,** *m.* warming cabinet. **-schutz,** *m.,* **-schutzmittel,** *n.* heat insulator (or insulation), protection against heat. **-schwankung,** *f.* heat fluctuation. **-schwingung,** *f.* heat vibration.

-speicher, *m.* heat accumulator, regenerator.
-spektrum, *n.* heat spectrum, thermal spectrum. -stich, *m.* fever-producing puncture. -stoff, *m.* caloric, thermogen. -strahl, *m.* heat ray. -strahlung, *f.* heat radiation. -strömung, *f.* heat convection. -summe, *f.* heat sum. -theorie, *f.* theory of heat. -tisch, *m.* warming table. -tönung, *f.* heat effect (of a reaction), heat of reaction, heat change, heat tone. -übergang, *m.* passage of heat, heat transmission. -übertragung, *f.* heat transfer. -vergütung, *f.* (*Metal.*) heat treatment. -verlust, *m.* loss of heat, heat loss. -vermögen, *n.* heat capacity. -vorgang, *m.* thermal process or phenomenon. -wert, *m.* heat value, calorific value.

wärmewiderstehend, *a.* heat-resistant.

Wärme-wirkung, *f.* effect or action of heat, thermal effect. -wirkungsgrad, *m.* thermal efficiency. -zahl, *f.* temperature coefficient.

wärmezehrend, *a.* heat-consuming, specif. endothermic.

Wärme-zufuhr, *f.* addition (or supplying) of heat. -zustand, *m.* thermal condition.

warmgepresst, *p.a.* hot-pressed.

Warmluft-. hot-air.

Wärm-ofen, *m.* heating furnace; reheating furnace. -platte, *f.* warming plate.

Warmprobe, *f.* hot test.

Wärmung, *f.* warming; heating.

Warmwasser-. hot-water. -bad, *m.* hot-water bath

Warmwind, *m.* (*Metal.*) hot blast.

warnen, *v.t.* warn, caution.

Warte, *f.* observatory; lookout.

warten, *v.i.* wait; attend (to).—*v.t.* take care of, nurse.

-wärts. -ward, -wards.

Wartung, *f.* attendance, attention; nursing.

warum, *adv.* why?

Warze, *f.* wart; nipple, teat; mastoid; pin, knob, boss, excrescence.

warzen-ähnlich, -artig, *a.* wartlike, mammillary, (*Biol.*) papillary. -förmig, *a.* wart-shaped, wartlike, mammillary, (*Biol.*) papillary.

Warzenkraut, *n.* warty plant, specif. marigold.

warzig, *a.* warty, verrucose.

was, *pron.* what, that, which; something.— — für, what, what a, what sort of.

Wasch-anlage, *f.* washing plant. -anstalt, *f.* laundry. -apparat, *m.* washing apparatus, washer. -aufsatz, *m.* washing attachment.

waschbar, *a.* washable, fast (color).

Wasch-benzol, *n.* a grade of commercial benzene. -blau, *n.* bluing. -bottich, *m.* washing vat (tub, etc.). -bürste, *f.* washing brush, cleaning brush.

Wäsche, *f.* washing, wash; washery; clothes, linen.

waschecht, *a.* fast to washing.

waschen, *v.t.& i.* wash; scrub, clean.

Wascher, Wäscher, *m.* washer; scrubber.

Wascherde, *f.* fuller's earth.

Wäscherei, *f.* washhouse, laundry; gossip.

Wasch-flasche, *f.* washing bottle, wash bottle. -flotte, -flüssigkeit, *f.* wash(ing) liquid. -gefäss, *n.* washing vessel. -gold, *n.* placer gold. -holländer, *m.* (*Paper*) washing engine. -kristall, *n.* washing crystals, soda crystals ($Na_2CO_3 \cdot 10H_2O$). -lauge, *f.* washing liquor. -leder, *n.* wash leather. -lösung, *f.* wash(ing) solution. -maschine, *f.* washing machine, washer. -mittel, *n.* washing agent, detergent; (*Med.*) lotion. -mittelfabrikation, *f.* manufacture of detergents. -öl, *n.* (*Gas*, etc.) washing oil, wash oil. -probe, *f.* assay of washed (buddled) ore. -pulver, *n.* washing powder. -seife, *f.* washing soap. -soda, *f.* washing soda.

wäscht, *pr. 3 sing.* of waschen.

Wasch-trommel, *f.* washing drum, washing cylinder. -turm, *m.* washing tower.

Waschung, *f.* washing; lotion, wash.

Wasch-verfahren, *n.* washing process. -vorrichtung, *f.* washing apparatus or device. -wasser, *n.* wash water. -wirkung, *f.* cleansing action (or effect). -wurzel, *f.* soapwort. -zinn, *n.* stream tin.

Wasen, *m.* vapor, exhalation; lawn, turf.

Wasser, *n.* water.

Wasser-. water, watery, aqueous, hydro-, hygro-, hydraulic. -abgabe, *f.* giving off (or elimination) of water.

wasserabhaltend, *a.* waterproof.

Wasser-ablass, *m.*, -ableitung, *f.* drainage, draining. -abscheidung, *f.* separation of water; secretion or excretion of water. -abspaltung, *f.* separation of water, dehydration.

wasser-abstossend, *p.a.* repelling water. -ähnlich, *a.* like water, watery.

Wasseranalyse, *f.* water analysis.

wasser-anziehend, *p.a.* attracting moisture, hygroscopic. -arm, *a.* having little water. -artig, *a.* like water, watery, aqueous.

Wasseraufnahme, *f.* absorption of water.

wasseraufsaugend, *a.* absorbing water.

Wasser-ausscheidung, *f.* = Wasserabscheidung. -ausspülung, *f.* rinsing with water. -austritt, *m.* elimination of water. -auszug, *m.* water extract, aqueous extract. -bad, *n.* water bath. -balg, *m.* (*Med.*) serous cyst. -baukunst, *f.* hydraulic engineering. -bedarf, *m.* water requirement.

wasserbegierig, *a.* readily absorbing, or combining with, water.

**Wasserbehälter,** *m.* (water) reservoir, tank, cistern; (*Brewing*) water back.

**wasserbeständig,** *a.* stable in water; resistant to water, waterproof.

**Wasser-bestimmung,** *f.* water determination. **-bildung,** *f.* formation of water. **-bindung,** *f.* combination of or with water. **-blase,** *f.* bubble; (*Med.*) vesicle; vessel for heating water.

**wasserblau,** *a.* blue like water, sea-blue.

**Wasser-blau,** *n.* water blue. **-blei,** *n.* molybdenite; graphite. **-bleiocker,** *m.* molybdic ocher, molybdite. **-bleisäure,** *f.* molybdic acid. **-bruch,** *m.* hydrocele.

**Wasserdampf,** *m.* water vapor, steam. **-bad,** *n.* steam bath; (*Med.*) vapor bath. **-destillation,** *f.* distillation with steam. **-entwickler, -erzeuger,** *m.* (steam) boiler.

**wasserdicht,** *a.* waterproof, water-tight.

**Wasser-dichte, -dichtheit, -dichtigkeit,** *f.* imperviousness to water, waterproofness. **-dichtmachen,** *n.* waterproofing. **-druck,** *m.* water pressure. **-dunst,** *m.* water vapor. **-durchlässigkeit,** *f.* permeability to water.

**wasserecht,** *a.* fast to water.

**Wasser-echtmachungsmittel,** *n.* water-resisting agent. **-enteisenung,** *f.* removal of iron from water. **-enthärtung,** *f.* water softening.

**wasserentziehend,** *a.* removing water, dehydrating.

**Wasser-entziehung,** *f.* removal of water, dehydration. **-entziehungsmittel,** *n.* dehydrating agent. **-erguss,** *m.* watery effusion, edema. **-farbe,** *f.* water color; color of water. **-fass,** *n.* water cask, water tub. **-fenchel,** *m.* water fennel.

**wasserfest,** *a.* water-tight, waterproof.

**Wasser-fläche,** *f.* water level; surface of water; sheet of water. **-flasche,** *f.* water bottle. **-fleck,** *m.* water stain.

**wasser-förmig,** *a.* like water, watery. **-frei,** *a.* anhydrous, free from water. **-führend,** *p.a.* water-bearing.

**Wasser-gang,** *m.* aqueduct; drain; waterway. **-gas,** *n.* water gas. **-gasteer,** *m.* water-gas tar. **-gefäss,** *n.* water vessel; (*Med.*) lymphatic vessel. **-gehalt,** *m.* water content, moisture content.

**wassergekühlt,** *p.a.* water-cooled.

**Wasser-geschwulst,** *f.* edema; hygroma. **-gewächs,** *n.* aquatic plant. **-glas,** *n.* water glass; glass for water.

**wassergleich,** *a.* like water, watery; level.

**Wasser-grün,** *n.* water green (a finely ground green verditer). **-hahn,** *m.* water cock, water tap.

**wasser-haltend,** *p.a.* containing water; water-retaining. **-haltig,** *a.* hydrous, hydrated; containing water, aqueous.

**Wasser-härtung,** *f.* water hardening. **-harz,** *n.* Burgundy pitch. **-haut,** *f.* water film; hyaloid membrane; amnion. **-heilkunde,** *f.* hydropathy.

**wasserhell,** *a.* clear as water, transparent.

**wässerig,** *a.* watery, aqueous, hydrous, (*Med.*) serous.

**Wässerigkeit,** *f.* wateriness; serosity.

**Wasser-kalk,** *m.* hydraulic lime, water lime. **-kessel,** *m.* water boiler, tank or kettle. **-kies,** *m.* (*Min.*) marcasite. **-kitt,** *m.* hydraulic cement.

**wasserklar,** *a.* clear as water.

**Wasser-klee,** *m.* buck bean, bog bean. **-kopf,** *m.* hydrocephalus. **-kraft,** *f.* water power. **-kraftlehre,** *f.* hydrodynamics. **-kran, -krahn,** *m.* water faucet. **-kristall,** *m.* rock crystal. **-kühler,** *m.* water cooler. **-kühlkasten,** *m.* water block. **-kühlung,** *f.* water cooling. **-kunst,** *f.* hydraulics; hydraulic engine; fountain; pumping engine.

**wasserl.,** *abbrev.* (wasserlöslich) water-soluble.

**wasserleer,** *a.* free from water, anhydrous.

**Wasserleitung,** *f.* water pipes, water piping, (also *Anat.*) aqueduct.

**Wasserleitungs-rohr,** *n.*, **-röhre,** *f.* water pipe, water tube. **-wasser,** *n.* tap water, city water.

**Wasserlinie,** *f.* water line.

**wasser-los,** *a.* waterless, without water, anhydrous. **-löslich,** *a.* water-soluble.

**Wasser-luftpumpe,** *f.* water vacuum pump. **-maische,** *f.* (aqueous) infusion; mash. **-malerei,** *f.* water-color painting. **-mantel,** *m.* water jacket. **-mass,** *n.* water gage. **-menge,** *f.* amount of water. **-messer,** *m.* water meter, water gage. **-moos,** *n.* alga; seaweed. **-mörtel,** *m.* hydraulic mortar.

**wässern,** *v.t.* water; soak; hydrate; dilute.— *v.i.* water.

**Wasser-nabel,** *m.* marsh pennywort (*Hydrocotyle*). **-niederschlag,** *m.* deposit of moisture. **-opal,** *m.* water opal, hyalite; hydrophane. **-papier,** *n.* (*Paper*) waterleaf. **-probe,** *f.* water test; sample of water. **-prüfer,** *m.* water tester. **-prüfung,** *f.* water testing, water analysis. **-pumpe,** *f.* water pump.

**wasserreich,** *a.* rich in water; of high humidity.

**Wasser-reinigung,** *f.* purification of water. **-rest,** *m.* water residue, hydroxyl. **-rohr,** *n.*, **-röhre,** *f.* water pipe, water tube. **-rohrkessel, -röhrenkessel,** *m.* water-tube boiler.

**wassersatt,** *a.* water-saturated.

**Wasser-säule,** *f.* water column. **-scheide,** *f.* water parting, watershed. **-scheu,** *f.* fear of water; (*Med.*) hydrophobia. **-schierling,** *m.* water hemlock (*Cicuta virosa*). **-schlange,** *f.* water snake; water hose;

bladderwort. **-schlauch,** *m.* water hose. **-schluss,** *m.* water seal, trap. **-spiegel,** *m.* water surface, water level. **-spritze,** *f.* syringe; water sprinkler. **-stand,** *m.* height of water, water level; constant (water) level device. **-standsglas,** *n.* gage glass. **-standshahn,** *m.* gage cock. **-stein,** *m.* scale (from water); whetstone. **-steinansatz,** *m.* deposit of scale.

**Wasserstoff,** *m.* hydrogen (in combination often best translated hydride, *e.g.* Äthylwasserstoff, ethyl hydride).

**wasserstoff-ähnlich,** *a.* resembling hydrogen. **-arm,** *a.* poor in hydrogen.

**Wasserstoffentwickelung,** *f.* evolution of hydrogen.

**wasserstoffentziehend,** *a.* abstracting hydrogen, dehydrogenating.

**Wasserstoffflasche,** *f.* hydrogen cylinder.

**wasserstofffrei,** *a.* free from hydrogen.

**Wasserstoff-gas,** *n.* hydrogen gas. **-gehalt,** *m.* hydrogen content.

**wasserstoffhaltig,** *a.* containing hydrogen, hydrogenous.

**Wasserstoff-hyperoxyd,** *n.* hydrogen peroxide. **-ion,** *n.* hydrogen ion. **-kalium,** *n.* potassium hydride. **-knallgas,** *n.* detonating gas (explosive mixture of hydrogen and oxygen.) **-palladium,** *n.* palladium hydride. **-peroxyd,** *n.* hydrogen peroxide.

**wasserstoffreich,** *a.* rich in hydrogen.

**Wasserstoffsalz,** *n.* hydrogen salt.

**wasserstoffsauer,** *a.* of, or combined with, a hydracid.

**Wasserstoff-säure,** *f.* hydracid. **-strom,** *m.* current of hydrogen. **-sulfid,** *n.* hydrogen sulfide. **-superoxyd,** *n.* hydrogen superoxide (hydrogen peroxide). **-verbindung,** *f.* hydrogen compound. **-wertigkeit,** *f.* hydrogen valence. **-zahl,** *f.* hydrogen-ion concentration, *p*H. **-zündmaschine,** *f.* hydrogen lamp, Döbereiner's lamp.

**Wasserstrahl,** *m.* jet of water, water jet. **-gebläse,** *n.* water-jet blast. **-luftpumpe,** *f.* water-jet vacuum pump.

**Wasser-strom,** *m.* stream or current of water. **-sturz,** *m.* waterfall. **-sucht,** *f.* dropsy. **-suppe,** *f.* water gruel. **-talk,** *m.* brucite. **-tiefe,** *f.* depth of water; draft (of ships). **-tier,** *n.* water animal, aquatic animal.

**wassertreibend,** *p.a.* (*Med.*) hydragog.

**Wasser-trockenschrank,** *m.* water-jacketed drying closet. **-tröpfchen,** *n.* water droplet. **-tropfen,** *n.* drop of water.

**wasserundurchlässig,** *a.* impervious to water, water-tight.

**Wässerung,** *f.* watering (specif. irrigation); soaking; hydration.

**wasserunlöslich,** *a.* insoluble in water.

**Wasser-untersuchung,** *f.* investigation of water, specif. water analysis. **-verbrauch,** *m.* consumption of water. **-vergoldung,** *f.* water gilding. **-verlust,** *m.* loss of water. **-vermögen,** *n.* (*Ceram.*) water-holding ability. **-verschluss,** *m.* water seal. **-versorgung,** *f.* water supply; waterworks. **-verunreinigung,** *f.* impurity in water; contamination of water. **-wa(a)ge,** *f.* water level (the instrument). **-wanne,** *f.* water trough, pneumatic trough. **-werk,** *n.* waterworks. **-wert,** *m.* water equivalent. **-zeichen,** *n.* (*Paper*) watermark. **-zement,** *m.* hydraulic cement. **-zersetzung,** *f.* decomposition of water. **-zufluss,** *m.,* **-zufuhr,** *f.* water supply, water feed. **-zusatz,** *m.* addition of water.

**wässrig,** *a.* = wässerig.

**Watte,** *f.* wadding (as of cotton or glass wool), wad, padding, pad; cotton wool. **-bausch,** *m.* cotton plug or pad. **-pfropf,** *m.* plug of wadding, wad. **-schicht,** *f.* layer of wadding. **-verschluss,** *m.* plug of wadding (esp. cotton).

**wattieren,** *v.t.* wad; pad.

**wattlos,** *a.* (*Elec.*) wattless.

**Watt-messer,** *m.* (*Elec.*) wattmeter. **-stunde,** *f.* (*Elec.*) watt-hour. **-zahl,** *f.* (*Elec.*) number of watts, wattage.

**Wau,** *m.* weld, dyer's weed (*Reseda luteola*). **-gelb,** *n.* luteolin.

**W.E., WE.,** *abbrev.* (Wärmeeinheit) heat unit.

**weben,** *v.t.* weave.

**Weber,** *m.* weaver. **-distel,** *f.* fuller's teasel (*Dipsacus*).

**Weberei,** *f.* weaving; texture, tissue; weaving mill.

**Weberzettel,** *m.* warp.

**Webstuhl,** *m.* loom.

**Wechsel,** *m.* change, shifting; alternation; variation; exchange; cock, tap; joint, junction; rotation (of crops); bill (of exchange), draft.

**wechselbar,** *a.* changeable.

**Wechsel-beziehung,** *f.* correlation; (*Com.*) drawing. **-fall,** *m.* vicissitude; alternative, dilemma.

**wechselfarbig,** *a.* changing color, iridescent.

**Wechsel-feld,** *n.* (*Elec.*) alternating field. **-fieber,** *n.* intermittent fever. **-gespräch,** *n.* dialog. **-hahn,** *m.* change cock. **-handel,** *m.* banking. **-kurs,** *m.* rate of exchange.

**wechseln,** *v.t.* change; vary; exchange; interchange.—*v.i.* alternate; change places.— **wechselnd,** *p.a.* varying, variable; alternating.

**Wechselsatz,** *m.* exchange principle.

**wechselseitig,** *a.* reciprocal; mutual; interchangeable; alternate.

Wechselspiel, *n.* alternation, fluctuation.

wechselständig, *a.* alternate.

Wechsel-stein, *m.* glazed tile, glazed brick. -strom, *m.* alternating current.

wechselsweise, *adv.* = wechselweise.

Wechselverhältnis, *n.* reciprocal relation; reciprocal proportion.

wechselweise, *adv.* alternately; reciprocally; mutually; interchangeably.

Wechsel-winkel, *m.pl.* alternate angles. -wirkung, *f.* reciprocal action or effect. -zersetzung, *f.* double (or mutual) decomposition.

Weck, Wecken, *m.*, Wecke, *f.* roll, small loaf.

wecken, *v.t.* wake, waken, rouse.

Wecker, *m.*, alarm; bell.

Wedel, *m.* fan; brush; (*Bot.*) frond.

weder, *conj.* neither.— — . . . noch, neither . . . nor.

weg, *adv.* away, off, gone.

Weg, *m.* way; passage, route, road, street; path; manner; means.

weg-. away, off, a-, ab-. -ätzen, *v.t.* remove by caustics, etch away. -begeben, *v.r.* go away, withdraw. -beizen, *v.t.* = wegätzen. -bekommen, *v.t.* get, catch; get away; get the knack of. -brennen, *v.t.* burn away, burn off. -bringen, *v.t.* carry or take away, remove.

Wege-bau, *m.* road making. -dorn, *m.* purging buckthorn (*Rhamnus cathartica*).

wegen, *prep. with gen.* (sometimes following its object). on account of, regarding.

Wegerich, *m.* plantain.

Wegfall, *m.* omission; suppression.—in — kommen, be omitted or suppressed.

wegfallen, *v.i.* fall off, drop; be omitted, cease.

wegfiltern, *n.* filtering off or away.

weg-gehen, *v.i.* go away, go off, escape. -giessen, *v.t.* pour away, pour off. -glühen, *v.t.* drive off by ignition. -kochen, *v.t.& i.* boil away, boil off. -kommen, *v.i.* get away; come off; get lost.

Weglänge, *f.* (length of) path.—mittlere freie —, mean free path.

weg-lassen, *v.t.* leave out, omit; let go, release. -leitend, *p.a.* efferent. -machen, *v.t.* remove.—*v.r.* make off.

Wegnahme, *f.* taking away, removal; seizure; (*Physiol.*) elimination.

weg-nehmen, *v.t.* take away, remove. -oxydieren, *v.t.* oxidize away or off. -räumen, *v.t.* remove, clear away.

wegsam, *a.* pervious, penetrable.

Wegsamkeit, *f.* perviousness, penetrability.

weg-saugen, *v.t.* suck away, remove by suction. -schaffen, *v.t.* remove, eliminate. -schmelzen, *v.t.* melt away, melt off; remove by fusion. -sein, *v.i.* be away, be gone; be faint. -setzen, *v.t.* put away.—

*v.i.* leap. -sieden, *v.t.* boil away, boil off. -spülen, *v.t.* rinse away, wash away.

Wegstrecke, *f.* distance, stretch.

weg-streichen, *v.t.* strike out; stroke away. -tun, *v.t.* put away, remove, dismiss.

Wegwartwurzel, *f.* chicory root.

weg-waschbar, *a.* removable by washing. -waschen, *v.t.* wash away.

Wegweiser, *m.* guide; sign post; directory.

weg-werfen, *v.t.* throw away; reject. -werfend, *p.a.* disparaging. -ziehen, *v.t.* draw away, pull away.—*v.i.* depart, move.

weh, *interj.* woe.—*a.* sore, painful, aching.— — tun, ache, give pain.

Weh, Wehe, *n.* woe, pain, grief, ache.

Wehe, *f.* (snow) drift.

wehen, *v.i.* blow; (of a flag) wave.

Wehenmittel, *n.* ecbolic.

Wehr, *n.& f.* weir, dam; dike.

Wehr, Wehre, *f.* defense.

wehren, *v.t.* check, keep, restrain, prevent.— *v.r.* resist.

wehrlos, *a.* unarmed, unprotected.

Weib, *n.* woman; wife.

weiblich, *a.* female; feminine; womanly; womanish.

weich, *a.* soft; tender, mellow, weak, gentle, mild.

Weichblei, *n.* soft lead, refined lead.

weichbleibend, *p.a.* remaining soft, nonhardening.

Weich-bottich, *m.* steeping tub. -brand, *m.* soft brick, place brick. -braunstein, *m.* pyrolusite. -bütte, *f.* (*Brewing*) steep tank, cistern. -dauer, *f.* time of steeping or soaking.

Weiche, *f.* softness; side, (*pl.*) groin; siding, switch; (*Leather*) soak pit, soak.

Weicheisen, *n.* soft iron. -kies, *m.* (*Min.*) marcasite.

weichen, *v.t.* soak, steep.—*v.i.* yield, give way, retreat, recede.

Weichen-. inguinal; switch.

Weichfass, *n.* steeping tub.

weichfeuern, *v.t.* (*Puddling*) melt down.

Weich-floss, *n.* (*Metal.*) porous white pig. -glühung, *f.* soft annealing. -gummi, *n.* soft rubber. -guss, *m.* malleable cast iron. -harz, *n.* soft resin, oleoresin. -heit, *f.* softness, etc. (see weich). -holz, *n.* soft wood. -kautschuk, *m.* soft rubber. -kohle, *f.* soft coal. -kufe, *f.* steeping vat, soaking tub, etc. -kupfer, *n.* soft copper. -leder, *n.* soft leather.

weichlich, *a.* soft, tender, delicate.

Weichlot, *n.* soft solder.

weichlöten, *v.t.* soft-solder.

Weich-machen, *n.* softening. -machungsmittel, *n.* softening agent, softener. -man-

gan, -manganerz, n. pyrolusite. -metall, n.
soft metal. -paraffin, n. soft paraffin.
-pech, n. soft pitch. -porzellan, n. soft
porcelain.

**Weichselkirsche,** f. mahaleb; morello.

**Weich-stahl,** m. mild steel, soft steel. -stock,
m. steeping tub; (Brewing) steep tank,
cistern. -teil, m. soft part. -tier, n. mollusk.
-wasser, n. steeping water, steep water,
soak liquor. -werden, n. softening.

**Weid,** m. woad.

**Weide,** f. willow; pasture, pasturage.

**weiden,** v.t.& i. pasture, feed.

**Weiden-bitter,** n. salicin. -kohle, f. willow
charcoal.

**weidlich,** adv. soundly, thoroly.

**Weife,** f. reel.

**weifen,** v.t. reel, wind.

**weigern,** v.t.& r. refuse, decline.

**Weihe,** f. consecration; sanction; kite (the
bird).

**weihen,** v.t. consecrate, ordain, devote.

**Weiher,** m. pond, pool.

**Weihnachten,** f.pl. Christmas.

**Weihnachtswurzel,** f. black hellebore.

**Weihrauch,** m. incense; specif., frankincense,
olibanum. -harz, n. incense resin; specif.,
frankincense.

**weil,** conj. because, since; while.

**Weilchen,** n. little while.

**Weile,** f. while, time; leisure.

**weilen,** v.i. tarry, stay.

**Wein,** m. wine; vine.

**weinähnlich,** a. like wine, vinaceous.

**Weinart,** f. kind of wine.

**weinartig,** a. vinous, winy.

**Wein-bau,** m. viniculture, viticulture. -bauer,
m. wine grower, grape grower. -beere, f.
grape. -berg, m. vineyard. -blau, n. wine
blue (enocyanin). -blume, f. bouquet (of
wine); enanthic ether (as an artificial
flavoring). -blüte, f. vine blossom. -brand,
-branntwein, m. brandy made from wine.

**weinen,** v.i. weep, cry.

**Weinernte,** f. vintage.

**weinerzeugend,** p.a. wine-producing.

**Wein-essig,** m. wine vinegar. -fabrik, f.
winery. -farbe, f. wine color.

**weinfarben,** a. wine-colored.

**Wein-farbstoff,** m. coloring matter of wine.
-fass, n. wine cask. -flasche, f. wine bottle.

**weingar,** a. see Maische.

**Wein-gärung,** f. vinous fermentation. -garten,
m. vineyard. -gegend, f. wine district.
-gehalt, m. wine content, vinosity.

**Weingeist,** m. (ethyl) alcohol, spirit of wine.
—versüsster —, (Pharm.) spirit of nitrous
ether.

**weingeistartig,** a. alcoholic.

**Weingeistfirnis,** m. spirit varnish.

**weingeisthaltig,** a. alcoholic.

**weingeistig,** a. spirituous, alcoholic.—wein-
geistiges Ammoniak, spirit of ammonia.

**Weingeist-lack,** m. spirit varnish. -messer,
m. alcoholometer.

**wein-gelb,** a. wine-yellow. -haltig, a. containing wine.

**Wein-handel,** m. wine trade. -hefe, f. wine
lees; wine yeast.

**weinig,** a. vinous.

**Wein-kamm,** m. grape pomace, rape. -kernöl,
n. grape-seed oil. -lese, f. vintage. -mes-
ser, m. vinometer, enometer. -most, m.
grape must, grape juice. -öl, n. oil of wine,
enanthic ether; (schweres) heavy oil of
wine (oily residue from preparation of
ether). -probe, f. sample of wine; sampling
of wine. -prüfung, f. wine testing. -raute,
f. (common) rue. -rebe, f. grapevine.
-rebenschwarz, n. Frankfort black.

**wein-rot,** a. wine-red. -sauer, a. of or combined with tartaric acid, tartrate of.
-säuerlich, a. sourish (like some wine).

**Wein-säure,** f. tartaric acid; acidity of wine.
-schöne, f. fining for wine. -stärkemesser,
m. wine hydrometer, enometer.

**Weinstein,** m. tartar.—roher —, crude tartar,
wine stone, argol.—gereinigter —, purified
tartar, cream of tartar.

**weinsteinartig,** a. tartar-like, tartareous.

**Weinstein-ersatz,** m. (Dyeing) tartar substitute, specif. acid sodium sulfate. -kohle,
f. black flux. -präparat, n. (Dyeing) acid
sodium sulfate. -rahm, m. cream of tartar.
-salz, n. salt of tartar (potassium carbonate).

**weinsteinsauer,** a. =weinsauer.

**Wein-steinsäure,** f. tartaric acid. -stock, m.
grapevine. -traube, f. grape, bunch of
grapes. -treber, f.pl., -trester, m.pl. marc
of grapes. -untersuchung, f. examination
(or investigation) of wine. -verfälschung,
f. adulteration of wine. -wa(a)ge, f. vinometer, enometer.

**weise,** a. wise, prudent.

**Weise,** f. manner, way; (Gram.) mood;
melody.—m. sage, philosopher.

-weise. in ... manner, by ... , -ly.

**weisen,** v.t. show; indicate, point out, direct,
send, teach.—v.i. point.

**Weiser,** m. pointer, indicator, hand; sign post;
guide, teacher.

**Weisheit,** f. wisdom, knowledge.

**weiss,** pr. 1 & 3 sing. of wissen.

**weiss,** a. white; blank; clean.—weisses
Eisenblech, tin plate.—weisser Fluss,
leucorrhea.—weiss gerben, taw.—weisse
Glut, white heat.—weisser Kupferstein,

(*Copper*) white metal.—**weisser Leim**, gelatin.—**weisse Magnesia**, magnesia alba (basic magnesium carbonate).—**weisses Nichts**, nihil album (zinc oxide).—**weiss sieden**, blanch.—**weisser Vitriol**, white vitriol (zinc sulfate).

**Weiss**, *n.* white.

**weissagen**, *v.t.& i.* predict, prophesy.

**Weiss-ätzung**, *f.* (*Calico*) white discharge. **-bad**, *n.* (in Turkey-red dyeing) white liquor bath. **-baumöl**, *n.* cajuput oil. **-bier**, *n.* pale beer; specif., weiss beer.

**weissblau**, *a.* whitish blue.

**Weiss-blech**, *n.* tin plate. **-blechwaren**, *f.pl.* tinware. **-blei**, *n.* tin. **-bleiche**, *f.* bleaching, full bleach. **-bleierz**, *n.* white lead ore, cerussite. **-blütigkeit**, *f.* leucocythemia. **-brennen**, *n.* calcining at white heat. **-brot**, *n.* white bread, wheat bread.

**weissbrüchig**, *a.* of white or pale fracture.

**Weiss-brühe**, *f.* dégras. **-buche**, *f.* hornbeam. **-dorn**, *m.* hawthorn.

**Weisse**, *m.& f.* white person, white.—*f.* whiteness; white; whitewash.

**Weisseisen**, *n.* white iron.

**weissen**, *v.t.* whiten, bleach; whitewash; (*Iron*) refine.

**Weiss-erde**, *f.* terra alba. **-erz**, *n.* arsenopyrite; siderite; krennerite; an impure marcasite.

**weissfärben**, *v.t.* bleach (and blue).

**Weiss-färber**, *m.* bleacher. **-feuer**, *n.* white fire.

**weiss-gar**, *a.* tawed. **-gelb**, *a.* pale yellow. **-gerben**, *v.t.* taw.

**Weiss-gerber**, *m.* tawer. **-gerberei**, *f.* tawing; tawery, alum tannery. **-glühen**, *n.* incandescence.

**weiss-glühen**, *v.t.* raise to white heat. **-glühend**, *p.a.* white-hot, incandescent.

**Weiss-glühhitze**, **-glut**, *f.* white heat, incandescence. **-gold**, *n.* platinum; white gold. **-golderz**, *n.* sylvanite.

**weissgrau**, *a.* light gray, pale gray.

**Weiss-gültigerz**, *n.* argentiferous tetrahedrite. **-guss**, *m.* white metal; white malleable cast iron. **-hitze**, *f.* white heat. **-kalk**, *m.* pyrolignite of lime (crude calcium acetate); fat lime. **-kies**, *m.* arsenopyrite. **-klee**, *m.* white clover.

**weisskochen**, *v.t.* degum (silk).

**Weiss-kupfer**, *n.* native copper arsenide; domeykite; white copper (paktong, German silver, etc.). **-kupfererz**, *n.* cubanite; an impure marcasite. **-lauge**, *f.* white liquor. **-leder**, *n.* white leather, tawed leather.

**weisslich**, *a.* whitish.

**Weisslot**, *n.* soft solder.

**weissmachen**, *v.t.* make white, bleach.

**Weiss-mehl**, *n.* white flour, wheat flour. **-messing**, *n.* white brass. **-metall**, *n.* white metal. **-nickelerz**, *n.*, **-nickelkies**, *m.* white nickel ore, chloanthite. **-ofen**, *m.* (*Metal.*) refining furnace. **-papp**, *m.* (*Calico*) white resist.

**weissrot**, *a.* whitish red.

**Weisssiedekessel**, *m.* blanching copper.

**weisssieden**, *v.t.* blanch.

**Weiss-siedlauge**, *f.* blanching liquor. **-spiessglanz**, *m.*, **-spiessglanzerz**, *n.* white antimony, valentinite. **-stein**, *m.* (*Copper*) white metal. **-strahl**, *m.* white pig iron resembling spiegeleisen.

**weissstrahlig**, *a.* white radiated.

**Weiss-stuck**, *m.* white stucco. **-sud**, *m.* blanching; blanching solution. **-sylvanerz**, *n.* sylvanite. **-tanne**, *f.* silver fir. **-tellur**, *n.* sylvanite. **-trockner**, *m.* (*Paints*) white drier. **-vitriol**, *n.* white vitriol (zinc sulfate). **-waren**, *f.pl.* white goods, linen goods.

**weisswarm**, *a.* white-hot.

**Weiss-wein**, *m.* white wine. **-wurzel**, *f.* Solomon's seal. **-zucker**, *m.* white sugar.

**Weisung**, *f.* order, direction, instructions.

**weit**, *a.* far, distant; long, great; wide, extended.—*adv.* far, much.—**bei weitem**, by far.

**weitaus**, *adv.* by far.

**Weite**, *f.* distance; wideness; width; extent, length, range.

**weiten**, *v.t.& r.* widen; extend.

**weiter**, *a.* farther; further, additional.—*adv.* farther, forward, on.

**Weiterbehandlung**, *f.* further or subsequent treatment.

**Weiteres**, *n.* remainder, rest.—**ohne —**, ohne weiteres, without more ado, directly.

**weiter-färben**, *v.t.* dye further, continue dyeing. **-gerben**, *v.t.* re-tan. **-hin**, *adv.* furthermore. **-oxydieren**, *v.t.* oxidize further.

**Weiterungen**, *f. pl.* formalities, red tape; complications.

**Weiter-verarbeitung**, *f.* further working or manufacture, subsequent treatment. **-wirkung**, *f.* further action, continued action.

**weitgehend**, *p.a.* far-reaching, extensive.

**Weithalsflasche**, *f.* wide-necked bottle.

**weithalsig**, *a.* wide-necked.

**Weithals-kölbchen**, *n.* small wide-mouthed flask. **-kolben**, *m.* wide-necked flask.

**weit-hin**, *adv.* far off, in wide extent. **-läufig**, *a.* wide, large, roomy; distant; widespread, scattered, straggling, diffuse, detailed. **-lochig**, *a.* large-holed, large-pored. **-maschig**, *a.* wide-meshed, coarse-meshed. **-mündig**, *a.* wide-mouthed. **-sichtig**, *a.* farsighted. **-tragend**, *p.a.* carrying a great distance; important. **-umfassend**, *a.* comprehensive, extensive.

**Weitung**, *f.* widening; width; space.

**Weizen**, *m.* wheat.—**türkischer** —, maize.

**Weizen-kleie**, *f.* wheat bran. **-malz**, *n.* wheat malt. **-mehl**, *n.* wheat flour. **-stärke**, *f.*, **-stärkemehl**, *n.* wheat starch. **-stroh**, *n.* wheat straw.

**welcher**, *pron.* which? what?; who, which, that; some, any.— **— auch**, whosoever; **welches auch**, whatsoever.

**welcherlei**, *a.* of what kind.

**Weldonschlamm**, *m.* Weldon mud.

**welk**, *a.* withered, faded; flaccid; languid.

**Welkboden**, *m.* (*Brewing*) withering floor.

**welken**, *v.i.* wither, fade, decay.—*v.t.* wither, dry.

**Welkmalz**, *n.* withered malt, air-dried malt.

**Well-baum**, *m.* arbor, shaft, axletree. **-blech**, *n.* corrugated plate or sheet, specif. corrugated iron.

**Welle**, *f.* wave; shaft, arbor, axle; roller, roll; stria (in glass); fagot, bundle.

**wellen**, *v.t.* boil, simmer; roll; wave; corrugate; wield.—**gewellt**, *p.a.* wavy; corrugated.

**wellenartig**, *a.* wavelike, undulatory.

**Wellen-bewegung**, *f.* wave motion, undulatory motion. **-bild**, *n.* wave form. **-filter**, *n.* wave filter. **-fläche**, *f.* wave surface.

**wellenförmig**, *a.* undulatory, wavy.

**Wellen-gleichung**, *f.* wave equation. **-kopf**, *m.* wave front. **-lager**, *n.* (*Mach.*) bearing, carriage. **-länge**, *f.* wave length. **-linie**, *f.* wavy line. **-mechanik**, *f.* wave mechanics.

**wellenmechanisch**, *a.* wave-mechanical.

**Wellenoptik**, *f.* wave optics.

**wellenoptisch**, *a.* of or pertaining to wave optics.

**Wellen-paket**, *n.* wave packet. **-schwingung**, *f.* undulation. **-strom**, *m.* (*Elec.*) pulsating current. **-stromlichtbogen**, *m.* pulsating-current arc. **-theorie**, *f.* wave theory, undulatory theory. **-zahl**, *f.* wave number.

**Weller**, *m.* loam, mud.

**wellig**, *a.* undulating, wavy.

**Well-packpapier**, **-papier**, *n.* corrugated paper. **-rad**, *n.* wheel and axle; arbor wheel. **-rohr**, *n.* corrugated tube.

**Wellung**, *f.* waving, undulation.

**Wellwurzel**, *f.* (*Pharm.*) symphytum.

**welsch**, *a.* foreign (specif. Italian or French); Welsh.

**Welt**, *f.* world; good breeding. **-all**, *n.* universe. **-alter**, *n.* age of the world; age. **-anschauung**, *f.* view of the world or of life. **-auge**, *f.* hydrophane. **-ausstellung**, *f.* world's fair. **-beschreibung**, *f.* cosmography.

**weltbürgerlich**, *a.* cosmopolitan.

**Weltenraum**, *m.* universal space, interstellar space.

**Welt-gegend**, *f.* quarter of the world. **-gürtel**, *m.* zone. **-handel**, *m.* world commerce. **-körper**, *m.* heavenly body. **-krieg**, *m.* world war. **-kugel**, *f.* globe.

**weltlich**, *a.* worldly, mundane; secular, temporal, civil, profane.

**Welt-meer**, *n.* ocean. **-postverein**, *m.* Postal Union. **-sprache**, *f.* universal language. **-stadt**, *f.* metropolis. **-teil**, *m.* continent; part of the world.

**wem**, *pron.* (dative of wer) whom, to whom.

**Wende**, *f.* turning, turning point, turn; epoch, era. **-kreis**, *m.* tropic.

**wenden**, *v.t.*, *i.& r.* turn; (*Elec.*) reverse.—**gewandt**, *p.a.* versed, skilled, clever, quick.

**Wendepunkt**, *m.* turning point, point of inflection.

**Wendung**, *f.* turning, turn; (*Elec.*) reversal.

**wenig**, *a.* little; (*pl.*) few.—*adv.* little.

**weniger**, *a.* less, fewer.—*adv.* less.

**Wenigkeit**, *f.* littleness, small amount, small number.

**wenigste**, *a.* least, fewest.

**wenigstens**, *adv.* at least.

**wenn**, *adv.* when.—*conj.* when; if.— **— auch**, **— gleich**, **— schon**, altho, even if.

**wer**, *pron.* who? which?; who, he who.—**— . . . nur**, **— . . . auch**, whoever.

**Werbe-**. advertizing, publicity, propaganda.

**werben**, *v.i.* advertize; carry on propaganda; sue, court.—*v.t.* levy, recruit.

**Werbeschrift**, *f.* advertizing publication; propaganda article or pamphlet.

**Werdegang**, *m.* development.

**werden**, *v.i.* become; turn; fall (to one's lot).—*v. aux.* shall, will, be, am, etc.—**es wird mir**, I feel.

**werfen**, *v.t.* throw; cast, fling, project.—*v.i.* bring forth young.—*v.r.* throw oneself, apply oneself; warp; (of beer) become turbid.

**Werft**, *f.* wharf, dock; weft.

**Werg**, *n.* tow, oakum.

**Werk**, *n.* work; works; apparatus, mechanism; (*Salt*) brine evaporated one time; (*Metal.*) pig of raw lead; (*Paper*) stuff. **-blei**, *n.* raw lead (usually containing silver). **-bottich**, *m.*, **-bütte**, *f.* (*Paper*) stuff vat. **-führer**, *m.* foreman. **-leute**, *pl.* workmen, hands. **-meister**, *m.* foreman. **-probe**, *f.* (*Metal.*) sample of metal. **-silber**, *n.* silver extracted from lead ore. **-statt**, **-stätte**, *f.* (work)shop, workroom, laboratory, studio. **-stein**, *m.* freestone, quarry stone. **-stoff**, *m.* (industrial) material. **-stück**, *n.* piece of metal (to be machined), work piece; hewn stone block.

werk-tägig, a. workaday, commonplace. -tätig, a. working, active, operative; practical.

Werkzeug, n. tool, instrument, implement; organ. -maschine, f. machine tool. -stahl, m. tool steel.

Werk-zink, n. raw zinc. -zinn, n. raw tin.

Wermut, m. wormwood; vermuth. -bitter, m. absinthin. -öl, n. oil of wormwood. -schnaps, m. vermuth.

wert, a. worth; worthy; dear, valued, respected.

Wert, m. value; valence; worth, merit. -angabe, f. statement of value. -bestimmung, f. determination of value, valuation; determination of valence.

wertgeschätzt, p.a. valued, esteemed.

-wertig. -valent.

Wertigkeit, f. valence.

Wertigkeitsformel, f. valence formula, linkage formula.

wertlos, a. worthless.

Wert-papier, n. valuable paper, security. -sachen, f.pl. valuables.

wertschätzen, v.t. value, esteem highly.

Wertverhältnis, n. relative value.

wertvoll, a. valuable.

Wesen, n. being, essence, substance; nature, character, condition, manner; affairs, concerns, matters; means, property.

wesentlich, a. essential; real, intrinsic.—im wesentlichen, essentially.

weshalb, adv. why, wherefore.

Wespe, f. wasp.

west-fälisch, a. Westphalian. -indisch, a. West India, West Indian. -lich, a. west, western, occidental.

weswegen, adv. why?

wett, adv. even, quits.

Wettbewerb, m. competition, rivalry.

Wette, f. bet, wager; rivalry, competition.

Wetteifer, m. emulation, competition.

wetteifern, v.i. vie, contend.

Wetter, n. weather; storm; (Mining) damp.

wetterbeständig, a. weatherproof.

Wetterdynamit, n. (Mining) permissible dynamite, wetterdynamite.

wetter-echt, a. fast to exposure. -fest, a. resistant to weather, weatherproof.

Wetter-fulminit, n. wetterfulminite (an explosive). -kunde, f. meteorology.

wettern, v.i. thunder and lighten; storm.

Wetter-prüfung, f. weathering test. -stein, m. belemnite.

Wett-kampf, m. contest. -lauf, m. race.

wettmachen, v.t. make good, compensate for.

Wettstreit, m. contest.

wetzen, v.t. whet, sharpen.

Wetzstein, m. whetstone, hone.

wf., abbrev. (wasserfrei) anhydrous, free from water.

wich, pret. of weichen.

Wichse, f. (polishing) wax, polish, blacking; drubbing.

wichsen, v.t. wax, polish; glaze.

Wichte, f. unit of weight; specific gravity.

wichtig, a. important, weighty; serious.

Wichtigkeit, f. importance; important matter.

Wicke, f. vetch.

Wickel, m. roller, roll; filler (of a cigar).

wickeln, v.t. wind, coil, roll, wrap, twist.

Wickelung, f. winding, wrapping, casing.

Wickenstroh, n. vetch straw.

Wicklung, f. winding, wrapping, casing.

Widder, m. ram.

widdern, v.t. turn (malt).

wider, prep. against, contrary to.

Wider-. counter-, contra-, re-, anti-, with-, gain-. -druck, m. counterpressure, reaction.

wider-fahren, v.i. happen, befall. -haarig, a. cross-grained, perverse.

Wider-haken, m. barb. -hall, m. echo, reverberation.

wider-legen, v.t. refute, disprove. -lich, a. repugnant, repulsive, disagreeable. -natürlich, a. unnatural, preternatural.

Widerrede, f. contradiction, objection.

widerrufen, v.t. recall, revoke.

Wider-sacher, m. adversary, opponent. -schein, m. reflection.

wider-setzen, v.t. resist, oppose. -sinnig, a. anticlinal; contradictory, nonsensical. -spenstig, a. refractory, stubborn. -spiegeln, v.t. reflect.

Widerspiel, n. contrary, opposition.

widersprechen, v.i. contradict.

Wider-spruch, m. contradiction, opposition, variance. -stand, m. resistance.

widerstandsfähig, a. resistant, capable of resistance, refractory.

Widerstands-fähigkeit, f. capability of resisting. -kasten, m. (Elec.) resistance box. -legierung, f. resistance alloy. -ofen, m. resistance furnace. -vermögen, n. resisting power, resistance.

widerstehen, v.i. resist, withstand; be repugnant.

Widerstoss, m. countershock.

widerwärtig, a. repugnant, disagreeable; adverse.

Widerwille, f. aversion, antipathy.

widerwillig, a. reluctant, unwilling.

widmen, v.t. dedicate, devote.

Widmung, f. dedication; devotion.

widrig, a. contrary, adverse; repugnant; (as a suffix) opposing, anti-, as fäulniswidrig, antiseptic.

**wie**, *adv.* how.—*conj.* as, like.— — ... **auch**, however.

**Wiebel**, *m.* weevil.

**Wied**, *m.* woad.

**wieder**, *adv.* again, anew, re-; back, in return. **-abdrucken**, *v.t.* reprint, republish.

**Wiederanreicherung**, *f.* reconcentration.

**wieder-auffüllen**, *v.t.* refill. **-aufladen**, *v.t.* (*Elec.*) recharge. **-auflösen**, *v.t.&r.* redissolve. **-aufsaugen**, *v.t.* reabsorb. **-beleben**, *v.t.* revive, revivify, reactivate, regenerate; (*Sugar*) reburn (char); (*Med.*) resuscitate.

**Wieder-belebung**, *f.* revival, etc. (see wiederbeleben). **-belebungsmittel**, *n.* (*Med.*) restorative. **-benutzung**, *f.* reutilization.

**wieder-beschicken**, *v.t.* reload, recharge. **-bilden**, *v.t.* form again.

**Wieder-brauchbarmachen**, *n.* regeneration. **-einschmelzen**, *n.* remelting.

**wieder-erhitzen**, *v.t.* reheat. **-erwärmen**, *v.t.* rewarm, reheat. **-erzeugen**, *v.t.* reproduce, regenerate.

**Wiedererzeugung**, *f.* reproduction, regeneration.

**wieder-fällen**, *v.t.* reprecipitate. **-färben**, *v.t.* recolor, redye.

**Wiedergabe**, *f.* reproduction; return; response; version.

**wieder-geben**, *v.t.* translate, render; return. **-gewinnen**, *v.t.* recover.

**Wieder-gewinnung**, *f.* recovery. **-hall**, *m.* echo, reverberation, resonance.

**wiederherstellen**, *v.t.* reprepare; reproduce; restore, revive; readjust.

**Wiederherstellung**, *f.* repreparation, etc. (see wiederherstellen).

**wieder-hervorbringen**, *v.t.* = wiedererzeugen. **-holbar**, *a.* capable of being repeated. **-holen**, *v.t.* repeat.—*v.r.* repeat oneself; recur. **-holt**, *p.a.* repeated.—*adv.* repeatedly.

**Wiederholung**, *f.* repetition.

**wiederkäuen**, *v.t.* ruminate; go over and over.

**Wieder-käuer**, *m.* ruminant. **-kehr**, *f.* return, recurrence.

**wieder-kehren**, *v.i.* return, recur. **-kristallisieren**, *v.t.* recrystallize.

**Wieder-kristallisierung**, *f.* recrystallization. **-oxydation**, *f.* reoxidation. **-schein**, *m.* reflection, reflex.

**wiederschmelzen**, *v.t.* remelt, re-fuse.

**Wiedersehen**, *n.* meeting again.—**auf —**, au revoir.

**wiederspiegeln**, *v.t.* reflect.

**Wieder-stoss**, *m.* countershock. **-strahl**, *m.* reflected ray.

**wieder-strahlen**, *v.t.* reflect. **-um**, *adv.* again, in return. **-vereinigen**, *v.t.* reunite; reconcile.

**Wiedervereinigung**, *f.* reunion, recombination.

**wieder-verstärken**, *v.t.* strengthen again; replenish. **-verwandeln**, *v.t.* reconvert.

**Wiederwässerung**, *f.* watering or soaking again; rehydration.

**Wiege**, *f.* cradle.

**Wiegegläschen**, *n.* weighing glass.

**wiegen**, *v.t.* weigh; rock.—*v.i.* weigh.— **gewogen**, *p.a.* weighed; well disposed, favorable.—**gewiegt**, *p.a.* skilled, experienced; rocked.

**Wiegevorrichtung**, *f.* weighing device.

**Wieke**, *f.* pledget.

**Wien**, *n.* Vienna.

**Wiener, wienerisch**, *a.* Vienna, Viennese.— **Wiener Ätzpulver**, Vienna paste, Vienna caustic.—**Wiener Grün**, Vienna green.— **Wiener Kalk**, French chalk.

**wies**, *pret.* of weisen.

**Wiese**, *f.* meadow.

**Wiesen-erz**, *n.* meadow ore, bog iron ore. **-flachs**, *m.* purging flax. **-heu**, *n.* meadow hay. **-kalk**, *m.* limestone from springs, fresh-water limestone. **-klee**, *m.* red clover. **-knöterich**, *m.* bistort (*Polygonum bistorta*). **-lein**, *n.* purging flax.

**wieviel**, *adv.* how much, how many.— — **Uhr ist es?** what time is it?

**wiewohl**, *conj.* altho.

**wild**, *a.* wild; savage, fierce, unruly.—**wilder Stahl**, wild steel.—**wildes Fleisch**, proud flesh.—**wildes Gestein**, rock containing no metal.

**Wilde**, *m.&f.* savage; wildness; wilderness.

**Wild-geschmack**, *m.* gamy taste. **-kirschenrinde**, *f.* wild cherry bark. **-leder**, *n.* buckskin, deerskin; chamois.

**Wildnis**, *f.* wilderness.

**will**, *pr.* 1 & 3 *sing.* of wollen.

**Wille**, *f.*, **Willen**, *m.* will, volition; design, intent; permission.

**willfahren**, *v.i.* yield to, comply with.

**willig**, *a.* willing, ready.

**willkommen**, *a.&adv.* welcome.

**Willkür**, *f.* free will, option; arbitrariness.

**willkürlich**, *a.* arbitrary; voluntary.

**wimmeln**, *v.i.* swarm, teem.

**Wimper**, *f.* eyelash.

**wimpernd**, *p.a.* ciliated, ciliary; winking.

**Wind**, *m.* wind, breeze; (*Metal.*) blast. **-bläser**, *m.* blower, blast apparatus. **-darm**, *m.* colon.

**winddicht**, *a.* airtight.

**Winddruck**, *m.* (*Metal.*) blast pressure; wind pressure.

**Winde**, *f.* windlass, winch; worm (screw); bindweed; (*Glass*) stria.

**winden**, *v.t.* wind, coil.—*v.r.* wind, coil, wriggle.

—gewunden, *p.a.* wound, coiled, twisted, spiral.

Wind-erhitzung, *f.* blast heating. -erhitzungsapparat, *m.* hot blast stove; regenerator. -fahne, *f.* vane. -flügel, *m.* (ventilator) fan; fan blade. -form, *f.* (*Metal.*) twyer, tuyère. -frischen, *n.* (*Metal.*) blast purifying, converting. -geschwulst, *f.* emphysema.

windig, *a.* windy, breezy; visionary, shaky.

Wind-kasten, *m.* wind chest, air chamber; (*Metal.*) twyer box. -leitung, *f.* (*Metal.*) blast main. -leitungsrohr, *n.* (*Metal.*) blast pipe. -ofen, *m.* wind furnace, air furnace. -pocken, *f.pl.* chicken pox. -pressung, *f.* (*Metal.*) blast pressure. -rohr, *n.* (*Metal.*) blast pipe, twyer pipe. -sammler, *m.* air reservoir.

windstill, *a.* calm.

Windstrom, *m.* air current, blast current.

wind-treibend, *p.a.* carminative. -trocken, *a.* wind-dried, air-dry.

Wind-trocknung, *f.* wind drying; blast drying; air drying. -trocknungsverfahren, *n.* dry-blast process.

Windung, *f.* winding, etc. (see winden).

Windzug, *m.* air current; ventilator.

Wink, *m.* wink; beckoning; nod; hint, suggestion.

Winkel, *m.* angle; corner. -abstand, *m.* angular distance. -abweichung, *f.* angular deviation. -bewegung, *f.* angular motion. -eisen, *n.* angle iron.

winkelförmig, *a.* angular.

Winkelgeschwindigkeit, *f.* angular velocity.

winkelig, *a.* angular, -angled, -cornered.

Winkel-linie, *f.* diagonal. -messer, *m.* goniometer.

winkelrecht, *a.* right-angled, rectangular.

Winkel-thermometer, *n.* bent-tube thermometer. -verschiebung, *f.* angular displacement. -zug, *m.* shift, pretext.

winken, *v.i.* wink; beckon; nod.

winklig, *a.* = winkelig.

Winter-grün, *n.* wintergreen; ivy; myrtle; periwinkle. -kresse, *f.* winter cress (*Barbarea*).

Wintersrinde, *f.* Winter's bark.

Winterweizen, *m.* winter wheat.

winzig, *a.* minute, tiny; mean.

Wipfel, *m.* top (of a tree).

Wippe, *f.* balancing; counterpoise; clipping (from coins); seesaw; (*Elec.*) tumbler switch.

wir, *pron.* we.

Wirbel, *m.* whirl, vortex; vertebra; whirlwind; eddy; (*Tech.*) spigot, button, collar, swivel, sheave, etc.; vertigo; intoxication; crown (of the head); warbling.

Wirbel-. whirl-, vortical; vertebral, vertebrate. -bein, *n.* vertebra. -bewegung, *f.* vortex motion. -knochen, *m.* vertebra.

wirbellos, *a.* invertebrate; free from eddies, nonvortical.

wirbeln, *v.i.* whirl, spin; warble; (of a drum) roll.—gewirbelt, *p.a.* whirled, etc.; vertebrate.

Wirbel-säule, *f.* vertebral column. -strom, *m.* whirlpool; (*Elec.*) eddy current. -sturm, *m.* tornado, cyclone. -tier, *n.* vertebrate.

wirbt, *pr. 3 sing.* of werben.

wird, *pr. 3 sing.* of werden.

wirft, *pr. 3 sing.* of werfen.

wirken, *v.i.* act, work, operate, have an effect. —*v.t.* work, effect, produce, perform, specif.: boil (salt); knead (dough); knit; weave.—wirkend, *p.a.* acting, working.—wirkendes Mittel, agent.

wirklich, *a.* real, actual, acting.—*adv.* really, actually, truly.

Wirklichkeit, *f.* reality, actuality.

wirksam, *a.* active; effective; efficient, efficacious.

Wirksamkeit, *f.* activity; agency; effectiveness, efficacy, efficiency; strength (of acids, etc.); operation.—in — setzen, set going, start; (*Mach.*) throw into gear.

Wirkstoff, *m.* active material or substance.

Wirkung, *f.* action; effect; working, operation, agency; efficacy.

Wirkungs-art, *f.* kind of action; mode of acting; mode of operation. -dauer *f.* period of action.

wirkungsfähig, *a.* capable of acting, active, effective, efficient.

Wirkungs-fähigkeit, *f.* activity, effectiveness, efficiency. -grad, *m.* efficiency, effect; strength (of a reagent). -kraft, *f.* effective force, working power, efficiency, efficacy. -kreis, *m.* sphere of action, sphere of activity.

wirkungslos, *a.* inactive, ineffectual, inefficient, inert.

Wirkungs-losigkeit, *f.* inactivity, ineffectiveness, inefficiency. -quantum, *n.* quantum of action. -querschnitt, *m.* effective cross section. -sphäre, *f.* sphere of action. -variabel, *n.* action variable. -vermögen, *n.* power of action, working power. -weise, *f.* mode of acting, mode of operation, action. -wert, *m.* effective value; (of an acid, etc.) strength; efficacy.

wirr, *a.* confused, tangled.

Wirre, *f.* confusion, disorder.

Wirrseide, *f.* silk waste.

Wirt, *m.* host, landlord.

Wirtel, *m.* whorl.

Wirtschaft, *f.* economy, management;

housekeeping; household; farm; hotel; inn.

**wirt-schaften,** *v.i.* keep house; keep an inn; run a farm; manage, go. **-schaftlich,** *a.* household; economic; economical.—*adv.* economically.

**Wirt-schaftlichkeit,** *f.* economy, thrift. **-schaftsbetrieb,** *m.* household management; farm management.

**Wisch,** *m.* rag; mop; whisk; piece of waste paper.

**wischen,** *v.t.* wipe.—*v.i.* whisk, slip (away).

**Wischer,** *m.* wiper; rubber, duster, (drawing) stump.

**Wischtuch,** *n.* wiping or dusting cloth.

**Wismut, Wismuth,** *n.& m.* bismuth. **-bleierz,** *n.* schapbachite. **-blende,** *f.* bismuth blende, eulytite. **-blüte,** *f.* bismuth ocher, bismite. **-bromid,** *n.* bismuth bromide. **-chlorid,** *n.* bismuth chloride, bismuth trichloride.

**wismuten,** *v.t.* solder with bismuth or bismuth solder.

**Wismut-erz,** *n.* bismuth ore. **-gehalt,** *m.* bismuth content. **-glanz,** *m.* bismuth glance, bismuthinite; **(prismatischer),** aikinite. **-glätte,** *f.* bismuth litharge, bismuth oxide.

**wismuthaltig,** *a.* bismuthiferous.

**Wismut-jodid,** *n.* bismuth iodide. **-kupfererz,** *n.* emplectite; klaprotholite; wittichenite. **-legierung,** *f.* bismuth alloy. **-lot,** *n.* bismuth solder (a fusible bismuth alloy). **-metall,** *n.* bismuth metal. **-nickel(kobalt)-kies,** *m.* grunauite. **-niederschlag,** *m.* bismuth precipitate; specif., bismuth oxynitrate. **-nitrat,** *n.* bismuth nitrate. **-ocker,** *m.* bismuth ocher, bismite ($Bi_2O_3$). **-oxyd,** *n.* bismuth oxide; specif., bismuth trioxide. **-salz,** *n.* bismuth salt. **-säure,** *f.* bismuthic acid. **-schwamm,** *m.* bismuth sponge. **-silber,** *n.* (*Min.*) schapbachite. **-spat,** *m.* bismutite. **-sulfid,** *n.* bismuth sulfide. **-tellur,** *n.* tetradymite, telluric bismuth. **-verbindung,** *f.* bismuth compound. **-weiss,** *n.* bismuth white.

**wissbegierig,** *a.* inquisitive, curious.

**wissen,** *v.t.& i.* know; know how.

**Wissen,** *n.* knowledge; learning. **-schaft,** *f.* science; learning, knowledge, intelligence.

**wissenschaftlich,** *a.* scientific.

**Wissen-schaftlichkeit,** *f.* scientific nature or quality. **-schaftslehre,** *f.* theory of science.

**Wissens-gebiet,** *n.* department of knowledge. **-zweig,** *m.* branch of knowledge.

**wissentlich,** *a.* knowing, deliberate.

**Wissmut,** *n.& m.* = Wismut.

**Witterung,** *f.* weather; scent, trail.

**Witterungs-kunde, -lehre,** *f.* meteorology.

**Wittsche Scheibe.** Witt plate.

**Witz,** *m.* wit; joke; sense.

**Witzelei,** *f.* witticism; quibble, quibbling.

**wl.,** *abbrev.* (wenig löslich) difficultly soluble.

**wlösl.,** *abbrev.* (wasserlöslich) soluble in water.

**wo,** *adv.* where; somewhere.—*conj.* if.

**w.o.,** *abbrev.* (weiter oben) above.

**wob,** *pret.* of weben.

**wobei,** *adv.* whereby, whereat.

**Woche,** *f.* week; (*pl.*) lying-in, confinement.

**Wochen-.** weekly; lying-in, obstetric, puerperal. **-bett,** *n.* childbed. **-fluss,** *m.* lochia. **-schrift,** *f.* weekly.

**wöchentlich,** *a.* weekly, week's.—*adv.* weekly.

**-wöchig.** -weekly, of . . . weeks' duration.

**Wöchnerin,** *f.* lying-in woman.

**wodurch,** *adv.* whereby, by what, by which.

**wofern,** *conj.* so far as, provided.

**wofür,** *adv.* for what, for which.

**wog,** *pret.* of wägen and of wiegen.

**wogegen,** *adv.& conj.* against what, against which; for what, for which; whereas.

**woher,** *adv.* whence, from where.

**wohin,** *adv.* whither, where. **-gegen,** *conj.* whereas, while.

**wohl,** *adv.* well; perhaps, probably; indeed.— **so — als,** as well as.

**Wohl,** *n.* weal, health, benefit, good.

**wohl-, Wohl-.** well, good.

**wohl-angebracht,** *p.a.* well-timed. **-auf,** *adv.* well.—*interj.* come on! now then! **-bedacht,** *p.a.* well-considered.

**Wohlbefinden,** *n.* good health.

**wohl-begründet,** *p.a.* well-founded. **-behalten,** *p.a.* in good condition. **-bekannt,** *p.a.* well-known. **-beleibt,** *p.a.* corpulent.

**Wohlbeleibtheit,** *f.* corpulence.

**wohl-belesen,** *p.a.* well-read. **-besetzt,** *p.a.* well-filled. **-bewusst,** *p.a.* well-known; conscious. **-definiert,** *p.a.* well-defined. **-erfahren,** *p.a.* experienced.

**Wohlergehen,** *n.* welfare, prosperity.

**wohl-erhalten,** *p.a.* well-preserved, in good condition. **-erwogen,** *p.a.* well-considered.

**Wohlfahrt,** *f.* welfare.

**wohlfeil,** *a.* cheap.

**Wohlfeilheit,** *f.* cheapness.

**wohl-gebaut,** *p.a.* well-built. **-gebildet,** *p.a.* well-formed.

**wohlgeboren,** *p.a.* well-born; Esquire.— **wohlgeborener Herr!** dear Sir.

**Wohlgefallen,** *n.* liking, pleasure, delight.

**wohl-gefällig,** *a.* pleasant, pleasing, pleased. **-gelitten,** *p.a.* popular. **-gemeint,** *p.a.* well-meant. **-gemut,** *a.* cheery, cheerful, merry. **-genährt,** *p.a.* well-nourished. **-geordnet,** *p.a.* well-arranged, well-ordered. **-geraten,** *p.a.* well-done, perfect; well-bred.

**Wohl-geruch,** *m.* agreeable odor, fragrance. **-geschmack,** *m.* agreeable taste or flavor.

**wohl-gesinnt,** *p.a.* well-disposed. **-geübt,** *p.a.*

practised, skilled. **-gewogen**, *p.a.* well-inclined. **-habend**, *p.a.* well-to-do, well off.

**Wohl-klang, -laut**, *m.* euphony; harmony. **-leben**, *n.* high living, luxury.

**wohl-redend**, *p.a.* eloquent, well-spoken. **-riechend**, *p.a.* fragrant, sweet-smelling. **-schmeckend**, *p.a.* savory, palatable.

**Wohl-sein**, *n.* good health, well-being. **-stand**, *m.* welfare, prosperity. **-tat**, *f.* good deed; benefit, kindness, blessing. **-täter**, *m.* benefactor.

**wohl-tätig**, *a.* beneficent, benevolent; beneficial, wholesome. **-tun**, *v.i.* do good, benefit, give pleasure.

**Wohlverlei**, *m.* arnica (*Arnica montana*). **-wurzel**, *f.* arnica root.

**wohl-verschlossen**, *p.a.* well-closed. **-versehen**, *p.a.* well-provided. **-weislich**, *adv.* very wisely. **-wollen**, *v.i.* wish well, be well-disposed.

**Wohlwollen**, *n.* good will, kind feeling, favor.

**wohnen**, *v.i.* live, dwell.

**wohnhaft**, *a.* dwelling, residing, resident.

**wohnlich**, *a.* habitable; comfortable.

**Wohn-ort, -platz**, *m.* dwelling place, residence. **-sitz**, *m.* domicile, residence. **-stube**, *f.* living room, sitting room.

**Wohnung**, *f.* dwelling, residence, housing.

**Wohnungsanzeiger**, *m.* directory.

**wölben**, *v.t.* vault, arch.—*v.r.* arch.

**Wölbung**, *f.* curvature; vault, vaulting.

**Wolf**, *m.* wolf; (*Iron*) lump, ball, bloom; (*Med.*) lupus; chafing.

**Wolfram**, *m.& n.* tungsten; wolframite.

**Wolframat**, *n.* tungstate, wolframate.

**Wolfram-blau**, *n.* wolfram blue, mineral blue (a tungsten oxide, $W_3O_8$?). **-bleierz**, *n.* stolzite. **-chlorid**, *n.* (any) tungsten chloride. **-erz**, *n.* tungsten ore. **-faden**, *m.* tungsten filament. **-gelb**, *n.* a yellow variety of tungsten bronze.

**wolframhaltig**, *a.* tungsteniferous.

**Wolfram-lampe**, *f.* tungsten lamp. **-metall**, *n.* metallic tungsten. **-ocker**, *m.* tungstic ocher, tungstite. **-oxyd**, *n.* tungsten oxide. **-salz**, *n.* tungsten salt.

**wolframsauer**, *a.* of or combined with tungstic acid, tungstate of.

**Wolframsäure**, *f.* tungstic acid, wolframic acid. **-anhydrid**, *n.* tungstic anhydride. **-salz**, *n.* salt of tungstic acid, tungstate.

**Wolfram-stahl**, *m.* tungsten steel. **-stickstoff**, *m.* tungsten nitride.

**Wolfs-bohne**, *f.* lupine. **-kirsche**, *f.* belladonna. **-milch**, *f.* wolf's milk, spurge (*Euphorbia* sp.). **-stahl**, *m.* natural steel. **-wurz**, *f.* baneberry.

**Wolke**, *f.* cloud; (*Warfare*) cloud, wave (of gas).

**Wolkenangriff**, *m.* wave attack, cloud gas attack.

**wolkig**, *a.* cloudy, clouded.

**Woll-abgang**, *m.*, **-abfälle**, *m.pl.* waste wool.

**woll-ähnlich, -artig**, *a.* wool-like, woolly.

**Woll-asche**, *f.* wool ashes. **-blumen**, *f.pl.* (*Pharm.*) mullen flowers.

**Wolle**, *f.* wool.—**philosophische —**, philosopher's wool (zinc oxide).

**wollen**, *v.i.& t.* will, be willing, choose, intend, mean, wish, want; be about, be going (to do something).—*a.* woolen.

**Wollen-**. wool, woolen, worsted.

**Woll-entfettung**, *f.* degreasing of wool. **-färber**, *m.* wool dyer.

**wollfarbig**, *a.* dyed in the wool.

**Woll-faser**, *f.* wool fiber. **-fett**, *n.* wool fat, wool grease. **-garn**, *n.* woolen yarn. **-grün**, *n.* wool green.

**wollig**, *a.* woolly.

**Woll-kraut**, *n.* mullen. **-öl**, *n.* wool oil. **-pulver**, *n.* flock. **-schmiere**, *f.* (wool) yolk, suint; wool softener. **-schwarz**, *n.* wool black.

**Wollschweiss**, *m.* (wool) yolk, suint. **-asche**, *f.* potash from suint. **-fett**, *n.* wool grease. **-salz**, *n.* suint salt.

**Wollstaub**, *m.* flock.

**womit**, *adv.* wherewith.

**womöglich**, *adv.* if possible.

**wonach**, *adv.* whereupon, after which, after what.

**Wonne**, *f.* bliss, delight, pleasure.

**wonnereich**, *a.* delightful, delicious.

**Wootzstahl**, *m.* wootz steel, wootz.

**woran**, *adv.* whereon, whereat, by what.

**worauf**, *adv.* whereon, whereupon, on what.

**woraus**, *adv.* from what, from which, by which.

**worein**, *adv.* into which, into what.

**worfeln**, *v.t.* winnow, fan.

**Wort**, *n.* word; term, expression. **-ableitung**, *f.* etymology. **-ausdruck**, *m.* phraseology.

**Wörterbuch**, *n.* dictionary; glossary.

**Wort-folge**, *f.* order of words. **-fügung**, *f.* sentence structure, syntax. **-führer**, *m.* spokesman, speaker.

**wortgetreu**, *a.* literal.

**Wort-kunde**, *f.* etymology. **-laut**, *m.* wording, text.

**wörtlich**, *a.* verbal, literal.—*adv.* verbatim, literally.

**Wort-register**, *n.* index of words, vocabulary, concordance. **-schatz**, *m.* vocabulary; thesaurus. **-verbindung**, *f.* connection of words, context. **-zeichen**, *n.* catchword.

**worüber**, *adv.* whereat, whereof, over, at, about or on which or what.

**worunter**, *adv.* under what, under which, among which.

**woselbst,** *adv.* where.

**Woulfische Flasche.** Woulfe bottle.

**wovon,** *adv.* whereof, of what, which or whom.

**wovor,** *adv.* before what, before which, of which.

**wozu,** *adv.* whereto, whereat, to what, why.

**Wrack,** *n.* wreck; refuse.

**wringen,** *v.t.* wring.

**Wrkg.,** *abbrev.* (Wirkung) action, effect.

**Ws.,** *abbrev.* (Wasser) water.

**W.-S.,** *abbrev.* (Wassersäule) water column.

**wss.,** *abbrev.* (wässerig) aqueous, hydrous.

**wuchern,** *v.i.* grow rapidly, (*Biol.*) proliferate; practise usury.

**Wucherung,** *f.* (*Biol.*) proliferation.

**wuchs,** *pret.* of wachsen.

**Wuchs,** *m.* growth; grain (of wood); form, stature.

**Wucht,** *f.* weight, burden; force; energy; fulcrum.

**wühlen,** *v.i.* rake, rummage, dig, root; agitate.

**Wulst,** *n.* pad, padding, roll; swelling, enlargement, elevation; bead.

**wulstig,** *a.* padded, stuffed, swelled, tumid.

**wund,** *a.* wounded, sore, chafed.

**Wundarzt,** *m.* surgeon.

**wundärztlich,** *a.* surgical.

**Wundbalsam,** *m.* vulnerary balsam.

**Wunde,** *f.* wound; injury.

**Wunder,** *n.* wonder, marvel; miracle.

**wunderbar,** *a.* wonderful, marvellous, strange.

**Wunder-baum,** *m.* castor-oil plant; locust tree. **-erde,** *f.* lithomarge. **-erscheinung,** *f.* miraculous phenomenon. **-kerze,** *f.* (*Pyro.*) sparkler.

**wunderlich,** *a.* strange, singular, odd, whimsical.

**wundern,** *v.t.* surprise, astonish.—*v.r.* wonder.

**Wunder-pfeffer,** *m.* allspice. **-salz,** *n.* sal mirabile, Glauber's salt.

**wunder-schön,** *a.* very beautiful. **-voll,** *a.* wonderful.

**Wunderwasser,** *n.* aqua mirabilis.

**Wund-klee,** *m.* kidney vetch. **-kraut,** *n.* vulnerary plant. **-pulver,** *n.* vulnerary powder. **-schwamm,** *m.* surgeon's agaric. **-stein,** *m.* copper aluminate.

**Wunsch,** *m.* wish, desire.

**wünschen,** *v.t.* wish, wish for.

**wünschenswert,** *a.* desirable.

**würbe,** *pret. subj.* of werben.

**wurde,** *pret.* of werden.

**Würde,** *f.* dignity; honor, preferment.

**würde-los,** *a.* undignified. **-voll,** *a.* dignified.

**würdig,** *a.* worthy, deserving, deserved.

**würdigen,** *v.t.* value, prize, appreciate; consider worthy.

**Wurf,** *m.* throw, cast; litter, brood; (*Mech.*) projection.

**würfe,** *pret. subj.* of werfen.

**Würfel,** *m.* cube; die (*pl.* dice). **-alaun,** *m.* cubic alum. **-eck,** *n.,* **-ecke,** *f.* corner of a cube, cubic summit. **-erz,** *n.* cube ore, pharmacosiderite.

**würfelförmig,** *a.* cubic, cubical.

**Würfelgips,** *m.* anhydrite.

**würfelig,** *a.* cubic, cubical; checkered.

**Würfel-inhalt,** *m.* cubic contents. **-kohle,** *f.* cob coal, cobbles.

**würfeln,** *v.i.* play at dice.—*v.t.* checker.—gewürfelt, *p.a.* checked, checkered.

**Würfel-nickel,** *m.& n.* cube nickel, nickel in cubes. **-pulver,** *n.* prismatic powder. **-salpeter,** *m.* cubic niter, cubic saltpeter (sodium nitrate). **-schiefer,** *m.* clay slate, argillite. **-spat,** *m.* anhydrite. **-stein,** *m.* boracite. **-zahl,** *f.* (*Math.*) cube. **-zeolith,** *m.* analcite. **-zucker,** *m.* cube sugar.

**Wurf-geschoss,** *n.* missile, projectile. **-kraft,** *f.* projectile force. **-lehre,** *f.* ballistics. **-linie,** *f.* line or curve of projection. **-mine,** *f.* trench-mortar shell or bomb. **-rauchkörper,** *n.* smoke maroon. **-schaufel,** *f.* shovel, scoop. **-weite,** *f.* range.

**Würgelpumpe,** *f.* rotary pump.

**würgen,** *v.t.* choke; strangle; destroy; gulp.—*v.i.* choke; retch.

**Wurm,** *m.* worm; vermin; reptile, snake; vermiform process.

**wurm-abtreibend,** *p.a.* vermifuge, anthelmintic. **-ähnlich, -artig,** *a.* wormlike, vermicular, vermiform.

**Wurm-arznei,** *f.* anthelmintic. **-farn,** *m.* male fern.

**wurmförmig,** *a.* worm-shaped, vermicular, vermiform.

**Wurm-fortsatz,** *m.* vermiform process. **-kraut,** *n.* anthelmintic herb, specif. (1) tansy, (2) (amerikanisches) pinkroot. **-mittel,** *n.* anthelmintic. **-moos,** *n.* worm moss, Corsican moss. **-pulver,** *n.* worm powder. **-rinde,** *f.* worm bark. **-samen,** *m.* wormseed. **-samenöl,** *n.* wormseed oil.

**wurmstichig,** *a.* worm-eaten.

**Wurmtang,** *m.* = Wurmmoos.

**wurm-treibend, -vertilgend, -vertreibend, -widrig,** *a.* anthelmintic.

**Wurst,** *f.* sausage; (black) pudding; roll, pad, padding. **-darm,** *m.* skin for sausages. **-fleisch,** *n.* sausage meat. **-gift,** *n.* sausage poison. **-kraut,** *n.* savory; marjoram. **-stein,** *m.* pudding stone.

**Wurz,** *f.* (in combination) -wort, herb.

**Würze,** *f.* spice, seasoning, condiment; (*Brewing*) wort. **-brechen,** *n.* breaking of the wort. **-kühler,** *m.* wort cooler.

**Wurzel,** *f.* root.

**Würzelchen,** *n.* rootlet, radicle.

**Wurzel-grösse,** *f.* (*Math.*) radical. **-keim,** *m.* (*Bot.*) radicle. **-knöllchen,** *n.* root nodule.

**wurzeln,** *v.i.* root, take root, be rooted.

**Wurzel-stock,** *m.* rootstock, rhizome. **-stoff,** *m.* (*Old Chem.*) radical principle. **-zeichen,** *n.* radical sign.

**würzen,** *v.t.* spice, season.—**gewürzt,** *p.a.* spiced, aromatic.

**Würze-pfanne,** *f.* wort kettle. **-siedepfanne,** *f.* wort boiler, brewing copper.

**Würz-geruch,** *m.* odor of spices, spicy odor. **-geschmack,** *m.* spicy taste.

**würzig,** *a.* spicy, aromatic.

**würzlos,** *a.* unspiced, unseasoned, flat.

**Würz-mittel,** *n.* condiment. **-nägelein,** *n.*, **-nelke,** *f.* clove. **-wein,** *m.* spiced wine.

**wusch,** *pret.* of waschen.

**wusste,** *pret.* of wissen.

**Wust,** *m.* confused mass, mess, jumble; rubbish.

**wüst,** *a.* waste; desert; wild.

**Wüste,** *f.* waste, desert, wilderness.

**wüsten,** *v.i.* waste.

**Wut,** *f.* rage, fury, madness; mania; rabies.

**wüten,** *v.i.* rage; fume, rave.—**wütend,** *p.a.* raging, furious.

**wütig,** *a.* raging, furious, mad.

**Wut-seuche, -krankheit,** *f.* rabies.

**Wutz, -stahl,** *m.* wootz steel, wootz.

# X

**Xanthanwasserstoff,** *m.* xanthane hydride (perthiocyanic acid, $C_2H_2N_2S_2$).

**xanthisch,** *a.* xanthic.

**Xantho-gensäure,** *f.* xanthogenic acid, xanthic acid. **-kobaltchlorid,** *n.* xanthocobaltic chloride. **-proteinsäure,** *f.* xanthoproteic acid.

**x-beliebig,** *a.* any.

**Xeres, Xereswein,** *m.* sherry.

**X-Strahlen,** *m.pl.* X-rays, Röntgen rays.

**Xylidinrot,** *n.* xylidine red.

**Xylo-chinol,** *n.* xyloquinol. **-chinon,** *n.* xyloquinone.

**Xylol,** *n.* xylene.

**Xylorcin,** *n.* xylorcinol, xylorcin.

**Xylylsäure,** *f.* xylic acid.

# Y

**Yamwurzel,** *f.* yam.

**Yerbastrauch,** *m.* maté, Paraguay tea.

**Y-förmig,** *a.* Y-shaped.

**Yohimboasäure,** *f.* yohimboaic acid (yohimbic acid).

**Y-Rohr,** *n.*, **Y-Röhre,** *f.* Y-tube.

**Ysop,** *m.* hyssop. **-öl,** *n.* oil of hyssop.

**Ytterbin,** *n.*, **-erde,** *f.* ytterbia.

**Ytter-erde,** *f.* yttria; (as class name) yttrium earth. **-flussspat,** *m.* yttrocerite.

**ytterhaltig,** *a.* containing yttrium, yttriferous, yttric.

**Ytter-oxyd,** *n.* ytterbium oxide. **-salz,** *n.* ytterbium salt. **-spat,** *m.* xenotime.

# Z

**z.,** *abbrev.* (zu, zum, zur) at, for, by; (ziemlich) rather.

**Z,** *abbrev.* (Zähigkeit) toughness.

**Z.,** *abbrev.* (Zeitschrift) periodical, journal; (Zahl) number; (Zeile) line; (Zeit) time; (Zoll) inch.

**za.,** *abbrev.* (zirka) about, approximately.

**Zachunöl, Zachäusöl,** *n.* bito oil, zachun (from *Balanites aegyptiaca*).

**Zacke,** *f.,* **Zacken,** *m.* prong, tooth, jag; twig, bough; scallop, edging; (*Metal.*) plate.

**zacken,** *v.t.* jag, tooth, indent, notch; scallop.

**zackig,** *a.* jagged, toothed, indented, serrated, (of a fracture) hackly.

**Zaffer,** *m.* zaffer, zaffre (impure oxide of cobalt).

**Zaffetika,** *f.* asafetida.

**Zageleisen,** *n.* slab iron.

**zäh, zähe,** *a.* tough, tenacious; (of liquids) viscous, viscid; stingy.

**Zähe,** *f.* = Zähigkeit.

**Zäheisen,** *n.* toughened iron.

**Zäheit,** *f.* = Zähigkeit.

**zähfestig,** *a.* tenacious.

**Zähfestigkeit,** *f.* tenacity.

**zähflüssig,** *a.* thickly liquid, viscous; difficultly fusible, refractory.

**Zähflüssigkeit,** *f.* viscosity; refractoriness.

**Zähigkeit,** *f.* toughness, tenacity; viscosity, viscidity.

**Zähigkeitsmesser,** *m.* viscosimeter, viscometer.

**Zähkupfer,** *n.* tough-pitch copper, tough pitch.

**Zahl,** *f.* number; numeral; (numerical) value.

**Zählapparat,** *m.* counting apparatus, counter.

**zahlbar,** *a.* payable, due.

**zahlen,** *v.t. & i.* pay.

**zählen,** *v.t. & i.* number, count, reckon.

**Zahlen-angaben,** *f.pl.* numerical data. **-folge,** *f.* numerical order. **-grösse,** *f.* numerical quantity.

**zahlenmässig,** *adv.* numerically.

**Zahlen-reihe,** *f.* numerical series. **-tafel,** *f.* table of figures, numerical table. **-wert,** *m.* numerical value.

**Zähler,** *m.* numerator; counter, marker; meter.

**Zähl-flasche,** *f.* counting bottle. **-kammer,** *f.* counting chamber.

**zahllos,** *a.* numberless, countless.

**zahlr.,** *abbrev.* (zahlreich) numerous.

**zahlreich,** *a.* numerous.

**Zahlung,** *f.* payment.

**Zählung,** *f.* counting, count, enumeration; calculation, computation.

**zahlungsfähig,** *a.* (*Com.*) solvent.

**Zahlungsschein,** *m.* receipt.

**zahlungsunfähig,** *a.* insolvent.

**Zählvorrichtung,** *f.* counting device.

**Zahl-wert,** *m.* numerical value. **-wort,** *n.* numeral. **-zeichen,** *n.* figure, numeral.

**zahm,** *a.* tame, gentle, domestic.

**zähmen,** *v.t.* tame, domesticate; restrain, control.

**Zahn,** *m.* tooth.

**Zahn-.** tooth, dental, odonto-, toothed, notched. **-arzt,** *m.* dentist.

**zahnärztlich,** *a.* dentist's, dental.

**Zahn-bein,** *n.* dentine. **-blei,** *n.* (*Bot.*) leadwort. **-bürste,** *f.* tooth brush.

**Zähne,** *m.pl.* teeth.

**zähneln,** *v.t.* tooth, indent, denticulate.

**Zahnemail,** *n.* dental enamel.

**zahnen,** *v.t.* tooth, indent.—*v.i.* teeth.— **gezahnt,** *p.a.* toothed, dentate, dentated, indented.

**Zahn-fleisch,** *n.* gum, gums. **-formel,** *f.* dental formula.

**zahnförmig,** *a.* tooth-shaped, odontoid.

**Zahnheilkunde,** *f.* dentistry.

**zahnig, zähnig,** *a.* toothed, dentate, indented, jagged.

**Zahn-keim,** *m.* dental pulp. **-kitt,** *m.* dental cement. **-latwerge,** *f.* tooth paste. **-paste,** *f.* tooth paste. **-pulpa,** *f.* dental pulp. **-pulver,** *n.* tooth powder. **-rad,** *n.* cog wheel. **-reinigungsmittel,** *n.* dentifrice. **-schmelz,** *m.* dental enamel. **-schmerz,** *m.* toothache. **-stange,** *f.* (*Mach.*) rack. **-stein,** *n.* tartar (on the teeth). **-substanz,** *f.* tooth substance, dentine.

**Zahnung,** *f.* toothing; serration; dentition.

**Zahn-wasser,** *n.* tooth wash, dental lotion. **-weh,** *n.* toothache. **-wehholz,** *n.* prickly ash (*Zanthoxylum*). **-weinstein,** *m.* tartar (on the teeth). **-werk,** *n.* gearing. **-zement,** *m.* dental cement.

**zäh-polen,** *v.t.* (*Metal.*) toughen by poling. **-schlackig,** *a.* of or forming tough clinker or slag. **-schleimig,** *a.* mucous.

**Zain,** *m.* ingot, bar, rod, pig.

**zainen,** *v.t.* make into ingots or bars; draw out, stretch (iron, etc.).

**Zainform,** *f.* ingot mold.

**Zange,** *f.* (pair of) tongs; pincers, nippers, forceps, pliers, tweezers.

**Zänge-.** (*Metal.*) shingling. **-arbeit,** *f.* (*Metal.*) shingling.

**Zängelchen,** *n.* pincers, nippers, tweezers.

**zängen,** *v.t.* (*Metal.*) shingle.

**Zangengriff,** *m.* handle of tongs, forceps, etc.

**Zänger,** *m.* shingler.

**Zänge-schlacke,** *f.* shingling slag. **-walzen,** *f.pl.* shingling rolls.

**Zäpfchen,** *n.* small pin, peg or plug; (*Anat.*) uvula.

**Zäpfchen-.** (*Anat.*) uvular.

**zapfen,** *v.t.* tap, draw (liquids).

**Zapfen,** *m.* peg, pin, plug, pivot; tap, spigot; bung; journal, trunnion; tenon; cone. **-baum,** *m.* conifer.

**zapfenförmig,** *a.* peg-shaped, cone-shaped, conical, (*Bot.*) strobiliform.

**Zapfen-korn,** *n.* ergot. **-lager,** *n.* (*Mach.*) bearing, socket, bush, collar. **-loch,** *n.* peg hole, pivot hole; (in casks) bung hole, tap hole.

**zapfentragend,** *p.a.* (*Bot.*) coniferous.

**Zapfenwein,** *m.* leaked wine.

**Zapf-hahn,** *m.* drain cock, tap. **-loch,** *n.* = Zapfenloch.

**Zapon,** *m.* varnish.

**zaponieren,** *v.t.* varnish with Zaponlack.

**Zaponlack,** *m.* cellulose ester (nitrate, acetate, etc.) varnish.

**zappeln,** *v.i.* struggle, flounder, writhe, fidget.

**Zarge,** *f.* border, rim, edge.

**zart,** *a.* tender; delicate; fragile; soft, fine.

**Zärul-, zärul-.** cerul-.

**Zaser,** *f.* fiber, filament.

**zaserig,** *a.* fibrous, filamentous.

**Zäsium,** *n.* cesium. For compounds see Cäsium-.

**Zaspel,** *f.* skein, hank.

**Zauber,** *m.* charm, spell; magic, witchcraft.

**Zauber-.** magic, fairy.

**Zauberei,** *f.* magic, sorcery.

**Zauberer,** *m.* magician, wizard.

**zauberhaft, zauberisch,** *a.* magic, enchanting.

**Zauber-hasel,** *f.* witch-hazel. **-laterne,** *f.* magic lantern. **-wurzel,** *f.* mandrake.

**zaudern,** *v.i.* delay, hesitate, waver.

**Zaum,** *m.* bridle, rein, check.

**Zaun,** *m.* fence, fencing; hedge. **-draht,** *m.* fence wire. **-gitter,** *n.* fence netting, wire fencing. **-rübe,** *f.* bryony.

**zausen, zauseln,** *v.t.* pull, pick, drag.

**z.B.,** *abbrev.* (zum Beispiel) for example, *e.g.*

**z.E.,** *abbrev.* (zum Exempel) for example, *e.g.*

**Zeche,** *f.* score, bill; mine, mining company.

**Zechen-koks,** *m.* furnace coke. **-teer,** *m.* coke tar.

**zechfrei,** *a.* scot-free.

**Zecke,** *f.* (*Zoöl.*) tick.

**Zeder,** *f.* cedar.

**Zeder(n)holzöl,** *n.* cedar-wood oil.

**Zederöl, Zedernöl,** *n.* cedar oil.

**zedieren,** *v.t.* cede, transfer.

**Zedratöl, Zedroöl,** *n.* citron oil.

**Zehe,** *f.,* **Zeh,** *m.* toe; clove (of garlic); knot, stick (of ginger).

**Zehen-.** digital, toe.

**zehn,** *a.* ten. **-basisch,** *a.* decabasic.

**Zehneck,** *n.* decagon.

**zehn-fach, -fältig,** *a.* tenfold.

**zehnte,** *a.* tenth.

**Zehntel,** *n.* tenth. **-grad,** *m.* tenth of a degree. **-lösung,** *f.* tenth-normal solution. **-silberlösung,** *f.* tenth-normal silver solution.

**zehren,** *v.i.* consume, waste; live, feed.

**Zehrung,** *f.* consumption; provisions, expenses; waste (of wine, etc.); (*Explosives*) priming.

**Zeichen,** *n.* symbol; sign; mark, stamp, brand; signal; symptom; token.

**Zeichen-.** symbolic, sign; drawing, marking. **-brett,** *n.* drawing board. **-ebene,** *f.* plane of the drawing, plane of the paper. **-erklärung,** *f.* explanation of symbols, marks or signs. **-kreide,** *f.* crayon, marking chalk. **-papier,** *n.* drawing paper. **-regel,** *f.* rule for drawing, construction rule. **-setzung,** *f.* punctuation. **-sprache,** *f.* symbolic notation, sign language. **-stab,** *m.* rule (for drawing). **-stift,** *m.* drawing pencil. **-tinte,** *f.* drawing ink, marking ink.

**zeichnen,** *v.t.& i.* draw, design; mark, brand; sign, subscribe.

**Zeichner,** *m.* drawer, draftsman, designer; signer.

**zeichnerisch,** *a.* pertaining to drawing, graphic, diagrammatic.—*adv.* graphically.

**Zeichnung,** *f.* drawing, diagram, sketch, design, plan, pattern; marking, marks; signature, subscription.

**Zeigefinger,** *m.* forefinger, index.

**zeigen,** *v.t.* show, exhibit; point out, indicate. —*v.r.* appear, show oneself, become evident; turn out, prove.—*v.i.* point.

**Zeiger,** *m.* pointer, indicator, hand, index, needle; (*Math.*) index; index finger; one that shows, presenter, bearer. **-ablesung,** *f.* pointer reading. **-ausschlag,** *m.* pointer deflection.

**Zeile,** *f.* line; row.

**Zein,** *m.* = Zain.—*n.* zein.

**Zeisig,** *m.* siskin.

**zeisig-gelb,** *a.* siskin-yellow, light greenish-yellow. **-grün,** *a.* siskin-green, light yellowish green.

**Zeit,** *f.* time; period, era, season; tense; tide.

—zur—, at the time; at present.—vor kurzer —, a short time ago.

**Zeit-abschnitt,** *m.* period, interval. **-alter,** *n.* age. **-angabe,** *f.* date. **-aufwand,** *m.* loss of time. **-dauer,** *f.* duration, period of time. **-einheit,** *f.* unit of time. **-folge,** *f.* chronological order or succession. **-frage,** *f.* topic of the day. **-geist,** *m.* spirit of the age.

**zeitgemäss,** *a.* timely, seasonable; up-to-date.

**Zeit-genoss,** *m.* contemporary. **-gleichung,** *f.* time equation. **-härtung,** *f.* age-hardening.

**zeither,** *adv.* hitherto, ever since.

**zeitig,** *a.* early, timely; ripe, mature.

**zeitigen,** *v.t.* mature, ripen.

**Zeitigung,** *f.* maturation, maturity.

**Zeitlang,** *f.* time.—**eine** —, for some time.

**zeit-lebens,** *adv.* for life, forever. **-lich,** *a.* temporary; temporal.

**Zeit-lose,** *f.* colchicum. **-mass,** *n.* measure of time; (*Music*) time; (*Gram.*) quantity. **-messer,** *m.* chronometer. **-punkt,** *m.* point of time, moment.

**zeitraubend,** *p.a.* time-consuming.

**Zeit-raum,** *m.* space of time, period. **-rechnung,** *f.* chronology.

**Zeitschr.,** *abbrev.* Zeitschrift.

**Zeit-schrift,** *f.* periodical, journal, magazine. **-schriftenliteratur,** *f.* journal literature. **-spanne,** *f.* length of time, time.

**Zeitung,** *f.* newspaper, paper; news.

**Zeitungs-ausgabe,** *f.* issue of a newspaper; newspaper office. **-papier,** *n.* (*Paper*) news; old newspapers. **-wesen,** *n.* newspaper business; journalism.

**Zeit-verlust,** *m.* loss of time. **-vertreib,** *m.* pastime.

**zeit-weilig,** *a.* temporary; present, actual. **-weise,** *adv.* temporarily; occasionally, at times.

**Zeit-wort,** *n.* verb. **-zünder,** *m.* time fuse. **-zwischenraum,** *m.* time interval.

**zelebrieren,** *v.t.* celebrate.

**zellähnlich,** *a.* cell-like, celloid.

**Zellchen,** *n.* cellule, small cell.

**Zelle,** *f.* cell.

**Zellen-,** cell, cellular. **-art,** *f.* kind of cell.

**zellen-artig,** *a.* cell-like, cellular. **-bildend,** *p.a.* cell-forming.

**Zellen-bildung,** *f.* cell formation. **-faser,** *f.* cell fiber. **-faserstoff,** *m.* cellulose. **-flüssigkeit,** *f.* cell fluid.

**zellenförmig,** *a.* in the form of cells, cellular.

**Zellen-gehalt,** *m.* cell contents. **-gewebe,** *n.* cellular tissue.

**zellenhaltig,** *a.* containing cells, cellular.

**Zellen-inhalt,** *m.* cell contents. **-kern,** *m.* cell nucleus. **-kies,** *m.* cellular pyrites. **-rad,** *n.* bucket wheel. **-saft,** *m.* cell fluid. **-schale,** *f.* cell membrane. **-schalter,** *m.* (*Elec.*)

battery switch. **-stoff,** *m.* cellulose. **-teilung,** *f.* cell division. **-tiefofen,** *m.* soaking-pit furnace. **-wand,** *f.* cell wall. **-zwischensubstanz,** *f.* intercellular substance.

**Zell-gewebe,** *n.* cellular tissue. **-gift,** *n.* intracellular toxin. **-horn,** *n.* celluloid or a similar product.

**zellig,** *a.* cellular, celled; honeycombed.

**Zellmasse,** *f.* cellular substance.

**Zellophan,** *n.* cellophane.

**Zell-pech,** *n.* cellulose pitch (a pitchy product from the evaporation of sulfite liquor). **-saft,** *m.* (*Bot.*) cell sap; (*Zoöl.*) cell juice.

**Zellstoff,** *n.* cellulose; (*Paper*) pulp. **-ausbeute,** *f.* (*Paper*) yield of pulp. **-chemie,** *f.* cellulose chemistry. **-fabrik,** *f.* (*Paper*) pulp factory, pulp mill. **-fabrikation,** *f.* cellulose manufacture; (*Paper*) pulp making. **-faser,** *f.* cellulose fiber. **-glashaut,** *f.* transparent cellulose film. **-pappe,** *f.* pulp board. **-prüfung,** *f.* cellulose testing, specif. pulp testing. **-schleim,** *m.* cellulose slime, pulp slime. **-seide,** *f.* cellulose silk, rayon. **-wechsel,** *m.* cell metabolism.

**Zellteilung,** *f.* cell division.

**Zelluloid,** *n.* celluloid.

**Zellulose,** *f.* cellulose. (For compounds see Cellulose-.)

**Zellwand,** *f.* cell wall.

**Zelt,** *n.* tent; awning; pavilion.

**Zeltchen,** *n.* lozenge, tablet.

**Zement,** *m.& n.* cement.

**zementartig,** *a.* cement-like.

**Zementation,** *f.* cementation.

**Zement-beton,** *m.* cement concrete. **-brei,** *m.* cement slurry. **-fabrik,** *f.* cement factory. **-gerbstahl,** *m.* shear steel.

**zementieren,** *v.t.* cement; subject to cementation.

**Zementier-fass,** *n.* precipitation vat. **-mittel,** *n.* cementing agent. **-ofen,** *m.* cementation furnace.

**Zementierung,** *f.* cementing; cementation.

**Zementit,** *n.* cementite.

**Zement-kalk,** *m.* hydraulic lime. **-kalkstein,** *m.* hydraulic limestone. **-kohle,** *f.* cementation carbon. **-kupfer,** *m.* cement copper. **-mastix,** *m.* mastic cement. **-mörtel,** *m.* cement mortar. **-ofen,** *m.* cement kiln. **-prüfung,** *f.* cement testing. **-schlacke,** *f.* cement clinker. **-silber,** *n.* precipitated silver. **-stahl,** *m.* cementation steel. **-werk,** *n.* cement plant.

**zensieren,** *v.t.* criticize.

**Zensur,** *f.* censorship; report.

**Zenti-,** centi-. **-gramm,** *n.* centigram. **-meter,** *n.* centimeter.

**Zentner,** *m.* hundredweight; quintal.

**zentral,** *a.* central.

Zentralblatt, *n.* central journal or paper (a name used by periodicals).

Zentrale, *f.* central office, center; central station; median (line); line joining centers.

Zentralgruppe, *f.* central group.

zentralisieren, *v.t.* centralize.

Zentral-kraftsystem, *n.* central force system. -lager, *n.* (*Com.*) central store or stock. -stelle, *f.* central place, office or station. -verein, *m.* central union or association.

Zentren, *pl.* of Zentrum.

zentrieren, *v.t.* center.

Zentrifuge, *f.* centrifuge; sling.

zentrifugieren, *v.t.* centrifuge, centrifugalize.

zentrisch, *a.* centric; central.

Zentrum, *n.* center; bull's-eye.

Zeolith, *m.* zeolite.

Zer, *n.* cerium.

zer-. apart, asunder, in pieces, dis-.

zerarbeiten, *v.t.* work, prepare by working; destroy by working, crumble; overwork.

Zerasin, *n.* cerasin.

Zerat, *n.* cerate.

zerätzen, *v.t.* destroy with caustics.

zerbrechen, *v.t.* break (in pieces), shatter.

zerbrechlich, *a.* breakable, fragile; brittle.

Zerbrechlichkeit, *f.* fragility; brittleness.

Zerbrechungsfestigkeit, *f.* resistance to breaking strain.

zerbröckeln, *v.t.& i.* crumble.—zerbröckelnd, *p.a.* crumbling, friable.

zerdrücken, *v.t.* crush.

Zerdrückungsfestigkeit, *f.* resistance to crushing strain.

Zerealien, *pl.* cereals.

zerebral, *a.* cerebral.

Zeremonie, *f.* ceremony.

zeremoniell, *a.* ceremonial.

Zeresin, *n.* ceresin.

zerfahren, *v.t.* injure (by driving over, as roads).—*p.a.* unsteady, inattentive, thoughtless.

Zerfall, *m.* decomposition; dissociation; disintegration; ruin.

zerfallen, *v.i.* decompose; dissociate; divide; disintegrate, crumble, fall to pieces; quarrel. —*v.t.* injure by falling.

Zerfall-geschwindigkeit, *f.* velocity of decomposition. -grad, *m.* degree of decomposition (or dissociation). -prozess, *m.* decomposition process. -schlacke, *f.* disintegrating slag.

Zerfalls-leuchten, *n.* decomposition luminescence. -produkt, *m.* decomposition (or dissociation) product. -reihe, *f.* disintegration series.

Zerfallwärme, *f.* heat of decomposition or dissociation.

Zerfaserer, *m.* (*Paper*) stuff grinder.

zerfasern, *v.t.* separate into fibers, rag.

zerfetzen, *v.t.* cut in pieces, shred; slash.

zerfl., *abbrev.* (zerfliesslich) deliquescent.

zerfleischen, *v.t.* lacerate.

zerfliessbar, *a.* deliquescent.

Zerfliessbarkeit, *f.* deliquescence.

zerfliessen, *v.i.* deliquesce; melt, be dissolved; (of colors) run.—zerfliessend, *p.a.* deliquescent.

zerfliesslich, *a.* deliquescent.

Zerfliesslichkeit, *f.* deliquescent property.

Zerfliessung, *f.* deliquescence.

Zerfluor, *m.* cerium fluoride.

zerfressen, *v.t.* eat away, corrode; cauterize. —zerfressend, *p.a.* corrosive.

Zerfressung, *f.* corrosion; cauterization.

zerfrieren, *v.i.* break (up) through freezing.

zergehen, *v.i.* deliquesce; disperse, dissolve, dwindle.

zergliedern, *v.t.* decompose, analyze; dismember; (*Med.*) dissect.

Zergliederung, *f.* decomposition, analysis; dissection; dismemberment.

zerhacken, *v.t.* cut to pieces, mince.

Zerin, *n.* cerin.

Zerit, *m.* cerite.

Zerium, *n.* cerium.

zerkleinern, *v.t.* reduce to small pieces, comminute, disintegrate, crush, pulverize.

zerklüften, *v.t.* cleave, split, fissure, divide, segment, separate.

zerknicken, *v.t.* crack (esp. by bending).

zerknistern, *v.i.* decrepitate.

zerknittern, *v.t.* crumple, rumple.

zerlassen, *v.t.* melt, liquefy, dissolve.

zerlegbar, *a.* decomposable, etc. (see zerlegen).

Zerlegbarkeit, *f.* decomposability, etc. (see zerlegen).

zerlegen, *v.t.* decompose; split up, take apart, cut up, dissect, analyze, resolve; (*Mach.*) dismount.

Zerlegung, *f.* decomposition, etc. (see zerlegen).

zerlöchern, *v.t.* perforate, punch.

zermahlen, *v.t.* grind fine, pulverize, triturate.

zermalmen, *v.t.* bruise, crush, grind.

Zermetall, *n.* cerium metal.

zermürben, *v.t.* rot (as fabrics).

Zernitrat, *n.* cerium nitrate.

zerpflücken, *v.t.* pull apart, pick apart, pick to pieces.

zerplatzen, *v.i.* burst, explode.

zerpulvern, *v.t.* pulverize.

zerquetschen, *v.t.* crush, mash, bruise.

zerreibbar, *a.* friable, triturable.

zerreiben, *v.t.* pulverize, powder, triturate.

zerreiblich, *a.* friable, crumbly, triturable.

Zerreiblichkeit, *f.* friability.

**Zerreibung,** *f.* pulverization, trituration.

**zerreissbar,** *a.* capable of being torn or rent.

**zerreissen,** *v.t.* tear, lacerate, break, rend, rupture; wear out.

**Zerreiss-festigkeit,** *f.* tensile strength. -probe, *f.* rending or breaking test; sample for tensile test. -versuch, *m.* tensile test.

**zerren,** *v.t.& r.* pull, tug, drag, tear.

**Zerrennboden,** *m.* (*Metal.*) slag bottom.

**zerrennen,** *v.t.* (*Metal.*) refine, fine.

**Zerrenner,** *m.* refiner.

**Zerrennfeuer,** *n.* (*Metal.*) refining fire.

**zerrieben,** *p.p.* of zerreiben.

**zerrieseln,** *v.i.* (of slag) disintegrate.

**zerrühren,** *v.t.* mix by stirring, beat up.

**Zerrung,** *f.* pulling, etc. (see zerren).

**zerrütten,** *v.t.* disturb, disorder, disorganize, derange, destroy.

**zers.,** *abbrev.* (zersetzend) decomposing; (zersetzt) decomposed; (zersetzbar) decomposable.

**Zers.,** *abbrev.* (Zersetzung) decomposition.

**zerschellen,** *v.t.* smash, shatter, shiver.

**zerschlagen,** *v.t.* break in pieces, smash, shatter, crush, batter.

**zerschmelzen,** *v.t.& i.* melt.

**zerschmettern,** *v.t.* shatter, smash, crush.

**zerschneiden,** *v.t.* cut up; mince, shred; dissect.

**zersetzbar,** *a.* decomposable.

**Zersetzbarkeit,** *f.* decomposability.

**zersetzen,** *v.t.& r.* decompose; disintegrate.

**Zersetzer,** *m.* decomposer, decomposing agent.

**zersetzlich,** *a.* liable to decompose, unstable.

**Zersetzlichkeit,** *f.* liability to decomposition, instability.

**Zersetzung,** *f.* decomposition; disintegration.

**Zersetzungs-destillation,** *f.* destructive distillation. -erzeugnis, *f.* decomposition product.

**zersetzungsfähig,** *a.* capable of decomposition.

**Zersetzungs-gefäss,** *n.* decomposition vessel. -kolben, *m.* decomposition flask, reaction flask. -kunst, *f.* analysis. -mittel, *n.* decomposing agent. -pfanne, *f.* decomposing pan. -produkt, *n.* decomposition product. -punkt, *m.* decomposition point. -spannung, *f.* (*Elec.*) decomposition voltage. -vorgang, *m.* process of decomposition. -wärme, *f.* heat of decomposition. -widerstand, *m.* (*Elec.*) electrolytic resistance.

**zerspalten,** *v.t.& i.* cleave, split (up).

**zersplittern,** *v.t.& i.* shiver, splinter, split up, break up, scatter.

**Zersplitterung,** *f.* shivering, etc. (see zersplittern).

**zersprengen,** *v.t.* burst, blow up, shatter, snap; disperse.

**zerspringen,** *v.i.* burst, explode, shiver, break, crack.

**zerstampfen,** *v.t.* pound, bray.

**zerstäuben,** *v.t.* reduce to dust, comminute, (of liquids) atomize, (of mercury) flour; scatter as dust, spatter, (of liquids) spray.

**Zerstäuber,** *m.* atomizer, sprayer, etc. (see zerstäuben).

**Zerstäubung,** *f.* comminution, fine disintegration, atomization; spattering, scattering; spraying, spray; (of mercury) flouring; (cathode) sputtering.

**Zerstäubungsapparat,** *m.* spray apparatus, atomizer.

**zerstieben,** *v.i.* scatter as dust, spray; vanish.

**zerstörbar,** *a.* destructible.

**zerstören,** *v.t.* destroy; break down, ruin.

**Zerstörung,** *f.* destruction; overthrow, ruin.

**Zerstörungsbombe,** *f.* demolition bomb.

**zerstossen,** *v.t.* pound (to pieces), bray, bruise, crush, powder, pulverize.

**zerstreuen,** *v.t.* disperse, scatter, disseminate, dissipate, diffuse; divert, distract.—zerstreut, *p.a.* dispersed, etc.; abstracted, distracted.

**Zerstreuung,** *f.* dispersion, etc. (see zerstreuen); (*Optics*) dispersion (sometimes, divergence); diversion, amusement.

**Zerstreuungsvermögen,** *n.* (*Optics*) dispersive power.

**zerstückeln,** *v.t.* divide into small pieces, cut up, parcel out, dismember.

**zerteilbar,** *a.* divisible.

**zerteilen,** *v.t.* divide; dissever, separate, resolve.—*v.r.* divide; disperse.

**Zerteilung,** *f.* division; separation, dissolution, resolution.

**Zerteilungs-grad,** *m.* degree of division, fineness. -mittel, *n.* (*Med.*) resolvent.

**zertrennen,** *v.t.* separate, etc. (= trennen).

**Zertrennung,** *f.* separation, etc. (see trennen).

**zertrümmern,** *v.t.* shatter, demolish, disrupt, destroy, wreck.

**Zertrümmerung,** *f.* shattering, destruction.

**Zerussit,** *m.* cerussite.

**Zervelatwurst,** *f.* saveloy.

**zerzupfen,** *v.t.* pick or pull to pieces.

**zessieren,** *v.i.* cease.

**Zettel,** *m.* slip (of paper), card, ticket, label, check, placard, handbill, note; warp. -katalog, *m.* card catalog.

**Zeug,** *n.& m.* stuff, material(s); tools implements; mortar; harness; rigging; trash; (*Paper*) stuff, pulp; (*Brewing*) yeast; (*Metal.*) metal; (*Fireworks*) composition; (*Weaving*) stuff, cloth, fabric. -bütte, *f.* (*Paper*) stuff chest, pulp vat. -druck, *m.* cloth printing, calico printing. -drucker, *m.*

cloth printer, calico printer. **-druckerei,** *f.* calico printing; print works.

**Zeuge,** *m.* witness.

**zeugen,** *v.t.* beget, procreate, generate, produce; demonstrate, prove.—*v.i.* testify; give evidence.

**Zeugen-.** of a witness, of testimony.

**Zeug-fabrik,** *f.* cloth factory, specif. woolen mill. **-fänger,** *m.* (*Paper*) stuff catcher. **-färberei,** *f.* dyeing; dye works. **-geben,** *n.* (*Brewing*) adding the yeast, pitching the wort. **-haus,** *n.* arsenal, armory. **-kasten,** *m.* (*Paper*) stuff chest; tool chest. **-lumpen,** *m.pl.* (*Paper*) cloth rags. **-nis,** *n.* testimony, witness, evidence; testimonial; certificate. **-sichter,** *m.* (*Paper*) pulp strainer.

**Zeugung,** *f.* procreation, generation, production.

**Zeugungs-.** generative, procreative. **-flüssigkeit,** *f.* seminal fluid. **-mittel,** *n.* aphrodisiac. **-stoff,** *m.* semen.

**Zeugwanne,** *f.* (*Brewing*) yeast tub.

**Zibebe,** *f.* cubeb; (large) raisin.

**Zibet, Zibeth,** *m.* civet.

**Zibeton,** *n.* civetone.

**Zichorie,** *f.* chicory.

**Zickelfell,** *n.* kid (leather).

**Zickzack,** *m.* zigzag.

**Ziege,** *f.* goat, she-goat.

**Ziegel,** *m.* brick; tile; briquet. **-brand,** *m.* brick burning, tile burning; batch of brick or tile. **-brennen,** *n.* brick burning, tile burning. **-brenner,** *m.* brick (or tile) burner (or maker). **-brennerei,** *f.* brick (or tile) burning; brick (or tile) factory. **-brennofen,** *m.* brick kiln, tile kiln.

**Ziegelei,** *f.* brickyard, tile works; brick kiln, tile kiln.

**Ziegel-erde,** *f.* brick earth, brick clay. **-erz,** *n.* tile ore. **-farbe,** *f.* brick color, brick red.

**ziegel-farbig, -farben,** *a.* brick (or tile)-colored, brick-red.

**Ziegel-hütte,** *f.* brick kiln, tile kiln. **-mehl,** *n.* brick dust. **-ofen,** *m.* brick kiln, tile kiln.

**ziegelrot,** *a.* brick-red.

**Ziegel-stein,** *m.* brick. **-ton,** *f.* brick clay, tile clay.

**Ziegen-.** goat's, goat. **-butter,** *f.* goat's butter. **-fell,** *n.* goat skin. **-käse,** *m.* goat's-milk cheese. **-leder,** *n.* goatskin or kid (leather). **-milch,** *f.* goat's milk. **-peter,** *m.* mumps. **-stein,** *m.* bezoar. **-talg,** *m.* goat tallow.

**Ziegler,** *m.* brickmaker, tile maker.

**zieh,** *pret.* of zeihen.

**Zieh-.** drawing, draw-, towing, tow-; foster-. **-arm,** *m.* arm, handle, crank.

**ziehbar,** *a.* ductile.

**Ziehbarkeit,** *f.* ductility.

**ziehen,** *v.t.* draw; pull, tug, drag; suck; raise;

breed; cultivate; rear, train, educate; extract (drugs); couch, floor (grain); dip, mold (candles), rifle (guns, etc.).—*v.r.* stretch; soak, penetrate; be ropy; warp; move.—*v.i.* draw; pull, etc.; have effect; move, go; (of colors) incline.—**Fäden —,** string, be ropy.

**Ziehen,** *n.* drawing, etc. (see ziehen); draft, traction; (of liquids) ropiness; move; twinge, twitch. **-lassen,** *n.* drawing, infusion.

**Zieh-feder,** *f.* drawing pen. **-kraft,** *f.* drawing power, tractive power. **-probe,** *f.* sample drawn (or to be drawn) out.

**Ziehung,** *f.* drawing, etc. (see ziehen); draft.

**Ziel,** *n.* goal, aim, object, end; limit, boundary; mark, target; term, time.

**zielbewusst,** *a.* clear-sighted, discerning.

**zielen,** *v.i.* aim (at); tend (to).—**zielendes Zeitwort,** transitive verb.

**ziellos,** *a.* aimless.

**Ziel-punkt,** *m.* aim, mark, bull's-eye. **-scheibe,** *f.* mark, target.

**ziemen,** *v.i.* become, be fitting, suit.

**ziemlich,** *a.* seemly, suitable; fair, moderate; considerable, rather large.—*adv.* fairly, tolerably, rather.

**Zier,** *f.* ornament, grace.

**Zier-.** ornamental, decorative, fancy.

**Zierat,** *m.* ornament, decoration, finery; foil.

**Zierde,** *f.* ornament, honor.

**zieren,** *v.t.* adorn, ornament, decorate.—*v.r.* be affected, coy, or prim.—**geziert,** *p.a.* adorned, etc.; affected, finical.

**zierlich,** *a.* elegant, graceful, pretty, dainty, smart.

**Ziffer,** *f.* figure, digit, number; cipher, cryptograph. **-blatt,** *n.* graduated face, dial.

**Zigarre,** *f.* cigar.

**Zimmer,** *n.* room, chamber, apartment.

**Zimmer-.** room, house, home; carpenter's. **-decke,** *f.* ceiling. **-gerät,** *n.* furniture, furnishings. **-holz,** *n.* timber. **-mann,** *m.* carpenter.

**zimmern,** *v.t.* frame, timber, build of wood; fabricate.

**Zimmer-temperatur, -wärme,** *f.* room temperature.

**Zimmet, Zimmt,** *m.* = Zimt.

**zimolisch,** *a.* = cimolisch.

**Zimt,** *m.* cinnamon.—**weisser —,** canella bark, canella.—**chinesischer —,** cassia bark.

**Zimt-.** cinnamic; cinnamon. **-aldehyd,** *n.* cinnamaldehyde, cinnamic aldehyde. **-alkohol,** *m.* cinnamic alcohol. **-blüte,** *f.* cinnamon flower, cassia bud.

**zimtbraun,** *a.* cinnamon-brown.

**Zimtcarbonsäure,** *f.* carboxycinnamic acid.

**zimt-farbig, -farben,** *a.* cinnamon-colored.

**Zimt-kaneel,** m. canella bark, canella. **-kassia,** f. cassia bark, cassia. **-kassienöl,** n. oil of cassia.

**Zimtöl,** n. oil of cinnamon.—**chinesisches —,** cassia oil.

**Zimtrinde,** f. cinnamon bark.

**zimtsauer,** a. of or combined with cinnamic acid, cinnamate of.

**Zimt-säure,** f. cinnamic acid. **-stein,** m. cinnamon stone, essonite. **-wasser,** n. cinnamon water.

**Zinder,** m. cinder.

**Zink,** n.& m. zinc.

**zinkartig,** a. zincky.

**Zink-asche,** f. zinc ash, zinc dross (oxide of zinc). **-äthyl,** n. zinc ethyl, diethylzinc. **-ätze,** f. zinc-etching solution. **-ätzung,** f. zinc etching. **-azetat,** n. zinc acetate. **-blech,** n. sheet zinc, zinc plate. **-blende,** f. zinc blende, sphalerite. **-blumen,** f.pl. flowers of zinc (zinc oxide). **-blüte,** f. zinc bloom, hydrozincite. **-butter,** f. (Old Chem.) butter of zinc (zinc chloride). **-dampf,** m. zinc vapor. **-destillierofen,** m. zinc-distillation furnace, zinc furnace.

**Zinke,** f. prong, spike, tooth, lug.

**Zinkeisen-erz,** n., **-stein,** m. franklinite. **-spat,** m. ferriferous smithsonite.

**Zinkerz,** n. zinc ore.—**rotes —,** zincite.

**Zink-fahlerz,** n. tennantite. **-farbe,** f. zinc paint. **-feile,** f., **-feilspäne,** m.pl. zinc filings. **-folie,** f. zinc foil.

**zinkführend,** a. zinc-bearing, zinciferous.

**Zink-gehalt,** m. zinc content. **-gekrätz,** n. zinc dross (oxide). **-gelb,** n. zinc yellow (zinc chromate). **-gewinnung,** f. extraction of zinc, zinc production. **-glas,** **-glaserz,** n. (siliceous) calamine. **-granalien,** f.pl. granulated zinc. **-grau,** n. zinc gray. **-grün,** n. zinc green.

**zinkhaltig,** a. containing zinc, zinciferous.

**Zinkhütte,** f. zinc works.

**zinkisch,** a. zincky, of zinc.

**Zink-jodid,** n. zinc iodide. **-kalk,** m. zinc calx, zinc ash. **-kiesel,** m., **-kieselerz,** n. (siliceous) calamine. **-kitt,** m. zinc cement. **-kohlenbatterie,** f. zinc-carbon battery. **-lösung,** f. zinc solution. **-mehl,** n. zinc powder, zinc dust. **-ofen,** m. zinc furnace. **-ofenbruch,** m. tutty, cadmia.

**zinkorganisch,** a. zinc-organic, organic zinc.

**Zinkoxyd,** n. zinc oxide.—**rotes —,** zincite.

**Zink-pecherz,** n. sphalerite. **-pol,** m. zinc pole, cathode. **-rauch,** m. zinc fume. **-salbe,** f. zinc ointment. **-salz,** n. zinc salt.

**zinksauer,** a. zincate of.

**Zink-schaum,** m. (Metal.) zinc scum. **-schlicker,** m. zinc dross. **-schwamm,** m. tutty, cadmia. **-spat,** m. zinc spar, smith-

sonite. **-stab,** m. zinc rod. **-staub,** m. zinc dust. **-überzug,** m. zinc coating. **-verbindung,** f. zinc compound. **-weiss,** n. zinc white (zinc oxide). **-werk,** n. zinc works. **-wolle,** f. flowers of zinc. **-zyanid,** n. zinc cyanide.

**Zinn,** n. tin. **-abstrich,** m. tin scum, tin dross. **-ader,** f. tin lode, tin vein. **-after,** m. tin (ore) refuse.

**zinnartig,** a. tin-like, tinny.

**Zinn-asche,** f. tin ashes, stannic oxide. **-bad,** n. tin bath. **-beize,** f. tin mordant, tin spirit. **-bergwerk,** n. tin mine. **-blatt,** n. tin foil. **-blech,** n. tin plate, sheet tin. **-bromid,** n. tin bromide, specif. stannic bromide. **-bromür,** n. stannous bromide.

**zinnbromwasserstoffsauer,** a. of or combined with bromostannic acid, bromostannate (or stannibromide) of.

**Zinn-bromwasserstoffsäure,** f. bromostannic acid. **-butter,** f. (Old Chem.) butter of tin (stannic chloride). **-chlorid,** n. tin chloride, specif. stannic chloride. **-chlorür,** n. stannous chloride.

**zinnchlorwasserstoffsauer,** a. of or combined with chlorostannic acid, chlorostannate (or stannichloride) of.

**Zinn-chlorwasserstoffsäure,** f. chlorostannic acid. **-diphenylchlorid,** n. diphenyltin chloride. **-draht,** m. tin wire.

**Zinne,** f. pinnacle.

**zinnen,** v.t. tin.

**zinnen, zinnern,** a. of tin, tin, pewter.

**Zinn-erz,** n. tin ore, cassiterite. **-farbe,** f. (Dyeing) tin-mordant color. **-feilicht,** n. **-feilspäne,** m.pl. tin filings. **-folie,** f. tin foil.

**zinnführend,** a. tin-bearing, stanniferous.

**Zinn-gehalt,** m. tin content. **-gekrätz,** n. tin refuse, tin sweepings. **-gerät,** n. tin ware, tin vessels, pewter. **-geschrei,** n. tin cry, crackling of tin. **-giesser,** m. tin founder.

**zinnglasiert,** p.a. tin-glazed.

**Zinn-glasur,** f. tin glazing, tin glaze. **-granalien,** f.pl. granulated tin. **-graupen,** f.pl. (Mining) cassiterite in twin crystals.

**zinnhaltig,** a. containing tin, stanniferous.

**Zinn-hütte,** f. tin smeltery, tin works. **-hydroxyd,** n. tin hydroxide, specif. stannic hydroxide. **-hydroxydul,** n. stannous hydroxide. **-jodid,** n. tin iodide, specif. stannic iodide. **-jodür,** n. stannous iodide. **-kalk,** m. tin calx, stannic oxide. **-kies,** m. tin pyrites, stannite. **-knirschen, -kreischen,** n.=Zinngeschrei. **-krätze,** f. tin dross, tin waste. **-legierung,** f. tin alloy. **-lösung,** f. tin solution; (Dyeing) tin spirit. **-lot,** n. tin solder.

**Zinnober,** m. cinnabar, (also, when used as a

pigment) vermilion. **-farbe,** *f.* vermilion (color).

**zinnobergrün,** *a.* cinnabar-green.

**Zinnober-rot,** *n.* vermilion. **-spat,** *m.* crystallized cinnabar.

**Zinnofen,** *m.* tin furnace.

**Zinnoxyd,** *n.* tin oxide, specif. stannic oxide. **-chlorid,** *n.* stannic chloride. **-hydrat,** *n.* tin hydroxide. **-natron,** *n.* sodium stannate. **-salz,** *n.* stannic salt.

**Zinnoxydul,** *n.* stannous oxide. **-chlorid,** *n.* stannous chloride. **-hydrat,** *n.* stannous hydroxide. **-salz,** *n.* stannous salt. **-verbindung,** *f.* stannous compound.

**Zinn-oxydverbindung,** *f.* stannic compound. **-pest,** *f.* tin plague. **-pfanne,** *f.* (*Tinning*) tin pot. **-platte,** *f.* tin plate, sheet of tin (plate). **-probe,** *f.* sample, test, or assay of tin. **-puder,** *m.* powdery tin dross. **-pulver,** *n.* powdered tin, grain tin.

**zinnreich,** *a.* rich in tin.

**Zinn-rohr,** *n.,* **-röhre,** *f.* tin pipe. **-salmiak,** *n.* ammonium chlorostannate, pink salt. **-salz,** *n.* tin salt; specif., (*Dyeing*) $SnCl_2 \cdot 2H_2O$.

**zinnsauer,** *a.* of or combined with stannic acid, stannate of.

**Zinn-saum,** *m.* list of tin, selvedge. **-säure,** *f.* stannic acid. **-säureanhydrid,** *n.* stannic anhydride, tin dioxide. **-schrei,** *m.* = Zinngeschrei. **-seife,** *f.* (*Mining*) stream tin. **-soda,** *f.* sodium stannate. **-staub,** *m.* tin dust. **-stein,** *m.* tinstone, cassiterite. **-sulfid,** *n.* tin sulfide, specif. stannic sulfide. **-sulfür,** *n.* stannous sulfide. **-verbindung,** *f.* tin compound. **-wolle,** *f.* mossy tin.

**Zins,** *m.* rent; (*pl.*) interest; tribute.

**zinsen,** *v.t. & i.* pay rent, interest, or tribute.

**Zipfel,** *m.* tip, point, end, summit.

**Zirbel-.** (*Anat.*) pineal. **-drüse,** *f.* pineal gland, pineal body. **-fichte,** **-kiefer,** *f.* Swiss pine (*Pinus cembra*). **-nuss,** *f.* cedar nut (from *Pinus cembra*).

**zirka,** *adv.* about, approximately.

**zirkassisch,** *a.* Circassian.

**Zirkel,** *m.* circle; (pair of) compasses.

**Zirkel-.** circular; compass.

**Zirkon,** *n.* zirconium; zircon. **-erde,** *f.* zirconia, zirconium oxide. **-glas,** *n.* zirconium glass.

**Zirkoniumverbindung,** *f.* zirconium compound.

**Zirkon-licht,** *n.* zircon light. **-oxyd,** *n.* zirconium oxide. **-präparat,** *n.* zirconium preparation. **-säure,** *f.* zirconic acid. **-stahl,** *m.* zirconium steel.

**Zirkular,** *n.* circular.

**zirkulieren,** *v.i.* circulate.

**zischen,** *v.i.* hiss, sizz, fizz.

**Zissoide,** *f.* cissoid.

**Zisterne,** *f.* cistern; tank.

**Zitat,** *n.* citation, quotation.

**zitieren,** *v.t.* quote, cite; summon.

**Zitr-, zitr-.** citr-.

**Zitrat,** *n.* citrate.

**zitratlöslich,** *a.* citrate-soluble.

**Zitraweinsäure,** *f.* citratartaric acid.

**Zitrin,** *n.* citrine.

**Zitronat,** *n.* candied lemon peel.

**Zitronbartgras,** *n.* lemon grass.

**Zitrone,** *f.* lemon; citron.

**Zitronell-al,** *n.* citronellal. **-asäure,** *f.* citronellic acid. **-ol,** *n.* citronellol. **-öl,** *n.* citronella oil. **-säure,** *f.* citronellic acid.

**Zitronenfarbe,** *f.* lemon color, citron color.

**zitronen-farben,** **-farbig,** *a.* lemon-colored, lemon-yellow. **-gelb,** *a.* lemon-yellow, citrine.

**Zitronengras,** *n.* lemon grass. **-öl,** *n.* lemongrass oil.

**zitronenlöslich,** *a.* citrate-soluble.

**Zitronen-melisse,** *f.* balm, balm mint (*Melissa officinalis*). **-öl,** *n.* lemon oil. **-saft,** *m.* lemon juice.

**zitronensauer,** *a.* = zitronsauer.

**Zitronen-säure,** *f.* citric acid. **-schale,** *f.* lemon peel. **-wasser,** *n.* lemonade.

**zitronsauer,** *a.* of or combined with citric acid, citrate of.

**Zitronsäure,** *f.* citric acid.

**Zitrulle,** *f.* watermelon.

**Zitrusöl,** *n.* citrus oil, specif. shaddock oil.

**zittern,** *v.i.* tremble, shake, quiver, vibrate.

**Zitterwurzel,** *f.* zedoary.

**Zitwer,** *m.* zedoary; aconite; sweet flag; ginger. **-kraut,** *m.* tarragon. **-samen,** *m.* wormseed, esp. santonica; zedoary seed. **-wurzel,** *f.* zedoary.

**Zitz,** *m.* chintz.

**Zitze,** *f.* nipple, teat.

**zitzenförmig,** *a.* mammillary; mastoid.

**Zitzentier,** *n.* mammal.

**zivil,** *a.* civil; moderate (price).

**zl.,** *abbrev.* (ziemlich löslich) fairly soluble.

**Zle.,** *abbrev.* (Zeile) line.

**Zobel,** *m.* sable.

**Zober,** *m.* tub.

**zog,** *pret.* of ziehen.

**zögern,** *v.i.* tarry, delay, hesitate.

**Zögling,** *m,* pupil.

**Zölestin,** *n.* celestite.

**Zoll,** *m.* duty, custom, toll; inch. **-amt,** *n.* customhouse; board of customs.

**zollbar,** *a.* dutiable.

**Zoll-beamte,** **-beamter,** *m.* customhouse officer, revenue officer.

**zollen,** *v.t.* pay, render.

**zollfrei,** *a.* duty-free.

**Zoll-freiheit**, *f.* exemption from duty. **-haus,** *n.* customhouse.

**zollpflichtig,** *a.* dutiable.

**Zoll-satz,** *m.* tariff rate. **-verein,** *m.* tariff union. **-verschluss,** *m.* bond.

**Zoochemie,** *f.* zoöchemistry.

**zoochemisch,** *a.* zoöchemical.

**Zoo-log,** *m.* zoölogist. **-logie,** *f.* zoölogy.

**zoologisch,** *a.* zoölogical.

**Zootinsalz,** *n.* Chile saltpeter.

**Zopf,** *m.* tuft; tress, plait; top (of a tree); red tape; pedantry.

**Zorn,** *m.* anger, wrath, rage, passion.

**Zotte, Zottel,** *f.* tuft, tangle; (*Anat.*) villus.

**Zottelwolle,** *f.* shaggy wool.

**Zottenhaut,** *f.* chorion.

**zottig,** *a.* shaggy, matted, (*Bot.*) villous.

**Zp.,** *abbrev.* (Zersetzungspunkt) decomposition point.

**z T., z.Th.,** *abbrev.* (zum Teil, zum Theil) in part.

**Ztg.,** *abbrev.* (Zeitung) newspaper, paper.

**zu,** *prep.* to, at, in, for.—*adv.* toward, on, too, closed; (on instruments, etc.) on.

**Zubehör,** *n.* belongings, accessories, fittings. **-teil,** *m.* accessory, fitting.

**zubekommen,** *v.t.* get in addition; get closed.

**zubenannt,** *p.a.* surnamed.

**Zuber,** *m.* tub.

**zubereiten,** *v.t.* prepare, dress, finish.

**Zubereitung,** *f.* preparation, dressing, finishing.

**zubilligen,** *v.t.* grant, allow.

**zubrennen,** *v.t.* roast, calcine; cauterize; close by heating.

**zubringen,** *v.t.* bring; convey; spend.

**Zubringer,** *m.* conveyor; feeder.

**Zubrühen,** *n.* (*Brewing*) addition of boiling water in mashing.

**Zubusse,** *f.* supply, contribution.

**Zucht,** *f.* breeding, rearing; cultivation, culture; breed, race; education; propriety; discipline.

**züchten,** *v.t.* breed, rear, grow, cultivate.

**Züchter,** *m.* breeder, raiser, grower.

**Züchtung,** *f.* breeding, growing, culture.

**zucken.** *v.i.* twitch, jerk, palpitate; flicker.— **zuckend,** *p.a.* convulsive, spasmodic.

**Zucker,** *m.* sugar.

**zuckerähnlich,** *a.* like sugar, saccharoid.

**Zucker-ahorn,** *m.* sugar maple. **-art,** *f.* kind or variety of sugar; (*pl.*) sugars.

**zuckerartig,** *a.* sugar-like, saccharine, saccharoid, sugary.

**Zucker-ausbeute,** *f.* yield of sugar, rendement. **-bäcker,** *m.* confectioner. **-baryt,** *n.* barium sucrate. **-bestimmung,** *f.* determination of sugar. **-bildung,** *f.* formation of sugar, saccharification, (*Physiol.*) glyco-

genesis. **-branntwein,** *m.* sugared spirit. **-brot,** *n.* sugar loaf; sweet bread. **-busch,** *m.* sugar bush, honey flower (*Protea mellifera*). **-couleur,** *f.* caramel. **-dicksaft,** *m.* molasses, treacle. **-erde,** *f.* animal charcoal for refining sugar; clay for refining sugar. **-fabrik,** *f.* sugar factory. **-fabrikation,** *f.* sugar manufacture. **-form,** *f.* sugar mold. **-gärung,** *f.* fermentation of sugar, saccharine fermentation. **-gehalt,** *m.* sugar content. **-gehaltmesser,** *m.* saccharimeter. **-geist,** *m.* rum. **-geschmack,** *m.* sugary taste. **-gewinnung,** *f.* extraction of sugar, sugar manufacture.

**zuckerhaltig,** *a.* containing sugar, saccharine, saccharated, sacchariferous.

**Zucker-harnen,** *n.* glycosuria. **-harnruhr,** *f.* diabetes mellitus. **-hirse,** *f.* sorghum. **-honig,** *m.* molasses, treacle. **-hut,** *m.* sugar loaf.

**zuckerig,** *a.* sugary, saccharine.

**Zuckerin,** *n.* saccharin.

**Zucker-industrie,** *f.* sugar industry. **-kalk,** *m.* calcium sucrate, sugar-lime. **-kand, -kandis,** *m.* sugar candy. **-kessel,** *m.* sugar kettle, sugar boiler. **-kohle,** *f.* charcoal from sugar. **-korn,** *n.* grain of sugar; sugar plum. **-krankheit,** *f.* diabetes mellitus. **-lauge,** *f.* (*Sugar*) limewater. **-lösung,** *f.* sugar solution; sirup. **-mehl,** *n.* powdered sugar. **-messer,** *m.* saccharimeter. **-messkunst, -messung,** *f.* saccharimetry. **-mühle,** *f.* sugar mill.

**zuckern,** *v.t.* sugar, sweeten.

**Zucker-pflanzung, -plantage,** *f.* sugar plantation. **-probe,** *f.* sample of sugar; sugar test.

**Zuckerrohr,** *n.* sugar cane.—**chinesisches —,** sorghum.

**Zuckerröhrchen,** *n.* sugar tube (small cylindrical funnel for sugar determinations).

**Zuckerroh-rückstände,** *m.pl.* bagasse. **-saft,** *m.* cane juice.

**Zucker-rose,** *f.* red rose. **-rübe,** *f.* sugar beet.

**Zuckerrüben-essig,** *m.* sugar-beet vinegar, beetroot vinegar. **-melasse,** *f.* beet molasses, beetroot molasses. **-saft,** *m.* sugar-beet juice. **-zucker,** *m.* beet sugar, beetroot sugar.

**Zucker-ruhr,** *f.* diabetes mellitus. **-saft,** *m.* saccharine juice. **-satz,** *m.* molasses.

**zuckersauer,** *a.* of or combined with saccharic acid, saccharate of.

**Zucker-säure,** *f.* saccharic acid; (*Old Chem.*) oxalic acid. **-schaum,** *m.* powdered animal charcoal. **-schlamm,** *m.* (*Beet Sugar*) lime scum. **-schleuder,** *f.* sugar centrifugal. **-schotenbaum,** *m.* honey locust. **-sieden,** *n.* sugar boiling, sugar refining. **-siederei,** *f.* sugar refinery, sugar house. **-stein,** *m.* finely granular albite. **-stoff**, *m.* saccharine matter.

**zuckerstoffhaltig**, *a.* saccharine.

**Zucker-strontian**, *m.* strontium sucrate. **-untersuchung**, *f.* examination (or investigation) of sugar. **-verbindung**, *f.* compound of sugar, specif. sucrate. **-waren**, *f.pl.*, **-werk**, *n.* confectionery, sweets.

**Zuckung**, *f.* convulsion, spasm; twitch.

**zudem**, *adv.* besides.

**zudrängen**, *v.r.* throng, crowd, intrude.

**zudrehen**, *v.t.* turn off, shut off.

**zudringlich**, *a.* intrusive, intruding.

**zudrücken**, *v.t.* shut, close.

**zueignen**, *v.t.* dedicate; attribute; appropriate.

**zuerkennen**, *v.t.* adjudge, award; admit, allow.

**zuerst**, *adv.* at first, first, above all.

**Zufall**, *m.* chance, accident; casualty; incident; attack.

**zufällig**, *a.* accidental, casual, chance.

**Zufälligkeitsfehler**, *m.* accidental error.

**Zufalls-gesetz**, *n.* law of chance or probability. **-kurve**, *f.* probability curve.

**zufliessen**, *v.i.* flow in.

**Zuflucht**, *f.* refuge, recourse.

**Zufluss**, *m.* flow, flux, afflux, influx; resources; (of a stream) tributary. **-rohr**, *n.* supply tube or pipe, feed pipe.

**zufolge**, *prep.* according to, owing to.

**zufrieden**, *a.* contented, satisfied, pleased. **-stellend**, *p.a.* satisfactory.

**zufrieren**, *v.i.* freeze up or over.

**zufügen**, *v.t.* add; inflict, cause (an injury).

**Zufügung**, *f.* addition; infliction.

**Zufuhr**, *f.* addition; supply, supplies; conveyance; importation.

**zuführen**, *v.t.* add, supply, feed; bring, conduct, convey; import.

**Zuführung**, *f.* (*Tech.*) supply, feed.

**Zug**, *m.* drawing, pulling, pull, traction, tug; stretch (of leather); motion, move; passage, progress; impulse, disposition; draft; train; procession, flock, team, etc.; range (of mountains); stroke, line; feature, trait; flue; pulley; piston; drawtube (of a microscope); etc.

**Zug-**. drawing, draw, pulling, traction, tractive, tensile, tension, extension; draft; train.

**Zugabe**, *f.* addition; extra, surplus; supplement.

**Zugang**, *m.* admittance, access.

**zugänglich**, *a.* accessible, approachable.

**Zugänglichkeit**, *f.* accessibility.

**Zug-beanspruchung**, *f.* tensile stress. **-druckversuch**, *m.* tensile-compression test.

**zugeben**, *v.t.* add; permit, allow.

**zugebracht**, *p.p.* of zubringen.

**zugegen**, *adv.& a.* present.

**zugehen**, *v.i.* go up (to), approach, go on;

come, arrive; close, meet; happen, come to pass.

**zugehören**, *v.i.* belong.

**zugehörig**, *a.* belonging, accompanying, proper.

**zugemischt**, *p.a.* admixed.

**zugeschmolzen**, *p.p.* of zuschmelzen.

**zugespitzt**, *p.a.* see zuspitzen.

**zugestehen**, *v.t.* concede, admit, permit.

**zugetan**, *p.a.* see zutun.

**Zugfestigkeit**, *f.* tensile strength, tenacity.

**zugfrei**, *a.* free from drafts.

**zugiessen**, *v.t.* fill up by pouring; pour to, pour in.

**zügig**, *a.* (of leather) flexible, pliant.

**Zug-kanal**, *m.* flue. **-kraft**, *f.* tractive force, traction; tension; attraction.

**zugleich**, *adv.* at the same time, at once, together.

**Zug-loch**, *n.* draft hole, air hole, vent hole. **-messer**, *m.* draft gage; draw knife. **-mittel**, *n.* attraction; (*Med.*) vesicant. **-muffel**, *f.* (*Ceram.*) continuous muffle. **-ofen**, *m.* wind furnace, draft furnace. **-pflaster**, *n.* blistering plaster, vesicatory.

**zugreifen**, *v.i.* lay hold, seize.

**Zug-rohr**, *n.*, **-röhre**, *f.* air pipe, vent pipe.

**zugrunde**, *adv.* =zu Grunde. (See Grund.)

**Zugrundelegung**, *f.* (literally) foundation laying.—**unter** —, on the basis (of).

**Zug-salbe**, *f.* (*Pharm.*) rosin cerate. **-spannung**, *f.* tensile stress.

**zugunsten**, *prep. with gen.* in favor of, for the sake of.

**Zuguss**, *m.* infusion; addition (of liquid).

**zugutemachen**, *v.t.* work up, work (ores, etc.).

**zuguterletzt**, *adv.* last, finally.

**Zug-versuch**, *m.* tensile test, tension test. **-wagen**, *m.* tractor. **-wirkung**, *f.* pulling effect, pull.

**zuheilen**, *v.i.* heal up.

**Zuhilfenahme**, *f.* utilization, aid.

**zuhören**, *v.i.* listen, attend.

**Zuhörer**, *m.* hearer, auditor. **-schaft**, *f.* audience.

**zukitten**, *v.t.* cement up.

**zukommen**, *v.i.* come up, come to, be due, belong; get on, manage.

**Zukunft**, *f.* future.

**zukünftig**, *a.* future, to come.—**zukünftige Woche**, next week.

**Zulage**, *f.* addition, increase (in pay), allowance.

**zulangen**, *v.i.* help oneself; suffice.

**zulänglich**, *a.* sufficient.

**Zulass**, *m.* admission.

**zulassen**, *v.t.* admit; permit; turn on (steam, etc.); leave closed.

**zulässig**, *a.* admissible, permissible.

**zulaufen,** *v.i.* run, crowd, flock; run on; run in. —*v.t.* run in, add.

**Zulauftemperatur,** *f.* temperature on admission.

**zulegen,** *v.t.* add; procure, get, take.—*v.i.* gain flesh.

**zuleimen,** *v.t.* glue up, cement.

**zuleiten,** *v.t.* lead, conduct (in or to).

**Zuleitung,** *f.* leading in or on; feed pipe, feed line, feed wire, etc.

**Zuleitungs-rohr,** *n.,* **-röhre,** *f.* inlet tube or pipe, feed pipe.

**zuletzt,** *adv.* at last, last, finally.

**zulöten,** *v.t.* solder up.

**zum.** =zu dem.

**zumachen,** *v.t.* shut, close.—*v.i.* be quick.

**zumal,** *adv.* chiefly, especially; all together.

**zumeist,** *adv.* for the most part.

**zumindest,** *adv.* at least.

**zumischen,** *v.t.* mix with, admix.

**Zumischstoff,** *m.* admixed material, admixture.

**zumuten,** *v.t.* expect, require.

**zunächst,** *adv.* nearest, next; first, above all.

**Zunahme,** *f.* increase; increment; growth; progress.

**Zuname,** *f.* surname, family name.

**Zünd-.** ignition, lighting, priming. **-apparat,** *m.* ignition apparatus; priming apparatus, primer.

**zündbar,** *a.* inflammable.

**Zünd-barkeit,** *f.* inflammability. **-einrichtung,** *f.* ignition device.

**zünden,** *v.i.* take fire, ignite.—*v.t.* set fire to, ignite, kindle.

**Zunder,** *m.* tinder; forge scale; cause, occasion.

**Zünder,** *m.* lighter, igniter; fuse, fusee; cinder.

**Zünderfüllmasse,** *f.,* **Zündersatz,** *m.* fuse composition.

**Zünd-flämmchen,** *n.* pilot flame. **-funke,** *f.,* **-funken,** *m.* ignition spark. **-holz,** hölzchen, *n.* match.—**schwedisches Zündhölzchen,** safety match.

**Zündholz-fabrik,** *f.* match factory. **-masse,** *f.,* **-satz,** *m.* match composition.

**Zündhütchen,** *n.* percussion cap, detonating cap. **-satz,** *m.* priming composition, priming.

**Zünd-kapsel,** *f.* =Zündhütchen. **-kerze,** *f.* spark plug; vesta, wax match. **-kirsche,** *f.* ignition pellet. **-ladung,** *f.* priming charge. **-masse,** *f.* igniting composition, ignition mixture. **-metall,** *n.* inflammable metal. **-mittel,** *n.* igniting agent, primer. **-papier,** *n.* touch paper. **-pille,** *f.* pellet primer. **-pulver,** *n.* priming powder, priming. **-punkt,** *m.* ignition point. **-satz,** *m.* priming composition. **-schnur,** *f.* fuse, match.

**-schwamm,** *m.* German tinder, punk. **-stelle,** *f.* place of ignition. **-stoff,** *m.* inflammable material; igniting agent, primer.

**Zündung,** *f.* ignition; priming.

**Zündungstemperatur,** *f.* temperature of ignition.

**Zünd-vorrichtung,** *f.* ignition device, igniter. **-waren,** *f.pl.* inflammable goods, inflammables. **-wärme,** *f.* heat of ignition.

**zunehmen,** *v.i.* increase, grow; grow larger, swell; advance, improve; prosper.—*v.t.* take (more).

**Zuneigung,** *f.* inclination; attachment.

**Zunft,** *f.* guild, corporation, profession, fraternity. **-gelehrter,** *m.* professional man.

**Zunge,** *f.* tongue; (of a balance) pointer, needle.

**züngeln,** *v.i.* (of flames) shoot out, lick.— **züngelnd,** *p.a.* lambent.

**Zungen-.** tongue, lingual, hyoid, glosso-, gloss-. **-zäpfchen,** *n.* epiglottis.

**zuoberst,** *adv.* uppermost.

**zupfen,** *v.t.* pick, pluck, tug, pull; pick apart, tease.

**Zupf-leinwand,** *f.* lint. **-nadel,** *f.* dissecting needle. **-präparat,** *n.* teased-out preparation.

**zupropfen,** *v.t.* cork up, stop up, plug up.

**zur.** =zu der.

**zuraten,** *v.i.* advise in favor.

**zurechnungsfähig,** *a.* accountable, responsible.

**zurecht,** *adv.* right, in order, in time. **-legen,** *v.t.* put right, arrange. **-machen,** *v.t.* get ready, prepare, adjust.

**zureden,** *v.i.* speak (to), encourage, persuade.

**zureichen,** *v.i.* suffice.—*v.t.* hand (to).

**zurichten,** *v.t.* prepare, make ready, dress, finish; curry (leather); leaven (dough); maltreat.

**Zurichtmasse,** *f.* (*Textiles*) sizing material.

**zurück,** *adv.* back, backward, behind. **-bilden,** *v.t.* form again, re-form. **-bleiben,** *v.i.* remain behind; be late, be slow; fall short, be inferior; survive. **-bleibend,** *p.a.* remaining behind, etc., residual. **-drängen,** *v.t.* push, drive or force back; repress, restrain. **-erhalten,** *v.t.* recover. **-fallen,** *v.t.* fall back, be reflected, revert, relapse. **-fliessen,** *v.i.* flow back; recede, ebb. **-führbar,** *a.* traceable; reducible. **-führen,** *v.t.* trace (back); lead back, reconvey; reduce; refer. **-gehen,** *v.i.* go back, return, revert; decline, deteriorate; fail.

**Zurückgehen,** *n.* return; reversion; decline; failure.

**zurück-gewinnen,** *v.t.* win back, recover. **-geworfen,** *p.p.* of zurückwerfen. **-halten,** *v.t.* keep back, retain, detain, repress.

-haltend, *p.a.* reserved, shy. -kehren, *v.i.* return; revert. -kommen, *v.i.* return, come back; decline. -lassen, *v.t.* leave behind, leave. -laufen, *v.i.* run back; recur; retrograde; recoil. -legen, *v.t.* put by; shelve; travel, go, live. -nehmen, *v.t.* take back, recall, retract. -prallen, *v.i.* rebound, recoil, be reflected; reverberate. -saugen, *v.t.* suck back, draw back (by suction). -schlagen, *v.i.* (of burners) strike back. -setzen, *v.t.* set back, put back; reduce; neglect; slight. -spiegeln, *v.t.* reflect. -spülen, *v.t.* rinse back, wash back. -steigen, *v.i.* rise back, mount back. -stossen, *v.t.* repel; push back.
Zurückstossung, *f.* repulsion; pushing back.
zurück-strahlen, *v.t.& i.* reflect. -titrieren, *v.t.* titrate back.
Zurück-titrieren, *n.*, -titrierung, *f.* return titration, back titration.
zurück-treiben, *v.t.* drive back, check. -treten, *v.i.* go back, recede, retire. -verwandeln, *v.t.* change back, reconvert. -weisen, *v.t.* send back, decline, refuse. -werfen, *v.t.* reflect; throw back.
zurunden, *v.t.* round, round off.
zurüsten, *v.t.* prepare, fit out, equip.
zurzeit, *adv.* at the time.
zus., *abbrev.* (zusammen) together.
Zus., *abbrev.* (Zusammensetzung) composition; (Zusatz) addition.
zusagen, *v.i.* agree, suit, please; consent, accept.—*v.t.* promise; assert.
zusammen, *adv.* together; altogether. -backen, *v.t.& i.* stick together, agglomerate. -ballen, *v.t.& r.* agglomerate, conglomerate, ball.
Zusammenballung, *f.* agglomeration, balling.
zusammen-bauen, *v.t.* assemble, erect. -brechen, *v.i.* break down, collapse. -brennen, *v.t.& i.* burn together.
Zusammendrehung, *f.* twisting, torsion.
zusammendrückbar, *a.* compressible.
Zusammendrückbarkeit, *f.* compressibility.
zusammendrücken, *v.t.* compress.
Zusammen-drücker, *m.* compressor. -drückung, *f.* compression. -drückungsmesser, *m.* compressometer.
zusammen-fallen, *v.i.* fall (in), collapse; converge; coincide. -falten, *v.t.* fold together, fold up. -fassen, *v.t.* grasp, comprehend; comprize; collect, summarize.
Zusammenfassung, *f.* summary, résumé; compilation; comprehension.
zusammen-fliessen, *v.i.* flow together; coalesce. -frieren, *v.i.* freeze together; freeze with contraction. -fügen, *v.t.* join, unite, combine. -gehörig, *a.* belonging together, corresponding, correlated, (*Biol.*) homologous.

Zusammengehörigkeit, *f.* correlation.
zusammen-geschliffen, *p.p.* of zusammenschleifen. -gesetzt, *p.a.* see zusammensetzen. -gewachsen, *p.p.* of zusammenwachsen. -giessen, *v.t.* pour together.
Zusammenhalt, *m.* cohesion; consistency; unity.
zusammen-haltbar, *a.* capable of holding together, cohesive; comparable; (formerly, of gases) coercible. -halten, *v.i.* cohere, hold together.—*v.t.* hold together; compare.
Zusammenhang, *m.* coherence, cohesion; relationship, connection, correlation; consistency.
zusammen-hangen, -hängen, *v.i.* cohere; be connected. -hangend, -hängend, *p.a.* cohesive; coherent; connected. -häufen, *v.t.* heap up, accumulate, aggregate. -kitten, *v.t.* cement. -kleben, *v.t.& i.* stick together, agglutinate.
Zusammen-klebung, *f.* adhesion; agglutination. -kunft, *f.* convention, assembly; conference. -lagerung, *f.* assemblage.
zusammen-laufen, *v.i.* run together, converge, blend, coagulate. -legen, *v.t.* put together, collect; fold, fold up. -leimen, *v.t.* agglutinate; glue together.
Zusammenleimung, *f.* agglutination; gluing together.
zusammen-löten, *v.t.* solder (together). -pressen, *v.t.* compress. -reiben, *v.t.* rub or grind together. -rücken, *v.t.* push together, crowd. -rühren, *v.t.* stir together, mix by stirring. -schleifen, *v.t.* grind together. -schmelzen, *v.t.* melt together, fuse.—*v.i.* melt, melt down; melt away, vanish. -schrumpfen, *v.i.* shrink, shrink up; wrinkle. -schütteln, *v.t.* shake together; shake down. -schütten, *v.t.* pour together, mix. -schweissen, *v.t.* weld together.
zusammensetzen, *v.t.* compose; combine; put together; set up, construct; compound.—*v.r.* be composed, consist; combine; sit together.—zusammensetzend, *p.a.* component, constituent.—zusammengesetzt, *p.a.* compound; composite; complex, complicated.
Zusammensetzung, *f.* composition; synthesis; combination; construction; structure; compound; complication.
zusammensintern, *v.t.& i.* sinter together, agglomerate.
Zusammenspiel, *n.* interplay.
zusammenstellen, *v.t.* put together, join, unite, group, compile, collate.
Zusammenstellung, *f.* putting together, grouping, classification, combination, compilation, juxtaposition, association.

**zusammenstimmen,** *v.i.* agree, accord, harmonize; vote together.

**Zusammenstoss,** *m.* collision, encounter, impact.

**zusammen-stossen,** *v.i.* come together, meet; collide; adjoin.—*v.t.* knock together; crush. **-stossend,** *p.a.* adjacent, contiguous. **-treffen,** *v.i.* meet; coincide, concur. **-trocknen,** *v.i.* dry up, shrivel. **-wachsen,** *v.i.* grow together, concrete, coalesce. **-wirken,** *v.i.* act together, coöperate; interact. **-ziehbar,** *a.* contractible; contractile. **-ziehen,** *v.t.* draw together, contract, abridge; assemble.—*v.r.* contract, shrink; gather. **-ziehend,** *p.a.* contractive; astringent.

**Zusammenziehung,** *f.* contraction, shrinking, etc. (see zusammenziehen).

**Zusatz,** *m.* addition; admixture; supplement, appendix; corollary.

**Zusatz-.** additional, supplementary, auxiliary. **-feld,** *n.* additional field, supplementary field. **-gerät,** *n.* supplementary apparatus, attachment. **-glied,** *n.* additional term, supplementary term.

**zusätzlich,** *a.* additional.

**Zusatz-linse,** *f.* supplementary lens. **-metall,** *n.* alloy. **-mittel,** *n.* addition agent, supplementary agent (something added to assist a reaction), admixed substance, substance used for admixture. **-patent,** *n.* addition to a patent. **-stoff,** *m.* admixed material; material for admixing.

**zuschärfen,** *v.t.* sharpen, point; (*Cryst.*) bevel.

**Zuschauer,** *m.* spectator.

**zuschieben,** *v.t.* push to, shut; shift (to someone else).

**Zuschlag,** *m.* addition; admixture; (*Metal.*) flux; increase; extra charge.

**zuschlagen,** *v.t.* add (as, a flux); hit hard, slam, bang; close up (casks).

**Zuschlag-erz,** *n.* fluxing ore. **-kalkstein,** *m.* limestone for flux.

**zuschmelzen,** *v.t.* close by melting, seal.

**zuschneiden,** *v.t.* cut out, cut.

**zuschreiben,** *v.t.* dedicate; credit; attribute; assign; add.

**Zuschrift,** *f.* letter, writing; dedication.

**Zuschuss,** *m.* extra sheet; addition; contribution.

**zusehen,** *v.i.* look (at, on or upon); witness.

**zusehends, zusehens,** *adv.* visibly, noticeably.

**zusetzen,** *v.t.* add; mix; alloy; adulterate; contribute; stop up; obstruct, bar; lose (money, etc.).

**zusichern,** *v.t.* assure, promise.

**Zus.-P.,** *abbrev.* (Zusatzpatent) addition to a patent.

**zuspitzen,** *v.t.* point, sharpen or taper to a point.—*v.r.* taper to a point; come to a crisis.—**zugespitzt,** *p.a.* tapering to a point, pointed, acuminate.

**Zuspitzung,** *f.* pointing, tapering to a point, acumination; point.

**zusprechen,** *v.t.* impart by speaking; adjudicate.—*v.i.* speak (to); cheer; call (on); agree (with), suit.

**Zuspruch,** *m.* encouragement; address; call.

**Zustand,** *m.* state; condition; situation, circumstances.

**zustande bringen.** carry thru, accomplish.

**zustande kommen.** come about, take place.

**zuständig,** *a.* belonging (to); appropriate, suitable.

**Zustands-änderung,** *f.* change of state. **-diagramm,** *n.* phase diagram. **-gleichung,** *f.* equation of state. **-schaubild,** *n.* phase diagram. **-verschiebung,** *f.* displacement of state, change in state.

**zustecken,** *v.t.* pin together; convey secretly.

**zustehen,** *v.i.* pertain, belong; be incumbent (on), become.

**zustellen,** *v.t.* block up, close; deliver.

**zustimmen,** *v.i.* agree, consent.

**zustöpseln,** *v.t.* stopper, cork.

**Zustrebekraft,** *f.* centripetal force.

**zuströmen,** *v.i.* flow in, stream in.

**zutage,** *adv.* to light, to or on the surface.— **— bringen,** bring to light, reveal.— **— kommen, — treten,** come to light, appear, become evident.— **— liegen,** be on the surface, be obvious.

**Zutat,** *f.* ingredient; addition, complement, trimming, furniture.

**zuteilen,** *v.t.* assign, allot, distribute.

**zuträglich,** *a.* good, profitable, beneficial.

**zutrauen,** *v.t.* credit (with), expect (of); confide (in).

**zutraulich,** *a.* confiding, confidential.

**zutreffen,** *v.i.* agree, correspond, prove correct.

**Zutritt,** *m.* access, admittance, admission.

**zutröpfeln, zutropfen,** *v.i.* drop in, drip in.— **— lassen,** add drop by drop.

**zutun,** *v.t.* close, shut; add; furnish.—**zugetan,** *p.a.* attached, devoted.

**Zutun,** *n.* coöperation, aid.

**zuverlässig,** *a.* reliable; certain, authentic.

**Zuverlässigkeit,** *f.* reliability, trustworthiness.

**Zuversicht,** *f.* reliance, confidence, certainty.

**zuversichtlich,** *a.* confident, positive, certain.

**zuvor,** *adv.* before, beforehand, previously. **-kommend,** *p.a.* anticipating; obliging. **-tun,** *v.t.* surpass, outdo.

**Zuwachs,** *m.* increase, increment, growth, accretion.

**zuwege bringen.** bring about, bring to pass.

**zuweilen,** *adv.* sometimes.

zuwenden, *v.t.& r.* turn.

zuwider, *prep.& adv.* against, contrary (to), repugnant (to).

zuziehen, *v.t.* draw shut or together; tighten; call in, invite, incur.—*v.i.* pull; move in, enter.

zuzüglich, *prep. with gen.* with addition of, including.

zw., *abbrev.* (zwischen) between; (zwar) indeed, to be sure; (zwecks) for the purpose of.

Zwackeisen, *n.* pincers.

zwacken, *v.t.* pinch; tease.

zwang, *pret.* cf zwingen.

Zwang, *m.* compulsion, coercion, force, pressure.

zwängen, *v.t.* force, press, coerce.

Zwangs-. forced, coercive, compulsory.

zwang(s)läufig, *a.* (*Mach.*) positive.

Zwang(s)-läufigkeit, *f.* guided motion, forced motion. -syndikat, *n.* compulsory syndicate.

zwangsweise, *adv.* by force.—*a.* compulsory, forcible.

zwanzig, *a.* twenty.

zwanzigste, *a.* twentieth.

zwar, *adv.* indeed, to be sure, truly.—und —, namely, that is.

Zweck, *m.* object, end, aim, goal, purpose; tack, pin, peg.

zweckdienlich, *a.* appropriate, efficient, useful.

Zwecke, *f.* tack, pin, peg.

zweck-los, *a.* aimless, useless. -mässig, *a.* suitable, appropriate, expedient.

Zweckmässigkeit, *f.* suitability, expediency.

zwecks, *prep. with gen.* for the purpose of.

zweckwidrig, *a.* inappropriate, unsuitable, inexpedient.

zwei, *a.* two.

zwei-, Zwei-. two-, di-, bi-, double.

zwei-achsig, *a.* biaxial. -armig, *a.* two-armed. -atomig, *a.* diatomic. -äugig, *a.* binocular. -badig, *a.* two-bath. -basisch, *a.* dibasic. -deutig, *a.* ambiguous, equivocal. -einhalbfach, *a.* two-and-a-half-fold. -einhalbmal, *adv.* two and a half times.

zweierlei, *a.* of two kinds, different; twofold.

Zweierstoss, *m.* collision of two bodies.

zweifach, *a.* twofold, double, bi-.— — kohlensaures Natron, sodium bicarbonate.

zweifachfrei, *a.* having two degrees of freedom, bivariant.

Zweifachschwefeleisen, *n.* iron disulfide.

zweifachschwefelsauer, *a.* bisulfate of.

Zweifachschwefelzinn, *n.* tin disulfide.

zweifachungesättigt, *a.* doubly unsaturated.

zweifarbig, *a.* two-colored, two-color, bicolored, dichromatic, dichroic.

Zweifarbigkeit, *f.* dichroism.

Zweifel, *m.* doubt, question, uncertainty.

zweifel-haft, *a.* doubtful, dubious. -los, *a.* doubtless, indubitable.

zweifelsohne, *adv.& a.* without doubt, doubtless.

Zweig, *m.* branch; sprig, twig; (mountain) spur.

zweigestaltig, *a.* dimorphous, dimorphic.

Zweigleitung, *f.* branch line.

zweigliedrig, *a.* two-membered; (*Math.*) binomial.

Zweig-rohr, *n.*, -röhre, *f.* branch tube or pipe, lateral.

zwei-halsig, *a.* two-necked. -jährig, *a.* of two years, biennial.

Zweikern-. binuclear; as, Zweikernchinon, binuclear quinone.

zweikernig, *a.* binuclear.

zweimal, *adv.* twice.

zweimalig, *a.* done twice, double, repeated.

Zweimalschmelzerei, *f.* (*Metal.*) two-stage melting process, specif. Walloon process.

zweimonatlich, *a.& adv.* bimonthly, every two months.

Zweiphasen-. (*Elec.*) two-phase.

zwei-phasig, *a.* two-phase, diphase. -polig, *a.* bipolar. -quantig, *a.* of two quanta, 2-quantum.

Zweirad, *n.* bicycle.

zwei-reihig, *a.* two-series. -säurig, *a.* diacid. -schalig, *a.* bivalve, bivalvular. -schenkelig, -schenklig, *a.* having two legs or branches. -schneidig, *a.* two-edged, double-edged. -seitig, *a.* two-sided, bilateral.

Zweistoff-. two-component, binary. -legierung, *f.* two-component alloy, binary alloy.

zwei-stufig, *a.* two-stage. -stündig, *a.* lasting two hours.

Zweitaktverfahren, *n.* two-stroke cycle.

zweite, *a.* second.

zweiteilig, *a.* two-part, bipartite.

zweitens, *adv.* secondly.

zweiwandig, *a.* two-walled, double-walled.

Zweiweg(e)hahn, *m.* two-way cock.

zweiwertig, *a.* bivalent, divalent.

Zweiwertigkeit, *f.* bivalence.

zweizählig, *a.* twofold, double, (*Bot.*) binate.

Zwerchfell, *n.* (*Anat.*) diaphragm.

Zwerg, *m.* dwarf.

Zwetsche, Zwetschge, Zwetschke, *f.* plum.

Zwickel, *m.* wedge; try cock, proof cock.

zwicken, *v.t.* pinch, nip; gripe; worry.

Zwickzange, *f.* pincers.

Zwieback, *m.* biscuit, specif. rusk, zwieback.

Zwiebel, *f.& m.* bulb, specif. onion.

zwiebelartig, *a.* bulbous; alliaceous.

Zwiebel-gewächs, *n.* bulbous plant. -marmor, *m.* cipolin. -öl, *n.* onion oil.

zwiebelrot, *a.* onion-red.

Zwiebelsaft, *m.* onion juice.

zwiefach, *a.* twofold, double.

Zwielicht, *n.* twilight.

Zwilling, *m.* twin.

Zwillingsachse, *f.* twinning axis.

zwillingsartig, *a.& adv.* in the form of twins, of the nature of twins.

Zwillings-bildung, *f.* twin formation. -doppel-verbindung, *f.* conjugated double linkage. -kerne, *m.pl.* twin nuclei. -kristall, *m.* twin crystal. -salz, *n.* double salt.

Zwinge, *f.* clamp, cramp; vise; ferrule, hoop.

zwingen, *v.t.* force, compel; subdue, conquer. —zwingend, *p.a.* cogent, compelling.

Zwinger, *m.* wedge.

Zwirn, *m.* thread (esp. linen thread). -band, *n.* tape.

zwirnen, *v.t.* twist, twine, throw (silk).

Zwirnfaden, *m.* (twisted) thread.

zwischen, *prep.* between, among.

zwischen-. inter-, intermediate, middle, mid-.

Zwischenbad, *n.* intermediate bath.

zwischendurch, *adv.* thru; at intervals.

Zwischen-erzeugnis, *f.* intermediate product, intermediate. -fall, *m.* incident, episode. -farbe, *f.* intermediate color. -gefäss, *n.* intermediate vessel or receptacle.

zwischengeschichtet, *a.* interstratified.

Zwischen-glasurmalerei, *f.* (*Ceram.*) painting between glazes. -glied, *n.* intermediate or connecting member, intermediate. -glühung, *f.* (*Metal.*) intermediate annealing. -händler, *m.* middleman, commission man; mediator. -körper, *m.* intermediate body (or substance). -kühler, *m.* intercooler. -lage, *f.* intermediate layer; intermediate position; interposition.

zwischen-legen, *v.t.* interpose. -liegend, *a.* intermediate.

Zwischen-mass, *n.* intermediate size. -masse, *f.* ground substance.

zwischenmolekular, *a.* intermolecular.

Zwischen-niveau, *n.* intermediate level. -optik, *f.* intermediate optical device or apparatus. -produkt, *n.* intermediate product; interposition. -raum, *m.* intermediate space; interstice, interspace, gap; interval. -reaktion, *f.* intermediate reaction. -schalten, *n.* insertion (between). -sorte, *f.* intermediate sort or quality. -stadium, *n.* intermediate stage.

zwischenständig, *a.* intermediate.

Zwischen-stein, *m.* (*Copper*) blue metal. -stellung, *f.* intermediate (or middle) position. -stück, *n.* intermediate piece or part. -stufe, *f.* intermediate stage. -ton, *m.* (of colors) medium or intermediate tone or shade. -träger, *m.* intermediate carrier or support; intermediary. -verbindung, *f.* intermediate compound. -wand, *f.* partition; shelf. -wärmung, *f.* intermediate heating. -weite, *f.* distance between, interval. -zeit, *f.* interval, interim.

zwischenzellig, *a.* intercellular.

Zwischen-zellraum, *m.* intercellular space. -zustand, *m.* intermediate state.

zwistig, *a.* disputing; in dispute.

Zwistigkeit, *f.* difference, dispute, discord.

Zwitter, *m.* hermaphrodite; hybrid; bastard; mongrel. -ion, *n.* hybrid ion, amphoteric ion.

zwl., *abbrev.* (ziemlich wenig löslich) rather difficultly soluble.

zwo, *a.* =zwei, two.

zwölf, *a.* twelve.

Zwölf-fingerdarm, *m.* duodenum. -flach, *n.* dodecahedron.

zwölfflächig, *a.* dodecahedral.

Zwölfflächner, *m.* dodecahedron.

zwölfseitig, *a.* twelve-sided, dodecahedral; dodecagonal.

zwölfte, *a.* twelfth.

Zyan, *n.* cyanogen. For compounds see Cyan-.

zyklisch, *a.* cyclic.

Zyklisieren, *n.* cyclization.

Zykloide, *f.* cycloid.

Zyklus, *m.* cycle, circle.

Zylinder, *m.* cylinder. -chen, *n.* small cylinder.

zylinderförmig, *a.* cylinder-shaped, cylindrical.

zylindern, zylindrieren, *v.t.* calender.

Zylinderöl, *n.* cylinder oil.

zylindrisch, *a.* cylindrical.

zymotechnisch, *a.* zymotechnic(al).

Zyper-. Cyprus, Cyprian.

Zypresse, *f.* cypress.

Zyst-. see also Cyst-.

Zyste, *f.* cyst.

Zyt-. cyt-.

Zytolyse, *f.* cytolysis.

z.Z., z.Zt., *abbrev.* (zur Zeit) at the time; at present; acting.